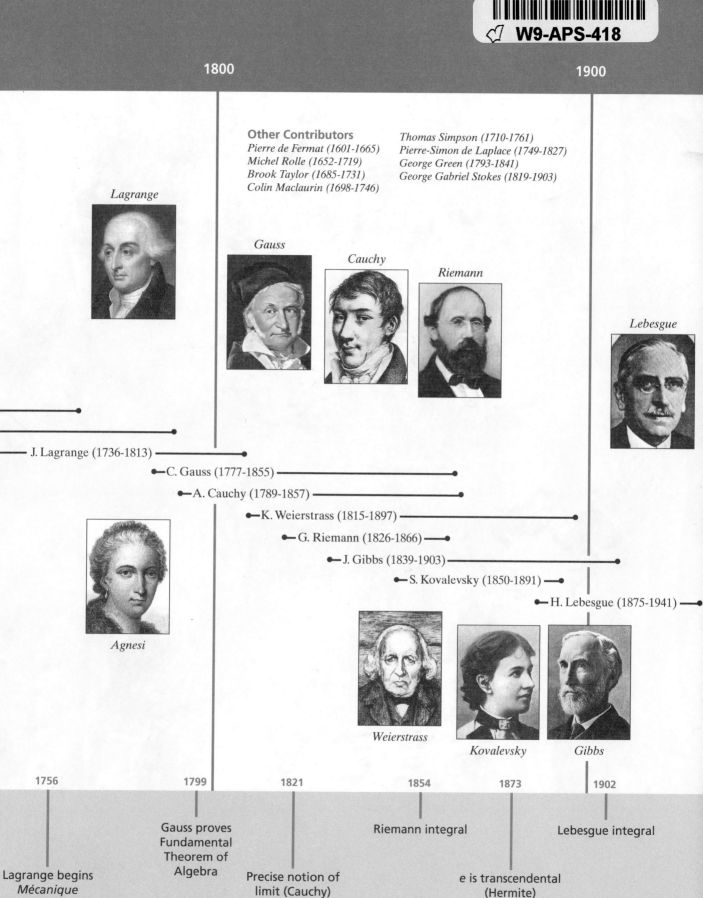

1800

1900

Other Contributors
Pierre de Fermat (1601-1665)
Michel Rolle (1652-1719)
Brook Taylor (1685-1731)
Colin Maclaurin (1698-1746)

Thomas Simpson (1710-1761)
Pierre-Simon de Laplace (1749-1827)
George Green (1793-1841)
George Gabriel Stokes (1819-1903)

Lagrange

Gauss

Cauchy

Riemann

Lebesgue

J. Lagrange (1736-1813)

C. Gauss (1777-1855)

A. Cauchy (1789-1857)

K. Weierstrass (1815-1897)

G. Riemann (1826-1866)

J. Gibbs (1839-1903)

S. Kovalevsky (1850-1891)

H. Lebesgue (1875-1941)

Agnesi

Weierstrass

Kovalevsky

Gibbs

1756

1799

1821

1854

1873

1902

Gauss proves
Fundamental
Theorem of
Algebra

Riemann integral

Lebesgue integral

Lagrange begins
*Mécanique
analytique*

Precise notion of
limit (Cauchy)

e is transcendental
(Hermite)

FORMULAS FROM GEOMETRY

Triangle

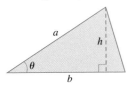

$$\text{Area} = \frac{1}{2}bh$$

$$\text{Area} = \frac{1}{2}ab\sin\theta$$

Parallelogram

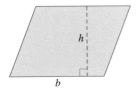

$$\text{Area} = bh$$

Trapezoid

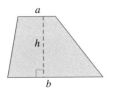

$$\text{Area} = \frac{a+b}{2}h$$

Circle

$$\text{Circumference} = 2\pi r$$

$$\text{Area} = \pi r^2$$

Sector of Circle

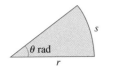

$$\text{Arc length } s = r\theta$$

$$\text{Area} = \frac{1}{2}r^2\theta$$

Polar Rectangle

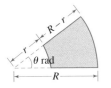

$$\text{Area} = \frac{R+r}{2}(R-r)\theta$$

Right Circular Cylinder

$$\text{Lateral area} = 2\pi rh$$

$$\text{Volume} = \pi r^2 h$$

Sphere

$$\text{Area} = 4\pi r^2$$

$$\text{Volume} = \frac{4}{3}\pi r^3$$

Right Circular Cone

$$\text{Lateral area} = \pi rs$$

$$\text{Volume} = \frac{1}{3}\pi r^2 h$$

Frustum of Right Circular Cone

$$\text{Lateral area} = \pi s(r+R)$$

$$\text{Volume} = \frac{1}{3}\pi(r^2 + rR + R^2)h$$

General Cone

$$\text{Volume} = \frac{1}{3}(\text{area }B)h$$

Wedge

$$\text{Area }A = (\text{area }B)\sec\theta$$

Calculus

EARLY TRANSCENDENTALS

CUSTOM EDITION FOR RYERSON UNIVERSITY

Dale Varberg
Edwin J. Purcell
Steven E. Rigdon

Taken from:

Calculus: Early Transcendentals
by Dale Varberg, Edwin J. Purcell and Steven E. Rigdon

Learning Solutions

New York Boston San Francisco
London Toronto Sydney Tokyo Singapore Madrid
Mexico City Munich Paris Cape Town Hong Kong Montreal

Cover Art: Courtesy of PhotoDisc/Getty Images

Taken from:

Calculus: Early Transcendentals
by Dale Varberg, Edwin J. Purcell and Steven E. Rigdon
Copyright © 2007 by Pearson Education, Inc.
Published by Prentice Hall
Upper Saddle River, New Jersey, 07458

This special edition published in cooperation with Pearson Learning Solutions.

All trademarks, service marks, registered trademarks, and registered service marks are the property of their respective owners and are used herein for identification purposes only.

Pearson Learning Solutions, 501 Boylston Street, Suite 900, Boston, MA 02116
A Pearson Education Company
www.pearsoned.com

Printed in Canada

1 2 3 4 5 6 7 8 9 10 VOFB 15 14 13 12 11 10

000200010270590886

LL

ISBN 10: 0-558-75198-9
ISBN 13: 978-0-558-75198-2

Contents

1.1

Real Numbers, Estimation, and Logic

Calculus is based on the real number system and its properties. But what are the real numbers and what are their properties? To answer, we start with some simpler number systems.

The Integers and the Rational Numbers The simplest numbers of all are the **natural numbers,**

$$\mathbb{N} \qquad 1, 2, 3, 4, 5, 6, \ldots$$

With them we can *count:* our books, our friends, and our money. If we include their negatives and zero, we obtain the **integers**

$$\mathbb{Z} \qquad \ldots, -3, -2, -1, 0, 1, 2, 3, \ldots$$

When we *measure* length, weight, or voltage, the integers are inadequate. They are spaced too far apart to give sufficient precision. We are led to consider quotients (ratios) of integers (Figure 1), numbers such as

$$\frac{3}{4}, \frac{-7}{8}, \frac{21}{5}, \frac{19}{-2}, \frac{16}{2}, \text{ and } \frac{-17}{1}$$

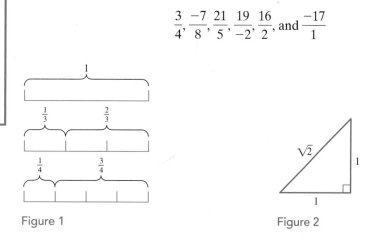

Figure 1

Figure 2

Note that we included $\frac{16}{2}$ and $\frac{-17}{1}$, though we would normally write them as 8 and -17 since they are equal to the latter by the ordinary meaning of division. We did not include $\frac{5}{0}$ or $\frac{-9}{0}$ since it is impossible to make sense out of these symbols (see Problem 30). Remember always that division by 0 is never allowed. Numbers that can be written in the form m/n, where m and n are integers with $n \neq 0$, are called **rational numbers.**

Do the rational numbers serve to measure all lengths? No. This surprising fact was discovered by the ancient Greeks in about the fifth century B.C. They showed that while $\sqrt{2}$ measures the hypotenuse of a right triangle with legs of length 1 (Figure 2), $\sqrt{2}$ cannot be written as a quotient of two integers (see Problem 77). Thus, $\sqrt{2}$ is an **irrational** (not rational) number. So are $\sqrt{3}, \sqrt{5}, \sqrt[3]{7}, \pi$, and a host of other numbers.

The Real Numbers Consider all numbers (rational and irrational) that can measure lengths, together with their negatives and zero. We call these numbers the **real numbers.**

The real numbers may be viewed as labels for points along a horizontal line. There they measure the distance to the right or left (the **directed distance**) from a

1

Figure 3

fixed point called the **origin** and labeled 0 (Figure 3). Though we cannot possibly show all the labels, each point does have a unique real number label. This number is called the **coordinate** of the point, and the resulting coordinate line is referred to as the **real line.** Figure 4 suggests the relationships among the sets of numbers discussed so far.

You may remember that the real number system can be enlarged still more—to the **complex numbers.** These are numbers of the form $a + bi$, where a and b are real numbers and $i = \sqrt{-1}$. Complex numbers will rarely be used in this book. In fact, if we say or suggest *number* without any qualifying adjective, you can assume that we mean real number. The real numbers are the principal characters in calculus.

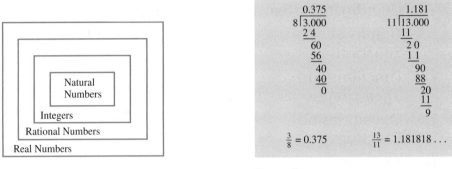

Figure 4

Figure 5

Repeating and Nonrepeating Decimals Every rational number can be written as a decimal, since by definition it can always be expressed as the quotient of two integers; if we divide the denominator into the numerator, we obtain a decimal (Figure 5). For example,

$$\frac{1}{2} = 0.5 \qquad \frac{3}{8} = 0.375 \qquad \frac{3}{7} = 0.428571428571428571\ldots$$

Irrational numbers, too, can be expressed as decimals. For instance,

$$\sqrt{2} = 1.4142135623\ldots, \qquad \pi = 3.1415926535\ldots$$

The decimal representation of a rational number either terminates (as in $\frac{3}{8} = 0.375$) or else repeats in regular cycles forever (as in $\frac{13}{11} = 1.181818\ldots$). A little experimenting with the long division algorithm will show you why. (Note that there can be only a finite number of different remainders.) A terminating decimal can be regarded as a repeating decimal with repeating zeros. For instance,

$$\frac{3}{8} = 0.375 = 0.3750000\ldots$$

Thus, every rational number can be written as a repeating decimal. In other words, if x is a rational number, then x can be written as a repeating decimal. It is a remarkable fact that the converse is also true; if x can be written as a repeating decimal, then x is a rational number. This is obvious in the case of a terminating decimal (for instance, $3.137 = 3137/1000$), and it is easy to show for the case of a nonterminating repeating decimal.

■ **EXAMPLE 1** **(Repeating decimals are rational.)** Show that $x = 0.136136136\ldots$ represents a rational number.

SOLUTION We subtract x from $1000x$ and then solve for x.

$$\begin{aligned} 1000x &= 136.136136\ldots \\ x &= 0.136136\ldots \\ \hline 999x &= 136 \\ x &= \frac{136}{999} \end{aligned}$$

The Real Numbers

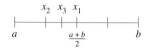

Rational Numbers (the repeating decimals)	Irrational Numbers (the nonrepeating decimals)

Figure 6

Figure 7

Figure 8

Many problems in this book are marked with a special sysmbol.

$\boxed{C}$ means use a calculator.

$\boxed{GC}$ means use a graphing calculator.

$\boxed{CAS}$ means use a computer algebra system.

$\boxed{EXPL}$ means the problem asks you to explore and go beyond the explanations given in the book.

The decimal representations of irrational numbers do not repeat in cycles. Conversely, a nonrepeating decimal must represent an irrational number. Thus, for example,

$$0.101001000100001\ldots$$

must represent an irrational number (note the pattern of more and more 0s between the 1s). The diagram in Figure 6 summarizes what we have said.

Denseness Between any two different real numbers a and b, no matter how close together, there is another real number. In particular, the number $x_1 = (a + b)/2$ is a real number that is midway between a and b (Figure 7). Since there is another real number, x_2, between a and x_1, and another real number, x_3, between x_1 and x_2, and since this argument can be repeated ad infinitum, we conclude that there are infinitely many real numbers between a and b. Thus, there is no such thing as "the real number just larger than 3."

Actually, we can say more. Between any two distinct real numbers, there are both a rational number and an irrational number. (In Problem 57 you are asked to show that there is a rational number between any two real numbers.) Hence, by the preceding argument, there are infinitely many of each.

One way that mathematicians describe the situation we have been discussing is to say that both the rational numbers and the irrational numbers are **dense** along the real line. Every number has both rational and irrational neighbors arbitrarily close to it.

One consequence of the density property is that any irrational number can be approximated as closely as we please by a rational number—in fact, by a rational number with a terminating decimal representation. Take $\sqrt{2}$ as an example. The sequence of rational numbers 1, 1.4, 1.41, 1.414, 1.4142, 1.41421, 1.414213,... marches steadily and inexorably toward $\sqrt{2}$ (Figure 8). By going far enough along in this sequence, we can get as near to $\sqrt{2}$ as we wish.

Calculators and Computers Today many calculators are capable of performing numerical, graphical, and symbolic operations. For decades now, calculators have been able to perform numerical operations such as giving decimal approximations to $\sqrt{12.2}$ and $1.25 \sin 22°$. By the early 1990s calculators could display the graph of almost any algebraic, trigonometric, exponential, or logarithmic function. Recent advances allow calculators to perform many symbolic operations, such as expanding $(x - 3y)^{12}$ or solving $x^3 - 2x^2 + x = 0$. Computer software such as *Mathematica* or *Maple* can perform symbolic operations like these, as well as a great many others.

Our recommendations regarding the use of a calculator are these:

1. Know when your calculator or computer gives you an exact answer and when it gives you an approximation. For example, if you ask for $\sin 60°$, your calculator may give the exact answer, $\sqrt{3}/2$, or it may give you a decimal approximation, 0.8660254.

2. In most cases, an exact answer is preferred. This is especially true when you must use the result in further calculations. For example, if you subsequently need to square the result of $\sin 60°$, it is easier, as well as being more accurate, to compute $(\sqrt{3}/2)^2 = 3/4$ than it is to compute 0.8660254^2.

3. In an applied problem, give an exact answer, if possible, as well as an approximation. You can often check whether your answer is reasonable, as it relates to the description of the problem, by looking at your numerical approximation to the solution.

Estimation Given a complicated arithmetic problem, a careless student might quickly press a few keys on a calculator and report the answer, not realizing that a missed parenthesis or a slip of the finger has given an incorrect result. A careful student with a feeling for numbers will press the same keys, immediately recognize

Figure 9

≈

In Example 3, we have used ≈ to mean "approximately equal." Use this symbol in your scratch work when making an approximation. In more formal work, never use this symbol without knowing how large the error could be.

Many problems are marked with this symbol.

≈ means make an estimate of the answer before working the problem; then check your answer against this estimate.

---

that the answer is wrong if it is far too big or far too small, and recalculate it correctly. It is important to know how to make a mental estimate.

EXAMPLE 2 Calculate $\left(\sqrt{430} + 72 + \sqrt[3]{7.5}\right)/2.75$.

SOLUTION A wise student approximated this as $(20 + 72 + 2)/3$ and said that the answer should be in the neighborhood of 30. Thus, when her calculator gave 93.448 for an answer, she was suspicious (she had actually calculated $\sqrt{430} + 72 + \sqrt[3]{7.5}/2.75$).

On recalculating, she got the correct answer: 34.434. ∎

EXAMPLE 3 Suppose that the shaded region R shown in Figure 9 is revolved about the x-axis. Estimate the volume of the resulting solid ring S.

SOLUTION The region R is about 3 units long and 0.9 units high. We estimate its area as $3(0.9) \approx 3$ square units. Imagine the solid ring S to be slit open and laid out flat, forming a box about $2\pi r \approx 2(3)(6) = 36$ units long. The volume of a box is its cross-sectional area times its length. Thus, we estimate the volume of the box to be $3(36) = 108$ cubic units. If you calculate it to be 1000 cubic units, you need to check your work. ∎

The process of *estimation* is just ordinary common sense combined with reasonable numerical approximations. We urge you to use it frequently, especially on word problems. Before you attempt to get a precise answer, make an estimate. If your answer is close to your estimate, there is no guarantee that your answer is correct. On the other hand, if your answer and your estimate are far apart, you should check your work. There is probably an error in your answer or in your approximation. Remember that $\pi \approx 3$, $\sqrt{2} \approx 1.4$, $2^{10} \approx 1000$, 1 foot $\approx$ 10 inches, 1 mile $\approx$ 5000 feet, and so on.

A central theme in this text is number sense. By this, we mean the ability to work through a problem and tell whether your solution is a reasonable one for the stated problem. A student with good number sense will immediately recognize and correct an answer that is obviously unreasonable. For many of the examples worked out in the text, we provide an initial estimate of the solution before proceeding to find the exact solution.

A Bit of Logic Important results in mathematics are called **theorems**; you will find many theorems in this book. The most important ones occur with the label *Theorem* and are usually given names (e.g., the Pythagorean Theorem). Others occur in the problem sets and are introduced with the words *show that* or *prove that*. In contrast to axioms or definitions, which are taken for granted, theorems require proof.

Many theorems are stated in the form "If P then Q" or they can be restated in this form. We often abbreviate the statement "If P then Q" by $P \Rightarrow Q$, which is also read "P implies Q." We call P the *hypothesis* and Q the *conclusion* of the theorem. A proof consists of showing that Q must be true whenever P is true.

Beginning students (and some mature ones) may confuse $P \Rightarrow Q$ with its **converse**, $Q \Rightarrow P$. These two statements are not equivalent. "If John is a Missourian, then John is an American" is a true statement, but its converse "If John is an American, then John is a Missourian" may not be true.

The **negation** of the statement P is written $\sim P$. For example, if P is the statement "It is raining," then $\sim P$ is the statement "It is not raining." The statement $\sim Q \Rightarrow \sim P$ is called the **contrapositive** of the statement $P \Rightarrow Q$ and it is equivalent to $P \Rightarrow Q$. By "equivalent" we mean that $P \Rightarrow Q$ and $\sim Q \Rightarrow \sim P$ are either both true or both false. For our example about John, the contrapositive of "If John is a Missourian, then John is an American" is "If John is not an American, then John is not a Missourian."

Because a statement and its contrapositive are equivalent, we can prove a theorem of the form "If P then Q" by proving its contrapositive "If $\sim Q$ then $\sim P$."

Thus, to prove $P \Rightarrow Q$, we can assume $\sim Q$ and try to deduce $\sim P$. Here is a simple example.

EXAMPLE 4 Prove that if n^2 is even, then n is even.

Proof The contrapositive of this sentence is "If n is not even, then n^2 is not even," which is equivalent to "If n is odd, then n^2 is odd." We will prove the contrapositive. If n is odd, then there exists an integer k such that $n = 2k + 1$. Then

$$n^2 = (2k + 1)^2 = 4k^2 + 4k + 1 = 2(2k^2 + 2k) + 1$$

Therefore, n^2 is equal to one more than twice an integer. Hence n^2 is odd. ■

The *Law of the Excluded Middle* says: Either R or $\sim R$, but not both. Any proof that begins by assuming the conclusion of a theorem is false and proceeds to show this assumption leads to a contradiction is called a **proof by contradiction.**

Occasionally, we will need another type of proof called **mathematical induction.** It would take us too far afield to describe this now, but we have given a complete discussion in Appendix A.1.

Sometimes both the statements $P \Rightarrow Q$ (if P then Q) and $Q \Rightarrow P$ (if Q then P) are true. In this case we write $P \Leftrightarrow Q$, which is read "P if and only if Q." In Example 4 we showed that "If n^2 is even, then n is even," but the converse "If n is even, then n^2 is even" is also true. Thus, we would say "n is even if and only if n^2 is even."

Order The nonzero real numbers separate nicely into two disjoint sets—the positive real numbers and the negative real numbers. This fact allows us to introduce the order relation $<$ (read "is less than") by

$$\boxed{x < y \Leftrightarrow y - x \text{ is positive}}$$

We agree that $x < y$ and $y > x$ shall mean the same thing. Thus, $3 < 4, 4 > 3, -3 < -2,$ and $-2 > -3$.

The order relation $\leq$ (read "is less than or equal to") is a first cousin of $<$. It is defined by

$$\boxed{x \leq y \Leftrightarrow y - x \text{ is positive or zero}}$$

Order properties 2, 3, and 4 in the margin box hold when the symbols $<$ and $>$ are replaced by $\leq$ and $\geq$.

Quantifiers Many mathematical statements involve a variable x, and the truth of the statement depends on the value of x. For example, the statement "$\sqrt{x}$ is a rational number" depends on the value of x; it is true for some values of x, such as $x = 1, 4, 9, \frac{4}{9}$, and $\frac{10,000}{49}$, and false for other values of x, such as $x = 2, 3, 77$, and π. Some statements, such as "$x^2 \geq 0$," are true for all real numbers x, and other statements, such as "x is an even integer greater than 2 and x is a prime number," are always false. We will let $P(x)$ denote a statement whose truth depends on the value of x.

We say "For all x, $P(x)$" or "For every x, $P(x)$" when the statement $P(x)$ is true for every value of x. When there is at least one value of x for which $P(x)$ is true, we say "There exists an x such that $P(x)$." The two important *quantifiers* are "for all" and "there exists."

EXAMPLE 5 Which of the following statements are true?
(a) For all x, $x^2 > 0$.
(b) For all x, $x < 0 \Rightarrow x^2 > 0$.
(c) For every x, there exists a y such that $y > x$.
(d) There exists a y such that, for all x, $y > x$.

Proof by Contradiction

Proof by contradiction also goes by the name *reductio ad absurdum*. Here is what the great mathematician G. H. Hardy had to say about it.

"Reductio ad absurdum, which Euclid loved so much, is one of a mathematician's finest weapons. It is a far finer gambit than any chess gambit; a chess player may offer the sacrifice of a pawn or even a piece, but a mathematician offers the game."

Order on the Real Line

To say that $x < y$ means that x is to the left of y on the real line.

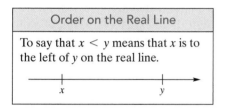

The Order Properties

1. **Trichotomy.** If x and y are numbers, then exactly one of the following holds:

    $x < y$ or $x = y$ or $x > y$

2. **Transitivity.** $x < y$ and $y < z$ $\Rightarrow x < z$.
3. **Addition.**
    $x < y \Leftrightarrow x + z < y + z$.
4. **Multiplication.** When z is positive, $x < y \Leftrightarrow xz < yz$. When z is negative, $x < y \Leftrightarrow xz > yz$.

SOLUTION

(a) False. If we choose $x = 0$, then it is not true that $x^2 > 0$.

(b) True. If x is negative, then x^2 will be positive.

(c) True. This statement contains two quantifiers, "for every" and "there exists." To read the statement correctly, we must apply them in the right order. The statement begins "for every," so if the statement is true, then what follows must be true for every value of x that we choose. If you are not sure whether the whole statement is true, try a few values of x and see whether the second part of the statement is true or false. For example, we might choose $x = 100$; given this choice, does there exist a y that is greater than x? In other words, is there a number greater than 100? Yes, of course. The number 101 would do. Next choose another value for x, say $x = 1,000,000$. Does there exist a y that is greater than this value of x? Again, yes; in this case the number 1,000,001 would do. Now, ask yourself: "If I let x be any real number, will I be able to find a y that is larger than x?" The answer is yes. Just choose y to be $x + 1$.

(d) False. This statement says that there is a real number that is larger than every other real number. In other words, there is a largest real number. This is false; here is a proof by contradiction. Suppose that there exists a largest real number y. Let $x = y + 1$. Then $x > y$, which is contrary to the assumption that y is the largest real number. ∎

The **negation** of the statement P is the statement "not P." (The statement "not P" is true provided P is false.) Consider the negation of the statement "for all x, $P(x)$." If this negated statement is true, then there must be at least one value of x for which $P(x)$ is false; in other words, there exists an x such that "not $P(x)$." Now consider the negation of the statement "there exists an x such that $P(x)$." If this negated statement is true, then there is not a single x for which $P(x)$ is true. This means that $P(x)$ is false no matter what the value of x. In other words, "for all x, not $P(x)$." In summary,

The negation of "for all x, $P(x)$" is "there exists an x such that not $P(x)$."

The negation of "there exists an x such that $P(x)$" is "for every x, not $P(x)$."

Concepts Review

1. Numbers that can be written as the ratio of two integers are called _____.

2. Between any two real numbers, there is another real number. This is what it means to say that the real numbers are _____.

3. The contrapositive of "If P then Q" is _____.

4. Axioms and definitions are taken for granted, but _____ require proof.

Problem Set 1.1

In Problems 1–16, simplify as much as possible. Be sure to remove all parentheses and reduce all fractions.

1. $4 - 2(8 - 11) + 6$

2. $3[2 - 4(7 - 12)]$

3. $-4[5(-3 + 12 - 4) + 2(13 - 7)]$

4. $5[-1(7 + 12 - 16) + 4] + 2$

5. $\frac{5}{7} - \frac{1}{13}$

6. $\frac{3}{4 - 7} + \frac{3}{21} - \frac{1}{6}$

7. $\frac{1}{3}\left[\frac{1}{2}\left(\frac{1}{4} - \frac{1}{3}\right) + \frac{1}{6}\right]$

8. $-\frac{1}{3}\left[\frac{2}{5} - \frac{1}{2}\left(\frac{1}{3} - \frac{1}{5}\right)\right]$

9. $\frac{14}{21}\left(\dfrac{2}{5 - \frac{1}{3}}\right)^2$

10. $\left(\frac{2}{7} - 5\right)/\left(1 - \frac{1}{7}\right)$

11. $\dfrac{\frac{11}{7} - \frac{12}{21}}{\frac{11}{7} + \frac{12}{21}}$

12. $\dfrac{\frac{1}{2} - \frac{3}{4} + \frac{7}{8}}{\frac{1}{2} + \frac{3}{4} - \frac{7}{8}}$

13. $1 - \dfrac{1}{1 + \frac{1}{2}}$

14. $2 + \dfrac{3}{1 + \frac{5}{2}}$

15. $\left(\sqrt{5} + \sqrt{3}\right)\left(\sqrt{5} - \sqrt{3}\right)$ **16.** $\left(\sqrt{5} - \sqrt{3}\right)^2$

In Problems 17–28, perform the indicated operations and simplify.

17. $(3x - 4)(x + 1)$

18. $(2x - 3)^2$

19. $(3x - 9)(2x + 1)$

20. $(4x - 11)(3x - 7)$

21. $(3t^2 - t + 1)^2$

22. $(2t + 3)^3$

23. $\dfrac{x^2 - 4}{x - 2}$

24. $\dfrac{x^2 - x - 6}{x - 3}$

25. $\dfrac{t^2 - 4t - 21}{t + 3}$

26. $\dfrac{2x - 2x^2}{x^3 - 2x^2 + x}$

27. $\dfrac{12}{x^2 + 2x} + \dfrac{4}{x} + \dfrac{2}{x + 2}$

28. $\dfrac{2}{6y - 2} + \dfrac{y}{9y^2 - 1}$

29. Find the value of each of the following; if undefined, say so.

(a) $0 \cdot 0$

(b) $\dfrac{0}{0}$

(c) $\dfrac{0}{17}$

(d) $\dfrac{3}{0}$

(e) 0^5

(f) 17^0

30. Show that division by 0 is meaningless as follows: Suppose that $a \neq 0$. If $a/0 = b$, then $a = 0 \cdot b = 0$, which is a contradiction. Now find a reason why $0/0$ is also meaningless.

In Problems 31–36, change each rational number to a decimal by performing long division.

31. $\frac{1}{12}$

32. $\frac{2}{7}$

33. $\frac{3}{21}$

34. $\frac{5}{17}$

35. $\frac{11}{3}$

36. $\frac{11}{13}$

In Problems 37–42, change each repeating decimal to a ratio of two integers (see Example 1).

37. $0.123123123\ldots$

38. $0.217171717\ldots$

39. $2.56565656\ldots$

40. $3.929292\ldots$

41. $0.199999\ldots$

42. $0.399999\ldots$

43. Since $0.199999\ldots = 0.200000\ldots$ and $0.399999\ldots = 0.400000\ldots$ (see Problems 41 and 42), we see that certain rational numbers have two different decimal expansions. Which rational numbers have this property?

44. Show that any rational number p/q, for which the prime factorization of q consists entirely of 2s and 5s, has a terminating decimal expansion.

45. Find a positive rational number and a positive irrational number both smaller than 0.00001.

46. What is the smallest positive integer? The smallest positive rational number? The smallest positive irrational number?

47. Find a rational number between 3.14159 and π. Note that $\pi = 3.141592\ldots$

48. Is there a number between $0.9999\ldots$ (repeating 9s) and 1? How do you resolve this with the statement that between any two different real numbers there is another real number?

49. Is $0.1234567891011121314\ldots$ rational or irrational? (You should see a pattern in the given sequence of digits.)

50. Find two irrational numbers whose sum is rational.

≈ *In Problems 51–56, find the best decimal approximation that your calculator allows. Begin by making a mental estimate.*

51. $\left(\sqrt{3} + 1\right)^3$

52. $\left(\sqrt{2} - \sqrt{3}\right)^4$

53. $\sqrt[4]{1.123} - \sqrt[3]{1.09}$

54. $(3.1415)^{-1/2}$

55. $\sqrt{8.9\pi^2 + 1} - 3\pi$

56. $\sqrt[4]{(6\pi^2 - 2)\pi}$

57. Show that between any two different real numbers there is a rational number. (*Hint:* If $a < b$, then $b - a > 0$, so there is a natural number n such that $1/n < b - a$. Consider the set $\{k : k/n > b\}$ and use the fact that a set of integers that is bounded from below contains a least element.) Show that between any

two different real numbers there are infinitely many rational numbers.

≈ 58. Estimate the number of cubic inches in your head.

≈ 59. Estimate the length of the equator in feet. Assume the radius of the earth to be 4000 miles.

≈ 60. About how many times has your heart beat by your twentieth birthday?

≈ 61. The General Sherman tree in California is about 270 feet tall and averages about 16 feet in diameter. Estimate the number of board feet (1 board foot equals 1 inch by 12 inches by 12 inches) of lumber that could be made from this tree, assuming no waste and ignoring the branches.

≈ 62. Assume that the General Sherman tree (Problem 61) produces an annual growth ring of thickness 0.004 foot. Estimate the resulting increase in the volume of its trunk each year.

63. Write the converse and the contrapositive to the following statements.

(a) If it rains today, then I will stay home from work.

(b) If the candidate meets all the qualifications, then she will be hired.

64. Write the converse and the contrapositive to the following statements.

(a) If I get an A on the final exam, I will pass the course.

(b) If I finish my research paper by Friday, then I will take off next week.

65. Write the converse and the contrapositive to the following statements.

(a) (Let a, b, and c be the lengths of sides of a triangle.) If $a^2 + b^2 = c^2$, then the triangle is a right triangle.

(b) If angle ABC is acute, then its measure is greater than $0°$ and less than $90°$.

66. Write the converse and the contrapositive to the following statements.

(a) If the measure of angle ABC is $45°$, then angle ABC is an acute angle.

(b) If $a < b$ then $a^2 < b^2$.

67. Consider the statements in Problem 65 along with their converses and contrapositives. Which are true?

68. Consider the statements in Problem 66 along with their converses and contrapositives. Which are true?

69. Use the rules regarding the negation of statements involving quantifiers to write the negation of the following statements. Which is true, the original statement or its negation?

(a) Every isosceles triangle is equilateral.

(b) There is a real number that is not an integer.

(c) Every natural number is less than or equal to its square.

70. Use the rules regarding the negation of statements involving quantifiers to write the negation of the following statements. Which is true, the original statement or its negation?

(a) Every natural number is rational.

(b) There is a circle whose area is larger than 9π.

(c) Every real number is larger than its square.

71. Which of the following are true? Assume that x and y are real numbers.

(a) For every x, $x > 0 \Rightarrow x^2 > 0$.

(b) For every x, $x > 0 \Leftrightarrow x^2 > 0$.

(c) For every x, $x^2 > x$.

(d) For every x, there exists a y such that $y > x^2$.

(e) For every positive number y, there exists another positive number x such that $0 < x < y$.

72. Which of the following are true? Unless it is stated otherwise, assume that x, y, and ε are real numbers.

(a) For every x, $x < x + 1$.

(b) There exists a natural number N such that all prime numbers are less than N. (A **prime number** is a natural number whose only factors are 1 and itself.)

(c) For every $x > 0$, there exists a y such that $y > \dfrac{1}{x}$.

(d) For every positive x, there exists a natural number n such that $\dfrac{1}{n} < x$.

(e) For every positive ε, there exists a natural number n such that $\dfrac{1}{2^n} < \varepsilon$.

73. Prove the following statements.

(a) If n is odd, then n^2 is odd. (*Hint:* If n is odd, then there exists an integer k such that $n = 2k + 1$.)

(b) If n^2 is odd, then n is odd. (*Hint:* Prove the contrapositive.)

74. Prove that n is odd if and only if n^2 is odd. (See Problem 73.)

75. According to the **Fundamental Theorem of Arithmetic,** every natural number greater than 1 can be written as the product of primes in a unique way, except for the order of the factors. For example, $45 = 3 \cdot 3 \cdot 5$. Write each of the following as a product of primes.

(a) 243   (b) 124   (c) 5100

76. Use the Fundamental Theorem of Arithmetic (Problem 75) to show that the square of any natural number greater than 1 can be written as the product of primes in a unique way, except for the order of the factors, with each prime occurring an *even* number of times. For example, $(45)^2 = 3 \cdot 3 \cdot 3 \cdot 3 \cdot 5 \cdot 5$.

77. Show that $\sqrt{2}$ is irrational. *Hint:* Try a proof by contradiction. Suppose that $\sqrt{2} = p/q$, where p and q are natural numbers (necessarily different from 1). Then $2 = p^2/q^2$, and so $2q^2 = p^2$. Now use Problem 76 to get a contradiction.

78. Show that $\sqrt{3}$ is irrational (see Problem 77).

79. Show that the sum of two rational numbers is rational.

80. Show that the product of a rational number (other than 0) and an irrational number is irrational. *Hint:* Try proof by contradiction.

81. Which of the following are rational and which are irrational?

(a) $-\sqrt{9}$ (b) 0.375

(c) $(3\sqrt{2})(5\sqrt{2})$ (d) $(1 + \sqrt{3})^2$

82. A number b is called an **upper bound** for a set S of numbers if $x \le b$ for all x in S. For example 5, 6.5, and 13 are upper bounds for the set $S = \{1, 2, 3, 4, 5\}$. The number 5 is the **least upper bound** for S (the smallest of all upper bounds). Similarly, 1.6, 2, and 2.5 are upper bounds for the infinite set $T = \{1.4, 1.49, 1.499, 1.4999, \dots\}$, whereas 1.5 is its least upper bound. Find the least upper bound of each of the following sets.

(a) $S = \{-10, -8, -6, -4, -2\}$

(b) $S = \{-2, -2.1, -2.11, -2.111, -2.1111, \dots\}$

(c) $S = \{2.4, 2.44, 2.444, 2.4444, \dots\}$

(d) $S = \left\{1 - \frac{1}{2}, 1 - \frac{1}{3}, 1 - \frac{1}{4}, 1 - \frac{1}{5}, \dots\right\}$

(e) $S = \{x: x = (-1)^n + 1/n, n \text{ a positive integer}\}$; that is, S is the set of all numbers x that have the form $x = (-1)^n + 1/n$, where n is a positive integer.

(f) $S = \{x: x^2 < 2, x \text{ a rational number}\}$

$\boxed{\text{EXPL}}$ **83. The Axiom of Completeness** for the real numbers says: Every set of real numbers that has an upper bound has a *least* upper bound that is a real number.

(a) Show that the italicized statement is false if the word *real* is replaced by *rational*.

(b) Would the italicized statement be true or false if the word *real* were replaced by *natural*?

Answers to Concepts Review: **1.** rational numbers **2.** dense **3.** "If not Q then not P." **4.** theorems

---

$$1.2$$

Inequalities and Absolute Values

Solving equations (for instance, $3x - 17 = 6$ or $x^2 - x - 6 = 0$) is one of the traditional tasks of mathematics; it will be important in this course and we assume that you remember how to do it. But of almost equal significance in calculus is the notion of solving an inequality (e.g., $3x - 17 < 6$ or $x^2 - x - 6 \ge 0$). To **solve** an inequality is to find the set of all real numbers that make the inequality true. In contrast to an equation, whose solution set normally consists of one number or perhaps a finite set of numbers, the solution set of an inequality is usually an entire interval of numbers or, in some cases, the union of such intervals.

Intervals   Several kinds of intervals will arise in our work and we introduce special terminology and notation for them. The inequality $a < x < b$, which is actually two inequalities, $a < x$ and $x < b$, describes the **open interval** consisting of all numbers between a and b, not including the end points a and b. We denote this interval by the symbol (a, b) (Figure 1). In contrast, the inequality $a \le x \le b$ describes the corresponding **closed interval,** which does include the end points a and

$(-1, 6) = \{x: -1 < x < 6\}$

Figure 1

$$[-1, 5] = \{x : -1 \leq x \leq 5\}$$

Figure 2

b. This interval is denoted by $[a, b]$ (Figure 2). The table indicates the wide variety of possibilities and introduces our notation.

Set Notation	Interval Notation	Graph
$\{x : a < x < b\}$	(a, b)	
$\{x : a \leq x \leq b\}$	$[a, b]$	
$\{x : a \leq x < b\}$	$[a, b)$	
$\{x : a < x \leq b\}$	$(a, b]$	
$\{x : x \leq b\}$	$(-\infty, b]$	
$\{x : x < b\}$	$(-\infty, b)$	
$\{x : x \geq a\}$	$[a, \infty)$	
$\{x : x > a\}$	(a, ∞)	
$\mathbb{R}$	$(-\infty, \infty)$	

Solving Inequalities As with equations, the procedure for solving an inequality consists of transforming the inequality one step at a time until the solution set is obvious. We may perform certain operations on both sides of an inequality without changing its solution set. In particular,

1. We may add the same number to both sides of an inequality.
2. We may multiply both sides of an inequality by the same positive number.
3. We may multiply both sides by the same negative number, but then we must reverse the direction of the inequality sign.

EXAMPLE 1 Solve the inequality $2x - 7 < 4x - 2$ and show the graph of its solution set.

SOLUTION

$$
\begin{aligned}
2x - 7 &< 4x - 2 \\
2x &< 4x + 5 \quad &\text{(adding 7)} \\
-2x &< 5 \quad &\text{(adding } -4x\text{)} \\
x &> -\tfrac{5}{2} \quad &\text{(multiplying by } -\tfrac{1}{2}\text{)}
\end{aligned}
$$

The graph appears in Figure 3.

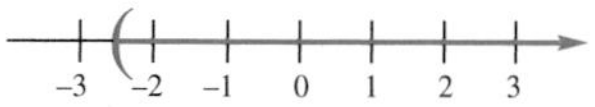

EXAMPLE 2 Solve $-5 \leq 2x + 6 < 4$.

SOLUTION

$$
\begin{aligned}
-5 &\leq 2x + 6 < 4 \\
-11 &\leq 2x \quad < -2 \quad &\text{(adding } -6\text{)} \\
-\tfrac{11}{2} &\leq \ x \quad\ \ < -1 \quad &\text{(multiplying by } \tfrac{1}{2}\text{)}
\end{aligned}
$$

Figure 4 shows the corresponding graph.

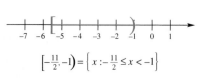

$$\left(-\tfrac{5}{2}, \infty\right) = \left\{x : x > -\tfrac{5}{2}\right\}$$

Figure 3

$$\left[-\tfrac{11}{2}, -1\right) = \left\{x : -\tfrac{11}{2} \leq x < -1\right\}$$

Figure 4

Before tackling a quadratic inequality, we point out that a linear factor of the form $x - a$ is positive for $x > a$ and negative for $x < a$. It follows that a product $(x - a)(x - b)$ can change from being positive to negative, or vice versa, only at a or b. These points, where a factor is zero, are called **split points.** They are the keys to determining the solution sets of quadratic and other more complicated inequalities.

EXAMPLE 3 Solve the quadratic inequality $x^2 - x < 6$.

SOLUTION As with quadratic equations, we move all nonzero terms to one side and factor.

$$x^2 - x < 6$$
$$x^2 - x - 6 < 0 \qquad \text{(adding } -6)$$
$$(x - 3)(x + 2) < 0 \qquad \text{(factoring)}$$

Test Point	Sign of $(x - 3)$	Sign of $(x + 2)$	Sign of $(x - 3)(x + 2)$
-3	$-$	$-$	$+$
0	$-$	$+$	$-$
5	$+$	$+$	$+$

We see that -2 and 3 are the split points; they divide the real line into the three intervals $(-\infty, -2), (-2, 3)$, and $(3, \infty)$. On each of these intervals, $(x - 3)(x + 2)$ is of one sign; that is, it is either always positive or always negative. To find this sign in each interval, we use the **test points** $-3, 0$, and 5 (any points in the three intervals would do). Our results are shown in the margin.

The information we have obtained is summarized in the top half of Figure 5. We conclude that the solution set for $(x - 3)(x + 2) < 0$ is the interval $(-2, 3)$. Its graph is shown in the bottom half of Figure 5.

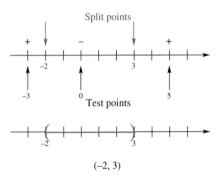

$(-2, 3)$

Figure 5

EXAMPLE 4 Solve $3x^2 - x - 2 > 0$.

SOLUTION Since

$$3x^2 - x - 2 = (3x + 2)(x - 1) = 3(x - 1)\left(x + \tfrac{2}{3}\right)$$

the split points are $-\tfrac{2}{3}$ and 1. These points, together with the test points $-2, 0$, and 2, establish the information shown in the top part of Figure 6. We conclude that the solution set of the inequality consists of the points in either $\left(-\infty, -\tfrac{2}{3}\right)$ or $(1, \infty)$. In set language, the solution set is the **union** (symbolized by $\cup$) of these two intervals; that is, it is $\left(-\infty, -\tfrac{2}{3}\right) \cup (1, \infty)$.

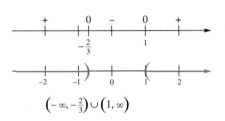

$\left(-\infty, -\tfrac{2}{3}\right) \cup \left(1, \infty\right)$

Figure 6

EXAMPLE 5 Solve $\dfrac{x - 1}{x + 2} \geq 0$.

SOLUTION Our inclination to multiply both sides by $x + 2$ leads to an immediate dilemma, since $x + 2$ may be either positive or negative. Should we reverse the inequality sign or leave it alone? Rather than try to untangle this problem (which would require breaking it into two cases), we observe that the quotient $(x - 1)/(x + 2)$ can change sign only at the split points of the numerator and denominator, that is, at 1 and -2. The test points $-3, 0$, and 2 yield the information displayed in the top part of Figure 7. The symbol u indicates that the quotient is undefined at -2. We conclude that the solution set is $(-\infty, -2) \cup [1, \infty)$. Note that -2 is not in the solution set because the quotient is undefined there. On the other hand, 1 is included because the inequality is true when $x = 1$.

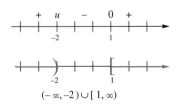

$(-\infty, -2) \cup [1, \infty)$

Figure 7

EXAMPLE 6 Solve $(x + 1)(x - 1)^2(x - 3) \leq 0$.

SOLUTION The split points are $-1, 1$ and 3, which divide the real line into four intervals, as shown in Figure 8. After testing these intervals, we conclude that the solution set is $[-1, 1] \cup [1, 3]$, which is the interval $[-1, 3]$.

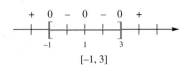

$[-1, 3]$

Figure 8

EXAMPLE 7 Solve $2.9 < \dfrac{1}{x} < 3.1$.

SOLUTION It is tempting to multiply through by x, but this again brings up the dilemma that x may be positive or negative. In this case, however, $\frac{1}{x}$ must be between 2.9 and 3.1, which guarantees that x is positive. It is therefore permissible to multiply by x and not reverse the inequalities. Thus,

$$2.9x < 1 < 3.1x$$

At this point, we must break this compound inequality into two inequalities, which we solve separately.

$$2.9x < 1 \qquad \text{and} \qquad 1 < 3.1x$$
$$x < \frac{1}{2.9} \qquad \text{and} \qquad \frac{1}{3.1} < x$$

Any value of x that satisfies the original inequality must satisfy both of these inequalities. The solution set thus consists of those values of x satisfying

$$\frac{1}{3.1} < x < \frac{1}{2.9}$$

This inequality can be written as

$$\frac{10}{31} < x < \frac{10}{29}$$

The interval $\left(\frac{10}{31}, \frac{10}{29}\right)$ is shown in Figure 9. ■

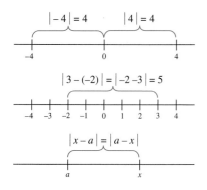

Figure 9

Absolute Values The concept of absolute value is extremely useful in calculus, and the reader should acquire skill in working with it. The **absolute value** of a real number x, denoted by $|x|$, is defined by

$$\boxed{\begin{aligned} |x| &= x && \text{if } x \geq 0 \\ |x| &= -x && \text{if } x < 0 \end{aligned}}$$

For example, $|6| = 6$, $|0| = 0$, and $|-5| = -(-5) = 5$. This two-pronged definition merits careful study. Note that it does not say that $|-x| = x$ (try $x = -5$ to see why). It is true that $|x|$ is always nonnegative; it is also true that $|-x| = |x|$.

One of the best ways to think of the absolute value of a number is as an undirected distance. In particular, $|x|$ is the distance between x and the origin. Similarly, $|x - a|$ is the distance between x and a (Figure 10).

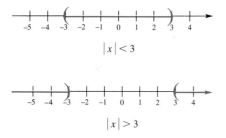

Figure 10

Properties Absolute values behave nicely under multiplication and division, but not so well under addition and subtraction.

Properties of Absolute Values

1. $|ab| = |a||b|$ 　　　　　　2. $\left|\dfrac{a}{b}\right| = \dfrac{|a|}{|b|}$

3. $|a + b| \leq |a| + |b|$ 　　(Triangle Inequality)

4. $|a - b| \geq ||a| - |b||$

Inequalities Involving Absolute Values If $|x| < 3$, then the distance between x and the origin must be less than 3. In other words, x must be simultaneously less than 3 *and* greater than -3; that is, $-3 < x < 3$. On the other hand, if $|x| > 3$, then the distance between x and the origin must be at least 3. This can happen when $x > 3$ *or* $x < -3$ (Figure 11). These are special cases of the following general statements that hold when $a > 0$.

(1) 　　　　　　$|x| < a \Leftrightarrow -a < x < a$
$$|x| > a \Leftrightarrow x < -a \ \text{ or } \ x > a$$

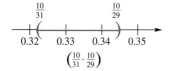

Figure 11

We can use these facts to solve inequalities involving absolute values, since they provide a way of removing absolute value signs.

EXAMPLE 8 Solve the inequality $|x - 4| < 2$ and show the solution set on the real line. Interpret the absolute value as a distance.

SOLUTION From the equations in (1), with x replaced by $|x - 4|$, we see that

$$|x - 4| < 2 \Leftrightarrow -2 < x - 4 < 2$$

When we add 4 to all three members of this latter inequality, we obtain $2 < x < 6$. The graph is shown in Figure 12.

In terms of distance, the symbol $|x - 4|$ represents the distance between x and 4. The inequality says that the distance between x and 4 is less than 2. The numbers x with this property are the numbers between 2 and 6; that is, $2 < x < 6$. ■

$|x-4| < 2$

Figure 12

The statements in the equations just before Example 8 are valid with $<$ and $>$ replaced by $\leq$ and $\geq$, respectively. We need the second statement in this form in our next example.

EXAMPLE 9 Solve the inequality $|3x - 5| \geq 1$ and show its solution set on the real line.

SOLUTION The given inequality may be written successively as

$$3x - 5 \leq -1 \quad \text{or} \quad 3x - 5 \geq 1$$
$$3x \leq 4 \quad \text{or} \quad 3x \geq 6$$
$$x \leq \tfrac{4}{3} \quad \text{or} \quad x \geq 2$$

The solution set is the union of two intervals, $\left(-\infty, \tfrac{4}{3}\right] \cup [2, \infty)$, and is shown in Figure 13. ■

$\left(-\infty, \tfrac{4}{3}\right] \cup [2, \infty)$

Figure 13

In Chapter 1, we will need to make the kind of manipulations illustrated by the next two examples. Delta (δ) and epsilon (ε) are the fourth and fifth letters, respectively, of the Greek alphabet and are traditionally used to stand for small positive numbers.

EXAMPLE 10 Let ε (epsilon) be a positive number. Show that

$$|x - 2| < \frac{\varepsilon}{5} \iff |5x - 10| < \varepsilon$$

In terms of distance, this says that the distance between x and 2 is less than $\varepsilon/5$ if and only if the distance between $5x$ and 10 is less than ε.

SOLUTION

$$
\begin{aligned}
|x - 2| < \frac{\varepsilon}{5} \iff & \quad 5|x - 2| \; < \varepsilon && \text{(multiplying by 5)} \\
\iff & \; |5||(x - 2)| \; < \varepsilon && (|5| = 5) \\
\iff & \quad |5(x - 2)| \; < \varepsilon && (|a||b| = |ab|) \\
\iff & \quad |5x - 10| \; < \varepsilon &&
\end{aligned}
$$
■

Finding Delta

Note two facts about our solution to Example 11.

1. The value we find for δ must depend on ε. Our choice is $\delta = \varepsilon/6$.
2. Any positive δ smaller than $\varepsilon/6$ is acceptable. For example $\delta = \varepsilon/7$ or $\delta = \varepsilon/(2\pi)$ are other correct choices.

EXAMPLE 11 Let ε be a positive number. Find a positive number δ (delta) such that

$$|x - 3| < \delta \implies |6x - 18| < \varepsilon$$

SOLUTION

$$
\begin{aligned}
|6x - 18| < \varepsilon \iff & \; |6(x - 3)| < \varepsilon \\
\iff & \; 6|x - 3| < \varepsilon && (|ab| = |a||b|) \\
\iff & \; |x - 3| < \frac{\varepsilon}{6} && \left(\text{multiplying by } \frac{1}{6}\right)
\end{aligned}
$$

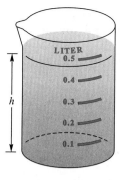

Figure 14

Therefore, we choose $\delta = \varepsilon/6$. Following the implications backward, we see that

$$|x - 3| < \delta \Rightarrow |x - 3| < \frac{\varepsilon}{6} \Rightarrow |6x - 18| < \varepsilon \quad \blacksquare$$

Here is a practical problem that uses the same type of reasoning.

EXAMPLE 12 A $\frac{1}{2}$-liter (500 cubic centimeter) glass beaker has an inner radius of 4 centimeters. How closely must we measure the height h of water in the beaker to be sure that we have $\frac{1}{2}$ liter of water with an error of less than 1%, that is, an error of less than 5 cubic centimeters? See Figure 14.

SOLUTION The volume V of water in the glass is given by the formula $V = 16\pi h$. We want $|V - 500| < 5$ or, equivalently, $|16\pi h - 500| < 5$. Now

$$|16\pi h - 500| < 5 \Leftrightarrow \left|16\pi\left(h - \frac{500}{16\pi}\right)\right| < 5$$

$$\Leftrightarrow \quad 16\pi\left|h - \frac{500}{16\pi}\right| < 5$$

$$\Leftrightarrow \quad \left|h - \frac{500}{16\pi}\right| < \frac{5}{16\pi}$$

$$\Leftrightarrow \quad |h - 9.947| < 0.09947 \approx 0.1$$

Thus, we must measure the height to an accuracy of about 0.1 centimeter, or 1 millimeter. $\blacksquare$

Quadratic Formula Most students will recall the **Quadratic Formula.** The solutions to the quadratic equation $ax^2 + bx + c = 0$ are given by

$$x = \frac{-b \pm \sqrt{b^2 - 4ac}}{2a}$$

The number $d = b^2 - 4ac$ is called the **discriminant** of the quadratic equation. The equation $ax^2 + bx + c = 0$ has two real solutions if $d > 0$, one real solution if $d = 0$, and no real solutions if $d < 0$. With the Quadratic Formula, we can easily solve quadratic inequalities even if they do not factor by inspection.

EXAMPLE 13 Solve $x^2 - 2x - 4 \leq 0$.

SOLUTION The two solutions of $x^2 - 2x - 4 = 0$ are

$$x_1 = \frac{-(-2) - \sqrt{4 + 16}}{2} = 1 - \sqrt{5} \approx -1.24$$

and

$$x_2 = \frac{-(-2) + \sqrt{4 + 16}}{2} = 1 + \sqrt{5} \approx 3.24$$

Thus,

$$x^2 - 2x - 4 = (x - x_1)(x - x_2) = \left(x - 1 + \sqrt{5}\right)\left(x - 1 - \sqrt{5}\right)$$

The split points $1 - \sqrt{5}$ and $1 + \sqrt{5}$ divide the real line into three intervals (Figure 15). When we test them with the test points -2, 0, and 4, we conclude that the solution set for $x^2 - 2x - 4 \leq 0$ is $\left[1 - \sqrt{5}, 1 + \sqrt{5}\right]$. $\blacksquare$

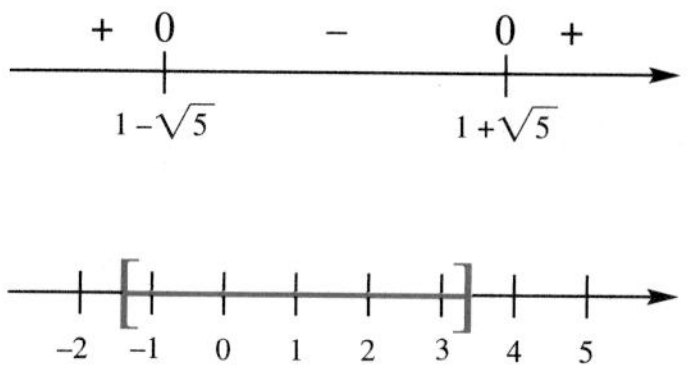

Squares Turning to squares, we notice that

$$|x|^2 = x^2 \quad \text{and} \quad |x| = \sqrt{x^2}$$

Notation for Square Roots

Every positive number has two square roots. For example, the two square roots of 9 are 3 and -3. We sometimes represent these two numbers as ± 3. For $a \geq 0$, the symbol $\sqrt{a}$, called the **principal square root** of a, denotes the nonnegative square root of a. Thus, $\sqrt{9} = 3$ and $\sqrt{121} = 11$. It is incorrect to write $\sqrt{16} = \pm 4$ because $\sqrt{16}$ means the nonnegative square root of 16, that is, 4. The number 7 has two square roots, which are written as $\pm\sqrt{7}$, but $\sqrt{7}$ represents a single real number. Just remember this:

$$a^2 = 16$$

has two solutions, $a = -4$ and $a = 4$, but

$$\sqrt{16} = 4$$

Figure 15

Notation for Roots
If n is even and $a \geq 0$ the symbol $\sqrt[n]{a}$ denotes the nonnegative nth root of a. When n is odd, there is only one real nth root of a, denoted by the symbol $\sqrt[n]{a}$. Thus, $\sqrt[4]{16} = 2$, $\sqrt[3]{27} = 3$, and $\sqrt[3]{-8} = -2$.

These follow from the property $|a||b| = |ab|$.

Does the squaring operation preserve inequalities? In general, the answer is no. For instance, $-3 < 2$, but $(-3)^2 > 2^2$. On the other hand, $2 < 3$ and $2^2 < 3^2$. If we are dealing with nonnegative numbers, then $a < b \Leftrightarrow a^2 < b^2$. A useful variant of this (see Problem 63) is

$$|x| < |y| \Leftrightarrow x^2 < y^2$$

EXAMPLE 14 Solve the inequality $|3x + 1| < 2|x - 6|$.

SOLUTION This inequality is more difficult to solve than our earlier examples, because there are two sets of absolute value signs. We can remove both of them by using the last boxed result.

$$
\begin{aligned}
|3x + 1| < 2|x - 6| &\Leftrightarrow & |3x + 1| < |2x - 12| \\
&\Leftrightarrow & (3x + 1)^2 < (2x - 12)^2 \\
&\Leftrightarrow & 9x^2 + 6x + 1 < 4x^2 - 48x + 144 \\
&\Leftrightarrow & 5x^2 + 54x - 143 < 0 \\
&\Leftrightarrow & (x + 13)(5x - 11) < 0
\end{aligned}
$$

The split points for this quadratic inequality are -13 and $\frac{11}{5}$; they divide the real line into the three intervals: $(-\infty, -13)$, $\left(-13, \frac{11}{5}\right)$, and $\left(\frac{11}{5}, \infty\right)$. When we use the test points $-14, 0$, and 3, we discover that only the points in $\left(-13, \frac{11}{5}\right)$ satisfy the inequality. ∎

Concepts Review

1. The set $\{x: -1 \leq x < 5\}$ is written in interval notation as _____ and the set $\{x: x \leq -2\}$ is written as _____.

2. If $a/b < 0$, then either $a < 0$ and _____ or $a > 0$ and _____.

3. Which of the following are always true?
(a) $|-x| = x$ (b) $|x|^2 = x^2$
(c) $|xy| = |x||y|$ (d) $\sqrt{x^2} = x$

4. The inequality $|x - 2| \leq 3$ is equivalent to

_____ $\leq x \leq$ _____.

Problem Set 1.2

1. Show each of the following intervals on the real line.
(a) $[-1, 1]$ (b) $(-4, 1]$
(c) $(-4, 1)$ (d) $[1, 4]$
(e) $[-1, \infty)$ (f) $(-\infty, 0]$

2. Use the notation of Problem 1 to describe the following intervals.

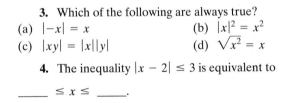

In each of Problems 3–26, express the solution set of the given inequality in interval notation and sketch its graph.

3. $x - 7 < 2x - 5$ **4.** $3x - 5 < 4x - 6$

5. $7x - 2 \leq 9x + 3$ **6.** $5x - 3 > 6x - 4$

7. $-4 < 3x + 2 < 5$ **8.** $-3 < 4x - 9 < 11$

9. $-3 < 1 - 6x \leq 4$ **10.** $4 < 5 - 3x < 7$

11. $x^2 + 2x - 12 < 0$ **12.** $x^2 - 5x - 6 > 0$

13. $2x^2 + 5x - 3 > 0$ **14.** $4x^2 - 5x - 6 < 0$

15. $\dfrac{x + 4}{x - 3} \leq 0$ **16.** $\dfrac{3x - 2}{x - 1} \geq 0$

17. $\dfrac{2}{x} < 5$ **18.** $\dfrac{7}{4x} \leq 7$

19. $\dfrac{1}{3x - 2} \leq 4$ **20.** $\dfrac{3}{x + 5} > 2$

21. $(x + 2)(x - 1)(x - 3) > 0$

22. $(2x + 3)(3x - 1)(x - 2) < 0$

23. $(2x - 3)(x - 1)^2(x - 3) \geq 0$

24. $(2x - 3)(x - 1)^2(x - 3) > 0$

25. $x^3 - 5x^2 - 6x < 0$ **26.** $x^3 - x^2 - x + 1 > 0$

27. Tell whether each of the following is true or false.

(a) $-3 < -7$ (b) $-1 > -17$ (c) $-3 < -\dfrac{22}{7}$

28. Tell whether each of the following is true or false.

(a) $-5 > -\sqrt{26}$ (b) $\dfrac{6}{7} < \dfrac{34}{39}$ (c) $-\dfrac{5}{7} < -\dfrac{44}{59}$

29. Assume that $a > 0, b > 0$. Prove each statement. *Hint:* Each part requires two proofs: one for $\Rightarrow$ and one for $\Leftarrow$.

(a) $a < b \Leftrightarrow a^2 < b^2$ (b) $a < b \Leftrightarrow \dfrac{1}{a} > \dfrac{1}{b}$

30. Which of the following are true if $a \leq b$?

(a) $a^2 \leq ab$ (b) $a - 3 \leq b - 3$

(c) $a^3 \leq a^2b$ (d) $-a \leq -b$

31. Find all values of x that satisfy both inequalities simultaneously.

(a) $3x + 7 > 1$ and $2x + 1 < 3$

(b) $3x + 7 > 1$ and $2x + 1 > -4$

(c) $3x + 7 > 1$ and $2x + 1 < -4$

32. Find all the values of x that satisfy at least one of the two inequalities.

(a) $2x - 7 > 1$ or $2x + 1 < 3$

(b) $2x - 7 \leq 1$ or $2x + 1 < 3$

(c) $2x - 7 \leq 1$ or $2x + 1 > 3$

33. Solve for x, expressing your answer in interval notation.

(a) $(x + 1)(x^2 + 2x - 7) \geq x^2 - 1$

(b) $x^4 - 2x^2 \geq 8$

(c) $(x^2 + 1)^2 - 7(x^2 + 1) + 10 < 0$

34. Solve each inequality. Express your solution in interval notation.

(a) $1.99 < \dfrac{1}{x} < 2.01$ (b) $2.99 < \dfrac{1}{x + 2} < 3.01$

In Problems 35–44, find the solution sets of the given inequalities.

35. $|x - 2| \geq 5$ **36.** $|x + 2| < 1$

37. $|4x + 5| \leq 10$ **38.** $|2x - 1| > 2$

39. $\left|\dfrac{2x}{7} - 5\right| \geq 7$ **40.** $\left|\dfrac{x}{4} + 1\right| < 1$

41. $|5x - 6| > 1$ **42.** $|2x - 7| > 3$

43. $\left|\dfrac{1}{x} - 3\right| > 6$ **44.** $\left|2 + \dfrac{5}{x}\right| > 1$

In Problems 45–48, solve the given quadratic inequality using the Quadratic Formula.

45. $x^2 - 3x - 4 \geq 0$ **46.** $x^2 - 4x + 4 \leq 0$

47. $3x^2 + 17x - 6 > 0$ **48.** $14x^2 + 11x - 15 \leq 0$

In Problems 49–52, show that the indicated implication is true.

49. $|x - 3| < 0.5 \Rightarrow |5x - 15| < 2.5$

50. $|x + 2| < 0.3 \Rightarrow |4x + 8| < 1.2$

51. $|x - 2| < \dfrac{\varepsilon}{6} \Rightarrow |6x - 12| < \varepsilon$

52. $|x + 4| < \dfrac{\varepsilon}{2} \Rightarrow |2x + 8| < \varepsilon$

In Problems 53–56, find δ (depending on ε) so that the given implication is true.

53. $|x - 5| < \delta \Rightarrow |3x - 15| < \varepsilon$

54. $|x - 2| < \delta \Rightarrow |4x - 8| < \varepsilon$

55. $|x + 6| < \delta \Rightarrow |6x + 36| < \varepsilon$

56. $|x + 5| < \delta \Rightarrow |5x + 25| < \varepsilon$

57. On a lathe, you are to turn out a disk (thin right circular cylinder) of circumference 10 inches. This is done by continually measuring the diameter as you make the disk smaller. How closely must you measure the diameter if you can tolerate an error of at most 0.02 inch in the circumference?

58. Fahrenheit temperatures and Celsius temperatures are related by the formula $C = \frac{5}{9}(F - 32)$. An experiment requires that a solution be kept at $50°C$ with an error of at most 3% (or $1.5°$). You have only a Fahrenheit thermometer. What error are you allowed on it?

In Problems 59–62, solve the inequalities.

59. $|x - 1| < 2|x - 3|$ **60.** $|2x - 1| \geq |x + 1|$

61. $2|2x - 3| < |x + 10|$ **62.** $|3x - 1| < 2|x + 6|$

63. Prove that $|x| < |y| \Leftrightarrow x^2 < y^2$ by giving a reason for each of these steps:

$$|x| < |y| \Rightarrow |x||x| \leq |x||y| \quad \text{and} \quad |x||y| < |y||y|$$
$$\Rightarrow |x|^2 < |y|^2$$
$$\Rightarrow x^2 < y^2$$

Conversely,

$$x^2 < y^2 \Rightarrow |x|^2 < |y|^2$$
$$\Rightarrow |x|^2 - |y|^2 < 0$$
$$\Rightarrow (|x| - |y|)(|x| + |y|) < 0$$
$$\Rightarrow |x| - |y| < 0$$
$$\Rightarrow |x| < |y|$$

64. Use the result of Problem 63 to show that

$$0 < a < b \Rightarrow \sqrt{a} < \sqrt{b}$$

65. Use the properties of the absolute value to show that each of the following is true.

(a) $|a - b| \leq |a| + |b|$ (b) $|a - b| \geq |a| - |b|$

(c) $|a + b + c| \leq |a| + |b| + |c|$

66. Use the Triangle Inequality and the fact that $0 < |a| < |b| \Rightarrow 1/|b| < 1/|a|$ to establish the following chain of inequalities.

$$\left|\frac{1}{x^2 + 3} - \frac{1}{|x| + 2}\right| \leq \frac{1}{x^2 + 3} + \frac{1}{|x| + 2} \leq \frac{1}{3} + \frac{1}{2}$$

67. Show that (see Problem 66)

$$\left|\frac{x - 2}{x^2 + 9}\right| \leq \frac{|x| + 2}{9}$$

68. Show that

$$|x| \leq 2 \Rightarrow \left|\frac{x^2 + 2x + 7}{x^2 + 1}\right| \leq 15$$

69. Show that

$$|x| \le 1 \Rightarrow \left|x^4 + \tfrac{1}{2}x^3 + \tfrac{1}{4}x^2 + \tfrac{1}{8}x + \tfrac{1}{16}\right| < 2$$

70. Show each of the following:

(a) $x < x^2$ for $x < 0$ or $x > 1$

(b) $x^2 < x$ for $0 < x < 1$

71. Show that $a \ne 0 \Rightarrow a^2 + 1/a^2 \ge 2$. *Hint:* Consider $(a - 1/a)^2$.

72. The number $\tfrac{1}{2}(a + b)$ is called the average, or **arithmetic mean,** of a and b. Show that the arithmetic mean of two numbers is between the two numbers; that is, prove that

$$a < b \Rightarrow a < \frac{a + b}{2} < b$$

73. The number $\sqrt{ab}$ is called the **geometric mean** of two positive numbers a and b. Prove that

$$0 < a < b \Rightarrow a < \sqrt{ab} < b$$

74. For two positive numbers a and b, prove that

$$\sqrt{ab} \le \tfrac{1}{2}(a + b)$$

This is the simplest version of a famous inequality called the **geometric mean–arithmetic mean inequality.**

75. Show that, among all rectangles with given perimeter p, the square has the largest area. *Hint:* If a and b denote the lengths of adjacent sides of a rectangle of perimeter p, then the area is ab, and for the square the area is $a^2 = [(a + b)/2]^2$. Now see Problem 74.

76. Solve $1 + x + x^2 + x^3 + \cdots + x^{99} \le 0$.

77. The formula $\dfrac{1}{R} = \dfrac{1}{R_1} + \dfrac{1}{R_2} + \dfrac{1}{R_3}$ gives the total resistance R in an electric circuit due to three resistances, R_1, R_2, and R_3, connected in parallel. If $10 \le R_1 \le 20, 20 \le R_2 \le 30$, and $30 \le R_3 \le 40$, find the range of values for R.

78. The radius of a sphere is measured to be about 10 inches. Determine a tolerance δ in this measurement that will ensure an error of less than 0.01 square inch in the calculated value of the surface area of the sphere.

Answers to Concepts Review **1.** $[-1, 5); (-\infty, -2]$
2. $b > 0; b < 0$ **3.** (b) and (c) **4.** $-1 \le x \le 5$

1.3
The Rectangular Coordinate System

In the plane, produce two copies of the real line, one horizontal and the other vertical, so that they intersect at the zero points of the two lines. The two lines are called **coordinate axes;** their intersection is labeled O and is called the **origin.** By convention, the horizontal line is called the **x-axis** and the vertical line is called the **y-axis.** The positive half of the x-axis is to the right; the positive half of the y-axis is upward. The coordinate axes divide the plane into four regions, called **quadrants,** labeled I, II, III, and IV, as shown in Figure 1.

Each point P in the plane can now be assigned a pair of numbers, called its **Cartesian coordinates.** If vertical and horizontal lines through P intersect the x- and y-axes at a and b, respectively, then P has coordinates (a, b) (see Figure 2). We call (a, b) an **ordered pair** of numbers because it makes a difference which number is first. The first number a is the **x-coordinate;** the second number b is the **y-coordinate.**

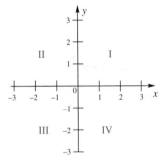

Figure 1

The Distance Formula With coordinates in hand, we can introduce a simple formula for the distance between any two points in the plane. It is based on the **Pythagorean Theorem,** which says that, if a and b measure the two legs of a right triangle and c measures its hypotenuse (Figure 3), then

$$a^2 + b^2 = c^2$$

Conversely, this relationship between the three sides of a triangle holds only for a right triangle.

Now consider any two points P and Q, with coordinates (x_1, y_1) and (x_2, y_2), respectively. Together with R, the point with coordinates (x_2, y_1), P and Q are vertices of a right triangle (Figure 4). The lengths of PR and RQ are $|x_2 - x_1|$ and $|y_2 - y_1|$, respectively. When we apply the Pythagorean Theorem and take the principal square root of both sides, we obtain the following expression for the **Distance Formula**

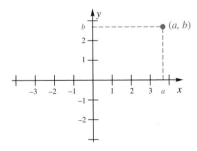

Figure 2

$$d(P, Q) = \sqrt{(x_2 - x_1)^2 + (y_2 - y_1)^2}$$

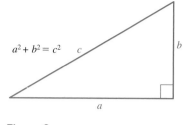

$$a^2 + b^2 = c^2$$

Figure 3

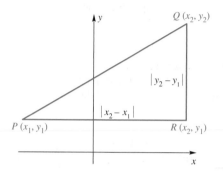

Figure 4

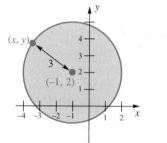

Figure 5

Circle ↔ Equation
To say that
$(x + 1)^2 + (y - 2)^2 = 9$
is the equation of the circle of radius 3 with center $(-1, 2)$ means two things:
1. If a point is on this circle, then its coordinates (x, y) satisfy the equation.
2. If x and y are numbers that satisfy the equation, then they are the coordinates of a point on the circle.

EXAMPLE 1 Find the distance between

(a) $P(-2, 3)$ and $Q(4, -1)$ 　　　　　　(b) $P(\sqrt{2}, \sqrt{3})$ and $Q(\pi, \pi)$

SOLUTION

(a) $d(P, Q) = \sqrt{(4 - (-2))^2 + (-1 - 3)^2} = \sqrt{36 + 16} = \sqrt{52} \approx 7.21$

(b) $d(P, Q) = \sqrt{(\pi - \sqrt{2})^2 + (\pi - \sqrt{3})^2} \approx \sqrt{4.971} \approx 2.23$ ■

The formula holds even if the two points lie on the same horizontal line or the same vertical line. Thus, the distance between $P(-2, 2)$ and $Q(6, 2)$ is

$$\sqrt{(6-(-2))^2 + (2 - 2)^2} = \sqrt{64} = 8$$

The Equation of a Circle　It is a small step from the distance formula to the equation of a circle. A **circle** is the set of points that lie at a fixed distance (the *radius*) from a fixed point (the *center*). Consider, for example, the circle of radius 3 with center at $(-1, 2)$ (Figure 5). Let (x, y) denote any point on this circle. By the Distance Formula,

$$\sqrt{(x + 1)^2 + (y - 2)^2} = 3$$

When we square both sides, we obtain

$$(x + 1)^2 + (y - 2)^2 = 9$$

which we call the equation of this circle.

　　More generally, the circle of radius r and center (h, k) has the equation

(1)　　　　　　$\boxed{(x - h)^2 + (y - k)^2 = r^2}$

We call this the **standard equation of a circle.**

EXAMPLE 2 Find the standard equation of a circle of radius 5 and center $(1, -5)$. Also find the y-coordinates of the two points on this circle with x-coordinate 2.

SOLUTION The desired equation is

$$(x - 1)^2 + (y + 5)^2 = 25$$

To accomplish the second task, we substitute $x = 2$ in the equation and solve for y.

$$(2 - 1)^2 + (y + 5)^2 = 25$$

$$(y + 5)^2 = 24$$

$$y + 5 = \pm\sqrt{24}$$

$$y = -5 \pm \sqrt{24} = -5 \pm 2\sqrt{6}$$ ■

　　If we expand the two squares in the boxed equation (1) and combine the constants, then the equation takes the form

$$x^2 + ax + y^2 + by = c$$

This suggests asking whether every equation of the latter form is the equation of a circle. The answer is yes, with some obvious exceptions.

EXAMPLE 3 Show that the equation

$$x^2 - 2x + y^2 + 6y = -6$$

represents a circle, and find its center and radius.

SOLUTION We need to *complete the square*, a process important in many contexts. To complete the square of $x^2 \pm bx$, add $(b/2)^2$. Thus, we add $(-2/2)^2 = 1$ to $x^2 - 2x$ and $(6/2)^2 = 9$ to $y^2 + 6y$, and of course we must add the same numbers to the right side of the equation, to obtain

$$x^2 - 2x + 1 + y^2 + 6y + 9 = -6 + 1 + 9$$
$$(x - 1)^2 + (y + 3)^2 = 4$$

The last equation is in standard form. It is the equation of a circle with center $(1, -3)$ and radius 2. If, as a result of this process, we had come up with a negative number on the right side of the final equation, the equation would not have represented any curve. If we had come up with zero, the equation would have represented the single point $(1, -3)$. ∎

The Midpoint Formula Consider two points $P(x_1, y_1)$ and $Q(x_2, y_2)$ with $x_1 \le x_2$ and $y_1 \le y_2$, as in Figure 6. The distance between x_1 and x_2 is $x_2 - x_1$. When we add half this distance, $\frac{1}{2}(x_2 - x_1)$, to x_1, we should get the number midway between x_1 and x_2.

$$x_1 + \frac{1}{2}(x_2 - x_1) = x_1 + \frac{1}{2}x_2 - \frac{1}{2}x_1 = \frac{1}{2}x_1 + \frac{1}{2}x_2 = \frac{x_1 + x_2}{2}$$

Thus, the point $(x_1 + x_2)/2$ is midway between x_1 and x_2 on the x-axis and, consequently, the midpoint M of the segment PQ has $(x_1 + x_2)/2$ as its x-coordinate. Similarly, we can show that $(y_1 + y_2)/2$ is the y-coordinate of M. Thus, we have the **Midpoint Formula.**

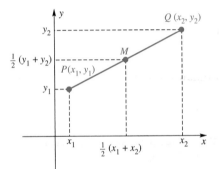

Figure 6

The midpoint of the line segment joining $P(x_1, y_1)$ and $Q(x_2, y_2)$ is

$$\left(\frac{x_1 + x_2}{2}, \frac{y_1 + y_2}{2} \right)$$

EXAMPLE 4 Find the equation of the circle having the segment from $(1, 3)$ to $(7, 11)$ as a diameter.

SOLUTION The center of the circle is at the midpoint of the diameter; thus, the center has coordinates $(1 + 7)/2 = 4$ and $(3 + 11)/2 = 7$. The length of the diameter, obtained from the distance formula, is

$$\sqrt{(7 - 1)^2 + (11 - 3)^2} = \sqrt{36 + 64} = 10$$

and so the radius of the circle is 5. The equation of the circle is

$$(x - 4)^2 + (y - 7)^2 = 25$$ ∎

Lines Consider the line in Figure 7. From point A to point B, there is a **rise** (vertical change) of 2 units and a **run** (horizontal change) of 5 units. We say that the line has a slope of $\frac{2}{5}$. In general (Figure 8), for a line through $A(x_1, y_1)$ and $B(x_2, y_2)$, where $x_1 \ne x_2$, we define the **slope** m of that line by

$$m = \frac{\text{rise}}{\text{run}} = \frac{y_2 - y_1}{x_2 - x_1}$$

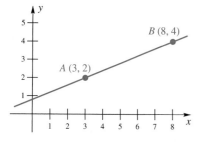

Figure 7

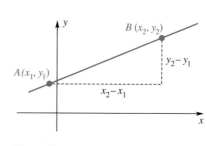

Figure 8

Figure 9

Does the value we get for the slope depend on which pair of points we use for A and B? The similar triangles in Figure 9 show us that

$$\frac{y_2' - y_1'}{x_2' - x_1'} = \frac{y_2 - y_1}{x_2 - x_1}$$

Thus, points A' and B' would do just as well as A and B. It does not even matter whether A is to the left or right of B, since

$$\frac{y_1 - y_2}{x_1 - x_2} = \frac{y_2 - y_1}{x_2 - x_1}$$

All that matters is that we subtract the coordinates in the same order in the numerator and the denominator.

The slope m is a measure of the steepness of a line, as Figure 10 illustrates. Notice that a horizontal line has zero slope, a line that rises to the right has positive slope, and a line that falls to the right has negative slope. The larger the absolute value of the slope is, the steeper the line. The concept of slope for a vertical line makes no sense, since it would involve division by zero. Therefore, slope for a vertical line is left undefined.

Grade and Pitch

The international symbol for the slope of a road (called the grade) is shown below. The grade is given as a percentage. A grade of 10% corresponds to a slope of ±0.10.

Carpenters use the term *pitch*. A 9:12 pitch corresponds to a slope of $\frac{9}{12}$.

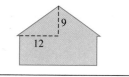

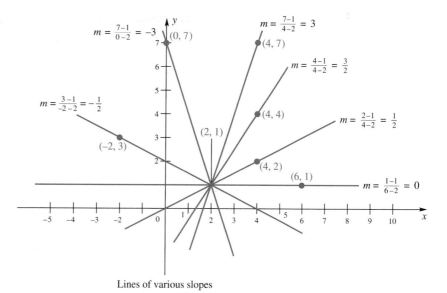

Lines of various slopes

Figure 10

The Point–Slope Form   Consider again the line of our opening discussion; it is reproduced in Figure 11. We know that this line

1. passes through $(3, 2)$ and
2. has slope $\frac{2}{5}$.

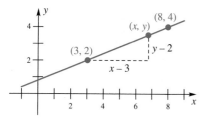

Figure 11

Take any other point on this line, such as one with coordinates (x, y). If we use this point and the point $(3, 2)$ to measure slope, we must get $\frac{2}{5}$, that is,

$$\frac{y - 2}{x - 3} = \frac{2}{5}$$

or, after multiplying by $x - 3$,

$$y - 2 = \tfrac{2}{5}(x - 3)$$

Notice that this last equation is satisfied by all points on the line, even by $(3, 2)$. Moreover, none of the points not on the line can satisfy this equation.

What we have just done in an example can be done in general. The line passing through the (fixed) point (x_1, y_1) with slope m has equation

$$\boxed{y - y_1 = m(x - x_1)}$$

We call this the **point–slope** form of the equation of a line.

Consider once more the line of our example. That line passes through $(8, 4)$ as well as $(3, 2)$. If we use $(8, 4)$ as (x_1, y_1), we get the equation

$$y - 4 = \tfrac{2}{5}(x - 8)$$

which looks quite different from $y - 2 = \tfrac{2}{5}(x - 3)$. However, both can be simplified to $5y - 2x = 4$; they are equivalent.

EXAMPLE 5 Find an equation of the line through $(-4, 2)$ and $(6, -1)$.

SOLUTION The slope is $m = (-1 - 2)/(6 + 4) = -\tfrac{3}{10}$. Thus, using $(-4, 2)$ as the fixed point, we obtain the equation

$$y - 2 = -\tfrac{3}{10}(x + 4) \qquad \blacksquare$$

The Slope–Intercept Form The equation of a line can be expressed in various forms. Suppose that we are given the slope m for a line and the y-intercept b (i.e., the line intersects the y-axis at $(0, b)$), as shown in Figure 12. Choosing $(0, b)$ as (x_1, y_1) and applying the point-slope form, we get

$$y - b = m(x - 0)$$

which we can rewrite as

$$\boxed{y = mx + b}$$

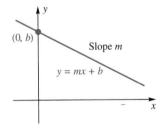

Figure 12

The latter is called the **slope–intercept** form. Any time we see an equation written this way, we recognize it as a line and can immediately read its slope and y-intercept. For example, consider the equation

$$3x - 2y + 4 = 0$$

If we solve for y, we get

$$y = \tfrac{3}{2}x + 2$$

It is the equation of a line with slope $\tfrac{3}{2}$ and y-intercept 2.

Equation of a Vertical Line Vertical lines do not fit within the preceding discussion since the concept of slope is not defined for them. But they do have equations, very simple ones. The line in Figure 13 has equation $x = \tfrac{5}{2}$, since a point is on the line if and only if it satisfies this equation. The equation of any vertical line can be put in the form $x = k$, where k is a constant. It should be noted that the equation of a horizontal line can be written in the form $y = k$.

The Form $Ax + By + C = 0$ It would be nice to have a form that covered all lines, including vertical lines. Consider, for example,

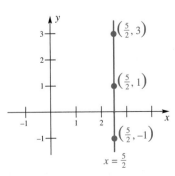

Figure 13

$$y - 2 = -4(x + 2)$$

$$y = 5x - 3$$

$$x = 5$$

These can be rewritten (by taking everything to the left-hand side) as follows:

$$4x + y + 6 = 0$$

$$-5x + y + 3 = 0$$

$$x + 0y - 5 = 0$$

All are of the form

$$Ax + By + C = 0, \qquad A \text{ and } B \text{ not both } 0$$

which we call the **general linear equation.** It takes only a moment's thought to see that the equation of any line can be put in this form. Conversely, the graph of the general linear equation is always a line.

Parallel Lines Two lines that have no points in common are said to be parallel. For example, the lines whose equations are $y = 2x + 2$ and $y = 2x + 5$ are parallel because, for every value of x, the second line is three units above the first (see Figure 14). Similarly, the lines with equations $-2x + 3y + 12 = 0$ and $4x - 6y = 5$ are parallel. To see this, solve each equation for y (i.e., put each in the slope–intercept form). This gives $y = \frac{2}{3}x - 4$ and $y = \frac{2}{3}x - \frac{5}{6}$, respectively. Again, because the slopes are equal, one line will be a fixed number of units above or below the other, so the lines will never intersect. If two lines have the same slope *and* the same y-intercept, then the two lines are the same, and they are not parallel.

We summarize by stating that two nonvertical lines are parallel if and only if they have the same slope and different y-intercepts. Two vertical lines are parallel if and only if they are distinct lines.

EXAMPLE 6 Find the equation of the line through $(6, 8)$ that is parallel to the line with equation $3x - 5y = 11$.

SOLUTION When we solve $3x - 5y = 11$ for y, we obtain $y = \frac{3}{5}x - \frac{11}{5}$, from which we read the slope of the line to be $\frac{3}{5}$. The equation of the desired line is

$$y - 8 = \frac{3}{5}(x - 6)$$

or, equivalently, $y = \frac{3}{5}x + \frac{22}{5}$. We know that these lines are distinct because the y-intercepts are different. ■

Perpendicular Lines Is there a simple slope condition that characterizes perpendicular lines? Yes; *two nonvertical lines are perpendicular if and only if their slopes are negative reciprocals of each other.* To see why this is true, consider Figure 15. This picture tells almost the whole story; it is left as an exercise (Problem 57) to construct a geometric proof that the two (nonvertical) lines are perpenicular if and only if $m_2 = -1/m_1$.

EXAMPLE 7 Find the equation of the line through the point of intersection of the lines with equations $3x + 4y = 8$ and $6x - 10y = 7$ that is perpendicular to the first of these two lines (Figure 16).

SOLUTION To find the point of intersection of the two lines, we multiply the first equation by -2 and add it to the second equation.

Summary: Equations of Lines

Vertical line: $x = k$

Horizontal line: $y = k$

Point–slope form:
$$y - y_1 = m(x - x_1)$$

Slope–intercept form:
$$y = mx + b$$

General linear equation:
$$Ax + By + C = 0$$

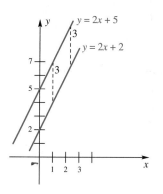

Figure 14

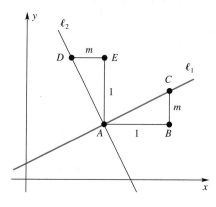

Figure 15

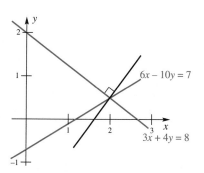

Figure 16

$$-6x - 8y = -16$$
$$\underline{6x - 10y = 7}$$
$$-18y = -9$$
$$y = \frac{1}{2}$$

Substituting $y = \frac{1}{2}$ in either of the original equations yields $x = 2$. The point of intersection is $\left(2, \frac{1}{2}\right)$. When we solve the first equation for y (to put it in slope-intercept form), we get $y = -\frac{3}{4}x + 2$. A line perpendicular to it has slope $\frac{4}{3}$. The equation of the required line is

$$y - \frac{1}{2} = \frac{4}{3}(x - 2) \qquad \blacksquare$$

Concepts Review

1. The distance between the points $(-2, 3)$ and (x, y) is _____.

2. The equation of the circle of radius 5 and center $(-4, 2)$ is _____.

3. The midpoint of the line segment joining $(-2, 3)$ and $(5, 7)$ is _____.

4. The line through (a, b) and (c, d) has slope $m =$ _____ provided $a \neq c$.

Problem Set 1.3

In Problems 1–4, plot the given points in the coordinate plane and then find the distance between them.

1. $(3, 1), (1, 1)$ **2.** $(-3, 5), (2, -2)$

3. $(4, 5), (5, -8)$ **4.** $(-1, 5), (6, 3)$

5. Show that the triangle whose vertices are $(5, 3), (-2, 4)$, and $(10, 8)$ is isosceles.

6. Show that the triangle whose vertices are $(2, -4), (4, 0)$, and $(8, -2)$ is a right triangle.

7. The points $(3, -1)$ and $(3, 3)$ are two vertices of a square. Give three other pairs of possible vertices.

8. Find the point on the x-axis that is equidistant from $(3, 1)$ and $(6, 4)$.

9. Find the distance between $(-2, 3)$ and the midpoint of the segment joining $(-2, -2)$ and $(4, 3)$.

10. Find the length of the line segment joining the midpoints of the segments AB and CD, where $A = (1, 3)$, $B = (2, 6)$, $C = (4, 7)$, and $D = (3, 4)$.

In Problems 11–16, find the equation of the circle satisfying the given conditions.

11. Center $(1, 1)$, radius 1

12. Center $(-2, 3)$, radius 4

13. Center $(2, -1)$, goes through $(5, 3)$

14. Center $(4, 3)$, goes through $(6, 2)$

15. Diameter AB, where $A = (1, 3)$ and $B = (3, 7)$

16. Center $(3, 4)$ and tangent to x-axis

In Problems 17–22, find the center and radius of the circle with the given equation.

17. $x^2 + 2x + 10 + y^2 - 6y - 10 = 0$

18. $x^2 + y^2 - 6y = 16$

19. $x^2 + y^2 - 12x + 35 = 0$

20. $x^2 + y^2 - 10x + 10y = 0$

21. $4x^2 + 16x + 15 + 4y^2 + 6y = 0$

22. $x^2 + 16x + \frac{105}{16} + 4y^2 + 3y = 0$

In Problems 23–28, find the slope of the line containing the given two points.

23. $(1, 1)$ and $(2, 2)$ **24.** $(3, 5)$ and $(4, 7)$

25. $(2, 3)$ and $(-5, -6)$ **26.** $(2, -4)$ and $(0, -6)$

27. $(3, 0)$ and $(0, 5)$ **28.** $(-6, 0)$ and $(0, 6)$

In Problems 29–34, find an equation for each line. Then write your answer in the form $Ax + By + C = 0$.

29. Through $(2, 2)$ with slope -1

30. Through $(3, 4)$ with slope -1

31. With y-intercept 3 and slope 2

32. With y-intercept 5 and slope 0

33. Through $(2, 3)$ and $(4, 8)$

34. Through $(4, 1)$ and $(8, 2)$

In Problems 35–38, find the slope and y-intercept of each line.

35. $3y = -2x + 1$ **36.** $-4y = 5x - 6$

37. $6 - 2y = 10x - 2$ **38.** $4x + 5y = -20$

39. Write an equation for the line through $(3, -3)$ that is
(a) parallel to the line $y = 2x + 5$;
(b) perpendicular to the line $y = 2x + 5$;
(c) parallel to the line $2x + 3y = 6$;
(d) perpendicular to the line $2x + 3y = 6$;
(e) parallel to the line through $(-1, 2)$ and $(3, -1)$;
(f) parallel to the line $x = 8$;
(g) perpendicular to the line $x = 8$.

40. Find the value of c for which the line $3x + cy = 5$
(a) passes through the point $(3, 1)$;
(b) is parallel to the y-axis;
(c) is parallel to the line $2x + y = -1$;
(d) has equal x- and y-intercepts;
(e) is perpendicular to the line $y - 2 = 3(x + 3)$.

41. Write the equation for the line through $(-2, -1)$ that is perpendicular to the line $y + 3 = -\frac{2}{3}(x - 5)$.

42. Find the value of k such that the line $kx - 3y = 10$
(a) is parallel to the line $y = 2x + 4$;
(b) is perpendicular to the line $y = 2x + 4$;
(c) is perpendicular to the line $2x + 3y = 6$.

43. Does $(3, 9)$ lie above or below the line $y = 3x - 1$?

44. Show that the equation of the line with x-intercept $a \neq 0$ and y-intercept $b \neq 0$ can be written as
$$\frac{x}{a} + \frac{y}{b} = 1$$

In Problems 45–48, find the coordinates of the point of intersection. Then write an equation for the line through that point perpendicular to the line given first.

45. $2x + 3y = 4$ **46.** $4x - 5y = 8$
        $-3x + y = 5$ $2x + y = -10$

47. $3x - 4y = 5$ **48.** $5x - 2y = 5$
        $2x + 3y = 9$ $2x + 3y = 6$

49. The points $(2, 3), (6, 3), (6, -1)$, and $(2, -1)$ are corners of a square. Find the equations of the inscribed and circumscribed circles.

50. A belt fits tightly around the two circles, with equations $(x - 1)^2 + (y + 2)^2 = 16$ and $(x + 9)^2 + (y - 10)^2 = 16$. How long is this belt?

51. Show that the midpoint of the hypotenuse of any right triangle is equidistant from the three vertices.

52. Find the equation of the circle circumscribed about the right triangle whose vertices are $(0, 0), (8, 0)$, and $(0, 6)$.

53. Show that the two circles $x^2 + y^2 - 4x - 2y - 11 = 0$ and $x^2 + y^2 + 20x - 12y + 72 = 0$ do not intersect. *Hint:* Find the distance between their centers.

54. What relationship between a, b, and c must hold if $x^2 + ax + y^2 + by + c = 0$ is the equation of a circle?

55. The ceiling of an attic makes an angle of $30°$ with the floor. A pipe of radius 2 inches is placed along the edge of the attic in such a way that one side of the pipe touches the ceiling and another side touches the floor (see Figure 17). What is the distance d from the edge of the attic to where the pipe touches the floor?

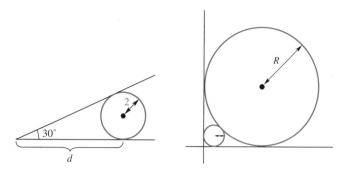

Figure 17   Figure 18

56. A circle of radius R is placed in the first quadrant as shown in Figure 18. What is the radius r of the largest circle that can be placed between the original circle and the origin?

57. Construct a geometric proof using Figure 15 that shows two lines are perpendicular if and only if their slopes are negative reciprocals of one another.

58. Show that the set of points that are twice as far from $(3, 4)$ as from $(1, 1)$ form a circle. Find its center and radius.

59. The Pythagorean Theorem says that the areas A, B, and C of the squares in Figure 19 satisfy $A + B = C$. Show that semicircles and equilateral triangles satisfy the same relation and then guess what a very general theorem says.

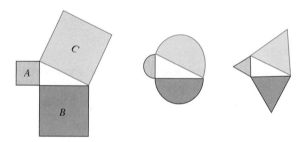

Figure 19

60. Consider a circle C and a point P exterior to the circle. Let line segment PT be tangent to C at T, and let the line through P and the center of C intersect C at M and N. Show that $(PM)(PN) = (PT)^2$.

61. A belt fits around the three circles $x^2 + y^2 = 4$, $(x - 8)^2 + y^2 = 4$, and $(x - 6)^2 + (y - 8)^2 = 4$, as shown in Figure 20. Find the length of this belt.

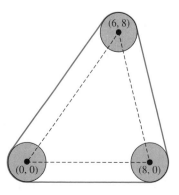

Figure 20

62. Study Problems 50 and 61. Consider a set of nonintersecting circles of radius r with centers at the vertices of a convex n-sided polygon having sides of lengths $d_1, d_2, \ldots, d_n$. How long is the belt that fits around these circles (in the manner of Figure 20)?

It can be shown that the distance d from the point (x_1, y_1) to the line $Ax + By + C = 0$ is

$$d = \frac{|Ax_1 + By_1 + C|}{\sqrt{A^2 + B^2}}$$

Use this result to find the distance from the given point to the given line.

63. $(-3, 2); 3x + 4y = 6$

64. $(4, -1); 2x - 2y + 4 = 0$

65. $(-2, -1); 5y = 12x + 1$

66. $(3, -1); y = 2x - 5$

In Problems 67 and 68, find the (perpendicular) distance between the given parallel lines. Hint: First find a point on one of the lines.

67. $2x + 4y = 7, 2x + 4y = 5$

68. $7x - 5y = 6, 7x - 5y = -1$

69. Find the equation for the line that bisects the line segment from $(-2, 3)$ to $(1, -2)$ and is at right angles to this line segment.

70. The center of the circumscribed circle of a triangle lies on the perpendicular bisectors of the sides. Use this fact to find the center of the circle that circumscribes the triangle with vertices $(0, 4), (2, 0)$, and $(4, 6)$.

71. Find the radius of the circle that is inscribed in a triangle with sides of lengths 3, 4, and 5 (see Figure 21).

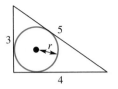

Figure 21

72. Suppose that (a, b) is on the circle $x^2 + y^2 = r^2$. Show that the line $ax + by = r^2$ is tangent to the circle at (a, b).

73. Find the equations of the two tangent lines to the circle $x^2 + y^2 = 36$ that go through $(12, 0)$. *Hint:* See Problem 72.

74. Express the perpendicular distance between the parallel lines $y = mx + b$ and $y = mx + B$ in terms of m, b, and B. *Hint:* The required distance is the same as that between $y = mx$ and $y = mx + B - b$.

75. Show that the line through the midpoints of two sides of a triangle is parallel to the third side. *Hint:* You may assume that the triangle has vertices at $(0, 0), (a, 0)$, and (b, c).

76. Show that the line segments joining the midpoints of adjacent sides of any quadrilateral (four-sided polygon) form a parallelogram.

77. A wheel whose rim has equation $x^2 + (y - 6)^2 = 25$ is rotating rapidly in the counterclockwise direction. A speck of dirt on the rim came loose at the point $(3, 2)$ and flew toward the wall $x = 11$. About how high up on the wall did it hit? *Hint:* The speck of dirt flies off on a tangent so fast that the effects of gravity are negligible by the time it has hit the wall.

Answers to Concepts Review: **1.** $\sqrt{(x + 2)^2 + (y - 3)^2}$ **2.** $(x + 4)^2 + (y - 2)^2 = 25$ **3.** $(1.5, 5)$ **4.** $(d - b)/(c - a)$

1.4
Graphs of Equations

The use of coordinates for points in the plane allows us to describe a curve (a geometric object) by an equation (an algebraic object). We saw how this was done for circles and lines in the previous section. Now we want to consider the reverse process: graphing an equation. The **graph of an equation** in x and y consists of those points in the plane whose coordinates (x, y) satisfy the equation, that is, make it a true equality.

The Graphing Procedure To graph an equation, for example, $y = 2x^3 - x + 19$, by hand, we can follow a simple three-step procedure:

Step 1: Obtain the coordinates of a few points that satisfy the equation.

Step 2: Plot these points in the plane.

Step 3: Connect the points with a smooth curve.

This simplistic method will have to suffice until Chapter 3 when we use more advanced methods to graph equations. The best way to do Step 1 is to make a table of values. Assign values to one of the variables, such as x, and determine the corresponding values of the other variable, listing the results in tabular form.

A graphing calculator or a computer algebra system will follow much the same procedure, although its procedure is transparent to the user. A user simply defines the function and asks the graphing calculator or computer to plot it.

EXAMPLE 1 Graph the equation $y = x^2 - 3$.

SOLUTION The three-step procedure is shown in Figure 1.

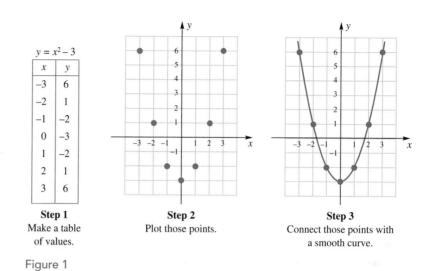

$y = x^2 - 3$	
x	y
-3	6
-2	1
-1	-2
0	-3
1	-2
2	1
3	6

Step 1
Make a table of values.

Step 2
Plot those points.

Step 3
Connect those points with a smooth curve.

Figure 1

Of course, you need to use common sense and even a little faith. When you have a point that seems out of place, check your calculations. When you connect the points you have plotted with a smooth curve, you are assuming that the curve behaves nicely between consecutive points, which is faith. This is why you should plot enough points so that the outline of the curve seems very clear; the more points you plot, the less faith you will need. Also, you should recognize that you can seldom display the whole curve. In our example, the curve has infinitely long arms, opening wider and wider. But our graph does show the essential features. This is our goal in graphing. Show enough of the graph so that the essential features are visible. Later (Section 3.5) we will use the tools of calculus to refine and improve our understanding of graphs.

Symmetry of a Graph   We can sometimes cut our graphing effort in half by recognizing certain symmetries of the graph as revealed by its equation. Look at the graph of $y = x^2 - 3$, drawn above and again in Figure 2. If the coordinate plane is folded along the y-axis, the two branches of the graph will coincide. For example, $(3, 6)$ will coincide with $(-3, 6)$, $(2, 1)$ will coincide with $(-2, 1)$, and, more generally, (x, y) will coincide with $(-x, y)$. Algebraically, this corresponds to the fact that replacing x by $-x$ in the equation $y = x^2 - 3$ results in an equivalent equation.

Consider an arbitrary graph. It is **symmetric with respect to the y-axis** if, whenever (x, y) is on the graph, $(-x, y)$ is also on the graph (Figure 2). Similarly, it is **symmetric with respect to the x-axis** if, whenever (x, y) is on the graph, $(x, -y)$ is also on the graph (Figure 3). Finally, a graph is **symmetric with respect to the origin** if, whenever (x, y) is on the graph, $(-x, -y)$ is also on the graph (see Example 2).

In terms of equations, we have three simple tests. The graph of an equation is

1. symmetric with respect to the y-axis if replacing x by $-x$ gives an equivalent equation (e.g., $y = x^2$);

2. symmetric with respect to the x-axis if replacing y by $-y$ gives an equivalent equation (e.g., $x = y^2 + 1$);

3. symmetric with respect to the origin if replacing x by $-x$ and y by $-y$ gives an equivalent equation ($y = x^3$ is a good example since $-y = (-x)^3$ is equivalent to $y = x^3$).

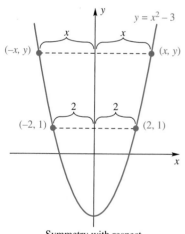

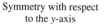

Symmetry with respect to the y-axis

Figure 2

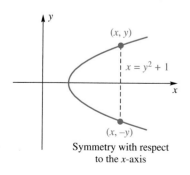

Symmetry with respect to the x-axis

Figure 3

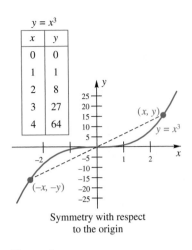

$y = x^3$

x	y
0	0
1	1
2	8
3	27
4	64

Symmetry with respect
to the origin

Figure 4

EXAMPLE 2 Sketch the graph of $y = x^3$.

SOLUTION We note, as pointed out above, that the graph will be symmetric with respect to the origin, so we need only get a table of values for nonnegative x's; we can find matching points by symmetry. For example, $(2, 8)$ being on the graph tells us that $(-2, -8)$ is on the graph, $(3, 27)$ being on the graph tells us that $(-3, -27)$ is on the graph, and so on. See Figure 4. ∎

In graphing $y = x^3$, we used a different scale on the y-axis than on the x-axis. This made it possible to show a larger portion of the graph (it also distorted the graph by flattening it). When you graph by hand we suggest that before putting scales on the two axes you should examine your table of values. Choose scales so that all or most of your points can be plotted and still keep your graph of reasonable size. A graphing calculator or a CAS will often choose the scale for the y's once you have chosen the x's to be used. The first choice you make, therefore, is the x values to plot. Most graphing calculators and CASs allow you to override the automatic y-axis scaling. In some cases you may want to use this option.

Intercepts The points where the graph of an equation crosses the two coordinate axes play a significant role in many problems. Consider, for example,

$$y = x^3 - 2x^2 - 5x + 6 = (x + 2)(x - 1)(x - 3)$$

Notice that $y = 0$ when $x = -2, 1, 3$. The numbers $-2, 1$, and 3 are called **x-intercepts.** Similarly, $y = 6$ when $x = 0$, and so 6 is called the **y-intercept.**

EXAMPLE 3 Find all intercepts of the graph of $y^2 - x + y - 6 = 0$.

SOLUTION Putting $y = 0$ in the given equation, we get $x = -6$, and so the x-intercept is -6. Putting $x = 0$ in the equation, we find that $y^2 + y - 6 = 0$, or $(y + 3)(y - 2) = 0$; the y-intercepts are -3 and 2. A check on symmetries indicates that the graph has none of the three types discussed earlier. The graph is displayed in Figure 5. ∎

Since quadratic and cubic equations will often be used as examples in later work, we display their typical graphs in Figure 6.

The graphs of quadratic equations are cup-shaped curves called **parabolas.** If an equation has the form $y = ax^2 + bx + c$ or $x = ay^2 + by + c$ with $a \neq 0$, its graph is a parabola. In the first case, the graph opens up if $a > 0$ and opens down if $a < 0$. In the second case, the graph opens right if $a > 0$ and opens left if $a < 0$. Note that the equation of Example 3 can be put in the form $x = y^2 + y - 6$.

Intersections of Graphs Frequently, we need to know the points of intersection of two graphs. These points are found by solving the two equations for the graphs simultaneously, as illustrated in the next example.

EXAMPLE 4 Find the points of intersection of the line $y = -2x + 2$ and the parabola $y = 2x^2 - 4x - 2$, and sketch both graphs on the same coordinate plane.

SOLUTION We must solve the two equations simultaneously. This is easy to do by substituting the expression for y from the first equation into the second equation and then solving the resulting equation for x.

$$-2x + 2 = 2x^2 - 4x - 2$$

$$0 = 2x^2 - 2x - 4$$

$$0 = 2(x + 1)(x - 2)$$

$$x = -1, \quad x = 2$$

Graphing Calculators

If you have a graphing calculator, use it whenever possible to reproduce the plots shown in the figures.

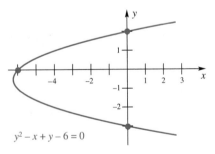

$y^2 - x + y - 6 = 0$

Figure 5

BASIC QUADRATIC AND CUBIC GRAPHS

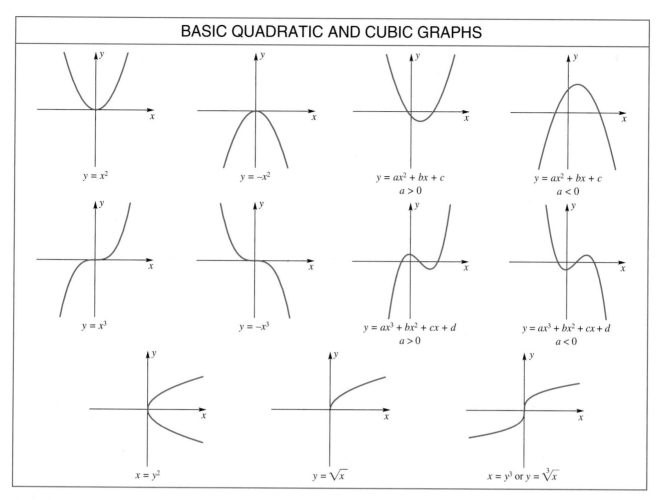

Figure 6

By substitution, we find the corresponding values of y to be 4 and -2; the intersection points are therefore $(-1, 4)$ and $(2, -2)$. The two graphs are shown in Figure 7.

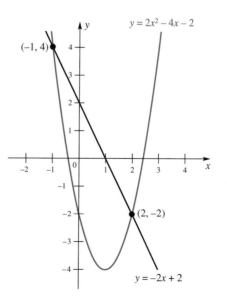

Figure 7

Concepts Review

1. If whenever (x, y) is on a graph, $(-x, y)$ is also on the graph, then the graph is symmetric with respect to the _____.

2. If $(-4, 2)$ is on a graph that is symmetric with respect to the origin, then _____ is also on the graph.

3. The graph of $y = (x + 2)(x - 1)(x - 4)$ has y-intercept _____ and x-intercepts _____.

4. The graph of $y = ax^2 + bx + c$ is a _____ if $a = 0$ and a _____ if $a \neq 0$.

Problem Set 1.4

In Problems 1–30, plot the graph of each equation. Begin by checking for symmetries and be sure to find all x- and y-intercepts.

1. $y = -x^2 + 1$

2. $x = -y^2 + 1$

3. $x = -4y^2 - 1$

4. $y = 4x^2 - 1$

5. $x^2 + y = 0$

6. $y = x^2 - 2x$

7. $7x^2 + 3y = 0$

8. $y = 3x^2 - 2x + 2$

9. $x^2 + y^2 = 4$

10. $3x^2 + 4y^2 = 12$

11. $y = -x^2 - 2x + 2$

12. $4x^2 + 3y^2 = 12$

13. $x^2 - y^2 = 4$

14. $x^2 + (y - 1)^2 = 9$

15. $4(x - 1)^2 + y^2 = 36$

16. $x^2 - 4x + 3y^2 = -2$

17. $x^2 + 9(y + 2)^2 = 36$

GC **18.** $x^4 + y^4 = 1$

GC **19.** $x^4 + y^4 = 16$

GC **20.** $y = x^3 - x$

GC **21.** $y = \dfrac{1}{x^2 + 1}$

GC **22.** $y = \dfrac{x}{x^2 + 1}$

GC **23.** $2x^2 - 4x + 3y^2 + 12y = -2$

GC **24.** $4(x - 5)^2 + 9(y + 2)^2 = 36$

GC **25.** $y = (x - 1)(x - 2)(x - 3)$

GC **26.** $y = x^2(x - 1)(x - 2)$

GC **27.** $y = x^2(x - 1)^2$

GC **28.** $y = x^4(x - 1)^4(x + 1)^4$

GC **29.** $|x| + |y| = 1$

GC **30.** $|x| + |y| = 4$

GC *In Problems 31–38, plot the graphs of both equations on the same coordinate plane. Find and label the points of intersection of the two graphs (see Example 4).*

31. $y = -x + 1$
$y = (x + 1)^2$

32. $y = 2x + 3$
$y = -(x - 1)^2$

33. $y = -2x + 3$
$y = -2(x - 4)^2$

34. $y = -2x + 3$
$y = 3x^2 - 3x + 12$

35. $y = x$
$x^2 + y^2 = 4$

36. $y = x - 1$
$2x^2 + 3y^2 = 12$

37. $y - 3x = 1$
$x^2 + 2x + y^2 = 15$

38. $y = 4x + 3$
$x^2 + y^2 = 81$

39. Choose the equation that corresponds to each graph in Figure 8.

(a) $y = ax^2$, with $a > 0$

(b) $y = ax^3 + bx^2 + cx + d$, with $a > 0$

(c) $y = ax^3 + bx^2 + cx + d$, with $a < 0$

(d) $y = ax^3$, with $a > 0$

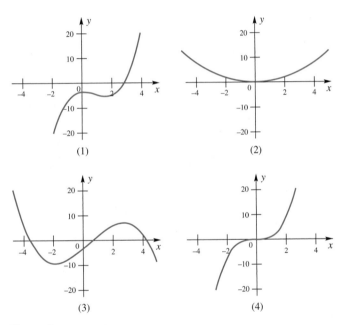

Figure 8

≈ **40.** Find the distance between the points on the circle $x^2 + y^2 = 13$ with the x-coordinates -2 and 2. How many such distances are there?

≈ **41.** Find the distance between the points on the circle $x^2 + 2x + y^2 - 2y = 20$ with the x-coordinates -2 and 2. How many such distances are there?

Answers to Concepts Review: **1.** y-axis **2.** $(4, -2)$
3. $8; -2, 1, 4$ **4.** line; parabola

1.5
Functions and Their Graphs

The concept of function is one of the most basic in all mathematics, and it plays an indispensable role in calculus.

> ### Definition
>
> A **function** f is a rule of correspondence that associates with each object x in one set, called the **domain,** a single value $f(x)$ from a second set. The set of all values so obtained is called the **range** of the function. (See Figure 1.)

Think of a function as a machine that takes as its input a value x and produces an output $f(x)$. (See Figure 2.) Each input value is matched with a *single* output value. It can, however, happen that several different input values give the same output value.

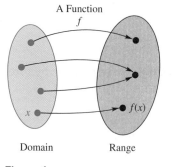

A Function
f

Domain   Range

Figure 1

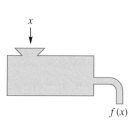

x

$f(x)$

Figure 2

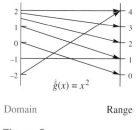

$g(x) = x^2$

Domain   Range

Figure 3

The definition puts no restriction on the domain and range sets. The domain might consist of the set of people in your calculus class, the range the set of grades $\{A, B, C, D, F\}$ that will be given, and the rule of correspondence the assignment of grades. Nearly all functions you encounter in this book will be functions of one or more real numbers. For example, the function g might take a real number x and square it, producing the real number x^2. In this case we have a formula that gives the rule of correspondence, that is, $g(x) = x^2$. A schematic diagram for this function is shown in Figure 3.

Function Notation   A single letter like f (or g or F) is used to name a function. Then $f(x)$, read "f of x" or "f at x," denotes the value that f assigns to x. Thus, if $f(x) = x^3 - 4$, then

$$f(2) = 2^3 - 4 = 4$$

$$f(a) = a^3 - 4$$

$$f(a + h) = (a + h)^3 - 4 = a^3 + 3a^2h + 3ah^2 + h^3 - 4$$

Study the following examples carefully. Although some of these examples may look odd now, they will play an important role in Chapter 3.

■ **EXAMPLE 1**   For $f(x) = x^2 - 2x$, find and simplify

(a) $f(4)$ (b) $f(4 + h)$
(c) $f(4 + h) - f(4)$ (d) $[f(4 + h) - f(4)]/h$

SOLUTION

(a) $f(4) = 4^2 - 2 \cdot 4 = 8$

(b) $f(4 + h) = (4 + h)^2 - 2(4 + h) = 16 + 8h + h^2 - 8 - 2h$
$$= 8 + 6h + h^2$$

(c) $f(4 + h) - f(4) = 8 + 6h + h^2 - 8 = 6h + h^2$

(d) $\dfrac{f(4 + h) - f(4)}{h} = \dfrac{6h + h^2}{h} = \dfrac{h(6 + h)}{h} = 6 + h$ ■

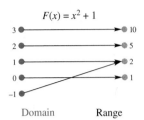

$F(x) = x^2 + 1$

Figure 4

Domain and Range To specify a function completely, we must state, in addition to the rule of correspondence, the domain of the function. For example, if F is the function defined by $F(x) = x^2 + 1$ with domain $\{-1, 0, 1, 2, 3\}$ (Figure 4), then the range is $\{1, 2, 5, 10\}$. The rule of correspondence, together with the domain, determines the range.

When no domain is specified for a function, we assume that it is the largest set of real numbers for which the rule for the function makes sense. This is called the **natural domain.** Numbers that you should remember to exclude from the natural domain are those values that would cause division by zero or the square root of a negative number.

EXAMPLE 2 Find the natural domains for

(a) $f(x) = 1/(x - 3)$ (b) $g(t) = \sqrt{9 - t^2}$

(c) $h(w) = 1/\sqrt{9 - w^2}$

SOLUTION

(a) We must exclude 3 from the domain because it would require division by zero. Thus, the natural domain is $\{x: x \neq 3\}$. This may be read "the set of x's such that x is not equal to 3."

(b) To avoid the square root of a negative number, we must choose t so that $9 - t^2 \geq 0$. Thus, t must satisfy $|t| \leq 3$. The natural domain is therefore $\{t: |t| \leq 3\}$, which we can write using interval notation as $[-3, 3]$.

(c) Now we must avoid division by zero *and* square roots of negative numbers, so we must exclude -3 and 3 from the natural domain. The natural domain is therefore the interval $(-3, 3)$. ∎

When the rule for a function is given by an equation of the form $y = f(x)$, we call x the **independent variable** and y the **dependent variable.** *Any* value in the domain may be substituted for the independent variable. Once selected, this value of x completely determines the corresponding value of the dependent variable y.

The input for a function need not be a single real number. In many important applications, a function depends on more than one independent variable. For example, the amount A of a monthly car payment depends on the loan's principal P, the rate of interest r, and the required number n of monthly payments. We could write such a function as $A(P, r, n)$. The value of $A(16000, 0.07, 48)$, that is, the required monthly payment to retire a $16,000 loan in 48 months at an annual interest rate of 7%, is $383.14. In this situation, there is no simple mathematical formula that gives the output A in terms of the input variables $P, r,$ and n.

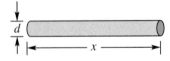

Figure 5

EXAMPLE 3 Let $V(x, d)$ denote the volume of a cylindrical rod of length x and diameter d. (See Figure 5.) Find

(a) a formula for $V(x, d)$
(b) the domain and range of V
(c) $V(4, 0.1)$

SOLUTION

(a) $V(x, d) = x \cdot \pi \left(\dfrac{d}{2}\right)^2 = \dfrac{\pi x d^2}{4}$

(b) Because the length and diameter of the rod must be positive, the domain is the set of all ordered pairs (x, d) where $x > 0$ and $d > 0$. Any positive volume is possible so the range is $(0, \infty)$.

(c) $V(4, 0.1) = \dfrac{\pi \cdot 4 \cdot 0.1^2}{4} = 0.01\pi$ ∎

Chapters 1 through 11 will deal mostly with functions of a single independent variable. Beginning in Chapter 12, we will study properties of functions of two or more independent variables.

Graphing Calculator

Remember, use your graphing calculator to reproduce the figures in this book. Experiment with various graphing windows until you are convinced that you understand all important aspects of the graph.

Graphs of Functions   When both the domain and range of a function are sets of real numbers, we can picture the function by drawing its graph on a coordinate plane. The **graph of a function** f is simply the graph of the equation $y = f(x)$.

EXAMPLE 4   Sketch the graphs of

(a) $f(x) = x^2 - 2$ (b) $g(x) = 2/(x - 1)$

SOLUTION The natural domains of f and g are, respectively, all real numbers and all real numbers except 1. Following the procedure described in Section 1.4 (make a table of values, plot the corresponding points, connect these points with a smooth curve), we obtain the two graphs shown in Figures 6 and 7a. ■

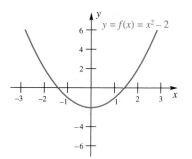

Figure 6

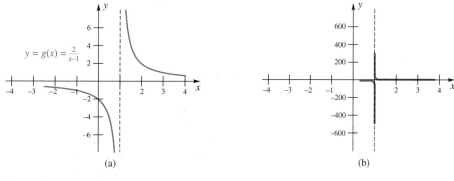

(a)   (b)

Figure 7

Pay special attention to the graph of g; it points to an oversimplification that we have made and now need to correct. When connecting the plotted points by a smooth curve, do not do so in a mechanical way that ignores special features that may be apparent from the formula for the function. In the case of $g(x) = 2/(x - 1)$, something dramatic happens as x nears 1. In fact, the values of $|g(x)|$ increase without bound; for example, $g(0.99) = 2/(0.99 - 1) = -200$ and $g(1.001) = 2000$. We have indicated this by drawing a dashed vertical line, called an **asymptote**, at $x = 1$. As x approaches 1, the graph gets closer and closer to this line, though this line itself is not part of the graph. Rather, it is a guideline. Notice that the graph of g also has a horizontal asymptote, the x-axis.

Functions like $g(x) = 2/(x - 1)$ can even cause problems when you graph them on a CAS. For example, *Maple*, when asked to plot $g(x) = 2/(x - 1)$ over the domain $[-4, 4]$ responded with the graph shown in Figure 7b. Computer Algebra Systems use an algorithm much like that described in Section 1.4; they choose a number of x-values over the stated domain, find the corresponding y-values, and plot these points with connecting lines. When *Maple* chose a number near 1, the resulting output was large, leading to the y-axis scaling in the figure. *Maple* also connected the points right across the break at $x = 1$. Always be cautious and careful when you use a graphing calculator or a CAS to plot functions.

The domains and ranges for the functions f and g are shown in the table below.

Function	Domain	Range
$f(x) = x^2 - 2$	all real numbers	$\{y: y \geq -2\}$
$g(x) = \dfrac{2}{x - 1}$	$\{x: x \neq 1\}$	$\{y: y \neq 0\}$

Even and Odd Functions   We can often predict the symmetries of the graph of a function by inspecting the formula for the function. If $f(-x) = f(x)$ for all x, then the graph is symmetric with respect to the y-axis. Such a function is called an

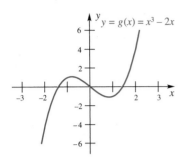

Figure 8

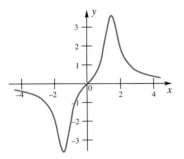

Figure 9

even function, probably because a function that specifies $f(x)$ as a sum of only even powers of x is even. The function $f(x) = x^2 - 2$ (graphed in Figure 6) is even; so are $f(x) = 3x^6 - 2x^4 + 11x^2 - 5$, $f(x) = x^2/(1 + x^4)$, and $f(x) = (x^3 - 2x)/3x$.

If $f(-x) = -f(x)$ for all x, the graph is symmetric with respect to the origin. We call such a function an **odd function.** A function that gives $f(x)$ as a sum of only odd powers of x is odd. Thus, $g(x) = x^3 - 2x$ (graphed in Figure 8) is odd. Note that

$$g(-x) = (-x)^3 - 2(-x) = -x^3 + 2x = -(x^3 - 2x) = -g(x)$$

Consider the function $g(x) = 2/(x - 1)$ from Example 4, which we graphed in Figure 7. It is neither even nor odd. To see this, observe that $g(-x) = 2/(-x - 1)$, which is not equal to either $g(x)$ or $-g(x)$. Note that the graph of $y = g(x)$ is neither symmetric with respect to the y-axis nor the origin.

EXAMPLE 5 Is $f(x) = \dfrac{x^3 + 3x}{x^4 - 3x^2 + 4}$ even, odd, or neither?

SOLUTION Since

$$f(-x) = \frac{(-x)^3 + 3(-x)}{(-x)^4 - 3(-x)^2 + 4} = \frac{-(x^3 + 3x)}{x^4 - 3x^2 + 4} = -f(x)$$

f is an odd function. The graph of $y = f(x)$ (Figure 9) is symmetric with respect to the origin. ∎

Two Special Functions Among the functions that will often be used as examples are two very special ones: the **absolute value function,** $|\ |$, and the **greatest integer function,** $[\![\ ]\!]$. They are defined by

$$|x| = \begin{cases} x & \text{if } x \geq 0 \\ -x & \text{if } x < 0 \end{cases}$$

and

$$[\![x]\!] = \text{the greatest integer less than or equal to } x$$

Thus, $|-3.1| = |3.1| = 3.1$, while $[\![-3.1]\!] = -4$ and $[\![3.1]\!] = 3$. We show the graphs of these two functions in Figures 10 and 11. The absolute value function is even, since $|-x| = |x|$. The greatest integer function is neither even nor odd, as you can see from its graph.

We will often appeal to the following special features of these graphs. The graph of $|x|$ has a sharp corner at the origin, while the graph of $[\![x]\!]$ takes a jump at each integer.

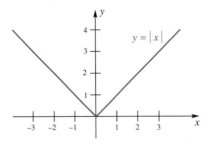

Figure 10

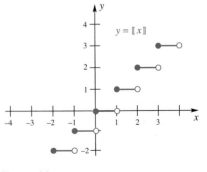

Figure 11

Concepts Review

1. The set of allowable inputs for a function is called the _____ of the function; the set of outputs that are obtained is called the _____ of the function.

2. If $f(x) = 3x^2$, then $f(2u) =$ _____ and $f(x + h) =$ _____.

3. If $f(x)$ gets closer and closer to L as $|x|$ increases indefinitely, then the line $y = L$ is a(an) _____ for the graph of f.

4. If $f(-x) = f(x)$ for all x in the domain of f, then f is called a(an) _____ function; if $f(-x) = -f(x)$ for all x in the domain of f, then f is called a(an) _____ function. In the first case, the graph of f is symmetric with respect to the _____; in the second case, it is symmetric with respect to the _____.

Problem Set 1.5

1. For $f(x) = 1 - x^2$, find each value.

(a) $f(1)$
(b) $f(-2)$
(c) $f(0)$
(d) $f(k)$
(e) $f(-5)$
(f) $f\left(\frac{1}{4}\right)$
(g) $f(1 + h)$
(h) $f(1 + h) - f(1)$
(i) $f(2 + h) - f(2)$

2. For $F(x) = x^3 + 3x$, find each value.

(a) $F(1)$
(b) $F(\sqrt{2})$
(c) $F\left(\frac{1}{4}\right)$
(d) $F(1 + h)$
(e) $F(1 + h) - F(1)$
(f) $F(2 + h) - F(2)$

3. For $G(y) = 1/(y - 1)$, find each value.

(a) $G(0)$
(b) $G(0.999)$
(c) $G(1.01)$
(d) $G(y^2)$
(e) $G(-x)$
(f) $G\left(\frac{1}{x^2}\right)$

4. For $\Phi(u) = \dfrac{u + u^2}{\sqrt{u}}$, find each value. ($\Phi$ is the uppercase Greek letter phi.)

(a) $\Phi(1)$
(b) $\Phi(-t)$
(c) $\Phi\left(\frac{1}{2}\right)$
(d) $\Phi(u + 1)$
(e) $\Phi(x^2)$
(f) $\Phi(x^2 + x)$

5. For
$$f(x) = \frac{1}{\sqrt{x - 3}}$$
find each value.

(a) $f(0.25)$
(b) $f(\pi)$
(c) $f(3 + \sqrt{2})$

[C] 6. For $f(x) = \sqrt{x^2 + 9}/(x - \sqrt{3})$, find each value.
(a) $f(0.79)$
(b) $f(12.26)$
(c) $f(\sqrt{3})$

7. Which of the following determine a function f with formula $y = f(x)$? For those that do, find $f(x)$. *Hint:* Solve for y in terms of x and note that the definition of a function requires a single y for each x.

(a) $x^2 + y^2 = 1$
(b) $xy + y + x = 1, x \neq -1$
(c) $x = \sqrt{2y + 1}$
(d) $x = \dfrac{y}{y + 1}$

8. Which of the graphs in Figure 12 are graphs of functions?

This problem suggests a rule: *For a graph to be the graph of a function, each vertical line must meet the graph in at most one point.*

9. For $f(x) = 2x^2 - 1$, find and simplify $[f(a + h) - f(a)]/h$.

10. For $F(t) = 4t^3$, find and simplify $[F(a + h) - F(a)]/h$.

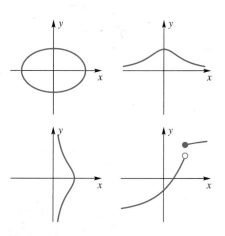

Figure 12

11. For $g(u) = 3/(u - 2)$, find and simplify $[g(x + h) - g(x)]/h$.

12. For $G(t) = t/(t + 4)$, find and simplify $[G(a + h) - G(a)]/h$.

13. Find the natural domain for each of the following.

(a) $F(z) = \sqrt{2z + 3}$
(b) $g(v) = 1/(4v - 1)$
(c) $\psi(x) = \sqrt{x^2 - 9}$
(d) $H(y) = -\sqrt{625 - y^4}$

14. Find the natural domain in each case.

(a) $f(x) = \dfrac{4 - x^2}{x^2 - x - 6}$
(b) $G(y) = \sqrt{(y + 1)^{-1}}$
(c) $\phi(u) = |2u + 3|$
(d) $F(t) = t^{2/3} - 4$

In Problems 15–30, specify whether the given function is even, odd, or neither, and then sketch its graph.

15. $f(x) = -4$
16. $f(x) = 3x$
17. $F(x) = 2x + 1$
18. $F(x) = 3x - \sqrt{2}$
19. $g(x) = 3x^2 + 2x - 1$
20. $g(u) = \dfrac{u^3}{8}$
21. $g(x) = \dfrac{x}{x^2 - 1}$
22. $\phi(z) = \dfrac{2z + 1}{z - 1}$
23. $f(w) = \sqrt{w - 1}$
24. $h(x) = \sqrt{x^2 + 4}$
25. $f(x) = |2x|$
26. $F(t) = -|t + 3|$
27. $g(x) = \left[\!\left[\dfrac{x}{2}\right]\!\right]$
28. $G(x) = [\![2x - 1]\!]$

29. $g(t) = \begin{cases} 1 & \text{if } t \le 0 \\ t + 1 & \text{if } 0 < t < 2 \\ t^2 - 1 & \text{if } t \ge 2 \end{cases}$

30. $h(x) = \begin{cases} -x^2 + 4 & \text{if } x \le 1 \\ 3x & \text{if } x > 1 \end{cases}$

31. A plant has the capacity to produce from 0 to 100 computers per day. The daily overhead for the plant is $5000, and the direct cost (labor and materials) of producing one computer is $805. Write a formula for $T(x)$, the total cost of producing x computers in one day, and also for the unit cost $u(x)$ (average cost per computer). What are the domains of these functions?

C **32.** It costs the ABC Company $400 + 5\sqrt{x(x - 4)}$ dollars to make x ($x \ge 4$) toy stoves that sell for $6 each.
(a) Find a formula for $P(x)$, the total profit in making x stoves.
(b) Evaluate $P(200)$ and $P(1000)$.
(c) How many stoves does ABC have to make to just break even?

C **33.** Find the formula for the amount $E(x)$ by which a number x exceeds its square. Plot a graph of $E(x)$ for $0 \le x \le 1$. Use the graph to estimate the positive number less than or equal to 1 that exceeds its square by the maximum amount.

34. Let p denote the perimeter of an equilateral triangle. Find a formula for $A(p)$, the area of such a triangle.

35. A right triangle has a fixed hypotenuse of length h and one leg that has length x. Find a formula for the length $L(x)$ of the other leg.

36. A right triangle has a fixed hypotenuse of length h and one leg that has length x. Find a formula for the area $A(x)$ of the triangle.

37. The Acme Car Rental Agency charges $24 a day for the rental of a car plus $0.40 per mile.
(a) Write a formula for the total rental expense $E(x)$ for one day, where x is the number of miles driven.
(b) If you rent a car for one day, how many miles can you drive for $120?

38. A right circular cylinder of radius r is inscribed in a sphere of radius $2r$. Find a formula for $V(r)$, the volume of the cylinder, in terms of r.

39. A 1-mile track has parallel sides and equal semicircular ends. Find a formula for the area enclosed by the track, $A(d)$, in terms of the diameter d of the semicircles. What is the natural domain for this function?

40. Let $A(c)$ denote the area of the region bounded from above by the line $y = x + 1$, from the left by the y-axis, from below by the x-axis, and from the right by the line $x = c$. Such a function is called an **accumulation function.** (See Figure 13.) Find
(a) $A(1)$ (b) $A(2)$
(c) $A(0)$ (d) $A(c)$
(e) Sketch the graph of $A(c)$.
(f) What are the domain and range of A?

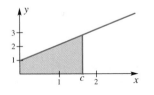

Figure 13

41. Let $B(c)$ denote the area of the region bounded from above by the graph of the curve $y = x(1 - x)$, from below by the x-axis, and from the right by the line $x = c$. The domain of B is the interval $[0, 1]$. (See Figure 14.) Given that $B(1) = \frac{1}{6}$,
(a) Find $B(0)$ (b) Find $B\left(\frac{1}{2}\right)$
(c) As best you can, sketch a graph of $B(c)$.

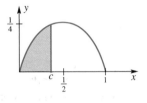

Figure 14

42. Which of the following functions satisfies $f(x + y) = f(x) + f(y)$ for all real numbers x and y?
(a) $f(t) = 2t$ (b) $f(t) = t^2$
(c) $f(t) = 2t + 1$ (d) $f(t) = -3t$

43. Let $f(x + y) = f(x) + f(y)$ for all x and y. Prove that there is a number m such that $f(t) = mt$ for all rational numbers t. *Hint:* First decide what m has to be. Then proceed in steps, starting with $f(0) = 0, f(p) = mp$ for a natural number p, $f(1/p) = m/p$, and so on.

44. A baseball diamond is a square with sides of 90 feet. A player, after hitting a home run, loped around the diamond at 10 feet per second. Let s represent the player's distance from home plate after t seconds.
(a) Express s as a function of t by means of a four-part formula.
(b) Express s as a function of t by means of a three-part formula.

GC *To use technology effectively, you need to discover its capabilities, its strengths, and its weaknesses. We urge you to practice graphing functions of various types using your own computer package or calculator. Problems 45–50 are designed for this purpose.*

45. Let $f(x) = (x^3 + 3x - 5)/(x^2 + 4)$.
(a) Evaluate $f(1.38)$ and $f(4.12)$.
(b) Construct a table of values for this function corresponding to $x = -4, -3, \ldots, 3, 4$.

46. Follow the instructions in Problem 45 for $f(x) = (\sin^2 x - 3 \tan x)/\cos x$.

47. Draw the graph of $f(x) = x^3 - 5x^2 + x + 8$ on the domain $[-2, 5]$.
(a) Determine the range of f.
(b) Where on this domain is $f(x) \ge 0$?

48. Superimpose the graph of $g(x) = 2x^2 - 8x - 1$ with domain $[-2, 5]$ on the graph of $f(x)$ of Problem 47.
(a) Estimate the x-values where $f(x) = g(x)$.
(b) Where on $[-2, 5]$ is $f(x) \ge g(x)$?
(c) Estimate the largest value of $|f(x) - g(x)|$ on $[-2, 5]$.

49. Graph $f(x) = (3x - 4)/(x^2 + x - 6)$ on the domain $[-6, 6]$.
(a) Determine the x- and y-intercepts.
(b) Determine the range of f for the given domain.
(c) Determine the vertical asymptotes of the graph.

(d) Determine the horizontal asymptote for the graph when the domain is enlarged to the natural domain.

50. Follow the directions in Problem 49 for the function $g(x) = (3x^2 - 4)/(x^2 + x - 6)$

Answers to Concepts Review: **1.** domain; range
2. $12u^2$; $3(x + h)^2 = 3x^2 + 6xh + 3h^2$ **3.** asymptote
4. even; odd; y-axis; origin

1.6
Operations on Functions

Just as two numbers a and b can be added to produce a new number $a + b$, so two functions f and g can be added to produce a new function $f + g$. This is just one of several operations on functions that we will describe in this section.

Sums, Differences, Products, Quotients, and Powers   Consider functions f and g with formulas

$$f(x) = \frac{x - 3}{2}, \qquad g(x) = \sqrt{x}$$

We can make a new function $f + g$ by having it assign to x the value $f(x) + g(x) = (x - 3)/2 + \sqrt{x}$; that is,

$$(f + g)(x) = f(x) + g(x) = \frac{x - 3}{2} + \sqrt{x}$$

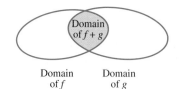

Domain
of f Domain
of g

Figure 1

Of course, we must be a little careful about domains. Clearly, x must be a number on which both f and g can work. In other words, the domain of $f + g$ is the intersection (common part) of the domains of f and g (Figure 1).

The functions $f - g$, $f \cdot g$, and f/g are introduced in a completely analogous way. Assuming that f and g have their natural domains, we have the following:

Formula	Domain
$(f + g)(x) = f(x) + g(x) = \dfrac{x - 3}{2} + \sqrt{x}$	$[0, \infty)$
$(f - g)(x) = f(x) - g(x) = \dfrac{x - 3}{2} - \sqrt{x}$	$[0, \infty)$
$(f \cdot g)(x) = f(x) \cdot g(x) = \dfrac{x - 3}{2}\sqrt{x}$	$[0, \infty)$
$\left(\dfrac{f}{g}\right)(x) = \dfrac{f(x)}{g(x)} = \dfrac{x - 3}{2\sqrt{x}}$	$(0, \infty)$

We had to exclude 0 from the domain of f/g to avoid division by 0.

We may also raise a function to a power. By f^n, we mean the function that assigns to x the value $[f(x)]^n$. Thus,

$$g^3(x) = [g(x)]^3 = \left(\sqrt{x}\right)^3 = x^{3/2}$$

There is one exception to the above agreement on exponents, namely, when $n = -1$. We reserve the symbol f^{-1} for the inverse function, which will be discussed later in this section. Thus, f^{-1} does not mean $1/f$.

EXAMPLE 1   Let $F(x) = \sqrt[4]{x + 1}$ and $G(x) = \sqrt{9 - x^2}$, with respective natural domains $[-1, \infty)$ and $[-3, 3]$. Find formulas for $F + G$, $F - G$, $F \cdot G$, F/G, and F^5 and give their natural domains.

SOLUTION

Formula	Domain
$(F + G)(x) = F(x) + G(x) = \sqrt[4]{x + 1} + \sqrt{9 - x^2}$	$[-1, 3]$
$(F - G)(x) = F(x) - G(x) = \sqrt[4]{x + 1} - \sqrt{9 - x^2}$	$[-1, 3]$
$(F \cdot G)(x) = F(x) \cdot G(x) = \sqrt[4]{x + 1}\sqrt{9 - x^2}$	$[-1, 3]$
$\left(\dfrac{F}{G}\right)(x) = \dfrac{F(x)}{G(x)} = \dfrac{\sqrt[4]{x + 1}}{\sqrt{9 - x^2}}$	$[-1, 3)$
$F^5(x) = [F(x)]^5 = \left(\sqrt[4]{x + 1}\right)^5 = (x + 1)^{5/4}$	$[-1, \infty)$ ∎

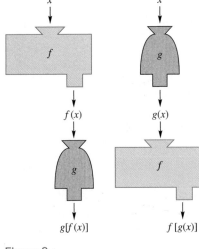

Composition of Functions Earlier, we asked you to think of a function as a machine. It accepts x as input, works on x, and produces $f(x)$ as output. Two machines may often be put together in tandem to make a more complicated machine; so may two functions f and g (Figure 2). If f works on x to produce $f(x)$ and g then works on $f(x)$ to produce $g(f(x))$, we say that we have *composed* g with f. The resulting function, called the **composition** of g with f, is denoted by $g \circ f$. Thus,

$$(g \circ f)(x) = g(f(x))$$

In our previous examples we had $f(x) = (x - 3)/2$ and $g(x) = \sqrt{x}$. We may compose these functions in two ways:

$$(g \circ f)(x) = g(f(x)) = g\left(\frac{x - 3}{2}\right) = \sqrt{\frac{x - 3}{2}}$$

$$(f \circ g)(x) = f(g(x)) = f\left(\sqrt{x}\right) = \frac{\sqrt{x} - 3}{2}$$

Right away we notice that $g \circ f$ does not equal $f \circ g$. Thus, we say that the composition of functions is not commutative.

We must be careful in describing the domain of a composite function. The domain of $g \circ f$ is equal to the set of those values x that satisfy the following properties:

1. x is in the domain of f.
2. $f(x)$ is in the domain of g.

In other words, x must be a valid input for f, and $f(x)$ must be a valid input for g. In our example, the value $x = 2$ is in the domain of f, but it is not in the domain of $g \circ f$ because this would lead to the square root of a negative number:

$$g(f(2)) = g((2 - 3)/2) = g\left(-\frac{1}{2}\right) = \sqrt{-\frac{1}{2}}$$

The domain for $g \circ f$ is the interval $[3, \infty)$ because $f(x)$ is nonnegative on this interval, and the input to g must be nonnegative. The domain for $f \circ g$ is the interval $[0, \infty)$ (why?), so we see that the domains of $g \circ f$ and $f \circ g$ can be different. Figure 3 shows how the domain of $g \circ f$ excludes those values of x for which $f(x)$ is not in the domain of g.

EXAMPLE 2 Let $f(x) = 6x/(x^2 - 9)$ and $g(x) = \sqrt{3x}$, with their natural domains. First, find $(f \circ g)(12)$; then find $(f \circ g)(x)$ and give its domain.

SOLUTION

$$(f \circ g)(12) = f(g(12)) = f\left(\sqrt{36}\right) = f(6) = \frac{6 \cdot 6}{6^2 - 9} = \frac{4}{3}$$

$$(f \circ g)(x) = f(g(x)) = f\left(\sqrt{3x}\right) = \frac{6\sqrt{3x}}{\left(\sqrt{3x}\right)^2 - 9}$$

Figure 2

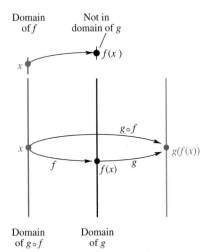

Figure 3

The expression $\sqrt{3x}$ appears in both the numera[tor]
negative number for x will lead to the square root of [n]or. Any
negative numbers must be excluded from the domain o[f.] hus, all
$\left(\sqrt{3x}\right)^2 = 3x$, allowing us to write ve have

$$(f \circ g)(x) = \frac{6\sqrt{3x}}{3x - 9} = \frac{2\sqrt{3x}}{x - 3}$$

We must also exclude $x = 3$ from the domain of $f \circ g$ be
domain of f. (It would cause division by 0.) Thus, th[e]n the
$[0, 3) \cup (3, \infty)$. g is

In calculus, we will often need to take a given function an[d]
position of two simpler functions. Usually, this can be done i[n] [s]om-
For example, $p(x) = \sqrt{x^2 + 4}$ can be written as ays.

$$p(x) = g(f(x)), \quad \text{where } g(x) = \sqrt{x} \quad \text{and} \quad f(x) =$$

or as

$$p(x) = g(f(x)), \quad \text{where } g(x) = \sqrt{x + 4} \quad \text{and} \quad f(x)$$

(You should check that both of these compositions give $p(x) =$
domain $(-\infty, \infty)$.) The decomposition $p(x) = g(f(x))$ with $f(x)$ [wi]th
$g(x) = \sqrt{x}$ is regarded as simpler and is usually preferred. We can t[hi]d
$p(x) = \sqrt{x^2 + 4}$ as the square root of a function of x. This way of loo[ki]ng
tions will be important in Chapter 3.

EXAMPLE 3 Write the function $p(x) = (x + 2)^5$ as a composit[e]
$g \circ f$.

SOLUTION The most obvious way to decompose p is to write

$$p(x) = g(f(x)), \quad \text{where } g(x) = x^5 \quad \text{and} \quad f(x) = x + 2$$

We thus view $p(x) = (x + 2)^5$ as the fifth power of a function of x.

Translations Observing how a function is built up from simpler on[es] [c]an be a
big aid in graphing. We may ask this question: How are the graphs of

$$y = f(x) \qquad y = f(x - 3) \qquad y = f(x) + 2 \qquad y = f(x - 3)2$$

related to each other? Consider $f(x) = |x|$ as an example. The corres[p]o[n]ding four
graphs are displayed in Figure 4.

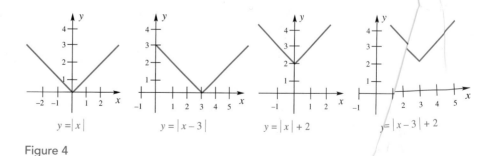

$$y = |x| \qquad\qquad y = |x - 3| \qquad\qquad y = |x| + 2 \qquad\qquad y = |x - 3| + 2$$

Figure 4

Notice that all four graphs have the same shape; the last three are just translations of the first. Replacing x by $x - 3$ translates the graph 3 units to the right;
adding 2 translates it upward by 2 units.

What happened with $f(x) = |x|$ is typical. Figure 5 offers an illustration for the
function $f(x) = x^3 + x^2$.

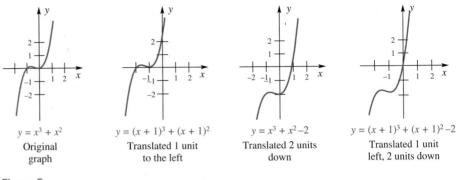

$y = x^3 + x^2$
Original
graph

$y = (x + 1)^3 + (x + 1)^2$
Translated 1 unit
to the left

$y = x^3 + x^2 - 2$
Translated 2 units
down

$y = (x + 1)^3 + (x + 1)^2 - 2$
Translated 1 unit
left, 2 units down

Figure 5

Exactly the same principles apply in the general situation. They are illustrated in Figure 6 with both h and k positive. If $h < 0$, the translation is to the left; if $k < 0$, the translation is downward.

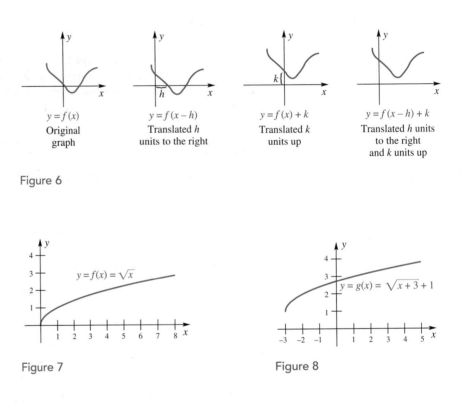

$y = f(x)$
Original
graph

$y = f(x - h)$
Translated h
units to the right

$y = f(x) + k$
Translated k
units up

$y = f(x - h) + k$
Translated h units
to the right
and k units up

Figure 6

$y = f(x) = \sqrt{x}$

Figure 7

$y = g(x) = \sqrt{x + 3} + 1$

Figure 8

■ **EXAMPLE 4** Sketch the graph of $g(x) = \sqrt{x + 3} + 1$ by first graphing $f(x) = \sqrt{x}$ and then making appropriate translations.

SOLUTION By translating the graph of f (Figure 7) 3 units left and 1 unit up, we obtain the graph of g (Figure 8). ■

The Inverse of a Function A function takes a number x from its domain D and assigns to it a single value y from its range R. In some cases, like the two functions graphed in Figures 9 and 10, we can reverse f; that is, for any given y in the range R, we can unambiguously go back and find the x from which it came. This new function that takes y and assigns x to it is denoted by f^{-1}. Note that its domain is R (the range of f) and its range is D (the domain of f). The function f^{-1} is called the inverse of f, or simply f-inverse. Note that we are using the superscript -1 in a new way. Earlier in this section, we defined f^n as the function defined by $f^n(x) = [f(x)]^n$ as long as $n \neq -1$. To us, the symbol f^{-1} means f-inverse, not $1/f$.

Sometimes, we can give a formula for f^{-1}. For example, if $y = f(x) = 2x$ then we can readily solve for x to get $x = \frac{1}{2}y$. This gives us a rule for determing what value of x gave a particular y. Thus, we write $x = f^{-1}(y) = \frac{1}{2}y$. If we preferred, we could write the inverse function with x as the argument and y as the output. In this case we would have $y = f^{-1}(x) = \frac{1}{2}x$. (These two ways of writing f^{-1}, namely $f^{-1}(y) = \frac{1}{2}y$ and $f^{-1}(x) = \frac{1}{2}x$, actually define the same function.)

Thus, to find the inverse f^{-1} of a function, we propose the following three-step procedure:

Step 1: Write $y = f(x)$ and solve for x in terms of y (if this is possible).

Step 2: Use the solution for x (in terms of y) to write $f^{-1}(y)$.

Step 3: Interchange the roles of x and y to get the formula for $f^{-1}(x)$.

If the function $y = f(x)$ has the property that every y in the range of f is associated with one and only one value of x, there is just one such x as suggested in Step 1. Geometrically, this says that a horizontal line can intersect the graph of $y = f(x)$ at most once. If a function satisfies this horizontal line test, then it will have an inverse. Yet another way of saying this is to say that different x's always lead to different y's. This leads to the following definition.

Definition One-to-one Function

A function f is said to be **one-to-one** if distinct values of x always lead to distinct values of $y = f(x)$; that is

$$x_1 \neq x_2 \iff f(x_1) \neq f(x_2)$$

EXAMPLE 5 Show that $f(x) = 2x + 6$ has an inverse and find it.

SOLUTION

Step 1: We set $y = f(x) = 2x + 6$ and attempt to solve for x. (If it is possible to solve unambiguously for x, then f has an inverse; otherwise it doesn't.) In this case we have

$$y = 2x + 6$$
$$y - 6 = 2x$$
$$x = \frac{y - 6}{2}$$

Step 2: Thus, $f^{-1}(y) = (y - 6)/2$.

Step 3: Interchanging the roles of x and y gives $f^{-1}(x) = (x - 6)/2$.   ∎

Not all functions have inverses. Consider, for instance, the function $f(x) = x^2$. If we set $y = x^2$ and attempt to solve for x we get $x = \pm \sqrt{y}$, which does not give us a single solution; f does not have an inverse. Figure 11 shows us why. For every positive y there exist two values for x that produce y.

There is a way of salvaging the notion of inverse for functions that do not have inverses on their natural domain. We simply *restrict the domain* to a subset of the natural domain. Thus, for $y = f(x) = x^2$, we may restrict the domain to $x \geq 0$ ($x \leq 0$ would work also). With this restriction, if we set $y = x^2$, we can solve unambiguously for x to get $x = \sqrt{y}$. Thus, $f^{-1}(x) = \sqrt{x}$. (See Figure 12.)

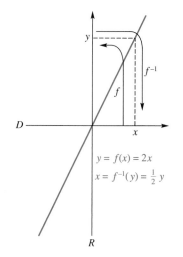

Figure 9

$y = f(x) = 2x$

$x = f^{-1}(y) = \frac{1}{2}y$

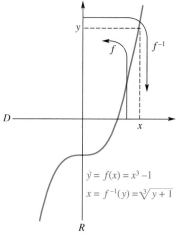

Figure 10

$y = f(x) = x^3 - 1$

$x = f^{-1}(y) = \sqrt[3]{y + 1}$

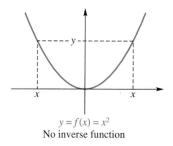

$y = f(x) = x^2$
No inverse function

Figure 11

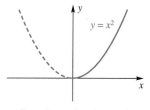

$y = x^2$

Domain restricted to $x \geq 0$

Figure 12

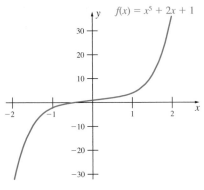

Figure 13

There are also cases where a function has an inverse, but it is not practical to find a formula for it. The function $f(x) = x^5 + 2x + 1$ is graphed in Figure 13. It seems evident that for every y, there is just one x satisfying $f(x) = y$. (In other words, it seems from looking at the graph that f is one-to-one.) The next theorem, which we will apply in Section 3.9, gives a condition that guarantees the existence of an inverse. First, though, we need to define a few terms.

Definition Increasing, Decreasing, Monotonic

Let I be an interval containing the points x_1 and x_2. A function f is **increasing** on I if $x_1 < x_2$ implies $f(x_1) < f(x_2)$. A function f is **decreasing** on I if $x_1 < x_2$ implies $f(x_1) > f(x_2)$. A function f is **monotonic** on I if it is either increasing or decreasing on I.

Theorem A

If f is monotonic on its domain, then f has an inverse.

Proof Let x_1 and x_2 be distinct numbers in the domain of f, with $x_1 < x_2$. Since f is monotonic, $f(x_1) < f(x_2)$ or $f(x_1) > f(x_2)$. Either way, $f(x_1) \neq f(x_2)$. Thus, $x_1 \neq x_2$ implies $f(x_1) \neq f(x_2)$, which means that f is one-to-one and therefore has an inverse. ∎

We will show in Section 3.9 that the function $f(x) = x^5 + 2x + 1$, graphed in Figure 13, is increasing and therefore, by Theorem A, has an inverse.

If the function f has an inverse f^{-1}, then f^{-1} has an inverse, namely, f. (With a little thought, that should appear obvious.) Thus, we may call f and f^{-1} a pair of inverse functions. One function undoes (or reverses) what the other did; in other words

$$f^{-1}(f(x)) = x \qquad \text{for every } x \text{ in the domain of } f$$

$$f(f^{-1}(y)) = y \qquad \text{for every } y \text{ in the range of } f$$

The Graph of $y = f^{-1}(x)$ If the function f has an inverse f^{-1}, then

$$y = f(x) \quad \Leftrightarrow \quad x = f^{-1}(y)$$

Consequently, $y = f(x)$ and $x = f^{-1}(y)$ determine the same (x, y) ordered pairs and so have identical graphs. However, it is conventional to use x as the argument for both functions, so we now inquire about the graph of $y = f^{-1}(x)$. Note that we have interchanged the roles of x and y here. To interchange the roles of x and y means that if (x, y) is on the graph of $y = f(x)$, then (y, x) is on the graph of $y = f^{-1}(x)$. Figure 14 illustrates this concept; the points (a, b) and (b, a) are symmetric about the line $y = x$. In other words, *the graph of $y = f^{-1}(x)$ is just the reflection of the graph of $y = f(x)$ across the line $y = x$* (Figure 15).

Undoing Machines

We may view a function as a machine that accepts an input and produces an output. If the f machine and the f^{-1} machine are hooked together in tandem, they undo each other.

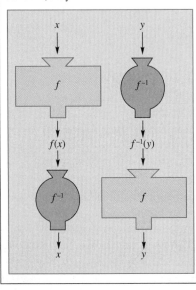

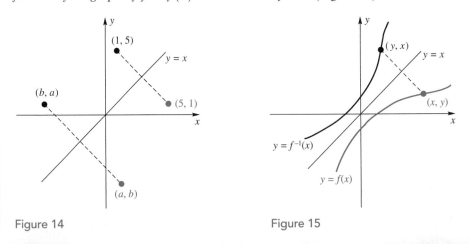

Figure 14   **Figure 15**

EXAMPLE 6 Find a formula for the inverse of $f(x) = x/(1 - x)$. Show that $f^{-1}(f(x)) = x$ for every x in the domain of f and $f(f^{-1}(y)) = y$ for every y in the range of f. Finally, graph both functions on the same set of axes.

SOLUTION   First, find the inverse of f.

Step 1: Write $y = f(x)$ and solve for x:

$$y = \frac{x}{1 - x}$$

$$(1 - x)y = x$$

$$y - xy = x$$

$$x + yx = y$$

$$x(1 + y) = y$$

$$x = \frac{y}{1 + y}$$

Step 2: $f^{-1}(y) = \dfrac{y}{1 + y}$

Step 3: $f^{-1}(x) = \dfrac{x}{1 + x}$

Next, consider $f^{-1}(f(x))$ and $f(f^{-1}(y))$. Let x be in the domain of f, that is, any number except 1. Then

$$f^{-1}(f(x)) = f^{-1}\left(\frac{x}{1 - x}\right) = \frac{\dfrac{x}{1 - x}}{1 + \dfrac{x}{1 - x}} = \frac{\dfrac{x}{1 - x}}{1 + \dfrac{x}{1 - x}} \frac{(1 - x)}{(1 - x)}$$

$$= \frac{x}{(1 - x) + x} = x$$

Now, let y be any number in the domain of f^{-1}, that is, any number except -1. Then

$$f(f^{-1}(y)) = f\left(\frac{y}{1 + y}\right) = \frac{\dfrac{y}{1 + y}}{1 - \dfrac{y}{1 + y}} = \frac{\dfrac{y}{1 + y}}{1 - \dfrac{y}{1 + y}} \frac{(1 + y)}{(1 + y)}$$

$$= \frac{y}{(1 + y) - y} = y$$

Figure 16 shows a graph of both $y = f(x)$ and $y = f^{-1}(x)$. As expected, the graphs are symmetric about the line $y = x$. ■

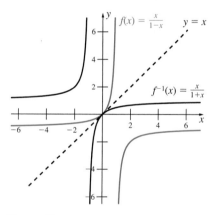

Figure 16

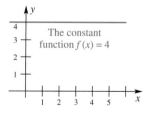

Figure 17

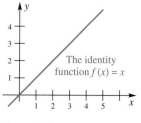

Figure 18

Partial Catalog of Functions   A function of the form $f(x) = k$, where k is a constant (real number), is called a **constant function.** Its graph is a horizontal line (Figure 17). The function $f(x) = x$ is called the **identity function.** Its graph is a line through the origin having slope 1 (Figure 18). From these simple functions, we can build many important functions.

Any function that can be obtained from the constant functions and the identity function by use of the operations of addition, subtraction, and multiplication is called a **polynomial function.** This amounts to saying that f is a polynomial function if it is of the form

$$f(x) = a_n x^n + a_{n-1} x^{n-1} + \cdots + a_1 x + a_0$$

where the a_j are real numbers and n is a nonnegative integer. If $a_n \neq 0$, n is the **degree** of the polynomial function. In particular, $f(x) = ax + b$ is a first-degree polynomial function, or **linear function,** and $f(x) = ax^2 + bx + c$ is a second-degree polynomial function, or **quadratic function.**

Quotients of polynomial functions are called **rational functions.** Thus, f is a rational function if it is of the form

$$f(x) = \frac{a_n x^n + a_{n-1}x^{n-1} + \cdots + a_1 x + a_0}{b_m x^m + b_{m-1}x^{m-1} + \cdots + b_1 x + b_0}$$

The domain of a rational function consists of those real numbers for which the denominator is nonzero.

An **explicit algebraic function** is one that can be obtained from the constant functions and the identity function via the five operations of addition, subtraction, multiplication, division, and root extraction. Examples are

$$f(x) = 3x^{2/5} = 3\sqrt[5]{x^2} \qquad g(x) = \frac{(x + 2)\sqrt{x}}{x^3 + \sqrt[3]{x^2} - 1}$$

Functions that do not fit into any of these categories are called **transcendental functions.** These include the trigonometric, inverse trigonometric, exponential, and logarithmic functions.

Concepts Review

1. If $f(x) = x^2 + 1$, then $f^3(x) = $ _____.

2. The value of the composite function $f \circ g$ at x is given by $(f \circ g)(x) = $ _____.

3. Compared to the graph of $y = f(x)$, the graph of $y = f(x + 2)$ is translated _____ units to the _____.

4. A rational function is defined as _____.

Problem Set 1.6

1. For $f(x) = x + 3$ and $g(x) = x^2$, find each value.
(a) $(f + g)(2)$ (b) $(f \cdot g)(0)$ (c) $(g/f)(3)$
(d) $(f \circ g)(1)$ (e) $(g \circ f)(1)$ (f) $(g \circ f)(-8)$

2. For $f(x) = x^2 + x$ and $g(x) = 2/(x + 3)$, find each value.
(a) $(f - g)(2)$ (b) $(f/g)(1)$ (c) $g^2(3)$
(d) $(f \circ g)(1)$ (e) $(g \circ f)(1)$ (f) $(g \circ g)(3)$

3. For $\Phi(u) = u^3 + 1$ and $\Psi(v) = 1/v$, find each value. (Ψ is the uppercase Greek letter psi.)
(a) $(\Phi + \Psi)(t)$ (b) $(\Phi \circ \Psi)(r)$
(c) $(\Psi \circ \Phi)(r)$ (d) $\Phi^3(z)$
(e) $(\Phi - \Psi)(5t)$ (f) $((\Phi - \Psi) \circ \Psi)(t)$

4. If $f(x) = \sqrt{x^2 - 1}$ and $g(x) = 2/x$, find formulas for the following and state their domains.
(a) $(f \cdot g)(x)$ (b) $f^4(x) + g^4(x)$
(c) $(f \circ g)(x)$ (d) $(g \circ f)(x)$

5. If $f(s) = \sqrt{s^2 - 4}$ and $g(w) = |1 + w|$, find formulas for $(f \circ g)(x)$ and $(g \circ f)(x)$.

6. If $g(x) = x^2 + 1$, find formulas for $g^3(x)$ and $(g \circ g \circ g)(x)$.

C **7.** Calculate $g(3.141)$ if $g(u) = \dfrac{\sqrt{u^3 + 2u}}{2 + u}$.

C **8.** Calculate $g(2.03)$ if $g(x) = \dfrac{(\sqrt{x} - \sqrt[3]{x})^4}{1 - x + x^2}$.

C **9.** Calculate $[g^2(\pi) - g(\pi)]^{1/3}$ if $g(v) = |11 - 7v|$.

C **10.** Calculate $[g^3(\pi) - g(\pi)]^{1/3}$ if $g(x) = 6x - 11$.

11. Find f and g so that $F = g \circ f$. (See Example 3.)
(a) $F(x) = \sqrt{x + 7}$ (b) $F(x) = (x^2 + x)^{15}$

12. Find f and g so that $p = f \circ g$.
(a) $p(x) = \dfrac{2}{(x^2 + x + 1)^3}$ (b) $p(x) = \dfrac{1}{x^3 + 3x}$

13. Write $p(x) = 1/\sqrt{x^2 + 1}$ as a composite of three functions in two different ways.

14. Write $p(x) = 1/\sqrt{x^2 + 1}$ as a composite of four functions.

15. Sketch the graph of $f(x) = \sqrt{x - 2} - 3$ by first sketching $g(x) = \sqrt{x}$ and then translating. (See Example 4.)

16. Sketch the graph of $g(x) = |x + 3| - 4$ by first sketching $h(x) = |x|$ and then translating.

17. Sketch the graph of $f(x) = (x - 2)^2 - 4$ using translations.

18. Sketch the graph of $g(x) = (x + 1)^3 - 3$ using translations.

19. Sketch the graphs of $f(x) = (x - 3)/2$ and $g(x) = \sqrt{x}$ using the same coordinate axes. Then sketch $f + g$ by adding y-coordinates.

20. Follow the directions of Problem 19 for $f(x) = x$ and $g(x) = |x|$.

21. Sketch the graph of $F(t) = \dfrac{|t| - t}{t}$.

22. State whether each of the following is an odd function, an even function, or neither. Prove your statements.
(a) The sum of two even functions
(b) The sum of two odd functions
(c) The product of two even functions
(d) The product of two odd functions
(e) The product of an even function and an odd function

23. Let F be any function whose domain contains $-x$ whenever it contains x. Prove each of the following.
(a) $F(x) - F(-x)$ is an odd function.
(b) $F(x) + F(-x)$ is an even function.
(c) F can always be expressed as the sum of an odd and an even function.

24. Is every polynomial of even degree an even function? Is every polynomial of odd degree an odd function? Explain.

In Problems 25–30, the graph of $y = f(x)$ is shown. In each case, decide whether f has an inverse and, if so, estimate $f^{-1}(2)$.

25.   **26.**

27.   **28.**

29.   **30.**

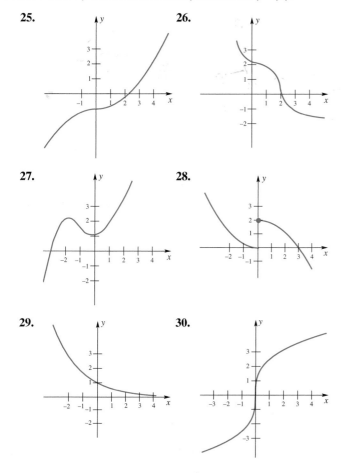

In Problems 31–44, find a formula for $f^{-1}(x)$ and then verify that $f^{-1}(f(x)) = x$ and $f(f^{-1}(x)) = x$.

31. $f(x) = x + 1$

32. $f(x) = -\dfrac{x}{3} + 1$

33. $f(x) = \sqrt{x + 1}$

34. $f(x) = -\sqrt{1 - x}$

35. $f(x) = -\dfrac{1}{x - 3}$

36. $f(x) = \sqrt{\dfrac{1}{x - 2}}$

37. $f(x) = 4x^2, x \le 0$

38. $f(x) = (x - 3)^2, x \ge 3$

39. $f(x) = (x - 1)^3$

40. $f(x) = x^{5/2}, x \ge 0$

41. $f(x) = \dfrac{x - 1}{x + 1}$

42. $f(x) = \left(\dfrac{x - 1}{x + 1}\right)^3$

43. $f(x) = \dfrac{x^3 + 2}{x^3 + 1}$

44. $f(x) = \left(\dfrac{x^3 + 2}{x^3 + 1}\right)^5$

45. Find the volume V of water in the conical tank of Figure 19 as a function of the height h. Then find the height h as a function of volume V.

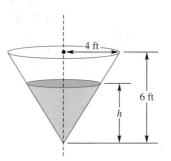

Figure 19

46. A ball is thrown vertically upward with velocity v_0. Find the maximum height H of the ball as a function of v_0. Then find the velocity v_0 required to achieve a height of H. *Hint:* The height of the ball after t seconds is $h = -16t^2 + v_0 t$. The vertex of the parabola $y = -ax^2 + bx$ is at $\left(b/(2a), b^2/(4a)\right)$.

In Problems 47 and 48, restrict the domain of f so that f has an inverse, yet keeping its range as large as possible. Then find $f^{-1}(x)$. Suggestion: First graph f.

47. $f(x) = 2x^2 + x - 4$ **48.** $f(x) = x^2 - 3x + 1$

49. Classify each of the following as a PF (polynomial function), RF (rational function but not a polynomial function), or neither.
(a) $f(x) = 3x^{1/2} + 1$
(b) $f(x) = 3$
(c) $f(x) = 3x^2 + 2x^{-1}$
(d) $f(x) = \pi x^3 - 3\pi$
(e) $f(x) = \dfrac{1}{x + 1}$
(f) $f(x) = \dfrac{x + 1}{\sqrt{x + 3}}$

50. After being in business for t years, a manufacturer of cars is producing $120 + 2t + 3t^2$ units per year. The sales price in dollars per unit has risen according to the formula $6000 + 700t$. Write a formula for the manufacturer's yearly revenue $R(t)$ after t years.

51. Starting at noon, airplane A flies due north at 400 miles per hour. Starting 1 hour later, airplane B flies due east at 300 miles per hour. Neglecting the curvature of the Earth and assuming that they fly at the same altitude, find a formula for $D(t)$, the distance between the two airplanes t hours after noon. *Hint:* There will be two formulas for $D(t)$, one if $0 < t < 1$ and the other if $t \ge 1$.

52. Find the distance between the airplanes of Problem 51 at 2:30 p.m.

53. Suppose that both f and g have inverses and that $h(x) = (f \circ g)(x) = f(g(x))$. Show that h has an inverse given by $h^{-1} = g^{-1} \circ f^{-1}$.

54. Verify the result of Problem 53 for $f(x) = 1/x$, $g(x) = 3x + 2$.

55. Let $f(x) = \dfrac{ax + b}{cx + d}$ and assume $bc - ad \neq 0$.

(a) Find the formula for $f^{-1}(x)$.

(b) Why is the condition $bc - ad \neq 0$ needed?

(c) What condition on $a, b, c,$ and d will make $f = f^{-1}$?

56. Let $f(x) = \dfrac{x - 3}{x + 1}$. Show that $f(f(f(x))) = x$, provided $x \neq \pm 1$.

57. Let $f(x) = \dfrac{x}{x - 1}$. Find and simplify each value.

(a) $f(1/x)$ (b) $f(f(x))$ (c) $f(1/f(x))$

58. Let $f(x) = \dfrac{x}{\sqrt{x} - 1}$. Find and simplify.

(a) $f\left(\dfrac{1}{x}\right)$ (b) $f(f(x))$

59. Prove that the operation of composition of functions is associative; that is, $f_1 \circ (f_2 \circ f_3) = (f_1 \circ f_2) \circ f_3$.

60. Let $f_1(x) = x$, $f_2(x) = 1/x$, $f_3(x) = 1 - x$, $f_4(x) = 1/(1 - x)$, $f_5(x) = (x - 1)/x$, and $f_6(x) = x/(x - 1)$. Note that $f_3(f_4(x)) = f_3(1/(1 - x)) = 1 - 1/(1 - x) = x/(x - 1) = f_6(x)$; that is, $f_3 \circ f_4 = f_6$. In fact, the composition of any two of these functions is another one in the list. Fill in the composition table in Figure 20.

Then use this table to find each of the following. From Problem 59, you know that the associative law holds.

(a) $f_3 \circ f_3 \circ f_3 \circ f_3 \circ f_3$

(b) $f_1 \circ f_2 \circ f_3 \circ f_4 \circ f_5 \circ f_6$

(c) F if $F \circ f_6 = f_1$

(d) G if $G \circ f_3 \circ f_6 = f_1$

(e) H if $f_2 \circ f_5 \circ H = f_5$

$\circ$	f_1	f_2	f_3	f_4	f_5	f_6
f_1						
f_2						
f_3				f_6		
f_4						
f_5						
f_6						

Figure 20

61. Use the table in Figure 20 to find the inverse of each f_i, $i = 1, 2, \ldots, 6$.

GC *Use a computer or a graphing calculator in Problems 62–65.*

62. Let $f(x) = x^2 - 3x$. Using the same axes, draw the graphs of $y = f(x)$, $y = f(x - 0.5) - 0.6$, and $y = f(1.5x)$, all on the domain $[-2, 5]$.

63. Let $f(x) = |x^3|$. Using the same axes, draw the graphs of $y = f(x)$, $y = f(3x)$, and $y = f(3(x - 0.8))$, all on the domain $[-3, 3]$.

64. Let $f(x) = 2\sqrt{x} - 2x + 0.25x^2$. Using the same axes, draw the graphs of $y = f(x)$, $y = f(1.5x)$, and $y = f(x - 1) + 0.5$, all on the domain $[1, 5]$.

65. Let $f(x) = 1/(x^2 + 1)$. Using the same axes, draw the graphs of $y = f(x)$, $y = f(2x)$, and $y = f(x - 2) + 0.6$, all on the domain $[-4, 4]$.

Answers to Concepts Review: **1.** $(x^2 + 1)^3$ **2.** $f(g(x))$
3. 2; left **4.** a quotient of two polynomial functions

1.7
Exponential and Logarithmic Functions

In algebra, we define exponentiation for successively larger classes of exponents. We begin by defining 2^n for positive integers, as in $2^4 = 2 \cdot 2 \cdot 2 \cdot 2$. Next, 2^0 is defined to be 1. Then for negative integer exponents, we define

$$2^{-n} = \frac{1}{2^n} \quad \text{if } n \text{ is a positive integer}$$

This means, for example, that $2^{-3} = 1/2^3 = 1/8$. Next, we use root functions to define 2^n for rational numbers. (Recall that a number is rational if it is the ratio of two integers.) Our definition was

$$2^{a/b} = \sqrt[b]{2^a}$$

Thus, $2^{1/2} = \sqrt[2]{2^1} = \sqrt{2}$ and $2^{7/3} = \sqrt[3]{2^7}$.

But what does it mean to raise a number to an irrational power, as in 2^π? (Recall that π is an irrational number, that is a number that cannot be expressed as a/b where a and b are integers.) One way to approach this question is to look at successive approximations to π, for example 3, 3.1, 3.14, 3.142, 3.1416, 3.14159, 3.141593, ... These numbers (each of which is rational, for example $3.1416 = 31416/10000$) are numerical approximations of π to successively more decimal places. To get at 2^{π}, we might consider the sequence

$$\begin{aligned}
2^3 &= 8 \\
2^{3.1} &\approx 8.57419 \\
2^{3.14} &\approx 8.81524 \\
2^{3.142} &\approx 8.82747 \\
2^{3.1416} &\approx 8.82502 \\
2^{3.14159} &\approx 8.82496 \\
2^{3.141593} &\approx 8.82498 \\
&\vdots
\end{aligned}$$

Intuitively, we might think that if we take an accurate (rational) approximation to π, and raise 2 to that power we would obtain a close approximation to 2^{π}. While this is true in some sense (we will revisit this issue in Section 2.6), it still does not give a *definition* for 2^{π}. A precise definition for 2^{π}, or in general, for a^x where a is positive and x is irrational, will have to wait until we cover some calculus. (We will define 2^{π} to be the limit of the sequence $2^3, 2^{3.1}, 2^{3.14}, 2^{3.142}, 2^{3.1416}, \ldots$, but that must wait until we define "limit" in the next chapter.)

From the above calculations, we suspect that 2^{π} is approximately 8.82498. This is correct to as many decimal places given. A calculator can always be used to obtain an approximation to numbers such as 2^{π} or $5^{\sqrt{2}}$. For now we will proceed with defining and working with exponential functions, even though the precise definition comes later. We will call any function of the form $f(x) = Ca^x$, or more generally $f(x) = Ca^{g(x)}$, an exponential function, provided a is a positive constant.

Graphs of Exponential Functions We consider first graphs of functions of the form $f(x) = a^x$ or $f(x) = a^{-x}$, where $a > 0$, and then we consider more complicated cases.

EXAMPLE 1 Sketch a graph of the functions $f(x) = 2^x$, $g(x) = \left(\frac{1}{2}\right)^x$, and $h(x) = 2^{-x}$.

SOLUTION For each, we make a table of values (see the table within each figure) and then sketch a plot (Figures 1 through 3).

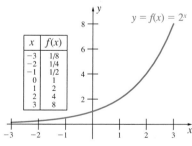

x	$f(x)$
−3	1/8
−2	1/4
−1	1/2
0	1
1	2
2	4
3	8

Figure 1

x	$g(x)$
−3	8
−2	4
−1	2
0	1
1	1/2
2	1/4
3	1/8

Figure 2

x	$h(x)$
−3	8
−2	4
−1	2
0	1
1	1/2
2	1/4
3	1/8

Figure 3

Example 1 suggests that the shape of the graph of $y = a^x$ can be increasing, as in Figure 1, or decreasing, as in Figure 2. The special case of $y = 1^x$ leads to a graph

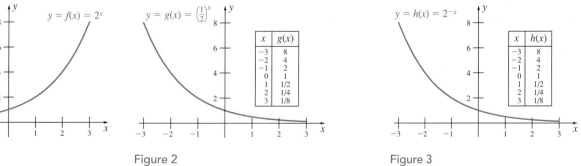

that is flat; this is because $1^x = 1$ for all x. Figure 4 illustrates for $a = \dfrac{1}{10}, \dfrac{1}{3}, \dfrac{1}{2}, 1, 2,$ 3, and 10 what the graphs of the exponential functions a^x can look like.

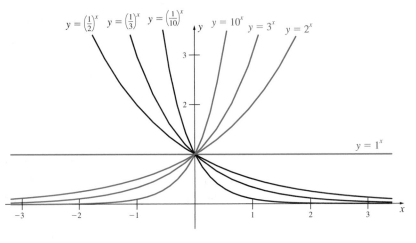

Figure 4

EXAMPLE 2 Sketch a graph and determine the domain and range of the functions $f(x) = 3^{\sqrt{x}}$ and $g(x) = 3^{-x^2/4}$.

SOLUTION Again, with the help of a calculator, we make a table of values and use them to sketch a plot. The graphs of $y = f(x)$ and $y = g(x)$ are shown in Figures 5 and 6.

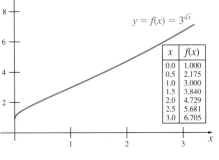

x	$f(x)$
0.0	1.000
0.5	2.175
1.0	3.000
1.5	3.840
2.0	4.729
2.5	5.681
3.0	6.705

Figure 5

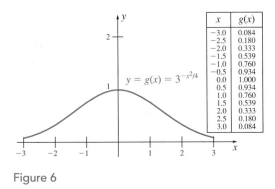

x	$g(x)$
−3.0	0.084
−2.5	0.180
−2.0	0.333
−1.5	0.539
−1.0	0.760
−0.5	0.934
0.0	1.000
0.5	0.934
1.0	0.760
1.5	0.539
2.0	0.333
2.5	0.180
3.0	0.084

Figure 6

The domain for $f(x) = 3^{\sqrt{x}}$ is the set of all nonnegative real numbers. (We can't take the square root of a negative number, so all negative numbers are excluded from the domain.) The function $g(x)$ makes sense for any real number argument, so the domain for g is the set of all real numbers.

The exponent in $3^{\sqrt{x}}$ is always nonnegative, so $3^{\sqrt{x}}$ is always greater than or equal to 1. Also, we can make the exponent $\sqrt{x}$ as large as we like; consequently, $f(x) = 3^{\sqrt{x}}$ can be made as large as we like. See Figure 5. Thus, the range for f is the interval $[1, \infty)$. The exponent in $3^{-x^2/4}$ is always less than or equal to zero, so $g(x)$ is always less than or equal to 1 (it is equal to 1 when $x = 0$). The function $g(x)$ can be made as close to zero as we like if we take x to be far enough away from 0. See Figure 6. Thus, the range for g is the interval $(0, 1]$.

While the conclusions about the range for f and g should seem evident by looking at the graphs of these functions in Figures 5 and 6, there are some issues that must be addressed before we can fully justify them.

We begin by looking at properties of exponents.

Properties of Exponents The usual properties of exponents hold even for irrational exponents. We will address the proofs of these properties in Section 2.6.

Theorem A **Properties of Exponents**

If $a > 0$, $b > 0$ and x and y are real numbers, then

(1) $a^x a^y = a^{x+y}$

(2) $\dfrac{a^x}{a^y} = a^{x-y}$

(3) $(a^x)^y = a^{xy}$

(4) $a^{-x} = \dfrac{1}{a^x}$

(5) $(ab)^x = a^x b^x$

(6) $\left(\dfrac{a}{b}\right)^x = \dfrac{a^x}{b^x}$

Note that in Example 1, Figures 2 and 3 look the same. In fact, they *are* the same; the functions g and h are identical, since we can use the properties of exponents to write

$$g(x) = \left(\frac{1}{2}\right)^x = (2^{-1})^x = 2^{-x} = h(x)$$

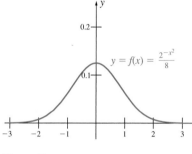

$y = f(x) = \dfrac{2^{-x^2}}{8}$

Figure 7

EXAMPLE 3 Simplify and then sketch a graph of the function defined by

$$F(x) = \frac{2^{-x^2}}{8}$$

SOLUTION We can use the fact that $8 = 2^3$, along with Property (ii), to write

$$F(x) = \frac{2^{-x^2}}{2^3} = 2^{-x^2-3}$$

We could then make a table and construct the plot shown in Figure 7. ∎

Logarithmic Functions Figure 4 suggests that the function $f(x) = a^x$ is increasing when $a > 1$ and decreasing when $0 < a < 1$. In both cases, a horizontal line intersects the graph of $y = f(x) = a^x$ at most once. Thus, the inverse function exists.

Definition

If $a > 0$ and $a \neq 1$, we define $\log_a x$ to be the inverse of the function a^x; that is,

$$y = a^x \iff x = \log_a y$$

From the properties of inverse functions (Section 1.6), we conclude that

$$a^{\log_a y} = y \quad \text{for every } y > 0$$

$$\log_a a^x = x \quad \text{for every } x$$

The next theorem states some of the familiar properties of logarithms.

Theorem B **Properties of Logarithms**

If a, b, and c are positive numbers, where $a \neq 1$, and if x is any real number, then

(1) $\log_a 1 = 0$

(2) $\log_a bc = \log_a b + \log_a c$

(3) $\log_a \dfrac{b}{c} = \log_a b - \log_a c$

(4) $\log_a b^x = x \log_a b$

Proof We prove (1) and (2) and leave the others as an exercise (see Problem 36).

(1) As long as a is positive and $a \neq 1$, $a^0 = 1$, so $\log_a 1 = 0$.

(2) By the properties of exponents,

$$a^{\log_a b + \log_a c} = a^{\log_a b} a^{\log_a c} = bc = a^{\log_a bc}$$

Thus, $\log_a bc = \log_a b + \log_a c$ because the function a^x is one-to-one. ∎

Recall that the domain of f is the range of f^{-1} and the range of f is the domain of f^{-1}. The domain for a^x is the set of all real numbers, so the range of $\log_a x$ is the set of all real numbers (as long as $a \neq 1$). Similarly, the range of a^x is the set of all positive numbers (again, assuming $a \neq 1$), so the domain of $\log_a x$ is the interval $(0, \infty)$.

▐ **EXAMPLE 4** Sketch the graphs of $f(x) = 2^x$ and $g(x) = \log_2 x$, and determine the domain and range for each function.

SOLUTION Tables of the function values are shown below. Note that since f and g are inverses of one another, the columns in the second table are obtained by interchanging the columns in the first table. Graphs for the two functions are shown in Figure 8. The domain for f is $(-\infty, \infty)$ and the range is $(0, \infty)$. For g, the domain is $(0, \infty)$ and the range is $(-\infty, \infty)$. ▐

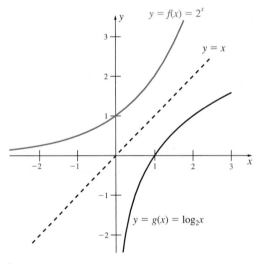

Figure 8

▐ **EXAMPLE 5** Find the inverse of $f(x) = \log_2 \dfrac{x}{1 - x}$ and graph f and f^{-1} on the same set of axes. Determine the domain and range for each function.

SOLUTION We begin by setting $y = f(x)$ and solving for x:

$$y = \log_2 \frac{x}{1 - x}$$

$$2^y = \frac{x}{1 - x}$$

$$(1 - x)2^y = x$$

$$2^y - x2^y = x$$

$$x + 2^y x = 2^y$$

$$x(1 + 2^y) = 2^y$$

$$x = \frac{2^y}{1 + 2^y} = f^{-1}(y)$$

Therefore, $f^{-1}(x) = 2^x/(1 + 2^x)$. Figure 9 shows both functions.

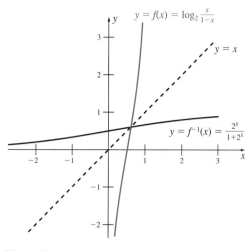

Figure 9

Since we can only take the log of a positive number, the argument $x/(1 - x)$ to the logarithmic function must be positive. Thus, we are led to the inequality $x/(1 - x) > 0$. The split points are 0 and 1. If $x < 0$, then the numerator is negative and the denominator is positive, so the fraction is negative. If $0 < x < 1$, then the numerator and the denominator are both positive, hence the fraction is positive. If $x > 1$, then the numerator is positive and the denominator is negative, so the fraction is negative. Thus, the only values of x that make $x/(1 - x)$ positive are those between 0 and 1. The domain for f is the interval $(0, 1)$. The domain for $f^{-1}(x) = 2^x/(1 + 2^x)$ is $(-\infty, \infty)$. The range for f is the domain for f^{-1}, that is $(-\infty, \infty)$ and the range for f^{-1} is the domain for f, that is $(0, 1)$. ∎

Most calculators have a button for the **common logarithm**, that is, the logarithm to the base 10. Another base that will become important in the next chapter, and nearly every subsequent chapter as well, is the **natural logarithm**, that is the logarithm to the base $e \approx 2.718$. We will have more to say about the number e and about natural logarithms in Chapter 2. For now, we will use logarithms, sometimes common logarithms, to solve equations involving exponential functions.

Notation for Logs
We will follow the convention of using $\log x$ (without explicitly giving the base) to mean common logarithms, that is logs to the base 10. We will use $\ln x$ to mean natural logs, that is, logs to the base e. (We will have more to say about $\ln x$ in the next chapter.) For all other bases we will explicitly give the base, e.g., $\log_2 x$ or $\log_5 x$.

EXAMPLE 6 Solve

(a) $2^{x^2-1} = 32$

(b) $3^{2x+1} = 17$

SOLUTION

(a) The base of 2 on the left side and the fact that $2^5 = 32$, suggest we take the log to the base 2 on both sides. This gives

$$\log_2 2^{x^2-1} = \log_2 32 = \log_2 2^5$$
$$(x^2 - 1)\log_2 2 = 5$$
$$x^2 - 1 = 5$$
$$x = \pm\sqrt{6}$$

(b) In this part, the base on the left is 3 but since 17 is not a perfect power of 3, taking log to the base 3 will not lead to a simplification. Anticipating the need for a calculator, we take the common log (base 10) on both sides.

$$\log_{10} 3^{2x+1} = \log_{10} 17$$
$$(2x + 1)\log_{10} 3 = \log_{10} 17$$

$$2x + 1 = \frac{\log_{10} 17}{\log_{10} 3}$$

$$x = \frac{1}{2}\left(\frac{\log_{10} 17}{\log_{10} 3} - 1\right) \approx 0.78945 \qquad \blacksquare$$

EXAMPLE 7 Carbon-14, an isotope of carbon, is radioactive and decays over time with a half life of 5730 years. Thus, if there is 1 gram of carbon-14 at time $t = 0$, then the amount remaining after t years is $2^{-t/5730}$.

(a) How much carbon-14 will be left after 10,000 years?
(b) How many years must pass until there is one-tenth of a gram remaining?

SOLUTION

(a) After 10,000 years, the amount of carbon-14 remaining is

$$2^{-10,000/5730} \approx 2^{-1.7452} \approx 0.29829 \text{ gram}$$

(b) To find when the amount is reduced to 0.1 gram, we set $0.1 = 2^{-t/5730}$ and solve for t. Since most calculators have a common log key, we take the common log of both sides to get

$$\log 0.1 = \log 2^{-t/5730}$$

$$-1 = -\frac{t}{5730}\log 2$$

$$t = \frac{5730}{\log 2} \approx 19{,}035 \text{ years} \qquad \blacksquare$$

(Recall that if we write log without explicitly giving the base, we mean the common logarithm; that is the logarithm to the base 10.) In this last example, the amount of carbon is halved every 5730 years, so 1 gram to begin with would be reduced to 0.5 grams after 5730 years, to 0.25 gram after $5730 \cdot 2 = 11{,}460$ years, 0.125 gram after $5730 \cdot 3 = 17{,}190$ years, and so on. What is not so clear is that the amount present after t years is given by $2^{-t/5730}$ if t is not a positive integer. It turns out that it is; we will return to this problem in Section 4.10.

Concepts Review

1. If p and q are integers, the expression $a^{p/q}$ can be written in terms of roots and integral powers as _____.

2. For any positive base a except 1, $\log_a 1 = $ _____.

3. $\log_a a^7 = $ _____, and in general, $\log_a a^x = $ _____.

4. $\log x - \log y$ can be written as the logarithm of a single quantity; namely, $\log x - \log y = $ _____.

Problem Set 1.7

In Problems 1–6, sketch a graph of the given exponential function.

1. $f(x) = 3^x$

2. $f(x) = \frac{1}{3}5^x$

3. $f(x) = 2^{2x}$

4. $f(x) = 2^{-3x}$

5. $f(x) = 2^{\sqrt{x}/4}$

6. $f(x) = \frac{1}{2}3^{-\sqrt{x}}$

In Problems 7–10, sketch a graph of the given logarithmic function.

7. $f(x) = \log_5 x$

8. $f(x) = \log_3 x$

9. $f(x) = \log_2 (x - 1)$

10. $f(x) = \log_{10} (x + 2)$

In Problems 11–16, find the inverse of the given function f and verify that $f(f^{-1}(x)) = x$ for all x in the domain of f^{-1}, and $f^{-1}(f(x)) = x$ for all x in the domain of f.

11. $f(x) = \dfrac{1}{1 + 2^x}$

12. $f(x) = 3 + 10^x$

13. $f(x) = \dfrac{10^x}{1 + 10^x}$

14. $f(x) = \dfrac{2^x}{4 + 2^x}$

15. $f(x) = \log_{10}(3x + 2)$

16. $f(x) = \log_2\left(\dfrac{x + 1}{2x}\right)$

In Problems 17–24, solve for x. Hint: $\log_a b = c \Leftrightarrow a^c = b$.

17. $\log_2 8 = x$

18. $\log_5 x = 2$

19. $\log_4 x = \frac{3}{2}$

20. $\log_x 64 = 4$

21. $2\log_9\left(\dfrac{x}{3}\right) = 1$

22. $\log_4\left(\dfrac{1}{2x}\right) = 3$

23. $\log_2(x + 3) - \log_2 x = 2$

24. $\log_5(x + 3) - \log_5 x = 1$

In Problems 25–28, the graph of an exponential function of the form $y = Ca^x$ is given. Use the graph to determine a and C.

25.

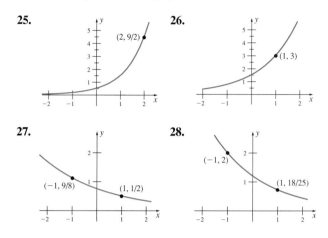

26.

27.

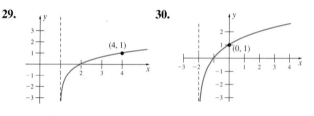

28.

In Problems 29 and 30, the graph of a logarithmic function of the form $y = \log_a (x - c)$ is given. Use the graph to determine a and c.

29.

30.

31. How are $\log_{1/2} x$ and $\log_2 x$ related?

32. Sketch the graphs of $\log_{1/3} x$ and $\log_3 x$ using the same coordinate axes.

C **33.** The magnitude M of an earthquake on the **Richter scale** is

$$M = 0.67 \log_{10}(0.37E) + 1.46$$

where E is the energy of the earthquake in kilowatt-hours. Find the energy of an earthquake of magnitude 7. Of magnitude 8.

C **34.** The loudness of sound is measured in decibels in honor of Alexander Graham Bell (1847–1922), inventor of the telephone. If the variation in pressure is P pounds per square inch, then the loudness L in decibels is

$$L = 20 \log_{10}(121.3P)$$

Find the variation in pressure caused by music at 115 decibels.

C **35.** In the equally tempered scale to which keyed instruments have been tuned since the days of J.S. Bach (1685–1750), the frequencies of successive notes C, C#, D, D#, E, F, F#, G, G#, A, A#, B, $\overline{C}$ form a geometric sequence (progression), with $\overline{C}$ having twice the frequency of C (C# is read C sharp and $\overline{C}$ indicates one octave above C). What is the ratio r between the frequencies of successive notes? If the frequency of A is 440, find the frequency of $\overline{C}$.

36. Prove parts (iii) and (iv) of Theorem B.

Answers to Concepts Review: **1.** $\sqrt[q]{a^p}$ **2.** 0   **3.** $7; x$
4. $\log \dfrac{x}{y}$

1.8
The Trigonometric Functions

You have probably seen the definitions of the trigonometric functions based on right triangles. Figure 1 summarizes the definitions of the sine, cosine, and tangent functions. You should review Figure 1 carefully, because these concepts are needed for many applications later in this book.

More generally, we define the trigonometric functions based on the unit circle. The unit circle, which we denote by C, is the circle with radius 1 and center at the origin; it has equation $x^2 + y^2 = 1$. Let A be the point $(1, 0)$ and let t be a positive number. There is a single point P on the circle C such that the distance, measured in the *counterclockwise* direction around the arc AP, is equal to t. (See Figure 2.) Recall that the circumference of a circle with radius r is $2\pi r$, so the circumference of C is 2π. Thus, if $t = \pi$, then the point P is exactly halfway around the circle from the point A; in this case, P is the point $(-1, 0)$. If $t = 3\pi/2$, then P is the point $(0, -1)$, and if $t = 2\pi$, then P is the point A. If $t > 2\pi$, then it will take more than one complete circuit of the circle C to trace the arc AP.

When $t < 0$, we trace the circle in a *clockwise* direction. There will be a single point P on the circle C such that the arc length measured in the clockwise direction from A is t. Thus, for every real number t, we can associate a unique point $P(x, y)$ on the unit circle. This allows us to make the key definitions of the sine and cosine functions. The functions sine and cosine are written as sin and cos, rather than as a single letter such as f or g. Parentheses around the independent variable are usually omitted unless there is some ambiguity.

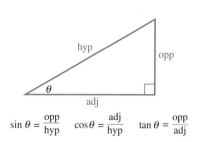

$$\sin \theta = \frac{\text{opp}}{\text{hyp}} \qquad \cos \theta = \frac{\text{adj}}{\text{hyp}} \qquad \tan \theta = \frac{\text{opp}}{\text{adj}}$$

Figure 1

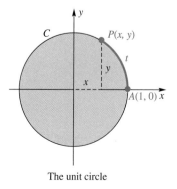

The unit circle

Figure 2

Definition   Sine and Cosine Functions
Let t be a real number that determines the point $P(x, y)$ as indicated above. Then
$$\sin t = y \quad \text{and} \quad \cos t = x$$

Basic Properties of Sine and Cosine A number of facts follow almost immediately from the definitions given above. First, since t can be any real number, the domain for both the sine and cosine functions is $(-\infty, \infty)$. Second, x and y are always between -1 and 1. Thus, the range for both the sine and cosine functions is the interval $[-1, 1]$.

Because the unit circle has circumference 2π, the values t and $t + 2\pi$ determine the *same* point $P(x, y)$. Thus,

$$\sin(t + 2\pi) = \sin t \quad \text{and} \quad \cos(t + 2\pi) = \cos t$$

(Notice that parentheses are needed to make it clear that we mean $\sin(t + 2\pi)$, rather than $(\sin t) + 2\pi$. The expression $\sin t + 2\pi$ would be ambiguous.)

The points P_1 and P_2 that correspond to t and $-t$, respectively, are symmetric about the x-axis (Figure 3). Thus, the x-coordinates for P_1 and P_2 are the same, and the y-coordinates differ only in sign. Consequently,

$$\sin(-t) = -\sin t \quad \text{and} \quad \cos(-t) = \cos t$$

In other words, sine is an odd function and cosine is an even function.

The points P_3 and P_4 corresponding to t and $\pi/2 - t$, respectively, are symmetric with respect to the line $y = x$ and thus they have their coordinates interchanged (Figure 4). This means that

$$\sin\left(\frac{\pi}{2} - t\right) = \cos t \quad \text{and} \quad \cos\left(\frac{\pi}{2} - t\right) = \sin t$$

Finally, we mention an important identity connecting the sine and cosine functions:

$$\sin^2 t + \cos^2 t = 1$$

for every real number t. This identity follows from the fact that since the point (x, y) is on the unit circle, x and y satisfy $x^2 + y^2 = 1$.

Graphs of Sine and Cosine To graph $y = \sin t$ and $y = \cos t$, we follow our usual procedure of making a table of values, plotting the corresponding points, and connecting these points with a smooth curve. So far, however, we know the values of sine and cosine for only a few values of t. A number of other values can be determined from geometric arguments. For example, if $t = \pi/4$, then t determines the point half of the way counterclockwise around the unit circle between the points $(1, 0)$ and $(0, 1)$. By symmetry, x and y will be on the line $y = x$, so $y = \sin t$ and $x = \cos t$ will be equal. Thus, the two legs of the right triangle OBP are equal, and the hypotenuse is 1 (Figure 5). The Pythagorean Theorem can be applied to give

$$1 = x^2 + x^2 = \cos^2\frac{\pi}{4} + \cos^2\frac{\pi}{4}$$

From this we conclude that $\cos(\pi/4) = 1/\sqrt{2} = \sqrt{2}/2$. Similarly, $\sin(\pi/4) = \sqrt{2}/2$. We can determine $\sin t$ and $\cos t$ for a number of other values of t. Some of these are shown in the table in the margin. Using these results, along with a number of results from a calculator (in radian mode), we obtain the graphs shown in Figure 6.

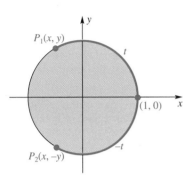

Figure 3

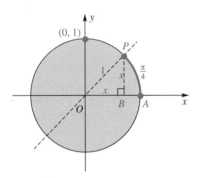

Figure 4

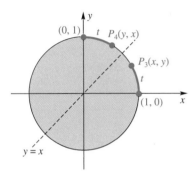

Figure 5

t	$\sin t$	$\cos t$
0	0	1
$\pi/6$	$1/2$	$\sqrt{3}/2$
$\pi/4$	$\sqrt{2}/2$	$\sqrt{2}/2$
$\pi/3$	$\sqrt{3}/2$	$1/2$
$\pi/2$	1	0
$2\pi/3$	$\sqrt{3}/2$	$-1/2$
$3\pi/4$	$\sqrt{2}/2$	$-\sqrt{2}/2$
$5\pi/6$	$1/2$	$-\sqrt{3}/2$
π	0	-1

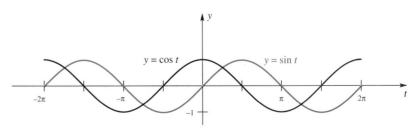

Figure 6

Four things are noticeable from these graphs:

1. Both sin t and cos t range from -1 to 1.
2. Both graphs repeat themselves on adjacent intervals of length 2π.
3. The graph of $y = \sin t$ is symmetric about the origin, and $y = \cos t$ is symmetric about the y-axis. (Thus, the sine function is odd and the cosine function is even.)
4. The graph of $y = \sin t$ is the same as that of $y = \cos t$, but translated $\pi/2$ units to the right.

The next example deals with functions of the form $\sin(at)$ or $\cos(at)$, which occur frequently in applications.

EXAMPLE 1 Sketch the graphs of

(a) $y = \sin(2\pi t)$ (b) $y = \cos(2t)$

SOLUTION

(a) As t goes from 0 to 1, the argument $2\pi t$ goes from 0 to 2π. Thus, the graph of this function will repeat itself on adjacent intervals of length 1. From the entries in the following table, we can sketch a graph of $y = \sin(2\pi t)$. Figure 7 shows a sketch.

t	$\sin(2\pi t)$	t	$\sin(2\pi t)$
0	$\sin(2\pi \cdot 0) = 0$	$\dfrac{5}{8}$	$\sin\left(2\pi \cdot \dfrac{5}{8}\right) = -\dfrac{\sqrt{2}}{2}$
$\dfrac{1}{8}$	$\sin\left(2\pi \cdot \dfrac{1}{8}\right) = \dfrac{\sqrt{2}}{2}$	$\dfrac{3}{4}$	$\sin\left(2\pi \cdot \dfrac{3}{4}\right) = -1$
$\dfrac{1}{4}$	$\sin\left(2\pi \cdot \dfrac{1}{4}\right) = 1$	$\dfrac{7}{8}$	$\sin\left(2\pi \cdot \dfrac{7}{8}\right) = -\dfrac{\sqrt{2}}{2}$
$\dfrac{3}{8}$	$\sin\left(2\pi \cdot \dfrac{3}{8}\right) = \dfrac{\sqrt{2}}{2}$	1	$\sin(2\pi \cdot 1) = 0$
$\dfrac{1}{2}$	$\sin\left(2\pi \cdot \dfrac{1}{2}\right) = 0$	$\dfrac{9}{8}$	$\sin\left(2\pi \cdot \dfrac{9}{8}\right) = \dfrac{\sqrt{2}}{2}$

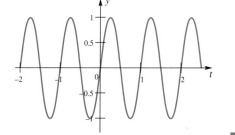

Figure 7

(b) As t goes from 0 to π, the argument $2t$ goes from 0 to 2π. Thus, the graph of $y = \cos(2t)$ will repeat itself on adjacent intervals of length π. Once we construct a table we can sketch a plot of $y = \cos(2t)$. Figure 8 shows the graph.

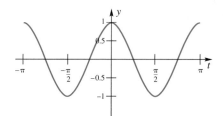

Figure 8

t	$\cos(2t)$	t	$\cos(2t)$
0	$\cos(2 \cdot 0) = 1$	$\dfrac{5\pi}{8}$	$\cos\left(2 \cdot \dfrac{5\pi}{8}\right) = -\dfrac{\sqrt{2}}{2}$
$\dfrac{\pi}{8}$	$\cos\left(2 \cdot \dfrac{\pi}{8}\right) = \dfrac{\sqrt{2}}{2}$	$\dfrac{3\pi}{4}$	$\cos\left(2 \cdot \dfrac{3\pi}{4}\right) = 0$
$\dfrac{\pi}{4}$	$\cos\left(2 \cdot \dfrac{\pi}{4}\right) = 0$	$\dfrac{7\pi}{8}$	$\cos\left(2 \cdot \dfrac{7\pi}{8}\right) = \dfrac{\sqrt{2}}{2}$
$\dfrac{3\pi}{8}$	$\cos\left(2 \cdot \dfrac{3\pi}{8}\right) = -\dfrac{\sqrt{2}}{2}$	π	$\cos(2 \cdot \pi) = 1$
$\dfrac{\pi}{2}$	$\cos\left(2 \cdot \dfrac{\pi}{2}\right) = -1$	$\dfrac{9\pi}{8}$	$\cos\left(2 \cdot \dfrac{9\pi}{8}\right) = \dfrac{\sqrt{2}}{2}$

Period and Amplitude of the Trigonometric Functions A function f is **periodic** if there is a positive number p such that

$$f(x + p) = f(x)$$

for all real numbers x in the domain of f. If f is nonconstant, the smallest such positive number p is called the **period** of f. The sine function is periodic because $\sin(x + 2\pi) = \sin x$ for all x. It is also true that

$$\sin(x + 4\pi) = \sin(x - 2\pi) = \sin(x + 12\pi) = \sin x$$

for all x. Thus, $4\pi, -2\pi,$ and 12π are all numbers p with the property $\sin(x + p) = \sin x$. The period is defined to be the *smallest* such positive number p. For the sine function, the smallest positive p with the property that $\sin(x + p) = \sin x$ is $p = 2\pi$. We therefore say that the sine function is periodic with period 2π. The cosine function is also periodic with period 2π.

The function $\sin(at)$ has period $2\pi/a$ since

$$\sin\left[a\left(t + \frac{2\pi}{a}\right)\right] = \sin[at + 2\pi] = \sin(at)$$

The period of the function $\cos(at)$ is also $2\pi/a$.

EXAMPLE 2 What are the periods of the following functions?

(a) $\sin(2\pi t)$ (b) $\cos(2t)$ (c) $\sin(2\pi t/12)$

SOLUTION

(a) Because the function $\sin(2\pi t)$ is of the form $\sin(at)$ with $a = 2\pi$, its period is $p = \dfrac{2\pi}{2\pi} = 1$.

(b) The function $\cos(2t)$ is of the form $\cos(at)$ with $a = 2$. Thus, the period of $\cos(2t)$ is $p = \dfrac{2\pi}{2} = \pi$.

(c) The function $\sin(2\pi t/12)$ has period $p = \dfrac{2\pi}{2\pi/12} = 12$. ■

If the periodic function f attains a minimum and a maximum, we define the **amplitude** A to be half the vertical distance between the highest point and the lowest point on the graph.

EXAMPLE 3 Find the amplitude of the following periodic functions.

(a) $\sin(2\pi t/12)$ (b) $3 \cos (2t)$
(c) $50 + 21 \sin(2\pi t/12 + 3)$

SOLUTION

(a) Since the range of the function $\sin(2\pi t/12)$ is $[-1, 1]$, its amplitude is $A = 1$.

(b) The function $3 \cos (2t)$ will take on values from -3 (which occurs when $t = \pm\dfrac{\pi}{2}, \pm\dfrac{3\pi}{2}, \dots$) to 3 (which occurs when $t = 0, \pm\pi, \pm 2\pi, \dots$). The amplitude is therefore $A = 3$.

(c) The function $21 \sin(2\pi t/12 + 3)$ takes on values from -21 to 21. Thus, $50 + 21 \sin(2\pi t/12 + 3)$ takes on values from $50 - 21 = 29$ to $50 + 21 = 71$. The amplitude is therefore 21. ■

In general, for $a > 0$ and $A > 0$,

$C + A \sin(a(t + b))$ and $C + A \cos(a(t + b))$ have period $\dfrac{2\pi}{a}$ and amplitude A.

Trigonometric functions can be used to model a number of physical phenomena, including daily tide levels and yearly temperatures.

EXAMPLE 4 The normal high temperature for St. Louis, Missouri, ranges from 37°F for January 15 to 89°F for July 15. The normal high temperature follows roughly a sinusoidal curve.

(a) Find values of $C, A, a,$ and b such that

$$T(t) = C + A\sin(a(t + b))$$

where t, expressed in months since January 1, is a reasonable model for the normal high temperature.

(b) Use this model to approximate the normal high temperature for May 15.

SOLUTION

(a) The required function must have period $t = 12$ since the seasons repeat every 12 months. Thus, $\dfrac{2\pi}{a} = 12$, so we have $a = \dfrac{2\pi}{12}$. The amplitude is half the difference between the lowest and highest points; in this case, $A = \dfrac{1}{2}(89 - 37) = 26$. The value of C is equal to the midpoint of the low and high temperatures, so $C = \dfrac{1}{2}(89 + 37) = 63$. The function $T(t)$ must therefore be of the form

$$T(t) = 63 + 26\sin\left(\frac{2\pi}{12}(t + b)\right)$$

The only constant left to find is b. The lowest normal high temperature is 37, which occurs on January 15, roughly in the middle of January. Thus, our function must satisfy $T(1/2) = 37$, and the function must reach its minimum of 37 when $t = 1/2$. Figure 9 summarizes the information that we have so far. The function $63 + 26\sin(2\pi t/12)$ reaches its minimum when $2\pi t/12 = -\pi/2$, that is, when $t = -3$. We must therefore translate the curve defined by $y = 63 + 26\sin(2\pi t/12)$ to the right by the amount $1/2 - (-3) = 7/2$. In Section 1.6, we showed that replacing x with $x - c$ translates the graph of $y = f(x)$ to the right by c units. Thus, in order to translate the graph of $y = 63 + 26\sin(2\pi t/12)$ to the right by $7/2$ units, we must replace t with $t - 7/2$. Thus,

$$T(t) = 63 + 26\sin\left(\frac{2\pi}{12}\left(t - \frac{7}{2}\right)\right)$$

Figure 10 shows a plot of the normal high temperature T as a function of time t, where t is given in months.

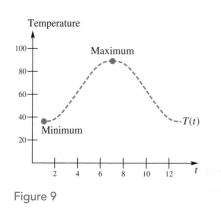

Figure 9

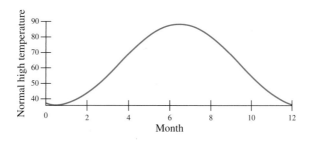

Figure 10

Models and Modeling

It is important to keep in mind that all models such as this are simplifications of reality. (That is why they are called *models*.) Although such models are inherently simplifications of reality, many of them are still useful for prediction.

(b) To estimate the normal high temperature for May 15, we substitute $t = 4.5$ (because the middle of May is four and one-half months into the year) and obtain

$$T(4.5) = 63 + 26 \sin(2\pi(4.5 - 3.5)/12) = 76$$

The normal high temperature for St. Louis on May 15 is actually 75°F. Thus, our model overpredicts by 1°, which is remarkably accurate considering how little information was given. ∎

Four Other Trigonometric Functions   We could get by with just the sine and cosine functions, but it is convenient to introduce four additional trigonometric functions: tangent, cotangent, secant, and cosecant.

$$\tan t = \frac{\sin t}{\cos t} \qquad \cot t = \frac{\cos t}{\sin t}$$

$$\sec t = \frac{1}{\cos t} \qquad \csc t = \frac{1}{\sin t}$$

What we know about sine and cosine will automatically give us knowledge about these four new functions.

EXAMPLE 5   Show that tangent is an odd function.

SOLUTION

$$\tan(-t) = \frac{\sin(-t)}{\cos(-t)} = \frac{-\sin t}{\cos t} = -\tan t$$ ∎

EXAMPLE 6   Verify that the following are identities.

$$1 + \tan^2 t = \sec^2 t \qquad 1 + \cot^2 t = \csc^2 t$$

SOLUTION

$$1 + \tan^2 t = 1 + \frac{\sin^2 t}{\cos^2 t} = \frac{\cos^2 t + \sin^2 t}{\cos^2 t} = \frac{1}{\cos^2 t} = \sec^2 t$$

$$1 + \cot^2 t = 1 + \frac{\cos^2 t}{\sin^2 t} = \frac{\sin^2 t + \cos^2 t}{\sin^2 t} = \frac{1}{\sin^2 t} = \csc^2 t$$ ∎

When we study the tangent function (Figure 11), we are in for two minor surprises. First, we notice that there are vertical asymptotes at $\pm\pi/2, \pm3\pi/2, \ldots$. We should have anticipated this since $\cos t = 0$ at these values of t, which means that $\sin t/\cos t$ would involve a division by zero. Second, it appears that the tangent is periodic (which we expected), but with period π (which we might not have expected). You will see the analytic reason for this in Problem 33.

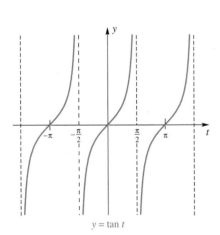

$y = \tan t$

Figure 11

Relation to Angle Trigonometry   Angles are commonly measured either in degrees or in radians. One radian is by definition the angle corresponding to an arc of length 1 on the unit circle. See Figure 12. The angle corresponding to a complete revolution measures 360°, but only 2π radians. Equivalently, a straight angle measures 180° or π radians, a fact worth remembering.

$$180° = \pi \text{ radians} \approx 3.1415927 \text{ radians}$$

This leads to the results

$$1 \text{ radian} \approx 57.29578° \qquad 1° \approx 0.0174533 \text{ radian}$$

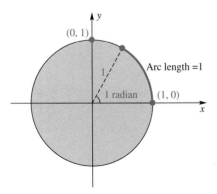

(0, 1)

Arc length = 1

1 radian   (1, 0)

Figure 12

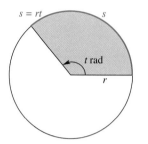

Degrees	Radians
0	0
30	$\pi/6$
45	$\pi/4$
60	$\pi/3$
90	$\pi/2$
120	$2\pi/3$
135	$3\pi/4$
150	$5\pi/6$
180	π
360	2π

Figure 13

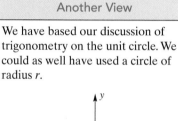

Figure 14

Figure 13 shows some other common conversions between degrees and radians.
The division of a revolution into 360 parts is quite arbitrary (due to the ancient Babylonians, who liked multiples of 60). The division into 2π parts is more fundamental and lies behind the almost universal use of radian measure in calculus. Notice, in particular, that the length s of the arc cut off on a circle of radius r by a central angle of t radians satisfies (see Figure 14)

$$\frac{s}{2\pi r} = \frac{t}{2\pi}$$

That is, the fraction of the total circumference $2\pi r$ corresponding to an angle t is the same as the fraction of the unit circle corresponding to the same angle t. This implies that $s = rt$.

When $r = 1$, this gives $s = t$. This means that *the length of the arc on the unit circle cut off by a central angle of t radians is t*. This is correct even if t is negative, provided that we interpret length to be negative when measured in the clockwise direction.

EXAMPLE 7 Find the distance traveled by a bicycle with wheels of radius 30 centimeters when the wheels turn through 100 revolutions.

SOLUTION We use the fact that $s = rt$, recognizing that 100 revolutions correspond to $100 \cdot (2\pi)$ radians.

$$s = (30)(100)(2\pi) = 6000\pi \approx 18{,}849.6 \text{ centimeters} \approx 188.5 \text{ meters} \quad \blacksquare$$

Now we can make the connection between angle trigonometry and unit circle trigonometry. If θ is an angle measuring t radians, that is, if θ is an angle that cuts off an arc of length t from the unit circle, then

$$\sin \theta = \sin t \qquad \cos \theta = \cos t$$

In calculus, when we meet an angle measured in degrees, we almost always change it to radians before doing any calculations. For example,

$$\sin 31.6° = \sin\left(31.6 \cdot \frac{\pi}{180} \text{radian}\right) \approx \sin 0.552$$

List of Important Identities We will not take space to verify all the following identities. We simply assert their truth and suggest that most of them will be needed somewhere in this book.

Another View

We have based our discussion of trigonometry on the unit circle. We could as well have used a circle of radius r.

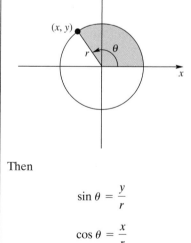

Then

$$\sin \theta = \frac{y}{r}$$

$$\cos \theta = \frac{x}{r}$$

Trigonometric Identities The following are true for all x and y, provided that both sides are defined at the chosen x and y.

Odd–even identities	**Cofunction identities**
$\sin(-x) = -\sin x$	$\sin\left(\dfrac{\pi}{2} - x\right) = \cos x$
$\cos(-x) = \cos x$	$\cos\left(\dfrac{\pi}{2} - x\right) = \sin x$
$\tan(-x) = -\tan x$	$\tan\left(\dfrac{\pi}{2} - x\right) = \cot x$

Pythagorean identities	**Addition identities**
$\sin^2 x + \cos^2 x = 1$	$\sin(x + y) = \sin x \cos y + \cos x \sin y$

$$1 + \tan^2 x = \sec^2 x$$

$$1 + \cot^2 x = \csc^2 x$$

$$\cos(x + y) = \cos x \cos y - \sin x \sin y$$

$$\tan(x + y) = \frac{\tan x + \tan y}{1 - \tan x \tan y}$$

Double-angle identities

$$\sin 2x = 2 \sin x \cos x$$

$$\cos 2x = \cos^2 x - \sin^2 x$$

$$= 2 \cos^2 x - 1$$

$$= 1 - 2 \sin^2 x$$

Half-angle identities

$$\sin\left(\frac{x}{2}\right) = \pm\sqrt{\frac{1 - \cos x}{2}}$$

$$\cos\left(\frac{x}{2}\right) = \pm\sqrt{\frac{1 + \cos x}{2}}$$

Sum identities

$$\sin x + \sin y = 2 \sin\left(\frac{x + y}{2}\right)\cos\left(\frac{x - y}{2}\right)$$

$$\cos x + \cos y = 2 \cos\left(\frac{x + y}{2}\right)\cos\left(\frac{x - y}{2}\right)$$

Product identities

$$\sin x \sin y = -\tfrac{1}{2}[\cos(x + y) - \cos(x - y)]$$

$$\cos x \cos y = \tfrac{1}{2}[\cos(x + y) + \cos(x - y)]$$

$$\sin x \cos y = \tfrac{1}{2}[\sin(x + y) + \sin(x - y)]$$

Concepts Review

1. The natural domain of the sine function is _____; its range is _____.

2. The period of the cosine function is _____; the period of the sine function is _____; the period of the tangent function is _____.

3. Since $\sin(-x) = -\sin x$, the sine function is _____, and since $\cos(-x) = \cos x$, the cosine function is _____.

4. If $(-4, 3)$ lies on the terminal side of an angle θ whose vertex is at the origin and initial side is along the positive x-axis, then $\cos \theta = $ _____.

Problem Set 1.8

1. Convert the following degree measures to radians (leave π in your answer).

(a) $30°$ (b) $45°$ (c) $-60°$

(d) $240°$ (e) $-370°$ (f) $10°$

2. Convert the following radian measures to degrees.

(a) $\frac{7}{6}\pi$ (b) $\frac{3}{4}\pi$ (c) $-\frac{1}{3}\pi$

(d) $\frac{4}{3}\pi$ (e) $-\frac{35}{18}\pi$ (f) $\frac{3}{18}\pi$

[C] **3.** Convert the following degree measures to radians $(1° = \pi/180 \approx 1.7453 \times 10^{-2}\text{ radian})$.

(a) $33.3°$ (b) $46°$ (c) $-66.6°$

(d) $240.11°$ (e) $-369°$ (f) $11°$

[C] **4.** Convert the following radian measures to degrees $(1\text{ radian} = 180/\pi \approx 57.296\text{ degrees})$.

(a) 3.141 (b) 6.28 (c) 5.00

(d) 0.001 (e) -0.1 (f) 36.0

[C] **5.** Calculate (be sure that your calculator is in radian or degree mode as needed).

(a) $\dfrac{56.4 \tan 34.2°}{\sin 34.1°}$ (b) $\dfrac{5.34 \tan 21.3°}{\sin 3.1° + \cot 23.5°}$

(c) $\tan 0.452$ (d) $\sin(-0.361)$

[C] **6.** Calculate.

(a) $\dfrac{234.1 \sin 1.56}{\cos 0.34}$ (b) $\sin^2 2.51 + \sqrt{\cos 0.51}$

[C] **7.** Calculate.

(a) $\dfrac{56.3 \tan 34.2°}{\sin 56.1°}$ (b) $\left(\dfrac{\sin 35°}{\sin 26° + \cos 26°}\right)^3$

8. Verify the values of $\sin t$ and $\cos t$ in the table used to construct Figure 6.

9. Evaluate without using a calculator.

(a) $\tan\dfrac{\pi}{6}$ (b) $\sec \pi$ (c) $\sec\dfrac{3\pi}{4}$

(d) $\csc \dfrac{\pi}{2}$ (e) $\cot \dfrac{\pi}{4}$ (f) $\tan\left(-\dfrac{\pi}{4}\right)$

10. Evaluate without using a calculator.

(a) $\tan \dfrac{\pi}{3}$ (b) $\sec \dfrac{\pi}{3}$ (c) $\cot \dfrac{\pi}{3}$

(d) $\csc \dfrac{\pi}{4}$ (e) $\tan\left(-\dfrac{\pi}{6}\right)$ (f) $\cos\left(-\dfrac{\pi}{3}\right)$

11. Verify that the following are identities (see Example 6).

(a) $(1 + \sin z)(1 - \sin z) = \dfrac{1}{\sec^2 z}$

(b) $(\sec t - 1)(\sec t + 1) = \tan^2 t$

(c) $\sec t - \sin t \tan t = \cos t$

(d) $\dfrac{\sec^2 t - 1}{\sec^2 t} = \sin^2 t$

12. Verify that the following are identities (see Example 6).

(a) $\sin^2 v + \dfrac{1}{\sec^2 v} = 1$

(b) $\cos 3t = 4 \cos^3 t - 3 \cos t$ *Hint:* Use a double-angle identity.

(c) $\sin 4x = 8 \sin x \cos^3 x - 4 \sin x \cos x$ *Hint:* Use a double-angle identity twice.

(d) $(1 + \cos \theta)(1 - \cos \theta) = \sin^2 \theta$

13. Verify the following are identities.

(a) $\dfrac{\sin u}{\csc u} + \dfrac{\cos u}{\sec u} = 1$

(b) $(1 - \cos^2 x)(1 + \cot^2 x) = 1$

(c) $\sin t(\csc t - \sin t) = \cos^2 t$

(d) $\dfrac{1 - \csc^2 t}{\csc^2 t} = \dfrac{-1}{\sec^2 t}$

14. Sketch the graphs of the following on $[-\pi, 2\pi]$.

(a) $y = \sin 2x$ (b) $y = 2 \sin t$

(c) $y = \cos\left(x - \dfrac{\pi}{4}\right)$ (d) $y = \sec t$

15. Sketch the graphs of the following on $[-\pi, 2\pi]$.

(a) $y = \csc t$ (b) $y = 2 \cos t$

(c) $y = \cos 3t$ (d) $y = \cos\left(t + \dfrac{\pi}{3}\right)$

Determine the period, amplitude, and shifts (both horizontal and vertical) and draw a graph over the interval $-5 \le x \le 5$ for the functions listed in Problems 16–23.

16. $y = 3 \cos \dfrac{x}{2}$ **17.** $y = 2 \sin 2x$

18. $y = \tan x$ **19.** $y = 2 + \dfrac{1}{6} \cot 2x$

20. $y = 3 + \sec(x - \pi)$ **21.** $y = 21 + 7 \sin(2x + 3)$

22. $y = 3 \cos\left(x - \dfrac{\pi}{2}\right) - 1$ **23.** $y = \tan\left(2x - \dfrac{\pi}{3}\right)$

24. Which of the following represent the same graph? Check your result analytically using trigonometric identities.

(a) $y = \sin\left(x + \dfrac{\pi}{2}\right)$ (b) $y = \cos\left(x + \dfrac{\pi}{2}\right)$

(c) $y = -\sin(x + \pi)$ (d) $y = \cos(x - \pi)$

(e) $y = -\sin(\pi - x)$ (f) $y = \cos\left(x - \dfrac{\pi}{2}\right)$

(g) $y = -\cos(\pi - x)$ (h) $y = \sin\left(x - \dfrac{\pi}{2}\right)$

25. Which of the following are odd functions? Even functions? Neither?

(a) $t \sin t$ (b) $\sin^2 t$ (c) $\csc t$

(d) $|\sin t|$ (e) $\sin (\cos t)$ (f) $x + \sin x$

26. Which of the following are odd functions? Even functions? Neither?

(a) $\cot t + \sin t$ (b) $\sin^3 t$ (c) $\sec t$

(d) $\sqrt{\sin^4 t}$ (e) $\cos (\sin t)$ (f) $x^2 + \sin x$

Find the exact values in Problems 27–31. Hint: Half-angle identities may be helpful.

27. $\cos^2 \dfrac{\pi}{3}$ **28.** $\sin^2 \dfrac{\pi}{6}$

29. $\sin^3 \dfrac{\pi}{6}$ **30.** $\cos^2 \dfrac{\pi}{12}$

31. $\sin^2 \dfrac{\pi}{8}$

32. Find identities analogous to the addition identities for each expression.

(a) $\sin(x - y)$ (b) $\cos(x - y)$ (c) $\tan(x - y)$

33. Use the addition identity for the tangent to show that $\tan(t + \pi) = \tan t$ for all t in the domain of $\tan t$.

34. Show that $\cos(x - \pi) = -\cos x$ for all x.

≈ C **35.** Suppose that a tire on a truck has an outer radius of 2.5 feet. How many revolutions per minute does the tire make when the truck is traveling 60 miles per hour?

≈ **36.** How far does a wheel of radius 2 feet roll along level ground in making 150 revolutions?

≈ C **37.** A belt passes around two wheels, as shown in Figure 15. How many revolutions per second does the small wheel make when the large wheel makes 21 revolutions per second?

6 in.   8 in.

Figure 15

38. The **angle of inclination** α of a line is the smallest positive angle from the positive x-axis to the line ($\alpha = 0$ for a horizontal line). Show that the slope m of the line is equal to $\tan \alpha$.

39. Find the angle of inclination of the following lines (see Problem 38).

(a) $y = \sqrt{3} x - 7$ (b) $\sqrt{3} x + 3y = 6$

40. Let ℓ_1 and ℓ_2 be two nonvertical intersecting lines with slopes m_1 and m_2, respectively. If θ, the angle from ℓ_1 to ℓ_2, is not a right angle, then

$$\tan \theta = \dfrac{m_2 - m_1}{1 + m_1 m_2}$$

Show this using the fact that $\theta = \theta_2 - \theta_1$ in Figure 16.

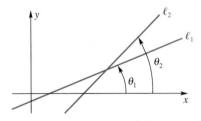

Figure 16

C **41.** Find the angle (in radians) from the first line to the second (see Problem 40).

(a) $y = 2x, y = 3x$

(b) $y = \dfrac{x}{2}, y = -x$

(c) $2x - 6y = 12, 2x + y = 0$

42. Derive the formula $A = \frac{1}{2}r^2 t$ for the area of a sector of a circle. Here r is the radius and t is the radian measure of the central angle (see Figure 17).

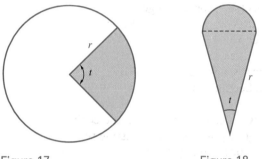

Figure 17   **Figure 18**

43. Find the area of the sector of a circle of radius 5 centimeters and central angle 2 radians (see Problem 42).

44. A regular polygon of n sides is inscribed in a circle of radius r. Find formulas for the perimeter, P, and area, A, of the polygon in terms of n and r.

45. An isosceles triangle is topped by a semicircle, as shown in Figure 18. Find a formula for the area A of the whole figure in terms of the side length r and angle t (radians). (We say that A is a function of the two independent variables r and t.)

46. From a product identity, we obtain

$$\cos \frac{x}{2} \cos \frac{x}{4} = \frac{1}{2}\left[\cos\left(\frac{3}{4}x\right) + \cos\left(\frac{1}{4}x\right)\right]$$

Find the corresponding sum of cosines for

$$\cos \frac{x}{2} \cos \frac{x}{4} \cos \frac{x}{8} \cos \frac{x}{16}$$

Do you see a generalization?

47. The normal high temperature for Las Vegas, Nevada, is 55°F for January 15 and 105° for July 15. Assuming that these are the extreme high and low temperatures for the year, use this information to approximate the average high temperature for November 15.

48. Tides are often measured by arbitrary height markings at some location. Suppose that a high tide occurs at noon when the water level is at 12 feet. Six hours later, a low tide with a water level of 5 feet occurs, and by midnight another high tide with a water level of 12 feet occurs. Assuming that the water level is periodic, use this information to find a formula that gives the water level as a function of time. Then use this function to approximate the water level at 5:30 P.M.

EXPL **49.** Circular motion can be modeled by using the parametric representations of the form $x(t) = \sin t$ and $y(t) = \cos t$. (A *parametric representation* means that a variable, t in this case, determines both $x(t)$ and $y(t)$.) This will give the full circle for $0 \leq t \leq 2\pi$. If we consider a 4-foot-diameter wheel making one complete rotation clockwise once every 10 seconds, show that the motion of a point on the rim of the wheel can be represented by $x(t) = 2\sin(\pi t/5)$ and $y(t) = 2\cos(\pi t/5)$.

(a) Find the positions of the point on the rim of the wheel when $t = 2$ seconds, 6 seconds, and 10 seconds. Where was this point when the wheel started to rotate at $t = 0$?

(b) How will the formulas giving the motion of the point change if the wheel is rotating *counterclockwise*.

(c) At what value of t is the point at $(2, 0)$ for the first time?

EXPL **50.** The circular frequency v of oscillation of a point is given by $v = \dfrac{2\pi}{\text{period}}$. What happens when you add two motions that have the same frequency or period? To investigate, we can graph the functions $y(t) = 2\sin(\pi t/5)$ and $y(t) = \sin(\pi t/5) + \cos(\pi t/5)$ and look for similarities. Armed with this information, we can investigate by graphing the following functions over the interval $[-5, 5]$:

(a) $y(t) = 3\sin(\pi t/5) - 5\cos(\pi t/5) + 2\sin((\pi t/5) - 3)$

(b) $y(t) = 3\cos(\pi t/5 - 2) + \cos(\pi t/5) + \cos((\pi t/5) - 3)$

EXPL **51.** We now explore the relationship between $A\sin(\omega t) + B\cos(\omega t)$ and $C\sin(\omega t + \phi)$.

(a) By expanding $\sin(\omega t + \phi)$ using the sum of the angles formula, show that the two expressions are equivalent if $A = C\cos\phi$ and $B = C\sin\phi$.

(b) Consequently, show that $A^2 + B^2 = C^2$ and that ϕ then satisfies the equation $\tan\phi = \dfrac{B}{A}$.

(c) Generalize your result to state a proposition about $A_1\sin(\omega t + \phi_1) + A_2\sin(\omega t + \phi_2) + A_3\sin(\omega t + \phi_3)$.

(d) Write an essay, in your own words, that expresses the importance of the identity between $A\sin(\omega t) + B\cos(\omega t)$ and $C\sin(\omega t + \phi)$. Be sure to note that $|C| \geq \max(|A|, |B|)$ and that the identity holds only when you are forming a linear combination (adding and/or subtracting multiples of single powers) of sine and cosine of the same frequency.

Trigonometric functions that have high frequencies pose special problems for graphing. We now explore how to plot such functions.

GC **52.** Graph the function $f(x) = \sin 50x$ using the window given by a y range of $-1.5 \leq y \leq 1.5$ and the x range given by

(a) $[-15, 15]$ (b) $[-10, 10]$ (c) $[-8, 8]$

(d) $[-1, 1]$ (e) $[-0.25, 0.25]$

Indicate briefly which x-window shows the true behavior of the function, and discuss reasons why the other x-windows give results that look different.

GC **53.** Graph the function $f(x) = \cos x + \dfrac{1}{50}\sin 50x$ using the windows given by the following ranges of x and y.

(a) $-5 \le x \le 5, -1 \le y \le 1$

(b) $-1 \le x \le 1, 0.5 \le y \le 1.5$

(c) $-0.1 \le x \le 0.1, 0.9 \le y \le 1.1$

Indicate briefly which (x, y)-window shows the true behavior of the function, and discuss reasons why the other (x, y)-windows give results that look different. In this case, is it true that only one window gives the important behavior, or do we need more than one window to graphically communicate the behavior of this function?

GC EXPL **54.** Let $f(x) = \dfrac{3x + 2}{x^2 + 1}$ and $g(x) = \dfrac{1}{100}\cos(100x)$.

(a) Use functional composition to form $h(x) = (f \circ g)(x)$, as well as $j(x) = (g \circ f)(x)$.

(b) Find the appropriate window or windows that give a clear picture of $h(x)$.

(c) Find the appropriate window or windows that give a clear picture of $j(x)$.

55. Suppose that a continuous function is periodic with period 1 and is linear between 0 and 0.25 and linear between -0.75 and 0. In addition, it has the value 1 at 0 and 2 at 0.25. Sketch the function over the domain $[-1, 1]$, and give a piecewise definition of the function.

56. Suppose that a continuous function is periodic with period 2 and is quadratic between -0.25 and 0.25 and linear between -1.75 and -0.25. In addition, it has the value 0 at 0 and 0.0625 at ± 0.25. Sketch the function over the domain $[-2, 2]$, and give a piecewise definition of the function.

Answers to Concepts Review: **1.** $(-\infty, \infty); [-1, 1]$
2. $2\pi; 2\pi; \pi$ **3.** odd; even **4.** $-4/5$

1.9
The Inverse Trigonometric Functions

The six basic trigonometric functions (sine, cosine, tangent, cotangent, secant, and cosecant) were defined in Section 1.8. With respect to the notion of inverse, they are miserable functions, since for each y in their range there are infinitely many x's that correspond to it (Figure 1). Nonetheless, we are going to introduce a notion of inverse for them. That this is possible rests on a procedure called **restricting the domain,** which was discussed briefly in Section 1.6.

Inverse Sine and Inverse Cosine In the case of sine and cosine, we restrict the domain, keeping the range as large as possible while insisting that the resulting function have an inverse. This can be done in many ways, but the agreed procedure is suggested by Figures 2 and 3. We also show the graph of the corresponding inverse function, obtained, as usual, by reflecting across the line $y = x$.

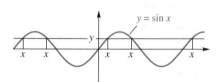

$y = \sin x$

Figure 1

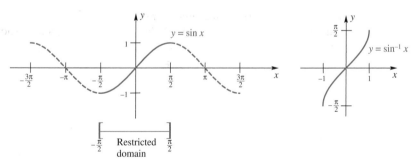

Figure 2

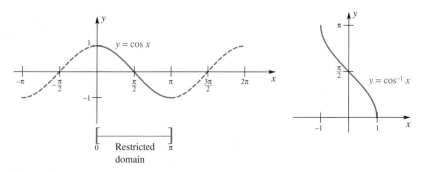

Figure 3

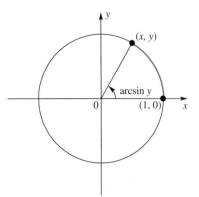

Figure 4

We formalize what we have shown in a definition.

Definition

To obtain inverses for sine and cosine, we restrict their domains to $[-\pi/2, \pi/2]$ and $[0, \pi]$, respectively. Thus,

$$x = \sin^{-1} y \quad \Leftrightarrow \quad y = \sin x, -\frac{\pi}{2} \leq x \leq \frac{\pi}{2}$$

$$x = \cos^{-1} y \quad \Leftrightarrow \quad y = \cos x, 0 \leq x \leq \pi$$

The symbol arcsin is often used for $\sin^{-1}$, and arccos is similarly used for $\cos^{-1}$. Think of arcsin as meaning "the arc whose sine is" or "the angle whose sine is" (Figure 4). We will use both forms throughout the rest of this book.

EXAMPLE 1 Calculate

(a) $\sin^{-1}\left(\sqrt{2}/2\right)$,

(b) $\cos^{-1}\left(-\frac{1}{2}\right)$,

(c) $\cos(\cos^{-1} 0.6)$,

(d) $\sin^{-1}(\sin 3\pi/2)$

SOLUTION

(a) $\sin^{-1}\left(\dfrac{\sqrt{2}}{2}\right) = \dfrac{\pi}{4}$

(b) $\cos^{-1}\left(-\dfrac{1}{2}\right) = \dfrac{2\pi}{3}$

(c) $\cos(\cos^{-1} 0.6) = 0.6$

(d) $\sin^{-1}\left(\sin\dfrac{3\pi}{2}\right) = -\dfrac{\pi}{2}$

The only one of these that is tricky is (d). Note that it would be wrong to give $3\pi/2$ as the answer, since $\sin^{-1} y$ is always in the interval $[-\pi/2, \pi/2]$. Work the problem in steps, as follows.

$$\sin^{-1}\left(\sin\frac{3\pi}{2}\right) = \sin^{-1}(-1) = -\pi/2 \qquad \blacksquare$$

EXAMPLE 2 Use a calculator to find

(a) $\cos^{-1}(-0.61)$,

(b) $\sin^{-1}(1.21)$,

(c) $\sin^{-1}(\sin 4.13)$

SOLUTION Use a calculator in radian mode. It has been programmed to give answers that are consistent with the definitions that we have given.

(a) $\cos^{-1}(-0.61) = 2.2268569$

(b) Your calculator should indicate an error, since $\sin^{-1}(1.21)$ does not exist.

(c) $\sin^{-1}(\sin 4.13) = -0.9884073 \qquad \blacksquare$

Inverse Tangent and Inverse Secant In Figure 5, we show the graph of the tangent function, its restricted domain, and the graph of $y = \tan^{-1} x$.

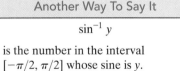

Another Way To Say It

$\sin^{-1} y$

is the number in the interval $[-\pi/2, \pi/2]$ whose sine is y.

$\cos^{-1} y$

is the number in the interval $[0, \pi]$ whose cosine is y.

$\tan^{-1} y$

is the number in the interval $(-\pi/2, \pi/2)$ whose tangent is y.

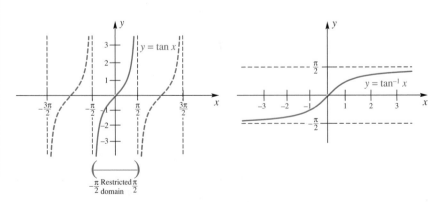

Figure 5

There is a standard way to restrict the domain of the cotangent function, that is, to $(0, \pi)$, so that it has an inverse. However, this function does not play a significant role in calculus.

To obtain an inverse for secant, we graph $y = \sec x$, restrict its domain appropriately, and then graph $y = \sec^{-1} x$ (Figure 6).

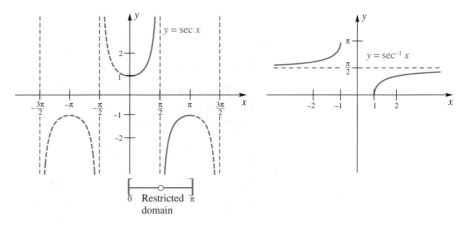

Figure 6

Definition

To obtain inverses for tangent and secant, we restrict their domains to $(-\pi/2, \pi/2)$ and $[0, \pi/2) \cup (\pi/2, \pi]$, respectively. Thus,

$$x = \tan^{-1} y \quad \Leftrightarrow \quad y = \tan x, -\frac{\pi}{2} < x < \frac{\pi}{2}$$

$$x = \sec^{-1} y \quad \Leftrightarrow \quad y = \sec x, 0 \le x \le \pi, x \neq \frac{\pi}{2}$$

Some authors restrict the domain of the secant in a different way. Thus, if you refer to another book, you must check that author's definition. We will have no need to define $\csc^{-1}$, though this can also be done.

EXAMPLE 3 Calculate

(a) $\tan^{-1}(1)$,

(b) $\tan^{-1}\left(-\sqrt{3}\right)$,

(c) $\tan^{-1}(\tan 5.236)$,

(d) $\sec^{-1}(-1)$,

(e) $\sec^{-1}(2)$,

(f) $\sec^{-1}(-1.32)$

SOLUTION

(a) $\tan^{-1}(1) = \dfrac{\pi}{4}$

(b) $\tan^{-1}\left(-\sqrt{3}\right) = -\dfrac{\pi}{3}$

(c) $\tan^{-1}(\tan 5.236) = -1.0471853$

Most of us have trouble remembering our secants; moreover, most calculators fail to have a secant button. Therefore, we suggest that you remember that $\sec x = 1/\cos x$. From this, it follows that

$$\sec^{-1} y = \cos^{-1}\left(\frac{1}{y}\right)$$

and this allows us to use known facts about the cosine.

(d) $\sec^{-1}(-1) = \cos^{-1}(-1) = \pi$

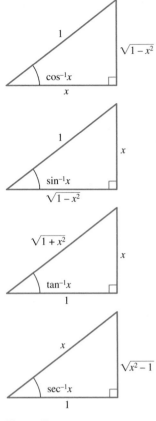

Figure 7

(e) $\sec^{-1}(2) = \cos^{-1}\left(\frac{1}{2}\right) = \frac{\pi}{3}$

(f) $\sec^{-1}(-1.32) = \cos^{-1}\left(-\frac{1}{1.32}\right) = \cos^{-1}(0.7575758)$

$$= 2.4303875$$

Four Useful Identities Theorem A gives some useful identities. You can recall them by reference to the triangles in Figure 7.

Theorem A

(1) $\sin(\cos^{-1} x) = \sqrt{1 - x^2}$

(2) $\cos(\sin^{-1} x) = \sqrt{1 - x^2}$

(3) $\sec(\tan^{-1} x) = \sqrt{1 + x^2}$

(4) $\tan(\sec^{-1} x) = \begin{cases} \sqrt{x^2 - 1}, & \text{if } x \geq 1 \\ -\sqrt{x^2 - 1}, & \text{if } x \leq -1 \end{cases}$

Proof To prove (1), recall that $\sin^2 \theta + \cos^2 \theta = 1$. If $0 \leq \theta \leq \pi$, then

$$\sin \theta = \sqrt{1 - \cos^2 \theta}$$

Now apply this with $\theta = \cos^{-1} x$ and use the fact that $\cos(\cos^{-1} x) = x$ to get

$$\sin(\cos^{-1} x) = \sqrt{1 - \cos^2(\cos^{-1} x)} = \sqrt{1 - x^2}$$

Identity (2) is proved in a completely similar manner. To prove (3) and (4), use the identity $\sec^2 \theta = 1 + \tan^2 \theta$ in place of $\sin^2 \theta + \cos^2 \theta = 1$. ∎

EXAMPLE 4 Calculate $\sin\left[2 \cos^{-1}\left(\frac{2}{3}\right)\right]$.

SOLUTION Recall the double-angle identity $\sin 2\theta = 2 \sin \theta \cos \theta$. Thus,

$$\sin\left[2 \cos^{-1}\left(\frac{2}{3}\right)\right] = 2 \sin\left[\cos^{-1}\left(\frac{2}{3}\right)\right] \cos\left[\cos^{-1}\left(\frac{2}{3}\right)\right]$$

$$= 2 \cdot \sqrt{1 - \left(\frac{2}{3}\right)^2} \cdot \frac{2}{3} = \frac{4\sqrt{5}}{9}$$

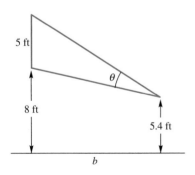

Figure 8

EXAMPLE 5 A picture 5 feet in height is hung on a wall so that its bottom is 8 feet from the floor, as shown in Figure 8. A viewer with eye level at 5.4 feet stands b feet from the wall. Express θ, the vertical angle subtended by the picture at her eye, in terms of b, and then find θ if $b = 12.9$ feet.

SOLUTION The top of the picture is 13 feet above the ground and 7.6 feet above eye level. The bottom of the picture is 2.6 feet above eye level. Let θ_1 denote the angle between the horizontal and the viewer's line of the sight to the bottom of the picture (Figure 9). Then

$$\tan(\theta_1 + \theta) = \frac{7.6}{b}$$

$$\tan \theta_1 = \frac{2.6}{b}$$

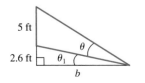

Figure 9

Thus,

$$\theta_1 + \theta = \tan^{-1}\left(\frac{7.6}{b}\right)$$

$$\theta_1 = \tan^{-1}\left(\frac{2.6}{b}\right)$$

Subtracting θ_1 from both sides of the first equation and making use of the second equation gives

$$\theta = \tan^{-1}\left(\frac{7.6}{b}\right) - \tan^{-1}\left(\frac{2.6}{b}\right)$$

If $b = 12.9$, then

$$\theta = \tan^{-1}\left(\frac{7.6}{10}\right) - \tan^{-1}\left(\frac{2.6}{10}\right) \approx 0.3955 \text{ radian} \approx 23° \qquad ■$$

Concepts Review

1. To obtain an inverse for the sine function, we restrict its domain to _____. The resulting inverse function is denoted by $\sin^{-1}$ or by _____.

2. To obtain an inverse for the tangent function, we restrict the domain to _____. The resulting inverse function is denoted by $\tan^{-1}$ or by _____.

3. The domain of $\tan^{-1}$ is _____, and the range is _____.

4. For $-1 \le x \le 1$, $\cos(\sin^{-1}x) =$ _____.

Problem Set 1.9

In Problems 1–10, find the exact value without using a calculator.

1. $\arccos\left(\dfrac{\sqrt{2}}{2}\right)$

2. $\arcsin\left(-\dfrac{\sqrt{3}}{2}\right)$

3. $\sin^{-1}\left(-\dfrac{\sqrt{3}}{2}\right)$

4. $\sin^{-1}\left(-\dfrac{\sqrt{2}}{2}\right)$

5. $\arctan\left(\sqrt{3}\right)$

6. $\text{arcsec}\,(2)$

7. $\arcsin\left(-\dfrac{1}{2}\right)$

8. $\tan^{-1}\left(-\dfrac{\sqrt{3}}{3}\right)$

9. $\sin(\sin^{-1}0.4567)$

10. $\cos(\sin^{-1}0.56)$

[C] *In Problems 11–18, use a calculator to approximate each value.*

11. $\sin^{-1}(0.1113)$

12. $\arccos(0.6341)$

13. $\cos(\text{arcsec}\,3.212)$

14. $\sec(\arccos 0.5111)$

15. $\sec^{-1}(-2.222)$

16. $\tan^{-1}(-60.11)$

17. $\cos(\sin(\tan^{-1}2.001))$

18. $\sin^2(\ln(\cos 0.5555))$

In Problems 19–24, express θ in terms of x using the inverse trigonometric functions $\sin^{-1}$, $\cos^{-1}$, $\tan^{-1}$, and $\sec^{-1}$.

19.

20.

21.

22.

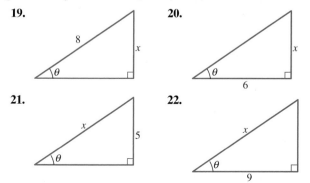

23.

24.

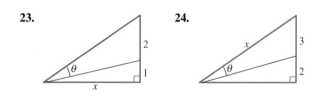

In Problems 25–28, find each value without using a calculator (see Example 4).

25. $\cos\left[2\sin^{-1}\left(-\dfrac{2}{3}\right)\right]$

26. $\tan\left[2\tan^{-1}\left(\dfrac{1}{3}\right)\right]$

27. $\sin\left[\cos^{-1}\left(\dfrac{3}{5}\right) + \cos^{-1}\left(\dfrac{5}{13}\right)\right]$

28. $\cos\left[\cos^{-1}\left(\dfrac{4}{5}\right) + \sin^{-1}\left(\dfrac{12}{13}\right)\right]$

In Problems 29–32, show that each equation is an identity.

29. $\tan(\sin^{-1}x) = \dfrac{x}{\sqrt{1-x^2}}$

30. $\sin(\tan^{-1}x) = \dfrac{x}{\sqrt{1+x^2}}$

31. $\cos(2\sin^{-1}x) = 1 - 2x^2$

32. $\tan(2\tan^{-1}x) = \dfrac{2x}{1-x^2}$

33. By repeated use of the addition formula

$$\tan(x+y) = (\tan x + \tan y)/(1 - \tan x \tan y)$$

show that

$$\frac{\pi}{4} = 3\tan^{-1}\left(\frac{1}{4}\right) + \tan^{-1}\left(\frac{5}{99}\right)$$

34. Verify that

$$\frac{\pi}{4} = 4 \tan^{-1}\left(\frac{1}{5}\right) - \tan^{-1}\left(\frac{1}{239}\right)$$

a result discovered by John Machin in 1706 and used by him to calculate the first 100 decimal places of π.

35. Find formulas for $f^{-1}(x)$ for each of the following functions f, first indicating how you would restrict the domain so that f has an inverse. For example, if $f(x) = 3 \sin 2x$ and we restrict the domain to $-\pi/4 \leq x \leq \pi/4$, then $f^{-1}(x) = \frac{1}{2}\sin^{-1}(x/3)$.

(a) $f(x) = 3 \cos 2x$

(b) $f(x) = 2 \sin 3x$

(c) $f(x) = \frac{1}{2} \tan x$

(d) $f(x) = \sin \dfrac{1}{x}$

GC **36.** Draw the graphs of

$$y = \arcsin x \qquad \text{and} \qquad y = \arctan\left(x/\sqrt{1 - x^2}\right)$$

using the same axes. Make a conjecture. Prove it.

GC **37.** Draw the graph of $y = \pi/2 - \arcsin x$. Make a conjecture. Prove it.

GC **38.** Draw the graph of $y = \sin(\arcsin x)$ on $[-1, 1]$. Then draw the graph of $y = \arcsin(\sin x)$ on $[-2\pi, 2\pi]$. Explain the differences that you observe.

Answers to Concepts Review: **1.** $[-\pi/2, \pi/2]$; arcsin **2.** $(-\pi/2, \pi/2)$; arctan **3.** $(-\infty, \infty)$; $(-\pi/2, \pi/2)$ **4.** $\sqrt{1 - x^2}$

1.10 Chapter Review

Concepts Test

Respond with true or false to each of the following assertions. Be prepared to justify your answer. Normally, this means that you should supply a reason if you answer true and provide a counterexample if you answer false.

1. Any number that can be written as a fraction p/q is rational.

2. The difference of any two rational numbers is rational.

3. The difference of any two irrational numbers is irrational.

4. Between two distinct irrational numbers, there is always another irrational number.

5. $0.999\ldots$ (repeating 9s) is less than 1.

6. The operation of exponentiation is commutative; that is, $(a^m)^n = (a^n)^m$.

7. The inequalities $x \leq y$, $y \leq z$, and $z \leq x$ together imply that $x = y = z$.

8. If $|x| < \varepsilon$ for every positive number ε, then $x = 0$.

9. If x and y are real numbers, then $(x - y)(y - x) \leq 0$.

10. If $a < b < 0$, then $1/a > 1/b$.

11. It is possible for two closed intervals to have exactly one point in common.

12. If two open intervals have a point in common, then they have infinitely many points in common.

13. If $x < 0$, then $\sqrt{x^2} = -x$.

14. If $|x| < |y|$, then $x < y$.

15. If $|x| < |y|$, then $x^4 < y^4$.

16. If x and y are both negative, then $|x + y| = |x| + |y|$.

17. If $|r| < 1$, then $\dfrac{1}{1 + |r|} \leq \dfrac{1}{1 - r} \leq \dfrac{1}{1 - |r|}$.

18. If $|r| > 1$, then $\dfrac{1}{1 - |r|} \leq \dfrac{1}{1 - r} \leq \dfrac{1}{1 + |r|}$.

19. It is always true that $||x| - |y|| \leq |x + y|$.

20. For every positive real number y, there exists a real number x such that $x^2 = y$.

21. For every real number y, there exists a real number x such that $x^3 = y$.

22. It is possible to have an inequality whose solution set consists of exactly one number.

23. The equation $x^2 + y^2 + ax + y = 0$ represents a circle for every real number a.

24. The equation $x^2 + y^2 + ax + by = c$ represents a circle for all real numbers a, b, c.

25. If (a, b) is on a line with slope $\frac{3}{4}$, then $(a + 4, b + 3)$ is also on that line.

26. If (a, b), (c, d) and (e, f) are on the same line, then $\dfrac{a - c}{b - d} = \dfrac{a - e}{b - f} = \dfrac{e - c}{f - d}$ provided all three points are different.

27. If $ab > 0$, then (a, b) lies in either the first or third quadrant.

28. For every $\varepsilon > 0$, there exists a positive number x such that $x < \varepsilon$.

29. If $ab = 0$, then (a, b) lies on either the x-axis or the y-axis.

30. If $\sqrt{(x_2 - x_1)^2 + (y_2 - y_1)^2} = |x_2 - x_1|$, then (x_1, y_1) and (x_2, y_2) lie on the same horizontal line.

31. The distance between $(a + b, a)$ and $(a - b, a)$ is $|2b|$.

32. The equation of every line can be written in point–slope form.

33. The equation of every line can be written in the general linear form $Ax + By + C = 0$.

34. If two nonvertical lines are parallel, they have the same slope.

35. It is possible for two lines to have positive slopes and be perpendicular.

36. If the x- and y-intercepts of a line are rational and nonzero, then the slope of the line is rational.

37. The lines $ax + y = c$ and $ax - y = c$ are perpendicular.

38. $(3x - 2y + 4) + m(2x + 6y - 2) = 0$ is the equation of a line for each real number m.

39. The natural domain of
$$f(x) = \sqrt{-(x^2 + 4x + 3)}$$
is the interval $-3 \le x \le -1$.

40. $\log_2|x|$ is defined for all real x.

41. The graph of an invertible function is intersected exactly once by every horizontal line.

42. $\log x/\log y = \log x - \log y$

43. $(\log x)^4 = 4 \log x$

44. The natural domain of $T(\theta) = \sec(\theta) + \cos(\theta)$ is $(-\infty, \infty)$.

45. The range of $f(x) = x^2 - 6$ is the interval $[-6, \infty)$.

46. The range of the function $f(x) = \tan x - \sec x$ is the set $(-\infty, -1] \cup [1, \infty)$.

47. The range of the function $f(x) = \csc x - \sec x$ is the set $(-\infty, -1] \cup [1, \infty)$.

48. The sum of two even functions is an even function.

49. The sum of two odd functions is an odd function.

50. The product of two odd functions is an odd function.

51. The product of an even function with an odd function is an odd function.

52. The composition of an even function with an odd function is an odd function.

53. The composition of two odd functions is an even function.

54. The function $f(x) = (2x^3 + x)/(x^2 + 1)$ is odd.

55. The function
$$f(t) = \frac{(\sin t)^2 + \cos t}{\tan t \csc t}$$
is even.

56. If the range of a function consists of just one number, then its domain also consists of just one number.

57. If the domain of a function contains at least two numbers then the range also contains at least two numbers.

58. If $g(x) = [\![x/2]\!]$, then $g(-1.8) = -1$.

59. If $f(x) = x^2$ and $g(x) = x^3$, then $f \circ g = g \circ f$.

60. If $f(x) = x^2$ and $g(x) = x^3$, then $(f \circ g)(x) = f(x) \cdot g(x)$.

61. If f and g have the same domain, then f/g also has that domain.

62. If the graph of $y = f(x)$ has an x-intercept at $x = a$, then the graph of $y = f(x + h)$ has an x-intercept at $x = a - h$.

63. The cotangent is an odd function.

64. The natural domain of the tangent function is the set of all real numbers.

65. If $\cos s = \cos t$, then $s = t$.

66. The domain for $\tan^{-1} x$ is $(-\pi/2, \pi/2)$.

67. The range of $\sin^{-1} x$ is $(-\pi/2, \pi/2)$.

68. $\sin(\arcsin x) = x$ for all real numbers x.

69. $\arcsin(\sin x) = x$ for all real numbers x.

Sample Test Problems

1. Calculate each value for $n = 1, 2$, and -2.

(a) $\left(n + \dfrac{1}{n}\right)^n$

(b) $(n^2 - n + 1)^2$

(c) $4^{3/n}$

2. Simplify.

(a) $\left(1 + \dfrac{1}{m} + \dfrac{1}{n}\right)\left(1 - \dfrac{1}{m} + \dfrac{1}{n}\right)^{-1}$

(b) $\dfrac{\dfrac{2}{x+1} - \dfrac{x}{x^2 - x - 2}}{\dfrac{3}{x+1} - \dfrac{2}{x-2}}$

(c) $\dfrac{t^3 - 1}{t - 1}$

3. Show that the average of two rational numbers is a rational number.

4. Write the repeating decimal $4.1282828\ldots$ as a ratio of two integers.

5. Find an irrational number between $\frac{1}{2}$ and $\frac{13}{25}$.

© **6.** Calculate $\left(\sqrt[3]{8.15 \times 10^4} - 1.32\right)^2/3.24$.

© **7.** Calculate $\left(\pi - \sqrt{2.0}\right)^{2.5} - \sqrt[3]{2.0}$.

© **8.** Calculate $\sin^2(2.45) + \cos^2(2.40) - 1.00$.

In Problems 9–18, find the solution set, graph this set on the real line, and express this set in interval notation.

9. $1 - 3x > 0$ **10.** $6x + 3 > 2x - 5$

11. $3 - 2x \le 4x + 1 \le 2x + 7$

12. $2x^2 + 5x - 3 < 0$ **13.** $21t^2 - 44t + 12 \le -3$

14. $\dfrac{2x - 1}{x - 2} > 0$

15. $(x + 4)(2x - 1)^2(x - 3) \le 0$

16. $|3x - 4| < 6$

17. $\dfrac{3}{1 - x} \le 2$

18. $|12 - 3x| \ge |x|$

19. Find a value of x for which $|-x| \ne x$.

20. For what values of x does the equation $|-x| = x$ hold?

21. For what values of t does the equation $|t - 5| = 5 - t$ hold?

22. For what values of a and t does the equation $|t - a| = a - t$ hold?

23. Suppose $|x| \le 2$. Use properties of absolute values to show that
$$\left|\frac{2x^2 + 3x + 2}{x^2 + 2}\right| \le 8$$

24. Write a sentence involving the word *distance* to express the following algebraic sentences:

(a) $|x - 5| = 3$ (b) $|x + 1| \le 2$

(c) $|x - a| > b$

25. Sketch the triangle with vertices $A(-2, 6)$, $B(1, 2)$, and $C(5, 5)$, and show that it is a right triangle.

26. Find the distance from $(3, -6)$ to the midpoint of the line segment from $(1, 2)$ to $(7, 8)$.

27. Find the equation of the circle with diameter AB if $A = (2, 0)$ and $B = (10, 4)$.

28. Find the center and radius of the circle with equation $x^2 + y^2 - 8x + 6y = 0$.

29. Find the distance between the centers of the circles with equations

$$x^2 - 2x + y^2 + 2y = 2 \quad \text{and} \quad x^2 + 6x + y^2 - 4y = -7$$

30. Find the equation of the line through the indicated point that is parallel to the indicated line, and sketch both lines.

(a) $(3, 2)$: $3x + 2y = 6$
(b) $(1, -1)$: $y = \frac{2}{3}x + 1$
(c) $(5, 9)$: $y = 10$
(d) $(-3, 4)$: $x = -2$

31. Write the equation of the line through $(-2, 1)$ that

(a) goes through $(7, 3)$;
(b) is parallel to $3x - 2y = 5$;
(c) is perpendicular to $3x + 4y = 9$;
(d) is perpendicular to $y = 4$;
(e) has y-intercept 3.

32. Show that $(2, -1)$, $(5, 3)$, and $(11, 11)$ are on the same line.

33. Figure 1 can be represented by which equation?

(a) $y = x^3$
(b) $x = y^3$
(c) $y = x^2$
(d) $x = y^2$

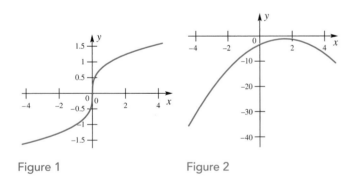

Figure 1   Figure 2

34. Figure 2 can be represented by which equation?

(a) $y = ax^2 + bx + c$, with $a > 0$, $b > 0$, and $c > 0$
(b) $y = ax^2 + bx + c$, with $a < 0$, $b > 0$, and $c > 0$
(c) $y = ax^2 + bx + c$, with $a < 0$, $b > 0$, and $c < 0$
(d) $y = ax^2 + bx + c$, with $a > 0$, $b > 0$, and $c < 0$

In Problems 35–38, sketch the graph of each equation.

35. $3y - 4x = 6$
36. $x^2 - 2x + y^2 = 3$

GC **37.** $y = \dfrac{2x}{x^2 + 2}$
GC **38.** $x = y^2 - 3$

GC **39.** Find the points of intersection of the graphs of $y = x^2 - 2x + 4$ and $y - x = 4$.

40. Among all lines perpendicular to $4x - y = 2$, find the equation of the one that, together with the positive x- and y-axes, forms a triangle of area 8.

41. For $f(x) = 1/(x + 1) - 1/x$, find each value (if possible).

(a) $f(1)$
(b) $f\left(-\frac{1}{2}\right)$
(c) $f(-1)$
(d) $f(t - 1)$
(e) $f\left(\dfrac{1}{t}\right)$

42. For $g(x) = (x + 1)/x$, find and simplify each value.

(a) $g(2)$
(b) $g\left(\frac{1}{2}\right)$
(c) $\dfrac{g(2 + h) - g(2)}{h}$

43. Describe the natural domain of each function.

(a) $f(x) = \dfrac{x}{x^2 - 1}$
(b) $g(x) = \sqrt{4 - x^2}$

44. Which of the following functions are odd? Even? Neither even nor odd?

(a) $f(x) = \dfrac{3x}{x^2 + 1}$
(b) $g(x) = |\sin x| + \cos x$
(c) $h(x) = x^3 + \sin x$
(d) $k(x) = \dfrac{x^2 + 1}{|x| + x^4}$

45. Sketch the graph of each function.

(a) $f(x) = x^2 - 1$
(b) $g(x) = \dfrac{x}{x^2 + 1}$
(c) $h(x) = \begin{cases} x^2 & \text{if } 0 \le x \le 2 \\ 6 - x & \text{if } x > 2 \end{cases}$

46. Suppose that f is an even function satisfying $f(x) = -1 + \sqrt{x}$ for $x \ge 0$. Sketch the graph of f for $-4 \le x \le 4$.

47. An open box is made by cutting squares of side x inches from the four corners of a sheet of cardboard 24 inches by 32 inches and then turning up the sides. Express the volume $V(x)$ in terms of x. What is the domain for this function?

48. Let $f(x) = x - 1/x$ and $g(x) = x^2 + 1$. Find each value.

(a) $(f + g)(2)$
(b) $(f \cdot g)(2)$
(c) $(f \circ g)(2)$
(d) $(g \circ f)(2)$
(e) $f^3(-1)$
(f) $f^2(2) + g^2(2)$

49. Sketch the graph of each of the following, making use of translations.

(a) $y = \frac{1}{4}x^2$
(b) $y = \frac{1}{4}(x + 2)^2$
(c) $y = -1 + \frac{1}{4}(x + 2)^2$

50. Let $f(x) = \sqrt{16 - x}$ and $g(x) = x^4$. What is the domain of each of the following?

(a) f
(b) $f \circ g$
(c) $g \circ f$

51. Write $F(x) = \sqrt{1 + \sin^2 x}$ as the composite of four functions, $f \circ g \circ h \circ k$.

52. Calculate each of the following without using a calculator.

(a) $\sin 570°$
(b) $\cos \dfrac{9\pi}{2}$
(c) $\cos\left(\dfrac{-13\pi}{6}\right)$

53. Find the inverse of the given function f and verify that $f\big(f^{-1}(x)\big) = x$ for all x in the domain of f^{-1}, and $f^{-1}\big(f(x)\big) = x$ for all x in the domain of f.

(a) $f(x) = 3x - 7$

(b) $f(x) = 2x^3 - 1$

54. Find the inverse of the given function f and verify that $f\big(f^{-1}(x)\big) = x$ for all x in the domain of f^{-1}, and $f^{-1}\big(f(x)\big) = x$ for all x in the domain of f.

(a) $f(x) = \dfrac{2^x}{5}$

(b) $f(x) = 2 + \log(x - 1)$

55. If $\sin t = 0.8$ and $\cos t < 0$, find each value.

(a) $\sin(-t)$

(b) $\cos t$

(c) $\sin 2t$

(d) $\tan t$

(e) $\cos\left(\dfrac{\pi}{2} - t\right)$

(f) $\sin(\pi + t)$

56. Write $\sin 3t$ in terms of $\sin t$. *Hint:* $3t = 2t + t$.

57. A fly sits on the rim of a wheel spinning at the rate of 20 revolutions per minute. If the radius of the wheel is 9 inches, how far does the fly travel in 1 second?

58. Find the exact value of the following without using a calculator.

(a) $\cos^{-1}\left(-\dfrac{\sqrt{2}}{2}\right)$

(b) $\sec^{-1}(-2)$

(c) $\arcsin\left(\dfrac{\sqrt{3}}{2}\right)$

(d) $\arctan(1)$

1. Solve the following inequalities:

(a) $1 < 2x + 1 < 5$

(b) $-3 < \dfrac{x}{2} < 8$

2. Solve the following inequalities:

(a) $14 < 2x + 1 < 15$

(b) $-3 < 1 - \dfrac{x}{2} < 8$

3. Solve $|x - 7| = 3$ for x.

4. Solve $|x + 3| = 2$ for x.

5. The distance along the number line between x and 7 is equal to 3. What are the possible values for x?

6. The distance along the number line between x and 7 is equal to d. What are the possible values for x?

7. Solve the following inequalities:

(a) $|x - 7| < 3$

(b) $|x - 7| \le 3$

(c) $|x - 7| \le 1$

(d) $|x - 7| < 0.1$

8. Solve the following inequalities:

(a) $|x - 2| < 1$

(b) $|x - 2| \ge 1$

(c) $|x - 2| < 0.1$

(d) $|x - 2| < 0.01$

9. What are the natural domains of the following functions?

(a) $f(x) = \dfrac{x^2 - 1}{x - 1}$

(b) $g(x) = \dfrac{x^2 - 2x + 1}{2x^2 - x - 1}$

10. What are the natural domains of the following functions?

(a) $F(x) = \dfrac{|x|}{x}$

(b) $G(x) = \dfrac{\sin x}{x}$

11. Evaluate the functions $f(x)$ and $g(x)$ from Problem 9 at the following values of x: $0, 0.9, 0.99, 0.999, 1.001, 1.01, 1.1, 2$.

12. Evaluate the functions $F(x)$ and $G(x)$ from Problem 10 at the following values of x: $-1, -0.1, -0.01, -0.001, 0.001, 0.01, 0.1, 1$.

13. The distance between x and 5 is less than 0.1. What are the possible values for x?

14. The distance between x and 5 is less than ε, where ε is a positive number. What are the possible values for x?

15. True or false. Assume that a, x, and y are real numbers and n is a natural number.

(a) For every $x > 0$, there exists a y such that $y > x$.

(b) For every $a \ge 0$, there exists an n such that $\dfrac{1}{n} < a$.

(c) For every $a > 0$, there exists an n such that $\dfrac{1}{n} < a$.

(d) For every circle C in the plane, there exists an n such that the circle C and its interior are all within n units of the origin.

16. Use the Addition Identity for the sine function to find $\sin(c + h)$ in terms of $\sin c$, $\sin h$, $\cos c$, and $\cos h$.

CHAPTER 2 Limits

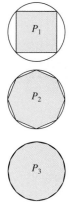

Figure 1

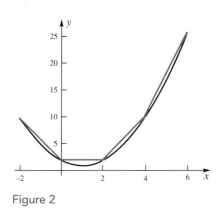

Figure 2

2.1

Introduction to Limits

The topics discussed in the previous chapter are part of what is called *precalculus*. They provide the foundation for calculus, but they are not calculus. Now we are ready for an important new idea, the notion of *limit*. It is this idea that distinguishes calculus from other branches of mathematics. In fact, we define calculus this way:

> Calculus is the study of limits.

Problems Leading to the Limit Concept The concept of **limit** is central to many problems in the physical, engineering, and social sciences. Basically the question is this: what happens to the function $f(x)$ as x gets close to some constant c? There are variations on this theme, but the basic idea is the same in many circumstances.

Suppose that as an object steadily moves forward we know its position at any given time. We denote the position at time t by $s(t)$. How fast is the object moving at time $t = 1$? We can use the formula "distance equals rate times time" to find the speed (rate of change of position) over any interval of time; in other words

$$\text{speed} = \frac{\text{distance}}{\text{time}}$$

We call this the "average" speed over the interval since, no matter how small the interval is, we never know whether the speed is constant over this interval. For example, over the interval $[1, 2]$, the average speed is $\frac{s(2) - s(1)}{2 - 1}$; over the interval $[1, 1.2]$, the average speed is $\frac{s(1.2) - s(1)}{1.2 - 1}$; over the interval $[1, 1.02]$, the average speed is $\frac{s(1.02) - s(1)}{1.02 - 1}$, etc. How fast is the object traveling at time $t = 1$? To give meaning to this "instantaneous" velocity we must talk about the *limit* of the average speed over smaller and smaller intervals.

We can find areas of rectangles and triangles using formulas from geometry, but what about regions with curved boundaries, such as a circle? Archimedes had this idea over two thousand years ago. Imagine regular polygons inscribed in a circle as shown in Figure 1. Archimedes was able to find the area of a regular polygon with n sides, and by taking the regular polygon with more and more sides, he was able to approximate the area of a circle to any desired level of accuracy. In other words, the area of the circle is the *limit* of the areas of the inscribed polygons as n (the number of sides in the polygon) increases without bound.

Consider the graph of the function $y = f(x)$ for $a \le x \le b$. If the graph is a straight line, the length of the curve is easy to find using the distance formula. But what if the graph is curved? We can find numerous points along the curve and connect them with line segments as shown in Figure 2. If we add up the lengths of these line segments we should get a sum that is approximately the length of the curve. In fact, by "length of the curve" we mean the *limit* of the sum of the lengths of these line segments as the number of line segments increases without bound.

The last three paragraphs describe situations that lead to the concept of *limit*. There are many others, and we will study them throughout this book. We begin with an intuitive explanation of limits. The precise definition is given in the next section.

An Intuitive Understanding   Consider the function defined by

$$f(x) = \frac{x^3 - 1}{x - 1}$$

Note that it is not defined at $x = 1$ since at this point $f(x)$ has the form $\frac{0}{0}$, which is meaningless. We can, however, still ask what is happening to $f(x)$ as x approaches 1. More precisely, is $f(x)$ approaching some specific number as x approaches 1? To get at the answer, we can do three things. We can calculate some values of $f(x)$ for x near 1, we can show these values in a schematic diagram, and we can sketch the graph of $y = f(x)$. All this has been done, and the results are shown in Figure 3.

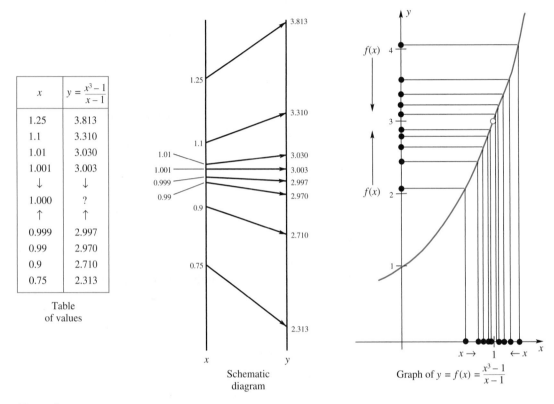

x	$y = \dfrac{x^3 - 1}{x - 1}$
1.25	3.813
1.1	3.310
1.01	3.030
1.001	3.003
↓	↓
1.000	?
↑	↑
0.999	2.997
0.99	2.970
0.9	2.710
0.75	2.313

Table
of values

Schematic
diagram

Graph of $y = f(x) = \dfrac{x^3 - 1}{x - 1}$

Figure 3

All the information we have assembled seems to point to the same conclusion: $f(x)$ approaches 3 as x approaches 1. In mathematical symbols, we write

$$\lim_{x \to 1} \frac{x^3 - 1}{x - 1} = 3$$

This is read "the limit as x approaches 1 of $(x^3 - 1)/(x - 1)$ is 3."

Being good algebraists (thus knowing how to factor the difference of cubes), we can provide more and better evidence.

$$\lim_{x \to 1} \frac{x^3 - 1}{x - 1} = \lim_{x \to 1} \frac{(x - 1)(x^2 + x + 1)}{x - 1}$$

$$= \lim_{x \to 1}(x^2 + x + 1) = 1^2 + 1 + 1 = 3$$

Note that $(x - 1)/(x - 1) = 1$ as long as $x \neq 1$. This justifies the second step. The third step should seem reasonable; a rigorous justification will come later.

To be sure that we are on the right track, we need to have a clearly understood meaning for the word *limit*. Here is our first attempt at a definition.

> **Definition** Intuitive Meaning of Limit
>
> To say that $\lim\limits_{x \to c} f(x) = L$ means that when x is near but different from c then $f(x)$ is near L.

Notice that we do not require anything *at c*. The function f need not even be defined at c; it was not in the example $f(x) = (x^3 - 1)/(x - 1)$ just considered. The notion of limit is associated with the behavior of a function *near c*, not *at c*.

A cautious reader is sure to object to our use of the word *near*. What does *near* mean? How near is near? For precise answers, you will have to study the next section; however, some further examples will help to clarify the idea.

More Examples   Our first example is almost trivial, but nonetheless important.

■ **EXAMPLE 1** Find $\lim\limits_{x \to 3} (4x - 5)$.

SOLUTION When x is near 3, $4x - 5$ is near $4 \cdot 3 - 5 = 7$. We write

$$\lim_{x \to 3} (4x - 5) = 7$$ ■

■ **EXAMPLE 2** Find $\lim\limits_{x \to 3} \dfrac{x^2 - x - 6}{x - 3}$.

SOLUTION Note that $(x^2 - x - 6)/(x - 3)$ is not defined at $x = 3$, but this is all right. To get an idea of what is happening as x approaches 3, we could use a calculator to evaluate the given expression, for example, at 3.1, 3.01, 3.001, and so on. But it is much better to use a little algebra to simplify the problem.

$$\lim_{x \to 3} \frac{x^2 - x - 6}{x - 3} = \lim_{x \to 3} \frac{(x - 3)(x + 2)}{x - 3} = \lim_{x \to 3} (x + 2) = 3 + 2 = 5$$

The cancellation of $x - 3$ in the second step is legitimate because the definition of limit ignores the behavior *at x = 3*. Remember, $\dfrac{x - 3}{x - 3} = 1$ as long as x is not equal to 3. ■

■ **EXAMPLE 3** Find $\lim\limits_{x \to 0} \dfrac{\sin x}{x}$.

SOLUTION No algebraic trick will simplify our task; certainly, we cannot cancel the x's. A calculator will help us to get an idea of the limit. Use your own calculator (radian mode) to check the values in the table of Figure 4. Figure 5 shows a plot of $y = (\sin x)/x$. Our conclusion, though we admit it is a bit shaky, is that

$$\lim_{x \to 0} \frac{\sin x}{x} = 1$$

We will give a rigorous demonstration in Section 2.5. ■

Some Warning Flags   Things are not quite as simple as they may appear. Calculators may mislead us; so may our own intuition. The examples that follow suggest some possible pitfalls.

x	$\dfrac{\sin x}{x}$
1.0	0.84147
0.1	0.99833
0.01	0.99998
↓	↓
0	?
↑	↑
−0.01	0.99998
−0.1	0.99833
−1.0	0.84147

Figure 4

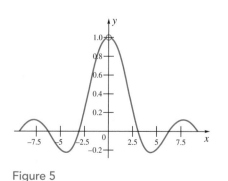

Figure 5

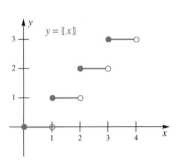

x	$x^2 - \dfrac{\cos x}{10{,}000}$
± 1	0.99995
± 0.5	0.24991
± 0.1	0.00990
± 0.01	0.000000005
$\downarrow$	$\downarrow$
0	?

Figure 6

Figure 7

x	$\sin \dfrac{1}{x}$
$2/\pi$	1
$2/(2\pi)$	0
$2/(3\pi)$	-1
$2/(4\pi)$	0
$2/(5\pi)$	1
$2/(6\pi)$	0
$2/(7\pi)$	-1
$2/(8\pi)$	0
$2/(9\pi)$	1
$2/(10\pi)$	0
$2/(11\pi)$	-1
$2/(12\pi)$	0
$\downarrow$	$\downarrow$
0	?

Figure 8

EXAMPLE 4 **(Your calculator may fool you.)** Find $\displaystyle\lim_{x\to 0}\left[x^2 - \frac{\cos x}{10{,}000}\right]$.

SOLUTION Following the procedure used in Example 3, we construct the table of values shown in Figure 6. The conclusion it suggests is that the desired limit is 0. But this is wrong. If we recall the graph of $y = \cos x$, we realize that $\cos x$ approaches 1 as x approaches 0. Thus,

$$\lim_{x\to 0}\left[x^2 - \frac{\cos x}{10{,}000}\right] = 0^2 - \frac{1}{10{,}000} = -\frac{1}{10{,}000}$$

EXAMPLE 5 **(No limit at a jump)** Find $\displaystyle\lim_{x\to 2}[\![x]\!]$.

SOLUTION Recall that $[\![x]\!]$ denotes the greatest integer less than or equal to x (see Section 1.5). The graph of $y = [\![x]\!]$ is shown in Figure 7. For all numbers x less than 2 but near 2, $[\![x]\!] = 1$, but for all numbers x greater than 2 but near 2, $[\![x]\!] = 2$. Is $[\![x]\!]$ near a single number L when x is near 2? No. No matter what number we propose for L, there will be x's arbitrarily close to 2 on one side or the other, where $[\![x]\!]$ differs from L by at least $\frac{1}{2}$. Our conclusion is that $\displaystyle\lim_{x\to 2}[\![x]\!]$ does not exist. If you check back, you will see that we have not claimed that every limit we can write must exist.

EXAMPLE 6 **(Too many wiggles)** Find $\displaystyle\lim_{x\to 0}\sin(1/x)$.

SOLUTION This example poses the most subtle limit question asked yet. Since we do not want to make too big a story out of it, we ask you to do two things. First, pick a sequence of x-values approaching 0. Use your calculator to evaluate $\sin(1/x)$ at these x's. Unless you happen on some very lucky choices, your values will oscillate wildly.

Second, consider trying to graph $y = \sin(1/x)$. No one will ever do this very well, but the table of values in Figure 8 gives a good clue about what is happening. In any neighborhood of the origin, the graph wiggles up and down between -1 and 1 infinitely many times (Figure 9). Clearly, $\sin(1/x)$ is not near a single number L when x is near 0. We conclude that $\displaystyle\lim_{x\to 0}\sin(1/x)$ does not exist.

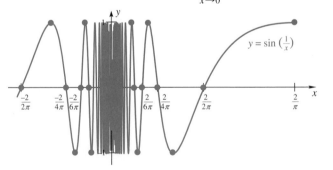

Figure 9

One-Sided Limits When a function takes a jump (as does $[\![x]\!]$ at each integer in Example 5), then the limit does not exist at the jump points. Such functions suggest the introduction of **one-sided limits.** Let the symbol $x \to c^+$ mean that x approaches c from the right, and let $x \to c^-$ mean that x approaches c from the left.

Definition **Right- and Left-Hand Limits**

To say that $\displaystyle\lim_{x\to c^+} f(x) = L$ means that when x is near but to the right of c then $f(x)$ is near L. Similarly, to say that $\displaystyle\lim_{x\to c^-} f(x) = L$ means that when x is near but to the left of c then $f(x)$ is near L.

Thus, while $\lim_{x \to 2} [\![x]\!]$ does not exist, it is correct to write (look at the graph in Figure 7)

$$\lim_{x \to 2^-} [\![x]\!] = 1 \quad \text{and} \quad \lim_{x \to 2^+} [\![x]\!] = 2$$

We believe that you will find the following theorem quite reasonable.

Theorem A

$\lim_{x \to c} f(x) = L$ if and only if $\lim_{x \to c^-} f(x) = L$ and $\lim_{x \to c^+} f(x) = L$.

Figure 10 should give additional insight. Two of the limits do not exist, although all but one of the one-sided limits exist.

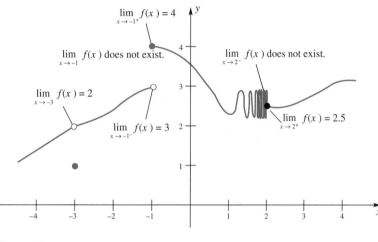

Figure 10

Concepts Review

1. $\lim_{x \to c} f(x) = L$ means that $f(x)$ gets close to _____ when x gets sufficiently close to (but is different from) _____.

2. Let $f(x) = (x^2 - 9)/(x - 3)$ and note that $f(3)$ is undefined. Nevertheless, $\lim_{x \to 3} f(x) =$ _____.

3. $\lim_{x \to c^+} f(x) = L$ means that $f(x)$ gets near to _____ when x approaches c from the _____.

4. If both $\lim_{x \to c^-} f(x) = M$ and $\lim_{x \to c^+} f(x) = M$, then _____.

Problem Set 2.1

In Problems 1–6, find the indicated limit.

1. $\lim_{x \to 3} (x - 5)$

2. $\lim_{t \to -1} (1 - 2t)$

3. $\lim_{x \to -2} (x^2 + 2x - 1)$

4. $\lim_{x \to -2} (x^2 + 2t - 1)$

5. $\lim_{t \to -1} (t^2 - 1)$

6. $\lim_{t \to -1} (t^2 - x^2)$

In Problems 7–18, find the indicated limit. In most cases, it will be wise to do some algebra first (see Example 2).

7. $\lim_{x \to 2} \dfrac{x^2 - 4}{x - 2}$

8. $\lim_{t \to -7} \dfrac{t^2 + 4t - 21}{t + 7}$

9. $\lim_{x \to -1} \dfrac{x^3 - 4x^2 + x + 6}{x + 1}$

10. $\lim_{x \to 0} \dfrac{x^4 + 2x^3 - x^2}{x^2}$

11. $\lim_{x \to -t} \dfrac{x^2 - t^2}{x + t}$

12. $\lim_{x \to 3} \dfrac{x^2 - 9}{x - 3}$

13. $\lim_{t \to 2} \dfrac{\sqrt{(t + 4)(t - 2)^4}}{(3t - 6)^2}$

14. $\lim_{t \to 7^+} \dfrac{\sqrt{(t - 7)^3}}{t - 7}$

15. $\lim_{x \to 3} \dfrac{x^4 - 18x^2 + 81}{(x - 3)^2}$

16. $\lim_{u \to 1} \dfrac{(3u + 4)(2u - 2)^3}{(u - 1)^2}$

17. $\lim_{h \to 0} \dfrac{(2 + h)^2 - 4}{h}$

18. $\lim_{h \to 0} \dfrac{(x + h)^2 - x^2}{h}$

[GC] *In Problems 19–28, use a calculator to find the indicated limit. Use a graphing calculator to plot the function near the limit point.*

19. $\lim_{x \to 0} \dfrac{\sin x}{2x}$

20. $\lim_{t \to 0} \dfrac{1 - \cos t}{2t}$

21. $\lim_{x \to 0} \dfrac{(x - \sin x)^2}{x^2}$

22. $\lim_{x \to 0} \dfrac{(1 - \cos x)^2}{x^2}$

23. $\lim_{t \to 1} \dfrac{t^2 - 1}{\sin(t - 1)}$

24. $\lim_{x \to 3} \dfrac{x - \sin(x - 3) - 3}{x - 3}$

25. $\lim_{x \to \pi} \dfrac{1 + \sin(x - 3\pi/2)}{x - \pi}$

26. $\lim_{t \to 0} \dfrac{1 - \cot t}{1/t}$

27. $\lim_{x \to \pi/4} \dfrac{(x - \pi/4)^2}{(\tan x - 1)^2}$

28. $\lim_{u \to \pi/2} \dfrac{2 - 2 \sin u}{3u}$

29. For the function f graphed in Figure 11, find the indicated limit or function value, or state that it does not exist.

(a) $\lim_{x \to -3} f(x)$ (b) $f(-3)$ (c) $f(-1)$

(d) $\lim_{x \to -1} f(x)$ (e) $f(1)$ (f) $\lim_{x \to 1} f(x)$

(g) $\lim_{x \to 1^-} f(x)$ (h) $\lim_{x \to 1^+} f(x)$ (i) $\lim_{x \to -1^+} f(x)$

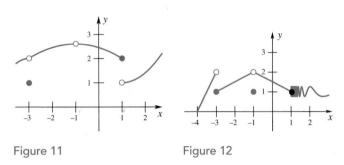

Figure 11   Figure 12

30. Follow the directions of Problem 29 for the function f graphed in Figure 12.

31. For the function f graphed in Figure 13, find the indicated limit or function value, or state that it does not exist.

(a) $f(-3)$ (b) $f(3)$ (c) $\lim_{x \to -3^-} f(x)$

(d) $\lim_{x \to -3^+} f(x)$ (e) $\lim_{x \to -3} f(x)$ (f) $\lim_{x \to 3^+} f(x)$

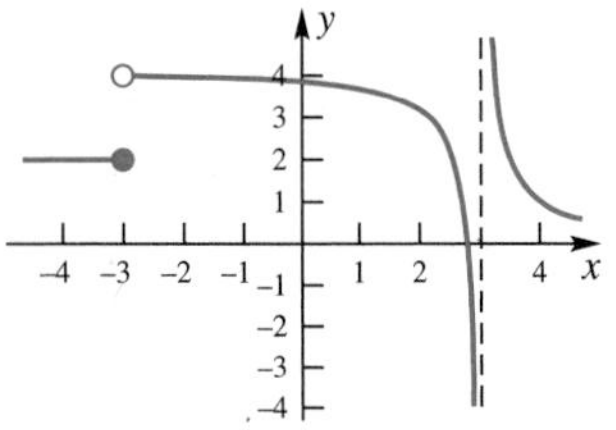

Figure 13 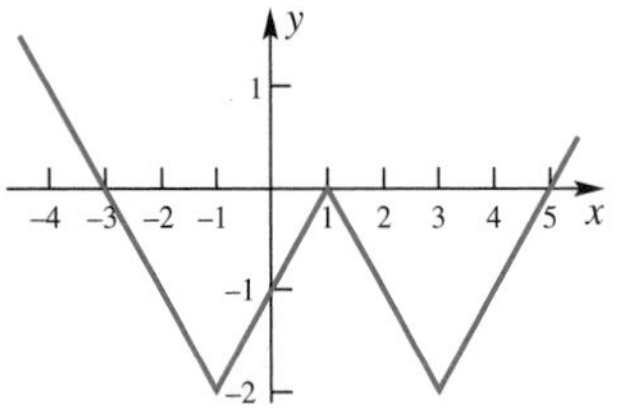   Figure 14

32. For the function f graphed in Figure 14, find the indicated limit or function value, or state that it does not exist.

(a) $\lim_{x \to -1^-} f(x)$ (b) $\lim_{x \to -1^+} f(x)$ (c) $\lim_{x \to -1} f(x)$

(d) $f(-1)$ (e) $\lim_{x \to 1} f(x)$ (f) $f(1)$

33. Sketch the graph of

$$f(x) = \begin{cases} -x & \text{if } x < 0 \\ x & \text{if } 0 \le x < 1 \\ 1 + x & \text{if } x \ge 1 \end{cases}$$

Then find each of the following or state that it does not exist.

(a) $\lim_{x \to 0} f(x)$ (b) $\lim_{x \to 1} f(x)$

(c) $f(1)$ (d) $\lim_{x \to 1^+} f(x)$

34. Sketch the graph of

$$g(x) = \begin{cases} -x + 1 & \text{if } x < 1 \\ x - 1 & \text{if } 1 < x < 2 \\ 5 - x^2 & \text{if } x \ge 2 \end{cases}$$

Then find each of the following or state that it does not exist.

(a) $\lim_{x \to 1} g(x)$ (b) $g(1)$

(c) $\lim_{x \to 2} g(x)$ (d) $\lim_{x \to 2^+} g(x)$

35. Sketch the graph of $f(x) = x - [\![x]\!]$; then find each of the following or state that it does not exist.

(a) $f(0)$ (b) $\lim_{x \to 0} f(x)$

(c) $\lim_{x \to 0^-} f(x)$ (d) $\lim_{x \to 1/2} f(x)$

36. Follow the directions of Problem 35 for $f(x) = x/|x|$.

37. Find $\lim_{x \to 1}(x^2 - 1)/|x - 1|$ or state that it does not exist.

38. Evaluate $\lim_{x \to 0}(\sqrt{x + 2} - \sqrt{2})/x$. *Hint:* Rationalize the numerator by multiplying the numerator and denominator by $\sqrt{x + 2} + \sqrt{2}$.

39. Let

$$f(x) = \begin{cases} x & \text{if } x \text{ is rational} \\ -x & \text{if } x \text{ is irrational} \end{cases}$$

Find each value, if possible.

(a) $\lim_{x \to 1} f(x)$ (b) $\lim_{x \to 0} f(x)$

40. Sketch, as best you can, the graph of a function f that satisfies all the following conditions.

(a) Its domain is the interval $[0, 4]$.

(b) $f(0) = f(1) = f(2) = f(3) = f(4) = 1$

(c) $\lim_{x \to 1} f(x) = 2$ (d) $\lim_{x \to 2} f(x) = 1$

(e) $\lim_{x \to 3^-} f(x) = 2$ (f) $\lim_{x \to 3^+} f(x) = 1$

41. Let

$$f(x) = \begin{cases} x^2 & \text{if } x \text{ is rational} \\ x^4 & \text{if } x \text{ is irrational} \end{cases}$$

For what values of a does $\lim_{x \to a} f(x)$ exist?

42. The function $f(x) = x^2$ had been carefully graphed, but during the night a mysterious visitor changed the values of f at a million different places. Does this affect the value of $\lim_{x \to a} f(x)$ at any a? Explain.

43. Find each of the following limits or state that it does not exist.

(a) $\lim_{x \to 1} \dfrac{|x - 1|}{x - 1}$ (b) $\lim_{x \to 1^-} \dfrac{|x - 1|}{x - 1}$

(c) $\lim_{x \to 1^-} \dfrac{x^2 - |x - 1| - 1}{|x - 1|}$ (d) $\lim_{x \to 1^-} \left[\dfrac{1}{x - 1} - \dfrac{1}{|x - 1|}\right]$

44. Find each of the following limits or state that it does not exist.

(a) $\lim_{x \to 1^+} \sqrt{x - [\![x]\!]}$ (b) $\lim_{x \to 0^+} [\![1/x]\!]$

(c) $\lim_{x \to 0^+} x(-1)^{[\![1/x]\!]}$ (d) $\lim_{x \to 0^+} [\![x]\!](-1)^{[\![1/x]\!]}$

45. Find each of the following limits or state that it does not exist.

(a) $\lim_{x \to 0^+} x[\![1/x]\!]$ (b) $\lim_{x \to 0^+} x^2[\![1/x]\!]$

(c) $\lim_{x \to 3^-} ([\![x]\!] + [\![-x]\!])$ (d) $\lim_{x \to 3^+} ([\![x]\!] + [\![-x]\!])$

46. Find each of the following limits or state that it does not exist.

(a) $\lim_{x \to 3} [\![x]\!]/x$ (b) $\lim_{x \to 0^+} [\![x]\!]/x$

(c) $\lim_{x \to 1.8} [\![x]\!]$ (d) $\lim_{x \to 1.8} [\![x]\!]/x$

CAS *Many software packages have programs for calculating limits, although you should be warned that they are not infallible. To develop confidence in your program, use it to recalculate some of the limits in Problems 1–28. Then for each of the following, find the limit or state that it does not exist.*

47. $\lim_{x \to 0} \sqrt{x}$ **48.** $\lim_{x \to 0^+} x^x$

49. $\lim_{x \to 0} \sqrt{|x|}$ **50.** $\lim_{x \to 0} |x|^x$

51. $\lim_{x \to 0} (\sin 2x)/4x$

52. $\lim_{x \to 0} (\sin 5x)/3x$

53. $\lim_{x \to 0} \cos(1/x)$

54. $\lim_{x \to 0} x \cos(1/x)$

55. $\lim_{x \to 1} \dfrac{x^3 - 1}{\sqrt{2x + 2} - 2}$

56. $\lim_{x \to 0} \dfrac{x \sin 2x}{\sin(x^2)}$

57. $\lim_{x \to 2^-} \dfrac{x^2 - x - 2}{|x - 2|}$

58. $\lim_{x \to 1^+} \dfrac{2}{1 + 2^{1/(x-1)}}$

CAS **59.** Since calculus software packages find $\lim_{x \to a} f(x)$ by sampling a few values of $f(x)$ for x near a, they can be fooled. Find a function f for which $\lim_{x \to 0} f(x)$ fails to exist but for which your software gives a value for the limit.

Answers to Concepts Review: **1.** $L; c$ **2.** 6 **3.** $L;$ right
4. $\lim_{x \to c} f(x) = M$

2.2
Rigorous Study of Limits

We gave an informal definition of *limit* in the previous section. Here is a slightly better, but still informal, rewording of that definition. To say that $\lim_{x \to c} f(x) = L$ means that $f(x)$ can be made to be as close as we like to L provided x is close enough, but not equal to c. The first example illustrates this point.

▮ **EXAMPLE 1** Use a plot of $y = f(x) = 3x^2$ to determine how close x must be to 2 to guarantee that $f(x)$ is within 0.05 of 12.

SOLUTION In order for $f(x)$ to be within 0.05 of 12, we must have $11.95 < f(x) < 12.05$. The lines $y = 11.95$ and $y = 12.05$ have been drawn in Figure 1. If we solve $y = 3x^2$ for x we get $x = \sqrt{y/3}$. Thus $f\left(\sqrt{11.95/3}\right) = 11.95$ and $f\left(\sqrt{12.05/3}\right) = 12.05$. Figure 1 indicates that if $\sqrt{11.95/3} < x < \sqrt{12.05/3}$ then $f(x)$ satisfies $11.95 < f(x) < 12.05$. This interval for x is approximately $1.99583 < x < 2.00416$. Of the two endpoints of this interval, the upper one, 2.00416, is closer to 2 and it is within 0.00416 of 2. Thus, if x is within 0.00416 of 2 then $f(x)$ is within 0.05 of 12. ▮

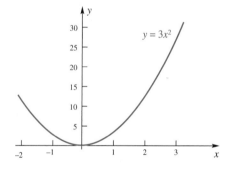

Figure 1

Absolute Value as Distance

Think of two points a and b on a number line. What is the distance between them? If $a < b$, then $b - a$ is the distance, but if $b < a$ then $a - b$ is the distance. We can combine these statements into one by saying that the distance is $|b - a|$. This geometric interpretation of the absolute value of a difference as the distance between two points on a number line is important in understanding our definition of the limit.

If we now asked how close x would have to be to 2 to guarantee that $f(x)$ is within 0.01 of 12, the solution would proceed along the same lines, and we would find that x would have to be in a smaller interval than we obtained above. If we wanted $f(x)$ to be within 0.001 of 12, we would require an interval that is narrower still. In this example, it seems plausible that no matter how close we want $f(x)$ to be to 12, we can accomplish this by taking x sufficiently close to 2.

We now make the definition of the limit precise.

Making the Definition Precise We follow the tradition in using the Greek letters ε (epsilon) and δ (delta) to stand for (usually small) arbitrary positive numbers.

To say that $f(x)$ is within ε of L means that $L - \varepsilon < f(x) < L + \varepsilon$, or equivalently, $|f(x) - L| < \varepsilon$. This means that $f(x)$ lies in the open interval $(L - \varepsilon, L + \varepsilon)$ shown on the graph in Figure 2.

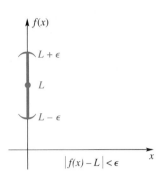

Figure 2

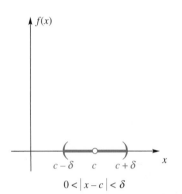

Figure 3

Next, to say that x is sufficiently close to but different from c is to say that, for some δ, x is in the open interval $(c - \delta, c + \delta)$ with c deleted. Perhaps the best way to say this is to write

$$0 < |x - c| < \delta$$

Note that $|x - c| < \delta$ would describe the interval $c - \delta < x < c + \delta$, while $0 < |x - c|$ requires that $x = c$ be excluded. The interval that we are describing is shown in Figure 3.

We are now ready for what some have called the most important definition in calculus.

Definition **Precise Meaning of Limit**

To say that $\lim_{x \to c} f(x) = L$ means that for each given $\varepsilon > 0$ (no matter how small) there is a corresponding $\delta > 0$ such that $|f(x) - L| < \varepsilon$, provided that $0 < |x - c| < \delta$; that is,

$$0 < |x - c| < \delta \Rightarrow |f(x) - L| < \varepsilon$$

The pictures in Figure 4 may help you absorb this definition.

We must emphasize that the real number ε must be given *first*; the number δ is to be produced, and it will usually depend on ε. Suppose that David wishes to prove to Emily that $\lim_{x \to c} f(x) = L$. Emily can challenge David with any particular

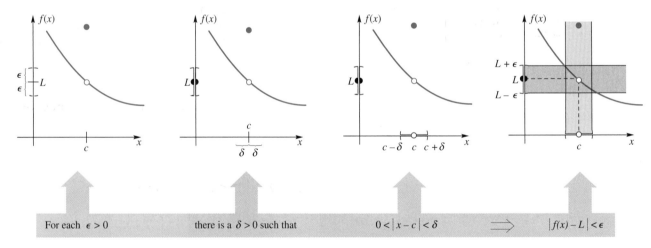

For each $\epsilon > 0$ there is a $\delta > 0$ such that $0 < |x - c| < \delta$ $\Longrightarrow$ $|f(x) - L| < \epsilon$

Figure 4

ε she chooses (e.g., $\varepsilon = 0.01$) and demand that David produce a corresponding δ. Let's apply David's reasoning to the limit $\lim_{x \to 3}(2x + 1)$. By inspection, David would conjecture that the limit is 7. Now, can David find a δ such that $|(2x + 1) - 7| < 0.01$ whenever $0 < |x - 3| < \delta$? A little algebra shows that

$$|(2x + 1) - 7| < 0.01 \Leftrightarrow 2|x - 3| < 0.01$$

$$\Leftrightarrow |x - 3| < \frac{0.01}{2}$$

Thus, the answer to the question is yes! David can choose $\delta = 0.01/2$ (or any smaller value) and this will guarantee that $|(2x + 1) - 7| < 0.01$ whenever $0 < |x - 3| < 0.01/2$. In other words, David can make $2x + 1$ within 0.01 of 7, provided that x is within 0.01/2 of 3.

Now suppose that Emily challenges David again, but this time she wants $|(2x + 1) - 7| < 0.000002$. Can David find a δ for this value of ε? Following the reasoning used above,

$$|(2x + 1) - 7| < 0.000002 \Leftrightarrow 2|x - 3| < 0.000002$$

$$\Leftrightarrow |x - 3| < \frac{0.000002}{2}$$

Thus, $|(2x + 1) - 7| < 0.000002$ whenever $|x - 3| < 0.000002/2$.

This kind of reasoning, while it may convince some, is not a proof that the limit is 7. The definition says that we must be able to find a δ for *every* $\varepsilon > 0$ (not for *some* $\varepsilon > 0$). Emily could challenge David repeatedly, but they would never *prove* that the limit is 7. David must be able to produce a δ for *every* positive ε (no matter how small).

David opts to take things into his own hands and proposes to let ε be any positive real number. He follows the same reasoning as above, but this time he uses ε instead of 0.000002.

$$|(2x + 1) - 7| < \varepsilon \Leftrightarrow 2|x - 3| < \varepsilon$$

$$\Leftrightarrow |x - 3| < \frac{\varepsilon}{2}$$

David can choose $\delta = \varepsilon/2$, and it follows that $|(2x + 1) - 7| < \varepsilon$ whenever $|x - 3| < \varepsilon/2$. In other words, he can make $2x + 1$ within ε of 7 provided x is within $\varepsilon/2$ of 3. Now David has met the requirements of the definition of the limit and has therefore verified that the limit is 7, as suspected.

Some Limit Proofs

In each of the following examples, we begin with what we call a preliminary analysis. We include it so that our choice of δ in each proof does not seem to suggest incredible insight on our part. It shows the kind of work you need to do on scratch paper in order to construct the proof. Once you feel that you grasp an example, take another look at it, but cover up the preliminary analysis and note how elegant, but mysterious, the proof seems to be.

> ### Two Different Limits?
>
> A natural question to ask is "Can a function have two different limits at c?" The obvious intuitive answer is no. If a function is getting closer and closer to L as $x \to c$, it cannot also be getting closer and closer to a different number M. You are asked to show this rigorously in Problem 23.

◼ EXAMPLE 2 Prove that $\lim\limits_{x \to 4}(3x - 7) = 5$.

PRELIMINARY ANALYSIS Let ε be any positive number. We must produce a $\delta > 0$ such that

$$0 < |x - 4| < \delta \Rightarrow |(3x - 7) - 5| < \varepsilon$$

Consider the inequality on the right.

$$
\begin{aligned}
|(3x - 7) - 5| < \varepsilon &\Leftrightarrow |3x - 12| < \varepsilon \\
&\Leftrightarrow |3(x - 4)| < \varepsilon \\
&\Leftrightarrow |3||(x - 4)| < \varepsilon \\
&\Leftrightarrow |x - 4| < \frac{\varepsilon}{3}
\end{aligned}
$$

Now we see how to choose δ; that is, $\delta = \varepsilon/3$. Of course, any smaller δ would work.

FORMAL PROOF Let $\varepsilon > 0$ be given. Choose $\delta = \varepsilon/3$. Then $0 < |x - 4| < \delta$ implies that

$$|(3x - 7) - 5| = |3x - 12| = |3(x - 4)| = 3|x - 4| < 3\delta = \varepsilon$$

If you read this chain of equalities and an inequality from left to right and use the transitive properties of $=$ and $<$, you see that

$$|(3x - 7) - 5| < \varepsilon$$

Now, David knows a rule for choosing the value of δ given Emily's challenge. If Emily were to challenge David with $\varepsilon = 0.01$, then David would respond with $\delta = 0.01/3$. If Emily said $\varepsilon = 0.000003$, then David would say $\delta = 0.000001$. If he gave a smaller value for δ, that would be fine, too.

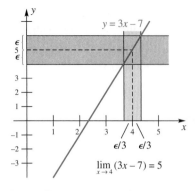

Figure 5

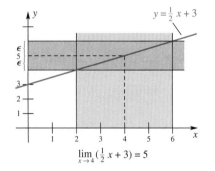

Figure 6

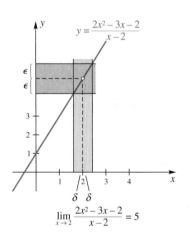

Figure 7

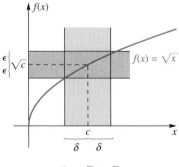

Figure 8

Of course, if you think about the graph of $y = 3x - 7$ (a line with slope 3, as in Figure 5), you know that to force $3x - 7$ to be close to 5 you had better make x even closer (closer by a factor of one-third) to 4. ■

Now look at Figure 6 and convince yourself that $\delta = 2\varepsilon$ would be an appropriate choice for δ in showing that $\lim_{x \to 4}\left(\frac{1}{2}x + 3\right) = 5$.

EXAMPLE 3 Prove that $\lim_{x \to 2} \dfrac{2x^2 - 3x - 2}{x - 2} = 5$.

PRELIMINARY ANALYSIS We are looking for a δ such that

$$0 < |x - 2| < \delta \Rightarrow \left|\frac{2x^2 - 3x - 2}{x - 2} - 5\right| < \varepsilon$$

Now, for $x \neq 2$,

$$\left|\frac{2x^2 - 3x - 2}{x - 2} - 5\right| < \varepsilon \Leftrightarrow \left|\frac{(2x + 1)(x - 2)}{x - 2} - 5\right| < \varepsilon$$

$$\Leftrightarrow |(2x + 1) - 5| < \varepsilon$$

$$\Leftrightarrow |2(x - 2)| < \varepsilon$$

$$\Leftrightarrow |2||x - 2| < \varepsilon$$

$$\Leftrightarrow |x - 2| < \frac{\varepsilon}{2}$$

This indicates that $\delta = \varepsilon/2$ will work (see Figure 7).

FORMAL PROOF Let $\varepsilon > 0$ be given. Choose $\delta = \varepsilon/2$. Then $0 < |x - 2| < \delta$ implies that

$$\left|\frac{2x^2 - 3x - 2}{x - 2} - 5\right| = \left|\frac{(2x + 1)(x - 2)}{x - 2} - 5\right| = |2x + 1 - 5|$$

$$= |2(x - 2)| = 2|x - 2| < 2\delta = \varepsilon$$

The cancellation of the factor $x - 2$ is legitimate because $0 < |x - 2|$ implies that $x \neq 2$, and $\dfrac{x - 2}{x - 2} = 1$ as long as $x \neq 2$. ■

EXAMPLE 4 Prove that $\lim_{x \to c}(mx + b) = mc + b$.

PRELIMINARY ANALYSIS We want to find δ such that

$$0 < |x - c| < \delta \Rightarrow |(mx + b) - (mc + b)| < \varepsilon$$

Now

$$|(mx + b) - (mc + b)| = |mx - mc| = |m(x - c)| = |m||x - c|$$

It appears that $\delta = \varepsilon/|m|$ should do as long as $m \neq 0$. (Note that m could be positive or negative, so we need to keep the absolute value bars. Recall from Chapter 1 that $|ab| = |a||b|$.)

FORMAL PROOF Let $\varepsilon > 0$ be given. Choose $\delta = \varepsilon/|m|$. Then $0 < |x - c| < \delta$ implies that

$$|(mx + b) - (mc + b)| = |mx - mc| = |m||x - c| < |m|\delta = \varepsilon$$

And in case $m = 0$, any δ will do just fine since

$$|(0x + b) - (0c + b)| = |0| = 0$$

The latter is less than ε for all x. ■

EXAMPLE 5 Prove that if $c > 0$ then $\lim_{x \to c} \sqrt{x} = \sqrt{c}$.

PRELIMINARY ANALYSIS Refer to Figure 8. We must find δ such that

$$0 < |x - c| < \delta \Rightarrow |\sqrt{x} - \sqrt{c}| < \varepsilon$$

Now

$$\left| \sqrt{x} - \sqrt{c} \right| = \left| \frac{\left(\sqrt{x} - \sqrt{c} \right)\left(\sqrt{x} + \sqrt{c} \right)}{\sqrt{x} + \sqrt{c}} \right| = \left| \frac{x - c}{\sqrt{x} + \sqrt{c}} \right|$$

$$= \frac{|x - c|}{\sqrt{x} + \sqrt{c}} \le \frac{|x - c|}{\sqrt{c}}$$

To make the latter less than ε requires that we have $|x - c| < \varepsilon\sqrt{c}$.

FORMAL PROOF Let $\varepsilon > 0$ be given. Choose $\delta = \varepsilon\sqrt{c}$. Then $0 < |x - c| < \delta$ implies that

$$\left| \sqrt{x} - \sqrt{c} \right| = \left| \frac{\left(\sqrt{x} - \sqrt{c} \right)\left(\sqrt{x} + \sqrt{c} \right)}{\sqrt{x} + \sqrt{c}} \right| = \left| \frac{x - c}{\sqrt{x} + \sqrt{c}} \right|$$

$$= \frac{|x - c|}{\sqrt{x} + \sqrt{c}} \le \frac{|x - c|}{\sqrt{c}} < \frac{\delta}{\sqrt{c}} = \varepsilon$$

There is one technical point here. We began with $c > 0$, but it could happen that c sits very close to 0 on the x-axis. We should insist that $\delta \le c$, for then $|x - c| < \delta$ implies that $x > 0$ so that $\sqrt{x}$ is defined. Thus, for absolute rigor, choose δ to be the smaller of c and $\varepsilon\sqrt{c}$. ∎

Our demonstration in Example 5 depended on *rationalizing the numerator*, a trick frequently useful in calculus.

EXAMPLE 6 Prove that $\lim_{x \to 3}(x^2 + x - 5) = 7$.

PRELIMINARY ANALYSIS Our task is to find δ such that

$$0 < |x - 3| < \delta \implies |(x^2 + x - 5) - 7| < \varepsilon$$

Now

$$|(x^2 + x - 5) - 7| = |x^2 + x - 12| = |x + 4||x - 3|$$

The factor $|x - 3|$ can be made as small as we wish, and we know that $|x + 4|$ will be about 7. We therefore seek an upper bound for $|x + 4|$. To do this, we first agree to make $\delta \le 1$. Then $|x - 3| < \delta$ implies that

$$|x + 4| = |x - 3 + 7|$$

$$\le |x - 3| + |7| \qquad \text{(Triangle Inequality)}$$

$$< 1 + 7 = 8$$

(Figure 9 offers an alternative demonstration of this fact.) If we also require that $\delta \le \varepsilon/8$, then the product $|x + 4||x - 3|$ will be less than ε.

FORMAL PROOF Let $\varepsilon > 0$ be given. Choose $\delta = \min\{1, \varepsilon/8\}$; that is, choose δ to be the smaller of 1 and $\varepsilon/8$. Then $0 < |x - 3| < \delta$ implies that

$$|(x^2 + x - 5) - 7| = |x^2 + x - 12| = |x + 4||x - 3| < 8 \cdot \frac{\varepsilon}{8} = \varepsilon \qquad ∎$$

$$\boxed{\begin{aligned} |x - 3| < 1 &\implies 2 < x < 4 \\ &\implies 6 < x + 4 < 8 \\ &\implies |x + 4| < 8 \end{aligned}}$$

Figure 9

EXAMPLE 7 Prove that $\lim_{x \to c} x^2 = c^2$.

PROOF We mimic the proof in Example 6. Let $\varepsilon > 0$ be given. Choose $\delta = \min\{1, \varepsilon/(1 + 2|c|)\}$. Then $0 < |x - c| < \delta$ implies that

$$|x^2 - c^2| = |x + c||x - c| = |x - c + 2c||x - c|$$

$$\le (|x - c| + 2|c|)|x - c| \qquad \text{(Triangle Inequality)}$$

$$< (1 + 2|c|)|x - c| < \frac{(1 + 2|c|) \cdot \varepsilon}{1 + 2|c|} = \varepsilon \qquad ∎$$

Although appearing incredibly insightful, we did not pull δ "out of the air" in Example 7. We simply did not show you the preliminary analysis this time.

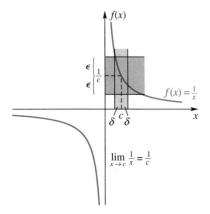

Figure 10

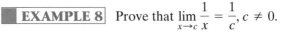

EXAMPLE 8 Prove that $\lim_{x \to c} \dfrac{1}{x} = \dfrac{1}{c}, c \neq 0$.

PRELIMINARY ANALYSIS Study Figure 10. We must find δ such that

$$0 < |x - c| < \delta \Rightarrow \left| \frac{1}{x} - \frac{1}{c} \right| < \varepsilon$$

Now

$$\left| \frac{1}{x} - \frac{1}{c} \right| = \left| \frac{c - x}{xc} \right| = \frac{1}{|x|} \cdot \frac{1}{|c|} \cdot |x - c|$$

The factor $1/|x|$ is troublesome, especially if x is near 0. We can bound this factor if we can keep x away from 0. To that end, note that

$$|c| = |c - x + x| \leq |c - x| + |x|$$

so

$$|x| \geq |c| - |x - c|$$

Thus, if we choose $\delta \leq |c|/2$, we succeed in making $|x| \geq |c|/2$. Finally, if we also require $\delta \leq \varepsilon c^2/2$, then

$$\frac{1}{|x|} \cdot \frac{1}{|c|} \cdot |x - c| < \frac{1}{|c|/2} \cdot \frac{1}{|c|} \cdot \frac{\varepsilon c^2}{2} = \varepsilon$$

FORMAL PROOF Let $\varepsilon > 0$ be given. Choose $\delta = \min\{|c|/2, \varepsilon c^2/2\}$. Then $0 < |x - c| < \delta$ implies

$$\left| \frac{1}{x} - \frac{1}{c} \right| = \left| \frac{c - x}{xc} \right| = \frac{1}{|x|} \cdot \frac{1}{|c|} \cdot |x - c| < \frac{1}{|c|/2} \cdot \frac{1}{|c|} \cdot \frac{\varepsilon c^2}{2} = \varepsilon \qquad \blacksquare$$

One-Sided Limits It does not take much imagination to give the ε–δ definitions of right- and left-hand limits.

Definition **Right-Hand Limit**

To say $\lim_{x \to c^+} f(x) = L$ means that for each $\varepsilon > 0$ there is a corresponding $\delta > 0$ such that

$$0 < x - c < \delta \Rightarrow |f(x) - L| < \varepsilon$$

We leave the ε–δ definition for the left-hand limit to the reader. (See Problem 5.)

The ε–δ concept presented in this section is probably the most intricate and elusive topic in a calculus course. It may take you some time to grasp this concept, but it is worth the effort. Calculus is the study of limits, so a clear understanding of the concept of limit is a worthy goal.

The discovery of calculus is usually attributed to Isaac Newton (1642–1727) and Gottfried Wilhelm von Leibniz (1646–1716), who worked independently in the late 1600s. Although Newton and Leibniz, along with their successors, discovered a number of properties of calculus, and calculus was found to have many applications in the physical sciences, it was not until the nineteenth century that a precise definition of a limit was proposed. Augustin Louis Cauchy (1789–1857), a French engineer and mathematician, gave this definition: "If the successive values attributed to the same variable approach indefinitely a fixed value, such that they finally differ from it by as little as one wishes, this latter is called the limit of all the others." Even Cauchy, a master at rigor, was somewhat vague in his definition of a limit. What are "successive values," and what does it mean to "finally differ"? The phrase "finally differ from it by as little as one wishes" contains the seed of the ε–δ

definition, because for the first time it indicates that the difference between $f(x)$ and its limit L can be made smaller than any given number, the number we labeled ε. The German mathematician Karl Weierstrass (1815–1897) first put together the definition that is equivalent to our ε–δ definition of a limit.

Concepts Review

1. The inequality $|f(x) - L| < \varepsilon$ is equivalent to _____ $< f(x) <$ _____.

2. The precise meaning of $\lim_{x \to a} f(x) = L$ is this: Given any positive number ε, there is a corresponding positive number δ such that _____ implies _____.

3. To be sure that $|3x - 3| < \varepsilon$, we would require that $|x - 1| <$ _____.

4. $\lim_{x \to a} (mx + b) =$ _____.

Problem Set 2.2

In Problems 1–6, give the appropriate ε–δ definition of each statement.

1. $\lim_{t \to a} f(t) = M$

2. $\lim_{u \to b} g(u) = L$

3. $\lim_{z \to d} h(z) = P$

4. $\lim_{y \to e} \phi(y) = B$

5. $\lim_{x \to c^-} f(x) = L$

6. $\lim_{t \to a^+} g(t) = D$

In Problems 7–10, plot the function $f(x)$ over the interval $[1.5, 2.5]$. Zoom in on the graph of each function to determine how close x must be to 2 in order that $f(x)$ is within 0.002 of 4. Your answer should be of the form "If x is within _____ of 2, then $f(x)$ is within 0.002 of 4."

7. $f(x) = 2x$

8. $f(x) = x^2$

9. $f(x) = \sqrt{8x}$

10. $f(x) = \dfrac{8}{x}$

In Problems 11–22, give an ε–δ proof of each limit fact.

11. $\lim_{x \to 0} (2x - 1) = -1$

12. $\lim_{x \to -21} (3x - 1) = -64$

13. $\lim_{x \to 5} \dfrac{x^2 - 25}{x - 5} = 10$

14. $\lim_{x \to 0} \left(\dfrac{2x^2 - x}{x} \right) = -1$

15. $\lim_{x \to 5} \dfrac{2x^2 - 11x + 5}{x - 5} = 9$

16. $\lim_{x \to 1} \sqrt{2x} = \sqrt{2}$

17. $\lim_{x \to 4} \dfrac{\sqrt{2x - 1}}{\sqrt{x - 3}} = \sqrt{7}$

18. $\lim_{x \to 1} \dfrac{14x^2 - 20x + 6}{x - 1} = 8$

19. $\lim_{x \to 1} \dfrac{10x^3 - 26x^2 + 22x - 6}{(x - 1)^2} = 4$

20. $\lim_{x \to 1} (2x^2 + 1) = 3$

21. $\lim_{x \to -1} (x^2 - 2x - 1) = 2$

22. $\lim_{x \to 0} x^4 = 0$

23. Prove that if $\lim_{x \to c} f(x) = L$ and $\lim_{x \to c} f(x) = M$, then $L = M$.

24. Let F and G be functions such that $0 \le F(x) \le G(x)$ for all x near c, except possibly at c. Prove that if $\lim_{x \to c} G(x) = 0$, then $\lim_{x \to c} F(x) = 0$.

25. Prove that $\lim_{x \to 0} x^4 \sin^2(1/x) = 0$. *Hint:* Use Problems 22 and 24.

26. Prove that $\lim_{x \to 0^+} \sqrt{x} = 0$.

27. By considering left- and right-hand limits, prove that $\lim_{x \to 0} |x| = 0$.

28. Prove that if $|f(x)| < B$ for $|x - a| < 1$ and $\lim_{x \to a} g(x) = 0$, then $\lim_{x \to a} f(x)g(x) = 0$.

29. Suppose that $\lim_{x \to a} f(x) = L$ and that $f(a)$ exists (though it may be different from L). Prove that f is bounded on some interval containing a; that is, show that there is an interval (c, d) with $c < a < d$ and a constant M such that $|f(x)| \le M$ for all x in (c, d).

30. Prove that if $f(x) \le g(x)$ for all x in some deleted interval about a and if $\lim_{x \to a} f(x) = L$ and $\lim_{x \to a} g(x) = M$, then $L \le M$.

31. Which of the following are equivalent to the definition of limit?

(a) For some $\varepsilon > 0$ and every $\delta > 0, 0 < |x - c| < \delta \Rightarrow |f(x) - L| < \varepsilon$.

(b) For every $\delta > 0$, there is a corresponding $\varepsilon > 0$ such that
$$0 < |x - c| < \varepsilon \Rightarrow |f(x) - L| < \delta$$

(c) For every positive integer N, there is a corresponding positive integer M such that $0 < |x - c| < 1/M \Rightarrow |f(x) - L| < 1/N$.

(d) For every $\varepsilon > 0$, there is a corresponding $\delta > 0$ such that $0 < |x - c| < \delta$ and $|f(x) - L| < \varepsilon$ for some x.

32. State in ε–δ language what it means to say $\lim_{x \to c} f(x) \ne L$.

GC **33.** Suppose we wish to give an ε–δ proof that
$$\lim_{x \to 3} \frac{x + 6}{x^4 - 4x^3 + x^2 + x + 6} = -1$$
We begin by writing $\dfrac{x + 6}{x^4 - 4x^3 + x^2 + x + 6} + 1$ in the form $(x - 3)g(x)$.

(a) Determine $g(x)$.

C (b) Could we choose $\delta = \min(1, \varepsilon/n)$ for some n? Explain.

(c) If we choose $\delta = \min\left(\frac{1}{4}, \varepsilon/m\right)$, what is the smallest integer m that we could use?

2.3
Limit Theorems

Most readers will agree that proving the existence and values of limits using the $\varepsilon{-}\delta$ definition of the preceding section is both time consuming and difficult. That is why the theorems of this section are so welcome. Our first theorem is the big one. With it, we can handle most limit problems that we will face for quite some time.

One-Sided Limits

Although stated in terms of two-sided limits, Theorem A remains true for both left- and right-hand limits.

Theorem A   Main Limit Theorem

Let n be a positive integer, k be a constant, and f and g be functions that have limits at c. Then

1. $\lim\limits_{x \to c} k = k$;

2. $\lim\limits_{x \to c} x = c$;

3. $\lim\limits_{x \to c} kf(x) = k \lim\limits_{x \to c} f(x)$;

4. $\lim\limits_{x \to c} [f(x) + g(x)] = \lim\limits_{x \to c} f(x) + \lim\limits_{x \to c} g(x)$;

5. $\lim\limits_{x \to c} [f(x) - g(x)] = \lim\limits_{x \to c} f(x) - \lim\limits_{x \to c} g(x)$;

6. $\lim\limits_{x \to c} [f(x) \cdot g(x)] = \lim\limits_{x \to c} f(x) \cdot \lim\limits_{x \to c} g(x)$;

7. $\lim\limits_{x \to c} \dfrac{f(x)}{g(x)} = \dfrac{\lim\limits_{x \to c} f(x)}{\lim\limits_{x \to c} g(x)}$, provided $\lim\limits_{x \to c} g(x) \neq 0$;

8. $\lim\limits_{x \to c} [f(x)]^n = \left[\lim\limits_{x \to c} f(x) \right]^n$;

9. $\lim\limits_{x \to c} \sqrt[n]{f(x)} = \sqrt[n]{\lim\limits_{x \to c} f(x)}$, provided $\lim\limits_{x \to c} f(x) > 0$ when n is even.

These important results are remembered best if learned in words. For example, Statement 4 translates as *The limit of a sum is the sum of the limits*.

Of course, Theorem A needs to be proved. We postpone that job till the end of the section, choosing first to show how this multipart theorem is used.

Applications of the Main Limit Theorem   In the next examples, the circled numbers refer to the numbered statements from Theorem A. Each equality is justified by the indicated statement.

■ **EXAMPLE 1**   Find $\lim\limits_{x \to 3} 2x^4$.

$$\lim_{x \to 3} 2x^4 \overset{(3)}{=} 2 \lim_{x \to 3} x^4 \overset{(8)}{=} 2 \left[\lim_{x \to 3} x \right]^4 \overset{(2)}{=} 2[3]^4 = 162$$

■

■ **EXAMPLE 2**   Find $\lim\limits_{x \to 4} (3x^2 - 2x)$.

SOLUTION

$$\lim_{x \to 4} (3x^2 - 2x) \overset{(5)}{=} \lim_{x \to 4} 3x^2 - \lim_{x \to 4} 2x \overset{(3)}{=} 3 \lim_{x \to 4} x^2 - 2 \lim_{x \to 4} x$$

$$\overset{(8)}{=} 3 \left(\lim_{x \to 4} x \right)^2 - 2 \lim_{x \to 4} x \overset{(2)}{=} 3(4)^2 - 2(4) = 40$$

■

EXAMPLE 3 Find $\displaystyle\lim_{x\to 4}\frac{\sqrt{x^2+9}}{x}$.

SOLUTION

$$\lim_{x\to 4}\frac{\sqrt{x^2+9}}{x}\overset{(7)}{=}\frac{\displaystyle\lim_{x\to 4}\sqrt{x^2+9}}{\displaystyle\lim_{x\to 4}x}\overset{(9,2)}{=}\frac{\sqrt{\displaystyle\lim_{x\to 4}(x^2+9)}}{4}\overset{(4)}{=}\frac{1}{4}\sqrt{\lim_{x\to 4}x^2+\lim_{x\to 4}9}$$

$$\overset{(8,1)}{=}\frac{1}{4}\sqrt{\left[\lim_{x\to 4}x\right]^2+9}\overset{(2)}{=}\frac{1}{4}\sqrt{4^2+9}=\frac{5}{4}$$

■

EXAMPLE 4 If $\displaystyle\lim_{x\to 3}f(x)=4$ and $\displaystyle\lim_{x\to 3}g(x)=8$, find

$$\lim_{x\to 3}\left[f^2(x)\cdot\sqrt[3]{g(x)}\right]$$

SOLUTION

$$\lim_{x\to 3}[f^2(x)\cdot\sqrt[3]{g(x)}]\overset{(6)}{=}\lim_{x\to 3}f^2(x)\cdot\lim_{x\to 3}\sqrt[3]{g(x)}$$

$$\overset{(8,9)}{=}\left[\lim_{x\to 3}f(x)\right]^2\cdot\sqrt[3]{\lim_{x\to 3}g(x)}$$

$$=[4]^2\cdot\sqrt[3]{8}=32$$

■

Recall that a polynomial function f has the form

$$f(x)=a_nx^n+a_{n-1}x^{n-1}+\cdots+a_1x+a_0$$

whereas a rational function f is the quotient of two polynomial functions, that is,

$$f(x)=\frac{a_nx^n+a_{n-1}x^{n-1}+\cdots+a_1x+a_0}{b_mx^m+b_{m-1}x^{m-1}+\cdots+b_1x+b_0}$$

Theorem B | Substitution Theorem

If f is a polynomial function or a rational function, then

$$\lim_{x\to c}f(x)=f(c)$$

provided $f(c)$ is defined. In the case of a rational function, this means that the value of the denominator at c is not zero.

Evaluating a Limit "by Substitution"

When we apply Theorem B, the Substitution Theorem, we say we evaluate the limit *by substitution*. Not all limits can be evaluated by substitution; consider $\displaystyle\lim_{x\to 1}\frac{x^2-1}{x-1}$. The Substitution Theorem does not apply here because the denominator is 0 when $x=1$, but the limit does exist.

The proof of Theorem B follows from repeated applications of Theorem A. Note that Theorem B allows us to find limits for polynomial and rational functions by simply substituting c for x throughout, provided the denominator of the rational function is not zero at c.

EXAMPLE 5 Find $\displaystyle\lim_{x\to 2}\frac{7x^5-10x^4-13x+6}{3x^2-6x-8}$.

SOLUTION

$$\lim_{x \to 2} \frac{7x^5 - 10x^4 - 13x + 6}{3x^2 - 6x - 8} = \frac{7(2)^5 - 10(2)^4 - 13(2) + 6}{3(2)^2 - 6(2) - 8} = -\frac{11}{2} \quad \blacksquare$$

EXAMPLE 6 Find $\lim_{x \to 1} \dfrac{x^3 + 3x + 7}{x^2 - 2x + 1} = \lim_{x \to 1} \dfrac{x^3 + 3x + 7}{(x - 1)^2}$.

SOLUTION Neither Theorem B nor Statement 7 of Theorem A applies, since the limit of the denominator is 0. However, since the limit of the numerator is 11, we see that as x nears 1 we are dividing a number near 11 by a positive number near 0. The result is a large positive number. In fact, the resulting number can be made as large as you like by letting x get close enough to 1. We say that the limit does not exist. (Later in this chapter (see Section 2.4) we will allow ourselves to say that the limit is $+\infty$.) $\quad \blacksquare$

In many cases, Theorem B cannot be applied because substitution of c causes the denominator to be 0. In cases like this, it sometimes happens that the function can be simplified, for example by factoring. For example, we can write

$$\frac{x^2 + 3x - 10}{x^2 + x - 6} = \frac{(x - 2)(x + 5)}{(x - 2)(x + 3)} = \frac{x + 5}{x + 3}$$

We have to be careful with this last step. The fraction $(x + 5)/(x + 3)$ is equal to the one on the left side of the equal sign only if x is not equal to 2. If $x = 2$, the left side is undefined (because the denominator is 0), whereas the right side is equal to $(2 + 5)/(2 + 3) = 7/5$. This brings up the question about whether the limits

$$\lim_{x \to 2} \frac{x^2 + 3x - 10}{x^2 + x - 6} \quad \text{and} \quad \lim_{x \to 2} \frac{x + 5}{x + 3}$$

are equal. The answer is contained in the following theorem.

Theorem C

If $f(x) = g(x)$ for all x in an open interval containing the number c, except possibly at the number c itself, and if $\lim_{x \to c} g(x)$ exists, then $\lim_{x \to c} f(x)$ exists and $\lim_{x \to c} f(x) = \lim_{x \to c} g(x)$.

EXAMPLE 7 Find $\lim_{x \to 2} \dfrac{x^2 + 3x - 10}{x^2 + x - 6}$.

SOLUTION Theorem B does not apply because the denominator is 0 when $x = 2$. When we substitute $x = 2$ in the numerator we also get 0, so the quotient takes on the meaningless form 0/0 at $x = 2$. When this happens we should look for some sort of simplification such as factoring.

$$\lim_{x \to 2} \frac{x^2 + 3x - 10}{x^2 + x - 6} = \lim_{x \to 2} \frac{(x - 2)(x + 5)}{(x - 2)(x + 3)} = \lim_{x \to 2} \frac{x + 5}{x + 3} = \frac{7}{5}$$

The second to last equality is justified by Theorem C since

$$\frac{(x - 2)(x + 5)}{(x - 2)(x + 3)} = \frac{x + 5}{x + 3}$$

for all x except $x = 2$. Once we apply Theorem C, we can evaluate the limit by substitution (i.e., by applying Theorem B). $\quad \blacksquare$

How much theorem proving should be done in a first calculus course? Mathematics teachers argue long and hard about this and about the right balance between

- logic and intuition
- proof and explanation
- theory and application

A great scientist of long ago had some sage advice.

"He who loves practice without theory is like the sailor who boards ship without a rudder and compass and never knows where he may cast."

Leonardo da Vinci

EXAMPLE 8 Find $\lim\limits_{x \to 1} \dfrac{x-1}{\sqrt{x}-1}$.

SOLUTION   Again, using Theorem C,

$$\lim_{x \to 1} \frac{x-1}{\sqrt{x}-1} = \lim_{x \to 1} \frac{(\sqrt{x}-1)(\sqrt{x}+1)}{\sqrt{x}-1} = \lim_{x \to 1}(\sqrt{x}+1) = \sqrt{1}+1 = 2 \quad \blacksquare$$

Proof of Theorem A (Optional)   You should not be too surprised when we say that the proofs of some parts of Theorem A are quite sophisticated. Because of this, we prove only the first five parts here, deferring the others to the Appendix (Section A.2, Theorem A). To get your feet wet, you might try Problems 35 and 36.

Proofs of Statements 1 and 2   These statements result from $\lim\limits_{x \to c}(mx+b)$ $= mc + b$ (Example 4 of Section 2.2) using first $m = 0$ and then $m = 1, b = 0$. $\quad\blacksquare$

Proof of Statement 3   If $k = 0$, the result is trivial, so we suppose that $k \neq 0$. Let $\varepsilon > 0$ be given. By hypothesis, $\lim\limits_{x \to c} f(x)$ exists; call its value L. By definition of limit, there is a number δ such that

$$0 < |x - c| < \delta \implies |f(x) - L| < \frac{\varepsilon}{|k|}$$

Someone is sure to complain that we put $\varepsilon/|k|$ rather than ε at the end of the inequality above. Well, isn't $\varepsilon/|k|$ a positive number? Yes. Doesn't the definition of limit require that for *any* positive number there be a corresponding δ? Yes.

Now, for δ so determined (again by a preliminary analysis that we have not shown here), we assert that $0 < |x - c| < \delta$ implies that

$$|kf(x) - kL| = |k||f(x) - L| < |k|\frac{\varepsilon}{|k|} = \varepsilon$$

This shows that

$$\lim_{x \to c} kf(x) = kL = k \lim_{x \to c} f(x) \quad\blacksquare$$

Proof of Statement 4   Refer to Figure 1. Let $\lim\limits_{x \to c} f(x) = L$ and $\lim\limits_{x \to c} g(x) = M$. If ε is any given positive number, then $\varepsilon/2$ is positive. Since $\lim\limits_{x \to c} f(x) = L$, there is a positive number δ_1 such that

$$0 < |x - c| < \delta_1 \implies |f(x) - L| < \frac{\varepsilon}{2}$$

Since $\lim\limits_{x \to c} g(x) = M$, there is a positive number δ_2 such that

$$0 < |x - c| < \delta_2 \implies |g(x) - M| < \frac{\varepsilon}{2}$$

Choose $\delta = \min\{\delta_1, \delta_2\}$; that is, choose δ to be the smaller of δ_1 and δ_2. Then $0 < |x - c| < \delta$ implies that

$$\begin{aligned} |f(x) + g(x) - (L + M)| &= |[f(x) - L] + [g(x) - M]| \\ &\leq |f(x) - L| + |g(x) - M| \\ &< \frac{\varepsilon}{2} + \frac{\varepsilon}{2} = \varepsilon \end{aligned}$$

In this chain, the first inequality is the Triangle Inequality (Section 1.2); the second results from the choice of δ. We have just shown that

$$0 < |x - c| < \delta \implies |f(x) + g(x) - (L + M)| < \varepsilon$$

Thus,

$$\lim_{x \to c} [f(x) + g(x)] = L + M = \lim_{x \to c} f(x) + \lim_{x \to c} g(x) \quad\blacksquare$$

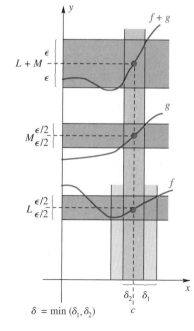

$\delta = \min(\delta_1, \delta_2)$

Figure 1

Proof of Statement 5

$$\lim_{x \to c} [f(x) - g(x)] = \lim_{x \to c} [f(x) + (-1)g(x)]$$
$$= \lim_{x \to c} f(x) + \lim_{x \to c} (-1)g(x)$$
$$= \lim_{x \to c} f(x) + (-1)\lim_{x \to c} g(x)$$
$$= \lim_{x \to c} f(x) - \lim_{x \to c} g(x) \quad \blacksquare$$

The Squeeze Theorem You have likely heard someone say, "I was caught between a rock and a hard place." This is what happens to g in the following theorem (see Figure 2).

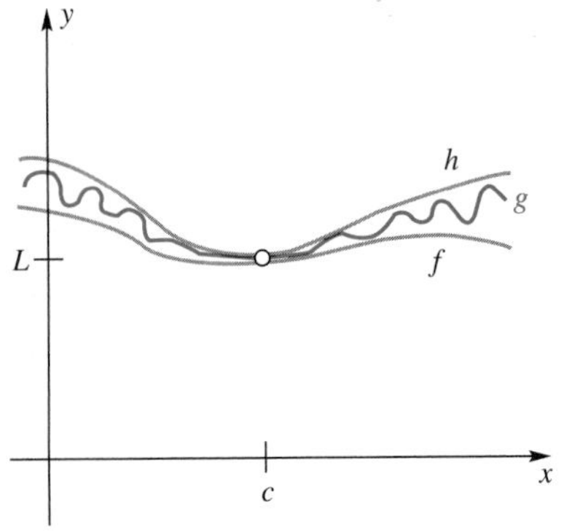

Theorem D **Squeeze Theorem**

Let f, g, and h be functions satisfying $f(x) \le g(x) \le h(x)$ for all x near c, except possibly at c. If $\lim_{x \to c} f(x) = \lim_{x \to c} h(x) = L$, then $\lim_{x \to c} g(x) = L$.

Figure 2

Proof (Optional) Let $\varepsilon > 0$ be given. Choose δ_1 such that

$$0 < |x - c| < \delta_1 \Rightarrow L - \varepsilon < f(x) < L + \varepsilon$$

and δ_2 such that

$$0 < |x - c| < \delta_2 \Rightarrow L - \varepsilon < h(x) < L + \varepsilon$$

Choose δ_3 so that

$$0 < |x - c| < \delta_3 \Rightarrow f(x) \le g(x) \le h(x)$$

Let $\delta = \min\{\delta_1, \delta_2, \delta_3\}$. Then

$$0 < |x - c| < \delta \Rightarrow L - \varepsilon < f(x) \le g(x) \le h(x) < L + \varepsilon$$

We conclude that $\lim_{x \to c} g(x) = L$. $\quad \blacksquare$

EXAMPLE 9 Assume that we have proved $1 - x^2/6 \le (\sin x)/x \le 1$ for all x near but different from 0. What can we conclude about $\lim_{x \to 0} \dfrac{\sin x}{x}$?

SOLUTION Let $f(x) = 1 - x^2/6$, $g(x) = (\sin x)/x$, and $h(x) = 1$. It follows that $\lim_{x \to 0} f(x) = 1 = \lim_{x \to 0} h(x)$ and so, by Theorem D,

$$\lim_{x \to 0} \frac{\sin x}{x} = 1 \quad \blacksquare$$

Concepts Review

1. If $\lim_{x \to 3} f(x) = 4$, then $\lim_{x \to 3} (x^2 + 3)f(x) = $ _____.

2. If $\lim_{x \to 2} g(x) = -2$, then $\lim_{x \to 2} \sqrt{g^2(x) + 12} = $ _____.

3. If $\lim_{x \to c} f(x) = 4$ and $\lim_{x \to c} g(x) = -2$, then $\lim_{x \to c} \dfrac{f^2(x)}{g(x)} = $
_____ and $\lim_{x \to c} \left[g(x) \sqrt{f(x)} + 5x \right] = $ _____.

4. If $\lim_{x \to c} f(x) = L$ and $\lim_{x \to c} g(x) = L$, then

$$\lim_{x \to c} [f(x) - L]g(x) = \underline{\qquad}.$$

Problem Set 2.3

In Problems 1–12, use Theorem A to find each of the limits. Justify each step by appealing to a numbered statement, as in Examples 1–4.

1. $\lim_{x \to 1} (2x + 1)$

2. $\lim_{x \to -1} (3x^2 - 1)$

3. $\lim_{x \to 0} [(2x + 1)(x - 3)]$

4. $\lim_{x \to \sqrt{2}} [(2x^2 + 1)(7x^2 + 13)]$

5. $\lim_{x \to 2} \dfrac{2x + 1}{5 - 3x}$

6. $\lim_{x \to -3} \dfrac{4x^3 + 1}{7 - 2x^2}$

7. $\lim_{x \to 3} \sqrt{3x - 5}$

8. $\lim_{x \to -3} \sqrt{5x^2 + 2x}$

9. $\lim_{t \to -2} (2t^3 + 15)^{13}$

10. $\lim_{w \to -2} \sqrt{-3w^3 + 7w^2}$

11. $\lim_{y \to 2} \left(\dfrac{4y^3 + 8y}{y + 4} \right)^{1/3}$

12. $\lim_{w \to 5} (2w^4 - 9w^3 + 19)^{-1/2}$

In Problems 13–24, find the indicated limit or state that it does not exist. In many cases, you will want to do some algebra before trying to evaluate the limit.

13. $\lim_{x \to 2} \dfrac{x^2 - 4}{x^2 + 4}$

14. $\lim_{x \to 2} \dfrac{x^2 - 5x + 6}{x - 2}$

15. $\lim_{x \to -1} \dfrac{x^2 - 2x - 3}{x + 1}$

16. $\lim_{x \to -1} \dfrac{x^2 + x}{x^2 + 1}$

17. $\lim_{x \to -1} \dfrac{x^3 - 6x^2 + 11x - 6}{x^3 + 4x^2 - 19x + 14}$

18. $\lim_{x \to 2} \dfrac{x^2 + 7x + 10}{x + 2}$

19. $\lim_{x \to 1} \dfrac{x^2 + x - 2}{x^2 - 1}$

20. $\lim_{x \to -3} \dfrac{x^2 - 14x - 51}{x^2 - 4x - 21}$

21. $\lim_{u \to -2} \dfrac{u^2 - ux + 2u - 2x}{u^2 - u - 6}$

22. $\lim_{x \to 1} \dfrac{x^2 + ux - x - u}{x^2 + 2x - 3}$

23. $\lim_{x \to \pi} \dfrac{2x^2 - 6x\pi + 4\pi^2}{x^2 - \pi^2}$

24. $\lim_{w \to -2} \dfrac{(w + 2)(w^2 - w - 6)}{w^2 + 4w + 4}$

In Problems 25–30, find the limits if $\lim_{x \to a} f(x) = 3$ and $\lim_{x \to a} g(x) = -1$ (see Example 4).

25. $\lim_{x \to a} \sqrt{f^2(x) + g^2(x)}$

26. $\lim_{x \to a} \dfrac{2f(x) - 3g(x)}{f(x) + g(x)}$

27. $\lim_{x \to a} \sqrt[3]{g(x)} \left[f(x) + 3 \right]$

28. $\lim_{x \to a} \left[f(x) - 3 \right]^4$

29. $\lim_{t \to a} \left[|f(t)| + |3g(t)| \right]$

30. $\lim_{u \to a} \left[f(u) + 3g(u) \right]^3$

In Problems 31–34, find $\lim_{x \to 2} [f(x) - f(2)]/(x - 2)$ for each given function f.

31. $f(x) = 3x^2$

32. $f(x) = 3x^2 + 2x + 1$

33. $f(x) = \dfrac{1}{x}$

34. $f(x) = \dfrac{3}{x^2}$

35. Prove Statement 6 of Theorem A. *Hint:*

$$|f(x)g(x) - LM| = |f(x)g(x) - Lg(x) + Lg(x) - LM|$$
$$= |g(x)[f(x) - L] + L[g(x) - M]|$$
$$\le |g(x)||f(x) - L| + |L||g(x) - M|$$

Now show that if $\lim_{x \to c} g(x) = M$, then there is a number δ_1 such that

$$0 < |x - c| < \delta_1 \Rightarrow |g(x)| < |M| + 1$$

36. Prove Statement 7 of Theorem A by first giving an ε–δ proof that $\lim_{x \to c} [1/g(x)] = 1/\left[\lim_{x \to c} g(x) \right]$ and then applying Statement 6.

37. Prove that $\lim_{x \to c} f(x) = L \Leftrightarrow \lim_{x \to c} [f(x) - L] = 0$.

38. Prove that $\lim_{x \to c} f(x) = 0 \Leftrightarrow \lim_{x \to c} |f(x)| = 0$.

39. Prove that $\lim_{x \to c} |x| = |c|$.

40. Find examples to show that if

(a) $\lim_{x \to c} \left[f(x) + g(x) \right]$ exists, this does not imply that either $\lim_{x \to c} f(x)$ or $\lim_{x \to c} g(x)$ exists;

(b) $\lim_{x \to c} \left[f(x) \cdot g(x) \right]$ exists, this does not imply that either $\lim_{x \to c} f(x)$ or $\lim_{x \to c} g(x)$ exists.

In Problems 41–48, find each of the right-hand and left-hand limits or state that they do not exist.

41. $\lim_{x \to -3^+} \dfrac{\sqrt{3 + x}}{x}$

42. $\lim_{x \to -\pi^+} \dfrac{\sqrt{\pi^3 + x^3}}{x}$

43. $\lim_{x \to 3^+} \dfrac{x - 3}{\sqrt{x^2 - 9}}$

44. $\lim_{x \to 1^-} \dfrac{\sqrt{1 + x}}{4 + 4x}$

45. $\lim_{x \to 2^+} \dfrac{(x^2 + 1)[\![x]\!]}{(3x - 1)^2}$

46. $\lim_{x \to 3^-} (x - [\![x]\!])$

47. $\lim_{x \to 0^-} \dfrac{x}{|x|}$

48. $\lim_{x \to 3^+} [\![x^2 + 2x]\!]$

49. Suppose that $f(x)g(x) = 1$ for all x and $\lim_{x \to a} g(x) = 0$. Prove that $\lim_{x \to a} f(x)$ does not exist.

50. Let R be the rectangle joining the midpoints of the sides of the quadrilateral Q having vertices $(\pm x, 0)$ and $(0, \pm 1)$. Calculate

$$\lim_{x \to 0^+} \dfrac{\text{perimeter of } R}{\text{perimeter of } Q}$$

51. Let $y = \sqrt{x}$ and consider the points M, N, O, and P with coordinates $(1, 0), (0, 1), (0, 0),$ and (x, y) on the graph of $y = \sqrt{x}$, respectively. Calculate

(a) $\lim_{x \to 0^+} \dfrac{\text{perimeter of } \Delta NOP}{\text{perimeter of } \Delta MOP}$

(b) $\lim_{x \to 0^+} \dfrac{\text{area of } \Delta NOP}{\text{area of } \Delta MOP}$

Answers to Concepts Review: **1.** 48 **2.** 4
3. -8; $-4 + 5c$ **4.** 0

2.4
Limits at Infinity; Infinite Limits

The deepest problems and most profound paradoxes of mathematics are often intertwined with the use of the concept of the infinite. Yet mathematical progress can in part be measured in terms of our understanding the concept of infinity. We have already used the symbols ∞ and $-\infty$ in our notation for certain intervals. Thus, $(3, \infty)$ is our way of denoting the set of all real numbers greater than 3. Note

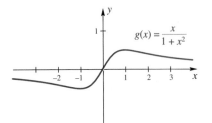

Figure 1

x	$\dfrac{x}{1+x^2}$
10	0.099
100	0.010
1000	0.001
10000	0.0001
$\downarrow$	$\downarrow$
∞	?

Figure 2

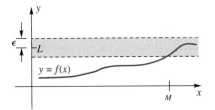

Figure 3

that we have never referred to ∞ as a number. For example, we have never added it to a number or divided it by a number. We will use the symbols ∞ and $-\infty$ in a new way in this section, but they will still not represent numbers.

Limits at Infinity   Consider the function $g(x) = x/(1 + x^2)$ whose graph is shown in Figure 1. We ask this question: What happens to $g(x)$ as x gets larger and larger? In symbols, we ask for the value of $\lim_{x \to \infty} g(x)$.

When we write $x \to \infty$, we are *not* implying that somewhere far, far to the right on the x-axis there is a number—bigger than all other numbers—that x is approaching. Rather, we use $x \to \infty$ as a shorthand way of saying that x gets larger and larger without bound.

In the table in Figure 2, we have listed values of $g(x) = x/(1 + x^2)$ for several values of x. It appears that $g(x)$ gets smaller and smaller as x gets larger and larger. We write

$$\lim_{x \to \infty} \frac{x}{1 + x^2} = 0$$

Experimenting with negative numbers far to the left of zero on the real number line would lead us to write

$$\lim_{x \to -\infty} \frac{x}{1 + x^2} = 0$$

Rigorous Definitions of Limits as $x \to \pm\infty$ In analogy with our ε–δ definition for ordinary limits, we make the following definition.

Definition   Limit as $x \to \infty$

Let f be defined on $[c, \infty)$ for some number c. We say that $\lim_{x \to \infty} f(x) = L$ if for each $\varepsilon > 0$ there is a corresponding number M such that

$$x > M \implies |f(x) - L| < \varepsilon$$

You will note that M can, and usually does, depend on ε. In general, the smaller ε is, the larger M will have to be. The graph in Figure 3 may help you to understand what we are saying.

Definition   Limit as $x \to -\infty$

Let f be defined on $(-\infty, c]$ for some number c. We say that $\lim_{x \to -\infty} f(x) = L$ if for each $\varepsilon > 0$ there is a corresponding number M such that

$$x < M \implies |f(x) - L| < \varepsilon$$

EXAMPLE 1   Show that if k is a positive integer, then

$$\lim_{x \to \infty} \frac{1}{x^k} = 0 \quad \text{and} \quad \lim_{x \to -\infty} \frac{1}{x^k} = 0$$

SOLUTION   Let $\varepsilon > 0$ be given. After a preliminary analysis (as in Section 2.2), we chose $M = \sqrt[k]{1/\varepsilon}$. Then $x > M$ implies that

$$\left| \frac{1}{x^k} - 0 \right| = \frac{1}{x^k} < \frac{1}{M^k} = \varepsilon$$

The proof of the second statement is similar.   ∎

Having given the definitions of these new kinds of limits, we must face the question of whether the Main Limit Theorem (Theorem 2.3A) holds for them. The answer is yes, and the proof is similar to the original one. Note how we use this theorem in the following examples.

EXAMPLE 2 Prove that $\lim\limits_{x\to\infty} \dfrac{x}{1+x^2} = 0$.

SOLUTION Here we use a standard trick: divide the numerator and denominator by the highest power of x that appears in the denominator, that is, x^2.

$$\lim_{x\to\infty} \frac{x}{1+x^2} = \lim_{x\to\infty} \frac{\dfrac{x}{x^2}}{\dfrac{1+x^2}{x^2}} = \lim_{x\to\infty} \frac{\dfrac{1}{x}}{\dfrac{1}{x^2}+1}$$

$$= \frac{\lim\limits_{x\to\infty} \dfrac{1}{x}}{\lim\limits_{x\to\infty} \dfrac{1}{x^2} + \lim\limits_{x\to\infty} 1} = \frac{0}{0+1} = 0 \qquad \blacksquare$$

EXAMPLE 3 Find $\lim\limits_{x\to-\infty} \dfrac{2x^3}{1+x^3}$.

SOLUTION The graph of $f(x) = 2x^3/(1+x^3)$ is shown in Figure 4. To find the limit, divide both the numerator and denominator by x^3.

$$\lim_{x\to-\infty} \frac{2x^3}{1+x^3} = \lim_{x\to-\infty} \frac{2}{1/x^3+1} = \frac{2}{0+1} = 2 \qquad \blacksquare$$

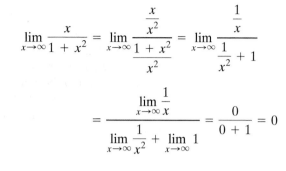

Limits of Sequences The domain for some functions is the set of natural numbers $\{1, 2, 3, \dots\}$. In this situation, we usually write a_n rather than $a(n)$ to denote the nth term of the sequence, or $\{a_n\}$ to denote the whole sequence. For example, we might define the sequence by $a_n = n/(n+1)$. Let's consider what happens as n gets large. A little calculation shows that

$$a_1 = \frac{1}{2}, \quad a_2 = \frac{2}{3}, \quad a_3 = \frac{3}{4}, \quad a_4 = \frac{4}{5}, \quad \dots, \quad a_{100} = \frac{100}{101}, \quad \dots$$

It looks as if these values are approaching 1, so it seems reasonable to say that for this sequence $\lim\limits_{n\to\infty} a_n = 1$. The next definition gives meaning to this idea of the limit of a sequence.

Definition Limit of a Sequence

Let a_n be defined for all natural numbers greater than or equal to some number c. We say that $\lim\limits_{n\to\infty} a_n = L$ if for each $\varepsilon > 0$ there is a corresponding natural number M such that

$$n > M \implies |a_n - L| < \varepsilon$$

Notice that this definition is nearly identical to the definition of $\lim\limits_{x\to\infty} f(x)$. The only difference is that now we are requiring that the argument to the function be a natural number. As we might expect, the Main Limit Theorem (Theorem 2.3A) holds for sequences.

EXAMPLE 4 Find $\lim\limits_{n\to\infty} \sqrt{\dfrac{n+1}{n+2}}$.

SOLUTION Figure 5 shows a graph of $a_n = \sqrt{\dfrac{n+1}{n+2}}$. Applying Theorem 2.3A gives

$$\lim_{n\to\infty} \sqrt{\frac{n+1}{n+2}} = \left(\lim_{n\to\infty} \frac{n+1}{n+2}\right)^{1/2} = \left(\lim_{n\to\infty} \frac{1+1/n}{1+2/n}\right)^{1/2} = \left(\frac{1+0}{1+0}\right)^{1/2} = 1 \qquad \blacksquare$$

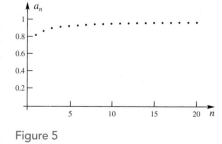

Figure 5

Figure 4

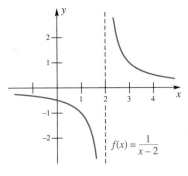

Figure 6

We will need the concept of the limit of a sequence in Section 4.7 and in Chapter 5. Sequences are covered more thoroughly in Chapter 9.

Infinite Limits Consider the function $f(x) = 1/(x - 2)$, which is graphed in Figure 6. As x gets close to 2 from the left, the function seems to decrease without bound. Similarly, as x approaches 2 from the right, the function seems to increase without bound. It therefore makes no sense to talk about $\lim_{x \to 2} 1/(x - 2)$, but we think it is reasonable to write

$$\lim_{x \to 2^-} \frac{1}{x - 2} = -\infty \quad \text{and} \quad \lim_{x \to 2^+} \frac{1}{x - 2} = \infty$$

Here is the precise definition.

Definition **Infinite Limit**

We say that $\lim_{x \to c^+} f(x) = \infty$ if for every positive number M, there exists a corresponding $\delta > 0$ such that

$$0 < x - c < \delta \Rightarrow f(x) > M$$

In other words, $f(x)$ can be made as large as we wish (greater than any M that we choose) by taking x to be sufficiently close to but to the right of c. There are corresponding definitions of

$$\lim_{x \to c^+} f(x) = -\infty \qquad \lim_{x \to c^-} f(x) = \infty \qquad \lim_{x \to c^-} f(x) = -\infty$$

$$\lim_{x \to \infty} f(x) = \infty \qquad \lim_{x \to \infty} f(x) = -\infty \qquad \lim_{x \to -\infty} f(x) = \infty \qquad \lim_{x \to -\infty} f(x) = -\infty$$

(See Problems 51 and 52.)

EXAMPLE 5 Find $\lim_{x \to 1^-} \dfrac{1}{(x - 1)^2}$ and $\lim_{x \to 1^+} \dfrac{1}{(x - 1)^2}$.

SOLUTION The graph of $f(x) = 1/(x - 1)^2$ is shown in Figure 7. As $x \to 1^+$, the denominator remains positive but goes to zero, while the numerator is 1 for all x. Thus, the ratio $1/(x - 1)^2$ can be made arbitrarily large by restricting x to be near, but to the right of, 1. Similarly, as $x \to 1^-$, the denominator is positive and can be made arbitrarily close to 0. Thus $1/(x - 1)^2$ can be made arbitrarily large by restricting x to be near, but to the left of, 1. We therefore conclude that

$$\lim_{x \to 1^+} \frac{1}{(x - 1)^2} = \infty \quad \text{and} \quad \lim_{x \to 1^-} \frac{1}{(x - 1)^2} = \infty$$

Since both limits are ∞, we could also write

$$\lim_{x \to 1} \frac{1}{(x - 1)^2} = \infty$$

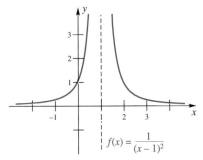

Figure 7

EXAMPLE 6 Find $\lim_{x \to 2^+} \dfrac{x + 1}{x^2 - 5x + 6}$.

SOLUTION

$$\lim_{x \to 2^+} \frac{x + 1}{x^2 - 5x + 6} = \lim_{x \to 2^+} \frac{x + 1}{(x - 3)(x - 2)}$$

As $x \to 2^+$ we see that $x + 1 \to 3$, $x - 3 \to -1$, and $x - 2 \to 0^+$; thus, the numerator is approaching 3, but the denominator is negative and approaching 0. We conclude that

$$\lim_{x \to 2^+} \frac{x + 1}{(x - 3)(x - 2)} = -\infty$$

<table>
<tr><td>

Do Infinite Limits Exist?

In previous sections we required that a limit be equal to a real number. For example, we said that

$$\lim_{x \to 2^+} \frac{1}{x - 2}$$ does not exist because

$1/(x - 2)$ does not approach a real number as x approaches 2 from the right. Many mathematicians maintain that this limit does not exist even though we write

$$\lim_{x \to 2^+} \frac{1}{x - 2} = \infty;$$ to say that the

limit is ∞ is to describe the particular way in which the limit does not exist. Here we will use the phrase "exists in the infinite sense" to describe such limits.

</td></tr>
</table>

Relation to Asymptotes Asymptotes were discussed briefly in Section 1.5, but now we can say more about them. The line $x = c$ is a **vertical asymptote** of the graph of $y = f(x)$ if any of the following four statements is true.

1. $\lim_{x \to c^+} f(x) = \infty$ 2. $\lim_{x \to c^+} f(x) = -\infty$

3. $\lim_{x \to c^-} f(x) = \infty$ 4. $\lim_{x \to c^-} f(x) = -\infty$

Thus, in Figure 6, the line $x = 2$ is a vertical asymptote. Likewise, the lines $x = 2$ and $x = 3$, although not shown graphically, are vertical asymptotes in Example 6.

In a similar vein, the line $y = b$ is a **horizontal asymptote** of the graph of $y = f(x)$ if either

$$\lim_{x \to \infty} f(x) = b \quad \text{or} \quad \lim_{x \to -\infty} f(x) = b$$

The line $y = 0$ is a horizontal asymptote in both Figures 6 and 7.

EXAMPLE 7 Find the vertical and horizontal asymptotes of the graph of $y = f(x)$ if

$$f(x) = \frac{2x}{x - 1}$$

SOLUTION We often have a vertical asymptote at a point where the denominator is zero, and in this case we do because

$$\lim_{x \to 1^+} \frac{2x}{x - 1} = \infty \quad \text{and} \quad \lim_{x \to 1^-} \frac{2x}{x - 1} = -\infty$$

On the other hand,

$$\lim_{x \to \infty} \frac{2x}{x - 1} = \lim_{x \to \infty} \frac{2}{1 - 1/x} = 2 \quad \text{and} \quad \lim_{x \to -\infty} \frac{2x}{x - 1} = 2$$

and so $y = 2$ is a horizontal asymptote. The graph of $y = 2x/(x - 1)$ is shown in Figure 8. ■

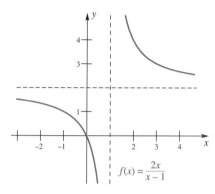

$$f(x) = \frac{2x}{x - 1}$$

Figure 8

Concepts Review

1. To say that $x \to \infty$ means that _____; to say that $\lim_{x \to \infty} f(x) = L$ means that _____. Give your answers in informal language.

2. To say that $\lim_{x \to c^+} f(x) = \infty$ means that _____; to say that $\lim_{x \to c^-} f(x) = -\infty$ means that _____. Give your answers in informal language.

3. If $\lim_{x \to \infty} f(x) = 6$, then the line _____ is a _____ asymptote of the graph of $y = f(x)$.

4. If $\lim_{x \to 6^+} f(x) = \infty$, then the line _____ is a _____ asymptote of the graph of $y = f(x)$.

Problem Set 2.4

In Problems 1–42, find the limits.

1. $\lim_{x \to \infty} \dfrac{x}{x - 5}$

2. $\lim_{x \to \infty} \dfrac{x^2}{5 - x^3}$

3. $\lim_{t \to -\infty} \dfrac{t^2}{7 - t^2}$

4. $\lim_{t \to -\infty} \dfrac{t}{t - 5}$

5. $\lim_{x \to \infty} \dfrac{x^2}{(x - 5)(3 - x)}$

6. $\lim_{x \to \infty} \dfrac{x^2}{x^2 - 8x + 15}$

7. $\lim_{x \to \infty} \dfrac{x^3}{2x^3 - 100x^2}$

8. $\lim_{\theta \to -\infty} \dfrac{\pi \theta^5}{\theta^5 - 5\theta^4}$

9. $\lim_{x \to \infty} \dfrac{3x^3 - x^2}{\pi x^3 - 5x^2}$

10. $\lim_{\theta \to \infty} \dfrac{\sin^2 \theta}{\theta^2 - 5}$

11. $\lim_{x \to \infty} \dfrac{3\sqrt{x^3} + 3x}{\sqrt{2x^3}}$

12. $\lim_{x \to \infty} \sqrt[3]{\dfrac{\pi x^3 + 3x}{\sqrt{2x^3} + 7x}}$

13. $\lim_{x \to \infty} \sqrt[3]{\dfrac{1 + 8x^2}{x^2 + 4}}$

14. $\lim_{x \to \infty} \sqrt{\dfrac{x^2 + x + 3}{(x - 1)(x + 1)}}$

15. $\lim_{n \to \infty} \dfrac{n}{2n + 1}$

16. $\lim_{n \to \infty} \dfrac{n^2}{n^2 + 1}$

17. $\displaystyle\lim_{n\to\infty}\frac{n^2}{n+1}$

18. $\displaystyle\lim_{n\to\infty}\frac{n}{n^2+1}$

19. $\displaystyle\lim_{x\to\infty}\frac{2x+1}{\sqrt{x^2+3}}$. *Hint:* Divide numerator and denominator by x. Note that, for $x>0$, $\sqrt{x^2+3}/x=\sqrt{(x^2+3)/x^2}$.

20. $\displaystyle\lim_{x\to\infty}\frac{\sqrt{2x+1}}{x+4}$

21. $\displaystyle\lim_{x\to\infty}\left(\sqrt{2x^2+3}-\sqrt{2x^2-5}\right)$. *Hint:* Multiply and divide by $\sqrt{2x^2+3}+\sqrt{2x^2-5}$.

22. $\displaystyle\lim_{x\to\infty}\left(\sqrt{x^2+2x}-x\right)$

23. $\displaystyle\lim_{y\to-\infty}\frac{9y^3+1}{y^2-2y+2}$. *Hint:* Divide numerator and denominator by y^2.

24. $\displaystyle\lim_{x\to\infty}\frac{a_0x^n+a_1x^{n-1}+\cdots+a_{n-1}x+a_n}{b_0x^n+b_1x^{n-1}+\cdots+b_{n-1}x+b_n}$, where $a_0\neq0$, $b_0\neq0$, and n is a natural number.

25. $\displaystyle\lim_{n\to\infty}\frac{n}{\sqrt{n^2+1}}$

26. $\displaystyle\lim_{n\to\infty}\frac{n^2}{\sqrt{n^3+2n+1}}$

27. $\displaystyle\lim_{x\to4^+}\frac{x}{x-4}$

28. $\displaystyle\lim_{t\to-3^+}\frac{t^2-9}{t+3}$

29. $\displaystyle\lim_{t\to3^-}\frac{t^2}{9-t^2}$

30. $\displaystyle\lim_{x\to\sqrt[3]{5}^+}\frac{x^2}{5-x^3}$

31. $\displaystyle\lim_{x\to5^-}\frac{x^2}{(x-5)(3-x)}$

32. $\displaystyle\lim_{\theta\to\pi^+}\frac{\theta^2}{\sin\theta}$

33. $\displaystyle\lim_{x\to3^-}\frac{x^3}{x-3}$

34. $\displaystyle\lim_{\theta\to(\pi/2)^+}\frac{\pi\theta}{\cos\theta}$

35. $\displaystyle\lim_{x\to3^-}\frac{x^2-x-6}{x-3}$

36. $\displaystyle\lim_{x\to2^+}\frac{x^2+2x-8}{x^2-4}$

37. $\displaystyle\lim_{x\to0^+}\frac{[\![x]\!]}{x}$

38. $\displaystyle\lim_{x\to0^-}\frac{[\![x]\!]}{x}$

39. $\displaystyle\lim_{x\to0^-}\frac{|x|}{x}$

40. $\displaystyle\lim_{x\to0^+}\frac{|x|}{x}$

41. $\displaystyle\lim_{x\to0^-}\frac{1+\cos x}{\sin x}$

42. $\displaystyle\lim_{x\to\infty}\frac{\sin x}{x}$

GC *In Problems 43–48, find the horizontal and vertical asymptotes for the graphs of the indicated functions. Then sketch their graphs.*

43. $f(x)=\dfrac{3}{x+1}$

44. $f(x)=\dfrac{3}{(x+1)^2}$

45. $F(x)=\dfrac{2x}{x-3}$

46. $F(x)=\dfrac{3}{9-x^2}$

47. $g(x)=\dfrac{14}{2x^2+7}$

48. $g(x)=\dfrac{2x}{\sqrt{x^2+5}}$

49. The line $y=ax+b$ is called an **oblique asymptote** to the graph of $y=f(x)$ if either $\displaystyle\lim_{x\to\infty}[f(x)-(ax+b)]=0$ or $\displaystyle\lim_{x\to-\infty}[f(x)-(ax+b)]=0$. Find the oblique asymptote for
$$f(x)=\frac{2x^4+3x^3-2x-4}{x^3-1}$$

Hint: Begin by dividing the denominator into the numerator.

50. Find the oblique asymptote for
$$f(x)=\frac{3x^3+4x^2-x+1}{x^2+1}$$

51. Using the symbols M and δ, give precise definitions of each expression.

(a) $\displaystyle\lim_{x\to c^+}f(x)=-\infty$

(b) $\displaystyle\lim_{x\to c^-}f(x)=\infty$

52. Using the symbols M and N, give precise definitions of each expression.

(a) $\displaystyle\lim_{x\to\infty}f(x)=\infty$

(b) $\displaystyle\lim_{x\to-\infty}f(x)=\infty$

53. Give a rigorous proof that if $\displaystyle\lim_{x\to\infty}f(x)=A$ and $\displaystyle\lim_{x\to\infty}g(x)=B$, then
$$\lim_{x\to\infty}[f(x)+g(x)]=A+B$$

54. We have given meaning to $\displaystyle\lim_{x\to A}f(x)$ for $A=a$, $a^-,a^+,-\infty,\infty$. Moreover, in each case, this limit may be L (finite), $-\infty$, ∞, or may fail to exist in any sense. Make a table illustrating each of the 20 possible cases.

55. Find each of the following limits or indicate that it does not exist even in the infinite sense.

(a) $\displaystyle\lim_{x\to\infty}\sin x$

(b) $\displaystyle\lim_{x\to\infty}\sin\frac{1}{x}$

(c) $\displaystyle\lim_{x\to\infty}x\sin\frac{1}{x}$

(d) $\displaystyle\lim_{x\to\infty}x^{3/2}\sin\frac{1}{x}$

(e) $\displaystyle\lim_{x\to\infty}x^{-1/2}\sin x$

(f) $\displaystyle\lim_{x\to\infty}\sin\left(\frac{\pi}{6}+\frac{1}{x}\right)$

(g) $\displaystyle\lim_{x\to\infty}\sin\left(x+\frac{1}{x}\right)$

(h) $\displaystyle\lim_{x\to\infty}\left[\sin\left(x+\frac{1}{x}\right)-\sin x\right]$

56. Einstein's Special Theory of Relativity says that the mass $m(v)$ of an object is related to its velocity v by
$$m(v)=\frac{m_0}{\sqrt{1-v^2/c^2}}$$

Here m_0 is the rest mass and c is the velocity of light. What is $\displaystyle\lim_{v\to c^-}m(v)$?

GC *Use a computer or a graphing calculator to find the limits in Problems 57–64. Begin by plotting the function in an appropriate window.*

57. $\displaystyle\lim_{x\to\infty}\frac{3x^2+x+1}{2x^2-1}$

58. $\displaystyle\lim_{x\to-\infty}\sqrt{\frac{2x^2-3x}{5x^2+1}}$

59. $\displaystyle\lim_{x\to-\infty}\left(\sqrt{2x^2+3x}-\sqrt{2x^2-5}\right)$

60. $\displaystyle\lim_{x\to\infty}\frac{2x+1}{\sqrt{3x^2+1}}$

61. $\displaystyle\lim_{x\to\infty}\left(1+\frac{1}{x}\right)^{10}$

62. $\displaystyle\lim_{x\to\infty}\left(1+\frac{1}{x}\right)^{x}$

63. $\displaystyle\lim_{x\to\infty}\left(1+\frac{1}{x}\right)^{x^2}$

64. $\displaystyle\lim_{x\to\infty}\left(1+\frac{1}{x}\right)^{\sin x}$

CAS *Find the one-sided limits in Problems 65–71. Begin by plotting the function in an appropriate window. Your computer may indicate that some of these limits do not exist, but, if so, you should be able to interpret the answer as either ∞ or $-\infty$.*

65. $\displaystyle\lim_{x\to3^-}\frac{\sin|x-3|}{x-3}$

66. $\displaystyle\lim_{x\to3^-}\frac{\sin|x-3|}{\tan(x-3)}$

67. $\displaystyle\lim_{x\to 3^-}\frac{\cos(x-3)}{x-3}$

68. $\displaystyle\lim_{x\to\frac{\pi}{2}^+}\frac{\cos x}{x-\pi/2}$

69. $\displaystyle\lim_{x\to 0^+}\left(1+\sqrt{x}\right)^{1/\sqrt{x}}$

70. $\displaystyle\lim_{x\to 0^+}\left(1+\sqrt{x}\right)^{1/x}$

71. $\displaystyle\lim_{x\to 0^+}\left(1+\sqrt{x}\right)^{x}$

Answers to Concepts Review: **1.** x increases without bound; $f(x)$ gets close to L as x increases without bound **2.** $f(x)$ increases without bound as x approaches c from the right; $f(x)$ decreases without bound as x approaches c from the left **3.** $y = 6$; horizontal **4.** $x = 6$; vertical

---

2.5
Limits Involving Trigonometric Functions

Theorem B of Section 2.3 says that limits of polynomial functions can always be found by substitution, and limits of rational functions can be found by substitution as long as the denominator is not zero at the limit point. This substitution rule applies to the trigonometric functions as well. This result is stated next.

Theorem A	Limits of Trigonometric Functions

For every real number c in the function's domain,

1. $\displaystyle\lim_{t\to c}\sin t = \sin c$ 2. $\displaystyle\lim_{t\to c}\cos t = \cos c$

3. $\displaystyle\lim_{t\to c}\tan t = \tan c$ 4. $\displaystyle\lim_{t\to c}\cot t = \cot c$

5. $\displaystyle\lim_{t\to c}\sec t = \sec c$ 6. $\displaystyle\lim_{t\to c}\csc t = \csc c$

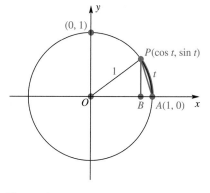

Figure 1

Proof of Statement 1 We first establish the special case in which $c = 0$. Suppose that $t > 0$ and let points A, B, and P be defined as in Figure 1. Then

$$0 < |BP| < |AP| < \operatorname{arc}(AP)$$

But $|BP| = \sin t$ and arc $(AP) = t$, so

$$0 < \sin t < t$$

If $t < 0$, then $t < \sin t < 0$. We can thus apply the Squeeze Theorem (Theorem 2.3D) and conclude that $\displaystyle\lim_{t\to 0}\sin t = 0$. To complete the proof, we will also need the result that $\displaystyle\lim_{t\to 0}\cos t = 1$. This follows by applying a trigonometric identity and Theorem 2.3A along with the fact that for t near 0, $\cos t = \sqrt{1-\sin^2 t}$:

$$\lim_{t\to 0}\cos t = \lim_{t\to 0}\sqrt{1-\sin^2 t} = \sqrt{1-\left(\lim_{t\to 0}\sin t\right)^2} = \sqrt{1-0^2} = 1$$

Now, to show that $\displaystyle\lim_{t\to c}\sin t = \sin c$, we first let $h = t - c$ so that $h \to 0$ as $t \to c$. Then

$$\lim_{t\to c}\sin t = \lim_{h\to 0}\sin(c+h)$$
$$= \lim_{h\to 0}\left(\sin c \cos h + \cos c \sin h\right) \qquad (\text{Addition Identity})$$
$$= (\sin c)\left(\lim_{h\to 0}\cos h\right) + (\cos c)\left(\lim_{h\to 0}\sin h\right)$$
$$= (\sin c)(1) + (\cos c)(0) = \sin c \qquad\blacksquare$$

Proof of Statement 2 We use another identity along with Theorem 2.3A. If $\cos c > 0$, then for t near c we have $\cos t = \sqrt{1-\sin^2 t}$. Thus,

$$\lim_{t\to c}\cos t = \lim_{t\to c}\sqrt{1-\sin^2 t} = \sqrt{1-\left(\lim_{t\to c}\sin t\right)^2} = \sqrt{1-\sin^2 c} = \cos c$$

On the other hand, if $\cos c < 0$, then for t near c we have $\cos t = -\sqrt{1-\sin^2 t}$. In this case,

$$\lim_{t\to c}\cos t = \lim_{t\to c}\left(-\sqrt{1-\sin^2 t}\right) = -\sqrt{1-\left(\lim_{t\to c}\sin t\right)^2} = -\sqrt{1-\sin^2 c}$$
$$= -\sqrt{\cos^2 c} = -|\cos c| = \cos c$$

The case $c = 0$ was handled in the proof of Statement 1. $\qquad\blacksquare$

The proofs for the other statements are left as exercises. (See Problems 21 and 22.) Theorem A can be used along with Theorem 2.3A to evaluate other limits.

EXAMPLE 1 Find $\lim\limits_{t \to 0} \dfrac{t^2 \cos t}{t + 1}$.

SOLUTION

$$\lim_{t \to 0} \frac{t^2 \cos t}{t + 1} = \left(\lim_{t \to 0} \frac{t^2}{t + 1} \right) \left(\lim_{t \to 0} \cos t \right) = 0 \cdot 1 = 0 \qquad \blacksquare$$

Two important limits that we cannot evaluate by substitution are

$$\lim_{t \to 0} \frac{\sin t}{t} \quad \text{and} \quad \lim_{t \to 0} \frac{1 - \cos t}{t}$$

We met the first of these limits in Section 2.1, where we conjectured that the limit was 1. Now we prove that 1 is indeed the limit.

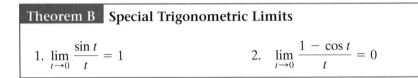

Theorem B	**Special Trigonometric Limits**

1. $\lim\limits_{t \to 0} \dfrac{\sin t}{t} = 1$ 2. $\lim\limits_{t \to 0} \dfrac{1 - \cos t}{t} = 0$

Proof of Statement 1 In the proof of Theorem A of this section, we showed that

$$\lim_{t \to 0} \cos t = 1 \quad \text{and} \quad \lim_{t \to 0} \sin t = 0$$

For $-\pi/2 \le t \le \pi/2, t \ne 0$ (remember, it does not matter what happens at $t = 0$), draw the vertical line segment BP and the circular arc BC, as shown in Figure 2. (If $t < 0$, then think of the shaded region as being reflected across the x-axis.) It is evident from Figure 2 that

$$\text{area (sector } OBC) \le \text{area } (\Delta OBP) \le \text{area (sector } OAP)$$

The area of a triangle is one-half its base times the height, and the area of a circular sector with central angle t and radius r is $\frac{1}{2} r^2 |t|$ (see Problem 42 of Section 1.8). Applying these results to the three regions gives

$$\frac{1}{2} (\cos t)^2 |t| \le \frac{1}{2} \cos t \, |\sin t| \le \frac{1}{2} 1^2 |t|$$

which, after multiplying by 2 and dividing by the positive number $|t| \cos t$, yields

$$\cos t \le \frac{|\sin t|}{|t|} \le \frac{1}{\cos t}$$

Since the expression $(\sin t)/t$ is positive for $-\pi/2 \le t \le \pi/2, t \ne 0$, we have $|\sin t|/|t| = (\sin t)/t$. Therefore,

$$\cos t \le \frac{\sin t}{t} \le \frac{1}{\cos t}$$

Since we are after the limit of the middle function and we know the limit of each "outside" function, this double inequality begs for the Squeeze Theorem. When we apply it, we get

$$\lim_{t \to 0} \frac{\sin t}{t} = 1 \qquad \blacksquare$$

Proof of Statement 2 The second limit follows easily from the first. Just multiply the numerator and denominator by $(1 + \cos t)$; this gives

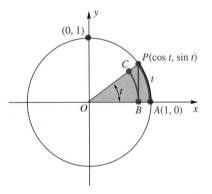

Figure 2

$$\lim_{t \to 0} \frac{1 - \cos t}{t} = \lim_{t \to 0} \frac{1 - \cos t}{t} \cdot \frac{1 + \cos t}{1 + \cos t} = \lim_{t \to 0} \frac{1 - \cos^2 t}{t(1 + \cos t)}$$

$$= \lim_{t \to 0} \frac{\sin^2 t}{t(1 + \cos t)}$$

$$= \left(\lim_{t \to 0} \frac{\sin t}{t} \right) \frac{\lim_{t \to 0} \sin t}{\lim_{t \to 0} (1 + \cos t)} = 1 \cdot \frac{0}{2} = 0 \qquad \blacksquare$$

We will make explicit use of these two limit statements in Chapter 3. Right now, we can use them to evaluate other limits.

EXAMPLE 2 Find each limit.

(a) $\displaystyle \lim_{x \to 0} \frac{\sin 3x}{x}$
(b) $\displaystyle \lim_{t \to 0} \frac{1 - \cos t}{\sin t}$
(c) $\displaystyle \lim_{x \to 0} \frac{\sin 4x}{\tan x}$

SOLUTION

(a) $\displaystyle \lim_{x \to 0} \frac{\sin 3x}{x} = \lim_{x \to 0} 3 \frac{\sin 3x}{3x} = 3 \lim_{x \to 0} \frac{\sin 3x}{3x}$

Here the argument to the sine function is $3x$, not simply x as required by Theorem B. Let $y = 3x$. Then $y \to 0$ if and only if $x \to 0$, so

$$\lim_{x \to 0} \frac{\sin 3x}{3x} = \lim_{y \to 0} \frac{\sin y}{y} = 1$$

Thus,

$$\lim_{x \to 0} \frac{\sin 3x}{x} = 3 \lim_{x \to 0} \frac{\sin 3x}{3x} = 3$$

(b)
$$\lim_{t \to 0} \frac{1 - \cos t}{\sin t} = \lim_{t \to 0} \frac{\dfrac{1 - \cos t}{t}}{\dfrac{\sin t}{t}} = \frac{\lim_{t \to 0} \dfrac{1 - \cos t}{t}}{\lim_{t \to 0} \dfrac{\sin t}{t}} = \frac{0}{1} = 0$$

(c)
$$\lim_{x \to 0} \frac{\sin 4x}{\tan x} = \lim_{x \to 0} \frac{\dfrac{4 \sin 4x}{4x}}{\dfrac{\sin x}{x \cos x}}$$

$$= \frac{4 \lim_{x \to 0} \dfrac{\sin 4x}{4x}}{\left(\lim_{x \to 0} \dfrac{\sin x}{x} \right) \left(\lim_{x \to 0} \dfrac{1}{\cos x} \right)} = \frac{4}{1 \cdot 1} = 4 \qquad \blacksquare$$

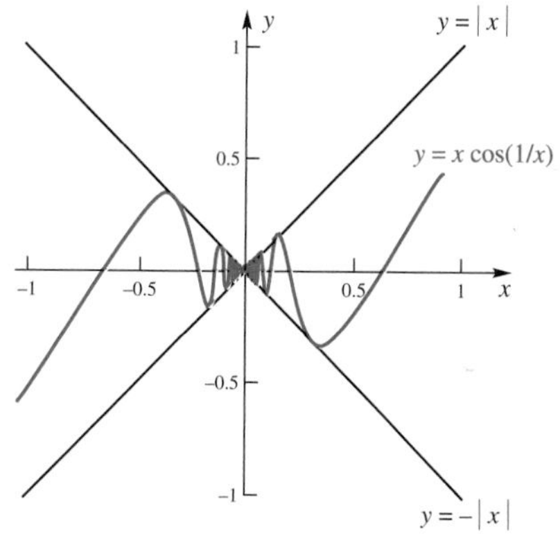

Figure 3

EXAMPLE 3 Sketch the graphs of $u(x) = |x|$, $l(x) = -|x|$, and $f(x) = x \cos(1/x)$. Use these graphs along with the Squeeze Theorem (Theorem D of Section 2.3) to determine $\lim_{x \to 0} f(x)$.

SOLUTION Note that $\cos(1/x)$ is always between -1 and 1. Thus, $x \cos(1/x)$ will always be between $-x$ and x if x is positive and between x and $-x$ if x is negative. In other words, the graph of $y = x \cos(1/x)$ is between the graphs of $y = |x|$ and $y = -|x|$, as shown in Figure 3. We know that $\lim_{x \to 0} |x| = \lim_{x \to 0} (-|x|) = 0$ (see Problem 27 of Section 2.2) and since the graph of $y = f(x) = x \cos(1/x)$ is "squeezed" between the graphs of $u(x) = |x|$ and $l(x) = -|x|$, both of which go to 0 as $x \to 0$, we can apply the Squeeze Theorem to conclude that $\lim_{x \to 0} f(x) = 0$. $\qquad \blacksquare$

Concepts Review

1. $\lim\limits_{t \to 0} \sin t = $ _____.

2. $\lim\limits_{t \to \pi/4} \tan t = $ _____.

3. The limit $\lim\limits_{t \to 0} \dfrac{\sin t}{t}$ cannot be evaluated by substitution because _____.

4. $\lim\limits_{t \to 0} \dfrac{\sin t}{t} = $ _____.

Problem Set 2.5

In Problems 1–14, evaluate each limit.

1. $\lim\limits_{x \to 0} \dfrac{\cos x}{x + 1}$

2. $\lim\limits_{\theta \to \pi/2} \theta \cos \theta$

3. $\lim\limits_{t \to 0} \dfrac{\cos^2 t}{1 + \sin t}$

4. $\lim\limits_{x \to 0} \dfrac{3x \tan x}{\sin x}$

5. $\lim\limits_{x \to 0} \dfrac{\sin x}{2x}$

6. $\lim\limits_{\theta \to 0} \dfrac{\sin 3\theta}{2\theta}$

7. $\lim\limits_{\theta \to 0} \dfrac{\sin 3\theta}{\tan \theta}$

8. $\lim\limits_{\theta \to 0} \dfrac{\tan 5\theta}{\sin 2\theta}$

9. $\lim\limits_{\theta \to 0} \dfrac{\cot (\pi\theta) \sin \theta}{2 \sec \theta}$

10. $\lim\limits_{t \to 0} \dfrac{\sin^2 3t}{2t}$

11. $\lim\limits_{t \to 0} \dfrac{\tan^2 3t}{2t}$

12. $\lim\limits_{t \to 0} \dfrac{\tan 2t}{\sin 2t - 1}$

13. $\lim\limits_{t \to 0} \dfrac{\sin 3t + 4t}{t \sec t}$

14. $\lim\limits_{\theta \to 0} \dfrac{\sin^2 \theta}{\theta^2}$

In Problems 15–19, plot the functions $u(x)$, $l(x)$, and $f(x)$. Then use these graphs along with the Squeeze Theorem to determine $\lim\limits_{x \to 0} f(x)$.

15. $u(x) = |x|, l(x) = -|x|, f(x) = x \sin(1/x)$

16. $u(x) = |x|, l(x) = -|x|, f(x) = x \sin(1/x^2)$

17. $u(x) = |x|, l(x) = -|x|, f(x) = (1 - \cos^2 x)/x$

18. $u(x) = 1, l(x) = 1 - x^2, f(x) = \cos^2 x$

19. $u(x) = 2, l(x) = 2 - x^2, f(x) = 1 + \dfrac{\sin x}{x}$

20. Prove that $\lim\limits_{t \to c} \cos t = \cos c$ using an argument similar to the one used in the proof that $\lim\limits_{t \to c} \sin t = \sin c$.

21. Prove statements 3 and 4 of Theorem A using Theorem 2.3A.

22. Prove statements 5 and 6 of Theorem A using Theorem 2.3A.

23. From area $(OBP) \leq$ area (sector OAP) $\leq$ area (OBP) + area $(ABPQ)$ in Figure 4, show that

$$\cos t \leq \dfrac{t}{\sin t} \leq 2 - \cos t$$

and thus obtain another proof that $\lim\limits_{t \to 0^+} (\sin t)/t = 1$.

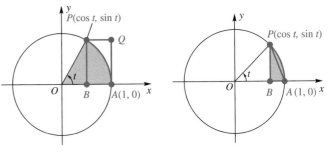

Figure 4   Figure 5

24. In Figure 5, let D be the area of triangle ABP and E the area of the shaded region.

(a) Guess the value of $\lim\limits_{t \to 0^+} \dfrac{D}{E}$ by looking at the figure.

(b) Find a formula for D/E in terms of t.

[C] (c) Use a calculator to get an accurate estimate of $\lim\limits_{t \to 0^+} \dfrac{D}{E}$.

Answers to Concepts Review: **1.** 0 **2.** 1 **3.** the denominator is zero when $t = 0$ **4.** 1

2.6

Natural Exponential, Natural Log, and Hyperbolic Functions

In Section 1.7, we presented an informal discussion of exponential and logarithmic functions. There were defined a^r $(a > 0)$ for rational values of r and we suggested that if we take an accurate (rational) approximation to an irrational number x, and raise a to that power we would obtain a close approximation of a^x. We would now like to make this idea more precise.

> **Definition**
>
> If r_n is a sequence of rational numbers that converges to the irrational number x, then a^x is defined to be
>
> $$a^x = \lim_{n \to \infty} a^{r_n}$$

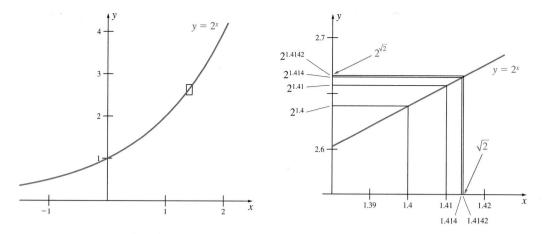

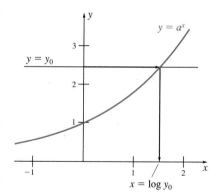

Figure 1

Figure 2

This defintion, which is illustrated in Figure 1, raises two important questions that we will address informally.

First, for a given irrational number x, is there such a sequence? The answer to this is yes. We could take as the nth term of the sequence of rational numbers the decimal expansion through the first n places of the number x. (Recall from Section 1.1 that an irrational number has a nonrepeating decimal expansion.) For example, $\sqrt{2}$ is the limit of the sequence

$$r_1 = 1.4, \ r_2 = 1.41, \ r_3 = 1.414, \ \ldots, \ r_{20} = 1.4142135623730950488, \ldots$$

This provides an increasing sequence of rational numbers, that is, $r_1 < r_2 < \ldots < r_n < r_{n+1} < \ldots < \sqrt{2}$, that converges to $\sqrt{2}$. We could as well have rounded up in the decimal expansion of $\sqrt{2}$, producing a decreasing sequence of rational numbers that converges to $\sqrt{2}$.

Second, what if two sequences of rational numbers, say r_n and s_n, both converge to x? Do we know that $\lim_{n \to \infty} a^{r_n} = \lim_{n \to \infty} a^{s_n}$? The answer is again yes, but this is more difficult to prove, and we omit a proof. Intuitively, the result is plausible because if r_n and s_n both converge to x, then for n sufficiently large, $|r_n - s_n|$ can be made arbitrarily small, and so $|a^{r_n} - a^{s_n}|$ will be small. This last step requires more justification than we can give it here. Books on advanced calculus or real analysis will contain a proof.

Another important question is this: does the exponential function described here have an inverse? In Chapter 1, we assumed that it did and defined the logarithmic function $\log_a x$ as the inverse of a^x (as long as $a > 0$ and $a \neq 1$). Graphs of exponential functions (Figure 2) suggest that every horizontal line of the form $y = y_0$, where $y_0 > 0$, will intersect the graph of $y = a^x$ exactly once (as long as $a \neq 1$), making the exponential function invertible. While we cannot give a rigorous proof of this, we assert that it is true, and proceed to discuss properties of exponential and logarithmic functions.

The next theorem restates the results of Theorem A and B of Section 1.7.

Theorem A	Properties of Exponential and Logarithmic Functions

If $a > 0, b > 0, c > 0, (c \neq 1)$ and x and y are real numbers, then

(1) $a^x a^y = a^{x+y}$ (2) $\dfrac{a^x}{a^y} = a^{x-y}$

(3) $(a^x)^y = a^{xy}$ (4) $a^{-x} = \dfrac{1}{a^x}$

(5) $(ab)^x = a^x b^x$ (6) $\left(\dfrac{a}{b}\right)^x = \dfrac{a^x}{b^x}$

(7) $\log_c 1 = 0$ (8) $\log_c ab = \log_c a + \log_c b$

(9) $\log_c \dfrac{a}{b} = \log_c a - \log_c b$ (10) $\log_c a^x = x \log_c a$

Proof We prove (1) and leave the proofs of parts (2) through (6) as an exercise (Problem 53). The proofs given in Section 1.7 for (7) through (10) are now valid once we have proved the results for exponents.

We assume that (1) is true for rational exponents and prove it for the case where at least one of the exponents is irrational. Let x be irrational and y be either rational or irrational. Suppose r_n and s_n are sequences of rational numbers satisfying

$$\lim_{n\to\infty} r_n = x \quad \text{and} \quad \lim_{n\to\infty} s_n = y$$

(Note, if y is rational, then the constant sequence $s_n = y$ for all n would do.) Then, since $\lim_{n\to\infty} (r_n + s_n) = x + y$,

$$a^x a^y = \left(\lim_{n\to\infty} a^{r_n}\right)\left(\lim_{n\to\infty} a^{s_n}\right) = \lim_{n\to\infty} (a^{r_n} a^{s_n}) = \lim_{n\to\infty} a^{r_n+s_n} = a^{x+y} \qquad \blacksquare$$

The first part of the next theorem is a "substitution result," analogous to Theorems 2.3B and 2.5A. The proof is rather difficult, but an outline of the proof is provided in Problem 56.

Theorem B | **Limits of Exponential Functions**

(1) $\lim_{x\to c} a^x = a^c$

(2) If $a > 1$, then $\lim_{x\to\infty} a^x = \infty$

(3) If $a > 1$, then $\lim_{x\to-\infty} a^x = 0$

We would like to have an analogous theorem for logarithms, or in general, the inverse of any given function. The next theorem provides us with the needed result.

Theorem C | **Limits for Inverse Functions**

If f has an inverse and $\lim_{x\to a} f(x) = f(a) = c$, then $\lim_{x\to c} f^{-1}(x) = f^{-1}(c) = a$.

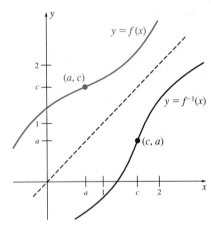

Figure 3

While Figure 3 makes this result plausible, the proof is rather difficult and we omit it. Theorem C also holds for one-sided limits, provided we approach a and c from the correct direction. For example, if f is increasing and $\lim_{x\to a^-} f(x) = f(a) = c$, then $\lim_{x\to c^-} f^{-1}(x) = f^{-1}(c) = a$, but if f is decreasing and $\lim_{x\to a^-} f(x) = f(a) = c$, then $\lim_{x\to c^+} f^{-1}(x) = f^{-1}(c) = a$. We will use this result in Section 2.7.

Theorem D | **Limits of Logarithmic Functions**

(1) If $a > 0$ and $c > 0$, $(c \neq 1)$, then $\lim_{x\to a} \log_c x = \log_c a$.

(2) If $c > 1$, then $\lim_{x\to\infty} \log_c x = \infty$.

(3) If $c > 1$, then $\lim_{x\to 0^+} \log_c x = -\infty$.

Proof Part (1) follows directly from Theorems B(1) and C. Parts (2) and (3) follow from Theorem B and symmetry. $\blacksquare$

EXAMPLE 1 Evaluate the limits (a) $\lim_{x\to\infty} \left(\dfrac{3}{2}\right)^{x^2}$ and (b) $\lim_{x\to\infty} \log_2\left(\dfrac{1}{x}\right)$.

SOLUTION

(a) As $x \to \infty$, the exponent x^2 grows without bound. Since $\frac{3}{2} > 1$, we can apply Theorem B(2) and conclude

$$\lim_{x \to \infty} \left(\frac{3}{2}\right)^{x^2} = \infty$$

(b) As $x \to \infty$, the expression $1/x$ goes to zero from the right. Thus, by Theorem D(3), we conclude

$$\lim_{x \to \infty} \log_2\left(\frac{1}{x}\right) = -\infty \qquad \blacksquare$$

The Natural Exponential Function and the Natural Logarithm If you invest \$100 at the rate of 6% annual interest, then after one year you would have $100(1 + 0.06) = 106.00. If interest is compounded twice per year, then for the second half of the year, you would receive interest on your interest. You would earn $6\%/2 = 3\%$ for the first six months, and another 3% for the second six months, so you would have $100(1.03)(1.03) = 106.09. If interest were compounded monthly, you would have $100(1 + 0.06/12)^{12} = 106.17$. In general, if you begin with A_0 dollars and compound interest n times per year at an interest rate of r, then you would have

$$A(1) = A_0\left(1 + \frac{r}{n}\right)^n$$

n	$\left(1 + \dfrac{1}{n}\right)^n$
10	2.5937425
100	2.7048138
1000	2.7169239
10,000	2.7181459
100,000	2.7182682

dollars after one year. A natural question to ask is: what happens to $A(1)$ as the number of compounding periods goes to infinity? Would our return go to infinity? It is clear that the answer hinges on the quantity $(1 + r/n)^n$. Let's investigate a special case of this sequence; specifically let's consider $(1 + 1/n)^n$. From the table in the margin, which shows a few calculations, it seems as if this sequence converges to a number near 2.718. This is the number that we call e. Its decimal expansion is known to thousands of places; the first few digits are

$$e \approx 2.718281828459045$$

Definition **The Number e**

$$e = \lim_{n \to \infty} \left(1 + \frac{1}{n}\right)^n$$

The limit in this definition is the same, whether we regard n as a natural number, the limit then being the limit of a sequence, or as a real number; that is,

$$e = \lim_{n \to \infty} \left(1 + \frac{1}{n}\right)^n = \lim_{x \to \infty} \left(1 + \frac{1}{x}\right)^x$$

If we let $h = 1/x$, then $x \to \infty$ if and only if $h \to 0^+$. Figure 4 suggests (correctly) that the limits as h approaches 0 from the left and right are the same. (See Problem 59.) Thus, another way to specify e is to say

$$e = \lim_{h \to 0} (1 + h)^{1/h}.$$

The limit of the expression $(1 + r/n)^n$ can then be written as

$$\lim_{n \to \infty} \left(1 + \frac{r}{n}\right)^n = \lim_{n \to \infty} \left[\left(1 + \frac{r}{n}\right)^{n/r}\right]^r = \left[\lim_{n \to \infty} \left(1 + \frac{r}{n}\right)^{n/r}\right]^r$$

$$= \left[\lim_{h \to 0} (1 + h)^{1/h}\right]^r = e^r$$

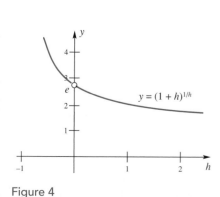

Figure 4

If the number of compounding periods goes to infinity, we say that interest is **compounded continuously.** The amount of money after one year is therefore $A(1) = A_0 e^r$. In general, after t the amount of money is

$$A(t) = A_0 e^{rt}.$$

Money compounded continuously grows this way, but so do other quantities that we will study in Section 4.10.

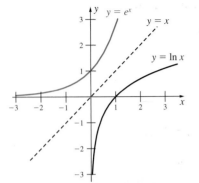

Figure 5

> **Definition** Natural Exponential and Natural Logarithm Functions
>
> The function $\exp(x) = e^x$ is called the natural exponential function, and its inverse, the logarithm to the base e, is called the natural logarithm function; it is denoted $\ln x$.

The natural exponential and logarithmic functions play a key role in this and subsequent chapters. The reason for the name "natural' will become apparent in the next chapter. Most calculators are capable of computing, or even graphing, e^x and $\ln x$. The domain for $\exp(x) = e^x$ is $(-\infty, \infty)$ and the range is $(0, \infty)$. For the natural logarithm function $\ln x$, the domain is $(0, \infty)$ and the range is $(-\infty, \infty)$. Graphs of these functions are shown in Figure 5.

EXAMPLE 2 Suppose $2000 is invested at 8% interest compounded continuously.

(a) How much is this investment worth after 5 years?
(b) How long will it take for the value of the investment to double?

SOLUTION

(a) After 5 years, the value is $A(5) = 2000e^{0.08(5)} = \$2983.60$.

(b) The value of the investment will double at time t_0, where t_0 satisfies

$$4000 = 2000e^{0.08t_0}$$
$$2 = e^{0.08t_0}$$
$$\ln 2 = \ln e^{0.08t_0} = 0.08t_0$$
$$t_0 = \frac{\ln 2}{0.08} \approx 8.66 \text{ years} \qquad \blacksquare$$

EXAMPLE 3 Evaluate the following limits:

$$\text{(a) } \lim_{h \to 0} (1 + h)^{500}, \quad \text{(b) } \lim_{n \to \infty} \left(\frac{n - 2}{n} \right)^{3n}.$$

SOLUTION

(a) Don't let the 500 in the exponent fool you. The exponent, while large, is fixed, so this is just the limit of a polynomial in h. Thus, the limit can be evaluated by substitution.

$$\lim_{h \to 0} (1 + h)^{500} = (1 + 0)^{500} = 1^{500} = 1$$

(b) We can write this as

$$\lim_{n \to \infty} \left(\frac{n - 2}{n} \right)^{3n} = \lim_{n \to \infty} \left[\left(1 + \frac{-2}{n} \right)^{n/(-2)} \right]^{-6} = \left[\lim_{h \to 0} (1 + h)^{1/h} \right]^{-6} = e^{-6} \qquad \blacksquare$$

EXAMPLE 4 Let $f(x) = e^{-x^2/2}$. (a) Find $\lim_{x \to \infty} f(x)$, and (b) graph this function.

SOLUTION

(a) As x grows large, the exponent on e becomes a negative number far to the left of 0. The exponent on e can be made to be to the left of any negative number, so by Theorem B(2), $\lim_{x \to \infty} f(x) = 0$.

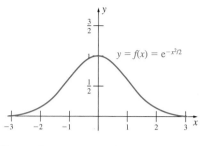

Figure 6

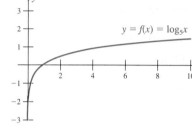

Figure 7

(b) We begin by noting that $f(x) = e^{-x^2/2}$ is an odd function, so its graph is symmetric about the y-axis. Also, $f(x) \geq 0$ for all x and $f(x) \leq e^{-0^2} = 1$. From part (a), $\lim_{x \to \infty} f(x) = 0$, and so by symmetry $\lim_{x \to -\infty} f(x) = 0$. This information, together with some computations of the function for a few values of x, yields the plot shown in Figure 6. ∎

Observe that if $y = \log_a x$, then $x = a^y$, which leads to

$$\ln x = \ln a^y = y \ln a = (\log_a x)(\ln a)$$

From this, the change of base formula follows.

$$\log_a x = \frac{\ln x}{\ln a}$$

EXAMPLE 5   Sketch the graph of $y = f(x) = \log_5 x$.

SOLUTION   We know what shape the graph of a logarithmic function will take, but to graph $y = f(x) = \log_5 x$ we need to find several points on the graph. Calculators usually have keys for common logs (base 10) and natural logs (base e), but usually not other bases. With the change of base formula, we can write

$$y = f(x) = \log_5 x = \frac{\ln x}{\ln 5}$$

With this formula, we could compute a few points on the curve, or, if we have a graphing calculator, we sketch the curve like the one in Figure 7. ∎

Hyperbolic Functions   In both mathematics and science, certain combinations of e^x and e^{-x} occur so often that they are given special names.

Definition   **Hyperbolic Functions**

The hyperbolic sine, hyperbolic cosine, and four related functions are defined by

$$\sinh x = \frac{e^x - e^{-x}}{2} \qquad \cosh x = \frac{e^x + e^{-x}}{2}$$

$$\tanh x = \frac{\sinh x}{\cosh x} \qquad \coth x = \frac{\cosh x}{\sinh x}$$

$$\operatorname{sech} x = \frac{1}{\cosh x} \qquad \operatorname{csch} x = \frac{1}{\sinh x}$$

The terminology suggests that there must be some connection with the trigonometric functions; there is. First, the fundamental identity for the hyperbolic functions (reminiscent of $\cos^2 x + \sin^2 x = 1$ in trigonometry) is

$$\boxed{\cosh^2 x - \sinh^2 x = 1}$$

To verify it, we write

$$\cosh^2 x - \sinh^2 x = \frac{e^{2x} + 2 + e^{-2x}}{4} - \frac{e^{2x} - 2 + e^{-2x}}{4} = 1$$

Since

$$\sinh(-x) = \frac{e^{-x} - e^x}{2} = -\frac{e^x - e^{-x}}{2} = -\sinh x$$

$\sinh x$ is an odd function. Similarly (see Problem 57) $\cosh(-x) = \cosh x$, so $\cosh x$ is an even function. Correspondingly, the graph of $y = \sinh x$ is symmetric with

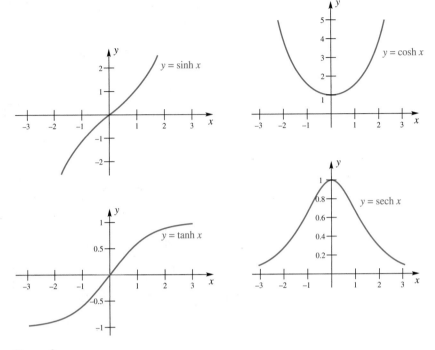

Figure 8

respect to the origin and the graph of $y = \cosh x$ is symmetric with respect to the y-axis. Similarly, $\tanh x$ is an odd function and $\text{sech } x$ is an even function. The graphs are shown in Figure 8.

Inverse Hyperbolic Functions

The hyperbolic sine and hyperbolic tangent are increasing functions and automatically have inverses. To obtain inverses for hyperbolic cosine and hyperbolic secant, we restrict their domains to $x \geq 0$. Thus,

$$x = \sinh^{-1} y \quad \Leftrightarrow \quad y = \sinh x$$

$$x = \cosh^{-1} y \quad \Leftrightarrow \quad y = \cosh x \quad \text{and} \quad x \geq 0$$

$$x = \tanh^{-1} y \quad \Leftrightarrow \quad y = \tanh x$$

$$x = \text{sech}^{-1} y \quad \Leftrightarrow \quad y = \text{sech } x \quad \text{and} \quad x \geq 0$$

Since the hyperbolic functions are defined in terms of e^x and e^{-x}, it is not too surprising that the inverse hyperbolic functions can be expressed in terms of the natural logarithm. For example, consider $y = \cosh x$ for $x \geq 0$; that is, consider

$$y = \frac{e^x + e^{-x}}{2}, \qquad x \geq 0$$

Our goal is to solve this equation for x, which will give $\cosh^{-1} y$. Multiplying both sides by $2e^x$, we get $2ye^x = e^{2x} + 1$, or

$$(e^x)^2 - 2ye^x + 1 = 0, \qquad x \geq 0$$

If we solve this quadratic equation in e^x, we obtain

$$e^x = \frac{2y + \sqrt{(2y)^2 - 4}}{2} = y + \sqrt{y^2 - 1}$$

The Quadratic Formula gives two solutions, the one given above and $\left(2y - \sqrt{(2y)^2 - 4}\right)/2$. This latter solution is extraneous because it is less than 1, whereas e^x is greater than 1 for all $x > 0$. Thus, $x = \ln\left(y + \sqrt{y^2 - 1}\right)$, so

$$x = \cosh^{-1} y = \ln\left(y + \sqrt{y^2 - 1}\right)$$

Similar arguments apply to each of the inverse hyperbolic functions. We obtain the following results (note that the roles of x and y have been interchanged). Figure 8 suggests the necessary domain restrictions. Graphs of the inverse hyperbolic functions are shown in Figure 9.

$$\sinh^{-1} x = \ln\left(x + \sqrt{x^2 + 1}\right)$$

$$\cosh^{-1} x = \ln\left(x + \sqrt{x^2 - 1}\right), \qquad x \geq 1$$

$$\tanh^{-1} x = \frac{1}{2}\ln\frac{1 + x}{1 - x}, \qquad -1 < x < 1$$

$$\text{sech}^{-1} x = \ln\left(\frac{1 + \sqrt{1 - x^2}}{x}\right), \qquad 0 < x \leq 1$$

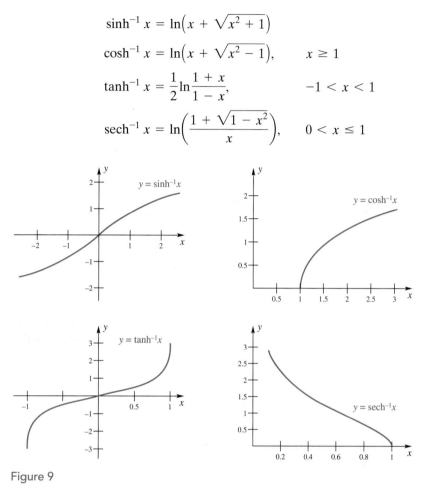

Figure 9

Concepts Review

1. If x is an irrational number and $a > 0$, then we define $a^x =$ _____ where r_n is a sequence of rational numbers that converges to x.

2. The inverse of the natural exponential function $\exp(x) = e^x$ is called the _____ and is denoted _____.

3. If interest is compounded continuously at the annual rate of 6%, then a \$1000 investment will be worth _____ after three years.

4. While the hyperbolic sine function is odd, the hyperbolic cosine function is _____ and the hyperbolic tangent is _____.

Problem Set 2.6

In Problems 1–10, simplify the given expression.

1. $10^{2 \log_{10} 5}$

2. $2^{2 \log_2 x}$

3. $e^{3 \ln x}$

4. $e^{-2 \ln x}$

5. $\ln e^{\cos x}$

6. $\ln e^{-2x-3}$

7. $\ln(x^3 e^{-3x})$

8. $e^{x - \ln x}$

9. $e^{\ln 3 + 2 \ln x}$

10. $e^{\ln x^2 - y \ln x}$

11. Match the graph to the right with the functions given below. The scales are the same on all four graphs.

(a) $f(x) = e^{x-1}$

(b) $f(x) = e^{-x^2}$

(c) $f(x) = e^x$

(d) $f(x) = e^{-x/4}$

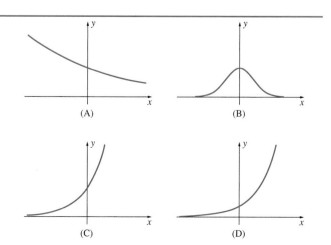

12. Match the graph below with the functions given. The scales are the same on all four graphs.

(a) $f(x) = \ln x$ (b) $f(x) = \ln(x - 1)$

(c) $f(x) = \ln \dfrac{1}{x}$ (d) $f(x) = \ln x^4$

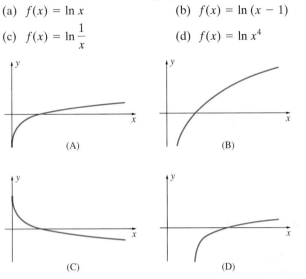

(A)

(B)

(C)

(D)

In Problems 13–16, make use of the known graph of $y = \ln x$ to sketch the graphs of the equations.

13. $y = \ln|x|$ **14.** $y = \ln \sqrt{x}$

15. $y = \ln\left(\dfrac{1}{x}\right)$ **16.** $y = \ln(x - 2)$

17. Sketch the graph of $y = \ln \cos x + \ln \sec x$ on $(-\pi/2, \pi/2)$, but think before you begin.

18. Find each of the following limits.

(a) $\lim\limits_{x \to 0}(1 + x)^{1000}$ (b) $\lim\limits_{x \to 0}(1)^{1/x}$

(c) $\lim\limits_{x \to 0^+}(1 + \varepsilon)^{1/x}, \varepsilon > 0$ (d) $\lim\limits_{x \to 0^-}(1 + \varepsilon)^{1/x}, \varepsilon > 0$

19. Use the fact that $e = \lim\limits_{h \to 0}(1 + h)^{1/h}$ to find each limit.

(a) $\lim\limits_{x \to 0}(1 - x)^{1/x}$ Hint: $(1 - x)^{1/x} = [(1 - x)^{1/(-x)}]^{-1}$

(b) $\lim\limits_{x \to 0}(1 + 3x)^{1/x}$ (c) $\lim\limits_{n \to \infty}\left(\dfrac{n + 2}{n}\right)^n$

(d) $\lim\limits_{n \to \infty}\left(\dfrac{n - 1}{n}\right)^{2n}$

20. Find each of the following limits.

(a) $\lim\limits_{n \to \infty}\left(1 + \dfrac{2}{n}\right)^{100}$ (b) $\lim\limits_{n \to \infty}(1.001)^n$

(c) $\lim\limits_{n \to \infty}\left(\dfrac{n + 3}{n}\right)^{n+1}$ (d) $\lim\limits_{x \to 0}(1 + x)^{1/x}$

21. Use the approximations $\ln 2 \approx 0.693$ and $\ln 3 \approx 1.099$ together with the properties stated in Theorem A to calculate approximations to each of the following. For example, $\ln 6 = \ln(2 \cdot 3) = \ln 2 + \ln 3 \approx 0.693 + 1.099 = 1.792$.

(a) $\ln 6$ (b) $\ln 1.5$ (c) $\ln 81$

(d) $\ln \sqrt{2}$ (e) $\ln\left(\dfrac{1}{36}\right)$ (f) $\ln 48$

22. Use your calculator to make the computations in Problem 21 directly.

In Problems 23–26, use Theorem A to write the expressions as the logarithm of a single quantity.

23. $2 \ln(x + 1) - \ln x$ **24.** $\frac{1}{2}\ln(x - 9) + \frac{1}{2}\ln x$

25. $\ln(x - 2) - \ln(x + 2) + 2 \ln x$

26. $\ln(x^2 - 9) - 2 \ln(x - 3) - \ln(x + 3)$

27. If \$375 is put in the bank today, what will it be worth at the end of 2 years if interest is 3.5% and is compounded as specified?

(a) Annually (b) Monthly

(c) Daily (d) Continuously

28. Do Problem 27 assuming that the interest rate is 4.6%.

29. How long does it take money to double in value for the specified interest rate?

(a) 6% compounded monthly

(b) 6% compounded continuously

30. Inflation between 1999 and 2004 ran at about 2.5% per year. On this basis, what would you expect a car that would have cost \$20,000 in 1999 to cost in 2004?

31. Manhattan Island is said to have been bought by Peter Minuit in 1626 for \$24. Suppose that Minuit had instead put the \$24 in the bank at 6% interest compounded continuously. What would that \$24 have been worth in 2000?

32. If Methuselah's parents had put \$100 in the bank for him at birth and he left it there, what would Methuselah have had at his death (969 years later) if interest was 4% compounded annually?

C Use $\log_a x = (\ln x)/(\ln a)$ to calculate each of the logarithms in Problems 33–36.

33. $\log_5 12$ **34.** $\log_7(0.11)$

35. $\log_{11}(8.12)^{1/5}$ **36.** $\log_{10}(8.57)^7$

C In Problems 37–40, use natural logarithms to solve each of the exponential equations. Hint: To solve $3^x = 11$, take ln of both sides, obtaining $x \ln 3 = \ln 11$; then $x = (\ln 11)/(\ln 3) \approx 2.1827$.

37. $2^x = 17$ **38.** $5^x = 13$

39. $5^{2s-3} = 4$ **40.** $12^{1/(\theta-1)} = 4$

In Problems 41–52, verify that the given equations are identities.

41. $e^x = \cosh x + \sinh x$

42 $e^{2x} = \cosh 2x + \sinh 2x$

43. $e^{-x} = \cosh x - \sinh x$

44. $e^{-2x} = \cosh 2x - \sinh 2x$

45. $\sinh(x + y) = \sinh x \cosh y + \cosh x \sinh y$

46. $\sinh(x - y) = \sinh x \cosh y - \cosh x \sinh y$

47. $\cosh(x + y) = \cosh x \cosh y + \sinh x \sinh y$

48. $\cosh(x - y) = \cosh x \cosh y - \sinh x \sinh y$

49. $\tanh(x + y) = \dfrac{\tanh x + \tanh y}{1 + \tanh x \tanh y}$

50. $\tanh(x - y) = \dfrac{\tanh x - \tanh y}{1 - \tanh x \tanh y}$

51. $\sinh 2x = 2 \sinh x \cosh x$

52. $\cosh 2x = \cosh^2 x + \sinh^2 x$

53. Assuming the properties of exponents for rational exponents, prove properties (2) through (6) of Theorem A for at least one irrational exponent.

54. State and prove a "substitution theorem" analogous to Theorems 2.3B and 2.5A for the inverse trigonometric functions.

55. State and prove a "substitution theorem" analogous to Theorems 2.3B and 2.5A for hyperbolic and inverse hyperbolic functions.

56. Prove Theorem B(1), that is, for $a > 0$, $\lim\limits_{x \to c} a^x = a^c$, by following these steps.

(a) Begin a proof by contradiction. Write down the negation of the statement "for every $\epsilon > 0$ there exists a $\delta > 0$ such that for all x, $|x - c| < \delta \Rightarrow |a^x - a^c| < \epsilon$." *Hint:* See the discussion at the end of Section 1.1.

(b) Let r_n be a sequence of rational numbers that converges to x, and reach a contradiction to the statement from part (a).

57. Show that $\cosh x$ is an even function.

58. Prove that $\lim\limits_{n \to \infty} \left(1 - \dfrac{1}{n}\right)^{-n} = e$. *Hint:* First show that

$$\left(1 - \frac{1}{n}\right)^{-n} = \left(1 + \frac{1}{n-1}\right)^{n} = \left(1 + \frac{1}{n-1}\right)^{n-1}\left(1 + \frac{1}{n-1}\right)$$

59. Use the result from Problem 58 to prove that $\lim\limits_{h \to 0^-} (1 + h)^{1/h} = e$.

Answers to Concepts Review: **1.** $\lim\limits_{n \to \infty} a^{r_n}$ **2.** natural logarithm; $\ln x$ **3.** $\$1000e^{0.06 \cdot 3}$ **4.** even; odd

---

2.7
Continuity
of Functions

In mathematics and science, we use the word *continuous* to describe a process that goes on without abrupt changes. In fact, our experience leads us to assume that this is an essential feature of many natural processes. It is this notion as it pertains to functions that we now want to make precise. In the three graphs shown in Figure 1, only the third graph exhibits continuity at c. In the first two graphs, either $\lim\limits_{x \to c} f(x)$ does not exist, or it exists but does not equal $f(c)$. Only in the third graph does $\lim\limits_{x \to c} f(x) = f(c)$.

A Discontinuous Machine

A good example of a discontinuous machine is the postage machine, which (in 2006) charged $0.39 for a 1-ounce letter but $0.63 for a letter the least little bit over 1 ounce.

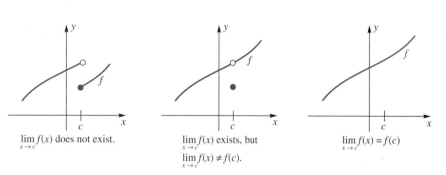

$\lim\limits_{x \to c} f(x)$ does not exist. $\lim\limits_{x \to c} f(x)$ exists, but $\lim\limits_{x \to c} f(x) \neq f(c)$. $\lim\limits_{x \to c} f(x) = f(c)$

Figure 1

Here is the formal definition.

Definition   **Continuity at a Point**

Let f be defined on an open interval containing c. We say that f is **continuous** at c if

$$\lim_{x \to c} f(x) = f(c)$$

We mean by this definition to require three things:

1. $\lim\limits_{x \to c} f(x)$ exists,

2. $f(c)$ exists (i.e., c is in the domain of f), and

3. $\lim\limits_{x \to c} f(x) = f(c)$.

If any one of these three fails, then f is **discontinuous** at c. Thus, the functions represented by the first and second graphs of Figure 1 are discontinuous at c. They do appear, however, to be continuous at other points of their domains.

EXAMPLE 1 Let $f(x) = \dfrac{x^2 - 4}{x - 2}$, $x \neq 2$. How should f be defined at $x = 2$ in order to make it continuous there?

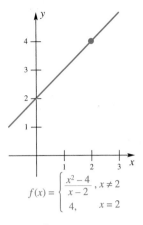

$$f(x) = \begin{cases} \dfrac{x^2 - 4}{x - 2}, & x \neq 2 \\ 4, & x = 2 \end{cases}$$

Figure 2

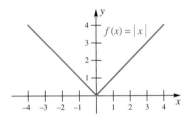

Figure 3

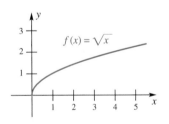

Figure 4

SOLUTION

$$\lim_{x \to 2} \frac{x^2 - 4}{x - 2} = \lim_{x \to 2} \frac{(x - 2)(x + 2)}{x - 2} = \lim_{x \to 2}(x + 2) = 4$$

Therefore, we define $f(2) = 4$. The graph of the resulting function is shown in Figure 2. In fact, we see that $f(x) = x + 2$ for all x. ∎

A point of discontinuity c is called **removable** if the function can be defined or redefined at c so as to make the function continuous. Otherwise, a point of discontinuity is called **nonremovable**. The function f in Example 1 has a removable discontinuity at 2 because we could define $f(2) = 4$ and the function would be continuous there.

Continuity of Familiar Functions Most functions that we will meet in this book are either (1) continuous everywhere or (2) continuous everywhere except at a few points. In particular, Theorem 2.3B implies the following result.

Theorem A **Continuity of Polynomial and Rational Functions**

A polynomial function is continuous at every real number c. A rational function is continuous at every real number c in its domain, that is, everywhere except where its denominator is zero.

Recall the absolute value function $f(x) = |x|$; its graph is shown in Figure 3. For $x < 0$, $f(x) = -x$, a polynomial; for $x > 0$, $f(x) = x$, another polynomial. Thus, $|x|$ is continuous at all numbers different from 0 by Theorem A. But

$$\lim_{x \to 0} |x| = 0 = |0|$$

(see Problem 27 of Section 2.2). Therefore, $|x|$ is also continuous at 0; it is continuous everywhere.

By the Main Limit Theorem (Theorem 2.3A)

$$\lim_{x \to c} \sqrt[n]{x} = \sqrt[n]{\lim_{x \to c} x} = \sqrt[n]{c}$$

provided $c > 0$ when n is even. This means that $f(x) = \sqrt[n]{x}$ is continuous at each point where it makes sense to talk about continuity. In particular, $f(x) = \sqrt{x}$ is continuous at each real number $c > 0$ (Figure 4). We summarize.

Theorem B **Continuity of Absolute Value and nth Root Functions**

The absolute value function is continuous at every real number c. If n is odd, the nth root function is continuous at every real number c; if n is even, the nth-root function is continuous at every positive real number c.

Continuity under Function Operations Do the standard function operations preserve continuity? Yes, according to the next theorem. In it, f and g are functions, k is a constant, and n is a positive integer.

Theorem C **Continuity under Function Operations**

If f and g are continuous at c, then so are kf, $f + g$, $f - g$, $f \cdot g$, f/g (provided that $g(c) \neq 0$), f^n, and $\sqrt[n]{f}$ (provided that $f(c) > 0$ if n is even).

Proof All these results are easy consequences of the corresponding facts for limits from Theorem 2.3A. For example, that theorem, combined with the fact that f and g are continuous at c, gives

$$\lim_{x \to c} f(x)g(x) = \lim_{x \to c} f(x) \cdot \lim_{x \to c} g(x) = f(c)g(c)$$

This is precisely what it means to say that $f \cdot g$ is continuous at c. ∎

EXAMPLE 2 At what numbers is $F(x) = (3|x| - x^2)/\left(\sqrt{x} + \sqrt[3]{x}\right)$ continuous?

SOLUTION We need not even consider nonpositive numbers, since F is not defined at such numbers. For any positive number, the functions $\sqrt{x}$, $\sqrt[3]{x}$, $|x|$, and x^2 are all continuous (Theorems A and B). It follows from Theorem C that $3|x|$, $3|x| - x^2$, $\sqrt{x} + \sqrt[3]{x}$, and finally,

$$\frac{(3|x| - x^2)}{\left(\sqrt{x} + \sqrt[3]{x}\right)}$$

are continuous at each positive number. ∎

The continuity of the trigonometric, inverse trigonometric, exponential, logarithmic, hyperbolic, and inverse hyperbolic functions is stated in the next theorem. Before we state this theorem, we must define the **interior** of an interval. Basically, by interor, we mean the interval, excluding the endpoints (if they were included in the first place). For example the interior of the interval $[1, 3]$ is the open interval $(1, 3)$; the interior of $(2, 4)$ is the interval $(2, 4)$ itself. This concept is needed because in order for the limit $\lim_{x \to c} f(x)$ to exist, we must be able to approach c from both sides, and this can be done only if c is in the interior of the domain of f.

Theorem D | **Continuity of Transcendental Functions**

The functions

  $\sin x$, $\cos x$, $\tan x$, $\cot x$, $\sec x$, $\csc x$

  $\sin^{-1} x$, $\cos^{-1} x$, $\tan^{-1} x$, $\cot^{-1} x$, $\sec^{-1} x$, $\csc^{-1} x$

  a^x, $\log_a x$ ($a > 0$ and $a \neq 1$)

  $\sinh x$, $\cosh x$, $\tanh x$, $\coth x$, $\operatorname{sech} x$, $\operatorname{csch} x$

  $\sinh^{-1} x$, $\cosh^{-1} x$, $\tanh^{-1} x$, $\coth^{-1} x$, $\operatorname{sech}^{-1} x$, $\operatorname{csch}^{-1} x$

are continuous at every point in the interior of their domain.

Proof That the trigonometric functions are continuous at every point in the domain follows from Theorem 2.5A. Applying Theorem 2.6C, we can conclude that the inverse trigonometric functions are continuous at every point on the interior of their domain. The continuity of the exponential and logarithmic functions follows directly from Theorems 2.6B and 2.6D. Hyperbolic functions are defined in terms of the exponential functions, so their continuity can be established using the continuity of the exponential functions (see Problem 55 of Section 2.6). Finally, inverse hyperbolic functions are continuous on the interior of their domain by Theorem 2.6C. ∎

Theorem D says, for example, that $\sin^{-1} x$ is continuous at every number c on the interior of its domain. The domain for the inverse sine is $[-1, 1]$, which has interior $(-1, 1)$. We conclude that $\sin^{-1} x$ is continuous at every number c in $(-1, 1)$.

EXAMPLE 3 Determine all points of discontinuity of $f(x) = \dfrac{\sin x}{x(1 - x)}$, $x \neq 0, 1$. Classify each point of discontinuity as removable or nonremovable.

SOLUTION By Theorem D, the numerator is continuous at every real number. The denominator is also continuous at every real number, but when $x = 0$ or

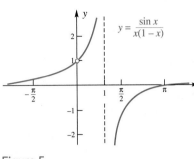

Figure 5

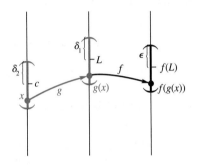

Figure 6

$x = 1$, the denominator is 0. Thus, by Theorem C, f is continuous at every real number except $x = 0$ and $x = 1$. Since

$$\lim_{x \to 0} \frac{\sin x}{x(1 - x)} = \lim_{x \to 0} \frac{\sin x}{x} \cdot \lim_{x \to 0} \frac{1}{(1 - x)} = (1)(1) = 1$$

we could define $f(0) = 1$ and the function would become continuous there. Thus, $x = 0$ is a removable discontinuity. Also, since

$$\lim_{x \to 1^+} \frac{\sin x}{x(1 - x)} = -\infty \quad \text{and} \quad \lim_{x \to 1^-} \frac{\sin x}{x(1 - x)} = \infty$$

there is no way to define $f(1)$ to make f continuous at $x = 1$. Thus $x = 1$ is a nonremovable discontinuity. A graph of $y = f(x)$ is shown in Figure 5. ∎

There is another functional operation, composition, that will be very important in later work. It, too, preserves continuity.

Theorem E | **Composite Limit Theorem**

If $\lim\limits_{x \to c} g(x) = L$ and if f is continuous at L, then

$$\lim_{x \to c} f(g(x)) = f\left(\lim_{x \to c} g(x)\right) = f(L)$$

In particular, if g is continuous at c and f is continuous at $g(c)$, then the composite $f \circ g$ is continuous at c.

Proof of Theorem E (Optional)

Proof Let $\varepsilon > 0$ be given. Since f is continuous at L, there is a corresponding $\delta_1 > 0$ such that

$$|t - L| < \delta_1 \Rightarrow |f(t) - f(L)| < \varepsilon$$

and so (see Figure 6)

$$|g(x) - L| < \delta_1 \Rightarrow |f(g(x)) - f(L)| < \varepsilon$$

But because $\lim\limits_{x \to c} g(x) = L$, for a given $\delta_1 > 0$ there is a corresponding $\delta_2 > 0$ such that

$$0 < |x - c| < \delta_2 \Rightarrow |g(x) - L| < \delta_1$$

When we put these two facts together, we have

$$0 < |x - c| < \delta_2 \Rightarrow |f(g(x)) - f(L)| < \varepsilon$$

This shows that

$$\lim_{x \to c} f(g(x)) = f(L)$$

The second statement in Theorem E follows from the observation that if g is continuous at c then $L = g(c)$. ∎

EXAMPLE 4 Show that $h(x) = |x^2 - 3x + 6|$ is continuous at each real number.

SOLUTION Let $f(x) = |x|$ and $g(x) = x^2 - 3x + 6$. Both are continuous at each real number, and so their composite

$$h(x) = f(g(x)) = |x^2 - 3x + 6|$$

is also. ∎

EXAMPLE 5 Show that

$$h(x) = \sin \frac{x^4 - 3x + 1}{x^2 - x - 6}$$

is continuous except at 3 and -2.

SOLUTION $x^2 - x - 6 = (x - 3)(x + 2)$. Thus, the rational function

$$g(x) = \frac{x^4 - 3x + 1}{x^2 - x - 6}$$

is continuous except at 3 and -2 (Theorem A). We know from Theorem D that the sine function is continuous at every real number. Thus, from Theorem E, we conclude that, since $h(x) = \sin(g(x))$, h is also continuous except at 3 and -2. ∎

Continuity on an Interval So far, we have been discussing continuity at a point. We now wish to discuss continuity on an interval. Continuity on an interval ought to mean continuity at each point of that interval. This is exactly what it does mean for an *open* interval.

When we consider a closed interval $[a, b]$, we face a problem. It might be that f is not even defined to the left of a (e.g., this occurs for $f(x) = \sqrt{x}$ at $a = 0$), so, strictly speaking, $\lim_{x \to a} f(x)$ does not exist. We choose to get around this problem by calling f continuous on $[a, b]$ if it is continuous at each point of (a, b) and if $\lim_{x \to a^+} f(x) = f(a)$ and $\lim_{x \to b^-} f(x) = f(b)$. We summarize in a formal definition.

Definition Continuity on an Interval

The function f is **right continuous** at a if $\lim_{x \to a^+} f(x) = f(a)$ and **left continuous** at b if $\lim_{x \to b^-} f(x) = f(b)$.

We say f is **continuous on an open interval** if it is continuous at each point of that interval. It is **continuous on the closed interval** $[a, b]$ if it is continuous on (a, b), right continuous at a, and left continuous at b.

For example, it is correct to say that $f(x) = 1/x$ is continuous on $(0, 1)$ and that $g(x) = \sqrt{x}$ is continuous on $[0, 1]$.

EXAMPLE 6 Using the definition above, describe the continuity properties of the function whose graph is sketched in Figure 7.

SOLUTION The function appears to be continuous on the open intervals $(-\infty, 0)$ $(0, 3)$, and $(5, \infty)$, and also on the closed interval $[3, 5]$. ∎

EXAMPLE 7 What is the largest interval over which the function defined by $g(x) = \sqrt{4 - x^2}$ is continuous?

SOLUTION The domain of g is the interval $[-2, 2]$. If c is in the open interval $(-2, 2)$, then g is continuous at c by Theorem E; hence, g is continuous on $(-2, 2)$. The one-sided limits are

$$\lim_{x \to -2^+} \sqrt{4 - x^2} = \sqrt{4 - \left(\lim_{x \to -2^+} x \right)^2} = \sqrt{4 - 4} = 0 = g(-2)$$

and

$$\lim_{x \to 2^-} \sqrt{4 - x^2} = \sqrt{4 - \left(\lim_{x \to 2^-} x \right)^2} = \sqrt{4 - 4} = 0 = g(2)$$

This implies that g is right continuous at -2 and left continuous at 2. Thus, g is continuous on its domain, the closed interval $[-2, 2]$. ∎

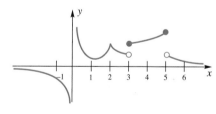

Figure 7

EXAMPLE 8 What is the largest interval over which the function defined by $f(x) = \cos^{-1} x$ is continuous?

SOLUTION The domain for $f(x) = \cos^{-1} x$ is the closed interval $[-1, 1]$. Theorem D says that this function is continuous at every point on the interior of its domain, that is, on the interval $(-1, 1)$. We must now address the continuity of f at the endpoints -1 and 1. By the discussion immediately following Theorem 2.6C, we can conclude that since $y = \cos x$ is decreasing on $[0, \pi]$,

$$\lim_{x \to \pi^-} \cos x = \cos \pi = -1 \quad \Rightarrow \quad \lim_{x \to -1^+} \cos^{-1} x = \cos^{-1}(-1) = \pi$$

and

$$\lim_{x \to 0^+} \cos x = \cos 0 = 1 \quad \Rightarrow \quad \lim_{x \to 1^-} \cos^{-1} x = \cos^{-1} 1 = 0$$

(See Figure 8). Thus $f(x) = \cos^{-1} x$ is right continuous at $x = -1$ and left continuous at $x = 1$. Since it is also continuous on the open interval $(-1, 1)$, we can conclude that $f(x) = \cos^{-1} x$ is continuous on the closed interval $[-1, 1]$. ∎

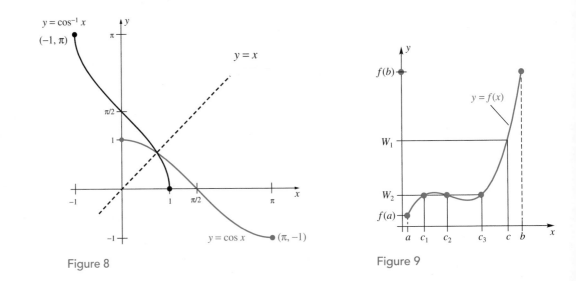

Figure 8

Figure 9

Intuitively, for f to be continuous on $[a, b]$ means that the graph of f on $[a, b]$ should have no jumps, so we should be able to "draw" the graph of f from the point $(a, f(a))$ to the point $(b, f(b))$ without lifting our pencil from the paper. Thus, the function f should take on every value between $f(a)$ and $f(b)$. This property is stated more precisely in Theorem F.

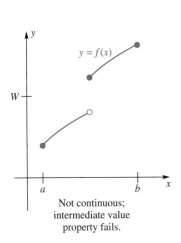

Not continuous; intermediate value property fails.

Figure 10

Theorem F | **Intermediate Value Theorem**

Let f be a function defined on $[a, b]$ and let W be a number between $f(a)$ and $f(b)$. If f is continuous on $[a, b]$, then there is at least one number c between a and b such that $f(c) = W$.

Figure 9 shows the graph of a function $f(x)$ that is continuous on $[a, b]$. The Intermediate Value Theorem says that for every W in $(f(a), f(b))$ there must be a c in $[a, b]$ such that $f(c) = W$. In other words, f takes on every value between $f(a)$ and $f(b)$. Continuity is needed for this theorem, for otherwise it is possible to find a function f and a number W between $f(a)$ and $f(b)$ such that there is no c in $[a, b]$ that satisfies $f(c) = W$. Figure 10 shows an example of such a function.

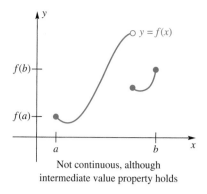

Not continuous, although intermediate value property holds

Figure 11

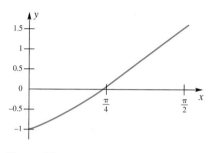

Figure 12

It seems clear that continuity is sufficient, although a formal proof of this result turns out to be difficult. We leave the proof to more advanced works.

The converse of this theorem, which is not true in general, says that if f takes on every value between $f(a)$ and $f(b)$ then f is continuous. Figures 9 and 11 show functions that take on all values between $f(a)$ and $f(b)$, but the function in Figure 11 is not continuous on $[a, b]$. Just because a function has the intermediate value property does not mean that it must be continuous.

The Intermediate Value Theorem can be used to tell us something about the solutions of equations, as the next example shows.

■ EXAMPLE 9 Use the Intermediate Value Theorem to show that the equation $x - \cos x = 0$ has a solution between $x = 0$ and $x = \pi/2$.

SOLUTION Let $f(x) = x - \cos x$, and let $W = 0$. Then $f(0) = 0 - \cos 0 = -1$ and $f(\pi/2) = \pi/2 - \cos \pi/2 = \pi/2$. Since f is continuous on $[0, \pi/2]$ and since $W = 0$ is between $f(0)$ and $f(\pi/2)$, the Intermediate Value Theorem implies the existence of a c in the interval $(0, \pi/2)$ with the property that $f(c) = 0$. Such a c is a solution to the equation $x - \cos x = 0$. Figure 12 suggests that there is exactly one such c.

We can go one step further. The midpoint of the interval $[0, \pi/2]$ is the point $x = \pi/4$. When we evaluate $f(\pi/4)$, we get

$$f(\pi/4) = \frac{\pi}{4} - \cos\frac{\pi}{4} = \frac{\pi}{4} - \frac{\sqrt{2}}{2} \approx 0.0782914$$

which is greater than 0. Thus, $f(0) < 0$ and $f(\pi/4) > 0$, so another application of the Intermediate Value Theorem tells us that there exists a c between 0 and $\pi/4$ such that $f(c) = 0$. We have thus narrowed down the interval containing the desired c from $[0, \pi/2]$ to $[0, \pi/4]$. There is nothing stopping us from selecting the midpoint of $[0, \pi/4]$ and evaluating f at that point, thereby narrowing even further the interval containing c. This process could be continued indefinitely until we find that c is in a sufficiently small interval. This method of zeroing in on a solution is called the *bisection method*, and we will study it further in Section 4.7. ■

The Intermediate Value Theorem can also lead to some surprising results.

■ EXAMPLE 10 Use the Intermediate Value Theorem to show that on a circular wire ring there are always two points opposite from each other with the same temperature.

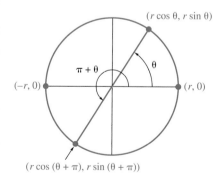

$(r \cos \theta, r \sin \theta)$

$(-r, 0)$ $\pi + \theta$ θ $(r, 0)$

$(r \cos (\theta + \pi), r \sin (\theta + \pi))$

Figure 13

SOLUTION Choose coordinates for this problem so that the center of the ring is the origin, and let r be the radius of the ring. (See Figure 13.) Define $T(x, y)$ to be the temperature at the point (x, y). Consider a diameter of the circle that makes an angle θ with the x-axis, and define $f(\theta)$ to be the temperature difference between the points that make angles of θ and $\theta + \pi$; that is,

$$f(\theta) = T(r \cos \theta, r \sin \theta) - T(r \cos(\theta + \pi), r \sin(\theta + \pi))$$

With this definition

$$f(0) = T(r, 0) - T(-r, 0)$$
$$f(\pi) = T(-r, 0) - T(r, 0) = -\left[T(r, 0) - T(-r, 0)\right] = -f(0)$$

Thus, either $f(0)$ and $f(\pi)$ are both zero, or one is positive and the other is negative. If both are zero, then we have found the required two points. Otherwise, we can apply the Intermediate Value Theorem. Assuming that temperature varies continuously, we conclude that there exists a c between 0 and π such that $f(c) = 0$. Thus, for the two points at the angles c and $c + \pi$, the temperatures are the same. ■

Concepts Review

1. A function f is continuous at c if _____ $= f(c)$.

2. The function $f(x) = [\![x]\!]$ is discontinuous at _____.

3. A function f is said to be continuous on a closed interval $[a, b]$ if it is continuous at every point of (a, b) and if _____ and _____.

4. The Intermediate Value Theorem says that if a function f is continuous on $[a, b]$ and W is a number between $f(a)$ and $f(b)$, then there is a number c between _____ and _____ such that _____.

Problem Set 2.7

In Problems 1–15, state whether the indicated function is continuous at 3. If it is not continuous, tell why.

1. $f(x) = (x - 3)(x - 4)$

2. $g(x) = x^2 - 9$

3. $h(x) = \dfrac{3}{x - 3}$

4. $g(t) = \sqrt{t - 4}$

5. $h(t) = \dfrac{|t - 3|}{t - 3}$

6. $h(t) = \dfrac{|\sqrt{(t - 3)^4}|}{t - 3}$

7. $f(t) = |t|$

8. $g(t) = |t - 2|$

9. $h(x) = \dfrac{x^2 - 9}{x - 3}$

10. $f(x) = \dfrac{21 - 7x}{x - 3}$

11. $r(t) = \begin{cases} \dfrac{t^3 - 27}{t - 3} & \text{if } t \neq 3 \\ 27 & \text{if } t = 3 \end{cases}$

12. $r(t) = \begin{cases} \dfrac{t^3 - 27}{t - 3} & \text{if } t \neq 3 \\ 23 & \text{if } t = 3 \end{cases}$

13. $f(t) = \begin{cases} t - 3 & \text{if } t \leq 3 \\ 3 - t & \text{if } t > 3 \end{cases}$

14. $f(t) = \begin{cases} t^2 - 9 & \text{if } t \leq 3 \\ (3 - t)^2 & \text{if } t > 3 \end{cases}$

15. $f(x) = \begin{cases} -3x + 7 & \text{if } x \leq 3 \\ -2 & \text{if } x > 3 \end{cases}$

16. From the graph of g (see Figure 14), indicate the values where g is discontinuous. For each of these values state whether g is continuous from the right, left, or neither.

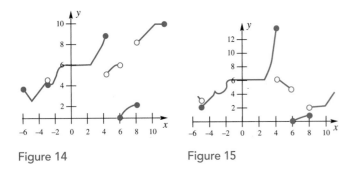

Figure 14   Figure 15

17. From the graph of h given in Figure 15, indicate the intervals on which h is continuous.

In Problems 18–23, the given function is not defined at a certain point. How should it be defined in order to make it continuous at that point? (See Example 1.)

18. $f(x) = \dfrac{x^2 - 49}{x - 7}$

19. $f(x) = \dfrac{2x^2 - 18}{3 - x}$

20. $g(\theta) = \dfrac{\sin \theta}{\theta}$

21. $H(t) = \dfrac{\sqrt{t} - 1}{t - 1}$

22. $\phi(x) = \dfrac{x^4 + 2x^2 - 3}{x + 1}$

23. $F(x) = \sin\dfrac{x^2 - 1}{x + 1}$

In Problems 24–35, at what points, if any, are the functions discontinuous?

24. $f(x) = \dfrac{3x + 7}{(x - 30)(x - \pi)}$

25. $f(x) = \dfrac{33 - x^2}{x\pi + 3x - 3\pi - x^2}$

26. $h(\theta) = |\sin \theta + \cos \theta|$

27. $r(\theta) = \tan \theta$

28. $f(u) = \dfrac{2u + 7}{\sqrt{u + 5}}$

29. $g(u) = \dfrac{u^2 + |u - 1|}{\sqrt[3]{u + 1}}$

30. $F(x) = \dfrac{1}{\sqrt{4 + x^2}}$

31. $G(x) = \dfrac{1}{\sqrt{4 - x^2}}$

32. $f(x) = \begin{cases} x & \text{if } x < 0 \\ x^2 & \text{if } 0 \leq x \leq 1 \\ 2 - x & \text{if } x > 1 \end{cases}$

33. $g(x) = \begin{cases} x^2 & \text{if } x < 0 \\ -x & \text{if } 0 \leq x \leq 1 \\ x & \text{if } x > 1 \end{cases}$

34. $f(t) = [\![t]\!]$

35. $g(t) = [\![t + \frac{1}{2}]\!]$

36. Sketch the graph of a function f that satisfies all the following conditions.
    (a) Its domain is $[-2, 2]$.
    (b) $f(-2) = f(-1) = f(1) = f(2) = 1$.
    (c) It is discontinuous at -1 and 1.
    (d) It is right continuous at -1 and left continuous at 1.

37. Sketch the graph of a function that has domain $[0, 2]$ and is continuous on $[0, 2)$ but not on $[0, 2]$.

38. Sketch the graph of a function that has domain $[0, 6]$ and is continuous on $[0, 2]$ and $(2, 6]$ but is not continuous on $[0, 6]$.

39. Sketch the graph of a function that has domain $[0, 6]$ and is continuous on $(0, 6)$ but not on $[0, 6]$.

40. Let

$$f(x) = \begin{cases} x & \text{if } x \text{ is rational} \\ -x & \text{if } x \text{ is irrational} \end{cases}$$

Sketch the graph of this function as best you can and decide where it is continuous.

In Problems 41–48, determine whether the function is continuous at the given point c. If the function is not continuous, determine whether the discontinuity is removable or nonremovable.

41. $f(x) = \sin x; c = 0$

42. $f(x) = \dfrac{x^2 - 100}{x - 10}; c = 10$

43. $f(x) = \dfrac{\sin x}{x}; c = 0$

44. $f(x) = \dfrac{\cos x}{x}; c = 0$

45. $g(x) = \begin{cases} \dfrac{\sin x}{x}, & x \neq 0 \\ 0, & x = 0 \end{cases}$

46. $F(x) = x \sin \dfrac{1}{x}; c = 0$

47. $f(x) = \sin \dfrac{1}{x}; c = 0$

48. $f(x) = \dfrac{4 - x}{2 - \sqrt{x}}; c = 4$

In Problems 49–54, determine the largest interval over which the given function is continuous.

49. $f(x) = \sqrt{25 - x^2}$

50. $f(x) = \dfrac{1}{\sqrt{25 - x^2}}$

51. $f(x) = \sin^{-1} x$

52. $f(x) = \operatorname{sech} x$

53. $f(x) = \sec^{-1} x, \ x \geq 0$

54. $f(x) = \operatorname{sech}^{-1} x$

55. A cell phone company charges $0.12 for connecting a call plus $0.08 per minute or any part thereof (e.g., a phone call lasting 2 minutes and 5 seconds costs $0.12 + 3 × $0.08). Sketch a graph of the cost of making a call as a function of the length of time t that the call lasts. Discuss the continuity of this function.

56. A rental car company charges $20 for one day, allowing up to 200 miles. For each additional 100 miles, or any fraction thereof, the company charges $18. Sketch a graph of the cost for renting a car for one day as a function of the miles driven. Discuss the continuity of this function.

57. A cab company charges $2.50 for the first $\frac{1}{4}$ mile and $0.20 for each additional $\frac{1}{8}$ mile. Sketch a graph of the cost of a cab ride as a function of the number of miles driven. Discuss the continuity of this function.

58. Use the Intermediate Value Theorem to prove that $x^3 + 3x - 2 = 0$ has a real solution between 0 and 1.

59. Use the Intermediate Value Theorem to prove that $(\cos t)t^3 + 6 \sin^5 t - 3 = 0$ has a real solution between 0 and 2π.

GC **60.** Use the Intermediate Value Theorem to show that $x^3 - 7x^2 + 14x - 8 = 0$ has at least one solution in the interval $[0, 5]$. Sketch the graph of $y = x^3 - 7x^2 + 14x - 8$ over $[0, 5]$. How many solutions does this equation really have?

GC **61.** Use the Intermediate Value Theorem to show that $\sqrt{x} - \cos x = 0$ has a solution between 0 and $\pi/2$. Zoom in on the graph of $y = \sqrt{x} - \cos x$ to find an interval having length 0.1 that contains this solution.

62. Show that the equation $x^5 + 4x^3 - 7x + 14 = 0$ has at least one real solution.

63. Prove that f is continuous at c if and only if $\lim_{t \to 0} f(c + t) = f(c)$.

64. Prove that if f is continuous at c and $f(c) > 0$ there is an interval $(c - \delta, c + \delta)$ such that $f(x) > 0$ on this interval.

65. Prove that if f is continuous on $[0, 1]$ and satisfies $0 \leq f(x) \leq 1$ there, then f has a *fixed point*; that is, there is a number c in $[0, 1]$ such that $f(c) = c$. *Hint:* Apply the Intermediate Value Theorem to $g(x) = x - f(x)$.

66. Find the values of a and b so that the following function is continuous everywhere.

$$f(x) = \begin{cases} x + 1 & \text{if } x < 1 \\ ax + b & \text{if } 1 \leq x < 2 \\ 3x & \text{if } x \geq 2 \end{cases}$$

67. A stretched elastic string covers the interval $[0, 1]$. The ends are released and the string contracts so that it covers the interval $[a, b], a \geq 0, b \leq 1$. Prove that this results in at least one point of the string being where it was originally. See Problem 65.

68. Let $f(x) = \dfrac{1}{x - 1}$. Then $f(-2) = -\dfrac{1}{3}$ and $f(2) = 1$. Does the Intermediate Value Theorem imply the existence of a number c between -2 and 2 such that $f(c) = 0$? Explain.

69. Starting at 4 A.M., a hiker slowly climbed to the top of a mountain, arriving at noon. The next day, he returned along the same path, starting at 5 A.M. and getting to the bottom at 11 A.M. Show that at some point along the path his watch showed the same time on both days.

70. Let D be a bounded, but otherwise arbitrary, region in the first quadrant. Given an angle $\theta, 0 \leq \theta \leq \pi/2$, D can be circumscribed by a rectangle whose base makes angle θ with the x-axis as shown in Figure 16. Prove that at some angle this rectangle is a square. (This means that *any* bounded region can be circumscribed by a *square*.)

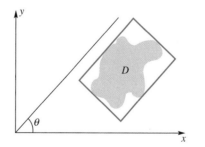

Figure 16

71. The gravitational force exerted by the earth on an object having mass m that is a distance r from the center of the earth is

$$g(r) = \begin{cases} \dfrac{GMmr}{R^3}, & \text{if } r < R \\ \dfrac{GMm}{r^2}, & \text{if } r \geq R \end{cases}$$

Here G is the gravitational constant, M is the mass of the earth, and R is the earth's radius. Is g a continuous function of r?

72. Suppose that f is continuous on $[a, b]$ and it is never zero there. Is it possible that f changes sign on $[a, b]$? Explain.

73. Let $f(x + y) = f(x) + f(y)$ for all x and y and suppose that f is continuous at $x = 0$.
(a) Prove that f is continuous everywhere.
(b) Prove that there is a constant m such that $f(t) = mt$ for all t (see Problem 43 of Section 1.5).

74. Prove that if $f(x)$ is a continuous function on an interval then so is the function $|f(x)| = \sqrt{(f(x))^2}$.

75. Show that if $g(x) = |f(x)|$ is continuous it is not necessarily true that $f(x)$ is continuous.

76. Let $f(x) = 0$ if x is irrational and let $f(x) = 1/q$ if x is the rational number p/q in reduced form $(q > 0)$.
(a) Sketch (as best you can) the graph of f on $(0, 1)$.
(b) Show that f is continuous at each irrational number in $(0, 1)$, but is discontinuous at each rational number in $(0, 1)$.

77. A thin equilateral triangular block of side length 1 unit has its face in the vertical xy-plane with a vertex V at the origin. Under the influence of gravity, it will rotate about V until a side hits the x-axis floor (Figure 17). Let x denote the initial x-coordinate of the midpoint M of the side opposite V, and let $f(x)$

denote the final x-coordinate of this point. Assume that the block balances when M is directly above V.
(a) Determine the domain and range of f.
(b) Where on this domain is f discontinuous?
(c) Identify any fixed points of f (see Problem 65).

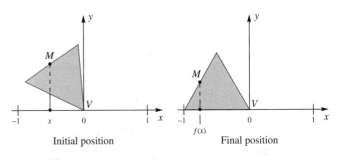
Initial position   Final position

Figure 17

Answers to Concepts Review: **1.** $\lim_{x \to c} f(x)$ **2.** every integer **3.** $\lim_{x \to a^+} f(x) = f(a); \lim_{x \to b^-} f(x) = f(b)$
4. $a; b; f(c) = W$

2.8 Chapter Review

Concepts Test

Respond with true or false to each of the following assertions. Be prepared to justify your answer.

1. If $f(c) = L$, then $\lim_{x \to c} f(x) = L$.

2. If $\lim_{x \to c} f(x) = L$, then $f(c) = L$.

3. If $\lim_{x \to c} f(x)$ exists, then $f(c)$ exists.

4. If $\lim_{x \to 0} f(x) = 0$, then for every $\varepsilon > 0$ there exists a $\delta > 0$ such that $0 < |x| < \delta$ implies $|f(x)| < \varepsilon$.

5. If $f(c)$ is undefined, then $\lim_{x \to c} f(x)$ does not exist.

6. The coordinates of the hole in the graph of $y = \dfrac{x^2 - 25}{x - 5}$ are $(5, 10)$.

7. If $p(x)$ is a polynomial, then $\lim_{x \to c} p(x) = p(c)$.

8. $\lim_{x \to 0} \dfrac{\sin x}{x}$ does not exist.

9. For every real number c, $\lim_{x \to c} \tan x = \tan c$.

10. $\tan x$ is continuous at every point of its domain.

11. The function $f(x) = 2 \sinh^2 x - \cosh x$ is continuous at every real number.

12. If f is continuous at c, then $f(c)$ exists.

13. If f is continuous on $[0, 4]$, then $\lim_{x \to 0} f(x)$ exists.

14. The function $f(x) = \cos^{-1} x$ is continuous at every point in $(-1, 1)$.

15. If f is an invertible function with inverse f^{-1}, and if $\lim_{x \to 1} f(x) = f(1)$, then $\lim_{x \to f(1)} f^{-1}(x) = 1$.

16. If r_n is a sequence of rational numbers that converges to π, then $\pi^\pi = \lim_{n \to \infty} \pi^{r_n}$.

17. If f is a continuous function such that $A \le f(x) \le B$ for all x, then $\lim_{x \to \infty} f(x)$ exists and it satisfies $A \le \lim_{x \to \infty} f(x) \le B$.

18. If f is continuous on (a, b) then $\lim_{x \to c} f(x) = f(c)$ for all c in (a, b).

19. $\lim_{x \to \infty} \tan^{-1} x = \dfrac{\pi}{2}$

20. If the line $y = 2$ is a horizontal asymptote of the graph of $y = f(x)$, then $\lim_{x \to \infty} f(x) = 2$.

21. The graph of $y = \tan x$ has many horizontal asymptotes.

22. The graph of $y = \dfrac{1}{x^2 - 4}$ has two vertical asymptotes.

23. $\lim_{t \to 1^+} \dfrac{e^t}{t - 1} = \infty$.

24. If $\lim_{x \to c^-} f(x) = \lim_{x \to c^+} f(x)$, then f is continuous at $x = c$.

25. If $\lim_{x \to c} f(x) = f\left(\lim_{x \to c} x\right)$, then f is continuous at $x = c$.

26. The function $f(x) = [x/2]$ is continuous at $x = 2.3$.

27. If $\lim_{x \to 2} f(x) = f(2) > 0$, then $f(x) < 1.001 f(2)$ for all x in some interval containing 2.

28. If $\lim_{x \to c} [f(x) + g(x)]$ exists, then $\lim_{x \to c} f(x)$ and $\lim_{x \to c} g(x)$ both exist.

29. If $0 \le f(x) \le 3x^2 + 2x^4$ for all x, then $\lim_{x \to 0} f(x) = 0$.

30. If $\lim_{x \to a} f(x) = L$ and $\lim_{x \to a} f(x) = M$, then $L = M$.

31. If $f(x) \ne g(x)$ for all x, then $\lim_{x \to c} f(x) \ne \lim_{x \to c} g(x)$.

32. If $f(x) < 10$ for all x and $\lim_{x \to 2} f(x)$ exists, then $\lim_{x \to 2} f(x) < 10$.

33. If $\lim_{x \to a} f(x) = b$, then $\lim_{x \to a} |f(x)| = |b|$.

34. If f is continuous and positive on $[a, b]$, then $1/f$ must assume every value between $1/f(a)$ and $1/f(b)$.

Sample Test Problems

In Problems 1–22, find the indicated limit or state that it does not exist.

1. $\lim_{x \to 2} \dfrac{x - 2}{x + 2}$

2. $\lim_{u \to 1} \dfrac{u^2 - 1}{u + 1}$

3. $\lim_{u \to 1} \dfrac{u^2 - 1}{u - 1}$

4. $\lim_{u \to 1} \dfrac{u + 1}{u^2 - 1}$

5. $\lim_{x \to 2} \dfrac{1 - 2/x}{x^2 - 4}$

6. $\lim_{z \to 2} \dfrac{z^2 - 4}{z^2 + z - 6}$

7. $\lim_{x \to 0} \dfrac{\tan x}{\sin 2x}$

8. $\lim_{y \to 1} \dfrac{y^3 - 1}{y^2 - 1}$

9. $\lim_{x \to 4} \dfrac{x - 4}{\sqrt{x} - 2}$

10. $\lim_{x \to 0} \dfrac{\cos x}{x}$

11. $\lim_{x \to 0^-} \dfrac{|x|}{x}$

12. $\lim_{x \to 1/2^+} [\![4x]\!]$

13. $\lim_{t \to 2^-} ([\![t]\!] - t)$

14. $\lim_{x \to 1^-} \dfrac{|x - 1|}{x - 1}$

15. $\lim_{x \to 0} \dfrac{\sin 5x}{3x}$

16. $\lim_{x \to 0} \dfrac{1 - \cos 2x}{3x}$

17. $\lim_{x \to \infty} \dfrac{x - 1}{x + 2}$

18. $\lim_{t \to \infty} \dfrac{\sin t}{t}$

19. $\lim_{x \to \infty} e^{x^2}$

20. $\lim_{x \to 0^+} \dfrac{\cos x}{x}$

21. $\lim_{x \to \pi/4^-} \tan 2x$

22. $\lim_{x \to 0^+} \ln x^2$

23. Prove using an ε–δ argument that $\lim_{x \to 3}(2x + 1) = 7$.

24. Let $f(x) = \begin{cases} x^3 & \text{if } x < -1 \\ x & \text{if } -1 < x < 1 \\ 1 - x & \text{if } x \geq 1 \end{cases}$

Find each value.

(a) $f(1)$

(b) $\lim_{x \to 1^+} f(x)$

(c) $\lim_{x \to 1^-} f(x)$

(d) $\lim_{x \to -1^-} f(x)$

25. Refer to f of Problem 24.

(a) What are the values of x at which f is discontinuous?

(b) How should f be defined at $x = -1$ to make it continuous there?

26. Give the ε–δ definition in each case.

(a) $\lim_{u \to a} g(u) = M$

(b) $\lim_{x \to a^-} f(x) = L$

27. If $\lim_{x \to 3} f(x) = 3$ and $\lim_{x \to 3} g(x) = -2$ and if g is continuous at $x = 3$, find each value.

(a) $\lim_{x \to 3} [2f(x) - 4g(x)]$

(b) $\lim_{x \to 3} g(x) \dfrac{x^2 - 9}{x - 3}$

(c) $g(3)$

(d) $\lim_{x \to 3} g(f(x))$

(e) $\lim_{x \to 3} \sqrt{f^2(x) - 8g(x)}$

(f) $\lim_{x \to 3} \dfrac{|g(x) - g(3)|}{f(x)}$

28. Sketch the graph of a function f that satisfies all the following conditions.

(a) Its domain is $[0, 6]$.

(b) $f(0) = f(2) = f(4) = f(6) = 2$.

(c) f is continuous except at $x = 2$.

(d) $\lim_{x \to 2^-} f(x) = 1$ and $\lim_{x \to 5^+} f(x) = 3$.

29. Let $f(x) = \begin{cases} -1 & \text{if } x \leq 0 \\ ax + b & \text{if } 0 < x < 1 \\ 1 & \text{if } x \geq 1 \end{cases}$

Determine a and b so that f is continuous everywhere.

30. Use the Intermediate Value Theorem to prove that the equation $x^5 - 4x^3 - 3x + 1 = 0$ has at least one solution between $x = 2$ and $x = 3$.

In Problems 31–36, find the equations of all vertical and horizontal asymptotes for the given function.

31. $f(x) = \dfrac{x}{x^2 + 1}$

32. $g(x) = \dfrac{x^2}{x^2 + 1}$

33. $F(x) = \dfrac{x^2}{x^2 - 1}$

34. $G(x) = \dfrac{x^3}{x^2 - 4}$

35. $h(x) = \tan 2x$

36. $H(x) = 2 \tan^{-1} x$

In Problems 37–38, determine the largest interval over which the given function is continuous.

37. $f(x) = \cos^{-1} \dfrac{x}{2}$

38. $f(x) = \ln(25 - x^2)$

1. Let $f(x) = x^2$. Find and simplify each of the following.

(a) $f(2)$

(b) $f(2.1)$

(c) $f(2.1) - f(2)$

(d) $\dfrac{f(2.1) - f(2)}{2.1 - 2}$

(e) $f(a + h)$

(f) $f(a + h) - f(a)$

(g) $\dfrac{f(a + h) - f(a)}{(a + h) - a}$

(h) $\displaystyle\lim_{h \to 0} \dfrac{f(a + h) - f(a)}{(a + h) - a}$

2. Repeat (a) through (h) of Problem 1 for the function $f(x) = 1/x$.

3. Repeat (a) through (h) of Problem 1 for the function $f(x) = \sqrt{x}$.

4. Repeat (a) through (h) of Problem 1 for the function $f(x) = x^3 + 1$.

5. Write the first two terms in the expansions of the following:

(a) $(a + b)^3$

(b) $(a + b)^4$

(c) $(a + b)^5$

6. Based on your results from Problem 5, make a conjecture about the first two terms in the expansion of $(a + b)^n$ for an arbitrary n.

7. Use a trigonometric identity to write $\sin(x + h)$ in terms of $\sin x$, $\sin h$, $\cos x$, and $\cos h$.

8. Use a trigonometric identity to write $\cos(x + h)$ in terms of $\cos x$, $\cos h$, $\sin x$, and $\sin h$.

9. A wheel centered at the origin and of radius 10 centimeters is rotating counterclockwise at a rate of 4 revolutions per second. A point P on the rim of the wheel is at position $(10, 0)$ at time $t = 0$.

(a) What are the coordinates of P at times $t = 1, 2, 3$?

(b) At what time does the point P first return to the starting position $(10, 0)$?

10. Assume that a soap bubble retains its spherical shape as it expands. At time $t = 0$ the soap bubble has radius 2 centimeters. At time $t = 1$, the radius has increased to 2.5 centimeters. How much has the volume changed in this 1 second interval?

11. One airplane leaves an airport at noon flying north at 300 miles per hour. Another leaves the same airport one hour later and flies east at 400 miles per hour.

(a) What are the positions of the airplanes at 2:00 P.M.?

(b) What is the distance between the two planes at 2:00 P.M.?

(c) What is the distance between the two planes at 2:15 P.M.?

12. Write as the logarithm of a single quantity:

$$\ln x + 2 \ln (x^2 + 4) - 3 \ln (x + 1)$$

In Problems 13–16, evaluate the given limits.

13. $\displaystyle\lim_{n \to \infty} \left(1 - \frac{2}{n}\right)^n$

14. $\displaystyle\lim_{h \to 0} \left(1 + \frac{h}{2}\right)^{2/h}$

15. $\displaystyle\lim_{h \to 0} \left(1 + \frac{h}{3}\right)^{1/h}$

16. $\displaystyle\lim_{h \to 0} \left(1 + \frac{h}{x}\right)^{1/h}$

The Derivative

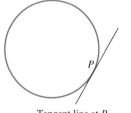

Tangent line at P

Figure 1

Tangent line at P

Figure 2

3.1
Two Problems with One Theme

Our first problem is very old; it dates back to the great Greek scientist Archimedes (287–212 B.C.). We refer to the problem of the *slope of the tangent line.* Our second problem is newer. It grew out of attempts by Kepler (1571–1630), Galileo (1564–1642), Newton (1642–1727), and others to describe the speed of a moving body. It is the problem of *instantaneous velocity.*

The two problems, one geometric and the other mechanical, appear to be quite unrelated. In this case, appearances are deceptive. The two problems are identical twins.

The Tangent Line   Euclid's notion of a tangent as a line touching a curve at just one point is all right for circles (Figure 1) but completely unsatisfactory for most other curves (Figure 2). The idea of a tangent to a curve at P as the line that best approximates the curve near P is better, but is still too vague for mathematical precision. The concept of limit provides a way of getting the best description.

Let P be a point on a curve and let Q be a nearby *movable point* on that curve. Consider the line through P and Q, called a **secant line.** The **tangent line** at P is the limiting position (if it exists) of the secant line as Q moves toward P along the curve (Figure 3).

Suppose that the curve is the graph of the equation $y = f(x)$. Then P has coordinates $(c, f(c))$, a nearby point Q has coordinates $(c + h, f(c + h))$, and the secant line through P and Q has slope m_{sec} given by (Figure 4):

$$m_{\text{sec}} = \frac{f(c + h) - f(c)}{h}$$

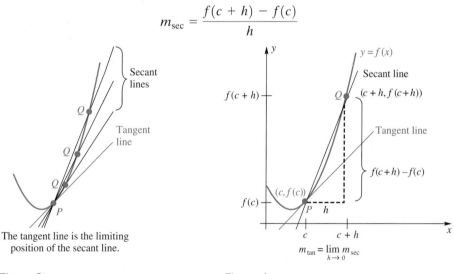

The tangent line is the limiting position of the secant line.

Figure 3

$$m_{\tan} = \lim_{h \to 0} m_{\text{sec}}$$

Figure 4

Using the concept of limit, which we studied in the last chapter, we can now give a formal definition of the tangent line.

Definition   Tangent Line

The **tangent line** to the curve $y = f(x)$ at the point $P(c, f(c))$ is that line through P with slope

$$m_{\tan} = \lim_{h \to 0} m_{\text{sec}} = \lim_{h \to 0} \frac{f(c + h) - f(c)}{h}$$

provided that this limit exists and is not ∞ or $-\infty$.

119

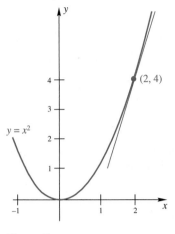

$y = x^2$

(2, 4)

Figure 5

EXAMPLE 1 Find the slope of the tangent line to the curve $y = f(x) = x^2$ at the point $(2, 4)$.

SOLUTION The line whose slope we are seeking is shown in Figure 5. Clearly it has a large positive slope.

$$m_{\tan} = \lim_{h \to 0} \frac{f(2 + h) - f(2)}{h}$$

$$= \lim_{h \to 0} \frac{(2 + h)^2 - 2^2}{h}$$

$$= \lim_{h \to 0} \frac{4 + 4h + h^2 - 4}{h}$$

$$= \lim_{h \to 0} \frac{h(4 + h)}{h}$$

$$= 4$$

EXAMPLE 2 Find the slopes of the tangent lines to the curve $y = f(x) = -x^2 + 2x + 2$ at the points with x-coordinates $-1, \frac{1}{2}, 2$, and 3.

SOLUTION Rather than make four separate calculations, it seems wise to calculate the slope at the point with x-coordinate c and then obtain the four desired answers by substitution.

$$m_{\tan} = \lim_{h \to 0} \frac{f(c + h) - f(c)}{h}$$

$$= \lim_{h \to 0} \frac{-(c + h)^2 + 2(c + h) + 2 - (-c^2 + 2c + 2)}{h}$$

$$= \lim_{h \to 0} \frac{-c^2 - 2ch - h^2 + 2c + 2h + 2 + c^2 - 2c - 2}{h}$$

$$= \lim_{h \to 0} \frac{h(-2c - h + 2)}{h}$$

$$= -2c + 2$$

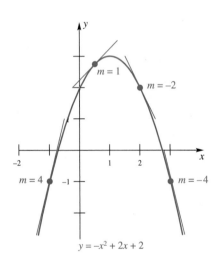

$m = 1$

$m = -2$

$m = 4$ -1

$m = -4$

$y = -x^2 + 2x + 2$

Figure 6

The four desired slopes (obtained by letting $c = -1, \frac{1}{2}, 2, 3$) are $4, 1, -2$, and -4. These answers do appear to be consistent with the graph in Figure 6.

EXAMPLE 3 Find the equation of the tangent line to the curve $y = 1/x$ at $\left(2, \frac{1}{2}\right)$ (see Figure 7).

SOLUTION Let $f(x) = 1/x$.

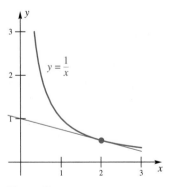

$y = \frac{1}{x}$

Figure 7

$$m_{\tan} = \lim_{h \to 0} \frac{f(2 + h) - f(2)}{h}$$

$$= \lim_{h \to 0} \frac{\dfrac{1}{2 + h} - \dfrac{1}{2}}{h}$$

$$= \lim_{h \to 0} \frac{\dfrac{2}{2(2 + h)} - \dfrac{2 + h}{2(2 + h)}}{h}$$

$$= \lim_{h \to 0} \frac{2 - (2 + h)}{2(2 + h)h}$$

$$= \lim_{h \to 0} \frac{-h}{2(2 + h)h}$$

$$= \lim_{h \to 0} \frac{-1}{2(2 + h)} = -\frac{1}{4}$$

Knowing that the slope of the tangent line is $-\frac{1}{4}$ and that the point $\left(2, \frac{1}{2}\right)$ is on it, we can easily write its equation by using the point-slope form $y - y_0 = m(x - x_0)$. The result is $y - \frac{1}{2} = -\frac{1}{4}(x - 2)$, or equivalently, $y = 1 - \frac{1}{4}x$. ∎

Average Velocity and Instantaneous Velocity If we drive an automobile from one town to another 80 miles away in 2 hours, our average velocity is 40 miles per hour. *Average velocity* is the distance from the first position to the second position divided by the elapsed time.

But during our trip the speedometer reading was often different from 40. At the start, it registered 0; at times it rose as high as 57; at the end it fell back to 0 again. Just what does the speedometer measure? Certainly, it does not indicate average velocity.

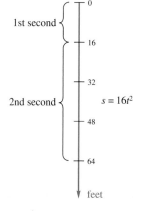

Figure 8

Consider the more precise example of an object P falling in a vacuum. Experiment shows that if it starts from rest, P falls $16t^2$ feet in t seconds. Thus, it falls 16 feet in the first second and 64 feet during the first 2 seconds (Figure 8); clearly, it falls faster and faster as time goes on. Figure 9 shows the distance traveled (on the vertical axis) as a function of time (on the horizontal axis).

During the second second (i.e., in the time interval from $t = 1$ to $t = 2$), P fell $64 - 16 = 48$ feet. Its average velocity was

$$v_{\text{avg}} = \frac{64 - 16}{2 - 1} = 48 \text{ feet per second}$$

During the time interval from $t = 1$ to $t = 1.5$, it fell $16(1.5)^2 - 16 = 20$ feet. Its average velocity was

$$v_{\text{avg}} = \frac{16(1.5)^2 - 16}{1.5 - 1} = \frac{20}{0.5} = 40 \text{ feet per second}$$

Similarly, on the time intervals $t = 1$ to $t = 1.1$ and $t = 1$ to $t = 1.01$, we calculate the respective average velocities to be

$$v_{\text{avg}} = \frac{16(1.1)^2 - 16}{1.1 - 1} = \frac{3.36}{0.1} = 33.6 \text{ feet per second}$$

$$v_{\text{avg}} = \frac{16(1.01)^2 - 16}{1.01 - 1} = \frac{0.3216}{0.01} = 32.16 \text{ feet per second}$$

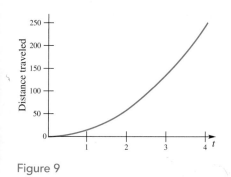

Figure 9

What we have done is to calculate the average velocity over shorter and shorter time intervals, each starting at $t = 1$. The shorter the time interval is, the better we should approximate the *instantaneous velocity* at the instant $t = 1$. Looking at the numbers 48, 40, 33.6, and 32.16, we might guess 32 feet per second to be the instantaneous velocity.

But let us be more precise. Suppose that an object P moves along a coordinate line so that its position at time t is given by $s = f(t)$. At time c the object is at $f(c)$; at the nearby time $c + h$, it is at $f(c + h)$ (see Figure 10). Thus the **average velocity** on this interval is

$$v_{\text{avg}} = \frac{f(c + h) - f(c)}{h}$$

We can now define instantaneous velocity.

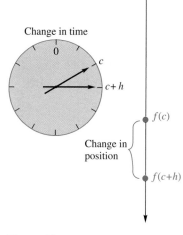

Figure 10

> **Definition** **Instantaneous Velocity**
>
> If an object moves along a coordinate line with position function $f(t)$, then its **instantaneous velocity** at time c is
>
> $$v = \lim_{h \to 0} v_{\text{avg}} = \lim_{h \to 0} \frac{f(c + h) - f(c)}{h}$$
>
> provided that the limit exists and is not ∞ or $-\infty$.

In the case where $f(t) = 16t^2$, the instantaneous velocity at $t = 1$ is

$$v = \lim_{h \to 0} \frac{f(1 + h) - f(1)}{h}$$

$$= \lim_{h \to 0} \frac{16(1 + h)^2 - 16}{h}$$

$$= \lim_{h \to 0} \frac{16 + 32h + 16h^2 - 16}{h}$$

$$= \lim_{h \to 0} (32 + 16h) = 32$$

This confirms our earlier guess.

EXAMPLE 4 An object, initially at rest, falls due to gravity. Find its instantaneous velocity at $t = 3.8$ seconds and at $t = 5.4$ seconds.

SOLUTION We calculate the instantaneous velocity at $t = c$ seconds. Since $f(t) = 16t^2$,

$$v = \lim_{h \to 0} \frac{f(c + h) - f(c)}{h}$$

$$= \lim_{h \to 0} \frac{16(c + h)^2 - 16c^2}{h}$$

$$= \lim_{h \to 0} \frac{16c^2 + 32ch + 16h^2 - 16c^2}{h}$$

$$= \lim_{h \to 0} (32c + 16h) = 32c$$

Thus, the instantaneous velocity at 3.8 seconds is $32(3.8) = 121.6$ feet per second; at 5.4 seconds, it is $32(5.4) = 172.8$ feet per second. ∎

EXAMPLE 5 How long will it take the falling object of Example 4 to reach an instantaneous velocity of 112 feet per second?

SOLUTION We learned in Example 4 that the instantaneous velocity after c seconds is $32c$. Thus, we must solve the equation $32c = 112$. The solution is $c = \frac{112}{32} = 3.5$ seconds. ∎

EXAMPLE 6 A particle moves along a coordinate line and s, its directed distance in centimeters from the origin after t seconds, is given by $s = f(t) = \sqrt{5t + 1}$. Find the instantaneous velocity of the particle after 3 seconds.

SOLUTION Figure 11 shows the distance traveled as a function of time. The instantaneous velocity at time $t = 3$ is equal to the slope of the tangent line at $t = 3$.

$$v = \lim_{h \to 0} \frac{f(3 + h) - f(3)}{h}$$

$$= \lim_{h \to 0} \frac{\sqrt{5(3 + h) + 1} - \sqrt{5(3) + 1}}{h}$$

$$= \lim_{h \to 0} \frac{\sqrt{16 + 5h} - 4}{h}$$

To evaluate this limit, we rationalize the numerator by multiplying the numerator and denominator by $\sqrt{16 + 5h} + 4$. We obtain

---

Two Problems with One Theme

Now you see why we called this section "Two Problems with One Theme." Look at the definitions of *slope of the tangent line* and *instantaneous velocity*. They give different names for the same mathematical concept.

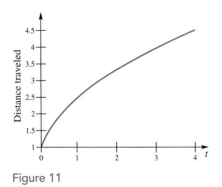

Figure 11

$$v = \lim_{h \to 0} \left(\frac{\sqrt{16 + 5h} - 4}{h} \cdot \frac{\sqrt{16 + 5h} + 4}{\sqrt{16 + 5h} + 4} \right)$$

$$= \lim_{h \to 0} \frac{16 + 5h - 16}{h(\sqrt{16 + 5h} + 4)}$$

$$= \lim_{h \to 0} \frac{5}{\sqrt{16 + 5h} + 4} = \frac{5}{8}$$

We conclude that the instantaneous velocity after 3 seconds is $\frac{5}{8}$ centimeter per second. ∎

Velocity or Speed
For the time being, we will use the terms *velocity* and *speed* interchangeably. Later in this chapter, we will distinguish between these two words.

Rates of Change Velocity is only one of many rates of change that will be important in this course; it is the rate of change of distance with respect to time. Other rates of change that will interest us are density for a wire (the rate of change of mass with respect to distance), marginal revenue (the rate of change of revenue with respect to the number of items produced), and current (the rate of change of electrical charge with respect to time). These rates and many more are discussed in the problem set. In each case, we must distinguish between an *average* rate of change on an interval and an *instantaneous* rate of change at a point. The phrase *rate of change* without an adjective will mean instantaneous rate of change.

Concepts Review

1. The line that most closely approximates a curve near the point P is the _____ through that point.

2. More precisely, the tangent line to a curve at P is the limiting position of the _____ line through P and Q as Q approaches P along the curve.

3. The slope m_{tan} of the tangent line to the curve $y = f(x)$ at $(c, f(c))$ is given by $m_{\text{tan}} = \lim_{h \to 0}$ _____.

4. The instantaneous velocity of a point P (moving along a line) at time c is the limit of the _____ on the time interval c to $c + h$ as h approaches zero.

Problem Set 3.1

In Problems 1 and 2, a tangent line to a curve is drawn. Estimate its slope (slope = rise/run). Be careful to note the difference in scales on the two axes.

1.

2.

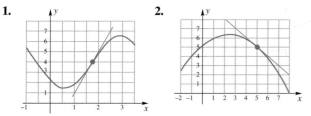

In Problems 3–6, draw the tangent line to the curve through the indicated point and estimate its slope.

3.

4.

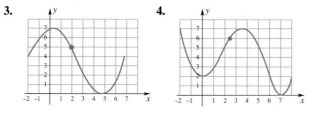

5.

6.

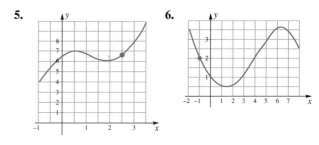

7. Consider $y = x^2 + 1$.

(a) Sketch its graph as carefully as you can.

(b) Draw the tangent line at $(1, 2)$.

≈ (c) Estimate the slope of this tangent line.

⊡ (d) Calculate the slope of the secant line through $(1, 2)$ and $(1.01, (1.01)^2 + 1.0)$.

(e) Find by the limit process (see Example 1) the slope of the tangent line at $(1, 2)$.

8. Consider $y = x^3 - 1$.

(a) Sketch its graph as carefully as you can.

(b) Draw the tangent line at $(2, 7)$.

≈ (c) Estimate the slope of this tangent line.

C (d) Calculate the slope of the secant line through $(2, 7)$ and $(2.01, (2.01)^3 - 1.0)$.

(e) Find by the limit process (see Example 1) the slope of the tangent line at $(2, 7)$.

9. Find the slopes of the tangent lines to the curve $y = x^2 - 1$ at the points where $x = -2, -1, 0, 1, 2$ (see Example 2).

10. Find the slopes of the tangent lines to the curve $y = x^3 - 3x$ at the points where $x = -2, -1, 0, 1, 2$.

11. Sketch the graph of $y = 1/(x + 1)$ and then find the equation of the tangent line at $\left(1, \frac{1}{2}\right)$ (see Example 3).

12. Find the equation of the tangent line to $y = 1/(x - 1)$ at $(0, -1)$.

13. Experiment suggests that a falling body will fall approximately $16t^2$ feet in t seconds.

(a) How far will it fall between $t = 0$ and $t = 1$?

(b) How far will it fall between $t = 1$ and $t = 2$?

(c) What is its average velocity on the interval $2 \le t \le 3$?

C (d) What is its average velocity on the interval $3 \le t \le 3.01$?

≈ (e) Find its instantaneous velocity at $t = 3$ (see Example 4).

14. An object travels along a line so that its position s is $s = t^2 + 1$ meters after t seconds.

(a) What is its average velocity on the interval $2 \le t \le 3$?

C (b) What is its average velocity on the interval $2 \le t \le 2.003$?

(c) What is its average velocity on the interval $2 \le t \le 2 + h$?

≈ (d) Find its instantaneous velocity at $t = 2$.

15. Suppose that an object moves along a coordinate line so that its directed distance from the origin after t seconds is $\sqrt{2t + 1}$ feet.

(a) Find its instantaneous velocity at $t = \alpha, \alpha > 0$.

(b) When will it reach a velocity of $\frac{1}{2}$ foot per second? (see Example 5.)

16. If a particle moves along a coordinate line so that its directed distance from the origin after t seconds is $(-t^2 + 4t)$ feet, when did the particle come to a momentary stop (i.e., when did its instantaneous velocity become zero)?

17. A certain bacterial culture is growing so that it has a mass of $\frac{1}{2}t^2 + 1$ grams after t hours.

C (a) How much did it grow during the interval $2 \le t \le 2.01$?

(b) What was its average growth rate during the interval $2 \le t \le 2.01$?

≈ (c) What was its instantaneous growth rate at $t = 2$?

18. A business is prospering in such a way that its total (accumulated) profit after t years is $1000t^2$ dollars.

(a) How much did the business make during the third year (between $t = 2$ and $t = 3$)?

(b) What was its average rate of profit during the first half of the third year, between $t = 2$ and $t = 2.5$? (The rate will be in dollars per year.)

(c) What was its instantaneous rate of profit at $t = 2$?

19. A wire of length 8 centimeters is such that the mass between its left end and a point x centimeters to the right is x^3 grams (Figure 12).

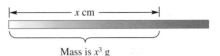

x cm

Mass is x^3 g

Figure 12

(a) What is the average density of the middle 2-centimeter segment of this wire? *Note:* Average density equals mass/length.

(b) What is the actual density at the point 3 centimeters from the left end?

20. Suppose that the revenue $R(n)$ in dollars from producing n computers is given by $R(n) = 0.4n - 0.001n^2$. Find the instantaneous rates of change of revenue when $n = 10$ and $n = 100$. (The instantaneous rate of change of revenue with respect to the amount of product produced is called the *marginal revenue.*)

21. The rate of change of velocity with respect to time is called **acceleration.** Suppose that the velocity at time t of a particle is given by $v(t) = 2t^2$. Find the instantaneous acceleration when $t = 1$ second.

22. A city is hit by an Asian flu epidemic. Officials estimate that t days after the beginning of the epidemic the number of persons sick with the flu is given by $p(t) = 120t^2 - 2t^3$, when $0 \le t \le 40$. At what rate is the flu spreading at time $t = 10; t = 20; t = 40$?

23. The graph in Figure 13 shows the amount of water in a city water tank during one day when no water was pumped into the tank. What was the average rate of water usage during the day? How fast was water being used at 8 A.M.?

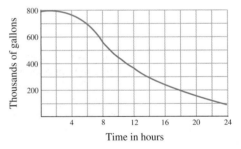

Figure 13

24. Passengers board an elevator at the ground floor (i.e., the zeroth floor) and take it to the seventh floor, which is 84 feet above the ground floor. The elevator's position s as a function of time t (measured in seconds) is shown in Figure 14.

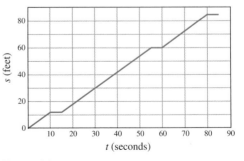

Figure 14

(a) What is the average velocity of the elevator from the time the elevator began moving until the time that it reached the seventh floor?

(b) What was the elevator's approximate velocity at time $t = 20$?

(c) How many stops did the elevator make between the ground floor and the seventh floor (excluding the ground and seventh floors)? On which floors do you think the elevator stopped?

25. Figure 15 shows the normal high temperature for St. Louis, Missouri, as a function of time (measured in days beginning January 1).

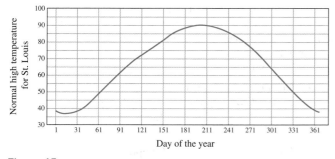

Figure 15

(a) What is the approximate rate of change in the normal high temperature on March 2 (i.e., on day number 61)? What are the units of this rate of change?

(b) What is the approximate rate of change in the normal high temperature on July 10 (i.e., on day number 191)?

(c) In what months is there a moment when the rate of change is equal to 0?

(d) In what months is the absolute value of the rate of change the greatest?

26. Figure 16 shows the population in millions of a developing country for the years 1900 to 1999. What is the approximate rate of change of the population in 1930? In 1990? The percentage growth is often a more appropriate measure of population growth. This is the rate of growth divided by the population size at that time. For this population, what was the approximate percentage growth in 1930? In 1990?

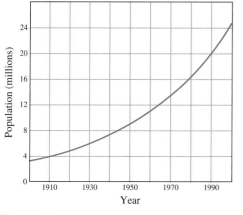

Figure 16

27. Figures 17a and 17b show the position s as a function of time t for two particles that are moving along a line. For each particle, is the velocity increasing or decreasing? Explain.

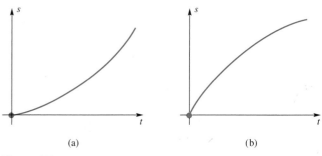

Figure 17

28. The rate of change of electric charge with respect to time is called **current.** Suppose that $\frac{1}{3}t^3 + t$ coulombs of charge flow through a wire in t seconds. Find the current in amperes (coulombs per second) after 3 seconds. When will a 20-ampere fuse in the line blow?

29. The radius of a circular oil spill is growing at a constant rate of 2 kilometers per day. At what rate is the area of the spill growing 3 days after it began?

30. The radius of a spherical balloon is increasing at the rate of 0.25 inch per second. If the radius is 0 at time $t = 0$, find the rate of change in the volume at time $t = 3$.

GC *Use a graphing calculator or a CAS to do Problems 31–34.*

31. Draw the graph of $y = f(x) = x^3 - 2x^2 + 1$. Then find the slope of the tangent line at

(a) -1 (b) 0   (c) 1   (d) 3.2

32. Draw the graph of $y = f(x) = \sin x \sin^2 2x$. Then find the slope of the tangent line at

(a) $\pi/3$ (b) 2.8   (c) π (d) 4.2

33. If a point moves along a line so that its distance s (in feet) from 0 is given by $s = t + t \cos^2 t$ at time t seconds, find its instantaneous velocity at $t = 3$.

34. If a point moves along a line so that its distance s (in meters) from 0 is given by $s = (t + 1)^3/(t + 2)$ at time t minutes, find its instantaneous velocity at $t = 1.6$.

Answers to Concepts Review: **1.** tangent line   **2.** secant
3. $[f(c + h) - f(c)]/h$ **4.** average velocity

3.2
The Derivative

We have seen that *slope of the tangent line* and *instantaneous velocity* are manifestations of the same basic idea. Rate of growth of an organism (biology), marginal profit (economics), density of a wire (physics), and dissolution rates (chemistry) are other versions of the same basic concept. Good mathematical sense suggests that we study this concept independently of these specialized vocabularies and diverse applications. We choose the neutral name *derivative*. Add it to *function* and *limit* as one of the key words in calculus.

Definition Derivative

The **derivative** of a function f is another function f' (read "f prime") whose value at any number x is

$$f'(x) = \lim_{h \to 0} \frac{f(x + h) - f(x)}{h}$$

If this limit does exist, we say that f is **differentiable** at x. Finding a derivative is called **differentiation**; the part of calculus associated with the derivative is called **differential calculus.**

Finding Derivatives   We illustrate with several examples.

EXAMPLE 1 Let $f(x) = 13x - 6$. Find $f'(4)$.

SOLUTION

$$f'(4) = \lim_{h \to 0} \frac{f(4 + h) - f(4)}{h} = \lim_{h \to 0} \frac{[13(4 + h) - 6] - [13(4) - 6]}{h}$$

$$= \lim_{h \to 0} \frac{13h}{h} = \lim_{h \to 0} 13 = 13 \qquad \blacksquare$$

EXAMPLE 2 If $f(x) = x^3 + 7x$, find $f'(x)$.

SOLUTION

$$f'(x) = \lim_{h \to 0} \frac{f(x + h) - f(x)}{h}$$

$$= \lim_{h \to 0} \frac{\left[(x + h)^3 + 7(x + h)\right] - \left[x^3 + 7x\right]}{h}$$

$$= \lim_{h \to 0} \frac{3x^2h + 3xh^2 + h^3 + 7h}{h}$$

$$= \lim_{h \to 0} (3x^2 + 3xh + h^2 + 7)$$

$$= 3x^2 + 7 \qquad \blacksquare$$

EXAMPLE 3 If $f(x) = 1/x$, find $f'(x)$.

SOLUTION

$$f'(x) = \lim_{h \to 0} \frac{f(x + h) - f(x)}{h} = \lim_{h \to 0} \frac{\dfrac{1}{x + h} - \dfrac{1}{x}}{h}$$

$$= \lim_{h \to 0} \left[\frac{x - (x + h)}{(x + h)x} \cdot \frac{1}{h}\right] = \lim_{h \to 0} \left[\frac{-h}{(x + h)x} \cdot \frac{1}{h}\right]$$

$$= \lim_{h \to 0} \frac{-1}{(x + h)x} = -\frac{1}{x^2}$$

Thus, f' is the function given by $f'(x) = -1/x^2$. Its domain is all real numbers except $x = 0$. ∎

■ EXAMPLE 4 Find $F'(x)$ if $F(x) = \sqrt{x}, x > 0$.

SOLUTION

$$F'(x) = \lim_{h \to 0} \frac{F(x + h) - F(x)}{h}$$

$$= \lim_{h \to 0} \frac{\sqrt{x + h} - \sqrt{x}}{h}$$

By this time you will have noticed that finding a derivative always involves taking the limit of a quotient where both numerator and denominator are approaching zero. Our task is to simplify this quotient so that we can cancel a factor h from the numerator and denominator, thereby allowing us to evaluate the limit by substitution. In the present example, this can be accomplished by rationalizing the numerator.

$$F'(x) = \lim_{h \to 0} \left[\frac{\sqrt{x + h} - \sqrt{x}}{h} \cdot \frac{\sqrt{x + h} + \sqrt{x}}{\sqrt{x + h} + \sqrt{x}} \right]$$

$$= \lim_{h \to 0} \frac{x + h - x}{h(\sqrt{x + h} + \sqrt{x})}$$

$$= \lim_{h \to 0} \frac{h}{h(\sqrt{x + h} + \sqrt{x})}$$

$$= \lim_{h \to 0} \frac{1}{\sqrt{x + h} + \sqrt{x}}$$

$$= \frac{1}{\sqrt{x} + \sqrt{x}} = \frac{1}{2\sqrt{x}}$$

Thus, F', the derivative of F, is given by $F'(x) = 1/(2\sqrt{x})$. Its domain is $(0, \infty)$. ∎

Equivalent Forms for the Derivative   There is nothing sacred about use of the letter h in defining $f'(c)$. Notice, for example, that

$$f'(c) = \lim_{h \to 0} \frac{f(c + h) - f(c)}{h}$$

$$= \lim_{p \to 0} \frac{f(c + p) - f(c)}{p}$$

$$= \lim_{s \to 0} \frac{f(c + s) - f(c)}{s}$$

A more radical change, but still just a change of notation, may be understood by comparing Figures 1 and 2. Note how x takes the place of $c + h$, and so $x - c$ replaces h. Thus,

$$f'(c) = \lim_{x \to c} \frac{f(x) - f(c)}{x - c}$$

Note that in all cases the number at which f' is evaluated is held fixed during the limit operation.

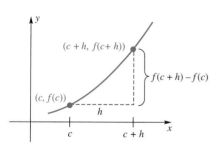

Figure 1

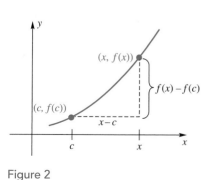

Figure 2

EXAMPLE 5 Use the last boxed result to find $g'(c)$ if $g(x) = 2/(x + 3)$.

SOLUTION

$$g'(c) = \lim_{x \to c} \frac{g(x) - g(c)}{x - c} = \lim_{x \to c} \frac{\dfrac{2}{x + 3} - \dfrac{2}{c + 3}}{x - c}$$

$$= \lim_{x \to c} \left[\frac{2(c + 3) - 2(x + 3)}{(x + 3)(c + 3)} \cdot \frac{1}{x - c} \right]$$

$$= \lim_{x \to c} \left[\frac{-2(x - c)}{(x + 3)(c + 3)} \cdot \frac{1}{x - c} \right]$$

$$= \lim_{x \to c} \frac{-2}{(x + 3)(c + 3)} = \frac{-2}{(c + 3)^2}$$

Here we manipulated the quotient until we could cancel a factor of $x - c$ from the numerator and denominator. Then we could evaluate the limit. ∎

EXAMPLE 6 Each of the following is a derivative, but of what function and at what point?

(a) $\displaystyle \lim_{h \to 0} \frac{(4 + h)^2 - 16}{h}$

(b) $\displaystyle \lim_{x \to 3} \frac{\dfrac{2}{x} - \dfrac{2}{3}}{x - 3}$

SOLUTION

(a) This is the derivative of $f(x) = x^2$ at $x = 4$.

(b) This is the derivative of $f(x) = 2/x$ at $x = 3$. ∎

Differentiability Implies Continuity If a curve has a tangent line at a point, then that curve cannot take a jump or wiggle too badly at the point. The precise formulation of this fact is an important theorem.

Theorem A **Differentiability Implies Continuity**

If $f'(c)$ exists, then f is continuous at c.

Proof We need to show that $\lim_{x \to c} f(x) = f(c)$. We begin by writing $f(x)$ in a fancy way.

$$f(x) = f(c) + \frac{f(x) - f(c)}{x - c} \cdot (x - c), \qquad x \neq c$$

Therefore,

$$\lim_{x \to c} f(x) = \lim_{x \to c} \left[f(c) + \frac{f(x) - f(c)}{x - c} \cdot (x - c) \right]$$

$$= \lim_{x \to c} f(c) + \lim_{x \to c} \frac{f(x) - f(c)}{x - c} \cdot \lim_{x \to c} (x - c)$$

$$= f(c) + f'(c) \cdot 0$$

$$= f(c) \qquad ∎$$

The converse of this theorem is false. If a function f is continuous at c, it does not follow that f has a derivative at c. This is easily seen by considering $f(x) = |x|$ at the origin (Figure 3). This function is certainly continuous at zero. However, it does not have a derivative there, as we now show. Note that for $f(x) = |x|$,

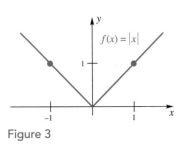

Figure 3

$$\frac{f(0 + h) - f(0)}{h} = \frac{|0 + h| - |0|}{h} = \frac{|h|}{h}$$

Thus,

$$\lim_{h \to 0^+} \frac{f(0 + h) - f(0)}{h} = \lim_{h \to 0^+} \frac{|h|}{h} = \lim_{h \to 0^+} \frac{h}{h} = 1$$

whereas

$$\lim_{h \to 0^-} \frac{f(0 + h) - f(0)}{h} = \lim_{h \to 0^-} \frac{|h|}{h} = \lim_{h \to 0^-} \frac{-h}{h} = -1$$

Since the right- and left-hand limits are different,

$$\lim_{h \to 0} \frac{f(0 + h) - f(0)}{h}$$

does not exist. Therefore, $f'(0)$ does not exist.

A similar argument shows that at any point where the graph of a continuous function has a sharp corner the function is not differentiable. The graph in Figure 4 indicates a number of ways for a function to be nondifferentiable at a point.

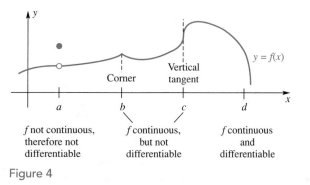

Figure 4

For the function shown in Figure 4 the derivative does not exist at the point c where the tangent line is vertical. This is because

$$\lim_{h \to 0} \frac{f(c + h) - f(c)}{h} = \infty$$

This corresponds to the fact that the slope of a vertical line is undefined.

Increments   If the value of a variable x changes from x_1 to x_2, then $x_2 - x_1$, the change in x, is called an **increment** of x and is commonly denoted by Δx (read "delta x"). Note that Δx does *not* mean Δ times x. If $x_1 = 4.1$ and $x_2 = 5.7$, then

$$\Delta x = x_2 - x_1 = 5.7 - 4.1 = 1.6$$

If $x_1 = c$ and $x_2 = c + h$, then

$$\Delta x = x_2 - x_1 = c + h - c = h$$

Suppose next that $y = f(x)$ determines a function. If x changes from x_1 to x_2, then y changes from $y_1 = f(x_1)$ to $y_2 = f(x_2)$. Thus, corresponding to the increment $\Delta x = x_2 - x_1$ in x, there is an increment in y given by

$$\Delta y = y_2 - y_1 = f(x_2) - f(x_1)$$

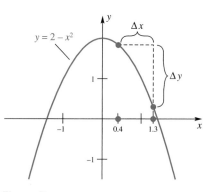

Figure 5

EXAMPLE 7   Let $y = f(x) = 2 - x^2$. Find Δy when x changes from 0.4 to 1.3 (see Figure 5).

SOLUTION

$$\Delta y = f(1.3) - f(0.4) = \left[2 - (1.3)^2\right] - \left[2 - (0.4)^2\right] = -1.53 \quad \blacksquare$$

Leibniz Notation for the Derivative Suppose now that the independent variable changes from x to $x + \Delta x$. The corresponding change in the dependent variable, y, will be

$$\Delta y = f(x + \Delta x) - f(x)$$

and the ratio

$$\frac{\Delta y}{\Delta x} = \frac{f(x + \Delta x) - f(x)}{\Delta x}$$

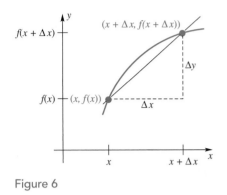

Figure 6

represents the slope of a secant line through $(x, f(x))$, as shown in Figure 6. As $\Delta x \to 0$, the slope of this secant line approaches that of the tangent line, and for this latter slope we use the symbol dy/dx. Thus,

$$\frac{dy}{dx} = \lim_{\Delta x \to 0} \frac{\Delta y}{\Delta x} = \lim_{\Delta x \to 0} \frac{f(x + \Delta x) - f(x)}{\Delta x} = f'(x)$$

Gottfried Wilhelm Leibniz, a contemporary of Isaac Newton, called dy/dx a quotient of two infinitesimals. The meaning of the word *infinitesimal* is vague, and we will not use it. However, dy/dx is a standard symbol for the derivative and we will use it frequently from now on.

The Graph of the Derivative The derivative $f'(x)$ gives the slope of the tangent line to the graph of $y = f(x)$ at the value of x. Thus, when the tangent line is sloping up to the right, the derivative is positive, and when the tangent line is sloping down to the right, the derivative is negative. We can therefore get a rough picture of the derivative given just the graph of the function.

EXAMPLE 8 Given the graph of $y = f(x)$ shown in the first part of Figure 7, sketch a graph of the derivative $f'(x)$.

SOLUTION For $x < 0$, the tangent line to the graph of $y = f(x)$ has positive slope. A rough calculation from the plot suggests that when $x = -2$, the slope is about 3. As we move from left to right along the curve in Figure 7, we see that the slope is still positive (for a while) but that the tangent lines become flatter and flatter. When $x = 0$, the tangent line is horizontal, telling us that $f'(0) = 0$. For x between 0 and 2, the tangent lines have negative slope, indicating that the derivative will be negative over this interval. When $x = 2$, we are again at a point where the tangent line is horizontal, so the derivative is equal to zero when $x = 2$. For $x > 2$, the tangent line again has positive slope. The graph of the derivative $f'(x)$ is shown in the last part of Figure 7. $\quad \blacksquare$

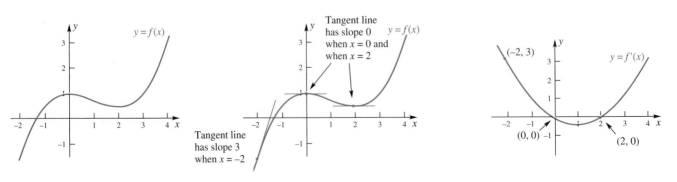

Figure 7

Concepts Review

1. The derivative of f at x is given by $f'(x) = \lim\limits_{h \to 0}$ ____. Equivalently, $f'(x) = \lim\limits_{t \to x}$ ____.

2. The slope of the tangent line to the graph of $y = f(x)$ at the point $(c, f(c))$ is ____.

3. If f is differentiable at c, then f is ____ at c. The converse is false, as is shown by the example $f(x) =$ ____.

4. If $y = f(x)$, we now have two different symbols for the derivative of y with respect to x. They are ____ and ____.

Problem Set 3.2

In Problems 1–4, use the definition

$$f'(c) = \lim_{h \to 0} \frac{f(c + h) - f(c)}{h}$$

to find the indicated derivative.

1. $f'(1)$ if $f(x) = x^2$

2. $f'(2)$ if $f(t) = (2t)^2$

3. $f'(3)$ if $f(t) = t^2 - t$

4. $f'(4)$ if $f(s) = \dfrac{1}{s - 1}$

In Problems 5–22, use $f'(x) = \lim\limits_{h \to 0} [f(x + h) - f(x)]/h$ to find the derivative at x.

5. $s(x) = 2x + 1$

6. $f(x) = \alpha x + \beta$

7. $r(x) = 3x^2 + 4$

8. $f(x) = x^2 + x + 1$

9. $f(x) = ax^2 + bx + c$

10. $f(x) = x^4$

11. $f(x) = x^3 + 2x^2 + 1$

12. $g(x) = x^4 + x^2$

13. $h(x) = \dfrac{2}{x}$

14. $S(x) = \dfrac{1}{x + 1}$

15. $F(x) = \dfrac{6}{x^2 + 1}$

16. $F(x) = \dfrac{x - 1}{x + 1}$

17. $G(x) = \dfrac{2x - 1}{x - 4}$

18. $G(x) = \dfrac{2x}{x^2 - x}$

19. $g(x) = \sqrt{3x}$

20. $g(x) = \dfrac{1}{\sqrt{3x}}$

21. $H(x) = \dfrac{3}{\sqrt{x - 2}}$

22. $H(x) = \sqrt{x^2 + 4}$

In Problems 23–26, use $f'(x) = \lim\limits_{t \to x} [f(t) - f(x)]/[t - x]$ to find $f'(x)$ (see Example 5).

23. $f(x) = x^2 - 3x$

24. $f(x) = x^3 + 5x$

25. $f(x) = \dfrac{x}{x - 5}$

26. $f(x) = \dfrac{x + 3}{x}$

In Problems 27–36, the given limit is a derivative, but of what function and at what point? (See Example 6.)

27. $\lim\limits_{h \to 0} \dfrac{2(5 + h)^3 - 2(5)^3}{h}$

28. $\lim\limits_{h \to 0} \dfrac{(3 + h)^2 + 2(3 + h) - 15}{h}$

29. $\lim\limits_{x \to 2} \dfrac{x^2 - 4}{x - 2}$

30. $\lim\limits_{x \to 3} \dfrac{x^3 + x - 30}{x - 3}$

31. $\lim\limits_{t \to x} \dfrac{t^2 - x^2}{t - x}$

32. $\lim\limits_{p \to x} \dfrac{p^3 - x^3}{p - x}$

33. $\lim\limits_{x \to t} \dfrac{\frac{2}{x} - \frac{2}{t}}{x - t}$

34. $\lim\limits_{x \to y} \dfrac{\sin x - \sin y}{x - y}$

35. $\lim\limits_{h \to 0} \dfrac{\cos(x + h) - \cos x}{h}$

36. $\lim\limits_{h \to 0} \dfrac{\tan(t + h) - \tan t}{h}$

In Problems 37–44, the graph of a function $y = f(x)$ is given. Use this graph to sketch the graph of $y = f'(x)$.

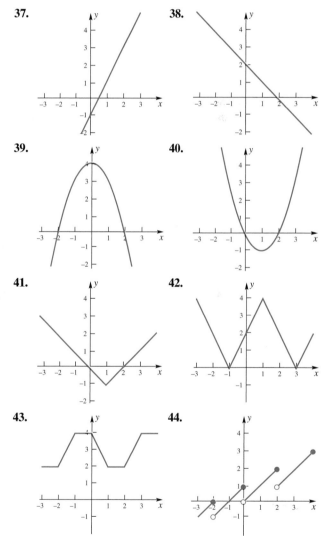

37.

38.

39.

40.

41.

42.

43.

44.

In Problems 45–50, find Δy for the given values of x_1 and x_2 (see Example 7).

45. $y = 3x + 2$, $x_1 = 1$, $x_2 = 1.5$

46. $y = 3x^2 + 2x + 1$, $x_1 = 0.0$, $x_2 = 0.1$

47. $y = \dfrac{1}{x}$, $x_1 = 1.0$, $x_2 = 1.2$

48. $y = \dfrac{2}{x + 1}$, $x_1 = 0$, $x_2 = 0.1$

49. $y = \dfrac{3}{x + 1}$, $x_1 = 2.34$, $x_2 = 2.31$

 50. $y = \cos 2x$, $x_1 = 0.571$, $x_2 = 0.573$

In Problems 51–56, first find and simplify

$$\frac{\Delta y}{\Delta x} = \frac{f(x + \Delta x) - f(x)}{\Delta x}$$

Then find dy/dx by taking the limit of your answer as $\Delta x \to 0$.

51. $y = x^2$

52. $y = x^3 - 3x^2$

53. $y = \dfrac{1}{x + 1}$

54. $y = 1 + \dfrac{1}{x}$

55. $y = \dfrac{x - 1}{x + 1}$

56. $y = \dfrac{x^2 - 1}{x}$

57. From Figure 8, estimate $f'(0)$, $f'(2)$, $f'(5)$, and $f'(7)$.

58. From Figure 9, estimate $g'(-1)$, $g'(1)$, $g'(4)$, and $g'(6)$.

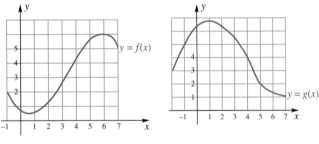

Figure 8

Figure 9

59. Sketch the graph of $y = f'(x)$ on $-1 < x < 7$ for the function f in Figure 8.

60. Sketch the graph of $y = g'(x)$ on $-1 < x < 7$ for the function g in Figure 9.

61. Consider the function $y = f(x)$, whose graph is sketched in Figure 10.

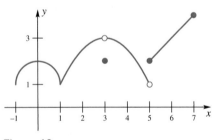

Figure 10

(a) Estimate $f(2)$, $f'(2)$, $f(0.5)$, and $f'(0.5)$.

(b) Estimate the average rate of change in f on the interval $0.5 \le x \le 2.5$.

(c) Where on the interval $-1 < x < 7$ does $\lim\limits_{u \to x} f(u)$ fail to exist?

(d) Where on the interval $-1 < x < 7$ does f fail to be continuous?

(e) Where on the interval $-1 < x < 7$ does f fail to have a derivative?

(f) Where on the interval $-1 < x < 7$ is $f'(x) = 0$?

(g) Where on the interval $-1 < x < 7$ is $f'(x) = 1$?

62. Figure 14 in Section 3.1 shows the position s of an elevator as a function of time t. At what points does the derivative exist? Sketch the derivative of s.

63. Figure 15 in Section 3.1 shows the normal high temperature for St. Louis, Missouri. Sketch the derivative.

64. Figure 11 shows two functions. One is the function f, and the other is its derivative f'. Which one is which?

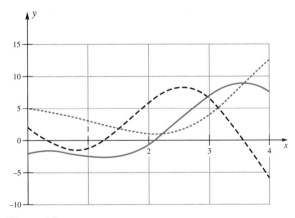

Figure 11

65. Figure 12 shows three functions. One is the function f; another is its derivative f', which we will call g; and the third is the derivative of g. Which one is which?

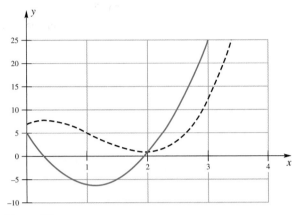

Figure 12

EXPL **66.** Suppose that $f(x + y) = f(x)f(y)$ for all x and y. Show that if $f'(0)$ exists then $f'(a)$ exists and $f'(a) = f(a)f'(0)$.

67. Let $f(x) = \begin{cases} mx + b & \text{if } x < 2 \\ x^2 & \text{if } x \ge 2 \end{cases}$

Determine m and b so that f is differentiable everywhere.

EXPL **68.** The **symmetric derivative** $f_s(x)$ is defined by

$$f_s(x) = \lim_{h \to 0} \frac{f(x + h) - f(x - h)}{2h}$$

Show that if $f'(x)$ exists then $f_s(x)$ exists, but that the converse is false.

69. Let f be differentiable and let $f'(x_0) = m$. Find $f'(-x_0)$ if

(a) f is an odd function.

(b) f is an even function.

70. Prove that the derivative of an odd function is an even function and that the derivative of an even function is an odd function.

CAS *Use a CAS to do Problems 71 and 72.*

EXPL **71.** Draw the graphs of $f(x) = x^3 - 4x^2 + 3$ and its derivative $f'(x)$ on the interval $[-2, 5]$ using the same axes.

(a) Where on this interval is $f'(x) < 0$?

(b) Where on this interval is $f(x)$ decreasing?

(c) Make a conjecture. Experiment with other intervals and other functions to support this conjecture.

EXPL **72.** Draw the graphs of $f(x) = \cos x - \sin(x/2)$ and its derivative $f'(x)$ on the interval $[0, 9]$ using the same axes.

(a) Where on this interval is $f'(x) > 0$?

(b) Where on this interval is $f(x)$ increasing?

(c) Make a conjecture. Experiment with other intervals and other functions to support this conjecture.

Answers to Concepts Review: **1.** $[f(x + h) - f(x)]/h$; $[f(t) - f(x)]/(t - x)$ **2.** $f'(c)$ **3.** continuous; $|x|$

4. $f'(x)$; $\dfrac{dy}{dx}$

3.3
Rules for Finding Derivatives

The process of finding the derivative of a function directly from the definition of the derivative, that is, by setting up the difference quotient

$$\frac{f(x + h) - f(x)}{h}$$

and evaluating its limit, can be time consuming and tedious. We are going to develop tools that will allow us to shortcut this lengthy process—that will, in fact, allow us to find derivatives of the most complicated looking functions.

Recall that the derivative of a function f is another function f'. We saw in Example 2 of the previous section that if $f(x) = x^3 + 7x$ is the formula for f, then $f'(x) = 3x^2 + 7$ is the formula for f'. When we take the derivative of f, we say that we are differentiating f. The derivative *operates* on f to produce f'. We often use the symbol D_x to indicate the operation of differentiating (Figure 1). The D_x symbol says that we are to take the derivative (with respect to the variable x) of what follows. Thus, we write $D_x f(x) = f'(x)$ or (in the case just mentioned) $D_x(x^3 + 7x) = 3x^2 + 7$. This D_x is an example of an **operator.** As Figure 1 suggests, an operator is a function whose input is a function and whose output is another function.

With Leibniz notation, introduced in the last section, we now have three notations for the derivative. If $y = f(x)$, we can denote the derivative of f by

$$f'(x) \qquad \text{or} \qquad D_x f(x) \qquad \text{or} \qquad \frac{dy}{dx}$$

We will use the notation $\dfrac{d}{dx}$ to mean the same as the operator D_x.

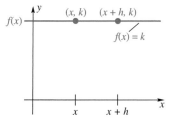

f
Input

Operation
D_x

f'
Output

An operator

Figure 1

The Constant and Power Rules The graph of the constant function $f(x) = k$ is a horizontal line (Figure 2), which therefore has slope zero everywhere. This is one way to understand our first theorem.

$f(x)$

(x, k) $(x + h, k)$

$f(x) = k$

x $x + h$

Figure 2

Theorem A	Constant Function Rule

If $f(x) = k$, where k is a constant, then for any x, $f'(x) = 0$; that is,

$$D_x(k) = 0$$

Proof

$$f'(x) = \lim_{h \to 0} \frac{f(x + h) - f(x)}{h} = \lim_{h \to 0} \frac{k - k}{h} = \lim_{h \to 0} 0 = 0 \qquad \blacksquare$$

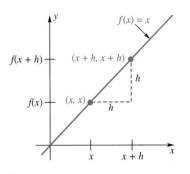

Figure 3

The graph of $f(x) = x$ is a line through the origin with slope 1 (Figure 3); so we should expect the derivative of this function to be 1 for all x.

Theorem B **Identity Function Rule**

If $f(x) = x$, then $f'(x) = 1$; that is,

$$D_x(x) = 1$$

Proof

$$f'(x) = \lim_{h \to 0} \frac{f(x+h) - f(x)}{h} = \lim_{h \to 0} \frac{x + h - x}{h} = \lim_{h \to 0} \frac{h}{h} = 1 \qquad ∎$$

Before stating our next theorem, we recall something from algebra: how to raise a binomial to a power.

$$(a + b)^2 = a^2 + 2ab + b^2$$
$$(a + b)^3 = a^3 + 3a^2b + 3ab^2 + b^3$$
$$(a + b)^4 = a^4 + 4a^3b + 6a^2b^2 + 4ab^3 + b^4$$
$$\vdots$$
$$(a + b)^n = a^n + na^{n-1}b + \frac{n(n-1)}{2}a^{n-2}b^2 + \cdots + nab^{n-1} + b^n$$

Theorem C **Power Rule**

If $f(x) = x^n$, where n is a positive integer, then $f'(x) = nx^{n-1}$; that is,

$$D_x(x^n) = nx^{n-1}$$

Proof

$$f'(x) = \lim_{h \to 0} \frac{f(x+h) - f(x)}{h} = \lim_{h \to 0} \frac{(x+h)^n - x^n}{h}$$

$$= \lim_{h \to 0} \frac{x^n + nx^{n-1}h + \dfrac{n(n-1)}{2}x^{n-2}h^2 + \cdots + nxh^{n-1} + h^n - x^n}{h}$$

$$= \lim_{h \to 0} \frac{h\left[nx^{n-1} + \dfrac{n(n-1)}{2}x^{n-2}h + \cdots + nxh^{n-2} + h^{n-1}\right]}{h}$$

Within the brackets, all terms except the first have h as a factor, and so for every value of x, each of these terms has limit zero as h approaches zero. Thus,

$$f'(x) = nx^{n-1} \qquad ∎$$

As illustrations of Theorem C, note that

$$D_x(x^3) = 3x^2 \qquad D_x(x^9) = 9x^8 \qquad D_x(x^{100}) = 100x^{99}$$

D_x Is a Linear Operator The operator D_x behaves very well when applied to constant multiples of functions or to sums of functions.

Theorem D **Constant Multiple Rule**

If k is a constant and f is a differentiable function, then $(kf)'(x) = k \cdot f'(x)$; that is,

$$D_x\left[k \cdot f(x)\right] = k \cdot D_x f(x)$$

In words, *a constant multiplier k can be passed across the operator D_x.*

Proof Let $F(x) = k \cdot f(x)$. Then

$$F'(x) = \lim_{h \to 0} \frac{F(x + h) - F(x)}{h} = \lim_{h \to 0} \frac{k \cdot f(x + h) - k \cdot f(x)}{h}$$

$$= \lim_{h \to 0} k \cdot \frac{f(x + h) - f(x)}{h} = k \cdot \lim_{h \to 0} \frac{f(x + h) - f(x)}{h}$$

$$= k \cdot f'(x)$$

The next-to-last step was the critical one. We could shift k past the limit sign because of the Main Limit Theorem Part 3. ∎

Examples that illustrate this result are

$$D_x(-7x^3) = -7D_x(x^3) = -7 \cdot 3x^2 = -21x^2$$

and

$$D_x\left(\tfrac{4}{3}x^9\right) = \tfrac{4}{3}D_x(x^9) = \tfrac{4}{3} \cdot 9x^8 = 12x^8$$

Theorem E **Sum Rule**

If f and g are differentiable functions, then $(f + g)'(x) = f'(x) + g'(x)$; that is,

$$D_x\big[f(x) + g(x)\big] = D_x f(x) + D_x g(x)$$

In words, *the derivative of a sum is the sum of the derivatives.*

Proof Let $F(x) = f(x) + g(x)$. Then

$$F'(x) = \lim_{h \to 0} \frac{\big[f(x + h) + g(x + h)\big] - \big[f(x) + g(x)\big]}{h}$$

$$= \lim_{h \to 0} \left[\frac{f(x + h) - f(x)}{h} + \frac{g(x + h) - g(x)}{h}\right]$$

$$= \lim_{h \to 0} \frac{f(x + h) - f(x)}{h} + \lim_{h \to 0} \frac{g(x + h) - g(x)}{h}$$

$$= f'(x) + g'(x)$$

Again, the next-to-last step was the critical one. It is justified by the Main Limit Theorem Part 4. ∎

Any operator L with the properties stated in Theorems D and E is called *linear*; that is, L is a **linear operator** if for all functions f and g:

1. $L(kf) = kL(f)$, for every constant k;
2. $L(f + g) = L(f) + L(g)$.

Linear operators will appear again and again in this book; D_x is a particularly important example. A linear operator always satisfies the difference rule $L(f - g) = L(f) - L(g)$, stated next for D_x.

Theorem F **Difference Rule**

If f and g are differentiable functions, then $(f - g)'(x) = f'(x) - g'(x)$; that is,

$$D_x\big[f(x) - g(x)\big] = D_x f(x) - D_x g(x)$$

The proof of Theorem F is left as an exercise (Problem 54).

Linear Operator

The fundamental meaning of the word *linear*, as used in mathematics, is that given in this section. An operator L is linear if it satisfies the two key conditions:

- $L(ku) = kL(u)$
- $L(u + v) = L(u) + L(v)$

Linear operators play a central role in the *linear algebra* course, which many readers of this book will take.

Functions of the form $f(x) = mx + b$ are called *linear functions* because of their connections with lines. This terminology can be confusing because linear functions are not linear in the operator sense. To see this, note that

$$f(kx) = m(kx) + b$$

whereas

$$kf(x) = k(mx + b)$$

Thus, $f(kx) \neq kf(x)$ unless b happens to be zero.

EXAMPLE 1 Find the derivatives of $5x^2 + 7x - 6$ and $4x^6 - 3x^5 - 10x^2 + 5x + 16$.

SOLUTION

$$
\begin{aligned}
D_x(5x^2 + 7x - 6) &= D_x(5x^2 + 7x) - D_x(6) &&\text{(Theorem F)} \\
&= D_x(5x^2) + D_x(7x) - D_x(6) &&\text{(Theorem E)} \\
&= 5D_x(x^2) + 7D_x(x) - D_x(6) &&\text{(Theorem D)} \\
&= 5 \cdot 2x + 7 \cdot 1 - 0 &&\text{(Theorems C, B, A)} \\
&= 10x + 7
\end{aligned}
$$

To find the next derivative, we note that the theorems on sums and differences extend to any finite number of terms. Thus,

$$
\begin{aligned}
D_x(4x^6 &- 3x^5 - 10x^2 + 5x + 16) \\
&= D_x(4x^6) - D_x(3x^5) - D_x(10x^2) + D_x(5x) + D_x(16) \\
&= 4D_x(x^6) - 3D_x(x^5) - 10D_x(x^2) + 5D_x(x) + D_x(16) \\
&= 4(6x^5) - 3(5x^4) - 10(2x) + 5(1) + 0 \\
&= 24x^5 - 15x^4 - 20x + 5 \qquad\blacksquare
\end{aligned}
$$

The method of Example 1 allows us to find the derivative of any polynomial. If you know the Power Rule and do what comes naturally, you are almost sure to get the right result. Also, with practice, you will find that you can write the derivative immediately, without having to write any intermediate steps.

Product and Quotient Rules Now we are in for a surprise. So far, we have seen that the limit of a sum or difference is equal to the sum or difference of the limits (Theorem 2.3A, Parts 4 and 5), the limit of a product or quotient is the product or quotient of the limits (Theorem 2.3A, Parts 6 and 7), and the derivative of a sum or difference is the sum or difference of the derivatives (Theorems E and F). So what could be more natural than to have the derivative of a product be the product of the derivatives?

This may seem natural, but it is wrong. To see why, let's look at the following example.

EXAMPLE 2 Let $g(x) = x, h(x) = 1 + 2x$, and $f(x) = g(x) \cdot h(x) = x(1 + 2x)$. Find $D_x f(x), D_x g(x)$, and $D_x h(x)$, and show that $D_x f(x) \neq [D_x g(x)][D_x h(x)]$.

SOLUTION

$$
\begin{aligned}
D_x f(x) &= D_x[x(1 + 2x)] \\
&= D_x(x + 2x^2) \\
&= 1 + 4x \\
D_x g(x) &= D_x x = 1 \\
D_x h(x) &= D_x(1 + 2x) = 2
\end{aligned}
$$

Notice that

$$ D_x(g(x))D_x(h(x)) = 1 \cdot 2 = 2 $$

whereas

$$ D_x f(x) = D_x[g(x)h(x)] = 1 + 4x $$

Thus, $D_x f(x) \neq [D_x g(x)][D_x h(x)]$. $\qquad\blacksquare$

That the derivative of a product should be the product of the derivatives seemed so natural that it even fooled Gottfried Wilhelm von Leibniz, one of the discoverers of calculus. In a manuscript of November 11, 1675, he computed the derivative of the product of two functions and said (without checking) that it was equal to the product of the derivatives. Ten days later, he caught the error and gave the correct product rule, which we present as Theorem G.

> **Theorem G** **Product Rule**
>
> If f and g are differentiable functions, then
> $$(f \cdot g)'(x) = f(x)g'(x) + g(x)f'(x)$$
>
> That is,
> $$D_x\big[f(x)g(x)\big] = f(x)D_xg(x) + g(x)D_xf(x)$$

This rule should be memorized in words as follows: *The derivative of a product of two functions is the first times the derivative of the second plus the second times the derivative of the first.*

Proof Let $F(x) = f(x)g(x)$. Then

$$F'(x) = \lim_{h \to 0} \frac{F(x + h) - F(x)}{h}$$

$$= \lim_{h \to 0} \frac{f(x + h)g(x + h) - f(x)g(x)}{h}$$

$$= \lim_{h \to 0} \frac{f(x + h)g(x + h) - f(x + h)g(x) + f(x + h)g(x) - f(x)g(x)}{h}$$

$$= \lim_{h \to 0} \left[f(x + h) \cdot \frac{g(x + h) - g(x)}{h} + g(x) \cdot \frac{f(x + h) - f(x)}{h} \right]$$

$$= \lim_{h \to 0} f(x + h) \cdot \lim_{h \to 0} \frac{g(x + h) - g(x)}{h} + g(x) \cdot \lim_{h \to 0} \frac{f(x + h) - f(x)}{h}$$

$$= f(x)g'(x) + g(x)f'(x)$$

The derivation just given relies first on the trick of adding and subtracting the same thing, that is, $f(x + h)g(x)$. Second, at the very end, we use the fact that

$$\lim_{h \to 0} f(x + h) = f(x)$$

This is just an application of Theorem 3.2A (which says that differentiability at a point implies continuity there) and the definition of continuity at a point. ∎

EXAMPLE 3 Find the derivative of $(3x^2 - 5)(2x^4 - x)$ by use of the Product Rule. Check the answer by doing the problem a different way.

SOLUTION

$$D_x\big[(3x^2 - 5)(2x^4 - x)\big] = (3x^2 - 5)D_x(2x^4 - x) + (2x^4 - x)D_x(3x^2 - 5)$$

$$= (3x^2 - 5)(8x^3 - 1) + (2x^4 - x)(6x)$$

$$= 24x^5 - 3x^2 - 40x^3 + 5 + 12x^5 - 6x^2$$

$$= 36x^5 - 40x^3 - 9x^2 + 5$$

To check, we first multiply and then take the derivative.

$$(3x^2 - 5)(2x^4 - x) = 6x^6 - 10x^4 - 3x^3 + 5x$$

Thus,

$$D_x\left[(3x^2 - 5)(2x^4 - x)\right] = D_x(6x^6) - D_x(10x^4) - D_x(3x^3) + D_x(5x)$$

$$= 36x^5 - 40x^3 - 9x^2 + 5 \qquad \blacksquare$$

Theorem H **Quotient Rule**

Let f and g be differentiable functions with $g(x) \neq 0$. Then

$$\left(\frac{f}{g}\right)'(x) = \frac{g(x)f'(x) - f(x)g'(x)}{g^2(x)}$$

That is,

$$D_x\left(\frac{f(x)}{g(x)}\right) = \frac{g(x)D_x f(x) - f(x)D_x g(x)}{g^2(x)}$$

We strongly urge you to memorize this in words, as follows: *The derivative of a quotient is equal to the denominator times the derivative of the numerator minus the numerator times the derivative of the denominator, all divided by the square of the denominator.*

Proof Let $F(x) = f(x)/g(x)$. Then

$$F'(x) = \lim_{h \to 0} \frac{F(x + h) - F(x)}{h}$$

$$= \lim_{h \to 0} \frac{\dfrac{f(x + h)}{g(x + h)} - \dfrac{f(x)}{g(x)}}{h}$$

$$= \lim_{h \to 0} \frac{g(x)f(x + h) - f(x)g(x + h)}{h} \cdot \frac{1}{g(x)g(x + h)}$$

$$= \lim_{h \to 0} \left[\frac{g(x)f(x + h) - g(x)f(x) + f(x)g(x) - f(x)g(x + h)}{h}\right.$$

$$\left. \cdot \frac{1}{g(x)g(x + h)}\right]$$

$$= \lim_{h \to 0} \left\{\left[g(x)\frac{f(x + h) - f(x)}{h} - f(x)\frac{g(x + h) - g(x)}{h}\right]\frac{1}{g(x)g(x + h)}\right\}$$

$$= \left[g(x)f'(x) - f(x)g'(x)\right]\frac{1}{g(x)g(x)} \qquad \blacksquare$$

EXAMPLE 4 Find $\dfrac{d}{dx}\dfrac{(3x - 5)}{(x^2 + 7)}$.

SOLUTION

$$\frac{d}{dx}\left[\frac{3x - 5}{x^2 + 7}\right] = \frac{(x^2 + 7)\dfrac{d}{dx}(3x - 5) - (3x - 5)\dfrac{d}{dx}(x^2 + 7)}{(x^2 + 7)^2}$$

$$= \frac{(x^2 + 7)(3) - (3x - 5)(2x)}{(x^2 + 7)^2}$$

$$= \frac{-3x^2 + 10x + 21}{(x^2 + 7)^2} \qquad \blacksquare$$

■ **EXAMPLE 5** Find $D_x y$ if $y = \dfrac{2}{x^4 + 1} + \dfrac{3}{x}$.

SOLUTION

$$D_x y = D_x\!\left(\frac{2}{x^4 + 1}\right) + D_x\!\left(\frac{3}{x}\right)$$

$$= \frac{(x^4 + 1)D_x(2) - 2D_x(x^4 + 1)}{(x^4 + 1)^2} + \frac{xD_x(3) - 3D_x(x)}{x^2}$$

$$= \frac{(x^4 + 1)(0) - (2)(4x^3)}{(x^4 + 1)^2} + \frac{(x)(0) - (3)(1)}{x^2}$$

$$= \frac{-8x^3}{(x^4 + 1)^2} - \frac{3}{x^2}$$

■

■ **EXAMPLE 6** Show that the Power Rule holds for negative integral exponents; that is,

$$\boxed{D_x\!\left(x^{-n}\right) = -nx^{-n-1}}$$

$$D_x(x^{-n}) = D_x\!\left(\frac{1}{x^n}\right) = \frac{x^n \cdot 0 - 1 \cdot nx^{n-1}}{(x^n)^2} = \frac{-nx^{n-1}}{x^{2n}} = -nx^{-n-1}$$

■

We saw as part of Example 5 that $D_x(3/x) = -3/x^2$. Now we have another way to see the same thing.

Concepts Review

1. The derivative of a product of two functions is the first times _____ plus the _____ times the derivative of the first. In symbols, $D_x\big[f(x)g(x)\big] = $ _____.

2. The derivative of a quotient is the _____ times the derivative of the numerator minus the numerator times the derivative of the _____, all divided by the _____. In symbols, $D_x\big[f(x)/g(x)\big] = $ _____.

3. The second term (the term involving h) in the expansion of $(x + h)^n$ is _____. It is this fact that leads to the formula $D_x\big[x^n\big] = $ _____.

4. L is called a linear operator if $L(kf) = $ _____ and $L(f + g) = $ _____. The derivative operator denoted by _____ is such an operator.

Problem Set 3.3

In Problems 1–44, find $D_x y$ using the rules of this section.

1. $y = 2x^2$

2. $y = 3x^3$

3. $y = \pi x$

4. $y = \pi x^3$

5. $y = 2x^{-2}$

6. $y = -3x^{-4}$

7. $y = \dfrac{\pi}{x}$

8. $y = \dfrac{\alpha}{x^3}$

9. $y = \dfrac{100}{x^5}$

10. $y = \dfrac{3\alpha}{4x^5}$

11. $y = x^2 + 2x$

12. $y = 3x^4 + x^3$

13. $y = x^4 + x^3 + x^2 + x + 1$

14. $y = 3x^4 - 2x^3 - 5x^2 + \pi x + \pi^2$

15. $y = \pi x^7 - 2x^5 - 5x^{-2}$

16. $y = x^{12} + 5x^{-2} - \pi x^{-10}$

17. $y = \dfrac{3}{x^3} + x^{-4}$

18. $y = 2x^{-6} + x^{-1}$

19. $y = \dfrac{2}{x} - \dfrac{1}{x^2}$

20. $y = \dfrac{3}{x^3} - \dfrac{1}{x^4}$

21. $y = \dfrac{1}{2x} + 2x$

22. $y = \dfrac{2}{3x} - \dfrac{2}{3}$

23. $y = x(x^2 + 1)$

24. $y = 3x(x^3 - 1)$

25. $y = (2x + 1)^2$

26. $y = (-3x + 2)^2$

27. $y = (x^2 + 2)(x^3 + 1)$

28. $y = (x^4 - 1)(x^2 + 1)$

29. $y = (x^2 + 17)(x^3 - 3x + 1)$

30. $y = (x^4 + 2x)(x^3 + 2x^2 + 1)$

31. $y = (5x^2 - 7)(3x^2 - 2x + 1)$

32. $y = (3x^2 + 2x)(x^4 - 3x + 1)$

33. $y = \dfrac{1}{3x^2 + 1}$

34. $y = \dfrac{2}{5x^2 - 1}$

35. $y = \dfrac{1}{4x^2 - 3x + 9}$

36. $y = \dfrac{4}{2x^3 - 3x}$

37. $y = \dfrac{x - 1}{x + 1}$

38. $y = \dfrac{2x - 1}{x - 1}$

39. $y = \dfrac{2x^2 - 1}{3x + 5}$

40. $y = \dfrac{5x - 4}{3x^2 + 1}$

41. $y = \dfrac{2x^2 - 3x + 1}{2x + 1}$

42. $y = \dfrac{5x^2 + 2x - 6}{3x - 1}$

43. $y = \dfrac{x^2 - x + 1}{x^2 + 1}$

44. $y = \dfrac{x^2 - 2x + 5}{x^2 + 2x - 3}$

45. If $f(0) = 4, f'(0) = -1, g(0) = -3$, and $g'(0) = 5$, find

(a) $(f \cdot g)'(0)$ (b) $(f + g)'(0)$ (c) $(f/g)'(0)$

46. If $f(3) = 7, f'(3) = 2, g(3) = 6$, and $g'(3) = -10$, find

(a) $(f - g)'(3)$ (b) $(f \cdot g)'(3)$ (c) $(g/f)'(3)$

47. Use the Product Rule to show that $D_x[f(x)]^2 = 2 \cdot f(x) \cdot D_x f(x)$.

[EXPL] **48.** Develop a rule for $D_x[f(x)g(x)h(x)]$.

49. Find the equation of the tangent line to $y = x^2 - 2x + 2$ at the point $(1, 1)$.

50. Find the equation of the tangent line to $y = 1/(x^2 + 4)$ at the point $(1, 1/5)$.

51. Find all points on the graph of $y = x^3 - x^2$ where the tangent line is horizontal.

52. Find all points on the graph of $y = \frac{1}{3}x^3 + x^2 - x$ where the tangent line has slope 1.

53. Find all points on the graph of $y = 100/x^5$ where the tangent line is perpendicular to the line $y = x$.

54. Prove Theorem F in two ways.

55. The height s in feet of a ball above the ground at t seconds is given by $s = -16t^2 + 40t + 100$.

(a) What is its instantaneous velocity at $t = 2$?

(b) When is its instantaneous velocity 0?

56. A ball rolls down a long inclined plane so that its distance s from its starting point after t seconds is $s = 4.5t^2 + 2t$ feet. When will its instantaneous velocity be 30 feet per second?

[≈] **57.** There are two tangent lines to the curve $y = 4x - x^2$ that go through $(2, 5)$. Find the equations of both of them. *Hint:* Let

(x_0, y_0) be a point of tangency. Find two conditions that (x_0, y_0) must satisfy. See Figure 4.

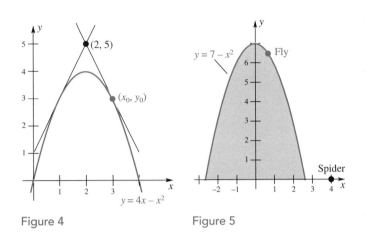

Figure 4   Figure 5

[≈] **58.** A space traveler is moving from left to right along the curve $y = x^2$. When she shuts off the engines, she will continue traveling along the tangent line at the point where she is at that time. At what point should she shut off the engines in order to reach the point $(4, 15)$?

[≈] **59.** A fly is crawling from left to right along the top of the curve $y = 7 - x^2$ (Figure 5). A spider waits at the point $(4, 0)$. Find the distance between the two insects when they first see each other.

60. Let $P(a, b)$ be a point on the first quadrant portion of the curve $y = 1/x$ and let the tangent line at P intersect the x-axis at A. Show that triangle AOP is isosceles and determine its area.

61. The radius of a spherical watermelon is growing at a constant rate of 2 centimeters per week. The thickness of the rind is always one-tenth of the radius. How fast is the volume of the rind growing at the end of the fifth week? Assume that the radius is initially 0.

[CAS] **62.** Redo Problems 29–44 on a computer and compare your answers with those you get by hand.

Answers to Concepts Review: **1.** the derivative of the second; second; $f(x)D_x g(x) + g(x)D_x f(x)$ **2.** denominator; denominator; square of the denominator; $[g(x)D_x f(x) - f(x)D_x g(x)]/g^2(x)$ **3.** $nx^{n-1}h; nx^{n-1}$ **4.** $kL(f); L(f) + L(g); D_x$

3.4

Derivatives of Trigonometric Functions

Figure 1 reminds us of the definition of the sine and cosine functions. In what follows, t should be thought of as a number measuring the length of an arc on the unit circle or, equivalently, as the number of radians in the corresponding angle. Thus, $f(t) = \sin t$ and $g(t) = \cos t$ are functions for which both domain and range are sets of real numbers. We may consider the problem of finding their derivatives.

The Derivative Formulas We choose to use x rather than t as our basic variable. To find $D_x(\sin x)$, we appeal to the definition of derivative and use the Addition Identity for $\sin(x + h)$.

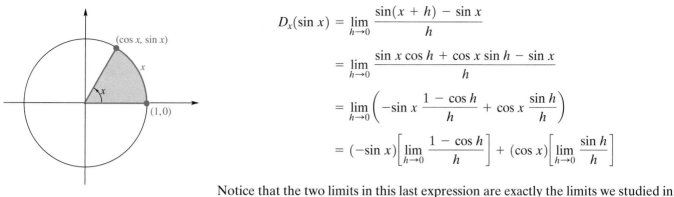

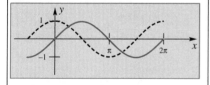

Figure 1

$$D_x(\sin x) = \lim_{h \to 0} \frac{\sin(x + h) - \sin x}{h}$$

$$= \lim_{h \to 0} \frac{\sin x \cos h + \cos x \sin h - \sin x}{h}$$

$$= \lim_{h \to 0} \left(-\sin x \frac{1 - \cos h}{h} + \cos x \frac{\sin h}{h} \right)$$

$$= (-\sin x)\left[\lim_{h \to 0} \frac{1 - \cos h}{h} \right] + (\cos x)\left[\lim_{h \to 0} \frac{\sin h}{h} \right]$$

Notice that the two limits in this last expression are exactly the limits we studied in Section 2.5. In Theorem 2.5B we proved that

$$\lim_{h \to 0} \frac{\sin h}{h} = 1 \quad \text{and} \quad \lim_{h \to 0} \frac{1 - \cos h}{h} = 0$$

Thus,

$$D_x(\sin x) = (-\sin x) \cdot 0 + (\cos x) \cdot 1 = \cos x$$

Similarly,

$$D_x(\cos x) = \lim_{h \to 0} \frac{\cos(x + h) - \cos x}{h}$$

$$= \lim_{h \to 0} \frac{\cos x \cos h - \sin x \sin h - \cos x}{h}$$

$$= \lim_{h \to 0} \left(-\cos x \frac{1 - \cos h}{h} - \sin x \frac{\sin h}{h} \right)$$

$$= (-\cos x) \cdot 0 - (\sin x) \cdot 1$$

$$= -\sin x$$

We summarize these results in an important theorem.

Could You Have Guessed?

The solid curve below is the graph of $y = \sin x$. Note that the slope is 1 at $0, 0$ at $\pi/2$, -1 at π, and so on. When we graph the slope function (the derivative), we obtain the dashed curve. Could you have guessed that $D_x \sin x = \cos x$?

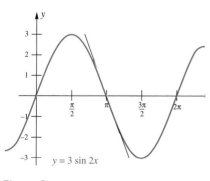

Try plotting these two functions in the same window on your CAS or graphing calculator.

> **Theorem A**
>
> The functions $f(x) = \sin x$ and $g(x) = \cos x$ are both differentiable and,
>
> $$D_x(\sin x) = \cos x \qquad D_x(\cos x) = -\sin x$$

EXAMPLE 1 Find $D_x(3 \sin x - 2 \cos x)$.

SOLUTION

$$D_x(3 \sin x - 2 \cos x) = 3D_x(\sin x) - 2D_x(\cos x)$$

$$= 3 \cos x + 2 \sin x \qquad \blacksquare$$

EXAMPLE 2 Find the equation of the tangent line to the graph of $y = 3 \sin x$ at the point $(\pi, 0)$. (See Figure 2.)

SOLUTION The derivative is $\dfrac{dy}{dx} = 3 \cos x$, so when $x = \pi$, the slope is $3 \cos \pi = -3$. Using the point-slope form for a line we find that the equation of the tangent line is

$y = 3 \sin 2x$

Figure 2

$$y - 0 = -3(x - \pi)$$
$$y = -3x + 3\pi \qquad \blacksquare$$

The Product and Quotient Rules are useful when evaluating derivatives of functions involving the trigonometric functions.

EXAMPLE 3 Find $D_x(x^2 \sin x)$.

SOLUTION The Product Rule is needed here.

$$D_x(x^2 \sin x) = x^2 D_x(\sin x) + \sin x(D_x x^2) = x^2 \cos x + 2x \sin x \qquad \blacksquare$$

EXAMPLE 4 Find $\dfrac{d}{dx}\left(\dfrac{1 + \sin x}{\cos x}\right)$.

SOLUTION For this problem, the Quotient Rule is needed.

$$\frac{d}{dx}\left(\frac{1 + \sin x}{\cos x}\right) = \frac{\cos x\left(\dfrac{d}{dx}(1 + \sin x)\right) - (1 + \sin x)\left(\dfrac{d}{dx}\cos x\right)}{\cos^2 x}$$

$$= \frac{\cos^2 x + \sin x + \sin^2 x}{\cos^2 x}$$

$$= \frac{1 + \sin x}{\cos^2 x} \qquad \blacksquare$$

EXAMPLE 5 At time t seconds, the center of a bobbing cork is $y = 2 \sin t$ centimeters above (or below) water level. What is the velocity of the cork at $t = 0, \pi/2, \pi$?

SOLUTION The velocity is the derivative of position, and $\dfrac{dy}{dt} = 2 \cos t$. Thus, when $t = 0$, $\dfrac{dy}{dt} = 2 \cos 0 = 2$, when $t = \pi/2$, $\dfrac{dy}{dt} = 2 \cos \dfrac{\pi}{2} = 0$, and when $t = \pi$, $\dfrac{dy}{dt} = 2 \cos \pi = -2$. $\qquad \blacksquare$

Since the tangent, cotangent, secant, and cosecant functions are defined in terms of the sine and cosine functions, the derivatives of these functions can be obtained from Theorem A by applying the Quotient Rule. The results are summarized in Theorem B; for proofs, see Problems 5–8.

Theorem B

For all points x in the function's domain,

$$D_x \tan x = \sec^2 x \qquad\qquad D_x \cot x = -\csc^2 x$$
$$D_x \sec x = \sec x \tan x \qquad\qquad D_x \csc x = -\csc x \cot x$$

EXAMPLE 6 Find $D_x(x^n \tan x)$ for $n \geq 1$.

SOLUTION We apply the Product Rule along with Theorem B.

$$D_x(x^n \tan x) = x^n D_x(\tan x) + \tan x(D_x x^n)$$
$$= x^n \sec^2 x + nx^{n-1} \tan x \qquad \blacksquare$$

EXAMPLE 7 Find the equation of the tangent line to the graph of $y = \tan x$ at the point $(\pi/4, 1)$.

SOLUTION The derivative of $y = \tan x$ is $\dfrac{dy}{dx} = \sec^2 x$. When $x = \pi/4$, the derivative is equal to $\sec^2 \dfrac{\pi}{4} = \left(\dfrac{2}{\sqrt{2}}\right)^2 = 2$. Thus the required line has slope 2 and passes through $(\pi/4, 1)$. Thus

$$y - 1 = 2\left(x - \frac{\pi}{4}\right)$$

$$y = 2x - \frac{\pi}{2} + 1$$ ■

EXAMPLE 8 Find all points on the graph of $y = \sin^2 x$ where the tangent line is horizontal.

SOLUTION The tangent line is horizontal when the derivative is equal to zero. To get the derivative of $\sin^2 x$, we use the Product Rule.

$$\frac{d}{dx}\sin^2 x = \frac{d}{dx}(\sin x \sin x) = \sin x \cos x + \sin x \cos x = 2 \sin x \cos x$$

The product of $\sin x$ and $\cos x$ is equal to zero when either $\sin x$ or $\cos x$ is equal to zero; that is, at $x = 0, \pm\dfrac{\pi}{2}, \pm\pi, \pm\dfrac{3\pi}{2}, \dots$. ■

Concepts Review

1. By definition, $D_x(\sin x) = \lim\limits_{h \to 0}$ _____.

2. To evaluate the limit in the preceding statement, we first use the Addition Identity for the sine function and then do a little algebra to obtain

$$D_x(\sin x) = (-\sin x)\left(\lim_{h \to 0}\frac{1 - \cos h}{h}\right) +$$
$$(\cos x)\left(\lim_{h \to 0}\frac{\sin h}{h}\right)$$

The two displayed limits have the values _____ and _____, respectively.

3. The result of the calculation in the preceding statement is the important derivative formula $D_x(\sin x) =$ _____. The corresponding derivative formula $D_x(\cos x) =$ _____ is obtained in a similar manner.

4. At $x = \pi/3$, $D_x(\sin x)$ has the value _____. Thus, the equation of the tangent line to $y = \sin x$ at $x = \pi/3$ is _____.

Problem Set 3.4

In Problems 1–18, find $D_x y$.

1. $y = 2 \sin x + 3 \cos x$

2. $y = \sin^2 x$

3. $y = \sin^2 x + \cos^2 x$

4. $y = 1 - \cos^2 x$

5. $y = \sec x = 1/\cos x$

6. $y = \csc x = 1/\sin x$

7. $y = \tan x = \dfrac{\sin x}{\cos x}$

8. $y = \cot x = \dfrac{\cos x}{\sin x}$

9. $y = \dfrac{\sin x + \cos x}{\cos x}$

10. $y = \dfrac{\sin x + \cos x}{\tan x}$

11. $y = \sin x \cos x$

12. $y = \sin x \tan x$

13. $y = \dfrac{\sin x}{x}$

14. $y = \dfrac{1 - \cos x}{x}$

15. $y = x^2 \cos x$

16. $y = \dfrac{x \cos x + \sin x}{x^2 + 1}$

17. $y = \tan^2 x$

18. $y = \sec^3 x$

C **19.** Find the equation of the tangent line to $y = \cos x$ at $x = 1$.

20. Find the equation of the tangent line to $y = \cot x$ at $x = \dfrac{\pi}{4}$.

21. Use the trigonometric identity $\sin 2x = 2 \sin x \cos x$ along with the Product Rule to find $D_x \sin 2x$.

22. Use the trigonometric identity $\cos 2x = 2 \cos^2 x - 1$ along with the Product Rule to find $D_x \cos 2x$.

23. A Ferris wheel of radius 30 feet is rotating counterclockwise with an angular velocity of 2 radians per second. How fast is a seat on the rim rising (in the vertical direction) when it is 15 feet above the horizontal line through the center of the wheel? *Hint:* Use the result of Problem 21.

24. A Ferris wheel of radius 20 feet is rotating counterclockwise with an angular velocity of 1 radian per second. One seat on the rim is at $(20, 0)$ at time $t = 0$.

(a) What are its coordinates at $t = \pi/6$?

(b) How fast is it rising (vertically) at $t = \pi/6$?

(c) How fast is it rising when it is rising at the fastest rate?

25. Find the equation of the tangent line to $y = \tan x$ at $x = 0$.

26. Find all points on the graph of $y = \tan^2 x$ where the tangent line is horizontal.

27. Find all points on the graph of $y = 9 \sin x \cos x$ where the tangent line is horizontal.

28. Let $f(x) = x - \sin x$. Find all points on the graph of $y = f(x)$ where the tangent line is horizontal. Find all points on the graph of $y = f(x)$ where the tangent line has slope 2.

29. Show that the curves $y = \sqrt{2} \sin x$ and $y = \sqrt{2} \cos x$ intersect at right angles at a certain point with $0 < x < \pi/2$.

30. At time t seconds, the center of a bobbing cork is $3 \sin 2t$ centimeters above (or below) water level. What is the velocity of the cork at $t = 0, \pi/2, \pi$?

31. Use the definition of the derivative to show that $D_x(\sin x^2) = 2x \cos x^2$.

32. Use the definition of the derivative to show that $D_x(\sin 5x) = 5 \cos 5x$.

GC *Problems 33 and 34 are computer or graphing calculator exercises.*

33. Let $f(x) = x \sin x$.

(a) Draw the graphs of $f(x)$ and $f'(x)$ on $[\pi, 6\pi]$.

(b) How many solutions does $f(x) = 0$ have on $[\pi, 6\pi]$? How many solutions does $f'(x) = 0$ have on this interval?

(c) What is wrong with the following conjecture? If f and f' are both continuous and differentiable on $[a, b]$, if $f(a) = f(b) = 0$, and if $f(x) = 0$ has exactly n solutions on $[a, b]$, then $f'(x) = 0$ has exactly $n - 1$ solutions on $[a, b]$.

(d) Determine the maximum value of $|f(x) - f'(x)|$ on $[\pi, 6\pi]$.

34. Let $f(x) = \cos^3 x - 1.25 \cos^2 x + 0.225$. Find $f'(x_0)$ at that point x_0 in $[\pi/2, \pi]$ where $f(x_0) = 0$.

Answers to Concepts Review: **1.** $[\sin(x + h) - \sin x]/h$
2. $0; 1$ **3.** $\cos x; -\sin x$ **4.** $\frac{1}{2}; y - \sqrt{3}/2 = \frac{1}{2}(x - \pi/3)$

3.5
The Chain Rule

Imagine trying to find the derivative of

$$F(x) = (2x^2 - 4x + 1)^{60}$$

We could find the derivative, but we would first have to multiply together the 60 quadratic factors of $2x^2 - 4x + 1$ and then differentiate the resulting polynomial. Or, how about trying to find the derivative of

$$G(x) = \sin 3x$$

We might be able to use some trigonometric identities to reduce it to something that depends on $\sin x$ and $\cos x$ and then use the rules from the previous section.

Fortunately, there is a better way. After learning the *Chain Rule*, we will be able to write the answers

$$F'(x) = 60(2x^2 - 4x + 1)^{59}(4x - 4)$$

and

$$G'(x) = 3 \cos 3x$$

The Chain Rule is so important that we will seldom again differentiate any function without using it.

Differentiating a Composite Function If David can type twice as fast as Mary and Mary can type three times as fast as Joe, then David can type $2 \times 3 = 6$ times as fast as Joe.

Consider the composite function $y = f(g(x))$. If we let $u = g(x)$, we can then think of f as a function of u. Suppose that $f(u)$ changes twice as fast as u, and $u = g(x)$ changes three times as fast as x. How fast is y changing? The statements

"$y = f(u)$ changes twice as fast as u" and "$u = g(x)$ changes three times as fast as x" can be restated as

$$\frac{dy}{du} = 2 \quad \text{and} \quad \frac{du}{dx} = 3$$

Just as in the previous paragraph, it seems as if the rates should multiply; that is, the rate of change of y with respect to x should equal the rate of change of y with respect to u times the rate of change of u with respect to x. In other words,

$$\frac{dy}{dx} = \frac{dy}{du} \times \frac{du}{dx}$$

This is in fact true, and we will sketch the proof at the end of this section. The result is called the **Chain Rule.**

Theorem A   **Chain Rule**

Let $y = f(u)$ and $u = g(x)$. If g is differentiable at x and f is differentiable at $u = g(x)$, then the composite function $f \circ g$, defined by $(f \circ g)(x) = f(g(x))$, is differentiable at x and

$$(f \circ g)'(x) = f'(g(x))g'(x)$$

That is,

$$D_x(f(g(x))) = f'(g(x))g'(x)$$

or

$$\frac{dy}{dx} = \frac{dy}{du}\frac{du}{dx}$$

You can remember the Chain Rule this way: *The derivative of a composite function is the derivative of the outer function evaluated at the inner function, times the derivative of the inner function.*

Applications of the Chain Rule   We begin with the example $(2x^2 - 4x + 1)^{60}$ introduced at the beginning of this section.

EXAMPLE 1   If $y = (2x^2 - 4x + 1)^{60}$, find $D_x y$.

SOLUTION   We think of y as the 60th power of a function of x; that is

$$y = u^{60} \quad \text{and} \quad u = 2x^2 - 4x + 1$$

The outer function is $f(u) = u^{60}$ and the inner function is $u = g(x) = 2x^2 - 4x + 1$. Thus,

$$D_x y = D_x f(g(x))$$
$$= f'(u)g'(x)$$
$$= (60u^{59})(4x - 4)$$
$$= 60(2x^2 - 4x + 1)^{59}(4x - 4) \qquad \blacksquare$$

EXAMPLE 2   If $y = 1/(2x^5 - 7)^3$, find $\dfrac{dy}{dx}$.

SOLUTION   Think of it this way.

$$y = \frac{1}{u^3} = u^{-3} \quad \text{and} \quad u = 2x^5 - 7$$

Thus,

$$\frac{dy}{dx} = \frac{dy}{du}\frac{du}{dx}$$

$$= (-3u^{-4})(10x^4)$$

$$= \frac{-3}{u^4} \cdot 10x^4$$

$$= \frac{-30x^4}{(2x^5 - 7)^4} \qquad \blacksquare$$

> ### The Last First
>
> Here is an informal rule that may help you in using the derivative rules.
>
> *The last step in calculation corresponds to the first step in differentiation.*
>
> For example, the last step in calculating $(2x + 1)^3$ is to cube $2x + 1$, so you would first apply the Chain Rule to the cube function. The last step in calculating
>
> $$\frac{x^2 - 1}{x^2 + 1}$$
>
> is to take the quotient, so the first rule to use in differentiating is the Quotient Rule.

EXAMPLE 3   Find $D_t\left(\dfrac{t^3 - 2t + 1}{t^4 + 3}\right)^{13}$.

SOLUTION   The last step in calculating this expression would be to raise the expression on the inside to the power 13. Thus, we begin by applying the Chain Rule to the function $y = u^{13}$, where $u = (t^3 - 2t + 1)/(t^4 + 3)$. The Chain Rule followed by the Quotient Rule gives

$$D_t\left(\frac{t^3 - 2t + 1}{t^4 + 3}\right)^{13} = 13\left(\frac{t^3 - 2t + 1}{t^4 + 3}\right)^{13-1} D_t\left(\frac{t^3 - 2t + 1}{t^4 + 3}\right)$$

$$= 13\left(\frac{t^3 - 2t + 1}{t^4 + 3}\right)^{12} \frac{(t^4 + 3)(3t^2 - 2) - (t^3 - 2t + 1)(4t^3)}{(t^4 + 3)^2}$$

$$= 13\left(\frac{t^3 - 2t + 1}{t^4 + 3}\right)^{12} \frac{-t^6 + 6t^4 - 4t^3 + 9t^2 - 6}{(t^4 + 3)^2} \qquad \blacksquare$$

The Chain Rule simplifies computation of many derivatives involving the trigonometric functions. Although it is possible to differentiate $y = \sin 2x$ using trigonometric identities (see Problem 21 of the previous section), it is much easier to use the Chain Rule.

EXAMPLE 4   If $y = \sin 2x$, find $\dfrac{dy}{dx}$.

SOLUTION   The last step in calculating this expression would be to take the sine of the quantity $2x$. Thus we use the Chain Rule on the function $y = \sin u$ where $u = 2x$.

$$\frac{dy}{dx} = (\cos 2x)\left(\frac{d}{dx} 2x\right) = 2\cos 2x \qquad \blacksquare$$

EXAMPLE 5   Find $F'(y)$ where $F(y) = y \sin y^2$.

SOLUTION   The last step in calculating this expression would be to multiply y and $\sin y^2$, so we begin by applying the Product Rule. The Chain Rule is needed when we differentiate $\sin y^2$.

$$F'(y) = yD_y[\sin y^2] + (\sin y^2)D_y(y)$$

$$= y(\cos y^2)D_y(y^2) + (\sin y^2)(1)$$

$$= 2y^2 \cos y^2 + \sin y^2 \qquad \blacksquare$$

EXAMPLE 6 Find $D_x\left(\dfrac{x^2(1-x)^3}{1+x}\right)$.

SOLUTION The last step in calculating this expression would be to take the quotient. Thus, the Quotient Rule is the first to be applied. But notice that when we take the derivative of the numerator, we must apply the Product Rule and then the Chain Rule.

$$D_x\left(\frac{x^2(1-x)^3}{1+x}\right) = \frac{(1+x)D_x(x^2(1-x)^3) - x^2(1-x)^3 D_x(1+x)}{(1+x)^2}$$

$$= \frac{(1+x)[x^2 D_x(1-x)^3 + (1-x)^3 D_x(x^2)] - x^2(1-x)^3(1)}{(1+x)^2}$$

$$= \frac{(1+x)[x^2(3(1-x)^2(-1)) + (1-x)^3(2x)] - x^2(1-x)^3}{(1+x)^2}$$

$$= \frac{(1+x)[-3x^2(1-x)^2 + 2x(1-x)^3] - x^2(1-x)^3}{(1+x)^2}$$

$$= \frac{(1+x)(1-x)^2 x(2-5x) - x^2(1-x)^3}{(1+x)^2} \qquad \blacksquare$$

EXAMPLE 7 Find $\dfrac{d}{dx}\dfrac{1}{(2x-1)^3}$.

SOLUTION

$$\frac{d}{dx}\frac{1}{(2x-1)^3} = \frac{d}{dx}(2x-1)^{-3} = -3(2x-1)^{-3-1}\frac{d}{dx}(2x-1) = -\frac{6}{(2x-1)^4} \qquad \blacksquare$$

In this last example we were able to avoid use of the Quotient Rule. If you use the Quotient Rule, you would notice that the derivative of the numerator is 0, which simplifies the calculation. (You should check that the Quotient Rule gives the same answer as above.) As a general rule, if the numerator of a fraction is a constant, then do not use the Quotient Rule; instead write the quotient as the product of the constant and the expression in the denominator raised to a negative power, and then use the Chain Rule.

EXAMPLE 8 Express the following derivatives in terms of the function $F(x)$. Assume that F is differentiable.

$$\text{(a) } D_x(F(x^3)) \quad \text{and} \quad \text{(b) } D_x[(F(x))^3]$$

SOLUTION

(a) The last step in calculating this expression would be to apply the function F. (Here the inner function is $u = x^3$ and the outer function is $F(u)$.) Thus

$$D_x(F(x^3)) = F'(x^3)D_x(x^3) = 3x^2\, F'(x^3)$$

(b) For this expression we would first evaluate $F(x)$ and then cube the result. (Here the inner function is $u = F(x)$ and the outer function is u^3.) Thus we apply the Power Rule first, then the Chain Rule.

$$D_x[(F(x))^3] = 3[F(x)]^2 D_x(F(x)) = 3[F(x)]^2 F'(x) \qquad \blacksquare$$

Applying the Chain Rule More than Once   Sometimes when we apply the Chain Rule to a composite function we find that differentiation of the inner function also requires the Chain Rule. In cases like this, we simply have to use the Chain Rule a second time.

Notations for the Derivative

In this section, we have used all the various notations for the derivative, namely,

$$f'(x)$$

$$\frac{dy}{dx}$$

and

$$D_x f(x)$$

You should by now be familiar with all of these notations. They will all be used in the remainder of the book.

EXAMPLE 9 Find $D_x \sin^3(4x)$.

SOLUTION Remember, $\sin^3(4x) = [\sin(4x)]^3$, so we view this as the cube of a function of x. Thus, using our rule "derivative of the outer function evaluated at the inner function times the derivative of the inner function," we have

$$D_x \sin^3(4x) = D_x[\sin(4x)]^3 = 3[\sin(4x)]^{3-1}D_x[\sin(4x)]$$

Now we apply the Chain Rule once again for the derivative of the inner function.

$$\begin{aligned} D_x \sin^3(4x) &= 3[\sin(4x)]^{3-1}D_x \sin(4x) \\ &= 3[\sin(4x)]^2 \cos(4x)D_x(4x) \\ &= 3[\sin(4x)]^2 \cos(4x)(4) \\ &= 12 \cos(4x) \sin^2(4x) \end{aligned}$$ ∎

EXAMPLE 10 Find $D_x \sin[\cos(x^2)]$.

SOLUTION

$$\begin{aligned} D_x \sin[\cos(x^2)] &= \cos[\cos(x^2)] \cdot [-\sin(x^2)] \cdot 2x \\ &= -2x \sin(x^2) \cos[\cos(x^2)] \end{aligned}$$ ∎

EXAMPLE 11 Suppose that the graphs of $y = f(x)$ and $y = g(x)$ are as shown in Figure 1. Use these graphs to approximate (a) $(f - g)'(2)$ and (b) $(f \circ g)'(2)$.

SOLUTION

(a) By Theorem 3.3F, $(f - g)'(2) = f'(2) - g'(2)$. From Figure 1, we can determine that $f'(2) \approx 1$ and $g'(2) \approx -\dfrac{1}{2}$. Thus,

$$(f - g)'(2) \approx 1 - \left(-\frac{1}{2}\right) = \frac{3}{2}.$$

(b) From Figure 1 we can determine that $f'(1) \approx \dfrac{1}{2}$. Thus, by the Chain Rule,

$$(f \circ g)'(2) = f'(g(2))g'(2) = f'(1)g'(2) \approx \frac{1}{2}\left(-\frac{1}{2}\right) = -\frac{1}{4}$$ ∎

A Partial Proof of the Chain Rule We can now give a sketch of the proof of the Chain Rule.

Proof We suppose that $y = f(u)$ and $u = g(x)$, that g is differentiable at x, and that f is differentiable at $u = g(x)$. When x is given an increment Δx, there are corresponding increments in u and y given by

$$\Delta u = g(x + \Delta x) - g(x)$$

$$\begin{aligned} \Delta y &= f(g(x + \Delta x)) - f(g(x)) \\ &= f(u + \Delta u) - f(u) \end{aligned}$$

Thus,

$$\begin{aligned} \frac{dy}{dx} &= \lim_{\Delta x \to 0} \frac{\Delta y}{\Delta x} = \lim_{\Delta x \to 0} \frac{\Delta y}{\Delta u} \frac{\Delta u}{\Delta x} \\ &= \lim_{\Delta x \to 0} \frac{\Delta y}{\Delta u} \cdot \lim_{\Delta x \to 0} \frac{\Delta u}{\Delta x} \end{aligned}$$

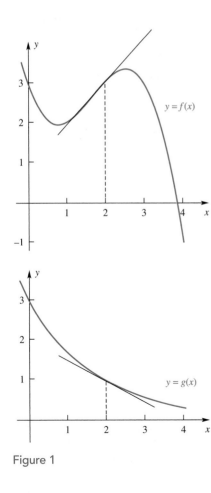

Figure 1

Since g is differentiable at x, it is continuous there (Theorem 3.2A), and so $\Delta x \to 0$ forces $\Delta u \to 0$. Hence,

$$\frac{dy}{dx} = \lim_{\Delta u \to 0} \frac{\Delta y}{\Delta u} \cdot \lim_{\Delta x \to 0} \frac{\Delta u}{\Delta x} = \frac{dy}{du} \cdot \frac{du}{dx}$$

This proof was very slick, but unfortunately it contains a subtle flaw. There are functions $u = g(x)$ that have the property that $\Delta u = 0$ for some points in every neighborhood of x (the constant function $g(x) = k$ is a good example). This means the division by Δu at our first step might not be legal. There is no simple way to get around this difficulty, though the Chain Rule is valid even in this case. We give a complete proof of the Chain Rule in the appendix (Section A.2, Theorem B). ∎

Concepts Review

1. If $y = f(u)$, where $u = g(t)$, then $D_t y = D_u y \cdot$ _____. In function notation, $(f \circ g)'(t) =$ _____ _____.

2. If $w = G(v)$, where $v = H(s)$, then $D_s w =$ _____ $D_s v$. In function notation $(G \circ H)'(s) =$ _____ _____.

3. $D_x \cos[(f(x))^2] = -\sin($ _____ $) \cdot D_x($ _____ $)$.

4. If $y = (2x + 1)^3 \sin(x^2)$, then $D_x y =$
$(2x + 1)^3 \cdot$ _____ $+ \sin(x^2) \cdot$ _____ .

Problem Set 3.5

In Problems 1–20, find $D_x y$.

1. $y = (1 + x)^{15}$

2. $y = (7 + x)^5$

3. $y = (3 - 2x)^5$

4. $y = (4 + 2x^2)^7$

5. $y = (x^3 - 2x^2 + 3x + 1)^{11}$ **6.** $y = (x^2 - x + 1)^{-7}$

7. $y = \dfrac{1}{(x + 3)^5}$

8. $y = \dfrac{1}{(3x^2 + x - 3)^9}$

9. $y = \sin(x^2 + x)$

10. $y = \cos(3x^2 - 2x)$

11. $y = \cos^3 x$

12. $y = \sin^4(3x^2)$

13. $y = \left(\dfrac{x + 1}{x - 1}\right)^3$

14. $y = \left(\dfrac{x - 2}{x - \pi}\right)^{-3}$

15. $y = \cos\left(\dfrac{3x^2}{x + 2}\right)$

16. $y = \cos^3\left(\dfrac{x^2}{1 - x}\right)$

17. $y = (3x - 2)^2(3 - x^2)^2$ **18.** $y = (2 - 3x^2)^4(x^7 + 3)^3$

19. $y = \dfrac{(x + 1)^2}{3x - 4}$

20. $y = \dfrac{2x - 3}{(x^2 + 4)^2}$

In Problems 21–28, find the indicated derivative.

21. y' where $y = (x^2 + 4)^2$ **22.** y' where $y = (x + \sin x)^2$

23. $D_t\left(\dfrac{3t - 2}{t + 5}\right)^3$

24. $D_s\left(\dfrac{s^2 - 9}{s + 4}\right)$

25. $\dfrac{d}{dt}\left(\dfrac{(3t - 2)^3}{t + 5}\right)$

26. $\dfrac{d}{d\theta}(\sin^3 \theta)$

27. $\dfrac{dy}{dx}$, where $y = \left(\dfrac{\sin x}{\cos 2x}\right)^3$

28. $\dfrac{dy}{dt}$, where $y = [\sin t \tan(t^2 + 1)]$

In Problems 29–32, evaluate the indicated derivative.

29. $f'(3)$ if $f(x) = \left(\dfrac{x^2 + 1}{x + 2}\right)^3$

30. $G'(1)$ if $G(t) = (t^2 + 9)^3(t^2 - 2)^4$

C **31.** $F'(1)$ if $F(t) = \sin(t^2 + 3t + 1)$

32. $g'\left(\dfrac{1}{2}\right)$ if $g(s) = \cos \pi s \sin^2 \pi s$

In Problems 33–40, apply the Chain Rule more than once to find the indicated derivative.

33. $D_x[\sin^4(x^2 + 3x)]$

34. $D_t[\cos^5(4t - 19)]$

35. $D_t[\sin^3(\cos t)]$

36. $D_u\left[\cos^4\left(\dfrac{u + 1}{u - 1}\right)\right]$

37. $D_\theta[\cos^4(\sin \theta^2)]$

38. $D_x[x \sin^2(2x)]$

39. $\dfrac{d}{dx}\{\sin[\cos(\sin 2x)]\}$

40. $\dfrac{d}{dt}\{\cos^2[\cos(\cos t)]\}$

In Problems 41–46, use Figures 2 and 3 to approximate the indicated expressions.

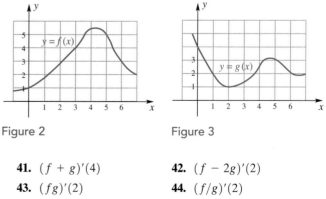

Figure 2

Figure 3

41. $(f + g)'(4)$

42. $(f - 2g)'(2)$

43. $(fg)'(2)$

44. $(f/g)'(2)$

45. $(f \circ g)'(6)$

46. $(g \circ f)'(3)$

In Problems 47–58, express the indicated derivative in terms of the function $F(x)$. Assume that F is differentiable.

47. $D_x(F(2x))$

48. $D_x(F(x^2 + 1))$

49. $D_t((F(t))^{-2})$

50. $\dfrac{d}{dz}\left(\dfrac{1}{(F(z))^2}\right)$

51. $\dfrac{d}{dz}(1 + (F(2z)))^2$

52. $\dfrac{d}{dy}\left(y^2 + \dfrac{1}{F(y^2)}\right)$

53. $\dfrac{d}{dx}F(\cos x)$

54. $\dfrac{d}{dx}\cos F(x)$

55. $D_x \tan F(2x)$

56. $\dfrac{d}{dx}g(\tan 2x)$

57. $D_x(F(x)\sin^2 F(x))$

58. $D_x \sec^3 F(x)$

59. Given that $f(0) = 1$ and $f'(0) = 2$, find $g'(0)$ where $g(x) = \cos f(x)$.

60. Given that $F(0) = 2$ and $F'(0) = -1$, find $G'(0)$ where
$$G(x) = \dfrac{x}{1 + \sec F(2x)}.$$

61. Given that $f(1) = 2$, $f'(1) = -1$, $g(1) = 0$ and $g'(1) = 1$, find $F'(1)$ where $F(x) = f(x)\cos g(x)$.

62. Find the equation of the tangent line to the graph of $y = 1 + x \sin 3x$ at $\left(\dfrac{\pi}{3}, 1\right)$. Where does this line cross the x-axis?

63. Find all points on the graph of $y = \sin^2 x$ where the tangent line has slope 1.

64. Find the equation of the tangent line to $y = (x^2 + 1)^3(x^4 + 1)^2$ at $(1, 32)$.

65. Find the equation of the tangent line to $y = (x^2 + 1)^{-2}$ at $\left(1, \frac{1}{4}\right)$.

66. Where does the tangent line to $y = (2x + 1)^3$ at $(0, 1)$ cross the x-axis?

67. Where does the tangent line to $y = (x^2 + 1)^{-2}$ at $\left(1, \frac{1}{4}\right)$ cross the x-axis?

68. A point P is moving in the plane so that its coordinates after t seconds are $(4 \cos 2t, 7 \sin 2t)$, measured in feet.

(a) Show that P is following an elliptical path. *Hint:* Show that $(x/4)^2 + (y/7)^2 = 1$, which is an equation of an ellipse.

(b) Obtain an expression for L, the distance of P from the origin at time t.

(c) How fast is the distance between P and the origin changing when $t = \pi/8$? You will need the fact that $D_u(\sqrt{u}) = 1/(2\sqrt{u})$ (see Example 4 of Section 3.2).

69. A wheel centered at the origin and of radius 10 centimeters is rotating counterclockwise at a rate of 4 revolutions per second. A point P on the rim is at $(10, 0)$ at $t = 0$.

(a) What are the coordinates of P at time t seconds?

(b) At what rate is P rising (or falling) at time $t = 1$?

70. Consider the wheel-piston device in Figure 4. The wheel has radius 1 foot and rotates counterclockwise at 2 radians per second. The connecting rod is 5 feet long. The point P is at $(1, 0)$ at time $t = 0$.

(a) Find the coordinates of P at time t.

(b) Find the y-coordinate of Q at time t (the x-coordinate is always zero).

(c) Find the velocity of Q at time t. You will need the fact that $D_u(\sqrt{u}) = 1/(2\sqrt{u})$.

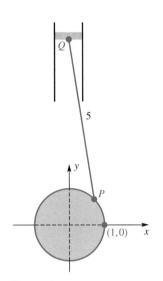

Figure 4

71. Do Problem 70, assuming that the wheel is rotating at 60 revolutions per minute and t is measured in seconds.

72. The dial of a standard clock has a 10-centimeter radius. One end of an elastic string is attached to the rim at 12 and the other to the tip of the 10-centimeter minute hand. At what rate is the string stretching at 12:15 (assuming that the clock is not slowed down by this stretching)?

C **73.** The hour and minute hands of a clock are 6 and 8 inches long, respectively. How fast are the tips of the hands separating at 12:20 (see Figure 5). *Hint:* Law of Cosines.

Figure 5

≈ GC **74.** Find the approximate time between 12:00 and 1:00 when the distance s between the tips of the hands of the clock of Figure 5 is increasing most rapidly, that is, when the derivative ds/dt is largest.

75. Let x_0 be the smallest positive value of x at which the curves $y = \sin x$ and $y = \sin 2x$ intersect. Find x_0 and also the acute angle at which the two curves intersect at x_0 (see Problem 40 of Section 1.8).

76. An isosceles triangle is topped by a semicircle, as shown in Figure 6. Let D be the area of triangle AOB and E be the area of the shaded region. Find a formula for D/E in terms of t and then calculate
$$\lim_{t \to 0^+}\dfrac{D}{E} \quad\text{and}\quad \lim_{t \to \pi^-}\dfrac{D}{E}$$

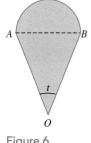

Figure 6

77. Show that $D_x|x| = |x|/x$, $x \neq 0$. *Hint:* Write $|x| = \sqrt{x^2}$ and use the Chain Rule with $u = x^2$.

78. Apply the result of Problem 77 to find $D_x|x^2 - 1|$.

79. Apply the result of Problem 77 to find $D_x|\sin x|$.

80. Let $f(0) = 1$ and $f'(0) = 2$. Find the derivative of $f(f(x) - 1)$ at $x = 0$.

81. Let $f(0) = 0$ and $f'(0) = 2$. Find the derivative of $f(f(f(f(x))))$ at $x = 0$.

82. Suppose that f is a differentiable function.

(a) Find $\dfrac{d}{dx} f(f(x))$.

(b) Find $\dfrac{d}{dx} f(f(f(x)))$.

(c) Let $f^{[n]}$ denote the function defined as follows: $f^{[1]} = f$ and $f^{[n]} = f \circ f^{[n-1]}$ for $n \geq 2$. Thus $f^{[2]} = f \circ f$, $f^{[3]} = f \circ f \circ f$, etc. Based on your results from parts (a) and (b), make a conjecture regarding $\dfrac{d}{dx} f^{[n]}$. Prove your conjecture.

83. Give a second proof of the Quotient Rule. Write

$$D_x\left(\frac{f(x)}{g(x)}\right) = D_x\left(f(x)\frac{1}{g(x)}\right)$$

and use the Product Rule and the Chain Rule.

84. Suppose that f is differentiable and that there are real numbers x_1 and x_2 such that $f(x_1) = x_2$ and $f(x_2) = x_1$. Let $g(x) = f(f(f(f(x))))$. Show that $g'(x_1) = g'(x_2)$.

Answers to Concepts Review: **1.** $D_t u$; $f'(g(t))g'(t)$
2. $D_v w$; $G'(H(s))H'(s)$ **3.** $(f(x))^2$; $(f(x))^2$
4. $2x \cos(x^2)$; $6(2x + 1)^2$

3.6

Higher-Order Derivatives

The operation of differentiation takes a function f and produces a new function f'. If we now differentiate f', we produce still another function, denoted by f'' (read "f double prime") and called the **second derivative** of f. It in turn, may be differentiated, thereby producing f''', which is called the **third derivative** of f, and so on. The **fourth derivative** is denoted $f^{(4)}$, the **fifth derivative** is denoted $f^{(5)}$, and so on.

If, for example

$$f(x) = 2x^3 - 4x^2 + 7x - 8$$

then

$$f'(x) = 6x^2 - 8x + 7$$
$$f''(x) = 12x - 8$$
$$f'''(x) = 12$$
$$f^{(4)}(x) = 0$$

Since the derivative of the zero function is zero, the fourth derivative and all *higher-order derivatives* of f will be zero.

We have introduced three notations for the derivative (now also called the *first derivative*) of $y = f(x)$. They are

$$f'(x) \qquad D_x y \qquad \frac{dy}{dx}$$

called, respectively, the *prime notation*, the *D notation*, and the *Leibniz notation*. There is a variation of the prime notation, y', that we will also use occasionally. All these notations have extensions for higher-order derivatives, as shown in the accompanying table. Note especially the Leibniz notation, which, though complicated, seemed most appropriate to Leibniz. What, thought he, is more natural than to write

$$\frac{d}{dx}\left(\frac{dy}{dx}\right) \qquad \text{as} \qquad \frac{d^2 y}{dx^2}$$

Leibniz's notation for the second derivative is read *the second derivative of y with respect to x.*

Derivative	f' Notation	y' Notation	D Notation	Leibniz Notation
First	$f'(x)$	y'	$D_x y$	$\dfrac{dy}{dx}$
Second	$f''(x)$	y''	$D_x^2 y$	$\dfrac{d^2 y}{dx^2}$
Third	$f'''(x)$	y'''	$D_x^3 y$	$\dfrac{d^3 y}{dx^3}$
Fourth	$f^{(4)}(x)$	$y^{(4)}$	$D_x^4 y$	$\dfrac{d^4 y}{dx^4}$
$\vdots$	$\vdots$	$\vdots$	$\vdots$	$\vdots$
nth	$f^{(n)}(x)$	$y^{(n)}$	$D_x^n y$	$\dfrac{d^n y}{dx^n}$

Notations for Derivatives of $y = f(x)$

■ **EXAMPLE 1** If $y = \sin 2x$, find $d^3 y/dx^3$, $d^4 y/dx^4$, and $d^{12} y/dx^{12}$.

SOLUTION

$$\frac{dy}{dx} = 2 \cos 2x$$

$$\frac{d^2 y}{dx^2} = -2^2 \sin 2x$$

$$\frac{d^3 y}{dx^3} = -2^3 \cos 2x$$

$$\frac{d^4 y}{dx^4} = 2^4 \sin 2x$$

$$\frac{d^5 y}{dx^5} = 2^5 \cos 2x$$

$$\vdots$$

$$\frac{d^{12} y}{dx^{12}} = 2^{12} \sin 2x$$

■

Velocity and Acceleration In Section 3.1, we used the notion of instantaneous velocity to motivate the definition of the derivative. Let's review this notion by means of an example. Also, from now on we will use the single word *velocity* in place of the more cumbersome phrase *instantaneous velocity*.

■ **EXAMPLE 2** An object moves along a coordinate line so that its position s satisfies $s = 2t^2 - 12t + 8$, where s is measured in centimeters and t in seconds with $t \geq 0$. Determine the velocity of the object when $t = 1$ and when $t = 6$. When is the velocity 0? When is it positive?

SOLUTION If we use the symbol $v(t)$ for the velocity at time t, then

$$v(t) = \frac{ds}{dt} = 4t - 12$$

Thus,

$$v(1) = 4(1) - 12 = -8 \text{ centimeters per second}$$

$$v(6) = 4(6) - 12 = 12 \text{ centimeters per second}$$

The velocity is 0 when $4t - 12 = 0$, that is, when $t = 3$. The velocity is positive when $4t - 12 > 0$, or when $t > 3$. All this is shown schematically in Figure 1.

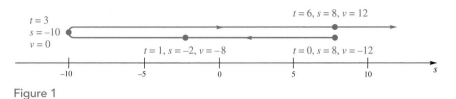

Figure 1

The object is, of course, moving along the s-axis, not on the colored path above it. But the colored path shows what happens to the object. Between $t = 0$ and $t = 3$, the velocity is negative; the object is moving to the left (backing up). By the time $t = 3$, it has "slowed" to a zero velocity. It then starts moving to the right as its velocity becomes positive. Thus, negative velocity corresponds to moving in the direction of decreasing s; positive velocity corresponds to moving in the direction of increasing s. A rigorous discussion of these points will be given in Chapter 4. ■

There is a technical distinction between the words *velocity* and *speed*. Velocity has a sign associated with it; it may be positive or negative. **Speed** is defined to be the absolute value of the velocity. Thus, in the example above, the speed at $t = 1$ is $|-8| = 8$ centimeters per second. The meter in most cars is a *speed*ometer; it always gives nonnegative values.

Now we want to give a physical interpretation of the second derivative d^2s/dt^2. It is, of course, just the first derivative of the velocity. Thus, it measures the rate of change of velocity with respect to time, which has the name **acceleration.** If it is denoted by a, then

$$a = \frac{dv}{dt} = \frac{d^2s}{dt^2}$$

In Example 2, $s = 2t^2 - 12t + 8$. Thus,

$$v = \frac{ds}{dt} = 4t - 12$$

$$a = \frac{d^2s}{dt^2} = 4$$

This means that the velocity is increasing at a constant rate of 4 centimeters per second every second, which we write as 4 centimeters per second per second, or as 4 cm/sec^2.

EXAMPLE 3 An object moves along a horizontal coordinate line in such a way that its position at time t is specified by

$$s = t^3 - 12t^2 + 36t - 30$$

Here s is measured in feet and t in seconds.
(a) When is the velocity 0?
(b) When is the velocity positive?
(c) When is the object moving to the left (that is, in the negative direction)?
(d) When is the acceleration positive?

SOLUTION
(a) $v = ds/dt = 3t^2 - 24t + 36 = 3(t - 2)(t - 6)$. Thus, $v = 0$ at $t = 2$ and at $t = 6$.
(b) $v > 0$ when $(t - 2)(t - 6) > 0$. We learned how to solve quadratic inequalities in Section 1.2. The solution is $\{t : t < 2 \text{ or } t > 6\}$ or, in interval notation, $(-\infty, 2) \cup (6, \infty)$; see Figure 2.

Measuring Time

If $t = 0$ corresponds to the present moment, then $t < 0$ corresponds to the past, and $t > 0$ to the future. In many problems, it will be obvious that we are concerned only with the future. However, since the statement of Example 3 does not specify this, it seems reasonable to allow t to have negative as well as positive values.

Figure 2

(c) The object is moving to the left when $v < 0$; that is, when $(t - 2)(t - 6) < 0$. This inequality has as its solution the interval $(2, 6)$.

(d) $a = dv/dt = 6t - 24 = 6(t - 4)$. Thus, $a > 0$ when $t > 4$. The motion of the object is shown schematically in Figure 3.

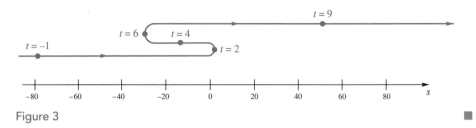

Figure 3

Falling-Body Problems

If an object is thrown straight upward (or downward) from an initial height of s_0 feet with an initial velocity of v_0 feet per second and if s is its height above the ground in feet after t seconds, then

$$s = -16t^2 + v_0 t + s_0$$

This assumes that the experiment takes place near sea level and that air resistance can be neglected. The diagram in Figure 4 portrays the situation we have in mind. Notice that positive velocity means that the object is moving upward.

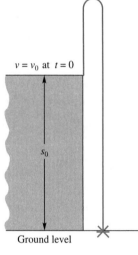

$v = v_0$ at $t = 0$

s_0

Ground level

Figure 4

EXAMPLE 4 From the top of a building 160 feet high, a ball is thrown upward with an initial velocity of 64 feet per second.

(a) When does it reach its maximum height?
(b) What is its maximum height?
(c) When does it hit the ground?
(d) With what speed does it hit the ground?
(e) What is its acceleration at $t = 2$?

SOLUTION Let $t = 0$ correspond to the instant when the ball was thrown. Then $s_0 = 160$ and $v_0 = 64$ (v_0 is positive because the ball was thrown *upward*). Thus,

$$s = -16t^2 + 64t + 160$$

$$v = \frac{ds}{dt} = -32t + 64$$

$$a = \frac{dv}{dt} = -32$$

(a) The ball reached its maximum height at the time its velocity was 0, that is, when $-32t + 64 = 0$ or when $t = 2$ seconds.

(b) At $t = 2$, $s = -16(2)^2 + 64(2) + 160 = 224$ feet.

(c) The ball hit the ground when $s = 0$, that is, when

$$-16t^2 + 64t + 160 = 0$$

Dividing by -16 yields

$$t^2 - 4t - 10 = 0$$

The quadratic formula then gives

$$t = \frac{4 \pm \sqrt{16 + 40}}{2} = \frac{4 \pm 2\sqrt{14}}{2} = 2 \pm \sqrt{14}$$

Only the positive answer makes sense. Thus, the ball hit the ground at $t = 2 + \sqrt{14} \approx 5.74$ seconds.

(d) At $t = 2 + \sqrt{14}$, $v = -32(2 + \sqrt{14}) + 64 \approx -119.73$. Thus, the ball hit the ground with a speed of 119.73 feet per second.

(e) The acceleration is always -32 feet per second per second. This is the acceleration of gravity near sea level. ∎

Concepts Review

1. If $y = f(x)$, then the third derivative of y with respect to x can be denoted by any one of the following four symbols: _____.

2. If $s = f(t)$ denotes the position of a particle on a coordinate line at time t, then its velocity is given by _____, its speed is given by _____, and its acceleration is given by _____.

3. If $s = f(t)$ denotes the position of an object at time t, then the object is moving to the right if _____ .

4. Assume that an object is thrown straight upward so that its height s at time t is given by $s = f(t)$. The object reaches its maximum height when $ds/dt =$ _____, after which, ds/dt _____.

Problem Set 3.6

In Problems 1–8, find d^3y/dx^3.

1. $y = x^3 + 3x^2 + 6x$

2. $y = x^5 + x^4$

3. $y = (3x + 5)^3$

4. $y = (3 - 5x)^5$

5. $y = \sin(7x)$

6. $y = \sin(x^3)$

7. $y = \dfrac{1}{x - 1}$

8. $y = \dfrac{3x}{1 - x}$

In Problems 9–16, find $f''(2)$.

9. $f(x) = x^2 + 1$

10. $f(x) = 5x^3 + 2x^2 + x$

11. $f(t) = \dfrac{2}{t}$

12. $f(u) = \dfrac{2u^2}{5 - u}$

13. $f(\theta) = (\cos \theta\pi)^{-2}$

14. $f(t) = t \sin(\pi/t)$

15. $f(s) = s(1 - s^2)^3$

16. $f(x) = \dfrac{(x + 1)^2}{x - 1}$

17. Let $n! = n(n - 1)(n - 2)\cdots 3\cdot 2\cdot 1$. Thus, $4! = 4\cdot 3\cdot 2\cdot 1 = 24$ and $5! = 5\cdot 4\cdot 3\cdot 2\cdot 1$. We give $n!$ the name n **factorial.** Show that $D_x^n(x^n) = n!$.

18. Find a formula for

$$D_x^n(a_{n-1}x^{n-1} + \cdots + a_1x + a_0)$$

19. Without doing any calculating, find each derivative.

(a) $D_x^4(3x^3 + 2x - 19)$

(b) $D_x^{12}(100x^{11} - 79x^{10})$

(c) $D_x^{11}(x^2 - 3)^5$

20. Find a formula for $D_x^n(1/x)$.

21. If $f(x) = x^3 + 3x^2 - 45x - 6$, find the value of f'' at each zero of f', that is, at each point c where $f'(c) = 0$.

22. Suppose that $g(t) = at^2 + bt + c$ and $g(1) = 5$, $g'(1) = 3$, and $g''(1) = -4$. Find $a, b,$ and c.

In Problems 23–28, an object is moving along a horizontal coordinate line according to the formula $s = f(t)$, where s, the directed distance from the origin, is in feet and t is in seconds. In each case, answer the following questions (see Examples 2 and 3).

(a) What are $v(t)$ and $a(t)$, the velocity and acceleration, at time t?

(b) When is the object moving to the right?

(c) When is it moving to the left?

(d) When is its acceleration negative?

(e) Draw a schematic diagram that shows the motion of the object.

23. $s = 12t - 2t^2$

24. $s = t^3 - 6t^2$

25. $s = t^3 - 9t^2 + 24t$

26. $s = 2t^3 - 6t + 5$

27. $s = t^2 + \dfrac{16}{t}, t > 0$

28. $s = t + \dfrac{4}{t}, t > 0$

29. If $s = \frac{1}{2}t^4 - 5t^3 + 12t^2$, find the velocity of the moving object when its acceleration is zero.

30. If $s = \frac{1}{10}(t^4 - 14t^3 + 60t^2)$, find the velocity of the moving object when its acceleration is zero.

31. Two objects move along a coordinate line. At the end of t seconds their directed distances from the origin, in feet, are given by $s_1 = 4t - 3t^2$ and $s_2 = t^2 - 2t$, respectively.

(a) When do they have the same velocity?

(b) When do they have the same speed?

(c) When do they have the same position?

32. The positions of two objects, P_1 and P_2, on a coordinate line at the end of t seconds are given by $s_1 = 3t^3 - 12t^2 + 18t + 5$ and $s_2 = -t^3 + 9t^2 - 12t$, respectively. When do the two objects have the same velocity?

33. An object thrown directly upward is at a height of $s = -16t^2 + 48t + 256$ feet after t seconds (see Example 4).

(a) What is its initial velocity?

(b) When does it reach its maximum height?

(c) What is its maximum height?

[C](d) When does it hit the ground?

[C](e) With what speed does it hit the ground?

34. An object thrown directly upward from ground level with an initial velocity of 48 feet per second is $s = 48t - 16t^2$ feet high at the end of t seconds.

(a) What is the maximum height attained?

(b) How fast is the object moving, and in which direction, at the end of 1 second?

(c) How long does it take to return to its original position?

[C] **35.** A projectile is fired directly upward from the ground with an initial velocity of v_0 feet per second. Its height in t seconds is given by $s = v_0t - 16t^2$ feet. What must its initial velocity be for the projectile to reach a maximum height of 1 mile?

36. An object thrown directly downward from the top of a cliff with an initial velocity of v_0 feet per second falls $s = v_0t + 16t^2$ feet in t seconds. If it strikes the ocean below in 3 seconds with a speed of 140 feet per second, how high is the cliff?

37. An object moves along a horizontal coordinate line in such a way that its position at time t is specified by $s = t^3 - 3t^2 - 24t - 6$. Here s is measured in centimeters and t in seconds. When is the object slowing down; that is, when is its *speed* decreasing?

38. Explain why an object moving along a line is slowing down when its velocity and acceleration have opposite signs (see Problem 37).

EXPL **39.** Leibniz obtained a general formula for $D_x^n(uv)$, where u and v are both functions of x. See if you can find it. *Hint:* Begin by considering the cases $n = 1, n = 2$, and $n = 3$.

40. Use the formula of Problem 39 to find $D_x^4(x^4 \sin x)$.

GC **41.** Let $f(x) = x[\sin x - \cos(x/2)]$.

(a) Draw the graphs of $f(x), f'(x), f''(x)$, and $f'''(x)$ on $[0, 6]$ using the same axes.

(b) Evaluate $f'''(2.13)$.

GC **42.** Repeat Problem 41 for $f(x) = (x + 1)/(x^2 + 2)$.

Answers to Concepts Review: **1.** $f'''(x); D_x^3 y; d^3y/dx^3; y'''$
2. $ds/dt; |ds/dt|; d^2s/dt^2$ **3.** $f'(t) > 0$ **4.** $0; < 0$

3.7
Implicit Differentiation

In the equation

$$y^3 + 7y = x^3$$

we cannot solve for y in terms of x. It still may be the case, however, that there is exactly one y corresponding to each x. For example, we may ask what y-values (if any) correspond to $x = 2$. To answer this question, we must solve

$$y^3 + 7y = 8$$

Certainly, $y = 1$ is one solution, and it turns out that $y = 1$ is the *only* real solution. Given $x = 2$, the equation $y^3 + 7y = x^3$ determines a corresponding y-value. We say that the equation defines y as an **implicit** function of x. The graph of this equation, shown in Figure 1, certainly looks like the graph of a differentiable function. The new element is that we do not have an equation of the form $y = f(x)$. Based on the graph, we assume that y is some unknown function of x. If we denote this function by $y(x)$, we can write the equation as

$$[y(x)]^3 + 7y(x) = x^3$$

Even though we do not have a formula for $y(x)$, we can nevertheless get a relation between x, $y(x)$, and $y'(x)$ by differentiating both sides of the equation with respect to x. Remembering to apply the Chain Rule, we get

$$\frac{d}{dx}(y^3) + \frac{d}{dx}(7y) = \frac{d}{dx}x^3$$

$$3y^2\frac{dy}{dx} + 7\frac{dy}{dx} = 3x^2$$

$$\frac{dy}{dx}(3y^2 + 7) = 3x^2$$

$$\frac{dy}{dx} = \frac{3x^2}{3y^2 + 7}$$

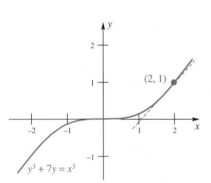

Figure 1

Note that our expression for dy/dx involves both x and y, a fact that is often a nuisance. But if we wish only to find a slope at a point where we know both coordinates, no difficulty exists. At $(2, 1)$,

$$\frac{dy}{dx} = \frac{3(2)^2}{3(1)^2 + 7} = \frac{12}{10} = \frac{6}{5}$$

The slope is $\frac{6}{5}$.

The method just illustrated for finding dy/dx without first solving the given equation for y explicitly in terms of x is called **implicit differentiation.** But is the method legitimate—does it give the right answer?

An Example That Can Be Checked To give some evidence for the correctness of the method, consider the following example, which can be worked two ways.

▇ **EXAMPLE 1** Find dy/dx if $4x^2y - 3y = x^3 - 1$.

SOLUTION

Method 1 We can solve the given equation explicitly for y as follows:

$$y(4x^2 - 3) = x^3 - 1$$

$$y = \frac{x^3 - 1}{4x^2 - 3}$$

Thus,

$$\frac{dy}{dx} = \frac{(4x^2 - 3)(3x^2) - (x^3 - 1)(8x)}{(4x^2 - 3)^2} = \frac{4x^4 - 9x^2 + 8x}{(4x^2 - 3)^2}$$

Method 2 Implicit Differentiation We equate the derivatives of the two sides.

$$\frac{d}{dx}(4x^2y - 3y) = \frac{d}{dx}(x^3 - 1)$$

We obtain, after using the Product Rule on the first term,

$$4x^2 \cdot \frac{dy}{dx} + y \cdot 8x - 3\frac{dy}{dx} = 3x^2$$

$$\frac{dy}{dx}(4x^2 - 3) = 3x^2 - 8xy$$

$$\frac{dy}{dx} = \frac{3x^2 - 8xy}{4x^2 - 3}$$

These two answers look different. For one thing, the answer obtained from Method 1 involves x only, whereas the answer from Method 2 involves both x and y. Remember, however, that the original equation could be solved for y in terms of x to give $y = (x^3 - 1)/(4x^2 - 3)$. When we substitute $y = (x^3 - 1)/(4x^2 - 3)$ into the expression just obtained for dy/dx, we get the following:

$$\frac{dy}{dx} = \frac{3x^2 - 8xy}{4x^2 - 3} = \frac{3x^2 - 8x\dfrac{x^3 - 1}{4x^2 - 3}}{4x^2 - 3}$$

$$= \frac{12x^4 - 9x^2 - 8x^4 + 8x}{(4x^2 - 3)^2} = \frac{4x^4 - 9x^2 + 8x}{(4x^2 - 3)^2} \qquad ▇$$

Some Subtle Difficulties If an equation in x and y determines a function $y = f(x)$ and if this function is differentiable, then the method of implicit differentiation will yield a correct expression for dy/dx. But notice there are two big *ifs* in this statement.

Consider the equation

$$x^2 + y^2 = 25$$

which determines both the function $y = f(x) = \sqrt{25 - x^2}$ and the function $y = g(x) = -\sqrt{25 - x^2}$. Their graphs are shown in Figure 2.

Happily, both of these functions are differentiable on $(-5, 5)$. Consider f first. It satisfies

$$x^2 + [f(x)]^2 = 25$$

When we differentiate implicitly and solve for $f'(x)$, we obtain

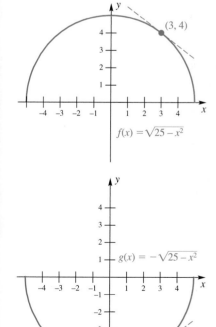

Figure 2

$$2x + 2f(x)f'(x) = 0$$

$$f'(x) = -\frac{x}{f(x)} = -\frac{x}{\sqrt{25 - x^2}}$$

A similar treatment of $g(x)$ yields

$$g'(x) = -\frac{x}{g(x)} = \frac{x}{\sqrt{25 - x^2}}$$

For practical purposes, we can obtain both of these results simultaneously by implicit differentiation of $x^2 + y^2 = 25$. This gives

$$2x + 2y\frac{dy}{dx} = 0$$

$$\frac{dy}{dx} = -\frac{x}{y} = \begin{cases} \dfrac{-x}{\sqrt{25 - x^2}} & \text{if } y = f(x) \\[2ex] \dfrac{-x}{-\sqrt{25 - x^2}} & \text{if } y = g(x) \end{cases}$$

Naturally, the results are identical with those obtained above.

Note that it is often enough to know that $dy/dx = -x/y$ in order to apply our results. Suppose we want to know the slopes of the tangent lines to the circle $x^2 + y^2 = 25$ when $x = 3$. For $x = 3$, the corresponding y-values are 4 and -4. The slopes at $(3, 4)$ and $(3, -4)$, obtained by substituting in $-x/y$, are $-\frac{3}{4}$ and $\frac{3}{4}$, respectively (see Figure 2).

To complicate matters, we point out that

$$x^2 + y^2 = 25$$

determines many other functions. For example, consider the function h defined by

$$h(x) = \begin{cases} \sqrt{25 - x^2} & \text{if } -5 \le x \le 3 \\ -\sqrt{25 - x^2} & \text{if } 3 < x \le 5 \end{cases}$$

It too satisfies $x^2 + y^2 = 25$, since $x^2 + [h(x)]^2 = 25$. But it is not even continuous at $x = 3$, so it certainly does not have a derivative there (see Figure 3).

While the subject of implicit functions leads to difficult technical questions (treated in advanced calculus), the problems we study have straightforward solutions.

More Examples In the examples that follow, we assume that the given equation determines one or more differentiable functions whose derivatives can be found by implicit differentiation. Note that in each case we begin by taking the derivative of each side of the given equation with respect to the appropriate variable. Then we use the Chain Rule as needed.

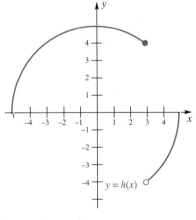

Figure 3

EXAMPLE 2 Find dy/dx if $x^2 + 5y^3 = x + 9$.

SOLUTION

$$\frac{d}{dx}(x^2 + 5y^3) = \frac{d}{dx}(x + 9)$$

$$2x + 15y^2\frac{dy}{dx} = 1$$

$$\frac{dy}{dx} = \frac{1 - 2x}{15y^2}$$

EXAMPLE 3 Find the equation of the tangent line to the curve

$$y^3 - xy^2 + \cos xy = 2$$

at the point $(0, 1)$.

SOLUTION For simplicity, let us use the notation y' for dy/dx. When we differentiate both sides and equate the results, we obtain

$$3y^2y' - x(2yy') - y^2 - (\sin xy)(xy' + y) = 0$$

$$y'(3y^2 - 2xy - x \sin xy) = y^2 + y \sin xy$$

$$y' = \frac{y^2 + y \sin xy}{3y^2 - 2xy - x \sin xy}$$

At $(0, 1)$, $y' = \frac{1}{3}$. Thus, the equation of the tangent line at $(0, 1)$ is

$$y - 1 = \tfrac{1}{3}(x - 0)$$

or

$$y = \tfrac{1}{3}x + 1$$ ■

The Power Rule Again We have learned that $D_x(x^n) = nx^{n-1}$, where n is any nonzero integer. We now extend this to the case where n is any nonzero rational number.

| Theorem A | **Power Rule** |

Let r be any nonzero rational number. Then, for $x > 0$,

$$D_x(x^r) = rx^{r-1}$$

If r can be written in lowest terms as $r = p/q$, where q is odd, then $D_x(x^r) = rx^{r-1}$ for all x.

Proof Since r is rational, r may be written as p/q, where p and q are integers with $q > 0$. Let

$$y = x^r = x^{p/q}$$

Then

$$y^q = x^p$$

and, by implicit differentiation,

$$qy^{q-1}D_xy = px^{p-1}$$

Thus,

$$D_xy = \frac{px^{p-1}}{qy^{q-1}} = \frac{p}{q}\frac{x^{p-1}}{(x^{p/q})^{q-1}} = \frac{p}{q}\frac{x^{p-1}}{x^{p-p/q}}$$

$$= \frac{p}{q}x^{p-1-p+p/q} = \frac{p}{q}x^{p/q-1} = rx^{r-1}$$

We have obtained the desired result, but, to be honest, we must point out a flaw in our argument. In the implicit differentiation step, we assumed that D_xy exists, that is, that $y = x^{p/q}$ is differentiable. We can fill this gap, but since it is hard work we relegate the complete proof to the appendix (Section A.2, Theorem C).   ■

EXAMPLE 4 If $y = 2x^{5/3} + \sqrt{x^2 + 1}$, find D_xy.

SOLUTION Using Theorem A and the Chain Rule, we have

$$D_x y = 2D_x x^{5/3} + D_x (x^2 + 1)^{1/2}$$

$$= 2 \cdot \frac{5}{3} x^{5/3-1} + \frac{1}{2}(x^2 + 1)^{1/2-1} \cdot (2x)$$

$$= \frac{10}{3} x^{2/3} + \frac{x}{\sqrt{x^2 + 1}} \qquad \blacksquare$$

Concepts Review

1. The implicit relation $yx^3 - 3y = 9$ can be solved explicitly for y giving $y = $ _____.

2. Implicit differentiation of $y^3 + x^3 = 2x$ with respect to x gives _____ $+ 3x^2 = 2$.

3. Implicit differentiation of $xy^2 + y^3 - y = x^3$ with respect to x gives _____ = _____.

4. The Power Rule with rational exponents says that $D_x(x^{p/q}) = $ _____. This rule, together with the Chain Rule, implies that $D_x[(x^2 - 5x)^{5/3}] = $ _____.

Problem Set 3.7

Assuming that each equation in Problems 1–12 defines a differentiable function of x, find $D_x y$ by implicit differentiation.

1. $y^2 - x^2 = 1$ **2.** $9x^2 + 4y^2 = 36$

3. $xy = 1$

4. $x^2 + \alpha^2 y^2 = 4\alpha^2$, where α is a constant.

5. $xy^2 = x - 8$ **6.** $x^2 + 2x^2 y + 3xy = 0$

7. $4x^3 + 7xy^2 = 2y^3$ **8.** $x^2 y = 1 + y^2 x$

9. $\sqrt{5xy} + 2y = y^2 + xy^3$ **10.** $x\sqrt{y + 1} = xy + 1$

11. $xy + \sin(xy) = 1$ **12.** $\cos(xy^2) = y^2 + x$

In Problems 13–18, find the equation of the tangent line at the indicated point (see Example 3).

13. $x^3 y + y^3 x = 30$; $(1, 3)$

14. $x^2 y^2 + 4xy = 12y$; $(2, 1)$

15. $\sin(xy) = y$; $(\pi/2, 1)$

16. $y + \cos(xy^2) + 3x^2 = 4$; $(1, 0)$

17. $x^{2/3} - y^{2/3} - 2y = 2$; $(1, -1)$

18. $\sqrt{y} + xy^2 = 5$; $(4, 1)$

In Problems 19–32, find dy/dx.

19. $y = 3x^{5/3} + \sqrt{x}$ **20.** $y = \sqrt[3]{x} - 2x^{7/2}$

21. $y = \sqrt[3]{x} + \dfrac{1}{\sqrt[3]{x}}$ **22.** $y = \sqrt[4]{2x + 1}$

23. $y = \sqrt[4]{3x^2 - 4x}$ **24.** $y = (x^3 - 2x)^{1/3}$

25. $y = \dfrac{1}{(x^3 + 2x)^{2/3}}$ **26.** $y = (3x - 9)^{-5/3}$

27. $y = \sqrt{x^2 + \sin x}$ **28.** $y = \sqrt{x^2 \cos x}$

29. $y = \dfrac{1}{\sqrt[3]{x^2 \sin x}}$ **30.** $y = \sqrt[4]{1 + \sin 5x}$

31. $y = \sqrt[4]{1 + \cos(x^2 + 2x)}$ **32.** $y = \sqrt{\tan^2 x + \sin^2 x}$

33. If $s^2 t + t^3 = 1$, find ds/dt and dt/ds.

34. If $y = \sin(x^2) + 2x^3$, find dx/dy.

35. Sketch the graph of the circle $x^2 + 4x + y^2 + 3 = 0$ and then find equations of the two tangent lines that pass through the origin.

36. Find the equation of the **normal line** (line perpendicular to the tangent line) to the curve $8(x^2 + y^2)^2 = 100(x^2 - y^2)$ at $(3, 1)$.

37. Suppose that $xy + y^3 = 2$. Then implicit differentiation twice with respect to x yields in turn:

(a) $xy' + y + 3y^2 y' = 0$;

(b) $xy'' + y' + y' + 3y^2 y'' + 6y(y')^2 = 0$.

Solve (a) for y' and substitute in (b), and then solve for y''.

38. Find y'' if $x^3 - 4y^2 + 3 = 0$ (see Problem 37).

39. Find y'' at $(2, 1)$ if $2x^2 y - 4y^3 = 4$ (see Problem 37).

40. Use implicit differentiation twice to find y'' at $(3, 4)$ if $x^2 + y^2 = 25$.

41. Show that the normal line to $x^3 + y^3 = 3xy$ at $\left(\frac{3}{2}, \frac{3}{2}\right)$ passes through the origin.

42. Show that the hyperbolas $xy = 1$ and $x^2 - y^2 = 1$ intersect at right angles.

43. Show that the graphs of $2x^2 + y^2 = 6$ and $y^2 = 4x$ intersect at right angles.

44. Suppose that curves C_1 and C_2 intersect at (x_0, y_0) with slopes m_1 and m_2, respectively, as in Figure 4. Then (see Problem 40 of Section 1.8) the positive angle θ from C_1 (i.e., from the tangent line to C_1 at (x_0, y_0)) to C_2 satisfies

$$\tan \theta = \frac{m_2 - m_1}{1 + m_1 m_2}$$

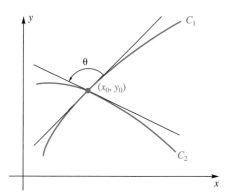

Figure 4

Find the angles from the circle $x^2 + y^2 = 1$ to the circle $(x - 1)^2 + y^2 = 1$ at the two points of intersection.

45. Find the angle from the line $y = 2x$ to the curve $x^2 - xy + 2y^2 = 28$ at their point of intersection in the first quadrant (see Problem 44).

46. A particle of mass m moves along the x-axis so that its position x and velocity $v = dx/dt$ satisfy

$$m(v^2 - v_0^2) = k(x_0^2 - x^2)$$

where v_0, x_0, and k are constants. Show by implicit differentiation that

$$m\frac{dv}{dt} = -kx$$

whenever $v \neq 0$.

47. The curve $x^2 - xy + y^2 = 16$ is an ellipse centered at the origin and with the line $y = x$ as its major axis. Find the equations of the tangent lines at the two points where the ellipse intersects the x-axis.

48. Find all points on the curve $x^2y - xy^2 = 2$ where the tangent line is vertical, that is, where $dx/dy = 0$.

⊠ **49.** How high h must the light bulb in Figure 5 be if the point $(1.25, 0)$ is on the edge of the illuminated region?

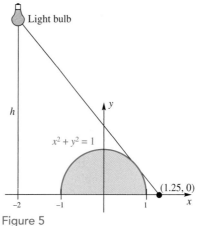

Figure 5

Answers to Concepts Review: **1.** $9/(x^3 - 3)$

2. $3y^2\dfrac{dy}{dx}$ **3.** $x \cdot 2y\dfrac{dy}{dx} + y^2 + 3y^2\dfrac{dy}{dx} - \dfrac{dy}{dx} = 3x^2$

4. $\dfrac{p}{q}x^{p/q-1}; \frac{5}{3}(x^2 - 5x)^{2/3}(2x - 5)$

3.8
Related Rates

If a variable y depends on time t, then its derivative dy/dt is called a **time rate of change.** Of course, if y measures distance, then this time rate of change is also called velocity. We are interested in a wide variety of time rates: the rate at which water is flowing into a bucket, the rate at which the area of an oil spill is growing, the rate at which the value of a piece of real estate is increasing, and so on. If y is given explicitly in terms of t, the problem is simple; we just differentiate and then evaluate the derivative at the required time.

It may be that, in place of knowing y explicitly in terms of t, we know a relationship that connects y and another variable x, and that we also know something about dx/dt. We may still be able to find dy/dt, since dy/dt and dx/dt are **related rates.** This will usually require implicit differentiation.

Two Simple Examples In preparation for outlining a systematic procedure for solving related rate problems, we discuss two examples.

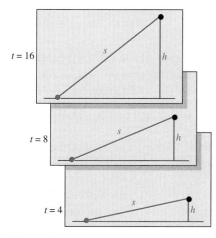

Figure 1

▮ **EXAMPLE 1** A small balloon is released at a point 150 feet away from an observer, who is on level ground. If the balloon goes straight up at a rate of 8 feet per second, how fast is the distance from the observer to the balloon increasing when the balloon is 50 feet high?

SOLUTION Let t denote the number of seconds after the balloon is released. Let h denote the height of the balloon and s its distance from the observer (see Figure 1). Both h and s are variables that depend on t; however, the base of the

Figure 2

triangle (the distance from the observer to the point of release) remains unchanged as t increases. Figure 2 shows the key quantities in one simple diagram.

≈ Before going farther, we pick up a theme discussed earlier in the book, *estimating the answer*. Note that, initially, s changes hardly at all ($ds/dt \approx 0$), but eventually s changes about as fast as h changes ($ds/dt \approx dh/dt = 8$). An estimate for ds/dt when $h = 50$ might be about one-third to one-half of dh/dt, or 3. If we get an answer far from this value, we will know we have made a mistake. For example, answers such as 17 and even 7 are clearly wrong.

We continue with the exact solution. For emphasis, we ask and answer three fundamental questions.

(a) What is given? *Answer: $dh/dt = 8$.*
(b) What do we want to know? *Answer:* We want to know ds/dt at the instant when $h = 50$.
(c) How are s and h related? *Answer:* The variables s and h change with time (they are implicit functions of t), but they are always related by the Pythagorean equation

$$s^2 = h^2 + (150)^2$$

If we differentiate implicitly with respect to t and use the Chain Rule, we obtain

$$2s\frac{ds}{dt} = 2h\frac{dh}{dt}$$

or

$$s\frac{ds}{dt} = h\frac{dh}{dt}$$

This relationship holds for all $t > 0$.

Now, and *not before now*, we turn to the specific instant when $h = 50$. From the Pythagorean Theorem, we see that, when $h = 50$,

$$s = \sqrt{(50)^2 + (150)^2} = 50\sqrt{10}$$

Substituting in $s(ds/dt) = h(dh/dt)$ yields

$$50\sqrt{10}\,\frac{ds}{dt} = 50(8)$$

or

$$\frac{ds}{dt} = \frac{8}{\sqrt{10}} \approx 2.53$$

At the instant when $h = 50$, the distance between the balloon and the observer is increasing at the rate of 2.53 feet per second. ∎

Similar Triangles

Two triangles are similar if their corresponding angles are congruent.

From geometry, we learn that ratios of corresponding sides of similar triangles are equal. For example,

$$\frac{b}{a} = \frac{B}{A}$$

This fact, used in Example 2, will be needed often in the problem set.

EXAMPLE 2 Water is pouring into a conical tank at the rate of 8 cubic feet per minute. If the height of the tank is 12 feet and the radius of its circular opening is 6 feet, how fast is the water level rising when the water is 4 feet deep?

SOLUTION Denote the depth of the water by h and let r be the corresponding radius of the surface of the water (see Figure 3).

We are *given* that the volume, V, of water in the tank is increasing at the rate of 8 cubic feet per minute; that is, $dV/dt = 8$. We *want to know* how fast the water is rising (that is, dh/dt) at the instant when $h = 4$.

We need to find an equation relating V and h; we will then differentiate it to get a relationship between dV/dt and dh/dt. The formula for the volume of water in the tank, $V = \frac{1}{3}\pi r^2 h$, contains the unwanted variable r; it is unwanted because we do not know its rate dr/dt. However, by similar triangles (see the marginal box), we have $r/h = 6/12$, so $r = h/2$. Substituting this in $V = \frac{1}{3}\pi r^2 h$ gives

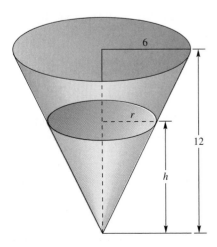

Figure 3

$$V = \frac{1}{3}\pi\left(\frac{h}{2}\right)^2 h = \frac{\pi h^3}{12}$$

Now we differentiate implicitly, keeping in mind that both V and h depend on t. We obtain

$$\frac{dV}{dt} = \frac{3\pi h^2}{12}\frac{dh}{dt} = \frac{\pi h^2}{4}\frac{dh}{dt}$$

Now that we have a relationship between dV/dt and dh/dt, and not earlier, we consider the situation when $h = 4$. Substituting $h = 4$ and $dV/dt = 8$, we obtain

$$8 = \frac{\pi(4)^2}{4}\frac{dh}{dt}$$

from which

$$\frac{dh}{dt} = \frac{2}{\pi} \approx 0.637$$

When the depth of the water is 4 feet, the water level is rising at 0.637 foot per minute. ∎

If you think about Example 2 for a moment, you realize that the water level will rise more and more slowly as time goes on. For example, when $h = 10$

$$8 = \frac{\pi(10)^2}{4}\frac{dh}{dt}$$

so $dh/dt = 32/100\pi \approx 0.102$ foot per minute.

What we are really saying is that the acceleration d^2h/dt^2 is negative. We can calculate an expression for it. At any time t,

$$8 = \frac{\pi h^2}{4}\frac{dh}{dt}$$

so

$$\frac{32}{\pi} = h^2\frac{dh}{dt}$$

If we differentiate implicitly again, we get

$$0 = h^2\frac{d^2h}{dt^2} + \frac{dh}{dt}\left(2h\frac{dh}{dt}\right)$$

from which

$$\frac{d^2h}{dt^2} = \frac{-2\left(\frac{dh}{dt}\right)^2}{h}$$

This is clearly negative.

A Systematic Procedure Examples 1 and 2 suggest the following method for solving a related rates problem.

Step 1: Let t denote the elapsed time. Draw a diagram that is valid for all $t > 0$. Label those quantities whose values do not change as t increases with their given *constant* values. Assign letters to the quantities that vary with t, and label the appropriate parts of the figure with these variables.

Step 2: State what is given about the variables and what information is wanted about them. This information will be in the form of derivatives with respect to t.

Step 3: Relate the variables by writing an equation that is valid at all times $t > 0$, not just at some particular instant.

Step 4: Differentiate the equation found in Step 3 implicitly with respect to t. The resulting equation, containing derivatives with respect to t, is true for all $t > 0$.

Step 5: At this point, and not earlier, substitute in the equation found in Step 4 all data that are valid *at the particular instant* for which the answer to the problem is required. Solve for the desired derivative.

EXAMPLE 3 An airplane flying north at 640 miles per hour passes over a certain town at noon. A second airplane going east at 600 miles per hour is directly over the same town 15 minutes later. If the airplanes are flying at the same altitude, how fast will they be separating at 1:15 P.M.?

SOLUTION

Step 1: Let t denote the number of hours after 12:15 P.M., y the distance in miles flown by the northbound airplane after 12:15 P.M., x the distance flown by the eastbound airplane after 12:15 P.M., and s the distance between the airplanes. In the 15 minutes from noon to 12:15 P.M. the northbound airplane will have flown $\frac{640}{4} = 160$ miles, so the distance from the town to the northbound airplane at time t will be $y + 160$. (See Figure 4.)

Step 2: We are given that, for all $t > 0$, $dy/dt = 640$ and $dx/dt = 600$. We want to know ds/dt at $t = 1$, that is, at 1:15 P.M.

Step 3: By the Pythagorean Theorem,

$$s^2 = x^2 + (y + 160)^2$$

Step 4: Differentiating implicitly with respect to t and using the Chain Rule, we have

$$2s\frac{ds}{dt} = 2x\frac{dx}{dt} + 2(y + 160)\frac{dy}{dt}$$

or

$$s\frac{ds}{dt} = x\frac{dx}{dt} + (y + 160)\frac{dy}{dt}$$

Step 5: For all $t > 0$, $dx/dt = 600$ and $dy/dt = 640$, while at the particular instant $t = 1$, $x = 600$, $y = 640$, and $s = \sqrt{(600)^2 + (640 + 160)^2} = 1000$. When we substitute these data in the equation of Step 4, we obtain

$$1000\frac{ds}{dt} = (600)(600) + (640 + 160)(640)$$

from which

$$\frac{ds}{dt} = 872$$

At 1:15 P.M., the airplanes are separating at 872 miles per hour.

≈ Now let's see if our answer makes sense. Look at Figure 4 again. Clearly, s is increasing faster than either x or y is increasing, so ds/dt exceeds 640. On the other hand, s is surely increasing more slowly than the sum of x and y; that is, $ds/dt < 600 + 640 = 1240$. Our answer, $ds/dt = 872$, is reasonable. ∎

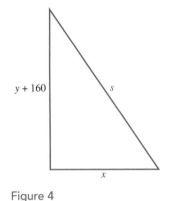

$y + 160$ s

x

Figure 4

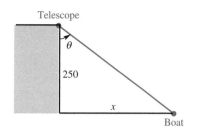

Figure 5

EXAMPLE 4 A woman standing on a cliff is watching a motorboat through a telescope as the boat approaches the shoreline directly below her. If the telescope is 250 feet above the water level and if the boat is approaching at 20 feet per second, at what rate is the angle of the telescope changing when the boat is 250 feet from the shore?

SOLUTION

Step 1: We draw a figure (Figure 5) and introduce variables x and θ, as shown.

Step 2: We are given that $dx/dt = -20$; the sign is negative because x is decreasing with time. We want to know $d\theta/dt$ at the instant when $x = 250$.

Step 3: From trigonometry,

$$\tan \theta = \frac{x}{250}$$

Step 4: We differentiate implicitly using the fact that $D_\theta \tan \theta = \sec^2 \theta$ (Theorem 3.4B). This gives

$$\sec^2 \theta \frac{d\theta}{dt} = \frac{1}{250} \frac{dx}{dt}$$

Step 5: At the instant when $x = 250$, θ is $\pi/4$ radians and $\sec^2 \theta = \sec^2(\pi/4) = 2$. Thus,

$$2\frac{d\theta}{dt} = \frac{1}{250}(-20)$$

or

$$\frac{d\theta}{dt} = \frac{-1}{25} = -0.04$$

The angle is changing at -0.04 radian per second. The negative sign shows that θ is decreasing with time. ∎

EXAMPLE 5 As the sun sets behind a 120-foot building, the building's shadow grows. How fast is the shadow growing (in feet per second) when the sun's rays make an angle of $45°$ (or $\pi/4$ radians)?

SOLUTION

Step 1: Let t denote time in seconds since midnight. Let x denote the length of the shadow in feet, and let θ denote the angle of the sun's ray. See Figure 6.

Step 2: Since the earth rotates once every 24 hours, or 86,400 seconds, we know that $d\theta/dt = -2\pi/86{,}400$. (The negative sign is needed because θ *decreases* as the sun sets.) We want to know dx/dt when $\theta = \pi/4$.

Step 3: Figure 6 indicates that the quantities x and θ satisfy $\cot \theta = x/120$, so $x = 120 \cot \theta$.

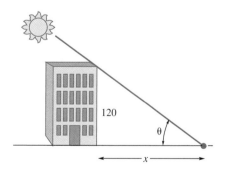

Figure 6

Step 4: Differentiating both sides of $x = 120 \cot \theta$ with respect to t gives

$$\frac{dx}{dt} = 120(-\csc^2 \theta)\frac{d\theta}{dt} = -120(\csc^2 \theta)\left(-\frac{2\pi}{86{,}400}\right) = \frac{\pi}{360}\csc^2 \theta$$

Step 5: When $\theta = \pi/4$, we have

$$\frac{dx}{dt} = \frac{\pi}{360}\csc^2\frac{\pi}{4} = \frac{\pi}{360}\left(\sqrt{2}\right)^2 = \frac{\pi}{180} \approx 0.0175 \frac{\text{ft}}{\text{sec}}$$

Notice that as the sun sets, θ is decreasing (hence $d\theta/dt$ is negative), while the shadow x is increasing (hence dx/dt is positive). ∎

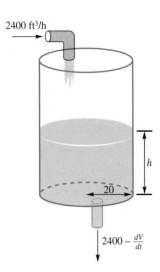

2400 ft³/h

h

20

$2400 - \frac{dV}{dt}$

Figure 7

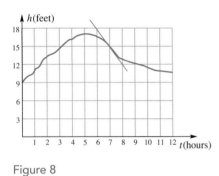

Figure 8

A Graphical Related Rates Problem

Often in a real-life situation, we do not know a formula for a certain function, but rather have an empirically determined graph for it. We may still be able to answer questions about rates.

EXAMPLE 6 Webster City monitors the height of the water in its cylindrical water tank with an automatic recording device. Water is constantly pumped into the tank at a rate of 2400 cubic feet per hour, as shown in Figure 7. During a certain 12-hour period (beginning at midnight), the water level rose and fell according to the graph in Figure 8. If the radius of the tank is 20 feet, at what rate was water being used at 7:00 A.M.?

SOLUTION Let t denote the number of hours past midnight, h the height of the water in the tank at time t, and V the volume of water in the tank at that time (see Figure 7). Then dV/dt is the rate in minus the rate out, so $2400 - dV/dt$ is the rate at which water is being used at any time t. Since the slope of the tangent line at $t = 7$ is approximately -3 (Figure 8), we conclude that $dh/dt \approx -3$ at that time. For a cylinder, $V = \pi r^2 h$, and so

$$V = \pi(20)^2 h$$

from which

$$\frac{dV}{dt} = 400\pi \frac{dh}{dt}$$

At $t = 7$,

$$\frac{dV}{dt} \approx 400\pi(-3) \approx -3770$$

Thus Webster City residents were using water at the rate of $2400 + 3770 = 6170$ cubic feet per hour at 7:00 A.M. ∎

Concepts Review

1. To ask how fast u is changing with respect to time t after 2 hours is to ask the value of _____ at _____.

2. An airplane with a constant speed of 400 miles per hour flew directly over an observer. The distance between the observer and plane grew at an increasing rate, eventually approaching a rate of _____.

3. If dh/dt is decreasing as time t increases, then d^2h/dt^2 is _____.

4. If water is pouring into a spherical tank at a constant rate, then the height of the water grows at a variable and positive rate dh/dt, but d^2h/dt^2 is _____ until h reaches half the height of the tank, after which d^2h/dt^2 becomes _____.

Problem Set 3.8

1. Each edge of a variable cube is increasing at a rate of 3 inches per second. How fast is the volume of the cube increasing when an edge is 12 inches long?

2. Assuming that a soap bubble retains its spherical shape as it expands, how fast is its radius increasing when its radius is 3 inches if air is blown into it at a rate of 3 cubic inches per second?

≈ **3.** An airplane, flying horizontally at an altitude of 1 mile, passes directly over an observer. If the constant speed of the airplane is 400 miles per hour, how fast is its distance from the observer increasing 45 seconds later? *Hint:* Note that in 45 seconds $\left(\frac{3}{4} \cdot \frac{1}{60} = \frac{1}{80} \text{ hour}\right)$, the airplane goes 5 miles.

4. A student is using a straw to drink from a conical paper cup, whose axis is vertical, at a rate of 3 cubic centimeters per second. If the height of the cup is 10 centimeters and the diameter of

its opening is 6 centimeters, how fast is the level of the liquid falling when the depth of the liquid is 5 centimeters?

≈ **5.** An airplane flying west at 300 miles per hour goes over the control tower at noon, and a second airplane at the same altitude, flying north at 400 miles per hour, goes over the tower an hour later. How fast is the distance between the airplanes changing at 2:00 P.M.? *Hint:* See Example 3.

≈ **6.** A woman on a dock is pulling in a rope fastened to the bow of a small boat. If the woman's hands are 10 feet higher than the point where the rope is attached to the boat and if she is retrieving the rope at a rate of 2 feet per second, how fast is the boat approaching the dock when 25 feet of rope is still out?

≈ **7.** A 20-foot ladder is leaning against a building. If the bottom of the ladder is sliding along the level pavement directly away from the building at 1 foot per second, how fast is the top of the ladder moving down when the foot of the ladder is 5 feet from the wall?

8. We assume that an oil spill is being cleaned up by deploying bacteria that consume the oil at 4 cubic feet per hour. The oil spill itself is modeled in the form of a very thin cylinder whose height is the thickness of the oil slick. When the thickness of the slick is 0.001 foot, the cylinder is 500 feet in diameter. If the height is decreasing at 0.0005 foot per hour, at what rate is the area of the slick changing?

9. Sand is pouring from a pipe at the rate of 16 cubic feet per second. If the falling sand forms a conical pile on the ground whose altitude is always $\frac{1}{4}$ the diameter of the base, how fast is the altitude increasing when the pile is 4 feet high? *Hint:* Refer to Figure 9 and use the fact that $V = \frac{1}{3}\pi r^2 h$.

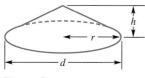

Figure 9

 10. A child is flying a kite. If the kite is 90 feet above the child's hand level and the wind is blowing it on a horizontal course at 5 feet per second, how fast is the child paying out cord when 150 feet of cord is out? (Assume that the cord remains straight from hand to kite, actually an unrealistic assumption.)

11. A rectangular swimming pool is 40 feet long, 20 feet wide, 8 feet deep at the deep end, and 3 feet deep at the shallow end (see Figure 10). If the pool is filled by pumping water into it at the rate of 40 cubic feet per minute, how fast is the water level rising when it is 3 feet deep at the deep end?

Figure 10

 12. A particle P is moving along the graph of $y = \sqrt{x^2 - 4}$, $x \geq 2$, so that the x-coordinate of P is increasing at the rate of 5 units per second. How fast is the y-coordinate of P increasing when $x = 3$?

13. A metal disk expands during heating. If its radius increases at the rate of 0.02 inch per second, how fast is the area of one of its faces increasing when its radius is 8.1 inches?

 14. Two ships sail from the same island port, one going north at 24 knots (24 nautical miles per hour) and the other east at 30 knots. The northbound ship departed at 9:00 A.M. and the eastbound ship left at 11:00 A.M. How fast is the distance between them increasing at 2:00 P.M.? *Hint:* Let $t = 0$ at 11:00 A.M.

15. A light in a lighthouse 1 kilometer offshore from a straight shoreline is rotating at 2 revolutions per minute. How fast is the beam moving along the shoreline when it passes the point $\frac{1}{2}$ kilometer from the point opposite the lighthouse?

16. An aircraft spotter observes a plane flying at a constant altitude of 4000 feet toward a point directly above her head. She notes that when the angle of elevation is $\frac{1}{2}$ radian it is increasing

at a rate of $\frac{1}{10}$ radian per second. What is the speed of the airplane?

17. Chris, who is 6 feet tall, is walking away from a street light pole 30 feet high at a rate of 2 feet per second.
(a) How fast is his shadow increasing in length when Chris is 24 feet from the pole? 30 feet?
(b) How fast is the tip of his shadow moving?
(c) To follow the tip of his shadow, at what angular rate must Chris be lifting his eyes when his shadow is 6 feet long?

18. The vertex angle θ opposite the base of an isosceles triangle with equal sides of length 100 centimeters is increasing at $\frac{1}{10}$ radian per minute. How fast is the area of the triangle increasing when the vertex angle measures $\pi/6$ radians? *Hint:* $A = \frac{1}{2}ab \sin \theta$.

19. A long, level highway bridge passes over a railroad track that is 100 feet below it and at right angles to it. If an automobile traveling 45 miles per hour (66 feet per second) is directly above a train engine going 60 miles per hour (88 feet per second), how fast will they be separating 10 seconds later?

20. Water is pumped at a uniform rate of 2 liters (1 liter = 1000 cubic centimeters) per minute into a tank shaped like a frustum of a right circular cone. The tank has altitude 80 centimeters and lower and upper radii of 20 and 40 centimeters, respectively (Figure 11). How fast is the water level rising when the depth of the water is 30 centimeters? *Note:* The volume, V, of a frustum of a right circular cone of altitude h and lower and upper radii a and b is $V = \frac{1}{3}\pi h \cdot (a^2 + ab + b^2)$.

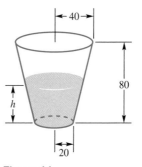

Figure 11

21. Water is leaking out the bottom of a hemispherical tank of radius 8 feet at a rate of 2 cubic feet per hour. The tank was full at a certain time. How fast is the water level changing when its height h is 3 feet? *Note:* The volume of a segment of height h in a hemisphere of radius r is $\pi h^2[r - (h/3)]$. (See Figure 12.)

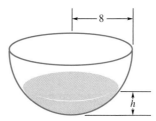

Figure 12

22. The hands on a clock are of length 5 inches (minute hand) and 4 inches (hour hand). How fast is the distance between the tips of the hands changing at 3:00?

23. A steel ball will drop $16t^2$ feet in t seconds. Such a ball is dropped from a height of 64 feet at a horizontal distance 10 feet from a 48-foot street light. How fast is the ball's shadow moving when the ball hits the ground?

24. Rework Example 6 assuming that the water tank is a sphere of radius 20 feet. (See Problem 21 for the volume of a spherical segment.)

25. Rework Example 6 assuming that the water tank is in the shape of an upper hemisphere of radius 20 feet. (See Problem 21 for the volume of a spherical segment.)

26. Refer to Example 6. How much water did Webster City use during this 12-hour period from midnight to noon? *Hint:* This is not a differentiation problem.

27. An 18-foot ladder leans against a 12-foot vertical wall, its top extending over the wall. The bottom end of the ladder is pulled along the ground away from the wall at 2 feet per second.
(a) Find the vertical velocity of the top end when the ladder makes an angle of 60° with the ground.
(b) Find the vertical acceleration at the same instant.

28. A spherical steel ball rests at the bottom of the tank of Problem 21. Answer the question posed there if the ball has radius
(a) 6 inches, and   (b) 2 feet.
(Assume that the ball does not affect the flow from the tank.)

29. A snowball melts at a rate proportional to its surface area.
(a) Show that its radius shrinks at a constant rate.
(b) If it melts to $\frac{8}{27}$ its original volume in one hour, how long will it take to melt completely?

30. A right circular cylinder with a piston at one end is filled with gas. Its volume is continually changing because of the movement of the piston. If the temperature of the gas is kept constant,

then, by **Boyle's Law,** $PV = k$, where P is the pressure (pounds per square inch), V is the volume (cubic inches), and k is a constant. The pressure was monitored by a recording device over one 10-minute period. The results are shown in Figure 13. Approximately how fast was the volume changing at $t = 6.5$ if its volume was 300 cubic inches at that instant? (See Example 6.)

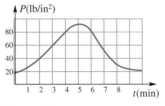

Figure 13

31. A girl 5 feet tall walks toward a street light 20 feet high at a rate of 4 feet per second. Her little brother, 3 feet tall, follows at a constant distance of 4 feet directly behind her (Figure 14).

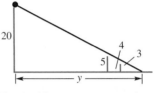

Figure 14

Determine how fast the tip of the shadow is moving, that is, determine dy/dt. *Note:* When the girl is far from the light, she controls the tip of the shadow, whereas her brother controls it near the light.

Answers to Concepts Review: **1.** du/dt; $t = 2$ **2.** 400 mi/h **3.** negative **4.** negative; positive

---

3.9
Derivatives of Exponential and Logarithmic Functions

Exponential and logarithmic functions are inverses of one another, so to get their derivatives, as well as the derivatives of the inverse trigonometric functions, we begin by studying inverse functions more thoroughly. Specifically, we will see how the derivative of a function is related to the derivative of its inverse.

Inverse Functions   We have seen in Theorem 1.6A that a function that is strictly monotonic (i.e., increasing or decreasing) on its domain must have an inverse. We have also seen in this chapter how the derivative $f'(x)$ gives us the slope of the tangent line to the graph at x. Thus, if $f'(x) > 0$, then the tangent line is rising to the right, suggesting that f is increasing. (See Figure 1.) Similarly, if $f'(x) < 0$, then the tangent line is falling to the right, suggesting that f is decreasing. Theorem A states this result, which at this point should seem plausible. A rigorous proof must wait until Section 4.6.

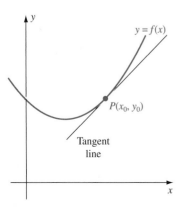

Figure 1

Theorem A   Monotonicity Theorem
Let f be continuous on an interval I and differentiable at every interior point of I.
(1) If $f'(x) > 0$ for all x interior to I, then f is increasing on I.
(2) If $f'(x) < 0$ for all x interior to I, then f is decreasing on I.

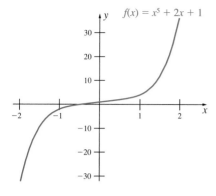

Figure 2

In Section 4.2, we will make use of this theorem as we use calculus to help us graph functions. For now, we will use it, along with the result stated above that a monotonic function has an inverse, to determine whether a given function has an inverse.

EXAMPLE 1 Show that $f(x) = x^5 + 2x + 1$ has an inverse.

SOLUTION $f'(x) = 5x^4 + 2 > 0$ for all x. Thus f is increasing on the whole real line and so it has an inverse there. (See Figure 2.) ∎

We do not claim that we can always give a formula for f^{-1}. In Example 1, this would require that we be able to solve $y = x^5 + 2x + 1$ for every x. Although we could use a CAS or a graphing calculator to solve this equation for x for a particular value of y, there is no simple formula that would give us x in terms of y for an arbitrary y.

Next, we investigate the relationship between the derivative of a function, and the derivative of its inverse. Consider what happens to a line l_1 when it is reflected across the line $y = x$. As the left half of Figure 3 makes clear, l_1 is reflected into a line l_2; moreover, their respective slopes m_1 and m_2 are related by $m_2 = 1/m_1$, provided $m_1 \neq 0$. If l_1 happens to be the tangent line to the graph of f at the point (c, d), then l_2 is the tangent line to the graph of f^{-1} at the point (d, c) (see the right half of Figure 3). We are led to the conclusion that

$$(f^{-1})'(d) = m_2 = \frac{1}{m_1} = \frac{1}{f'(c)}$$

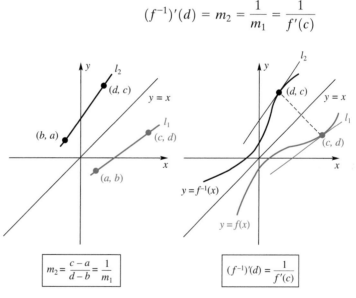

Figure 3

Pictures are sometimes deceptive, so we claim only to have made the following result plausible.

Theorem B | **Inverse Function Theorem**

Let f be differentiable and strictly monotonic on an interval I. If $f'(x) \neq 0$ at a certain x in I, then (1) f^{-1} is differentiable at the corresponding point $y = f(x)$ in the range of f and (2)

$$(f^{-1})'(y) = \frac{1}{f'(x)}$$

The proof that f^{-1} is differentiable is omitted, but see Problem 59 for a proof of the second part. The conclusion to Theorem B is often written symbolically as

$$\frac{dx}{dy} = \frac{1}{dy/dx}$$

EXAMPLE 2 Let $y = f(x) = x^5 + 2x + 1$, as in Example 1. Find $(f^{-1})'(4)$.

SOLUTION Even though we cannot find a formula for f^{-1} in this case, we note that $y = 4$ corresponds to $x = 1$, and since $f'(x) = 5x^4 + 2$,

$$(f^{-1})'(4) = \frac{1}{f'(1)} = \frac{1}{5 + 2} = \frac{1}{7}$$ ■

EXAMPLE 3 Let $f(x) = x^3 + 1$. Find $(f^{-1})'(9)$ in two ways.

SOLUTION **Method 1:** We find the inverse of f and then take its derivative.

$$y = x^3 + 1$$
$$x = \sqrt[3]{y - 1}$$
$$f^{-1}(x) = \sqrt[3]{x - 1}$$

Then

$$(f^{-1})'(x) = \frac{1}{3}(x - 1)^{-2/3}$$
$$(f^{-1})'(9) = \frac{1}{3}(9 - 1)^{-2/3} = \frac{1}{12}$$

Method 2: We use the Inverse Function Theorem. Note that $f'(x) = 3x^2$, and that $f(2) = 9$, so $f^{-1}(9) = 2$. Then

$$(f^{-1})'(9) = \frac{1}{f'(2)} = \frac{1}{3 \cdot 2^2} = \frac{1}{12}$$ ■

Derivatives of Exponential and Logarithmic Functions Armed with Theorems A and B, we are now ready to find formulas for the derivatives of the logarithmic and exponential functions. We begin with the natural logarithmic function $f(x) = \ln x$ and then address its inverse, the natural exponential function $g(x) = e^x$. Since these are inverses of one another, we need only find the derivative of one; then use the result, along with Theorem B, to find the derivative of the other. These results are given in Theorem C.

Theorem C	Derivatives of Natural Logarithmic and Exponential Functions
(1) $D_x(\ln x) = \dfrac{1}{x}$	(2) $D_x(e^x) = e^x$

Proof We begin by proving that $D_x(\ln x) = 1/x$. To complete the proof, we must assume the continuity of $\ln x$, something we think is plausible, but which we assumed without proof in Chapter 2. Using the definition of the derivative, and the properties of logs, we have

$$D_x(\ln x) = \lim_{h \to 0} \frac{\ln(x + h) - \ln x}{h} = \lim_{h \to 0} \frac{1}{h} \ln \frac{x + h}{x} = \lim_{h \to 0} \ln \left(1 + \frac{h}{x}\right)^{1/h}$$

This last limit can be written as

$$D_x(\ln x) = \lim_{h \to 0} \ln \left[\left(1 + \frac{h}{x}\right)^{x/h}\right]^{1/x}$$

$$= \ln \lim_{h \to 0} \left[\left(1 + \frac{h}{x}\right)^{x/h}\right]^{1/x} = \ln e^{1/x} = \frac{1}{x}$$

Here we have used the continuity of the natural log function and the result from Chapter 2 that

$$\lim_{h \to 0} \left(1 + \frac{h}{x} \right)^{x/h} = \lim_{h \to 0} (1 + h)^{1/h} = e$$

Once the derivative of $\ln x$ is obtained, it is a matter of applying Theorem B to find the derivative of $f(x) = e^x$. If we let $y = e^x$, then $\ln y = x$, so $dx/dy = 1/y$. Thus,

$$\frac{dy}{dx} = \frac{1}{dx/dy} = \frac{1}{1/y} = y = e^x. \qquad \blacksquare$$

Note the remarkable simplicity in the formulas for the derivatives of $\ln x$ and e^x. In particular, we have shown that $f(x) = e^x$ is a function that is its own derivative! When used along with the Chain Rule, the formulas in Theorem C become

$$(1) \qquad D_x \ln u = \frac{1}{u} D_x u \qquad\qquad (2) \qquad D_x e^u = e^u D_x u$$

Once we have Theorem C, we can use it, together with the Product Rule, Quotient Rule, and Chain Rule, to evaluate a number of derivatives.

EXAMPLE 4 Find the derivatives

(a) $D_x \ln(x^2 - 1)$, $\qquad$ (b) $D_x \left(e^{-x^2} \right)$ $\qquad$ (c) $D_x \left(\dfrac{\ln x}{1 + e^x} \right)$

SOLUTION Parts (a) and (b) require just the Chain Rule, whereas part (c) requires the Quotient Rule.

(a) $D_x \ln(x^2 - 1) = \dfrac{1}{x^2 - 1} D_x (x^2 - 1) = \dfrac{2x}{x^2 - 1}$

(b) $D_x \left(e^{-x^2} \right) = e^{-x^2} D_x (-x^2) = -2xe^{-x^2}$

(c) $D_x \left(\dfrac{\ln x}{1 + e^x} \right) = \dfrac{(1 + e^x) D_x \ln x - (\ln x) D_x (1 + e^x)}{(1 + e^x)^2} = \dfrac{(1 + e^x)/x - e^x \ln x}{(1 + e^x)^2}$ $\qquad\blacksquare$

We can now obtain the derivative formulas for the general exponential function:

$$D_x a^x = D_x e^{x \ln a} = e^{x \ln a} (\ln a) = a^x \ln a$$

If we let $y = \log_a x$, then $a^y = x$. Taking the natural log of both sides gives $y \ln a = \ln x$, so

$$y = \frac{\ln x}{\ln a}$$

from which we conclude

$$D_x \log_a x = \frac{1}{x \ln a}$$

EXAMPLE 5 If $y = \log_{10} (x^4 + 13)$ and $z = 2^{-x^2}$, find (a) $\dfrac{dy}{dx}$, and (b) $\dfrac{dz}{dx}$.

SOLUTION Both derivatives require the Chain Rule.

(a) $\dfrac{dy}{dx} = \dfrac{1}{(x^4 + 13) \ln 10} D_x (x^4 + 13) = \dfrac{4x^3}{(x^4 + 13) \ln 10}$

(b) $\dfrac{dz}{dx} = 2^{-x^2} (\ln 2) D_x (-x^2) = -2x2^{-x^2} \ln 2 = -x2^{-x^2+1} \ln 2$ $\qquad\blacksquare$

Logarithmic Differentiation The labor of differentiating expressions involving quotients, products, or powers can often be substantially reduced by first applying the natural logarithm function and using its properties. This method, called **logarithmic differentiation,** is illustrated in Example 6.

EXAMPLE 6 Differentiate $y = \dfrac{\sqrt{1 - x^2}}{(x + 1)^{2/3}}$.

SOLUTION First we take natural logarithms; then we differentiate implicitly with respect to x (recall Section 3.7).

$$\ln y = \frac{1}{2} \ln(1 - x^2) - \frac{2}{3} \ln(x + 1)$$

$$\frac{1}{y} \frac{dy}{dx} = \frac{-2x}{2(1 - x^2)} - \frac{2}{3(x + 1)} = \frac{-(x + 2)}{3(1 - x^2)}$$

Thus,

$$\frac{dy}{dx} = \frac{-y(x + 2)}{3(1 - x^2)} = \frac{-\sqrt{1 - x^2}\,(x + 2)}{3(x + 1)^{2/3}(1 - x^2)}$$

$$= \frac{-(x + 2)}{3(x + 1)^{2/3}(1 - x^2)^{1/2}} \qquad \blacksquare$$

Example 6 could have been done directly, without first taking logarithms, and we suggest you try it. You should be able to make the two answers agree.

The Functions a^x, x^a, and x^x Begin by comparing the three graphs in Figure 4. More generally, let a be a constant. Do not confuse $f(x) = a^x$, an *exponential function*, with $g(x) = x^a$, a *power function*. And do not confuse their derivatives. We have just learned that

$$\boxed{D_x(a^x) = a^x \ln a}$$

What about $D_x(x^a)$? For a rational, we proved the Power Rule in Section 3.7, which says that

$$D_x(x^a) = ax^{a-1}$$

Now we assert that this is true even if a is irrational. To see this, write

$$D_x(x^a) = D_x(e^{a \ln x}) = e^{a \ln x} \cdot \frac{a}{x}$$

$$= x^a \cdot \frac{a}{x} = ax^{a-1}$$

Finally, we consider $f(x) = x^x$, a variable to a variable power. There is a formula for $D_x(x^x)$, but we do not recommend that you memorize it. Rather, we suggest that you learn two methods for finding it, as illustrated below.

EXAMPLE 7 If $y = x^x$, $x > 0$, find $D_x y$ by two different methods.

SOLUTION

Method 1 We may write

$$y = x^x = e^{x \ln x}$$

Thus, using the Chain Rule and the Product Rule,

$$D_x y = e^{x \ln x} D_x(x \ln x) = x^x \left(x \cdot \frac{1}{x} + \ln x \right) = x^x(1 + \ln x)$$

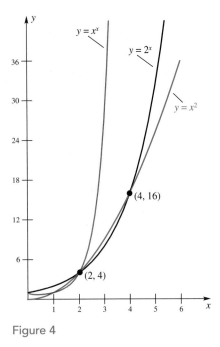

Figure 4

Method 2 Apply the *logarithmic differentiation* technique.

$$y = x^x$$

$$\ln y = x \ln x$$

$$\frac{1}{y} D_x y = x \cdot \frac{1}{x} + \ln x$$

$$D_x y = y(1 + \ln x) = x^x(1 + \ln x) \quad \blacksquare$$

EXAMPLE 8 If $y = (x^2 + 1)^\pi + \pi^{\sin x}$, find dy/dx.

SOLUTION

$$\frac{dy}{dx} = \pi(x^2 + 1)^{\pi-1}(2x) + \pi^{\sin x} \ln \pi \cdot \cos x \quad \blacksquare$$

From a^x to $[f(x)]^{g(x)}$

Note the increasing complexity of the functions that we have considered. The progression a^x to x^a to x^x is one chain. A more complex chain is $a^{f(x)}$ to $[f(x)]^a$ to $[f(x)]^{g(x)}$. We now know how to find the derivatives of all these functions. Finding the derivative of the last of these is best accomplished by logarithmic differentiation.

EXAMPLE 9 If $y = (x^2 + 1)^{\sin x}$, find $\dfrac{dy}{dx}$.

SOLUTION We use logarithmic differentiation.

$$\ln y = (\sin x) \ln(x^2 + 1)$$

$$\frac{1}{y}\frac{dy}{dx} = (\sin x)\frac{2x}{x^2 + 1} + (\cos x) \ln(x^2 + 1)$$

$$\frac{dy}{dx} = (x^2 + 1)^{\sin x}\left[\frac{2x \sin x}{x^2 + 1} + (\cos x) \ln(x^2 + 1)\right] \quad \blacksquare$$

Concepts Review

1. A function that is strictly _____ on its domain has an inverse.

2. The derivative of the natural logarithmic function is $D_x (\ln x) =$ _____.

3. An example of a function that is its own derivative is $f(x) =$ _____.

4. If $x > 0$, then the power rule $D_x (x^a) =$ _____, is true for all real numbers a in the interval _____.

Problem Set 3.9

In Problems 1–6, show that f has an inverse by showing that it is strictly monotonic (see Example 1).

1. $f(x) = -x^5 - x^3 - x$

2. $f(x) = x^7 + x^5 + x^3 + x$

3. $f(\theta) = \cos \theta, 0 \le \theta \le \pi$

4. $f(x) = \cot x = \dfrac{\cos x}{\sin x}, 0 < x < \dfrac{\pi}{2}$

5. $f(z) = (z - 1)^2, z \ge 1$

6. $f(x) = x^2 + x - 6, x \ge 2$

In each of Problems 7–10, the graph of $y = f(x)$ is shown. Sketch the graph of $y = f^{-1}(x)$ and estimate $(f^{-1})'(3)$.

7.

8.

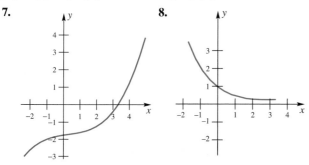

9.

10.

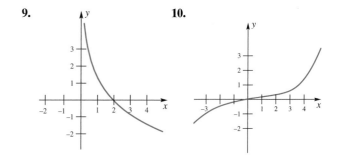

In Problems 11–14, find $(f^{-1})'(2)$ by using Theorem B (see Example 2). Note that you can find the x corresponding to $y = 2$ by inspection.

11. $f(x) = 3x^5 + x - 2$

12. $f(x) = x^5 + 5x - 4$

13. $f(x) = 2 \tan x, -\dfrac{\pi}{2} < x < \dfrac{\pi}{2}$

14. $f(x) = \sqrt{x + 1}$

In Problems 15–52, find the indicated derivative.

15. $D_x \ln(x^2 + 3x + \pi)$

16. $D_x \ln(3x^3 + 2x)$

17. $D_x \ln(x - 4)^3$

18. $D_x \ln \sqrt{3x - 2}$

19. $\dfrac{dy}{dx}$ if $y = 3 \ln x$

20. $\dfrac{dy}{dx}$ if $y = x^2 \ln x$

21. $\dfrac{dz}{dx}$ if $z = x^2 \ln x^2 + (\ln x)^3$

22. $\dfrac{dr}{dx}$ if $r = \dfrac{\ln x}{x^2 \ln x^2} + \left(\ln \dfrac{1}{x}\right)^3$

23. $g'(x)$ if $g(x) = \ln\left(x + \sqrt{x^2 + 1}\right)$

24. $h'(x)$ if $h(x) = \ln\left(x + \sqrt{x^2 - 1}\right)$

25. $f'(81)$ if $f(x) = \ln \sqrt[3]{x}$

26 $f'\left(\dfrac{\pi}{4}\right)$ if $f(x) = \ln(\cos x)$

27. $D_x e^{x+2}$

28. $D_x e^{2x^2-x}$

29. $D_x e^{\sqrt{x+2}}$

30. $D_x e^{-1/x^2}$

31. y' if $y = e^{2 \ln x}$

32. y' if $y = e^{x/\ln x}$

33. $D_x x^3 e^x$

34. $D_x e^{x^3 \ln x}$

35. $D_x\left(\sqrt{e^{x^2}} + e^{\sqrt{x^2}}\right)$

36. $D_x (e^{1/x^2} + 1/e^{x^2})$

37. $\dfrac{dy}{dx}$ if $e^{xy} + xy = 2$ *Hint:* Use implicit differentiation.

38. $\dfrac{dy}{dx}$ if $e^{x+y} = 4 + x + y$

39. $D_x(6^{2x})$

40. $D_x(3^{2x^2-3x})$

41. $D_x \log_3 e^x$

42. $D_x \log_{10}(x^3 + 9)$

43. $D_z[3^z \ln(z + 5)]$

44. $D_\theta \sqrt{\log_{10}(3^{\theta^2-\theta})}$

45. $D_x\left(10^{(x^2)} + (x^2)^{10}\right)$

46. $D_x (\sin^2 x + 2^{\sin x})$

47. $D_x [x^{\pi+1} + (\pi + 1)^x]$

48. $D_x [2^{(e^x)} + (2^e)^x]$

49. $D_x (x^2 + 1)^{\ln x}$

50. $D_x (\ln x^2)^{2x+3}$

51. $f'(1)$ if $f(x) = x^{\sin x}$

52. $D_x x^{(2^x)}$

In Problems 53–56, find dy/dx by logarithmic differentiation (see Example 6).

53. $y = \dfrac{x + 11}{\sqrt{x^3 - 4}}$

54. $y = (x^2 + 3x)(x - 2)(x^2 + 1)$

55. $y = \dfrac{\sqrt{x + 13}}{(x - 4)\sqrt[3]{2x + 1}}$

56. $y = \dfrac{(x^2 + 3)^{2/3}(3x + 2)^2}{\sqrt{x + 1}}$

57. Find and simplify $f'(1)$ if

$$f(x) = \ln\left(\dfrac{ax - b}{ax + b}\right)^c, \text{ where } c = \dfrac{a^2 - b^2}{2ab}.$$

58. Convince yourself that $f(x) = (x^x)^x$ and $g(x) = x^{(x^x)}$ are not the same function. Then find $f'(x)$ and $g'(x)$. *Note:* When mathematicians write x^{x^x}, they mean $x^{(x^x)}$.

59. Prove the second part of Theorem B. *Hint:* Let $g(x) = f^{-1}(x)$. Then $g(f(x)) = x$. Differentiate both sides and use the Chain Rule.

Answers to Concepts Review: **1.** monotonic **2.** $\dfrac{1}{x}$ **3.** e^x
4. $ax^{a-1}; (-\infty, \infty)$

3.10
Derivatives of Hyperbolic and Inverse Trigonometric Functions

In Section 2.6 we defined the hyperbolic functions. We repeat these definitions for easy reference.

Definition Hyperbolic Functions

The hyperbolic sine, hyperbolic cosine, and four related functions are defined by

$$\sinh x = \dfrac{e^x - e^{-x}}{2} \qquad \cosh x = \dfrac{e^x + e^{-x}}{2}$$

$$\tanh x = \dfrac{\sinh x}{\cosh x} \qquad \coth x = \dfrac{\cosh x}{\sinh x}$$

$$\operatorname{sech} x = \dfrac{1}{\cosh x} \qquad \operatorname{csch} x = \dfrac{1}{\sinh x}$$

Derivatives of Hyperbolic Functions We can find $D_x \sinh x$ and $D_x \cosh x$ directly from the definitions.

$$D_x \sinh x = D_x\left(\dfrac{e^x - e^{-x}}{2}\right) = \dfrac{e^x + e^{-x}}{2} = \cosh x$$

and

$$D_x \cosh x = D_x\left(\dfrac{e^x + e^{-x}}{2}\right) = \dfrac{e^x - e^{-x}}{2} = \sinh x$$

Note that these facts confirm the character of the graphs in Figure 7 of Section 2.6. For example, since $D_x(\sinh x) = \cosh x > 0$, the graph of hyperbolic sine is always increasing.

The derivatives of the other four hyperbolic functions follow from those for the first two, combined with the Quotient Rule. The results are summarized in Theorem A.

Theorem A   **Derivatives of Hyperbolic Functions**

$$D_x \sinh x = \cosh x \qquad\qquad D_x \cosh x = \sinh x$$

$$D_x \tanh x = \operatorname{sech}^2 x \qquad\qquad D_x \coth x = -\operatorname{csch}^2 x$$

$$D_x \operatorname{sech} x = -\operatorname{sech} x \tanh x \qquad D_x \operatorname{csch} x = -\operatorname{csch} x \coth x$$

EXAMPLE 1   Find $D_x \tanh(\sin x)$.

SOLUTION

$$D_x \tanh(\sin x) = \operatorname{sech}^2(\sin x)\, D_x(\sin x)$$
$$= \cos x \cdot \operatorname{sech}^2(\sin x) \qquad\qquad \blacksquare$$

EXAMPLE 2   Find $D_x \cosh^2(3x - 1)$.

SOLUTION   We apply the Chain Rule twice.

$$D_x \cosh^2(3x - 1) = 2 \cosh(3x - 1)\, D_x \cosh(3x - 1)$$
$$= 2 \cosh(3x - 1) \sinh(3x - 1)\, D_x(3x - 1)$$
$$= 6 \cosh(3x - 1) \sinh(3x - 1) \qquad\qquad \blacksquare$$

The inverse hyperbolic functions were also derived in Section 2.6. They are

$$\sinh^{-1} x = \ln\left(x + \sqrt{x^2 + 1}\right)$$

$$\cosh^{-1} x = \ln\left(x + \sqrt{x^2 - 1}\right), \qquad x \geq 1$$

$$\tanh^{-1} x = \frac{1}{2}\ln\frac{1 + x}{1 - x}, \qquad -1 < x < 1$$

$$\operatorname{sech}^{-1} x = \ln\left(\frac{1 + \sqrt{1 - x^2}}{x}\right), \qquad 0 < x \leq 1$$

Graphs of the inverse hyperbolic functions are shown in Figure 1. Each of these functions is differentiable. In fact,

$$D_x \sinh^{-1} x = \frac{1}{\sqrt{x^2 + 1}}$$

$$D_x \cosh^{-1} x = \frac{1}{\sqrt{x^2 - 1}}, \qquad x > 1$$

$$D_x \tanh^{-1} x = \frac{1}{1 - x^2}, \qquad -1 < x < 1$$

$$D_x \operatorname{sech}^{-1} x = -\frac{1}{x\sqrt{1 - x^2}}, \qquad 0 < x < 1$$

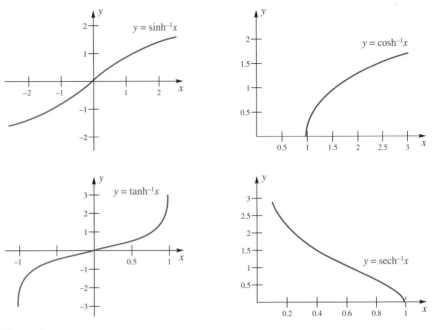

Figure 1

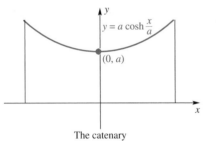

$(0, a)$

The catenary

Figure 2

An Inverted Catenary

EXAMPLE 3   Show that $D_x \sinh^{-1} x = 1/\sqrt{x^2 + 1}$ by two different methods.

SOLUTION

Method 1 Use implicit differentiation. Let $y = \sinh^{-1} x$, so

$$x = \sinh y$$

Now differentiate both sides with respect to x.

$$1 = (\cosh y)\, D_x y$$

Thus,

$$D_x y = D_x(\sinh^{-1} x) = \frac{1}{\cosh y} = \frac{1}{\sqrt{1 + \sinh^2 y}} = \frac{1}{\sqrt{1 + x^2}}$$

Method 2 Use the logarithmic expression for $\sinh^{-1} x$.

$$D_x(\sinh^{-1} x) = D_x \ln\left(x + \sqrt{x^2 + 1}\right)$$

$$= \frac{1}{x + \sqrt{x^2 + 1}} D_x\left(x + \sqrt{x^2 + 1}\right)$$

$$= \frac{1}{x + \sqrt{x^2 + 1}}\left(1 + \frac{x}{\sqrt{x^2 + 1}}\right)$$

$$= \frac{1}{\sqrt{x^2 + 1}}$$

$\blacksquare$

If a homogeneous flexible cable or chain is suspended between two fixed points at the same height, it forms a curve called a **catenary** (Figure 2). Furthermore (see Problem 38 of Section 4.9), a catenary can be placed in a coordinate system so that its equation takes the form

$$y = a \cosh \frac{x}{a}$$

The Gateway Arch in St. Louis, Missouri, shown in the photo, is the shape of an inverted caternary. The arch, designed by Eero Saarinen (1910–1961), is 630 feet high and 630 feet wide. His original plan, from 1948, was for a 590-foot parabolic arch.

Inverse Trigonometric Functions From the Inverse Function Theorem (Theorem 3.9B), we conclude that $\sin^{-1} x$, $\cos^{-1} x$, $\tan^{-1} x$, and $\sec^{-1} x$ are differentiable. Our aim is to find formulas for their derivatives. We state the results and then show how they can be derived.

Theorem B | **Derivatives of Four Inverse Trigonometric Functions**

(1) $D_x \sin^{-1} x = \dfrac{1}{\sqrt{1 - x^2}}$, $-1 < x < 1$

(2) $D_x \cos^{-1} x = -\dfrac{1}{\sqrt{1 - x^2}}$, $-1 < x < 1$

(3) $D_x \tan^{-1} x = \dfrac{1}{1 + x^2}$

(4) $D_x \sec^{-1} x = \dfrac{1}{|x|\sqrt{x^2 - 1}}$, $|x| > 1$

Proof Our proofs follow the same pattern in each case. To prove (1), let $y = \sin^{-1} x$, so that

$$x = \sin y$$

Now differentiate both sides with respect to x, using the Chain Rule on the right-hand side. Then

$$1 = \cos y \, D_x y = \cos(\sin^{-1} x) \, D_x(\sin^{-1} x)$$

$$= \sqrt{1 - x^2} \, D_x(\sin^{-1} x)$$

At the last step, we used Theorem 1.9A(2). We conclude that $D_x(\sin^{-1} x) = 1/\sqrt{1 - x^2}$.

Results (2), (3), and (4) are proved similarly, but (4) has a little twist. Let $y = \sec^{-1} x$, so $x = \sec y$. Differentiating both sides with respect to x and using Theorem 1.9A(4), we obtain

$$1 = \sec y \tan y \, D_x y$$

$$= \sec(\sec^{-1} x) \tan(\sec^{-1} x) \, D_x(\sec^{-1} x)$$

$$= \begin{cases} x\sqrt{x^2 - 1} \, D_x(\sec^{-1} x), & \text{if } x \geq 1 \\ x\left(-\sqrt{x^2 - 1}\right) D_x(\sec^{-1} x), & \text{if } x \leq -1 \end{cases}$$

$$= |x|\sqrt{x^2 - 1} \, D_x(\sec^{-1} x)$$

The desired result follows immediately. ∎

EXAMPLE 4 Find $D_x \sin^{-1}(3x - 1)$.

SOLUTION We use Theorem B(1) and the Chain Rule.

$$D_x \sin^{-1}(3x - 1) = \frac{1}{\sqrt{1 - (3x - 1)^2}} D_x(3x - 1)$$

$$= \frac{3}{\sqrt{-9x^2 + 6x}}$$ ∎

EXAMPLE 5 Find $\dfrac{d^2 y}{dx^2}$ if $y = \tan^{-1} 2x$.

SOLUTION

$$\frac{dy}{dx} = D_x \tan^{-1} 2x = \frac{1}{1 + (2x)^2} D_x(2x) = \frac{2}{1 + 4x^2} = 2\left(1 + 4x^2\right)^{-1}$$

$D_x \sec^{-1} x$

Here is another way to derive the formula for the derivative of $\sec^{-1} x$.

$$D_x \sec^{-1} x = D_x \cos^{-1}\left(\frac{1}{x}\right)$$

$$= \frac{-1}{\sqrt{1 - 1/x^2}} \cdot \frac{-1}{x^2}$$

$$= \frac{1}{\sqrt{x^2 - 1}} \cdot \frac{\sqrt{x^2}}{x^2}$$

$$= \frac{1}{\sqrt{x^2 - 1}} \cdot \frac{|x|}{x^2}$$

$$= \frac{1}{|x|\sqrt{x^2 - 1}}$$

$$\frac{d^2y}{dx^2} = D_x\left(2(1 + 4x^2)^{-1}\right) = -2(1 + 4x^2)^{-2} D_x (1 + 4x^2) = -\frac{16x}{(1 + 4x^2)^2} \quad \blacksquare$$

EXAMPLE 6 A woman, whose eye-level is 5 feet from the floor, is looking at a 6-foot high painting that is hanging 8 feet from the floor as shown in Figure 3. Suppose that the woman is walking (backwards) away from the wall at the rate of 2 feet per second. How fast is the angle θ changing when she is 10 feet from the wall?

SOLUTION Let x denote the woman's distance from the wall. The triangle from the top of the picture, to the woman's eye, to the point on the wall that is level with her eye is a right triangle. Thus, $\tan (\theta + \theta_1) = 9/x$, so $\theta + \theta_1 = \tan^{-1}(9/x)$. Similarly, $\tan \theta_1 = 3/x$ and $\theta_1 = \tan^{-1}(3/x)$. The angle θ therefore satisfies

$$\theta = \tan^{-1}\frac{9}{x} - \theta_1 = \tan^{-1}\frac{9}{x} - \tan^{-1}\frac{3}{x}$$

Differentiating both sides with respect to time t, and using the fact that $dx/dt = 2$, we obtain,

$$\frac{d\theta}{dt} = \frac{1}{1 + 81/x^2}\left(-\frac{9}{x^2}\right)\frac{dx}{dt} - \frac{1}{1 + 9/x^2}\left(-\frac{3}{x^2}\right)\frac{dx}{dt}$$

$$= -\frac{9}{x^2 + 81}(2) + \frac{3}{x^2 + 9}(2) = -\frac{18}{10^2 + 81} + \frac{6}{10^2 + 9} = -0.0444$$

The angle θ is decreasing at the rate of 0.0444 radian per second. $\quad\blacksquare$

Summary In this and previous sections, we have seen a number of derivative formulas. For reference, some of these formulas are listed in the table below.

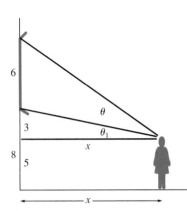

Figure 3

$D_x x^r = rx^{r-1}$	$D_x[f(x) \pm g(x)] = f'(x) \pm g'(x)$
$D_x[f(x)g(x)] = f(x)g'(x) + g(x)f'(x)$	$D_x\dfrac{f(x)}{g(x)} = \dfrac{g(x)f'(x) - f(x)g'(x)}{[g(x)]^2}$
$D_x \sin x = \cos x$	$D_x \sin^{-1} x = \dfrac{1}{\sqrt{1 - x^2}}, \; -1 < x < 1$
$D_x \cos x = -\sin x$	$D_x \cos^{-1} x = -\dfrac{1}{\sqrt{1 - x^2}}, \; -1 < x < 1$
$D_x \tan x = \sec^2 x$	$D_x \tan^{-1} x = \dfrac{1}{1 + x^2}$
$D_x \cot x = -\csc^2 x$	$D_x \sec^{-1} x = \dfrac{1}{|x|\sqrt{x^2 - 1}}, \; |x| > 1$
$D_x \sec x = \sec x \tan x$	$D_x \sinh x = \cosh x$
$D_x \csc x = -\csc x \cot x$	$D_x \cosh x = \sinh x$
$D_x \ln x = \dfrac{1}{x}$	$D_x \tanh x = \operatorname{sech}^2 x$
$D_x e^x = e^x$	$D_x \coth x = -\operatorname{csch}^2 x$
$D_x \log_a x = \dfrac{1}{x \ln a}$	$D_x \operatorname{sech} x = -\operatorname{sech} x \tanh x$
$D_x a^x = a^x \ln a$	$D_x \operatorname{csch} x = -\operatorname{csch} x \coth x$
$D_x \sinh^{-1} x = \dfrac{1}{\sqrt{x^2 + 1}}$	$D_x \tanh^{-1} x = \dfrac{1}{1 - x^2}, \; -1 < x < 1$
$D_x \cosh^{-1} x = \dfrac{1}{\sqrt{x^2 - 1}}, \; x > 1$	$D_x \operatorname{sech}^{-1} x = -\dfrac{1}{x\sqrt{1 - x^2}}, \; 0 < x < 1$

Concepts Review

1. If $y = \sinh x$, then $y' =$ _____ and $y'' =$ _____.

2. If a cable is suspended between two fixed points at the same height, then the resulting shape is a _____.

3. The inverse sine function, $f(x) = \sin^{-1}x$, is differentiable on the interval _____.

4. The derivative of the inverse tangent function is $D_x (\arctan x) =$ _____, which has domain _____.

Problem Set 3.10

In Problems 1–36, find $D_x y$.

1. $y = \sinh^2 x$

2. $y = \cosh^2 x$

3. $y = 5 \sinh^2 x$

4. $y = \cosh^3 x$

5. $y = \cosh(3x + 1)$

6. $y = \sinh(x^2 + x)$

7. $y = \ln(\sinh x)$

8. $y = \ln(\coth x)$

9. $y = x^2 \cosh x$

10. $y = x^{-2} \sinh x$

11. $y = \cosh 3x \sinh x$

12. $y = \sinh x \cosh 4x$

13. $y = \tanh x \sinh 2x$

14. $y = \coth 4x \sinh x$

15. $y = \sinh^{-1}(x^2)$

16. $y = \cosh^{-1}(x^3)$

17. $y = \tanh^{-1}(2x - 3)$

18. $y = \coth^{-1}(x^5)$

19. $y = x \cosh^{-1}(3x)$

20. $y = x^2 \sinh^{-1}(x^5)$

21. $y = \ln(\cosh^{-1} x)$

22. $y = \cosh^{-1}(\cos x)$

23. $y = \tanh(\cot x)$

24. $y = \coth^{-1}(\tanh x)$

25. $y = \sin^{-1}(2x^2)$

26. $y = \arccos(e^x)$

27. $y = x^3 \tan^{-1}(e^x)$

28. $y = e^x \arcsin x^2$

29. $y = (\tan^{-1} x)^3$

30. $y = \tan(\cos^{-1} x)$

31. $y = \sec^{-1}(x^3)$

32. $y = (\sec^{-1} x)^3$

33. $y = (1 + \sin^{-1} x)^3$

34. $y = \sin^{-1}\left(\dfrac{1}{x^2 + 4}\right)$

35. $y = \tan^{-1}(\ln x^2)$

36. $y = x \operatorname{arcsec}(x^2 + 1)$

GC **37.** Draw the graphs of $y = \sinh x$, $y = \ln\left(x + \sqrt{x^2 + 1}\right)$, and $y = x$ using the same axes and scaled so that $-3 \le x \le 3$ and $-3 \le y \le 3$. What does this demonstrate?

C **38.** Call the graph of $y = b - a \cosh(x/a)$ an inverted catenary and imagine it to be an arch sitting on the x-axis. Show that if the width of this arch along the x-axis is $2a$ then each of the following is true.

(a) $b = a \cosh 1 \approx 1.54308a$.

(b) The height of the arch is approximately $0.54308a$.

(c) The height of an arch of width 48 is approximately 13.

39. Find the equation of the Gateway Arch in St. Louis, Missouri, given that it is an inverted catenary (see Problem 38). Assume that it stands on the x-axis, that it is symmetric with respect to the y-axis, and that it is 630 feet wide at the base and 630 feet high at the center.

40. Express $d\theta/dt$ in terms of x, dx/dt, and the constants a and b.

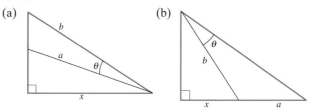

(a)   (b)

41. The structural steel work of a new office building is finished. Across the street, 60 feet from the ground floor of the freight elevator shaft in the building, a spectator is standing and watching the freight elevator ascend at a constant rate of 15 feet per second. How fast is the angle of elevation of the spectator's line of sight to the elevator increasing 6 seconds after his line of sight passes the horizontal?

42. An airplane is flying at a constant altitude of 2 miles and a constant speed of 600 miles per hour on a straight course that will take it directly over an observer on the ground. How fast is the angle of elevation of the observer's line of sight increasing when the distance from her to the plane is 3 miles? Give your result in radians per minute.

43. A revolving beacon light is located on an island and is 2 miles away from the nearest point P of the straight shoreline of the mainland. The beacon throws a spot of light that moves along the shoreline as the beacon revolves. If the speed of the spot of light on the shoreline is 5π miles per minute when the spot is 1 mile from P, how fast is the beacon revolving?

44. A man on a dock is pulling in a rope attached to a rowboat at a rate of 5 feet per second. If the man's hands are 8 feet higher than the point where the rope is attached to the boat, how fast is the angle of depression of the rope changing when there are still 17 feet of rope out?

C **45.** A visitor from outer space is approaching the earth (radius = 6376 kilometers) at 2 kilometers per second. How fast is the angle θ subtended by the earth at her eye increasing when she is 3000 kilometers from the surface?

Answers to Concepts Review: **1.** $\cosh x; \sinh x$ **2.** catenary   **3.** $(-1, 1)$ **4.** $\dfrac{1}{1 + x^2}; (-\infty, \infty)$

3.11
Differentials and Approximations

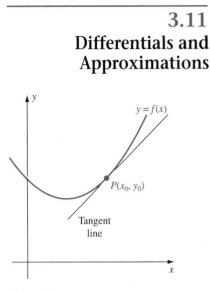

Figure 1

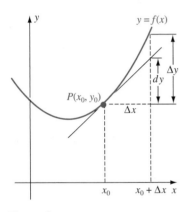

Figure 2

The Leibniz notation dy/dx has been used to mean the derivative of y with respect to x. The notation d/dx has been used as an operator to mean the derivative (of whatever follows d/dx) with respect to x. Thus, d/dx and D_x are synonymous. Up to now, we have treated dy/dx (or d/dx) as a *single* symbol and have not tried to give separate meanings to the symbols dy and dx. In this section we will give meanings to dy and to dx.

Let f be a differentiable function. To motivate our definitions, let $P(x_0, y_0)$ be a point on the graph of $y = f(x)$ as shown in Figure 1. Since f is differentiable,

$$\lim_{\Delta x \to 0} \frac{f(x_0 + \Delta x) - f(x_0)}{\Delta x} = f'(x_0)$$

Thus, if Δx is small, the quotient $[f(x_0 + \Delta x) - f(x_0)]/\Delta x$ will be approximately $f'(x_0)$, so

$$f(x_0 + \Delta x) - f(x_0) \approx \Delta x \, f'(x_0)$$

The left side of this expression is called Δy; this is the *actual* change in y as x changes from x_0 to $x_0 + \Delta x$. The right side is called dy, and it serves as an approximation to Δy. As Figure 2 indicates, the quantity dy is equal to the change in the tangent line to the curve at P as x changes from x_0 to $x_0 + \Delta x$. When Δx is small, we expect dy to be a good approximation to Δy, and being just a constant times Δx, it is usually easier to calculate.

Differentials Defined   Here are the formal definitions of the differentials dx and dy.

Definition **Differentials**

Let $y = f(x)$ be a differentiable function of the independent variable x.

Δx is an arbitrary increment in the independent variable x.

dx, called the **differential of the independent variable** x, is equal to Δx.

Δy is the actual change in the variable y as x changes from x to $x + \Delta x$; that is, $\Delta y = f(x + \Delta x) - f(x)$.

dy, called the **differential of the dependent variable** y, is defined by $dy = f'(x) \, dx$.

EXAMPLE 1   Find dy if
(a) $y = x^3 - 3x + 1$ 　　　　(b) $y = \sqrt{x^2 + 3x}$
(c) $y = \sin(x^4 - 3x^2 + 11)$

SOLUTION   If we know how to calculate derivatives, we know how to calculate differentials. We simply calculate the derivative and multiply it by dx.

(a) $dy = (3x^2 - 3) \, dx$

(b) $dy = \frac{1}{2}(x^2 + 3x)^{-1/2}(2x + 3) \, dx = \dfrac{2x + 3}{2\sqrt{x^2 + 3x}} \, dx$

(c) $dy = \cos(x^4 - 3x^2 + 11) \cdot (4x^3 - 6x) \, dx$ ∎

We ask you to note two things. First, since $dy = f'(x) \, dx$, division of both sides by dx yields

$$f'(x) = \frac{dy}{dx}$$

and we can, if we wish, interpret the derivative as a quotient of two differentials. Second, corresponding to every derivative rule, there is a differential rule obtained from the former by "multiplying" through by dx. We illustrate the major rules in the following table.

<table>
<tr><td>Distinguish between Derivatives and Differentials</td></tr>
</table>

Derivatives and differentials are not the same. When you write $D_x y$ or dy/dx, you are using a symbol for the derivative; when you write dy, you are denoting a differential. Do not be sloppy and write dy when you mean to label a derivative. This will lead to boundless confusion.

Derivative Rule	**Differential Rule**
1. $\dfrac{dk}{dx} = 0$	1. $dk = 0$
2. $\dfrac{d(ku)}{dx} = k\dfrac{du}{dx}$	2. $d(ku) = k\,du$
3. $\dfrac{d(u+v)}{dx} = \dfrac{du}{dx} + \dfrac{dv}{dx}$	3. $d(u+v) = du + dv$
4. $\dfrac{d(uv)}{dx} = u\dfrac{dv}{dx} + v\dfrac{du}{dx}$	4. $d(uv) = u\,dv + v\,du$
5. $\dfrac{d(u/v)}{dx} = \dfrac{v(du/dx) - u(dv/dx)}{v^2}$	5. $d\left(\dfrac{u}{v}\right) = \dfrac{v\,du - u\,dv}{v^2}$
6. $\dfrac{d(u^r)}{dx} = ru^{r-1}\dfrac{du}{dx}$	6. $d(u^r) = ru^{r-1}\,du$

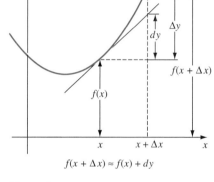

Figure 3

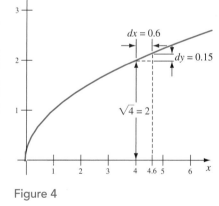

Figure 4

Approximations   Differentials will play several roles in this book, but for now their chief use is in providing approximations. We hinted at this earlier.

Suppose that $y = f(x)$, as shown in Figure 3. An increment Δx produces a corresponding increment Δy in y, which can be approximated by dy. Thus, $f(x + \Delta x)$ is approximated by

$$f(x + \Delta x) \approx f(x) + dy = f(x) + f'(x)\,\Delta x$$

This is the basis for the solutions to all the examples that follow.

EXAMPLE 2   Suppose you need good approximations to $\sqrt{4.6}$ and $\sqrt{8.2}$, but your calculator has died. What might you do?

SOLUTION   Consider the graph of $y = \sqrt{x}$ sketched in Figure 4. When x changes from 4 to 4.6, $\sqrt{x}$ changes from $\sqrt{4} = 2$ to (approximately) $\sqrt{4} + dy$. Now

$$dy = \frac{1}{2}x^{-1/2}\,dx = \frac{1}{2\sqrt{x}}\,dx$$

which, at $x = 4$ and $dx = 0.6$, has the value

$$dy = \frac{1}{2\sqrt{4}}(0.6) = \frac{0.6}{4} = 0.15$$

Thus,

$$\sqrt{4.6} \approx \sqrt{4} + dy = 2 + 0.15 = 2.15$$

Similarly, at $x = 9$ and $dx = -0.8$,

$$dy = \frac{1}{2\sqrt{9}}(-0.8) = \frac{-0.8}{6} \approx -0.133$$

Hence,

$$\sqrt{8.2} \approx \sqrt{9} + dy \approx 3 - 0.133 = 2.867$$

Note that both dx and dy were negative in this case.

The approximate values 2.15 and 2.867 may be compared to the true values (to four decimal places) of 2.1448 and 2.8636. ∎

EXAMPLE 3   Use differentials to approximate the increase in the area of a soap bubble when its radius increases from 3 inches to 3.025 inches.

SOLUTION The area of a spherical soap bubble is given by $A = 4\pi r^2$. We may approximate the exact change, ΔA, by the differential dA, where

$$dA = 8\pi r\, dr$$

At $r = 3$ and $dr = \Delta r = 0.025$,

$$dA = 8\pi(3)(0.025) \approx 1.885 \text{ square inches} \qquad \blacksquare$$

Estimating Errors Here is a typical problem in science. A researcher measures a certain variable x to have a value x_0 with a possible error of size $\pm\Delta x$. The value x_0 is then used to calculate a value y_0 for y that depends on x. The value y_0 is contaminated by the error in x, but how badly? The standard procedure is to estimate this error by means of differentials.

EXAMPLE 4 The side of a cube is measured as 11.4 centimeters with a possible error of ± 0.05 centimeter. Evaluate the volume of the cube and give an estimate for the possible error in this value.

SOLUTION The volume V of a cube of side x is $V = x^3$. Thus, $dV = 3x^2\, dx$. If $x = 11.4$ and $dx = 0.05$, then $V = (11.4)^3 \approx 1482$ and

$$\Delta V \approx dV = 3(11.4)^2(0.05) \approx 19$$

Thus, we might report the volume of the cube as 1482 ± 19 cubic centimeters. $\blacksquare$

The quantity ΔV in Example 4 is called the **absolute error.** Another measure of error is the **relative error,** which is found by dividing the absolute error by the total volume. We can approximate the relative error $\Delta V/V$ by dV/V. In Example 4, the relative error is

$$\frac{\Delta V}{V} \approx \frac{dV}{V} \approx \frac{19}{1482} \approx 0.0128$$

The relative error is often expressed in terms of a percentage. Thus, we say that for the cube in Example 4 the relative error is approximately 1.28%.

EXAMPLE 5 Poiseuille's Law for blood flow says that the volume flowing through an artery is proportional to the fourth power of the radius, that is, $V = kR^4$. By how much must the radius be increased in order to increase the blood flow by 50%?

SOLUTION The differentials satisfy $dV = 4kR^3\, dR$. The relative change in the volume is

$$\frac{\Delta V}{V} \approx \frac{dV}{V} = \frac{4kR^3\, dR}{kR^4} = 4\frac{dR}{R}$$

so for a 50% change in volume,

$$0.5 \approx \frac{dV}{V} = 4\frac{dR}{R}$$

The relative change in R must be

$$\frac{\Delta R}{R} \approx \frac{dR}{R} \approx \frac{0.5}{4} = 0.125$$

Thus, just a 12.5% increase in the radius of an artery will increase the blood flow by about 50%. $\blacksquare$

Linear Approximation   If f is differentiable at a, then from the point-slope form of a line, the tangent line to f at $(a, f(a))$ is given by $y = f(a) + f'(a)(x - a)$. The function

$$L(x) = f(a) + f'(a)(x - a)$$

is called the **linear approximation** to the function f at a, and it is often a very good approximation to f when x is close to a.

▮ **EXAMPLE 6**   Find and plot the linear approximation to $f(x) = 1 + \sin 2x$ at $x = \pi/2$.

SOLUTION: The derivative of f is $f'(x) = 2 \cos 2x$, so the linear approximation is

$$L(x) = f(\pi/2) + f'(\pi/2)(x - \pi/2)$$
$$= (1 + \sin \pi) + (2 \cos \pi)(x - \pi/2)$$
$$= 1 - 2(x - \pi/2) = (1 + \pi) - 2x$$

Figure 5a shows both the graph of the function f and the linear approximation L over the interval $[0, \pi]$. We can see that the approximation is good near $\pi/2$, but not so good as you move away from $\pi/2$. Figures 5b and c also show plots of the functions L and f over smaller and smaller intervals. For values of x close to $\pi/2$, we see that the linear approximation is very close to the function f.   ▮

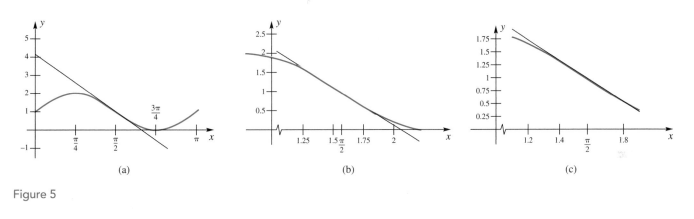

(a)   (b)   (c)

Figure 5

Concepts Review

1. Let $y = f(x)$. The differential of y in terms of dx is defined by $dy = $ _____.

2. Consider the curve $y = f(x)$ and suppose that x is given an increment Δx. The corresponding change in y on the curve is denoted by _____, whereas the corresponding change in y on the tangent line is denoted by _____.

3. We can expect dy to be a good approximation to Δy, provided that _____.

4. On the curve $y = \sqrt{x}$, we should expect dy to be close to Δy, but always _____ than Δy. On the curve $y = x^2$, $x \geq 0$, we should expect dy to be _____ than Δy.

Problem Set 3.11

In Problems 1–8, find dy.

1. $y = x^2 + x - 3$

2. $y = 7x^3 + 3x^2 + 1$

3. $y = (2x + 3)^{-4}$

4. $y = (3x^2 + x + 1)^{-2}$

5. $y = (\sin x + \cos x)^3$

6. $y = (\tan x + 1)^3$

7. $y = (1 - e^x) \ln x$

8. $y = (1 + \sinh^3 2x)^{1/2}$

9. If $s = \sqrt{(t^2 - \cot t + 2)^3}$, find ds.

10. Let $y = f(x) = x^3$. Find the value of dy in each case.

(a) $x = 0.5, dx = 1$

(b) $x = -1, dx = 0.75$

11. For the function defined in Problem 10, make a careful drawing of the graph of f for $-1.5 \leq x \leq 1.5$ and the tangents to the curve at $x = 0.5$ and $x = -1$; on this drawing label dy and dx for each of the given sets of data in parts (a) and (b).

12. Let $y = 1/x$. Find the value of dy in each case.

(a) $x = 1, dx = 0.5$ (b) $x = -2, dx = 0.75$

13. For the function defined in Problem 12, make a careful drawing (as in Problem 11) for $-3 \leq x < 0$ and $0 < x \leq 3$.

C **14.** For the data of Problem 10, find the actual changes in y, that is, Δy.

C **15.** For the data of Problem 12, find the actual changes in y, that is, Δy.

16. If $y = x^2 - 3$, find the values of Δy and dy in each case.

(a) $x = 2$ and $dx = \Delta x = 0.5$

C (b) $x = 3$ and $dx = \Delta x = -0.12$

17. If $y = x^4 + 2x$, find the values of Δy and dy in each case.

(a) $x = 2$ and $dx = \Delta x = 1$

C (b) $x = 2$ and $dx = \Delta x = 0.005$

In Problems 18–20, use differentials to approximate the given number (see Example 2). Compare with calculator values.

18. $\sqrt{402}$ **19.** $\sqrt{35.9}$

20. $\sqrt[3]{26.91}$

C **21.** Approximate the volume of material in a spherical shell of inner radius 5 centimeters and outer radius 5.125 centimeters (see Example 3).

C **22.** All six sides of a cubical metal box are 0.25 inch thick, and the volume of the interior of the box is 40 cubic inches. Use differentials to find the approximate volume of metal used to make the box.

23. The outside diameter of a thin spherical shell is 12 feet. If the shell is 0.3 inch thick, use differentials to approximate the volume of the region interior to the shell.

24. The interior of an open cylindrical tank is 12 feet in diameter and 8 feet deep. The bottom is copper and the sides are steel. Use differentials to find approximately how many gallons of waterproofing paint are needed to apply a 0.05-inch coat to the steel part of the inside of the tank (1 gallon $\approx$ 231 cubic inches).

25. Assuming that the equator is a circle whose radius is approximately 4000 miles, how much longer than the equator would a concentric, coplanar circle be if each point on it were 2 feet above the equator? Use differentials.

26. The period of a simple pendulum of length L feet is given by $T = 2\pi\sqrt{L/g}$ seconds. We assume that g, the acceleration due to gravity on (or very near) the surface of the earth, is 32 feet per second per second. If the pendulum is that of a clock that keeps good time when $L = 4$ feet, how much time will the clock gain in 24 hours if the length of the pendulum is decreased to 3.97 feet?

27. The diameter of a sphere is measured as 20 ± 0.1 centimeters. Calculate the volume and estimate the absolute error and the relative error (see Example 4).

28. A cylindrical roller is exactly 12 inches long and its diameter is measured as 6 ± 0.005 inches. Calculate its volume with an estimate for the absolute error and the relative error.

C **29.** The angle θ between the two equal sides of an isosceles triangle measures 0.53 ± 0.005 radian. The two equal sides are exactly 151 centimeters long. Calculate the length of the third side with an estimate for the absolute error and the relative error.

C **30.** Calculate the area of the triangle of Problem 29 with an estimate for the absolute error and the relative error. *Hint:* $A = \frac{1}{2}ab \sin\theta$.

31. It can be shown that if $|d^2y/dx^2| \leq M$ on a closed interval with c and $c + \Delta x$ as end points, then

$$|\Delta y - dy| \leq \frac{1}{2}M(\Delta x)^2$$

Find, using differentials, the change in $y = 3x^2 - 2x + 11$ when x increases from 2 to 2.001 and then give a bound for the error that you have made by using differentials.

32. Suppose that f is a function satisfying $f(1) = 10$, and $f'(1.02) = 12$. Use this information to approximate $f(1.02)$.

33. Suppose f is a function satisfying $f(3) = 8$ and $f'(3.05) = \frac{1}{4}$. Use this information to approximate $f(3.05)$.

34. A conical cup, 10 centimeters high and 8 centimeters wide at the top, is filled with water to a depth of 9 centimeters. An ice cube 3 centimeters on a side is about to be dropped in. Use differentials to decide whether the cup will overflow.

35. A tank has the shape of a cylinder with hemispherical ends. If the cylindrical part is 100 centimeters long and has an outside diameter of 20 centimeters, about how much paint is required to coat the outside of the tank to a thickness of 1 millimeter?

C **36.** Einstein's Special Theory of Relativity says that an object's mass m is related to its velocity v by the formula

$$m = \frac{m_0}{\sqrt{1 - v^2/c^2}} = m_0\left(1 - \frac{v^2}{c^2}\right)^{-1/2}$$

Here m_0 is the rest mass and c is the speed of light. Use differentials to determine the percent increase in mass of an object when its velocity increases from $0.9c$ to $0.92c$.

In Problems 37–44, find the linear approximation to the given functions at the specified points. Plot the function and its linear approximation over the indicated interval.

37. $f(x) = x^2$ at $a = 2$, $[0, 3]$

38. $g(x) = x^2 \cos x$ at $a = \pi/2$, $[0, \pi]$

39. $h(x) = \sin x$ at $a = 0$, $[-\pi, \pi]$

40. $F(x) = 3x + 4$ at $a = 3$, $[0, 6]$

41. $f(x) = \sqrt{1 - x^2}$ at $a = 0$, $[-1, 1]$

42. $g(x) = \sin^{-1} x$ at $a = 0$, $[-1, 1]$

43. $h(x) = x \sec x$ at $a = 0$, $(-\pi/2, \pi/2)$

44. $G(x) = x + \sin 2x$, at $a = \pi/2$, $[0, \pi]$

45. Find the linear approximation to $f(x) = mx + b$ at an arbitrary a. What is the relationship between $f(x)$ and $L(x)$?

46. Show that for every $a > 0$ the linear approximation $L(x)$ to the function $f(x) = \sqrt{x}$ at a satisfies $f(x) \leq L(x)$ for all $x > 0$.

47. Show that for every a the linear approximation $L(x)$ to the function $f(x) = x^2$ at a satisfies $L(x) \leq f(x)$ for all x.

EXPL **48.** Find a linear approximation to $f(x) = (1 + x)^\alpha$ at $x = 0$, where α is any number. For various values of α, plot $f(x)$ and its linear approximation $L(x)$. For what values of α does the linear approximation always overestimate $f(x)$? For what values of α does the linear approximation always underestimate $f(x)$?

EXPL **49.** Suppose f is differentiable. If we use the approximation $f(x + h) \approx f(x) + f'(x) h$ the error is $\varepsilon(h) = f(x + h) - f(x) - f'(x) h$. Show that

(a) $\lim_{h\to0} \varepsilon(h) = 0$ and (b) $\lim_{h\to0} \dfrac{\varepsilon(h)}{h} = 0$.

Answers to Concepts Review: **1.** $f'(x) \, dx$ **2.** $\Delta y; dy$ **3.** Δx is small **4.** larger; smaller

3.12 Chapter Review

Concepts Test

Respond with true or false to each of the following assertions. Be prepared to justify your answer.

1. The tangent line to a curve at a point cannot cross the curve at that point.

2. The tangent line to a curve can touch the curve at only one point.

3. The slope of the tangent line to the curve $y = x^4$ is different at every point of the curve.

4. The slope of the tangent line to the curve $y = \cos x$ is different at every point on the curve.

5. It is possible for the velocity of an object to be increasing while its speed is decreasing.

6. It is possible for the speed of an object to be increasing while its velocity is decreasing.

7. If the tangent line to the graph of $y = f(x)$ is horizontal at $x = c$, then $f'(c) = 0$.

8. If $f'(x) = g'(x)$ for all x, then $f(x) = g(x)$ for all x.

9. If $g(x) = x$, and f is a differentiable function, then $f'(g(x)) = D_x f(g(x))$.

10. If $y = \pi^5$, then $D_x y = 5\pi^4$.

11. If $f'(c)$ exists, then f is continuous at c.

12. The graph of $y = \sqrt[3]{x}$ has a tangent line at $x = 0$ and yet $D_x y$ does not exist there.

13. The derivative of a product is always the product of the derivatives.

14. If the acceleration of an object is negative, then its velocity is decreasing.

15. If x^3 is a factor of the differentiable function $f(x)$, then x^2 is a factor of its derivative.

16. The equation of the line tangent to the graph of $y = x^3$ at $(1, 1)$ is $y - 1 = 3x^2(x - 1)$.

17. If $y = f(x)g(x)$, then $D_x^2 y = f(x)g''(x) + g(x)f''(x)$.

18. If $y = (x^3 + x)^8$, then $D_x^{25} y = 0$.

19. The derivative of a polynomial is a polynomial.

20. The derivative of a rational function is a rational function.

21. If $f'(c) = g'(c) = 0$ and $h(x) = f(x)g(x)$, then $h'(c) = 0$.

22. The expression

$$\lim_{x\to\pi/2} \frac{\sin x - 1}{x - \pi/2}$$

is the derivative of $f(x) = \sin x$ at $x = \pi/2$.

23. The operator D^2 is linear.

24. If $h(x) = f(g(x))$ where both f and g are differentiable, then $g'(c) = 0$ implies that $h'(c) = 0$.

25. If $f'(2) = g'(2) = g(2) = 2$, then $(f \circ g)'(2) = 4$.

26. The tangent line to the graph of $y = \ln x$ at $(1, 0)$ is $y = x - 1$.

27. If the radius of a sphere is increasing at 3 feet per second, then its volume is increasing at 27 cubic feet per second.

28. If the radius of a circle is increasing at 4 feet per second, then its circumference is increasing at 8π feet per second.

29. $D_x^{n+4}(\sin x) = D_x^n(\sin x)$ for every positive integer n.

30. $D_x^{n+3}(\cos x) = -D_x^n(\sin x)$ for every positive integer n.

31. $h(x) = \sinh x$ is a function that is its own second derivative.

32. If $s = 5t^3 + 6t - 300$ gives the position of an object on a horizontal coordinate line at time t, then that object is always moving to the right (the direction of increasing s).

33. If air is being pumped into a spherical rubber balloon at a constant rate of 3 cubic inches per second, then the radius will increase, but at a slower and slower rate.

34. If water is being pumped into a spherical tank of fixed radius at a rate of 3 gallons per second, the height of the water in the tank will increase more and more rapidly as the tank nears being full.

35. If an error Δr is made in measuring the radius of a sphere, the corresponding error in the calculated volume will be approximately $S \cdot \Delta r$, where S is the surface area of the sphere.

36. If $y = \tan^{-1} x$, then $dy \geq 0$.

37. The linear approximation to the function defined by $f(x) = \cosh x$ at $x = 0$ has positive slope.

Sample Test Problems

1. Use $f'(x) = \lim_{h\to0} [f(x + h) - f(x)]/h$ to find the derivative of each of the following.

(a) $f(x) = 3x^3$

(b) $f(x) = 2x^5 + 3x$

(c) $f(x) = \dfrac{1}{3x}$

(d) $f(x) = \dfrac{1}{3x^2 + 2}$

(e) $f(x) = \sqrt{3x}$

(f) $f(x) = \sin 3x$

(g) $f(x) = \sqrt{x^2 + 5}$

(h) $f(x) = \cos \pi x$

2. Use $g'(x) = \lim_{t\to x} \dfrac{g(t) - g(x)}{t - x}$ to find $g'(x)$ in each case.

(a) $g(x) = 2x^2$

(b) $g(x) = x^3 + x$

(c) $g(x) = \dfrac{1}{x}$

(d) $g(x) = \dfrac{1}{x^2 + 1}$

(e) $g(x) = \sqrt{x}$

(f) $g(x) = \sin \pi x$

(g) $g(x) = \sqrt{x^3 + C}$

(h) $g(x) = \cos 2x$

3. The given limit is a derivative, but of what function f and at what point?

(a) $\displaystyle\lim_{h \to 0} \dfrac{3(1 + h) - 3}{h}$

(b) $\displaystyle\lim_{h \to 0} \dfrac{4(2 + h)^3 - 4(2)^3}{h}$

(c) $\displaystyle\lim_{\Delta x \to 0} \dfrac{\sqrt{(1 + \Delta x)^3} - 1}{\Delta x}$

(d) $\displaystyle\lim_{\Delta x \to 0} \dfrac{\sin(\pi + \Delta x)}{\Delta x}$

(e) $\displaystyle\lim_{t \to x} \dfrac{4/t - 4/x}{t - x}$

(f) $\displaystyle\lim_{t \to x} \dfrac{\sin 3x - \sin 3t}{t - x}$

(g) $\displaystyle\lim_{h \to 0} \dfrac{\tan(\pi/4 + h) - 1}{h}$

(h) $\displaystyle\lim_{h \to 0}\left(\dfrac{1}{\sqrt{5 + h}} - \dfrac{1}{\sqrt{5}}\right)\dfrac{1}{h}$

4. Use the sketch of $s = f(t)$ in Figure 1 to approximate each of the following.

(a) $f'(2)$

(b) $f'(6)$

(c) v_{avg} on $[3, 7]$

(d) $\dfrac{d}{dt} f(t^2)$ at $t = 2$

(e) $\dfrac{d}{dt} [f^2(t)]$ at $t = 2$

(f) $\dfrac{d}{dt}(f(f(t)))$ at $t = 2$

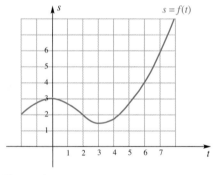

Figure 1

In Problems 5–29, find the indicated derivative by using the rules that we have developed.

5. $D_x(3x^5)$

6. $D_x(x^3 - 3x^2 + x^{-2})$

7. $D_z(z^3 + 4z^2 + 2z)$

8. $D_x\left(\dfrac{3x - 5}{x^2 + 1}\right)$

9. $D_t\left(\dfrac{4t - 5}{6t^2 + 2t}\right)$

10. $D_x^2(3x + 2)^{2/3}$

11. $\dfrac{d}{dx}\left(\dfrac{4x^2 - 2}{x^3 + x}\right)$

12. $D_t\left(t\sqrt{2t + 6}\right)$

13. $\dfrac{d}{dx}\left(\dfrac{1}{\sqrt{x^2 + 4}}\right)$

14. $\dfrac{d}{dx}\sqrt{\dfrac{x^2 - 1}{x^3 - x}}$

15. $D_\theta^2(\sin \theta + \cos^3 \theta)$

16. $\dfrac{d}{dt}\left[\sin(t^2) - \sin^2(t)\right]$

17. $D_\theta(\sin(\theta^2))$

18. $\dfrac{d}{dx} e^{4x}$

19. $\dfrac{d}{d\theta}\left[\sin^2(\sin(\pi\theta))\right]$

20. $\dfrac{d}{dt}\left[\sin^2(\cos 4t)\right]$

21. $D_\theta e^{3\theta}$

22. $\dfrac{d}{dx}\left[x \ln(x^2 + 4)\right]$

23. $D_x \tan^{-1}\left(\dfrac{1}{x}\right)$

24. $D_x^4 \cosh x$

25. $\dfrac{d}{dx}\left(\dfrac{\cot x}{\sec x^2}\right)$

26. $D_t\left(\dfrac{4t \sin t}{\cos t - \sin t}\right)$

27. $f'(2)$ if $f(x) = (x - 1)^3(\sin \pi x - x)^2$

28. $h''(0)$ if $h(t) = (\sin 2t + \cos 3t)^5$

29. $g'''(1)$ if $g(r) = \cos^3 5r$

In Problems 30–33, assume that all the functions given are differentiable, and find the indicated derivative.

30. $f'(t)$ if $f(t) = h(g(t)) + g^2(t)$

31. $G''(x)$ if $G(x) = F(r(x) + s(x)) + s(x)$

32. If $F(x) = Q(R(x))$, $R(x) = \cos x$, and $Q(R) = R^3$, find $F'(x)$.

33. If $F(z) = r(s(z))$, $r(x) = \sin 3x$, and $s(t) = 3t^3$, find $F'(z)$.

34. Find the coordinates of the point on the curve $y = (x - 2)^2$ where there is a tangent line that is perpendicular to the line $2x - y + 2 = 0$.

35. A spherical balloon is expanding from the sun's heat. Find the rate of change of the volume of the balloon with respect to its radius when the radius is 5 meters.

36 If the volume of the balloon of Problem 35 is increasing at a constant rate of 10 cubic meters per hour, how fast is its radius increasing when the radius is 5 meters?

37. A trough 12 feet long has a cross section in the form of an isosceles triangle (with base at the top) 4 feet deep and 6 feet across. If water is filling the trough at the rate of 9 cubic feet per minute, how fast is the water level rising when the water is 3 feet deep?

38. An object is projected directly upward from the ground with an initial velocity of 128 feet per second. Its height s at the end of t seconds is $s = 128t - 16t^2$ feet.

(a) When does it reach its maximum height and what is this height?

(b) When does it hit the ground and with what velocity?

39. An object moves on a horizontal coordinate line. Its directed distance s from the origin at the end of t seconds is $s = t^3 - 6t^2 + 9t$ feet.

(a) When is the object moving to the left?

(b) What is its acceleration when its velocity is zero?

(c) When is its acceleration positive?

40. Find $D_x^{20} y$ in each case.

(a) $y = x^{19} + x^{12} + x^5 + 10$

(b) $y = x^{20} + x^{19} + x^{18}$

(c) $y = 7x^{21} + 3x^{20}$

(d) $y = e^{2x + 1}$

(e) $y = \sin 2x$

(f) $y = \ln x$

(g) $y = \cosh x$

(h) $y = x^{19} + e^{-x}$

41. Find dy/dx in each case.

(a) $(x - 1)^2 + y^2 = 5$

(b) $xy^2 + yx^2 = 1$

(c) $x^3 + y^3 = x^3 y^3$

(d) $x \sin(xy) = x^2 + 1$

(e) $x \tan(xy) = 2$

(f) $e^{xy} = 2 - \dfrac{x}{4}$

42. Show that the tangent lines to the curves $y^2 = 4x^3$ and $2x^2 + 3y^2 = 14$ at $(1, 2)$ are perpendicular to each other. *Hint:* Use implicit differentiation.

43. Let $y = \sin(\pi x) + x^2$. If x changes from 2 to 2.01, approximately how much does y change?

44. Let $xy^2 + 2y(x + 2)^2 + 2 = 0$.

(a) If x changes from -2.00 to -2.01 and $y > 0$, approximately how much does y change?

(b) If x changes from -2.00 to -2.01 and $y < 0$, approximately how much does y change?

45. Suppose that $f(2) = 3$, $f'(2) = 4$, $f''(2) = -1$, $g(2) = 2$, and $g'(2) = 5$. Find each value.

(a) $\dfrac{d}{dx}[f^2(x) + g^3(x)]$ at $x = 2$

(b) $\dfrac{d}{dx}[f(x)g(x)]$ at $x = 2$

(c) $\dfrac{d}{dx}[f(g(x))]$ at $x = 2$ (d) $D_x^2[f^2(x)]$ at $x = 2$

46. A 13-foot ladder is leaning against a vertical wall. If the bottom of the ladder is being pulled away from the wall at a constant rate of 2 feet per second how fast is the top end of the ladder moving down the wall when it is 5 feet above the ground?

47. An airplane is climbing at a 15° angle to the horizontal. How fast is it gaining altitude if its speed is 400 miles per hour?

48. Given that $D_x|x| = \dfrac{|x|}{x}$, $x \neq 0$, find a formula for

(a) $D_x(|x|^2)$ (b) $D_x^2|x|$

(c) $D_x^3|x|$ (d) $D_x^2(|x|^2)$

49. Given that $D_t|t| = \dfrac{|t|}{t}$, $t \neq 0$, find a formula for

(a) $D_\theta|\sin\theta|$ (b) $D_\theta|\cos\theta|$

(c) $D_\theta|\tan\theta|$ (d) $D_x|\sinh x|$

50. Find the linear approximation to the following functions at the given points.

(a) $\sqrt{x + 1}$ at $a = 3$ (b) $x\cos x$ at $a = 1$

(c) e^{2x} at $a = 0$ (d) $\ln(x + 1)$ at $a = 0$

In Problems 1–6, solve the given inequalities. (See Section 1.2.)

1. $(x - 2)(x - 3) < 0$

2. $x^2 - x - 6 > 0$

3. $x(x - 1)(x - 2) \le 0$

4. $x^3 + 3x^2 + 2x \ge 0$

5. $\dfrac{x(x - 2)}{x^2 - 4} \ge 0$

6. $\dfrac{x^2 - 9}{x^2 + 2} > 0$

In Problems 7–14, find the derivative $f'(x)$ of the given function.

7. $f(x) = (2x + 1)^4$

8. $f(x) = \sin \pi x$

9. $f(x) = (x^2 - 1) \cos 2x$

10. $f(x) = \dfrac{\ln x}{x}$

11. $f(x) = \tan^2 3x$

12. $f(x) = \sqrt{1 + \sin^2 x}$

13. $f(x) = (x + 1)e^{-x^2/2}$

14. $f(x) = \sqrt{\sin^{-1} x}$

15. Find all points on the graph of $y = \tan^2 x$ where the tangent line is horizontal.

16. Find all points on the graph of $y = x + \sin x$ where the tangent line is horizontal.

17. Find all points on the graph of $y = x + \sin x$ where the tangent line is parallel to the line $y = 2 + x$.

18. A rectangular box is to be made from a piece of cardboard 24 inches long and 9 inches wide by cutting out identical squares from the four corners and turning up the sides as in Figure 1. If x is the length of the side of one of the squares that is cut out, what is the volume of the resulting box?

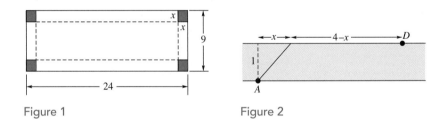

Figure 1   Figure 2

19. Andy wants to cross a river that is 1 kilometer wide and get to a point 4 kilometers downstream. (See Figure 2.) He can swim at 4 kilometers per hour and run 10 kilometers per hour. Assuming that he begins by swimming and that he swims toward a point x kilometers downstream from his initial starting point A, how long will it take him to reach his destination D?

20. Let $f(x) = x - \cos x$.

(a) Does the equation $x - \cos x = 0$ have a solution between $x = 0$ and $x = \pi$? How do you know?

(b) Find the equation of the tangent line at $x = \pi/2$.

(c) Where does the tangent line from part (b) intersect the x-axis?

21. Find a function whose derivative is

(a) $2x$ (b) $\sin x$ (c) $x^2 + x + 1$

22. Add 1 to each answer from Problem 21. Are these functions also solutions to Problem 21? Explain.

CHAPTER 4

Applications of the Derivative

4.1
Maxima and Minima

Often in life, we are faced with the problem of finding the *best* way to do something. For example, a farmer wants to choose the mix of crops that is likely to produce the largest profit. A doctor wishes to select the smallest dosage of a drug that will cure a certain disease. A manufacturer would like to minimize the cost of distributing its products. Often such a problem can be formulated so that it involves maximizing or minimizing a function over a specified set. If so, the methods of calculus provide a powerful tool for solving the problem.

Suppose then that we are given a function $f(x)$ and a domain S as in Figure 1. We now pose three questions:

1. Does $f(x)$ have a maximum or minimum value on S?
2. If it does have a maximum or a minimum, where are they attained?
3. If they exist, what are the maximum and minimum values?

Answering these questions is the principal goal of this section. We begin by introducing a precise vocabulary.

Definition

Let S, the domain of f, contain the point c. We say that

(i) $f(c)$ is the **maximum value** of f on S if $f(c) \geq f(x)$ for all x in S;
(ii) $f(c)$ is the **minimum value** of f on S if $f(c) \leq f(x)$ for all x in S;
(iii) $f(c)$ is an **extreme value** of f on S if it is either the maximum value or the minimum value;
(iv) the function we want to maximize or minimize is the **objective function.**

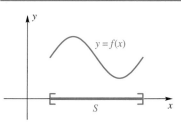

Figure 1

The Existence Question *Does f have a maximum (or minimum) value on S?* The answer depends first of all on the set S. Consider $f(x) = 1/x$ on $S = (0, \infty)$; it has neither a maximum value nor a minimum value (Figure 2). On the other hand, the same function on $S = [1, 3]$ has the maximum value of $f(1) = 1$ and the minimum value of $f(3) = \frac{1}{3}$. On $S = (1, 3]$, f has no maximum value and the minimum value is $f(3) = \frac{1}{3}$.

The answer also depends on the type of function. Consider the discontinuous function g (Figure 3) defined by

$$g(x) = \begin{cases} x & \text{if } 1 \leq x < 2 \\ x - 2 & \text{if } 2 \leq x \leq 3 \end{cases}$$

On $S = [1, 3]$, g has no maximum value (it gets arbitrarily close to 2 but never attains it). However, g has the minimum value $g(2) = 0$.

There is a nice theorem that answers the existence question for many of the problems that come up in practice. Though it is intuitively obvious, a rigorous proof is quite difficult; we leave that for more advanced textbooks.

Theorem A **Max–Min Existence Theorem**

If f is continuous on a closed interval $[a, b]$, then f attains both a maximum value and a minimum value there.

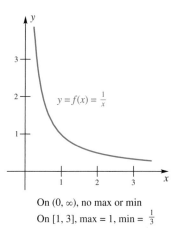

On $(0, \infty)$, no max or min
On $[1, 3]$, max = 1, min = $\frac{1}{3}$

Figure 2

189

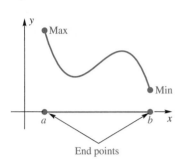

No max, min = 0

Figure 3

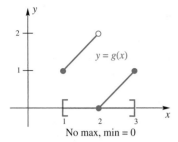

Note the key words in Theorem A; f is required to be *continuous* and the set S is required to be a *closed interval*.

Where Do Extreme Values Occur? Usually, the objective function will have an interval I as its domain. But this interval may be any of the nine types discussed in Section 1.2. Some of them contain their end points; some do not. For instance, $I = [a, b]$ contains both its end points; $[a, b)$ contains only its left end point; (a, b) contains neither end point. Extreme values of functions defined on closed intervals often occur at end points (see Figure 4).

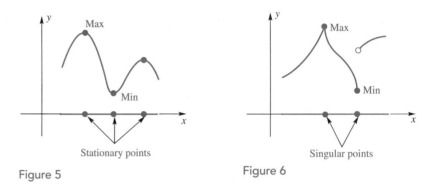

Figure 4

End points

Figure 5

Stationary points

Figure 6

Singular points

If c is a point at which $f'(c) = 0$, we call c a **stationary point.** The name derives from the fact that at a stationary point the graph of f levels off, since the tangent line is horizontal. Extreme values often occur at stationary points (see Figure 5).

Finally, if c is an interior point of I where f' fails to exist, we call c a **singular point.** It is a point where the graph of f has a sharp corner, a vertical tangent, or perhaps takes a jump, or near where the graph wiggles very badly. Extreme values can occur at singular points (Figure 6), though in practical problems this is quite rare.

These three kinds of points (end points, stationary points, and singular points) are the key points of max–min theory. Any point of one of these three types in the domain of a function f is called a **critical point** of f.

EXAMPLE 1 Find the critical points of $f(x) = -2x^3 + 3x^2$ on $\left[-\frac{1}{2}, 2\right]$.

SOLUTION The end points are $-\frac{1}{2}$ and 2. To find the stationary points, we solve $f'(x) = -6x^2 + 6x = 0$ for x, obtaining 0 and 1. There are no singular points. Thus, the critical points are $-\frac{1}{2}, 0, 1,$ and 2. ■

Theorem B **Critical Point Theorem**

Let f be defined on an interval I containing the point c. If $f(c)$ is an extreme value, then c must be a critical point; that is, either c is

(i)   an end point of I;
(ii)   a stationary point of f; that is, a point where $f'(c) = 0$; or
(iii) a singular point of f; that is, a point where $f'(c)$ does not exist.

Proof Consider first the case where $f(c)$ is the maximum value of f on I and suppose that c is neither an end point nor a singular point. We must show that c is a stationary point.

Now, since $f(c)$ is the maximum value, $f(x) \leq f(c)$ for all x in I; that is,

$$f(x) - f(c) \leq 0$$

Thus, if $x < c$, so that $x - c < 0$, then

(1) $$\frac{f(x) - f(c)}{x - c} \geq 0$$

whereas if $x > c$, then

(2)
$$\frac{f(x) - f(c)}{x - c} \le 0$$

But $f'(c)$ exists because c is not a singular point. Consequently, when we let $x \to c^-$ in (1) and $x \to c^+$ in (2), we obtain, respectively, $f'(c) \ge 0$ and $f'(c) \le 0$. We conclude that $f'(c) = 0$, as desired.

The case where $f(c)$ is the minimum value is handled similarly. ∎

In the proof just given, we used the fact that the inequality $\le$ is preserved under the operation of taking limits.

What Are the Extreme Values?   In view of Theorems A and B, we can now state a very simple procedure for finding the maximum value and minimum value of a continuous function f on a *closed interval I*.

Step 1:   Find the critical points of f on I.

Step 2:   Evaluate f at each of these critical points. The largest of these values is the maximum value; the smallest is the minimum value.

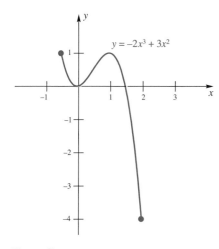

Figure 7

$y = -2x^3 + 3x^2$

EXAMPLE 2   Find the maximum and minimum values of $f(x) = x^3$ on $[-2, 2]$.

SOLUTION   The derivative is $f'(x) = 3x^2$, which is defined on $(-2, 2)$ and is zero only when $x = 0$. The critical points are therefore $x = 0$ and the end points $x = -2$ and $x = 2$. Evaluating f at the critical points yields $f(-2) = -8$, $f(0) = 0$, and $f(2) = 8$. Thus, the maximum value of f is 8 (attained at $x = 2$) and the minimum is -8 (attained at $x = -2$). ∎

Notice that in Example 2, $f'(0) = 0$, but f did not attain a minimum or a maximum at $x = 0$. This does not contradict Theorem B. Theorem B does not say that if c is a critical point then $f(c)$ is a minimum or maximum; it says that if $f(c)$ is a minimum or a maximum, then c is a critical point.

EXAMPLE 3   Find the maximum and minimum values of
$$f(x) = -2x^3 + 3x^2$$
on $\left[-\frac{1}{2}, 2\right]$.

SOLUTION   In Example 1, we identified $-\frac{1}{2}$, 0, 1, and 2 as the critical points. Now $f\left(-\frac{1}{2}\right) = 1$, $f(0) = 0$, $f(1) = 1$, and $f(2) = -4$. Thus, the maximum value is 1 (attained at both $x = -\frac{1}{2}$ and $x = 1$), and the minimum value is -4 (attained at $x = 2$). The graph of f is shown in Figure 7. ∎

Terminology

Notice the way that terms are used in Example 3. The maximum is 1, which is equal to $f\left(-\frac{1}{2}\right)$ and $f(1)$. We say that the maximum is attained at $-\frac{1}{2}$ and at 1. Similarly, the minimum is -4, which is attained at 2.

EXAMPLE 4   The function $F(x) = x^{2/3}$ is continuous everywhere. Find its maximum and minimum values on $[-1, 2]$.

SOLUTION $F'(x) = \frac{2}{3}x^{-1/3}$, which is never 0. However, $F'(0)$ does not exist, so 0 is a critical point, as are the end points -1 and 2. Now $F(-1) = 1$, $F(0) = 0$, and $F(2) = \sqrt[3]{4} \approx 1.59$. Thus, the maximum value is $\sqrt[3]{4}$; the minimum value is 0. The graph is shown in Figure 8. ∎

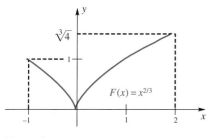

Figure 8

$\sqrt[3]{4}$

$F(x) = x^{2/3}$

EXAMPLE 5   Find the maximum and minimum values of $f(x) = x + 2\cos x$ on $[-\pi, 2\pi]$.

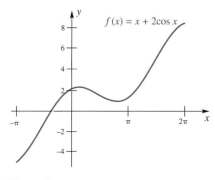

Figure 9

$f(x) = x + 2\cos x$

SOLUTION   Figure 9 shows a plot of $y = f(x)$. The derivative is $f'(x) = 1 - 2\sin x$, which is defined on $(-\pi, 2\pi)$ and is zero when $\sin x = 1/2$. The only values of x in the interval $[-\pi, 2\pi]$ that satisfy $\sin x = 1/2$ are $x = \pi/6$ and $x = 5\pi/6$. These two numbers, together with the end points $-\pi$ and 2π, are the critical points. Now, evaluate f at each critical point:

$$f(-\pi) = -2 - \pi \approx -5.14 \qquad f(\pi/6) = \sqrt{3} + \frac{\pi}{6} \approx 2.26$$

$$f(5\pi/6) = -\sqrt{3} + \frac{5\pi}{6} \approx 0.89 \qquad f(2\pi) = 2 + 2\pi \approx 8.28$$

Thus, $-2 - \pi$ is the minimum (attained at $x = -\pi$), and the maximum is $2 + 2\pi$ (attained at $x = 2\pi$). ∎

Concepts Review

1. A _____ function on a _____ interval will always have both a maximum value and a minimum value on that interval.

2. The term _____ value denotes either a maximum or a minimum value.

3. A function can attain an extreme value only at a critical point. Critical points are of three types: _____, _____, and _____.

4. A stationary point for f is a number c such that _____; a singular point for f is a number c such that _____.

Problem Set 4.1

In Problems 1–4, find all critical points and find the minimum and maximum of the function. Each function has domain $[-2, 4]$.

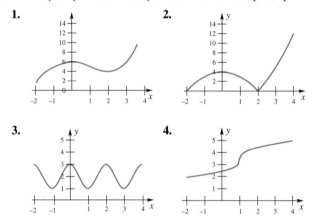

1.   **2.**

3.   **4.**

In Problems 5–26, identify the critical points and find the maximum value and minimum value on the given interval.

5. $f(x) = x^2 + 4x + 4; I = [-4, 0]$

6. $h(x) = x^2 + x; I = [-2, 2]$

7. $\Psi(x) = x^2 + 3x; I = [-2, 1]$

8. $G(x) = \frac{1}{5}(2x^3 + 3x^2 - 12x); I = [-3, 3]$

9. $f(x) = x^3 - 3x + 1; I = \left(-\frac{3}{2}, 3\right)$ *Hint:* Sketch the graph.

10. $f(x) = x^3 - 3x + 1; I = \left[-\frac{3}{2}, 3\right]$

11. $h(x) = e^{-x^2}; I = [-1, 3]$

12. $g(x) = \dfrac{1}{1 + x^2}; I = [-3, 1]$

13. $f(x) = x^4 - 2x^2 + 2; I = [-2, 2]$

14. $f(x) = x^5 - \dfrac{25}{3}x^3 + 20x - 1; I = [-3, 2]$

15. $g(x) = \dfrac{1}{1 + x^2}; I = (-\infty, \infty)$ *Hint:* Sketch the graph.

16. $f(x) = \dfrac{x}{1 + x^2}; I = [-1, 4]$

17. $r(\theta) = \sin \theta; I = \left[-\dfrac{\pi}{4}, \dfrac{\pi}{6}\right]$

18. $s(t) = \sin t - \cos t; I = [0, \pi]$

19. $a(x) = |x - 1|; I = [0, 3]$

20. $f(s) = |3s - 2|; I = [-1, 4]$

21. $g(x) = \sqrt[3]{x}; I = [-1, 27]$

22. $s(t) = t^{2/5}; I = [-1, 32]$

23. $f(x) = xe^{-x^2}; I = [-1, 2]$

24. $g(x) = \dfrac{\ln(x + 1)}{x + 1}; I = [0, 3]$

25. $g(\theta) = \theta^2 \sec \theta; I = \left[-\dfrac{\pi}{4}, \dfrac{\pi}{4}\right]$

26. $h(t) = \dfrac{t^{5/3}}{2 + t}; I = [-1, 8]$

GC **27.** Identify the critical points and find the extreme values on the interval $[-1, 5]$ for each function:

(a) $f(x) = x^3 - 6x^2 + x + 2$ (b) $g(x) = |f(x)|$

GC **28.** Identify the critical points and find the extreme values on the interval $[-1, 5]$ for each function:

(a) $f(x) = \cos x + x \sin x + 2$ (b) $g(x) = |f(x)|$

In Problems 29–36, sketch the graph of a function with the given properties.

29. f is differentiable, has domain $[0, 6]$, reaches a maximum of 6 (attained when $x = 3$) and a minimum of 0 (attained when $x = 0$). Additionally, $x = 5$ is a stationary point.

30. f is differentiable, has domain $[0, 6]$, reaches a maximum of 4 (attained when $x = 6$) and a minimum of -2 (attained when $x = 1$). Additionally, $x = 2, 3, 4, 5$ are stationary points.

31. f is continuous, but not necessarily differentiable, has domain $[0, 6]$, reaches a maximum of 6 (attained when $x = 5$), and a minimum of 2 (attained when $x = 3$). Additionally, $x = 1$ and $x = 5$ are the only stationary points.

32. f is continuous, but not necessarily differentiable, has domain $[0, 6]$, reaches a maximum of 4 (attained when $x = 4$), and a minimum of 2 (attained when $x = 2$). Additionally, f has no stationary points.

33. f is differentiable, has domain $[0, 6]$, reaches a maximum of 4 (attained at two different values of x, neither of which is an end point), and a minimum of 1 (attained at three different values of x, exactly one of which is an end point.)

34. f is continuous but not necessarily differentiable, has domain $[0, 6]$, reaches a maximum of 6 (attained when $x = 0$) and a minimum of 0 (attained when $x = 6$). Additionally, f has two stationary points and two singular points in $(0, 6)$.

35. f has domain $[0, 6]$, but is not necessarily continuous, and f does not attain a maximum.

36. f has domain $[0, 6]$, but is not necessarily continuous, and f attains neither a maximum nor a minimum.

Answers to Concepts Review: **1.** continuous; closed
2. extreme **3.** end points; stationary points; singular points
4. $f'(c) = 0$; $f'(c)$ does not exist

4.2
Monotonicity and Concavity

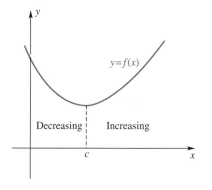

Figure 1

Consider the graph in Figure 1. No one will be surprised when we say that f is decreasing to the left of c and increasing to the right of c. These terms were introduced in Section 1.6 in the context of finding the inverse of a function, but for easy reference, we repeat the definitions here.

Definition

Let f be defined on an interval I (open, closed, or neither). We say that

(i) f is **increasing** on I if, for every pair of numbers x_1 and x_2 in I,

$$x_1 < x_2 \Rightarrow f(x_1) < f(x_2)$$

(ii) f is **decreasing** on I if, for every pair of numbers x_1 and x_2 in I,

$$x_1 < x_2 \Rightarrow f(x_1) > f(x_2)$$

(iii) f is **strictly monotonic** on I if it is either increasing on I or decreasing on I.

How shall we decide where a function is increasing? We could draw its graph and look at it, but a graph is usually drawn by plotting a few points and connecting those points with a smooth curve. Who can be sure that the graph does not wiggle between the plotted points? Even computer algebra systems and graphing calculators plot by simply connecting points. We need a better procedure.

The First Derivative and Monotonicity Recall that the first derivative $f'(x)$ gives us the slope of the tangent line to the graph of f at the point x. Thus, if $f'(x) > 0$, then the tangent line is rising to the right, suggesting that f is increasing. (See Figure 2.) Similarly, if $f'(x) < 0$, then the tangent line is falling to the right, suggesting that f is decreasing. We can also look at this in terms of motion along a line. Suppose an object is at position $s(t)$ at time t and that its velocity is always positive, that is, $s'(t) = ds/dt > 0$. Then it seems reasonable that the object will continue to move to the right as long as the derivative stays positive. In other words, $s(t)$ will be an *increasing* function of t. These observations are stated in Theorem A below, which we first saw in Section 3.9. We postpone a rigorous proof until Section 4.6.

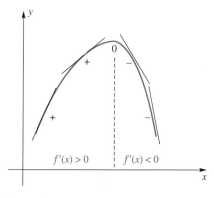

Figure 2

Theorem A **Monotonicity Theorem**

Let f be continuous on an interval I and differentiable at every interior point of I.

(1) If $f'(x) > 0$ for all x interior to I, then f is increasing on I.
(2) If $f'(x) < 0$ for all x interior to I, then f is decreasing on I.

This theorem usually allows us to determine precisely where a differentiable function increases and where it decreases. It is a matter of solving two inequalities.

EXAMPLE 1 If $f(x) = 2x^3 - 3x^2 - 12x + 7$, find where f is increasing and where it is decreasing.

SOLUTION We begin by finding the derivative of f.

$$f'(x) = 6x^2 - 6x - 12 = 6(x + 1)(x - 2)$$

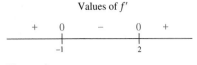

Values of f'

Figure 3

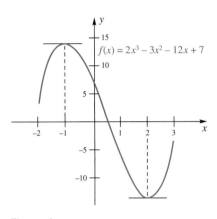

$f(x) = 2x^3 - 3x^2 - 12x + 7$

Figure 4

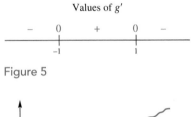

Values of g'

Figure 5

Increasing but wiggly

Figure 6

We need to determine where

$$(x + 1)(x - 2) > 0$$

and also where

$$(x + 1)(x - 2) < 0$$

This problem was discussed in great detail in Section 1.2, a section worth reviewing now. The split points are -1 and 2; they split the x-axis into three intervals: $(-\infty, -1), (-1, 2)$, and $(2, \infty)$. Using the test points $-2, 0$, and 3, we conclude that $f'(x) > 0$ on the first and last of these intervals and that $f'(x) < 0$ on the middle interval (Figure 3). Thus, by Theorem A, f is increasing on $(-\infty, -1]$ and $[2, \infty)$; it is decreasing on $[-1, 2]$. Note that the theorem allows us to include the end points of these intervals, even though $f'(x) = 0$ at those points. The graph of f is shown in Figure 4. ∎

EXAMPLE 2 Determine where $g(x) = x/(1 + x^2)$ is increasing and where it is decreasing.

SOLUTION

$$g'(x) = \frac{(1 + x^2) - x(2x)}{(1 + x^2)^2} = \frac{1 - x^2}{(1 + x^2)^2} = \frac{(1 - x)(1 + x)}{(1 + x^2)^2}$$

Since the denominator is always positive, $g'(x)$ has the same sign as the numerator $(1 - x)(1 + x)$. The split points, -1 and 1, determine the three intervals $(-\infty, -1), (-1, 1)$, and $(1, \infty)$. When we test them, we find that $g'(x) < 0$ on the first and last of these intervals and that $g'(x) > 0$ on the middle one (Figure 5). We conclude from Theorem A that g is decreasing on $(-\infty, -1]$ and $[1, \infty)$ and that it is increasing on $[-1, 1]$. We postpone graphing g until later, but if you want to see the graph, turn to Figure 11 and Example 4. ∎

The Second Derivative and Concavity A function may be increasing and still have a very wiggly graph (Figure 6). To analyze wiggles, we need to study how the tangent line turns as we move from left to right along the graph. If the tangent line turns steadily in the counterclockwise direction, we say that the graph is *concave up*; if the tangent turns in the clockwise direction, the graph is *concave down*. Both definitions are better stated in terms of functions and their derivatives.

Definition

Let f be differentiable on an open interval I. We say that f (as well as its graph) is **concave up** on I if f' is increasing on I, and we say that f is **concave down** on I if f' is decreasing on I.

The diagrams in Figure 7 will help to clarify these notions. Note that a curve that is concave *up* is shaped like a *cup*.

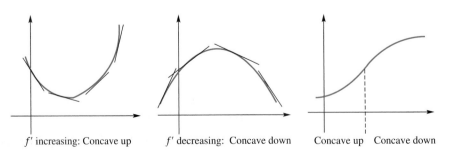

f' increasing: Concave up f' decreasing: Concave down   Concave up   Concave down

Figure 7

In view of Theorem A, we have a simple criterion for deciding where a curve is concave up and where it is concave down. We simply keep in mind that the second derivative of f is the first derivative of f'. Thus, f' is increasing if f'' is positive; it is decreasing if f'' is negative.

Conditions in Theorems A and B

The conditions regarding the derivatives in Theorems A and B are sufficient to guarantee the conclusions stated. These conditions are not, however, necessary. It is possible that a function is increasing on some interval even though the derivative isn't always positive on that interval. If we consider the function $f(x) = x^3$ over the interval $[-4, 4]$ we note that it is increasing but its derivative is not always positive on that interval ($f'(0) = 0$). The function $g(x) = x^4$ is concave up on the interval $[-4, 4]$, but the second derivative, $g''(x) = 12x^2$, is not always positive on that interval.

> **Theorem B   Concavity Theorem**
>
> Let f be twice differentiable on the open interval I.
>
> (1)   If $f''(x) > 0$ for all x in I, then f is concave up on I.
> (2)   If $f''(x) < 0$ for all x in I, then f is concave down on I.

For most functions, this theorem reduces the problem of determining concavity to the problem of solving inequalities. By now we are experts at this.

■ EXAMPLE 3   Where is $f(x) = \frac{1}{3}x^3 - x^2 - 3x + 4$ increasing, decreasing, concave up, and concave down?

SOLUTION

$$f'(x) = x^2 - 2x - 3 = (x + 1)(x - 3)$$
$$f''(x) = 2x - 2 = 2(x - 1)$$

By solving the inequalities $(x + 1)(x - 3) > 0$ and its opposite, $(x + 1)(x - 3) < 0$, we conclude that f is increasing on $(-\infty, -1]$ and $[3, \infty)$ and decreasing on $[-1, 3]$ (Figure 8). Similarly, solving $2(x - 1) > 0$ and $2(x - 1) < 0$ shows that f is concave up on $(1, \infty)$ and concave down on $(-\infty, 1)$. The graph of f is shown in Figure 9.   ■

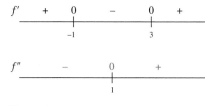

Figure 8

■ EXAMPLE 4   Where is $g(x) = x/(1 + x^2)$ concave up and where is it concave down? Sketch the graph of g.

SOLUTION   We began our study of this function in Example 2. There we learned that g is decreasing on $(-\infty, -1]$ and $[1, \infty)$ and increasing on $[-1, 1]$. To analyze concavity, we calculate g''.

$$g'(x) = \frac{1 - x^2}{(1 + x^2)^2}$$

$$g''(x) = \frac{(1 + x^2)^2(-2x) - (1 - x^2)(2)(1 + x^2)(2x)}{(1 + x^2)^4}$$

$$= \frac{(1 + x^2)[(1 + x^2)(-2x) - (1 - x^2)(4x)]}{(1 + x^2)^4}$$

$$= \frac{2x^3 - 6x}{(1 + x^2)^3}$$

$$= \frac{2x(x^2 - 3)}{(1 + x^2)^3}$$

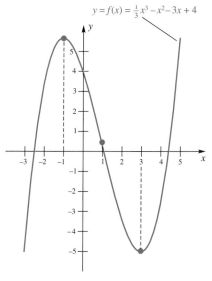

Figure 9

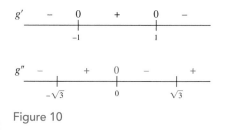

Figure 10

Since the denominator is always positive, we need only solve $x(x^2 - 3) > 0$ and its opposite. The split points are $-\sqrt{3}, 0,$ and $\sqrt{3}$. These three split points determine four intervals. After testing them (Figure 10), we conclude that g is concave up on $(-\sqrt{3}, 0)$ and $(\sqrt{3}, \infty)$ and that it is concave down on $(-\infty, -\sqrt{3})$ and $(0, \sqrt{3})$.

To sketch the graph of g, we make use of all the information obtained so far, plus the fact that g is an odd function whose graph is symmetric with respect to the origin (Figure 11).

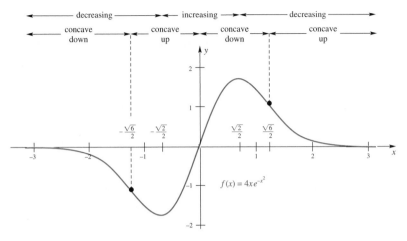

Figure 11

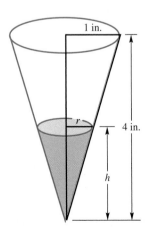

Figure 12

EXAMPLE 5 Suppose that water is poured into the conical container, as shown in Figure 12, at the constant rate of $\frac{1}{2}$ cubic inch per second. Determine the height h of the water as a function of time t and plot $h(t)$ from time $t = 0$ until the time that the container is full.

SOLUTION Before we solve this problem, let's think about what the graph will look like. At first, the height will increase rapidly, since it takes very little water to fill the bottom of the cone. As the container fills up, the height will increase less rapidly. What do these statements say about the function $h(t)$, its derivative $h'(t)$, and its second derivative $h''(t)$? Since the water is steadily pouring in, the height will always increase, so $h'(t)$ will be positive. The height will increase more slowly as the water level rises. Thus, the function $h'(t)$ is decreasing so $h''(t)$ is negative. The graph of $h(t)$ is therefore increasing (because $h'(t)$ is positive) and concave down (because $h''(t)$ is negative).

Now, once we have an intuitive idea about what the graph should look like (increasing and concave down), let's solve the problem analytically. The volume of a right circular cone is $V = \frac{1}{3}\pi r^2 h$, where V, r, and h are all functions of time. The functions h and r are related; notice the similar triangles in Figure 13. Using properties of similar triangles, we have

$$\frac{r}{h} = \frac{1}{4}$$

Thus, $r = h/4$. The volume of the water inside the cone is thus

$$V = \frac{1}{3}\pi r^2 h = \frac{\pi}{3}\left(\frac{h}{4}\right)^2 h = \frac{\pi}{48}h^3$$

On the other hand, since water is flowing into the container at the rate of $\frac{1}{2}$ cubic inch per second, the volume at time t is $V = \frac{1}{2}t$, where t is measured in seconds. Equating these two expressions for V gives

$$\frac{1}{2}t = \frac{\pi}{48}h^3$$

When $h = 4$, we have $t = \frac{2\pi}{48}4^3 = \frac{8}{3}\pi \approx 8.4$; thus, it takes about 8.4 seconds to fill the container. Now solve for h in the above equation relating h and t to obtain

$$h(t) = \sqrt[3]{\frac{24}{\pi}t}$$

Figure 13

Figure 14

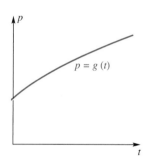

Figure 15

Figure 16

Terminology
While a function's minimum or maximum is a *number*, an inflection point is always an *ordered pair*, $(c, f(c))$.

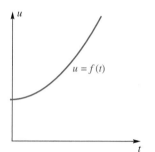

Figure 18

The first and second derivatives of h are

$$h'(t) = D_t \sqrt[3]{\frac{24}{\pi}t} = \frac{8}{\pi}\left(\frac{24}{\pi}t\right)^{-2/3} = \frac{2}{\sqrt[3]{9\pi t^2}}$$

which is positive, and

$$h''(t) = D_t \frac{2}{\sqrt[3]{9\pi t^2}} = -\frac{4}{3\sqrt[3]{9\pi t^5}}$$

which is negative. The graph of $h(t)$ is shown in Figure 14. As expected, the graph of h is increasing and concave down. ∎

EXAMPLE 6   A news agency reported in May 2005 that unemployment in eastern Asia was continuing to increase at an increasing rate. On the other hand, the price of food was increasing, but at a slower rate than before. Interpret these statements in terms of increasing/decreasing functions and concavity.

SOLUTION   Let $u = f(t)$ denote the number of people unemployed at time t. Although u actually jumps by unit amounts, we will follow standard practice in representing u by a smooth curve as in Figure 15. To say unemployment is increasing is to say that $du/dt > 0$. To say that it is increasing at an increasing rate is to say that the function du/dt is *increasing*; but this means that the derivative of du/dt must be positive. Thus, $d^2u/dt^2 > 0$. In Figure 15, notice that the slope of the tangent line increases as t increases. Unemployment is increasing and concave up.

Similarly, if $p = g(t)$ represents the price of food (e.g., the typical cost of one day's groceries for one person) at time t, then dp/dt is positive but *decreasing*. Thus, the derivative of dp/dt is negative, so $d^2p/dt^2 < 0$. In Figure 16, notice that the slope of the tangent line decreases as t increases. The price of food is increasing but concave down. ∎

Inflection Points   Let f be continuous at c. We call $(c, f(c))$ an **inflection point** of the graph of f if f is concave up on one side of c and concave down on the other side. The graph in Figure 17 indicates a number of possibilities.

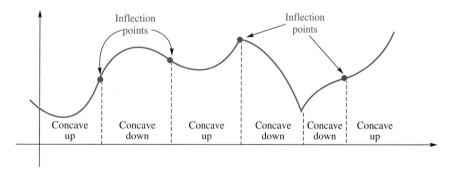

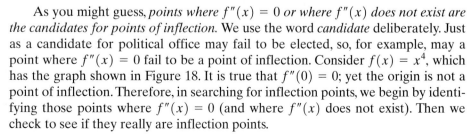

Figure 17

As you might guess, *points where $f''(x) = 0$ or where $f''(x)$ does not exist are the candidates for points of inflection.* We use the word *candidate* deliberately. Just as a candidate for political office may fail to be elected, so, for example, may a point where $f''(x) = 0$ fail to be a point of inflection. Consider $f(x) = x^4$, which has the graph shown in Figure 18. It is true that $f''(0) = 0$; yet the origin is not a point of inflection. Therefore, in searching for inflection points, we begin by identifying those points where $f''(x) = 0$ (and where $f''(x)$ does not exist). Then we check to see if they really are inflection points.

Look back at the graph in Example 4. You will see that it has three inflection points. They are $\left(-\sqrt{3}, -\sqrt{3}/4\right)$, $(0, 0)$, and $\left(\sqrt{3}, \sqrt{3}/4\right)$.

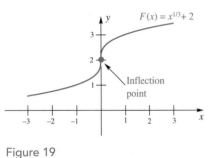

Figure 19

EXAMPLE 7 Find all points of inflection of $F(x) = x^{1/3} + 2$.

SOLUTION

$$F'(x) = \frac{1}{3x^{2/3}}, \qquad F''(x) = \frac{-2}{9x^{5/3}}$$

The second derivative, $F''(x)$, is never 0; however, it fails to exist at $x = 0$. The point $(0, 2)$ is an inflection point since $F''(x) > 0$ for $x < 0$ and $F''(x) < 0$ for $x > 0$. The graph is sketched in Figure 19. ∎

Concepts Review

1. If $f'(x) > 0$ everywhere, then f is _____ everywhere; if $f''(x) > 0$ everywhere, then f is _____ everywhere.

2. If _____ and _____ on an open interval I, then f is both increasing and concave down on I.

3. A point on the graph of a continuous function where the concavity changes is called _____.

4. In trying to locate the inflection points for the graph of a function f, we should look at numbers c, where either _____ or _____.

Problem Set 4.2

In Problems 1–10, use the Monotonicity Theorem to find where the given function is increasing and where it is decreasing.

1. $f(x) = 3x + 3$

2. $g(x) = (x + 1)(x - 2)$

3. $h(t) = t^2 + 2t - 3$

4. $f(x) = x^3 - 1$

5. $G(x) = 2x^3 - 9x^2 + 12x$

6. $f(t) = t^3 + 3t^2 - 12$

7. $h(z) = \dfrac{z^4}{4} - \dfrac{4z^3}{6}$

8. $f(x) = e^{-x}$

9. $H(t) = \sin t, 0 \le t \le 2\pi$

10. $f(x) = \dfrac{e^{-x}}{x^2}$

In Problems 11–18, use the Concavity Theorem to determine where the given function is concave up and where it is concave down. Also find all inflection points.

11. $f(x) = (x - 1)^2$

12. $G(w) = w^2 - 1$

13. $T(t) = 3t^3 - 18t$

14. $f(z) = z^2 - \dfrac{1}{z^2}$

15. $q(x) = x^4 - 6x^3 - 24x^2 + 3x + 1$

16. $f(x) = x^4 + 8x^3 - 2$

17. $F(x) = 2x^2 + \cos^2 x$

18. $G(x) = \arcsin 2x$

In Problems 19–28, determine where the graph of the given function is increasing, decreasing, concave up, and concave down. Then sketch the graph (see Example 4).

19. $f(x) = x^3 - 12x + 1$

20. $g(x) = 4x^3 - 3x^2 - 6x + 12$

21. $g(x) = 3x^4 - 4x^3 + 2$

22. $F(x) = x^6 - 3x^4$

23. $G(x) = 3x^5 - 5x^3 + 1$

24. $H(x) = \dfrac{x^2}{x^2 + 1}$

25. $f(x) = \sqrt{\sin x}$ on $[0, \pi]$

26. $g(x) = x\sqrt{x - 2}$

27. $f(x) = e^{-x^2}$

28. $g(x) = \dfrac{\ln(x + 1)}{x + 1}$

In Problems 29–34, sketch the graph of a continuous function f on $[0, 6]$ that satisfies all the stated conditions.

29. $f(0) = 1; f(6) = 3$; increasing and concave down on $(0, 6)$

30. $f(0) = 8; f(6) = -2$; decreasing on $(0, 6)$; inflection point at the ordered pair $(2, 3)$, concave up on $(2, 6)$

31. $f(0) = 3; f(3) = 0; f(6) = 4$;
$f'(x) < 0$ on $(0, 3); f'(x) > 0$ on $(3, 6)$;
$f''(x) > 0$ on $(0, 5); f''(x) < 0$ on $(5, 6)$

32. $f(0) = 3; f(2) = 2; f(6) = 0$;
$f'(x) < 0$ on $(0, 2) \cup (2, 6); f'(2) = 0$;
$f''(x) < 0$ on $(0, 1) \cup (2, 6); f''(x) > 0$ on $(1, 2)$

33. $f(0) = f(4) = 1; f(2) = 2; f(6) = 0$;
$f'(x) > 0$ on $(0, 2); f'(x) < 0$ on $(2, 4) \cup (4, 6)$;
$f'(2) = f'(4) = 0; f''(x) > 0$ on $(0, 1) \cup (3, 4)$;
$f''(x) < 0$ on $(1, 3) \cup (4, 6)$

34. $f(0) = f(3) = 3; f(2) = 4; f(4) = 2; f(6) = 0$;
$f'(x) > 0$ on $(0, 2); f'(x) < 0$ on $(2, 4) \cup (4, 5)$;
$f'(2) = f'(4) = 0; f'(x) = -1$ on $(5, 6)$;
$f''(x) < 0$ on $(0, 3) \cup (4, 5); f''(x) > 0$ on $(3, 4)$

35. Prove that a quadratic function has no point of inflection.

36. Prove that a cubic function has exactly one point of inflection.

37. Prove that, if $f'(x)$ exists and is continuous on an interval I and if $f'(x) \ne 0$ at all interior points of I, then either f is increasing throughout I or decreasing throughout I. *Hint:* Use the Intermediate Value Theorem to show that there cannot be two points x_1 and x_2 of I where f' has opposite signs.

38. Suppose that f is a function whose derivative is $f'(x) = (x^2 - x + 1)/(x^2 + 1)$. Use Problem 37 to prove that f is increasing everywhere.

39. Use the Monotonicity Theorem to prove each statement if $0 < x < y$.

(a) $x^2 < y^2$ (b) $\sqrt{x} < \sqrt{y}$ (c) $\dfrac{1}{x} > \dfrac{1}{y}$

40. What conditions on a, b, and c will make $f(x) = ax^3 + bx^2 + cx + d$ always increasing?

41. Determine a and b so that $f(x) = a\sqrt{x} + b/\sqrt{x}$ has the point $(4, 13)$ as an inflection point.

42. Suppose that the cubic function $f(x)$ has three real zeros, r_1, r_2, and r_3. Show that its inflection point has x-coordinate $(r_1 + r_2 + r_3)/3$. *Hint:* $f(x) = a(x - r_1)(x - r_2)(x - r_3)$.

43. Suppose that $f'(x) > 0$ and $g'(x) > 0$ for all x. What simple additional conditions (if any) are needed to guarantee that:

(a) $f(x) + g(x)$ is increasing for all x;
(b) $f(x) \cdot g(x)$ is increasing for all x;
(c) $f(g(x))$ is increasing for all x?

44. Suppose that $f''(x) > 0$ and $g''(x) > 0$ for all x. What simple additional conditions (if any) are needed to guarantee that

(a) $f(x) + g(x)$ is concave up for all x;
(b) $f(x) \cdot g(x)$ is concave up for all x;
(c) $f(g(x))$ is concave up for all x?

GC *Use a graphing calculator or a computer to do Problems 45–48.*

45. Let $f(x) = \sin x + \cos(x/2)$ on the interval $I = (-2, 7)$.
(a) Draw the graph of f on I.
(b) Use this graph to estimate where $f'(x) < 0$ on I.
(c) Use this graph to estimate where $f''(x) < 0$ on I.
(d) Plot the graph of f' to confirm your answer to part (b).
(e) Plot the graph of f'' to confirm your answer to part (c).

46. Repeat Problem 45 for $f(x) = x \cos^2(x/3)$ on $(0, 10)$.

47. Let $f'(x) = x^3 - 5x^2 + 2$ on $I = [-2, 4]$. Where on I is f increasing?

48. Let $f''(x) = x^4 - 5x^3 + 4x^2 + 4$ on $I = [-2, 3]$. Where on I is f concave down?

49. Translate each of the following into the language of derivatives of distance with respect to time. For each part, sketch a plot of the car's position s against time t, and indicate the concavity.

(a) The speed of the car is proportional to the distance it has traveled.
(b) The car is speeding up.
(c) I didn't say the car was slowing down; I said its rate of increase in speed was slowing down.
(d) The car's speed is increasing 10 miles per hour every minute.
(e) The car is slowing very gently to a stop.
(f) The car always travels the same distance in equal time intervals.

50. Translate each of the following into the language of derivatives, sketch a plot of the appropriate function and indicate the concavity.

(a) Water is evaporating from the tank at a constant rate.
(b) Water is being poured into the tank at 3 gallons per minute but is also leaking out at $\frac{1}{2}$ gallon per minute.
(c) Since water is being poured into the conical tank at a constant rate, the water level is rising at a slower and slower rate.
(d) Inflation held steady this year but is expected to rise more and more rapidly in the years ahead.
(e) At present the price of oil is dropping, but this trend is expected to slow and then reverse direction in 2 years.
(f) David's temperature is still rising, but the penicillin seems to be taking effect.

51. Translate each of the following statements into mathematical language, sketch a plot of the appropriate function, and indicate the concavity.

(a) The cost of a car continues to increase and at a faster and faster rate.
(b) During the last 2 years, the United States has continued to cut its consumption of oil, but at a slower and slower rate.
(c) World population continues to grow, but at a slower and slower rate.
(d) The angle that the Leaning Tower of Pisa makes with the vertical is increasing more and more rapidly.
(e) Upper Midwest firm's profit growth slows.
(f) The XYZ Company has been losing money, but will soon turn this situation around.

52. Translate each statement from the following newspaper column into a statement about derivatives.

(a) In the United States, the ratio R of government debt to national income remained unchanged at around 28% up to 1981, but
(b) then it began to increase more and more sharply, reaching 36% during 1983.

≈ **53.** Coffee is poured into the cup shown in Figure 20 at the rate of 2 cubic inches per second. The top diameter is 3.5 inches, the bottom diameter is 3 inches, and the height of the cup is 5 inches. This cup holds about 23 fluid ounces. Determine the height h of the coffee as a function of time t, and sketch the graph of $h(t)$ from time $t = 0$ until the time that the cup is full.

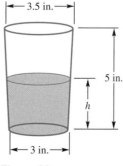

Figure 20

54. Water is being pumped into a cylindrical tank at a constant rate of 5 gallons per minute, as shown in Figure 21. The tank has diameter 3 feet and length 9.5 feet. The volume of the tank is $\pi r^2 l = \pi \times 1.5^2 \times 9.5 \approx 67.152$ cubic feet ≈ 500 gallons. Without doing any calculations, sketch a graph of the height h of the water as a function of time t (see Example 6). Where is h concave up? Concave down?

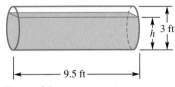

Figure 21

55. A liquid is poured into the container shown in Figure 22 at the rate of 3 cubic inches per second. The container holds about 24 cubic inches. Sketch a graph of the height h of the liquid as a function of time t. In your graph, pay special attention to the concavity of h.

56. A 20-gallon barrel, as shown in Figure 23, leaks at the constant rate of 0.1 gallon per day. Sketch a plot of the height h of the water as a function of time t, assuming that the barrel is full at time $t = 0$. In your graph, pay special attention to the concavity of h.

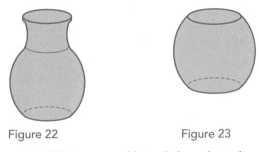

Figure 22　　　　　　　　　Figure 23

57. What are you able to deduce about the shape of a vase based on each of the following tables, which give measurements of the volume of the water as a function of the depth.

(a)

Depth	1	2	3	4	5	6
Volume	4	8	11	14	20	28

(b)

Depth	1	2	3	4	5	6
Volume	4	9	12	14	20	28

Answers to Concepts Review: **1.** increasing; concave up
2. $f'(x) > 0; f''(x) < 0$ **3.** an inflection point
4. $f''(c) = 0; f''(c)$ does not exist

4.3
Local Extrema and Extrema on Open Intervals

We recall from Section 4.1 that the maximum value (if it exists) of a function f on a set S is the largest value that f attains on the whole set S. It is sometimes referred to as the **global maximum value,** or the *absolute maximum value* of f. Thus, for the function f with domain $S = [a, b]$ whose graph is sketched in Figure 1, $f(a)$ is the global maximum value. But what about $f(c)$? It may not be king of the country, but at least it is chief of its own locality. We call it a **local maximum value,** or a *relative maximum value*. Of course, a global maximum value is automatically a local maximum value. Figure 2 illustrates a number of possibilities. Note that the global maximum value (if it exists) is simply the largest of the local maximum values. Similarly, the global minimum value is the smallest of the local minimum values.

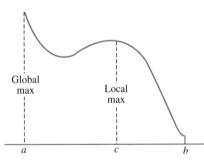

Figure 1

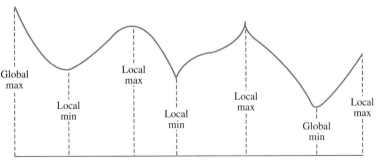

Figure 2

Here is the formal definition of local maxima and local minima. Recall that the symbol $\cap$ denotes the intersection (common part) of two sets.

Definition

Let S, the domain of f, contain the point c. We say that

(i)　$f(c)$ is a **local maximum value** of f if there is an interval (a, b) containing c such that $f(c)$ is the maximum value of f on $(a, b) \cap S$;

(ii)　$f(c)$ is a **local minimum value** of f if there is an interval (a, b) containing c such that $f(c)$ is the minimum value of f on $(a, b) \cap S$;

(iii)　$f(c)$ is a **local extreme value** of f if it is either a local maximum or a local minimum value.

Where Do Local Extreme Values Occur? The Critical Point Theorem (Theorem 4.1B) holds with the phrase *extreme value* replaced by *local extreme value*; the proof is essentially the same. Thus, the critical points (end points, stationary points, and singular points) are the candidates for points where local extrema may occur. We say *candidates* because we are not claiming that there must be a local extremum at every critical point. The left graph in Figure 3 makes this

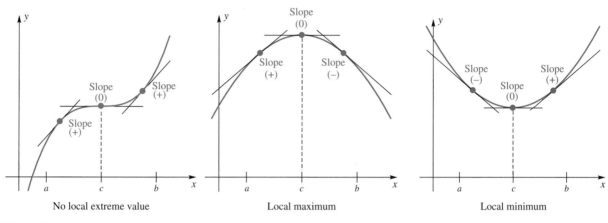

No local extreme value   Local maximum   Local minimum

Figure 3

clear. However, if the derivative is positive on one side of the critical point and negative on the other (and if the function is continuous), then we have a local extremum, as shown in the middle and right graphs of Figure 3.

Theorem A | **First Derivative Test**

Let f be continuous on an open interval (a, b) that contains a critical point c.

(1)   If $f'(x) > 0$ for all x in (a, c) and $f'(x) < 0$ for all x in (c, b), then $f(c)$ is a local maximum value of f.

(2)   If $f'(x) < 0$ for all x in (a, c) and $f'(x) > 0$ for all x in (c, b), then $f(c)$ is a local minimum value of f.

(3)   If $f'(x)$ has the same sign on both sides of c, then $f(c)$ is not a local extreme value of f.

Proof of (1) Since $f'(x) > 0$ for all x in (a, c), f is increasing on $(a, c]$ by the Monotonicity Theorem. Again, since $f'(x) < 0$ for all x in (c, b), f is decreasing on $[c, b)$. Thus, $f(x) < f(c)$ for all x in (a, b), except of course at $x = c$. We conclude that $f(c)$ is a local maximum.

The proofs of (2) and (3) are similar. ∎

EXAMPLE 1 Find the local extreme values of the function $f(x) = x^2 - 6x + 5$ on $(-\infty, \infty)$.

SOLUTION The polynomial function f is continuous everywhere, and its derivative, $f'(x) = 2x - 6$, exists for all x. Thus, the only critical point for f is the single solution of $f'(x) = 0$; that is, $x = 3$.

Since $f'(x) = 2(x - 3) < 0$ for $x < 3$, f is decreasing on $(-\infty, 3]$; and because $2(x - 3) > 0$ for $x > 3$, f is increasing on $[3, \infty)$. Therefore, by the First Derivative Test, $f(3) = -4$ is a local minimum value of f. Since 3 is the only critical point, there are no other extreme values. The graph of f is shown in Figure 4. Note that $f(3)$ is actually the (global) minimum value in this case. ∎

EXAMPLE 2 Find the local extreme values of $f(x) = \frac{1}{3}x^3 - x^2 - 3x + 4$ on $(-\infty, \infty)$.

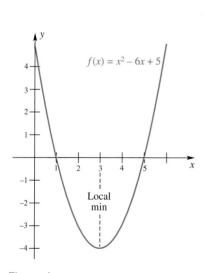

$f(x) = x^2 - 6x + 5$

Local min

Figure 4

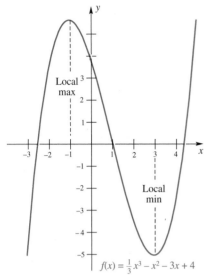

Local max

Local min

$f(x) = \frac{1}{3}x^3 - x^2 - 3x + 4$

Figure 5

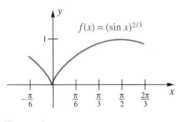

$f(x) = (\sin x)^{2/3}$

Figure 6

SOLUTION   Since $f'(x) = x^2 - 2x - 3 = (x + 1)(x - 3)$, the only critical points of f are -1 and 3. When we use the test points -2, 0, and 4, we learn that $(x + 1)(x - 3) > 0$ on $(-\infty, -1)$ and $(3, \infty)$ and $(x + 1)(x - 3) < 0$ on $(-1, 3)$. By the First Derivative Test, we conclude that $f(-1) = \frac{17}{3}$ is a local maximum value and that $f(3) = -5$ is a local minimum value (Figure 5). ∎

EXAMPLE 3   Find the local extreme values of $f(x) = (\sin x)^{2/3}$ on $(-\pi/6, 2\pi/3)$.

SOLUTION

$$f'(x) = \frac{2 \cos x}{3(\sin x)^{1/3}}, \qquad x \neq 0$$

The points 0 and $\pi/2$ are critical points, since $f'(0)$ does not exist and $f'(\pi/2) = 0$. Now $f'(x) < 0$ on $(-\pi/6, 0)$ and on $(\pi/2, 2\pi/3)$, while $f'(x) > 0$ on $(0, \pi/2)$. By the First Derivative Test, we conclude that $f(0) = 0$ is a local minimum value and that $f(\pi/2) = 1$ is a local maximum value. The graph of f is shown in Figure 6. ∎

The Second Derivative Test   There is another test for local maxima and minima that is sometimes easier to apply than the First Derivative Test. It involves evaluating the second derivative at the stationary points. It does not apply to singular points.

Theorem B   **Second Derivative Test**

Let f be a function such that f' and f'' exist at every point in an open interval (a, b) containing c, and suppose that $f'(c) = 0$.

(1)   If $f''(c) < 0$, then $f(c)$ is a local maximum value of f.
(2)   If $f''(c) > 0$, then $f(c)$ is a local minimum value of f.

Proof of (1)   It is tempting to say that, since $f''(c) < 0$, f is concave downward near c and to claim that this proves (1). However, to be sure that f is concave downward in a neighborhood of c, we need $f''(x) < 0$ in that neighborhood (not just at c), and nothing in our hypothesis guarantees that. We must be a bit more careful. By definition and hypothesis,

$$f''(c) = \lim_{x \to c} \frac{f'(x) - f'(c)}{x - c} = \lim_{x \to c} \frac{f'(x) - 0}{x - c} < 0$$

so we can conclude that there is a (possibly small) interval (α, β) around c where

$$\frac{f'(x)}{x - c} < 0, \qquad x \neq c$$

But this inequality implies that $f'(x) > 0$ for $\alpha < x < c$ and $f'(x) < 0$ for $c < x < \beta$. Thus, by the First Derivative Test, $f(c)$ is a local maximum value. The proof of (2) is similar. ∎

EXAMPLE 4   For $f(x) = x^2 - 6x + 5$, use the Second Derivative Test to identify local extrema.

SOLUTION   This is the function of Example 1. Note that

$$f'(x) = 2x - 6 = 2(x - 3)$$
$$f''(x) = 2$$

Thus, $f'(3) = 0$ and $f''(3) > 0$. Therefore, by the Second Derivative Test, $f(3)$ is a local minimum value. ∎

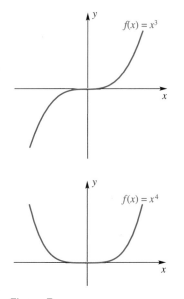

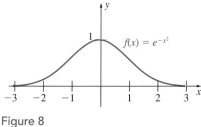

Figure 7

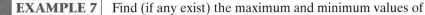

Figure 8

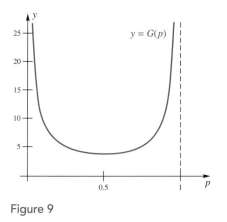

0.5   1 p

Figure 9

EXAMPLE 5 For $f(x) = \frac{1}{3}x^3 - x^2 - 3x + 4$, use the Second Derivative Test to identify local extrema.

SOLUTION This is the function of Example 2.

$$f'(x) = x^2 - 2x - 3 = (x + 1)(x - 3)$$
$$f''(x) = 2x - 2$$

The critical points are -1 and 3 ($f'(-1) = f'(3) = 0$). Since $f''(-1) = -4$ and $f''(3) = 4$, we conclude by the Second Derivative Test that $f(-1)$ is a local maximum value and that $f(3)$ is a local minimum value. ∎

Unfortunately, the Second Derivative Test sometimes fails, since $f''(x)$ may be 0 at a stationary point. For both $f(x) = x^3$ and $f(x) = x^4$, $f'(0) = 0$ and $f''(0) = 0$ (see Figure 7). The first does not have a local maximum or minimum value at 0; the second has a local minimum there. This shows that if $f''(x) = 0$ at a stationary point we are unable to draw a conclusion about maxima or minima without more information.

Extrema on Open Intervals The problems that we studied in this section and in Section 4.1 often assumed that the set on which we wanted to maximize or minimize a function was a *closed* interval. However, the intervals that arise in practice are not always closed; they are sometimes open, or even open on one end and closed on the other. We can still handle these problems if we correctly apply the theory developed in this section. Keep in mind that maximum (minimum) with no qualifying adjective means global maximum (minimum).

EXAMPLE 6 Find (if any exist) the minimum and maximum values of $f(x) = e^{-x^2/2}$ on $(-\infty, \infty)$.

SOLUTION The first derivative is

$$f'(x) = e^{-x^2/2}\left(\frac{-2x}{2}\right) = -xe^{-x^2/2}$$

Since f is differentiable everywhere and since $f'(x) = 0$ only when $x = 0$, there is only one critical point, $x = 0$. Note that $e^{-x^2/2}$ is always positive, so $f'(x) = -xe^{-x^2/2}$ is positive when x is negative, and negative when x is positive. Thus, f is increasing on $(-\infty, 0]$ and decreasing on $[0, \infty)$, so we conclude that $f(0) = 1$ is the global maximum. Note that these facts imply that f cannot have a minimum. As $x \to -\infty$ or $x \to \infty$, $f(x)$ approaches, but never attains, the value 0. A graph of f is shown in Figure 8. ∎

EXAMPLE 7 Find (if any exist) the maximum and minimum values of

$$G(p) = \frac{1}{p(1 - p)}$$

on $(0, 1)$.

SOLUTION

$$G'(p) = \frac{d}{dp}\left[\frac{1}{p(1 - p)}\right] = \frac{2p - 1}{p^2(1 - p)^2}$$

The only critical point is $p = 1/2$. For every value of p in the interval $(0, 1)$ the denominator is positive; thus, the numerator determines the sign. If p is in the interval $(0, 1/2)$, then the numerator is negative; hence, $G'(p) < 0$. Similarly, if p is in the interval $(1/2, 1)$, $G'(p) > 0$. Thus, by the First Derivative Test, $G(1/2) = 4$ is a local minimum. Since there are no end points or singular points to check, $G(1/2)$ is a global minimum. There is no maximum. The graph of $y = G(p)$ is shown in Figure 9. ∎

Concepts Review

1. If f is continuous at c, $f'(x) > 0$ near to c on the left, and $f'(x) < 0$ near to c on the right, then $f(c)$ is a local _____ value for f.

2. If $f'(x) = (x + 2)(x - 1)$, then $f(-2)$ is a local _____ value for f and $f(1)$ is a local _____ value for f.

3. If $f'(c) = 0$ and $f''(c) < 0$, we expect to find a local _____ value for f at c.

4. If $f(x) = x^3$, then $f(0)$ is neither a _____ nor a _____, even though $f''(0) = $ _____.

Problem Set 4.3

In Problems 1–10, identify the critical points. Then use (a) the First Derivative Test and (if possible) (b) the Second Derivative Test to decide which of the critical points give a local maximum and which give a local minimum.

1. $f(x) = x^3 - 6x^2 + 4$

2. $f(x) = x^3 - 12x + \pi$

3. $f(\theta) = \sin 2\theta, 0 < \theta < \dfrac{\pi}{4}$

4. $f(x) = \frac{1}{2}x + \sin x, 0 < x < 2\pi$

5. $\Psi(\theta) = \sin^2 \theta, -\pi/2 < \theta < \pi/2$

6. $r(z) = z^4 + 4$

7. $f(x) = \dfrac{x}{x^2 + 4}$

8. $g(z) = \dfrac{z^2}{1 + z^2}$

9. $h(y) = \tan^{-1} y^2$

10. $f(x) = \dfrac{\ln(x + 2)}{x + 2}$

In Problems 11–20, find the critical points and use the test of your choice to decide which critical points give a local maximum value and which give a local minimum value. What are these local maximum and minimum values?

11. $f(x) = x^3 - 3x$

12. $g(x) = x^4 + x^2 + 3$

13. $H(x) = x^4 - 2x^3$

14. $f(x) = (x - 2)^5$

15. $g(t) = \pi - (t - 2)^{2/3}$

16. $r(s) = 3s + s^{2/5}$

17. $f(t) = t - \dfrac{1}{t}, t \neq 0$

18. $f(x) = \dfrac{x^2}{\sqrt{x^2 + 4}}$

19. $\Lambda(\theta) = \dfrac{\cos \theta}{1 + \sin \theta}, 0 < \theta < 2\pi$

20. $g(\theta) = |\sin \theta|, 0 < \theta < 2\pi$

In Problems 21–30, find, if possible, the (global) maximum and minimum values of the given function on the indicated interval.

21. $f(x) = \sin^2 2x$ on $[0, 2]$

22. $f(x) = \dfrac{2x}{x^2 + 4}$ on $[0, \infty)$

23. $g(x) = \dfrac{x^2}{x^3 + 32}$ on $[0, \infty)$

24. $h(x) = \dfrac{1}{x^2 + 4}$ on $[0, \infty)$

25. $F(x) = 6\sqrt{x} - 4x$ on $[0, 4]$

26. $F(x) = 6\sqrt{x} - 4x$ on $[0, \infty)$

27. $f(x) = \dfrac{64}{\sin x} + \dfrac{27}{\cos x}$ on $(0, \pi/2)$

28. $g(x) = x^2 + \dfrac{16x^2}{(8 - x)^2}$ on $(8, \infty)$

29. $H(x) = |x^2 - 1|$ on $[-2, 2]$

30. $h(t) = \sin t^2$ on $[0, \pi]$

31. $f(x) = xe^{-x}$ on $[0, \infty)$

32. $g(x) = 2^{x^2}$ on $[-2, 2]$

In Problems 33–38, the first derivative f' is given. Find all values of x that make the function f (a) a local minimum and (b) a local maximum.

33. $f'(x) = x^3(1 - x)^2$

34. $f'(x) = -(x - 1)(x - 2)(x - 3)(x - 4)$

35. $f'(x) = (x - 1)^2(x - 2)^2(x - 3)(x - 4)$

36. $f'(x) = (x - 1)^2(x - 2)^2(x - 3)^2(x - 4)^2$

37. $f'(x) = (x - A)^2(x - B)^2, A \neq B$

38. $f'(x) = x(x - A)(x - B), 0 < A < B$

In Problems 39–44, sketch a graph of a function with the given properties. If it is impossible to graph such a function, then indicate this and justify your answer.

39. f is differentiable, has domain $[0, 6]$, and has two local maxima and two local minima on $(0, 6)$.

40. f is differentiable, has domain $[0, 6]$, and has three local maxima and two local minima on $(0, 6)$.

41. f is continuous, but not necessarily differentiable, has domain $[0, 6]$, and has one local minimum and one local maximum on $(0, 6)$.

42. f is continuous, but not necessarily differentiable, has domain $[0, 6]$, and has one local minimum and no local maximum on $(0, 6)$.

43. f has domain $[0, 6]$, but is not necessarily continuous, and has three local maxima and no local minimum on $(0, 6)$.

44. f has domain $[0, 6]$, but is not necessarily continuous, and has two local maxima and no local minimum on $(0, 6)$.

45. Consider $f(x) = Ax^2 + Bx + C$ with $A > 0$. Show that $f(x) \geq 0$ for all x if and only if $B^2 - 4AC \leq 0$.

46. Consider $f(x) = Ax^3 + Bx^2 + Cx + D$ with $A > 0$. Show that f has one local maximum and one local minimum if and only if $B^2 - 3AC > 0$.

47. What conclusions can you draw about f from the information that $f'(c) = f''(c) = 0$ and $f'''(c) > 0$?

Answers to Concepts Review: **1.** maximum **2.** maximum; minimum **3.** maximum **4.** local maximum; local minimum; 0

4.4
Practical Problems

Based on the examples and the theory developed in the first three sections of this chapter, we suggest the following step-by-step method that can be applied to many practical optimization problems. Do not follow it slavishly; common sense may sometimes suggest an alternative approach or omission of some steps.

Step 1: Draw a picture for the problem and assign appropriate variables to the important quantities.

Step 2: Write a formula for the objective function Q to be maximized or minimized in terms of the variables from step 1.

Step 3: Use the conditions of the problem to eliminate all but one of these variables, and thereby express Q as a function of a single variable.

Step 4: Find the critical points (end points, stationary points, singular points).

Step 5: Either substitute the critical values into the objective function or use the theory from the last section (i.e., the First and Second Derivative Tests) to determine the maximum or minimum.

Throughout, use your intuition to get some idea of what the solution of the problem should be. For many physical problems you can get a "ballpark" estimate of the optimal value before you begin to carry out the details.

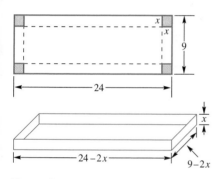

Figure 1

■ **EXAMPLE 1** A rectangular box is to be made from a piece of cardboard 24 inches long and 9 inches wide by cutting out identical squares from the four corners and turning up the sides, as in Figure 1. Find the dimensions of the box of maximum volume. What is this volume?

SOLUTION Let x be the width of the square to be cut out and V the volume of the resulting box. Then

$$V = x(9 - 2x)(24 - 2x) = 216x - 66x^2 + 4x^3$$

Now x cannot be less than 0 or more than 4.5. Thus, our problem is to maximize V on $[0, 4.5]$. The stationary points are found by setting dV/dx equal to 0 and solving the resulting equation:

$$\frac{dV}{dx} = 216 - 132x + 12x^2 = 12(18 - 11x + x^2) = 12(9 - x)(2 - x) = 0$$

This gives $x = 2$ or $x = 9$, but 9 is not in the interval $[0, 4.5]$. We see that there are only three critical points, 0, 2, and 4.5. At the end points 0 and 4.5, $V = 0$; at 2, $V = 200$. We conclude that the box has a maximum volume of 200 cubic inches if $x = 2$, that is, if the box is 20 inches long, 5 inches wide, and 2 inches deep. ■

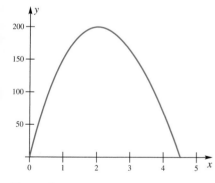

Figure 2

It is often helpful to plot the objective function. Plotting functions can be done easily with a graphing calculator or a CAS. Figure 2 shows a plot of the function $V(x) = 216x - 66x^2 + 4x^3$. When $x = 0$, $V(x)$ is equal to zero. In the context of folding the box, this means that when the width of the cut-out corner is zero there is nothing to fold up, so the volume is zero. Also, when $x = 4.5$, the cardboard gets folded in half, so there is no base to the box; this box will also have zero volume. Thus, $V(0) = 0$ and $V(4.5) = 0$. The greatest volume must be attained for some value of x between 0 and 4.5. The graph suggests that the maximum volume occurs when x is about 2; by using calculus, we can determine that the *exact* value of x that maximizes the volume of the box is $x = 2$.

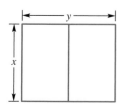

Figure 3

■ **EXAMPLE 2** A farmer has 100 meters of wire fence with which he plans to build two identical adjacent pens, as shown in Figure 3. What are the dimensions of the enclosure that has maximum area?

SOLUTION   Let x be the width and y the length of the total enclosure, both in meters. Because there are 100 meters of fence, $3x + 2y = 100$; that is,

$$y = 50 - \tfrac{3}{2}x$$

The total area A is given by

$$A = xy = 50x - \tfrac{3}{2}x^2$$

Since there must be three sides of length x, we see that $0 \le x \le \frac{100}{3}$. Thus, our problem is to maximize A on $\left[0, \frac{100}{3}\right]$. Now

$$\frac{dA}{dx} = 50 - 3x$$

When we set $50 - 3x$ equal to 0 and solve, we get $x = \frac{50}{3}$ as a stationary point. Thus, there are three critical points: 0, $\frac{50}{3}$, and $\frac{100}{3}$. The two end points 0 and $\frac{100}{3}$ give $A = 0$, while $x = \frac{50}{3}$ yields $A \approx 416.67$. The desired dimensions are $x = \frac{50}{3} \approx 16.67$ meters and $y = 50 - \frac{3}{2}\left(\frac{50}{3}\right) = 25$ meters.

≈ Is this answer sensible? Yes. We should expect to use more of the given fence in the y-direction than the x-direction because the former is fenced only twice, whereas the latter is fenced three times. ∎

EXAMPLE 3   Find the dimensions of the right circular cylinder of greatest volume that can be inscribed in a given right circular cone.

SOLUTION   Let a be the altitude and b the radius of the base of the given cone (both constants). Denote by h, r, and V the altitude, radius, and volume, respectively, of an inscribed cylinder (see Figure 4).

≈ Before proceeding, let's apply some intuition. If the cylinder's radius is close to the radius of the cone's base, then the cylinder's volume would be close to zero. Now, imagine inscribed cylinders with increasing height, but decreasing radius. Initially, the volumes would increase from zero, but then they would decrease to zero as the cylinders' heights get close to the cone's height. Intuitively, the volume should peak for some cylinder. Since the radius is squared in the volume formula, it counts more than the height and we would expect $r > h$ at the maximum.

The volume of the inscribed cylinder is

$$V = \pi r^2 h$$

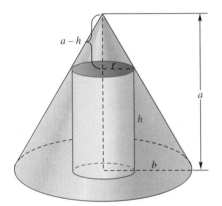

Figure 4

From similar triangles,

$$\frac{a - h}{r} = \frac{a}{b}$$

which gives $h = a - \dfrac{a}{b}r$. When we substitute this expression for h in the formula for V, we obtain

$$V = \pi r^2 \left(a - \frac{a}{b}r\right) = \pi a r^2 - \pi \frac{a}{b} r^3$$

Algebra and Geometry

Whenever possible, try to view a problem from both a geometric and an algebraic point of view. Example 3 is a good example for which this kind of thinking lends insight into the problem.

We wish to maximize V for r in the interval $[0, b]$. Now

$$\frac{dV}{dr} = 2\pi a r - 3\pi \frac{a}{b} r^2 = \pi a r \left(2 - \frac{3}{b}r\right)$$

This yields the stationary points $r = 0$ and $r = 2b/3$, giving us three critical points on $[0, b]$ to consider: 0, $2b/3$, and b. As expected, $r = 0$ and $r = b$ both give a volume of 0. Thus, $r = 2b/3$ has to give the maximum volume. When we substitute this value for r in the equation connecting r and h, we find that $h = a/3$. In other words, the inscribed cylinder has greatest volume when its radius is two-thirds the radius of the cone's base and its height is one-third the altitude of the cone. ∎

EXAMPLE 4 Suppose that a fish swims upstream with velocity v relative to the water and that the current of the river has velocity $-v_c$ (the negative sign indicates that the current's velocity is in the direction opposite that of the fish). The energy expended in traveling a distance d up the river is directly proportional to the time required to travel the distance d and the cube of the velocity. What velocity v minimizes the energy expended in swimming this distance?

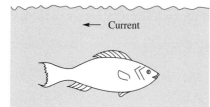

Figure 5

SOLUTION Figure 5 illustrates the situation. Since the fish's velocity up the stream (i.e., relative to the banks of the stream) is $v - v_c$, we have $d = (v - v_c)t$, where t is the required time. Thus $t = d/(v - v_c)$. For a fixed value of v, the energy required for the fish to travel the distance d is therefore

$$E(v) = k\frac{d}{v - v_c}v^3 = kd\frac{v^3}{v - v_c}$$

The domain for the function E is the open interval (v_c, ∞). To find the value of v that minimizes the required energy we set $E'(v) = 0$ and solve for v:

$$E'(v) = kd\frac{(v - v_c)3v^2 - v^3(1)}{(v - v_c)^2} = \frac{kd}{(v - v_c)^2}v^2(2v - 3v_c) = 0$$

The only critical point in the interval (v_0, ∞) is found by solving $2v - 3v_c = 0$, which leads to $v = \frac{3}{2}v_c$. The interval is open so there are no end points to check. The sign of $E'(v)$ depends entirely on the expression $2v - 3v_c$, since all the other expressions are positive. If $v < \frac{3}{2}v_c$, then $2v - 3v_c < 0$ so E is decreasing to the left of $\frac{3}{2}v_c$. If $v > \frac{3}{2}v_c$, then $2v - 3v_c > 0$ so E is increasing to the right of $\frac{3}{2}v_c$. Thus, by the First Derivative Test, $v = \frac{3}{2}v_c$ yields a local minimum. Since this is the only critical point on the interval (v_0, ∞), this must give a global minimum. The velocity that minimizes the expended energy is therefore one and a half times the speed of the current. ∎

EXAMPLE 5 A woman, whose eye-level is 5 feet from the floor, is looking at a 6-foot high painting that is hanging 8 feet from the floor as shown in Figure 6. How far from the wall should she stand to maximize her viewing angle?

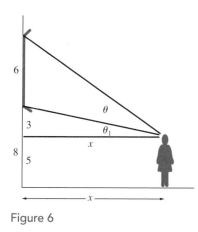

Figure 6

SOLUTION Let x denote the woman's distance from the wall as shown in Figure 6. In Example 6 of Section 3.10 we saw that the angle θ is

$$\theta(x) = \tan^{-1}\frac{9}{x} - \theta_1 = \tan^{-1}\frac{9}{x} - \tan^{-1}\frac{3}{x}$$

Differentiating with respect to x, and setting the result equal to zero gives

$$\theta'(x) = \frac{1}{1 + 81/x^2}\left(-\frac{9}{x^2}\right) - \frac{1}{1 + 9/x^2}\left(-\frac{3}{x^2}\right) = 0$$

$$-\frac{9}{x^2 + 81} + \frac{3}{x^2 + 9} = 0$$

$$\frac{-6(x^2 - 27)}{(x^2 + 81)(x^2 + 9)} = 0$$

The only positive solution to this last equation is $x = 3\sqrt{3}$. To the left of $3\sqrt{3}$, $\theta'(x)$ is positive, so $\theta(x)$ is increasing. To the right of $3\sqrt{3}$, $\theta'(x)$ is negative so $\theta(x)$ is decreasing. Thus $x = 3\sqrt{3} \approx 5.2$ feet maximizes the viewing angle. ∎

EXAMPLE 6 A 6-foot-wide hallway makes a right-angle turn. What is the length of the longest thin rod that can be carried around the corner assuming you cannot tilt the rod?

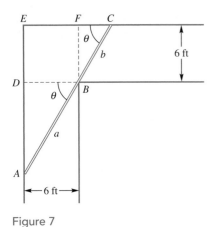

Figure 7

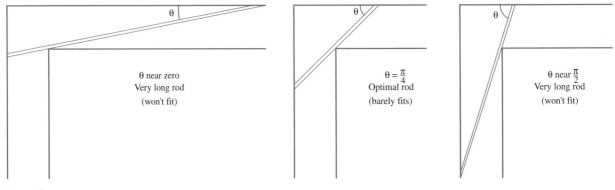

Figure 8

SOLUTION The rod that barely fits around the corner will touch the outside walls as well as the inside corner. As suggested in Figure 7, let a and b represent the lengths of the segments AB and BC, and let θ denote the angles $\angle DBA$ and $\angle FCB$. Consider the two similar right triangles, $\triangle ADB$ and $\triangle BFC$; these have hypotenuses a and b, respectively. Some trigonometry applied to these angles gives

$$a = \frac{6}{\cos \theta} = 6 \sec \theta \quad \text{and} \quad b = \frac{6}{\sin \theta} = 6 \csc \theta$$

Note that the angle θ determines the position of the rod. The total length of the rod in Figure 7 is thus

$$L(\theta) = a + b = 6 \sec \theta + 6 \csc \theta$$

The domain for θ is the open interval $(0, \pi/2)$. The derivative of L is

$$L'(\theta) = 6 \sec \theta \tan \theta - 6 \csc \theta \cot \theta$$

$$= 6\left(\frac{\sin \theta}{\cos^2 \theta} - \frac{\cos \theta}{\sin^2 \theta} \right) = 6 \frac{\sin^3 \theta - \cos^3 \theta}{\sin^2 \theta \cos^2 \theta}$$

Thus $L'(\theta) = 0$ provided $\sin^3 \theta - \cos^3 \theta = 0$. This leads to $\sin \theta = \cos \theta$. The only angle in $(0, \pi/2)$ for which $\sin \theta = \cos \theta$ is the angle $\pi/4$ (see Figure 8). We again apply the First Derivative Test. If $0 < \theta < \pi/4$, then $\sin \theta < \cos \theta$ (see Figure 8 again) so $\sin^3 \theta - \cos^3 \theta < 0$. Thus, $L(\theta)$ is decreasing on $(0, \pi/4)$. If $\pi/4 < \theta < \pi/2$ then $\sin \theta > \cos \theta$ so $\sin^3 \theta - \cos^3 \theta > 0$. Thus, $L(\theta)$ is increasing on $(\pi/4, \pi/2)$. By the First Derivative Test, $\theta = \pi/4$ yields a minimum. The problem, however, asks for the *longest* rod that fits around the corner. As Figure 9 below indicates, we are actually finding the *smallest* rod that satisfies the conditions in Figure 7; in other words, we are finding the smallest rod that doesn't fit around the corner. Therefore, the longest rod that does fit around the corner is $L(\pi/4) = 6 \sec \pi/4 + 6 \csc \pi/4 = 12\sqrt{2} \approx 16.97$ feet. ∎

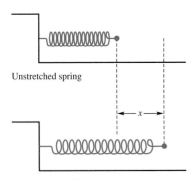

Unstretched spring

Spring stretched by amount x

Figure 10

Figure 9

θ near zero
Very long rod
(won't fit)

$\theta = \frac{\pi}{4}$
Optimal rod
(barely fits)

θ near $\frac{\pi}{2}$
Very long rod
(won't fit)

Least Squares (Optional) There are a number of physical, economic, and social phenomena in which one variable is proportional to another. For example, Newton's Second Law says that the force F on an object of mass m is proportional to its acceleration a ($F = ma$). Hooke's Law says that the force exerted by a spring is proportional to the distance it is stretched ($F = kx$). (Hooke's Law is often given as $F = -kx$, with the negative sign indicating that the force is in the direction opposite the stretch. For now, we will ignore the sign of the force.) Manufacturing costs are proportional to the number of units produced. The number of traffic accidents is proportional to the volume of traffic. These are *models*, and in an experiment we will rarely find that the observed data fit the model exactly.

Suppose that we observe the force exerted by a spring when it is stretched by x centimeters (Figure 10). For example, when we stretch the spring by 0.5 centimeter (0.005 meter), we observe a force of 8 newtons, when we stretch the spring

Distance Stretched, x (meters)	Force y Exerted by Spring (newtons)
0.005	8
0.010	17
0.015	22
0.020	32
0.025	36

Figure 11

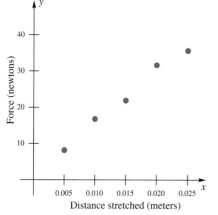

Figure 12

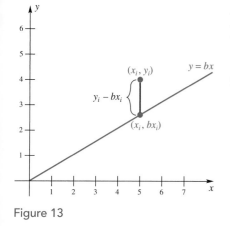

Figure 13

by 1.0 centimeter, we observe a force of 17 newtons, and so on. Figure 11 shows additional observations, and Figure 12 shows a plot of the ordered pairs (x_i, y_i), where x_i is the distance stretched and y_i is the force exerted on the spring. A plot of ordered pairs like this is called a **scatter plot.**

Let's generalize the problem to one in which we are given n points $(x_1, y_1), (x_2, y_2), \ldots, (x_n, y_n)$. Our goal is to find a line through the origin that *best fits* these points. Before proceeding, we must introduce sigma (Σ) notation.

The symbol $\displaystyle\sum_{i=1}^{n} a_i$ means the sum of the numbers $a_1, a_2, \ldots, a_n$. For example,

$$\sum_{i=1}^{3} i^2 = 1^2 + 2^2 + 3^2 = 14 \quad \text{and} \quad \sum_{i=1}^{n} x_i y_i = x_1 y_1 + x_2 y_2 + \cdots + x_n y_n$$

In the second case, we multiply x_i and y_i first and then sum.

To find the line that best fits these n points, we must be specific about how we measure the fit. Our *best-fit* line through the origin is defined to be the one that minimizes the sum of the squared vertical deviations between (x_i, y_i) and the line $y = bx$. If (x_i, y_i) is a point in the data set, then (x_i, bx_i) is the point on the line $y = bx$ that is directly above or below (x_i, y_i). The vertical deviation between (x_i, y_i) and (x_i, bx_i) is therefore $y_i - bx_i$. (See Figure 13.) The squared deviation is thus $(y_i - bx_i)^2$. The problem is to find the value of b that minimizes the sum of these squared deviations. If we define

$$S = \sum_{i=1}^{n} (y_i - bx_i)^2$$

then we must find the value of b that *minimizes S.* This is a minimization problem like the ones encountered before. Keep in mind, however, that the ordered pairs (x_i, y_i), $i = 1, 2, \ldots, n$ are *fixed;* the variable in this problem is b.

We proceed as before by finding dS/db, setting the result equal to 0, and solving for b. Since the derivative is a linear operator, we have

$$\frac{dS}{db} = \frac{d}{db}\sum_{i=1}^{n} (y_i - bx_i)^2 = \sum_{i=1}^{n} \frac{d}{db}(y_i - bx_i)^2$$

$$= \sum_{i=1}^{n} 2(y_i - bx_i)\left(\frac{d}{db}(y_i - bx_i)\right)$$

$$= -2\sum_{i=1}^{n} x_i(y_i - bx_i)$$

Setting this result equal to zero and solving yields

$$0 = -2\sum_{i=1}^{n} x_i(y_i - bx_i)$$

$$0 = \sum_{i=1}^{n} x_i y_i - b\sum_{i=1}^{n} x_i^2$$

$$b = \frac{\displaystyle\sum_{i=1}^{n} x_i y_i}{\displaystyle\sum_{i=1}^{n} x_i^2}$$

To see that this yields a minimum value for S, we note that

$$\frac{d^2 S}{db^2} = 2\sum_{i=1}^{n} x_i^2$$

which is always positive. There are no end points to check. Thus, by the Second Derivative Test, we conclude that the line $y = bx$, with $b = \displaystyle\sum_{i=1}^{n} x_i y_i \bigg/ \sum_{i=1}^{n} x_i^2$, is the

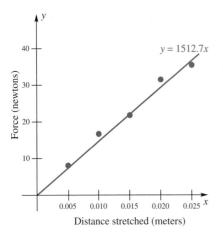

Figure 14

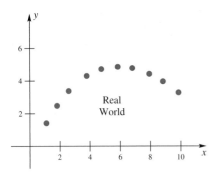

Figure 15

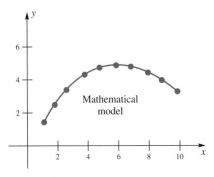

Figure 16

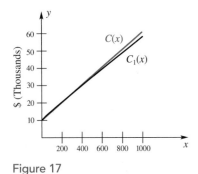

Figure 17

best-fit line, in the sense of minimizing S. The line $y = bx$ is called the **least-squares line through the origin.**

■ **EXAMPLE 7** Find the least-squares line through the origin for the spring data in Figure 11.

SOLUTION

$$b = \frac{0.005 \cdot 8 + 0.010 \cdot 17 + 0.015 \cdot 22 + 0.020 \cdot 32 + 0.025 \cdot 36}{0.005^2 + 0.010^2 + 0.015^2 + 0.020^2 + 0.025^2} \approx 1512.7$$

The least-squares line through the origin is therefore $y = 1512.7x$ and is shown in Figure 14. The estimate of the spring constant is therefore $k = 1512.7$. ■

For most line-fitting problems, it is unreasonable to assume that the line passes through the origin. A more reasonable assumption is that y is related to x by $y = a + bx$. In this case, however, the sum of squares is a function of both a and b so we are faced with the problem of minimizing a function of two variables, a problem we address in Chapter 12.

Economic Applications (Optional) Consider a typical company, the ABC Company. For simplicity, assume that ABC produces and markets a single product; it might be television sets, car batteries, or bars of soap. If it sells x units of the product in a fixed period of time (e.g., a year), it will be able to charge a **price,** $p(x)$, for each unit. In other words, $p(x)$ is the price required to attract a demand for x units. The **total revenue** that ABC can expect is given by $R(x) = xp(x)$, the number of units times the price per unit.

To produce and market x units, ABC will have a total cost, $C(x)$. This is normally the sum of a **fixed cost** (office utilities, real estate taxes, and so on) plus a **variable cost,** which depends directly on the number of units produced.

The key concept for a company is the **total profit,** $P(x)$. It is just the difference between revenue and cost; that is,

$$P(x) = R(x) - C(x) = xp(x) - C(x)$$

Generally, a company seeks to maximize its total profit.

There is a feature that tends to distinguish problems in economics from those in the physical sciences. In most cases, ABC's product will be in discrete units (you can't make or sell 8.23 television sets or π car batteries). Thus, the functions $R(x)$, $C(x)$, and $P(x)$ are usually defined only for $x = 0, 1, 2, \ldots$ and, consequently, their graphs consist of discrete points (Figure 15). In order to make the tools of calculus available, we connect these points with a smooth curve (Figure 16), thereby pretending that R, C, and P are nice differentiable functions. This illustrates an aspect of *mathematical modeling* that is almost always necessary, especially in economics. To model a real-world problem, we must make some simplifying assumptions. This means that the answers we get are only approximations of the answers that we seek—one of the reasons economics is a less than perfect science. A well-known statistician once said: No model is accurate, but many models are useful.

A related problem for an economist is how to obtain formulas for the functions $C(x)$ and $p(x)$. In a simple case, $C(x)$ might have the form

$$C(x) = 10,000 + 50x$$

If so, $10,000 is the **fixed cost** and $50x is the **variable cost,** based on a $50 direct cost for each unit produced. Perhaps a more typical situation is

$$C_1(x) = 10,000 + 45x + 100\sqrt{x}$$

Both cost functions are shown in Figure 17.

The cost function $C(x)$ indicates that the cost of making an additional unit is the same regardless of how many units have been made. On the other hand, the cost function $C_1(x)$ indicates that the cost of making additional units increases but

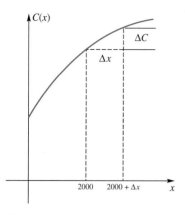

Figure 18

at a decreasing rate. Thus, $C_1(x)$ allows for what economists call economies of scale.

Selecting appropriate functions to model cost and price is a nontrivial task. Occasionally, they can be inferred from basic assumptions. In other cases, a careful study of the history of the firm will suggest reasonable choices. Sometimes, we must simply make intelligent guesses.

Use of the Word *Marginal* Suppose that ABC knows its cost function $C(x)$ and that it has tentatively planned to produce 2000 units this year. We would like to determine the additional cost per unit if ABC increased production slightly. Would it, for example, be less than the additional revenue per unit? If so, it would make good economic sense to increase production.

If the cost function is the one shown in Figure 18, we are asking for the value of $\Delta C / \Delta x$ when $\Delta x = 1$. But we expect that this will be very close to the value of

$$\lim_{\Delta x \to 0} \frac{\Delta C}{\Delta x}$$

when $x = 2000$. This limit is called the **marginal cost.** We mathematicians recognize it as dC/dx, the derivative of C with respect to x. In a similar vein, we define **marginal price** as dp/dx, **marginal revenue** as dR/dx, and **marginal profit** as dP/dx. We now illustrate how to solve a wide variety of economic problems.

EXAMPLE 8 Suppose that $C(x) = 8300 + 3.25x + 40\sqrt[3]{x}$ dollars. Find the average cost per unit and the marginal cost, and then evaluate them when $x = 1000$.

SOLUTION

$$\text{Average cost:} \quad \frac{C(x)}{x} = \frac{8300 + 3.25x + 40x^{1/3}}{x}$$

$$\text{Marginal cost:} \quad \frac{dC}{dx} = 3.25 + \frac{40}{3}x^{-2/3}$$

At $x = 1000$, these have the values 11.95 and 3.38, respectively. This means that it costs, on the average, $11.95 per unit to produce the first 1000 units; to produce one additional unit beyond 1000 costs only about $3.38. ∎

EXAMPLE 9 In manufacturing and selling x units of a certain commodity, the price function p and the cost function C (in dollars) are given by

$$p(x) = 5.00 - 0.002x$$

$$C(x) = 3.00 + 1.10x$$

Find expressions for the marginal revenue, marginal cost, and marginal profit. Determine the production level that will produce the maximum total profit.

SOLUTION

$$R(x) = xp(x) = 5.00x - 0.002x^2$$

$$P(x) = R(x) - C(x) = -3.00 + 3.90x - 0.002x^2$$

Thus, we have the following derivatives:

$$\text{Marginal revenue:} \quad \frac{dR}{dx} = 5 - 0.004x$$

$$\text{Marginal cost:} \quad \frac{dC}{dx} = 1.1$$

$$\text{Marginal profit:} \quad \frac{dP}{dx} = \frac{dR}{dx} - \frac{dC}{dx} = 3.9 - 0.004x$$

To maximize profit, we set $dP/dx = 0$ and solve. This gives $x = 975$ as the only critical point to consider. It does provide a maximum, as may be checked by the First Derivative Test. The maximum profit is $P(975) = \$1898.25$. ■

Note that at $x = 975$ both the marginal revenue and the marginal cost are $\$1.10$. In general, a company should expect to be at a maximum profit level when the cost of producing an additional unit equals the revenue from that unit.

Concepts Review

1. If a rectangle of area 100 has length x and width y, then the allowable values for x are _____.

2. The perimeter of the rectangle in Question 1, expressed in terms of x (only), is _____.

3. The least squares line through the origin minimizes

$$S = \sum_{i=1}^{n} (\underline{\hspace{1cm}})^2$$

4. In economics, $\dfrac{dR}{dx}$ is called _____ and $\dfrac{dC}{dx}$ is called _____.

Problem Set 4.4

1. Find two numbers whose product is -16 and the sum of whose squares is a minimum.

2. For what number does the principal square root exceed eight times the number by the largest amount?

3. For what number does the principal fourth root exceed twice the number by the largest amount?

4. Find two numbers whose product is -12 and the sum of whose squares is a minimum.

5. Find the points on the parabola $y = x^2$ that are closest to the point $(0, 5)$. *Hint:* Minimize the square of the distance between (x, y) and $(0, 5)$.

6. Find the points on the parabola $x = 2y^2$ that are closest to the point $(10, 0)$. *Hint:* Minimize the square of the distance between (x, y) and $(10, 0)$.

7. What number exceeds its square by the maximum amount? Begin by convincing yourself that this number is on the interval $[0, 1]$.

8. Show that for a rectangle of given perimeter K the one with maximum area is a square.

9. Find the volume of the largest open box that can be made from a piece of cardboard 24 inches square by cutting equal squares from the corners and turning up the sides (see Example 1).

≈ **10.** A farmer has 80 feet of fence with which he plans to enclose a rectangular pen along one side of his 100-foot barn, as shown in Figure 19 (the side along the barn needs no fence). What are the dimensions of the pen that has maximum area?

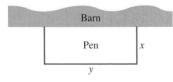

Figure 19

≈ **11.** The farmer of Problem 10 decides to make three identical pens with his 80 feet of fence, as shown in Figure 20. What

dimensions for the total enclosure make the area of the pens as large as possible?

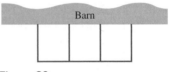

Figure 20

12. Suppose that the farmer of Problem 10 has 180 feet of fence and wants the pen to adjoin to the whole side of the 100-foot barn, as shown in Figure 21. What should the dimensions be for maximum area? Note that $0 \le x \le 40$ in this case.

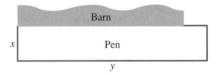

Figure 21

13. A farmer wishes to fence off two identical adjoining rectangular pens, each with 900 square feet of area, as shown in Figure 22. What are x and y so that the least amount of fence is required?

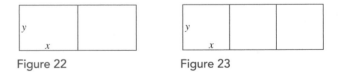

Figure 22　　　　　　　　Figure 23

14. A farmer wishes to fence off three identical adjoining rectangular pens (see Figure 23), each with 300 square feet of area. What should the width and length of each pen be so that the least amount of fence is required?

15. Suppose that the outer boundary of the pens in Problem 14 requires heavy fence that costs $\$3$ per foot, but that the two internal partitions require fence costing only $2 per foot. What dimensions x and y will produce the least expensive cost for the pens?

16. Solve Problem 14 assuming that the area of each pen is 900 square feet. Study the solution to this problem and to Problem 14 and make a conjecture about the ratio of x/y in all problems of this type. Try to prove your conjecture.

17. Find the points P and Q on the curve $y = x^2/4$, $0 \le x \le 2\sqrt{3}$, that are closest to and farthest from the point $(0, 4)$. *Hint:* The algebra is simpler if you consider the square of the required distance rather than the distance itself.

18. A right circular cone is to be inscribed in another right circular cone of given volume, with the same axis and with the vertex of the inner cone touching the base of the outer cone. What must be the ratio of their altitudes for the inscribed cone to have maximum volume?

⧉ 19. A small island is 2 miles from the nearest point P on the straight shoreline of a large lake. If a woman on the island can row a boat 3 miles per hour and can walk 4 miles per hour, where should the boat be landed in order to arrive at a town 10 miles down the shore from P in the least time?

⧉ 20. In Problem 19, suppose that the woman will be picked up by a car that will average 50 miles per hour when she gets to the shore. Then where should she land?

⧉ 21. In Problem 19, suppose that the woman uses a motorboat that goes 20 miles per hour. Then where should she land?

22. A powerhouse is located on one bank of a straight river that is w feet wide. A factory is situated on the opposite bank of the river, L feet downstream from the point A directly opposite the powerhouse. What is the most economical path for a cable connecting the powerhouse to the factory if it costs a dollars per foot to lay the cable under water and b dollars per foot on land $(a > b)$?

23. At 7:00 A.M. one ship was 60 miles due east from a second ship. If the first ship sailed west at 20 miles per hour and the second ship sailed southeast at 30 miles per hour, when were they closest together?

24. Find the equation of the line that is tangent to the ellipse $b^2x^2 + a^2y^2 = a^2b^2$ in the first quadrant and forms with the coordinate axes the triangle with smallest possible area (a and b are positive constants).

25. Find the greatest volume that a right circular cylinder can have if it is inscribed in a sphere of radius r.

26. Show that the rectangle with maximum perimeter that can be inscribed in a circle is a square.

27. What are the dimensions of the right circular cylinder with greatest curved surface area that can be inscribed in a sphere of radius r?

28. The illumination at a point is inversely proportional to the square of the distance of the point from the light source and directly proportional to the intensity of the light source. If two light sources are s feet apart and their intensities are I_1 and I_2, respectively, at what point between them will the sum of their illuminations be a minimum?

29. A wire of length 100 centimeters is cut into two pieces; one is bent to form a square, and the other is bent to form an equilateral triangle. Where should the cut be made if (a) the sum of the two areas is to be a minimum; (b) a maximum? (Allow the possibility of no cut.)

30. A closed box in the form of a rectangular parallelepiped with a square base is to have a given volume. If the material used in the bottom costs 20% more per square inch than the material in the sides, and the material in the top costs 50% more per square inch than that of the sides, find the most economical proportions for the box.

31. An observatory is to be in the form of a right circular cylinder surmounted by a hemispherical dome. If the hemispherical dome costs twice as much per square foot as the cylindrical wall, what are the most economical proportions for a given volume?

32. A weight connected to a spring moves along the x-axis so that its x-coordinate at time t is

$$x = \sin 2t + \sqrt{3} \cos 2t$$

What is the farthest that the weight gets from the origin?

33. A flower bed will be in the shape of a sector of a circle (a pie-shaped region) of radius r and vertex angle θ. Find r and θ if its area is a constant A and the perimeter is a minimum.

34. A fence h feet high runs parallel to a tall building and w feet from it (Figure 24). Find the length of the shortest ladder that will reach from the ground across the top of the fence to the wall of the building.

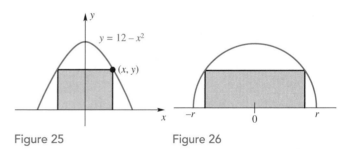

Figure 24

35. A rectangle has two corners on the x-axis and the other two on the parabola $y = 12 - x^2$, with $y \ge 0$ (Figure 25). What are the dimensions of the rectangle of this type with maximum area?

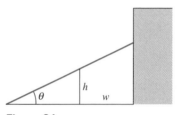

Figure 25   Figure 26

36. A rectangle is to be inscribed in a semicircle of radius r, as shown in Figure 26. What are the dimensions of the rectangle if its area is to be maximized?

37. Of all right circular cylinders with a given surface area, find the one with the maximum volume. *Note:* The ends of the cylinders are closed.

38. Find the dimensions of the rectangle of greatest area that can be inscribed in the ellipse $x^2/a^2 + y^2/b^2 = 1$.

39. Of all rectangles with a given diagonal, find the one with the maximum area.

40. A humidifier uses a rotating disk of radius r, which is partially submerged in water. The most evaporation occurs when the exposed wetted region (shown as the upper shaded region in Figure 27) is maximized. Show that this happens when h (the distance from the center to the water) is equal to $r/\sqrt{1 + \pi^2}$.

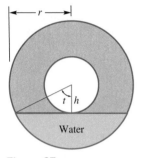

Figure 27

41. A metal rain gutter is to have 3-inch sides and a 3-inch horizontal bottom, the sides making an equal angle θ with the bottom (Figure 28). What should θ be in order to maximize the carrying capacity of the gutter? *Note:* $0 \leq \theta \leq \pi/2$.

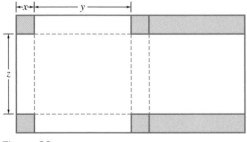

Figure 28   Figure 29

42. A huge conical tank is to be made from a circular piece of sheet metal of radius 10 meters by cutting out a sector with vertex angle θ and then welding together the straight edges of the remaining piece (Figure 29). Find θ so that the resulting cone has the largest possible volume.

43. A covered box is to be made from a rectangular sheet of cardboard measuring 5 feet by 8 feet. This is done by cutting out the shaded regions of Figure 30 and then folding on the dotted lines. What are the dimensions x, y, and z that maximize the volume?

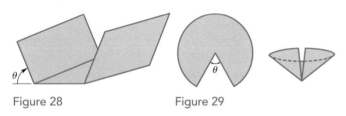

Figure 30

44. I have enough pure silver to coat 1 square meter of surface area. I plan to coat a sphere and a cube. What dimensions should they be if the total volume of the silvered solids is to be a maximum? A minimum? (Allow the possibility of all the silver going onto one solid.)

45. One corner of a long narrow strip of paper is folded over so that it just touches the opposite side, as shown in Figure 31. With parts labeled as indicated, determine x in order to

(a) maximize the area of triangle A;

(b) minimize the area of triangle B;

(c) minimize the length z.

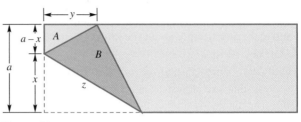

Figure 31

46. Determine θ so that the area of the symmetric cross shown in Figure 32 is maximized. Then find this maximum area.

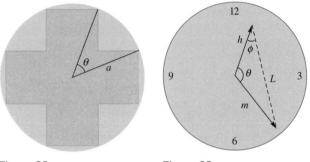

Figure 32   Figure 33

CAS **47.** A clock has hour and minute hands of lengths h and m, respectively, with $h \leq m$. We wish to study this clock at times between 12:00 and 12:30. Let θ, ϕ, and L be as in Figure 33 and note that θ increases at a constant rate. By the Law of Cosines, $L = L(\theta) = (h^2 + m^2 - 2hm \cos \theta)^{1/2}$, and so

$$L'(\theta) = hm(h^2 + m^2 - 2hm \cos \theta)^{-1/2} \sin \theta$$

(a) For $h = 3$ and $m = 5$, determine L', L, and ϕ at the instant when L' is largest.

(b) Rework part (a) when $h = 5$ and $m = 13$.

(c) Based on parts (a) and (b), make conjectures about the values of L', L, and ϕ at the instant when the tips of the hands are separating most rapidly.

(d) Try to prove your conjectures.

≈ C **48.** An object thrown from the edge of a 100-foot cliff follows the path given by $y = -\dfrac{x^2}{10} + x + 100$. An observer stands 2 feet from the bottom of the cliff.

(a) Find the position of the object when it is closest to the observer.

(b) Find the position of the object when it is farthest from the observer.

≈ CAS **49.** The earth's position in the solar system at time t can be described approximately by $P(93 \cos(2\pi t), 93 \sin(2\pi t))$, where the sun is at the origin and distances are measured in millions of miles. Suppose that an asteroid has position $Q(60 \cos[2\pi(1.51t - 1)], 120 \sin[2\pi(1.51t - 1)])$. When, over the time period $[0, 20]$ (i.e., over the next 20 years), does the asteroid come closest to the earth? How close does it come?

50. An advertising flyer is to contain 50 square inches of printed matter, with 2-inch margins at the top and bottom and 1-inch margins on each side. What dimensions for the flyer would use the least paper?

≈ **51.** One end of a 27-foot ladder rests on the ground and the other end rests on the top of an 8-foot wall. As the bottom end is pushed along the ground toward the wall, the top end extends beyond the wall. Find the maximum horizontal overhang of the top end.

C **52.** Brass is produced in long rolls of a thin sheet. To monitor the quality, inspectors select at random a piece of the sheet, measure its area, and count the number of surface imperfections on that piece. The area varies from piece to piece. The following table gives data on the area (in square feet) of the selected piece and the number of surface imperfections found on that piece.

Piece	Area in Square Feet	Number of Surface Imperfections
1	1.0	3
2	4.0	12
3	3.6	9
4	1.5	5
5	3.0	8

(a) Make a scatter plot with area on the horizontal axis and number of surface imperfections on the vertical axis.

(b) Does it look like a line through the origin would be a good model for these data? Explain.

(c) Find the equation of the least-squares line through the origin.

(d) Use the result of part (c) to predict how many surface imperfections there would be on a sheet with area 2.0 square feet.

C **53.** Suppose that every customer order taken by the XYZ Company requires exacty 5 hours of labor for handling the paperwork; this length of time is *fixed* and does not vary from lot to lot. The total number of hours y required to manufacture and sell a lot of size x would then be

$$y = (\text{number of hours to produce a lot of size } x) + 5$$

Some data on XYZ's bookcases are given in the following table.

Order	Lot Size x	Total Labor Hours y
1	11	38
2	16	52
3	8	29
4	7	25
5	10	38

(a) From the description of the problem, the least-squares line should have 5 as its y-intercept. Find a formula for the value of the slope b that minimizes the sum of squares

$$S = \sum_{i=1}^{n} [y_i - (5 + bx_i)]^2$$

(b) Use this formula to estimate the slope b.

(c) Use your least-squares line to predict the total number of labor hours to produce a lot consisting of 15 bookcases.

54. The fixed monthly cost of operating a plant that makes Zbars is \$7000, while the cost of manufacturing each unit is \$100. Write an expression for $C(x)$, the total cost of making x Zbars in a month.

55. The manufacturer of Zbars estimates that 100 units per month can be sold if the unit price is \$250 and that sales will increase by 10 units for each \$5 decrease in price. Write an expression for the price $p(n)$ and the revenue $R(n)$ if n units are sold in one month, $n \geq 100$

56. Use the information in Problems 54 and 55 to write an expression for the total monthly profit $P(n)$, $n \geq 100$.

57. Sketch the graph of $P(n)$ of Problem 56, and from it estimate the value of n that maximizes P. Find this n exactly by the methods of calculus.

C **58.** The total cost of producing and selling x units of Xbars per month is $C(x) = 100 + 3.002x - 0.0001x^2$. If the production level is 1600 units per month, find the average cost, $C(x)/x$, of each unit and the marginal cost.

59. The total cost of producing and selling n units of a certain commodity per week is $C(n) = 1000 + n^2/1200$. Find the average cost, $C(n)/n$, of each unit and the marginal cost at a production level of 800 units per week.

60. The total cost of producing and selling $100x$ units of a particular commodity per week is

$$C(x) = 1000 + 33x - 9x^2 + x^3$$

Find (a) the level of production at which the marginal cost is a minimum, and (b) the minimum marginal cost.

61. A price function, p, is defined by

$$p(x) = 20 + 4x - \frac{x^2}{3}$$

where $x \geq 0$ is the number of units.

(a) Find the total revenue function and the marginal revenue function.

(b) On what interval is the total revenue increasing?

(c) For what number x is the marginal revenue a maximum?

C **62.** For the price function defined by

$$p(x) = (182 - x/36)^{1/2}$$

find the number of units x_1 that makes the total revenue a maximum and state the maximum possible revenue. What is the marginal revenue when the optimum number of units, x_1, is sold?

63. For the price function given by

$$p(x) = 800/(x + 3) - 3$$

find the number of units x_1 that makes the total revenue a maximum and state the maximum possible revenue. What is the marginal revenue when the optimum number of units, x_1, is sold?

64. A riverboat company offers a fraternal organization a Fourth of July excursion with the understanding that there will be at least 400 passengers. The price of each ticket will be \$12.00, and the company agrees to discount the price by \$0.20 for each 10 passengers in excess of 400. Write an expression for the price function $p(x)$ and find the number x_1 of passengers that makes the total revenue a maximum.

65. The XYZ Company manufactures wicker chairs. With its present machines, it has a maximum yearly output of 500 units. If it makes x chairs, it can set a price of $p(x) = 200 - 0.15x$ dollars each and will have a total yearly cost of $C(x) = 5000 + 6x - 0.002x^2$ dollars. The company has the opportunity to buy a new machine for $4000 with which the company can make up to an additional 250 chairs per year. The cost function for values of x between 500 and 750 is thus $C(x) = 9000 + 6x - 0.002x^2$. Basing your analysis on the profit for the next year, answer the following questions.

(a) Should the company purchase the additional machine?

(b) What should be the level of production?

66. Repeat Problem 65, assuming that the additional machine costs $3000.

C **67.** The ZEE Company makes zingos, which it markets at a price of $p(x) = 10 - 0.001x$ dollars, where x is the number produced each month. Its total monthly cost is $C(x) = 200 + 4x - 0.01x^2$. At peak production, it can make 300 units. What is its maximum monthly profit and what level of production gives this profit?

C **68.** If the company of Problem 67 expands its facilities so that it can produce up to 450 units each month, its monthly cost function takes the form $C(x) = 800 + 3x - 0.01x^2$ for $300 < x \leq 450$. Find the production level that maximizes monthly profit and evaluate this profit. Sketch the graph of the monthly profit function $P(x)$ on $0 \leq x \leq 450$.

EXPL **69.** The arithmetic mean of the numbers a and b is $(a + b)/2$, and the geometric mean of two positive numbers a and b is $\sqrt{ab}$. Suppose that $a > 0$ and $b > 0$.

(a) Show that $\sqrt{ab} \leq (a + b)/2$ holds by squaring both sides and simplifying.

(b) Use calculus to show that $\sqrt{ab} \leq (a + b)/2$. *Hint:* Consider a to be fixed. Square both sides of the inequality and divide through by b. Define the function $F(b) = (a + b)^2/4b$. Show that F has its minimum at a.

(c) The geometric mean of three positive numbers $a, b,$ and c is $(abc)^{1/3}$. Show that the analogous inequality holds:

$$(abc)^{1/3} \leq \frac{a + b + c}{3}$$

Hint: Consider a and c to be fixed and define $F(b) = (a + b + c)^3/27b$. Show that F has a minimum at $b = (a + c)/2$ and that this minimum is $[(a + c)/2]^2$. Then use the result from (b).

EXPL **70.** Show that of all three-dimensional boxes with a given surface area, the cube has the greatest volume. *Hint:* The surface area is $S = 2(lw + lh + hw)$ and the volume is $V = lwh$. Let $a = lw, b = lh,$ and $c = hw$. Use the previous problem to show that $(V^2)^{1/3} \leq S/6$. When does equality hold?

Answers to Concepts Review: **1.** $0 < x < \infty$
2. $2x + 200/x$ **3.** $y_i - bx_i$ **4.** marginal revenue; marginal cost

---

4.5
Graphing Functions Using Calculus

Our treatment of graphing in Section 1.4 was elementary. We proposed plotting enough points so that the essential features of the graph were clear. We mentioned that symmetries of the graph could reduce the effort involved. We suggested that one should be alert to possible asymptotes. But if the equation to be graphed is complicated or if we want a very accurate graph, the techniques of that section are inadequate.

Calculus provides a powerful tool for analyzing the fine structure of a graph, especially in identifying those points where the character of the graph changes. We can locate local maximum points, local minimum points, and inflection points; we can determine precisely where the graph is increasing or where it is concave up. Inclusion of all these ideas in our graphing procedure is the program for this section.

Polynomial Functions A polynomial function of degree 1 or 2 is easy to graph by hand; one of degree 50 could be next to impossible. If the degree is of modest size, such as 3 to 6, we can use the tools of calculus to great advantage.

■ **EXAMPLE 1** Sketch the graph of $f(x) = \dfrac{3x^5 - 20x^3}{32}$.

SOLUTION Since $f(-x) = -f(x), f$ is an odd function, and therefore its graph is symmetric with respect to the origin. Setting $f(x) = 0$, we find the x-intercepts to be 0 and $\pm\sqrt{20/3} \approx \pm 2.6$. We can go this far without calculus.

When we differentiate f, we obtain

$$f'(x) = \frac{15x^4 - 60x^2}{32} = \frac{15x^2(x - 2)(x + 2)}{32}$$

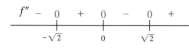

Figure 1

Figure 2

Thus, the critical points are $-2, 0$, and 2; we quickly discover (Figure 1) that $f'(x) > 0$ on $(-\infty, -2)$ and $(2, \infty)$ and that $f'(x) < 0$ on $(-2, 0)$ and $(0, 2)$. These facts tell us where f is increasing and where it is decreasing; they also confirm that $f(-2) = 2$ is a local maximum value and that $f(2) = -2$ is a local minimum value.

Differentiating again, we get

$$f''(x) = \frac{60x^3 - 120x}{32} = \frac{15x\left(x - \sqrt{2}\right)\left(x + \sqrt{2}\right)}{8}$$

By studying the sign of $f''(x)$ (Figure 2), we deduce that f is concave up on $\left(-\sqrt{2}, 0\right)$ and $\left(\sqrt{2}, \infty\right)$ and concave down on $\left(-\infty, -\sqrt{2}\right)$ and $\left(0, \sqrt{2}\right)$. Thus, there are three points of inflection: $\left(-\sqrt{2}, 7\sqrt{2}/8\right) \approx (-1.4, 1.2)$, $(0, 0)$, and $\left(\sqrt{2}, -7\sqrt{2}/8\right) \approx (1.4, -1.2)$.

Much of this information is collected at the top of Figure 3, which we use to sketch the graph directly below it.

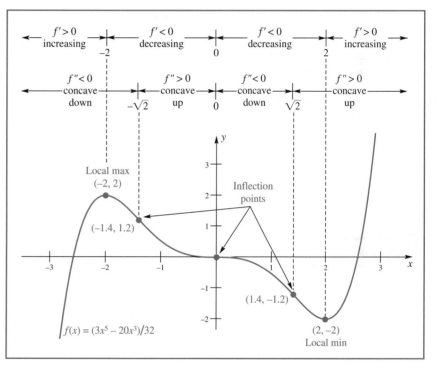

Figure 3

Rational Functions A rational function, being the quotient of two polynomial functions, is considerably more complicated to graph than a polynomial. In particular, we can expect dramatic behavior near where the denominator would be zero.

EXAMPLE 2 Sketch the graph of $f(x) = \dfrac{x^2 - 2x + 4}{x - 2}$.

SOLUTION This function is neither even nor odd, so we do not have any of the usual symmetries. There are no x-intercepts, since the solutions to $x^2 - 2x + 4 = 0$ are not real numbers. The y-intercept is -2. We anticipate a vertical asymptote at $x = 2$. In fact,

$$\lim_{x \to 2^-} \frac{x^2 - 2x + 4}{x - 2} = -\infty \qquad \text{and} \qquad \lim_{x \to 2^+} \frac{x^2 - 2x + 4}{x - 2} = \infty$$

Differentiation twice gives

$$f'(x) = \frac{x(x-4)}{(x-2)^2} \quad \text{and} \quad f''(x) = \frac{8}{(x-2)^3}$$

The stationary points are therefore $x = 0$ and $x = 4$.

Thus, $f'(x) > 0$ on $(-\infty, 0) \cup (4, \infty)$ and $f'(x) < 0$ on $(0, 2) \cup (2, 4)$. (Remember, $f'(x)$ does not exist when $x = 2$.) Also, $f''(x) > 0$ on $(2, \infty)$ and $f''(x) < 0$ on $(-\infty, 2)$. Since $f''(x)$ is never 0, there are no inflection points. On the other hand, $f(0) = -2$ and $f(4) = 6$ give local maximum and minimum values, respectively.

It is a good idea to check on the behavior of $f(x)$ for large $|x|$. Since

$$f(x) = \frac{x^2 - 2x + 4}{x - 2} = x + \frac{4}{x - 2}$$

the graph of $y = f(x)$ gets closer and closer to the line $y = x$ as $|x|$ gets larger and larger. We call the line $y = x$ an **oblique asymptote** for the graph of f (see Problem 49 of Section 2.4).

With all this information, we are able to sketch a rather accurate graph (Figure 4).

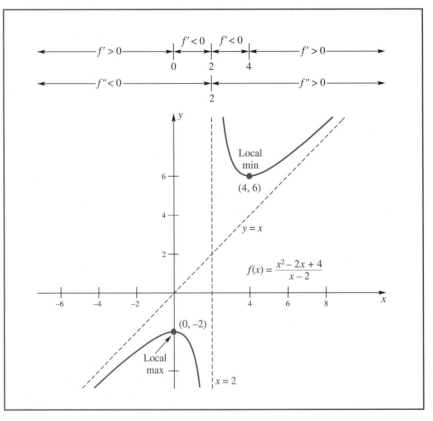

Figure 4

Functions Involving Roots

Functions Involving Roots There is an endless variety of functions involving roots. Here is one example.

EXAMPLE 3 Analyze the function

$$F(x) = \frac{\sqrt{x}(x - 5)^2}{4}$$

and sketch its graph.

SOLUTION The domain of F is $[0, \infty)$ and the range is $[0, \infty)$, so the graph of F is confined to the first quadrant and the positive coordinate axes. The x-intercepts are 0 and 5; the y-intercept is 0. From

$$F'(x) = \frac{5(x - 1)(x - 5)}{8\sqrt{x}}, \qquad x > 0$$

we find the stationary points 1 and 5. Since $F'(x) > 0$ on $(0, 1)$ and $(5, \infty)$, while $F'(x) < 0$ on $(1, 5)$, we conclude that $F(1) = 4$ is a local maximum value and $F(5) = 0$ is a local minimum value.

So far, it has been clear sailing. But on calculating the second derivative, we obtain

$$F''(x) = \frac{5(3x^2 - 6x - 5)}{16x^{3/2}}, \qquad x > 0$$

which is quite complicated. However, $3x^2 - 6x - 5 = 0$ has one solution in $(0, \infty)$, namely $1 + 2\sqrt{6}/3 \approx 2.6$.

Using the test points 1 and 3, we conclude that $f''(x) < 0$ on $(0, 1 + 2\sqrt{6}/3)$ and $f''(x) > 0$ on $(1 + 2\sqrt{6}/3, \infty)$. It then follows that the point $\left(1 + 2\sqrt{6}/3, F(1 + 2\sqrt{6}/3)\right)$, which is approximately $(2.6, 2.3)$, is an inflection point.

As x grows large, $F(x)$ grows without bound and much faster than any linear function; there are no asymptotes. The graph is sketched in Figure 5. ∎

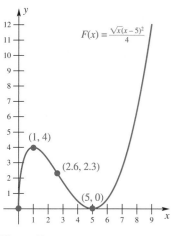

$F(x) = \frac{\sqrt{x}(x-5)^2}{4}$

Figure 5

Summary of the Method In graphing functions, there is no substitute for common sense. However, the following procedure will be helpful in most cases.

Step 1: Precalculus analysis.
(a) Check the *domain* and *range* of the function to see if any regions of the plane are excluded.
(b) Test for *symmetry* with respect to the y-axis and the origin. (Is the function even or odd?)
(c) Find the *intercepts*.

Step 2: Calculus analysis.
(a) Use the first derivative to find the critical points and to find out where the graph is *increasing* and *decreasing*.
(b) Test the critical points for *local maxima* and *minima*.
(c) Use the second derivative to find out where the graph is *concave up* and *concave down* and to locate *inflection points*.
(d) Find the *asymptotes*.

Step 3: Plot a few points (including all critical points and inflection points).

Step 4: Sketch the graph.

EXAMPLE 4 For the function $f(x) = 4xe^{-x^2}$,
(a) Find where f is increasing and where it is decreasing.
(b) Find where f is concave up and where it is concave down.
(c) Find all inflection points of f.
(d) Sketch the graph of $y = f(x)$.

SOLUTION
(a) The Product Rule gives

$$f'(x) = 4x\left(-2xe^{-x^2}\right) + 4e^{-x^2} = 4(1 - 2x^2)e^{-x^2}$$

Since $e^{-x^2} > 0$ for all x, the sign of $f'(x)$ depends on $1 - 2x^2$. We have

$$1 - 2x^2 > 0 \quad \Leftrightarrow \quad |x| < \frac{\sqrt{2}}{2}$$

Thus, f is increasing on $[-\sqrt{2}/2, \sqrt{2}/2]$. Since $1 - 2x^2 < 0$ on $(-\infty, -\sqrt{2}/2)$ and on $(\sqrt{2}/2, \infty)$, we conclude that f is decreasing on $(-\infty, -\sqrt{2}/2]$ and on $[\sqrt{2}/2, \infty)$.

(b) The Product Rule applied a second time gives

$$f''(x) = 4(1-2x^2)(-2x)e^{-x^2} + 4e^{-x^2}(-4x) = 8x(2x^2 - 3)e^{-x^2}$$

Again, $e^{-x^2} > 0$ for all x, so the sign of $f''(x)$ hinges on the quantity $8x(2x^2 - 3)$. The split points for the inequality $8x(2x^2 - 3) > 0$ are $x = \pm\sqrt{3/2} = \pm\sqrt{6}/2$ and $x = 0$. Substitution of some test points indicates that $f''(x) < 0$ on $(-\infty, -\sqrt{6}/2)$ and $(0, \sqrt{6}/2)$, so the graph is concave down there, and that $f''(x) > 0$ on $(-\sqrt{6}/2, 0)$ and $(\sqrt{6}/2, \infty)$, so the graph is concave up there.

(c) The concavity changes when $x = -\sqrt{6}/2, 0$, and $\sqrt{6}/2$, so the inflection points are the ordered pairs $(-\sqrt{6}/2, f(-\sqrt{6}/2))$, $(0, f(0))$, and $(\sqrt{6}/2, f(\sqrt{6}/2))$, which are (approximately for the first and last), $(-1.22, -1.09)$, $(0, 0)$, and $(1.22, 1.09)$.

(d) Much of the work leading to the graphing of the function has been done in parts (a) through (c). In addition, we make the following observations. The domain of f is $(-\infty, \infty)$. The maximum, which occurs at $x = \sqrt{2}/2$, is $f(\sqrt{2}/2) = 2\sqrt{2}e^{-1/2} \approx 1.716$. Similarly, the minimum, which occurs at $x = -\sqrt{2}/2$, is $f(-\sqrt{2}/2) = -2\sqrt{2}e^{-1/2} \approx -1.716$. Since $f(-x) = -f(x)$, we know that the function is odd, so its graph is symmetric with respect to the origin. Finally, there are no vertical asymptotes, and since

$$\lim_{x \to -\infty} f(x) = \lim_{x \to \infty} f(x) = 0$$

the line $y = 0$ is the only horizontal asymptote. A graph is shown in Figure 6. ∎

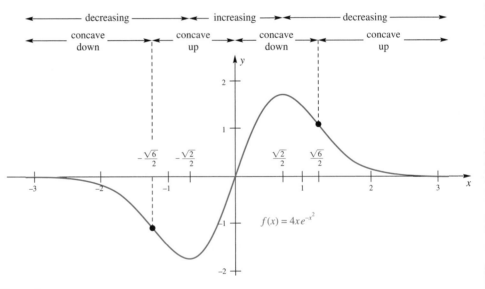

Figure 6

EXAMPLE 5 Sketch the graphs of $f(x) = x^{1/3}$ and $g(x) = x^{2/3}$ and their derivatives.

SOLUTION The domain for both functions is $(-\infty, \infty)$. (Remember, the cube root exists for every real number.) The range for $f(x)$ is $(-\infty, \infty)$ since every real number is the cube root of some other number. Writing $g(x)$ as $g(x) = x^{2/3} = (x^{1/3})^2$, we see that $g(x)$ must be nonnegative; it's range is $[0, \infty)$.

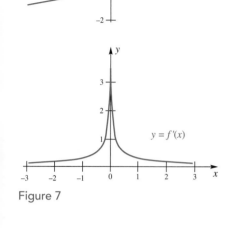

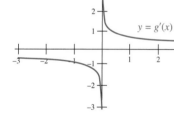

Figure 7

Since $f(-x) = (-x)^{1/3} = -x^{1/3} = -f(x)$, we see that f is an odd function. Similarly, since $g(-x) = (-x)^{2/3} = ((-x)^2)^{1/3} = (x^2)^{1/3} = g(x)$, we see that g is an even function. The first derivatives are

$$f'(x) = \frac{1}{3}x^{-2/3} = \frac{1}{3x^{2/3}}$$

and

$$g'(x) = \frac{2}{3}x^{-1/3} = \frac{2}{3x^{1/3}}$$

and the second derivatives are

$$f''(x) = -\frac{2}{9}x^{-5/3} = -\frac{2}{9x^{5/3}}$$

and

$$g''(x) = -\frac{2}{9}x^{-4/3} = -\frac{2}{9x^{4/3}}$$

For both functions the only critical point, in this case a point where the derivative doesn't exist, is $x = 0$.

Note that $f'(x) > 0$ for all x, except $x = 0$. Thus, f is increasing on $(-\infty, 0]$ and also on $[0, \infty)$, but because f is continuous on $(-\infty, \infty)$, we can conclude that f is always increasing. Consequently, f has no local maxima or minima. Since $f''(x)$ is positive when x is negative and negative when x is positive (and undefined when $x = 0$), we conclude that f is concave up on $(-\infty, 0)$ and concave down on $(0, \infty)$. The point $(0, 0)$ is an inflection point because that is where the concavity changes.

Now consider $g(x)$. Note that $g'(x)$ is negative when x is negative and positive when x is positive. Since g is decreasing on $(-\infty, 0]$ and increasing on $[0, \infty)$, $g(0) = 0$ is a local mimimum. Note also that $g''(x)$ is negative as long as $x \neq 0$. Thus g is concave down on $(-\infty, 0)$ and concave down on $(0, \infty)$, so $(0, 0)$ is not an inflection point. The graphs of $f(x), f'(x), g(x)$ and $g'(x)$ are shown in Figures 7 and 8. ∎

Note that in the above example both functions had one critical point, $x = 0$, where the derivative was undefined. Yet the graphs of the functions are fundamentally different. The graph of $y = f(x)$ has a tangent line at all points, but it is vertical when $x = 0$. (If the tangent line is vertical, then the derivative doesn't exist at that point.) The graph of $y = g(x)$ has a sharp point, called a **cusp**, at $x = 0$.

Using the Derivative's Graph to Graph a Function Knowing just a function's derivative can tell us a lot about the function itself and what its graph looks like.

EXAMPLE 6 Figure 9 shows a plot of $y = f'(x)$. Find all local extrema and points of inflection of f on the interval $[-1, 3]$. Given that $f(1) = 0$, sketch the graph of $y = f(x)$.

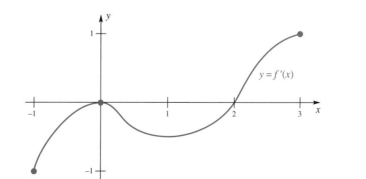

Figure 9

SOLUTION The derivative is negative on the intervals $(-1, 0)$ and $(0, 2)$, and positive on the interval $(2, 3)$. Thus, f is decreasing on $[-1, 0]$ and on $[0, 2]$ so there is a local maximum at the left end point $x = -1$. Since $f'(x)$ is positive on $(2, 3)$, f is increasing on $[2, 3]$ so there is a local maximum at the right end point $x = 3$. Since f is decreasing on $[-1, 2]$ and increasing on $[2, 3]$, there is a local minimum at $x = 2$. Figure 10 summarizes this information.

Inflection points for f occur when the concavity of f changes. Since f' is increasing on $(-1, 0)$ and on $(1, 3)$, f is concave up on $(-1, 0)$ and on $(1, 3)$. Since f' is decreasing on $(0, 1)$, f is concave down on $(0, 1)$. Thus, f changes concavity at $x = 0$ and $x = 1$. The inflection points are therefore $(0, f(0))$ and $(1, f(1))$.

The information given above, together with the fact that $f(1) = 0$, can be used to sketch the graph of $y = f(x)$. (The sketch cannot be too precise because we still have limited information about f.) A sketch is shown in Figure 11.

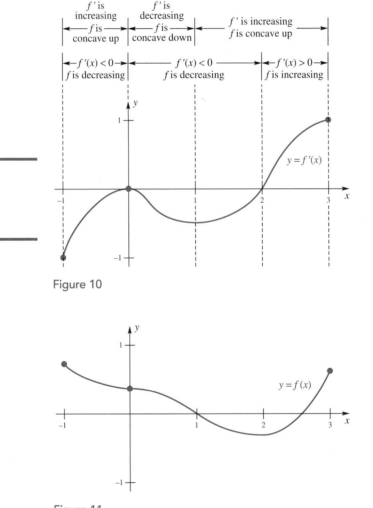

$f(-1)$	Local maximum
$f(2)$	Local minimum
$f(3)$	Local maximum
$(0, f(0))$	Inflection point
$(1, f(1))$	Inflection point

Figure 10

Figure 11

Concepts Review

1. The graph of f is symmetric with respect to the y-axis if $f(-x) =$ _____ for every x; the graph is symmetric with respect to the origin if $f(-x) =$ _____ for every x.

2. If $f'(x) < 0$ and $f''(x) > 0$ for all x in an interval I, then the graph of f is both _____ and _____ on I.

3. The graph of $f(x) = x^3/[(x + 1)(x - 2)(x - 3)]$ has as vertical asymptotes the lines _____ and as a horizontal asymptote the line _____.

4. We call $f(x) = 3x^5 - 2x^2 + 6$ a(n) _____ function, and we call $g(x) = (3x^5 - 2x^2 + 6)/(x^2 - 4)$ a(n) _____ function.

Problem Set 4.5

In Problems 1–27, make an analysis as suggested in the summary above and then sketch the graph.

1. $f(x) = x^3 - 3x + 5$ **2.** $f(x) = 2x^3 - 3x - 10$

3. $f(x) = 2x^3 - 3x^2 - 12x + 3$

4. $f(x) = (x - 1)^3$ **5.** $G(x) = (x - 1)^4$

6. $H(t) = t^2(t^2 - 1)$

7. $f(x) = x^3 - 3x^2 + 3x + 10$

8. $F(s) = \dfrac{4s^4 - 8s^2 - 12}{3}$

9. $g(x) = \dfrac{x}{x + 1}$ **10.** $g(s) = \sin^{-1} x$

11. $f(x) = \dfrac{x}{x^2 + 4}$ **12.** $\Lambda(\theta) = \dfrac{\theta^2}{\theta^2 + 1}$

13. $h(x) = \tan^{-1} x$ **14.** $P(x) = 1 - e^{-2x}$

15. $f(x) = \dfrac{(x - 1)(x - 3)}{(x + 1)(x - 2)}$ **16.** $w(z) = \dfrac{z^2 + 1}{z}$

17. $g(x) = \dfrac{x^2 + x - 6}{x - 1}$

18. $f(x) = |x|^3$ *Hint:* $\dfrac{d}{dx}|x| = \dfrac{|x|}{x}$

19. $R(z) = z|z|$ **20.** $H(q) = q^2|q|$

21. $g(x) = \dfrac{|x| + x}{2}(3x + 2)$

22. $h(x) = \dfrac{|x| - x}{2}(x^2 - x + 6)$

23. $f(x) = |\sin x|$ **24.** $f(x) = \sqrt{\sin x}$

25. $h(t) = \cos^2 t$ **26.** $g(t) = \tan^2 t$

C **27.** $f(x) = (\ln x)^2$

28. Sketch the graph of a function f that has the following properties:
(a) f is everywhere continuous;   (b) $f(0) = 0, f(1) = 2$;
(c) f is an even function;   (d) $f'(x) > 0$ for $x > 0$;
(e) $f''(x) > 0$ for $x > 0$.

29. Sketch the graph of a function f that has the following properties:
(a) f is everywhere continuous;   (b) $f(2) = -3, f(6) = 1$;
(c) $f'(2) = 0, f'(x) > 0$ for $x \neq 2, f'(6) = 3$;
(d) $f''(6) = 0, f''(x) > 0$ for $2 < x < 6, f''(x) < 0$ for $x > 6$.

30. Sketch the graph of a function g that has the following properties:
(a) g is everywhere *smooth* (continuous with a continuous first derivative);
(b) $g(0) = 0$;   (c) $g'(x) < 0$ for all x;
(d) $g''(x) < 0$ for $x < 0$ and $g''(x) > 0$ for $x > 0$.

31. Sketch the graph of a function f that has the following properties:
(a) f is everywhere continuous;
(b) $f(-3) = 1$;
(c) $f'(x) < 0$ for $x < -3, f'(x) > 0$ for $x > -3, f''(x) < 0$ for $x \neq -3$.

32. Sketch the graph of a function f that has the following properties:
(a) f is everywhere continuous;
(b) $f(-4) = -3, f(0) = 0, f(3) = 2$;
(c) $f'(-4) = 0, f'(3) = 0, f'(x) > 0$ for $x < -4, f'(x) > 0$ for $-4 < x < 3, f'(x) < 0$ for $x > 3$;
(d) $f''(-4) = 0, f''(0) = 0, f''(x) < 0$ for $x < -4, f''(x) > 0$ for $-4 < x < 0, f''(x) < 0$ for $x > 0$.

33. Sketch the graph of a function f that has the following properties.
(a) has a continuous first derivative;
(b) is decreasing and concave up for $x < 3$;
(c) has an extremum at $(3, 1)$;
(d) is increasing and concave up for $3 < x < 5$;
(e) has an inflection point at $(5, 4)$;
(f) is increasing and concave down for $5 < x < 6$;
(g) has an extremum at $(6, 7)$;
(h) is decreasing and concave down for $x > 6$.

GC *Linear approximations provide particularly good approximations near points of inflection. Using a graphing calculator, investigate this behavior in Problems 34–36.*

34. Graph $y = \sin x$ and its linear approximation $L(x) = x$ at $x = 0$.

35. Graph $y = \cos x$ and its linear approximation $L(x) = -x + \pi/2$ at $x = \pi/2$.

36. Find the linear approximation to the curve $y = (x - 1)^5 + 3$ at its point of inflection. Graph both the function and its linear approximation in the neighborhood of the inflection point.

37. Suppose $f'(x) = (x - 2)(x - 3)(x - 4)$ and $f(2) = 2$. Sketch a graph of $y = f(x)$.

38. Suppose $f'(x) = (x - 3)(x - 2)^2(x - 1)$ and $f(2) = 0$. Sketch a graph of $y = f(x)$.

39. Suppose $h'(x) = x^2(x - 1)^2(x - 2)$ and $h(0) = 0$. Sketch a graph of $y = h(x)$.

40. Consider a general quadratic curve $y = ax^2 + bx + c$. Show that such a curve has no inflection points.

41. Show that the curve $y = ax^3 + bx^2 + cx + d$ where $a \neq 0$, has exactly one inflection point.

42. Consider a general quartic curve $y = ax^4 + bx^3 + cx^2 + dx + e$, where $a \neq 0$. What is the maximum number of inflection points that such a curve can have?

EXPL CAS *In Problems 43–47, the graph of $y = f(x)$ depends on a parameter c. Using a CAS, investigate how the extremum and inflection points depend on the value of c. Identify the values of c at which the basic shape of the curve changes.*

43. $f(x) = x^2\sqrt{x^2 - c^2}$ **44.** $f(x) = \dfrac{cx}{4 + (cx)^2}$

45. $f(x) = \dfrac{1}{(cx^2 - 4)^2 + cx^2}$ **46.** $f(x) = \dfrac{1}{x^2 + 4x + c}$

47. $f(x) = c + \sin cx$

48. What conclusions can you draw about f from the information that $f'(c) = f''(c) = 0$ and $f'''(c) > 0$?

49. Let $g(x)$ be a function that has two derivatives and satisfies the following properties:

(a) $g(1) = 1$;

(b) $g'(x) > 0$ for all $x \neq 1$;

(c) g is concave down for all $x < 1$ and concave up for all $x > 1$;

(d) $f(x) = g(x^4)$;

Sketch a possible graph of $f(x)$ and justify your answer.

50. Let $H(x)$ have three continuous derivatives, and be such that $H(1) = H'(1) = H''(1) = 0$, but $H'''(1) \neq 0$. Does $H(x)$ have a local maximum, local minimum, or a point of inflection at $x = 1$? Justify your answer.

51. In each case, is it possible for a function F with two continuous derivatives to satisfy the following properties? If so sketch such a function. If not, justify your answer.

(a) $F'(x) > 0, F''(x) > 0$, while $F(x) < 0$ for all x.

(b) $F''(x) < 0$, while $F(x) > 0$.

(c) $F''(x) < 0$, while $F'(x) > 0$.

GC **52.** Use a graphing calculator or a CAS to plot the graphs of each of the following functions on the indicated interval. Determine the coordinates of any of the global extrema and any inflection points. You should be able to give answers that are accurate to at least one decimal place. Restrict the y-axis window to $-5 \leq y \leq 5$.

(a) $f(x) = x^2 \tan x; \left(-\dfrac{\pi}{2}, \dfrac{\pi}{2}\right)$

(b) $f(x) = x^3 \tan x; \left(-\dfrac{\pi}{2}, \dfrac{\pi}{2}\right)$

(c) $f(x) = 2x + \sin x; [-\pi, \pi]$

(d) $f(x) = x - \dfrac{\sin x}{2}; [-\pi, \pi]$

GC **53.** Each of the following functions is periodic. Use a graphing calculator or a CAS to plot the graph of each of the following functions over one full period with the center of the interval located at the origin. Determine the coordinates of any of the global extrema and any inflection points. You should be able to give answers that are accurate to at least one decimal place.

(a) $f(x) = 2 \sin x + \cos^2 x$ (b) $f(x) = 2 \sin x + \sin^2 x$

(c) $f(x) = \cos 2x - 2 \cos x$ (d) $f(x) = \sin 3x - \sin x$

(e) $f(x) = \sin 2x - \cos 3x$

54. Let f be a continuous function with $f(-3) = f(0) = 2$. If the graph of $y = f'(x)$ is as shown in Figure 12, sketch a possible graph for $y = f(x)$.

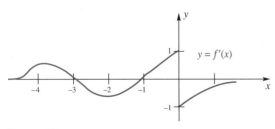

Figure 12

55. Let f be a continuous function and let f' have the graph shown in Figure 13. Sketch a possible graph for f and answer the following questions.

(a) Where is f increasing? Decreasing?

(b) Where is f concave up? Concave down?

(c) Where does f attain a local maximum? A local minimum?

(d) Where are there inflection points for f?

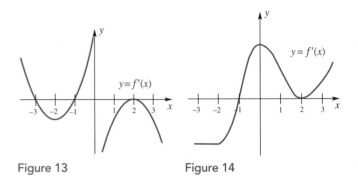

Figure 13   Figure 14

56. Repeat Problem 55 for Figure 14.

57. Let f be a continuous function with $f(0) = f(2) = 0$. If the graph of $y = f'(x)$ is as shown in Figure 15, sketch a possible graph for $y = f(x)$.

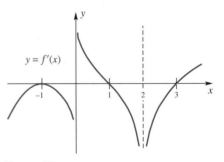

Figure 15

58. Suppose that $f'(x) = (x - 3)(x - 1)^2(x + 2)$ and $f(1) = 2$. Sketch a graph of f.

GC **59.** Use a graphing calculator or a CAS to plot the graph of each of the following functions on $[-1, 7]$. Determine the coordinates of any global extrema and any inflection points. You should be able to give answers that are accurate to at least one decimal place.

(a) $f(x) = x\sqrt{x^2 - 6x + 40}$

(b) $f(x) = \sqrt{|x|}(x^2 - 6x + 40)$

(c) $f(x) = \sqrt{x^2 - 6x + 40}/(x - 2)$

(d) $f(x) = \sin[(x^2 - 6x + 40)/6]$

GC **60.** Repeat Problem 59 for the following functions.

(a) $f(x) = x^3 - 8x^2 + 5x + 4$

(b) $f(x) = |x^3 - 8x^2 + 5x + 4|$

(c) $f(x) = (x^3 - 8x^2 + 5x + 4)/(x - 1)$

(d) $f(x) = (x^3 - 8x^2 + 5x + 4)/(x^3 + 1)$

Answers to Concepts Review: **1.** $f(x); -f(x)$

2. decreasing; concave up   **3.** $x = -1, x = 2, x = 3; y = 1$

4. polynomial; rational

4.6
The Mean Value Theorem for Derivatives

In geometric language, the Mean Value Theorem is easy to state and understand. It says that, if the graph of a continuous function has a nonvertical tangent line at every point between A and B, then there is at least one point C on the graph between A and B at which the tangent line is parallel to the secant line AB. In Figure 1, there is just one such point C; in Figure 2, there are several. First we state the theorem in the language of functions; then we prove it.

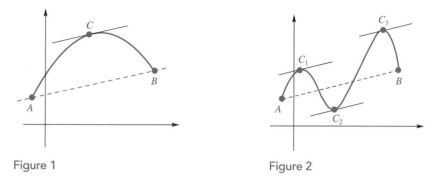

Figure 1   Figure 2

Theorem A   **Mean Value Theorem for Derivatives**

If f is continuous on a closed interval $[a, b]$ and differentiable on its interior (a, b), then there is at least one number c in (a, b) where

$$\frac{f(b) - f(a)}{b - a} = f'(c)$$

or, equivalently, where

$$f(b) - f(a) = f'(c)(b - a)$$

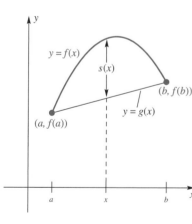

Figure 3

Proof   Our proof rests on a careful analysis of the function $s(x) = f(x) - g(x)$, introduced in Figure 3. Here $y = g(x)$ is the equation of the line through $(a, f(a))$ and $(b, f(b))$. Since this line has slope $[f(b) - f(a)]/(b - a)$ and goes through $(a, f(a))$, the point-slope form for its equation is

$$g(x) - f(a) = \frac{f(b) - f(a)}{b - a}(x - a)$$

This, in turn, yields a formula for $s(x)$:

$$s(x) = f(x) - g(x) = f(x) - f(a) - \frac{f(b) - f(a)}{b - a}(x - a)$$

Note immediately that $s(b) = s(a) = 0$ and that, for x in (a, b),

$$s'(x) = f'(x) - \frac{f(b) - f(a)}{b - a}$$

Now we make a crucial observation. If we knew that there was a number c in (a, b) satisfying $s'(c) = 0$, we would be all done. For then the last equation would say that

$$0 = f'(c) - \frac{f(b) - f(a)}{b - a}$$

which is equivalent to the conclusion of the theorem.

To see that $s'(c) = 0$ for some c in (a, b), reason as follows. Clearly, s is continuous on $[a, b]$, being the difference of two continuous functions. Thus, by the Max–Min Existence Theorem (Theorem 4.1A), s must attain both a maximum and

---

The Key to a Proof

The key to this proof is that c is the value at which $f'(c) = \dfrac{f(b) - f(a)}{b - a}$ *and* $s'(c) = 0$. Many proofs have one or two key ideas; if you understand the key, you will understand the proof.

a minimum value on $[a, b]$. If both of these values happen to be 0, then $s(x)$ is identically 0 on $[a, b]$, and consequently $s'(x) = 0$ for all x in (a, b), much more than we need.

If either the maximum value or the minimum value is different from 0, then that value is attained at an interior point c, since $s(a) = s(b) = 0$. Now s has a derivative at each point of (a, b), and so, by the Critical Point Theorem (Theorem 4.1B), $s'(c) = 0$. That is all we needed to know. ∎

The Theorem Illustrated

EXAMPLE 1 Find the number c guaranteed by the Mean Value Theorem for $f(x) = 2\sqrt{x}$ on $[1, 4]$.

SOLUTION

$$f'(x) = 2 \cdot \frac{1}{2} x^{-1/2} = \frac{1}{\sqrt{x}}$$

and

$$\frac{f(4) - f(1)}{4 - 1} = \frac{4 - 2}{3} = \frac{2}{3}$$

Thus, we must solve

$$\frac{1}{\sqrt{c}} = \frac{2}{3}$$

The single solution is $c = \frac{9}{4}$ (Figure 4). ∎

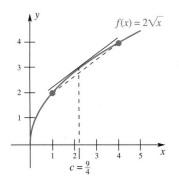

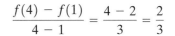

Figure 4

EXAMPLE 2 Let $f(x) = x^3 - x^2 - x + 1$ on $[-1, 2]$. Find all numbers c satisfying the conclusion to the Mean Value Theorem.

SOLUTION Figure 5 shows a graph of the function f. From this graph, it appears that there are two numbers c_1 and c_2 with the required property. We now find

$$f'(x) = 3x^2 - 2x - 1$$

and

$$\frac{f(2) - f(-1)}{2 - (-1)} = \frac{3 - 0}{3} = 1$$

Therefore, we must solve

$$3c^2 - 2c - 1 = 1$$

or, equivalently,

$$3c^2 - 2c - 2 = 0$$

By the Quadratic Formula, there are two solutions, $\left(2 \pm \sqrt{4 + 24}\right)/6$, which correspond to $c_1 \approx -0.55$ and $c_2 \approx 1.22$. Both numbers are in the interval $(-1, 2)$. ∎

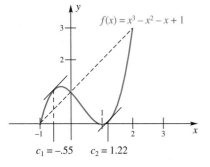

Figure 5

EXAMPLE 3 Let $h(x) = \sec^{-1} x$. Find all numbers c satisfying the conclusion to the Mean Value Theorem on the interval $[1, 2]$.

SOLUTION Using the result from Theorem 3.10B, we have

$$h'(x) = \frac{1}{|x|\sqrt{x^2 - 1}} = \frac{1}{x\sqrt{x^2 - 1}}$$

The absolute value in the denominator is not needed since x must be in the interval $[1, 2]$. We also have

$$\frac{h(2) - h(1)}{2 - 1} = \frac{\sec^{-1} 2 - \sec^{-1} 1}{1} = \frac{\pi}{3}$$

Therefore we must solve

$$\frac{1}{c\sqrt{c^2 - 1}} = \frac{\pi}{3}$$

$$c\sqrt{c^2 - 1} = \frac{3}{\pi}$$

$$c^2(c^2 - 1) = \frac{9}{\pi^2}$$

$$c^4 - c^2 - \frac{9}{\pi^2} = 0$$

This last equation is a quadratic in c^2. Thus,

$$c^2 = \frac{-(-1) \pm \sqrt{1 - 4(1)(-9/\pi^2)}}{2} = \frac{1 \pm \sqrt{1 + 36/\pi^2}}{2}$$

The negative sign gives a negative number for c^2, so we take the positive sign and obtain

$$c = \sqrt{\frac{1 + \sqrt{1 + 36/\pi^2}}{2}} \approx 1.2561$$

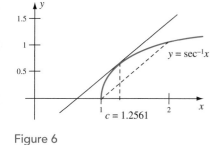

Figure 6

Figure 6 shows the graph of $h(x)$ along with the secant line and tangent line at $x = 1.2561$. ■

EXAMPLE 4 Let $f(x) = x^{2/3}$ on $[-8, 27]$. Show that the conclusion to the Mean Value Theorem fails and figure out why.

SOLUTION

$$f'(x) = \frac{2}{3}x^{-1/3}, \qquad x \neq 0$$

and

$$\frac{f(27) - f(-8)}{27 - (-8)} = \frac{9 - 4}{35} = \frac{1}{7}$$

We must solve

$$\frac{2}{3}c^{-1/3} = \frac{1}{7}$$

which gives

$$c = \left(\frac{14}{3}\right)^3 \approx 102$$

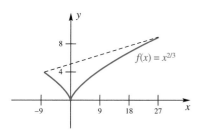

Figure 7

But $c = 102$ is not in the interval $(-8, 27)$ as required. As the graph of $y = f(x)$ suggests (Figure 7), $f'(0)$ fails to exist, so the problem is that $f(x)$ is not everywhere differentiable on $(-8, 27)$. ■

If the function $s(t)$ represents the position of an object at time t, then the Mean Value Theorem states that over any interval of time, there is some time for which the instantaneous velocity equals the average velocity.

EXAMPLE 5 Suppose that an object has position function $s(t) = t^2 - t - 2$. Find the average velocity over the interval $[3, 6]$ and find the time at which the instantaneous velocity equals the average velocity.

SOLUTION The average velocity over the interval $[3, 6]$ is equal to $(s(6) - s(3))/(6 - 3) = 8$. The instantaneous velocity is $s'(t) = 2t - 1$. To find the point where average velocity equals instantaneous velocity, we equate $8 = 2t - 1$ and solve to get $t = 9/2$. ∎

The Theorem Used In Section 4.2, we promised a rigorous proof of the Monotonicity Theorem (Theorem 4.2A). This is the theorem that relates the sign of the derivative of a function to whether that function is increasing or decreasing.

Proof of the Monotonicity Theorem We suppose that f is continuous on I and that $f'(x) > 0$ at each point x in the interior of I. Consider any two points x_1 and x_2 of I with $x_1 < x_2$. By the Mean Value Theorem applied to the interval $[x_1, x_2]$, there is a number c in (x_1, x_2) satisfying

$$f(x_2) - f(x_1) = f'(c)(x_2 - x_1)$$

Since $f'(c) > 0$, we see that $f(x_2) - f(x_1) > 0$; that is, $f(x_2) > f(x_1)$. This is what we mean when we say that f is increasing on I.

The case where $f'(x) < 0$ on I is handled similarly. ∎

Our next theorem will be used repeatedly in this and the next chapter. In words, it says that *two functions with the same derivative differ by a constant*, possibly the zero constant (see Figure 8).

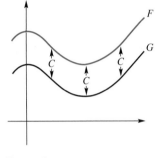

Figure 8

Theorem B
If $F'(x) = G'(x)$ for all x in (a, b), then there is a constant C such that $$F(x) = G(x) + C$$ for all x in (a, b).

Proof Let $H(x) = F(x) - G(x)$. Then

$$H'(x) = F'(x) - G'(x) = 0$$

for all x in (a, b). Choose x_1, as some (fixed) point in (a, b), and let x be any other point there. The function H satisfies the hypotheses of the Mean Value Theorem on the closed interval with end points x_1, and x. Thus, there is a number c between x_1 and x such that

$$H(x) - H(x_1) = H'(c)(x - x_1)$$

But $H'(c) = 0$ by hypothesis. Therefore, $H(x) - H(x_1) = 0$ or, equivalently, $H(x) = H(x_1)$ for all x in (a, b). Since $H(x) = F(x) - G(x)$, we conclude that $F(x) - G(x) = H(x_1)$. Now let $C = H(x_1)$, and we have the conclusion $F(x) = G(x) + C$. ∎

Geometry and Algebra

As with most topics in this book, you should try to see things from an algebraic and a geometrical point of view. Geometrically, Theorem B says that if F and G have the same derivative then the graph of G is a vertical translation of the graph of F.

Concepts Review

1. The Mean Value Theorem for Derivatives says that if f is _____ on $[a, b]$ and differentiable on _____ then there is a point c in (a, b) such that _____.

2. The function, $f(x) = |\sin x|$ would satisfy the hypotheses of the Mean Value Theorem on the interval $[0, 1]$ but would not satisfy them on the interval $[-1, 1]$ because _____.

3. If two functions F and G have the same derivative on the interval (a, b), then there is a constant C such that _____.

4. Since $D_x(x^4) = 4x^3$, it follows that every function F that satisfies $F'(x) = 4x^3$ has the form $F(x) =$ _____.

Problem Set 4.6

In each of the Problems 1–21, a function is defined and a closed interval is given. Decide whether the Mean Value Theorem applies to the given function on the given interval. If it does, find all possible values of c; if not, state the reason. In each problem, sketch the graph of the given function on the given interval.

1. $f(x) = |x|; [1, 2]$ **2.** $g(x) = |x|; [-2, 2]$

3. $f(x) = x^2 + x; [-2, 2]$ **4.** $g(x) = (x + 1)^3; [-1, 1]$

5. $H(s) = s^2 + 3s - 1; [-3, 1]$

6. $F(x) = \dfrac{x^3}{3}; [-2, 2]$

7. $f(z) = \frac{1}{3}(z^3 + z - 4); [-1, 2]$

8. $F(t) = \dfrac{1}{t-1}; [0, 2]$ **9.** $h(x) = e^{-x}; [0, 3]$

10. $f(x) = \dfrac{x-4}{x-3}; [0, 4]$ **11.** $h(t) = t^{2/3}; [0, 2]$

12. $h(t) = t^{2/3}; [-2, 2]$ **13.** $g(x) = x^{5/3}; [0, 1]$

14. $g(x) = x^{5/3}; [-1, 1]$ **15.** $S(\theta) = \sin \theta; [-\pi, \pi]$

16. $C(\theta) = \csc \theta; [-\pi, \pi]$ **17.** $T(\theta) = \tan \theta; [0, \pi]$

18. $f(x) = x + \dfrac{1}{x}; \left[-1, \frac{1}{2}\right]$ **19.** $f(x) = x + \dfrac{1}{x}; [1, 2]$

20. $f(x) = [\![x]\!]; [1, 2]$ **21.** $f(x) = \ln |x|; [-1, 1]$

22. (Rolle's Theorem) *If f is continuous on* $[a, b]$ *and differentiable on* (a, b), *and if* $f(a) = f(b)$, *then there is at least one number c in* (a, b) *such that* $f'(c) = 0$. Show that Rolle's Theorem is just a special case of the Mean Value Theorem. (Michel Rolle (1652–1719) was a French mathematician.)

23. For the function graphed in Figure 9, find (approximately) all points c that satisfy the conclusion to the Mean Value Theorem for the interval [0, 8].

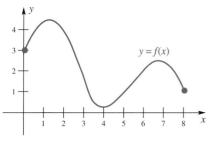

Figure 9

24. Show that if f is the quadratic function defined by $f(x) = \alpha x^2 + \beta x + \gamma, \alpha \neq 0$, then the number c of the Mean Value Theorem is always the midpoint of the given interval $[a, b]$.

25. Prove: If f is continuous on (a, b) and if $f'(x)$ exists and satisfies $f'(x) > 0$ except at one point x_0 in (a, b), then f is increasing on (a, b). *Hint:* Consider f on each of the intervals $(a, x_0]$ and $[x_0, b)$ separately.

26. Use Problem 25 to show that each of the following is increasing on $(-\infty, \infty)$.

(a) $f(x) = x^3$ (b) $f(x) = x^5$

(c) $f(x) = \begin{cases} x^3, & x \le 0 \\ x, & x > 0 \end{cases}$

27. Use the Mean Value Theorem to show that $s = 1/t$ decreases on any interval over which it is defined.

28. Use the Mean Value Theorem to show that $s = 1/t^2$ decreases on any interval to the right of the origin.

29. Prove that if $F'(x) = 0$ for all x in (a, b) then there is a constant C such that $F(x) = C$ for all x in (a, b). *Hint:* Let $G(x) = 0$ and apply Theorem B.

30. Suppose that you know that $\cos(0) = 1$, $\sin(0) = 0$, $D_x \cos x = -\sin x$, and $D_x \sin x = \cos x$, but nothing else about the sine and cosine functions. Show that $\cos^2 x + \sin^2 x = 1$. *Hint:* Let $F(x) = \cos^2 x + \sin^2 x$ and use Problem 29.

31. Prove that if $F'(x) = D$ for all x in (a, b) then there is a constant C such that $F(x) = Dx + C$ for all x in (a, b). *Hint:* Let $G(x) = Dx$ and apply Theorem B.

32. Suppose that $F'(x) = 5$ and $F(0) = 4$. Find a formula for $F(x)$. *Hint:* See Problem 31.

33. Prove: Let f be continuous on $[a, b]$ and differentiable on (a, b). If $f(a)$ and $f(b)$ have opposite signs and if $f'(x) \neq 0$ for all x in (a, b), then the equation $f(x) = 0$ has one and only one solution between a and b. *Hint:* Use the Intermediate Value Theorem and Rolle's Theorem (Problem 22).

34. Show that $f(x) = 2x^3 - 9x^2 + 1 = 0$ has exactly one solution on each of the intervals $(-1, 0)$, $(0, 1)$, and $(4, 5)$. *Hint:* Apply Problem 33.

35. Let f have a derivative on an interval I. Prove that between successive distinct zeros of f' there can be at most one zero of f. *Hint:* Try a proof by contradiction and use Rolle's Theorem (Problem 22).

36. Let g be continuous on $[a, b]$ and suppose that $g''(x)$ exists for all x in (a, b). Prove that if there are three values of x in $[a, b]$ for which $g(x) = 0$ then there is at least one value of x in (a, b) such that $g''(x) = 0$.

37. Let $f(x) = (x - 1)(x - 2)(x - 3)$. Prove by using Problem 36 that there is at least one value in the interval $[0, 4]$ where $f''(x) = 0$ and two values in the same interval where $f'(x) = 0$.

38. Prove that if $|f'(x)| \le M$ for all x in (a, b) and if x_1 and x_2 are any two points in (a, b) then

$$|f(x_2) - f(x_1)| \le M|x_2 - x_1|$$

Note: A function satisfying the above inequality is said to satisfy a *Lipschitz condition* with constant M. (Rudolph Lipschitz (1832–1903) was a German mathematician.)

39. Show that $f(x) = \sin 2x$ satisfies a Lipschitz condition with constant 2 on the interval $(-\infty, \infty)$. See Problem 38.

40. A function f is said to be **nondecreasing** on an interval I if $x_1 < x_2 \Rightarrow f(x_1) \le f(x_2)$ for x_1 and x_2 in I. Similarly, f is **nonincreasing** on I if $x_1 < x_2 \Rightarrow f(x_1) \ge f(x_2)$ for x_1 and x_2 in I.

(a) Sketch the graph of a function that is nondecreasing but not increasing.

(b) Sketch the graph of a function that is nonincreasing but not decreasing.

41. Prove that, if f is continuous on I and if $f'(x)$ exists and satisfies $f'(x) \ge 0$ on the interior of I, then f is nondecreasing on I. Similarly, if $f'(x) \le 0$, then f is nonincreasing on I.

42. Prove that if $f(x) \geq 0$ and $f'(x) \geq 0$ on I, then f^2 is nondecreasing on I.

43. Prove that if $g'(x) \leq h'(x)$ for all x in (a, b) then

$$x_1 < x_2 \Rightarrow g(x_2) - g(x_1) \leq h(x_2) - h(x_1)$$

for all x_1 and x_2 in (a, b). *Hint:* Apply Problem 41 with $f(x) = h(x) - g(x)$.

44. Use the Mean Value Theorem to prove that

$$\lim_{x \to \infty} \left(\sqrt{x + 2} - \sqrt{x} \right) = 0$$

45. Use the Mean Value Theorem to show that

$$|\sin x - \sin y| \leq |x - y|$$

46. Suppose that in a race, horse A and horse B begin at the same point and finish in a dead heat. Prove that their speeds were identical at some instant of the race.

47. In Problem 46, suppose that the two horses crossed the finish line together at the same speed. Show that they had the same acceleration at some instant.

48. Use the Mean Value Theorem to show that the graph of a concave up function f is always above its tangent line; that is, show that

$$f(x) > f(c) + f'(c)(x - c), \qquad x \neq c$$

49. Prove that if $|f(y) - f(x)| \leq M(y - x)^2$ for all x and y then f is a constant function.

50. Give an example of a function f that is continuous on $[0, 1]$, differentiable on $(0, 1)$, and *not* differentiable on $[0, 1]$, and has a tangent line at every point of $[0, 1]$.

51. John traveled 112 miles in 2 hours and claimed that he never exceeded 55 miles per hour. Use the Mean Value Theorem to disprove John's claim. *Hint:* Let $f(t)$ be the distance traveled in time t.

52. A car is stationary at a toll booth. Eighteen minutes later at a point 20 miles down the road the car is clocked at 60 miles per hour. Sketch a possible graph of v versus t. Sketch a possible graph of the distance traveled s against t. Use the Mean Value Theorem to show that the car must have exceeded the 60 mile per hour speed limit at some time after leaving the toll booth, but before the car was clocked at 60 miles per hour.

53. A car is stationary at a toll booth. Twenty minutes later at a point 20 miles down the road the car is clocked at 60 miles per hour. Explain why the car must have exceeded 60 miles per hour at some time after leaving the toll booth, but before the car was clocked at 60 miles per hour.

54. Show that if an object's position function is given by $s(t) = at^2 + bt + c$, then the average velocity over the interval $[A, B]$ is equal to the instantaneous velocity at the midpoint of $[A, B]$.

Answers to Concepts Review: **1.** continuous; (a, b); $f(b) - f(a) = f'(c)(b - a)$ **2.** $f'(0)$ does not exist **3.** $F(x) = G(x) + C$ **4.** $x^4 + C$

4.7
Solving Equations Numerically

In mathematics and science, we often need to find the roots (solutions) of an equation $f(x) = 0$. To be sure, if $f(x)$ is a linear or quadratic polynomial, formulas for writing exact solutions exist and are well known. But for other algebraic equations, and certainly for equations involving transcendental functions, formulas for exact solutions are rarely available. What can be done in such cases?

There is a general method of solving problems known to all resourceful people. Given a cup of tea, we add sugar a bit at a time until it tastes just right. Given a stopper too large for a hole, we whittle it down until it fits. We change the solution a bit at a time, improving the accuracy, until we are satisfied. Mathematicians call this the *method of successive approximations*, or the *method of iterations*.

In this section, we present three such methods for solving equations: the Bisection Method, Newton's Method, and the Fixed-Point Method. All are designed to approximate the real roots of $f(x) = 0$, and they all require many computations. You will want to keep your calculator handy.

The Bisection Method In Example 9 of Section 2.7 we saw how to use the Intermediate Value Theorem to approximate a solution of $f(x) = 0$ by successively bisecting an interval known to contain a solution. This Bisection Method has two great virtues—simplicity and reliability. It also has a major vice—the large number of steps needed to achieve the desired accuracy (otherwise known as slowness of convergence).

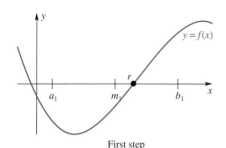

First step

Figure 1

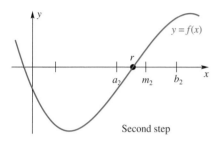

Second step

Figure 2

Begin the process by sketching the graph of f, which is assumed to be a continuous function (see Figure 1). A real root r of $f(x) = 0$ is a point (technically, the x-coordinate of a point) where the graph crosses the x-axis. As a first step in pinning down this point, locate two points, $a_1 < b_1$, at which you are sure that f has opposite signs; if f has opposite signs at a_1 and b_1, then the product $f(a_1) \cdot f(b_1)$ will be negative. (Try choosing a_1 and b_1 on opposite sides of your best guess at r.) The Intermediate Value Theorem guarantees the existence of a root between a_1 and b_1. Now evaluate f at the midpoint $m_1 = (a_1 + b_1)/2$ of $[a_1, b_1]$. The number m_1 is our first approximation to r.

Either $f(m_1) = 0$, in which case we are done, or $f(m_1)$ differs in sign from $f(a_1)$ or $f(b_1)$. Denote the one of the subintervals $[a_1, m_1]$ or $[m_1, b_1]$ on which the sign change occurs by the symbol $[a_2, b_2]$, and evaluate f at its midpoint $m_2 = (a_2 + b_2)/2$ (Figure 2). The number m_2 is our second approximation to r.

Repeat the process, thus determining a sequence of approximations $m_1, m_2, m_3, \ldots$, and subintervals $[a_1, b_1], [a_2, b_2], [a_3, b_3], \ldots$, each subinterval containing the root r and each half the length of its predecessor. Stop when r is determined to the desired accuracy, that is, when $(b_n - a_n)/2$ is less than the allowable error, which we will denote by E.

Algorithm   Bisection Method

Let $f(x)$ be a continuous function, and let a_1 and b_1 be numbers satisfying $a_1 < b_1$ and $f(a_1) \cdot f(b_1) < 0$. Let E denote the desired bound for the error $|r - m_n|$. Repeat steps 1 to 5 for $n = 1, 2, \ldots$ until $h_n < E$:

1.   Calculate $m_n = (a_n + b_n)/2$.
2.   Calculate $f(m_n)$, and if $f(m_n) = 0$, then STOP.
3.   Calculate $h_n = (b_n - a_n)/2$.
4.   If $f(a_n) \cdot f(m_n) < 0$, then set $a_{n+1} = a_n$ and $b_{n+1} = m_n$.
5.   If $f(a_n) \cdot f(m_n) > 0$, then set $a_{n+1} = m_n$ and $b_{n+1} = b_n$.

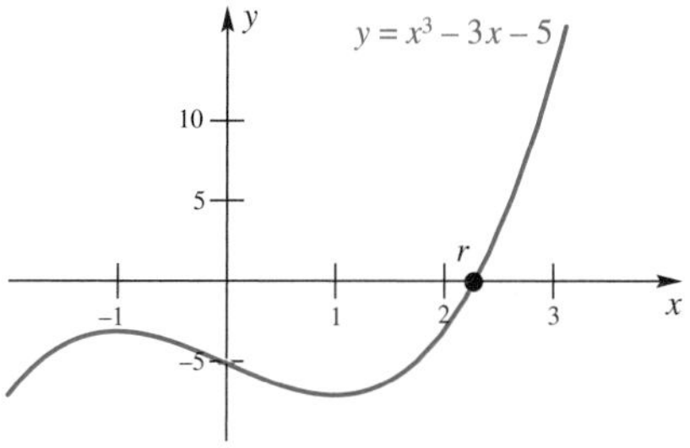

$y = x^3 - 3x - 5$

Figure 3

EXAMPLE 1   Determine the real root of $f(x) = x^3 - 3x - 5 = 0$ to accuracy within 0.0000001.

SOLUTION   We first sketch the graph of $y = x^3 - 3x - 5$ (Figure 3) and, noting that it crosses the x-axis between 2 and 3, we begin with $a_1 = 2$ and $b_1 = 3$.

Step 1: $m_1 = (a_1 + b_1)/2 = (2 + 3)/2 = 2.5$

Step 2: $f(m_1) = f(2.5) = 2.5^3 - 3 \cdot 2.5 - 5 = 3.125$

Step 3: $h_1 = (b_1 - a_1)/2 = (3 - 2)/2 = 0.5$

Step 4: Since

$$f(a_1) \cdot f(m_1) = f(2)f(2.5) = (-3)(3.125) = -9.375 < 0$$

we set $a_2 = a_1 = 2$ and $b_2 = m_1 = 2.5$.

Step 5: The condition $f(a_n) \cdot f(m_n) > 0$ is false.

Next we increment n so that it has the value 2 and repeat these steps. We can continue this process to obtain the entries in the following table:

n	h_n	m_n	$f(m_n)$
1	0.5	2.5	3.125
2	0.25	2.25	−0.359
3	0.125	2.375	1.271
4	0.0625	2.3125	0.429
5	0.03125	2.28125	0.02811
6	0.015625	2.265625	−0.16729
7	0.0078125	2.2734375	−0.07001
8	0.0039063	2.2773438	−0.02106
9	0.0019531	2.2792969	0.00350
10	0.0009766	2.2783203	−0.00878
11	0.0004883	2.2788086	−0.00264
12	0.0002441	2.2790528	0.00043
13	0.0001221	2.2789307	−0.00111
14	0.0000610	2.2789918	−0.00034
15	0.0000305	2.2790224	0.00005
16	0.0000153	2.2790071	−0.00015
17	0.0000076	2.2790148	−0.00005
18	0.0000038	2.2790187	−0.000001
19	0.0000019	2.2790207	0.000024
20	0.0000010	2.2790197	0.000011
21	0.0000005	2.2790192	0.000005
22	0.0000002	2.2790189	0.0000014
23	0.0000001	2.2790187	−0.0000011
24	0.0000001	2.2790188	0.0000001

We conclude that $r = 2.2790188$ with an error of at most 0.0000001. ∎

Example 1 illustrates the shortcoming of the Bisection Method. The approximations $m_1, m_2, m_3, \ldots$ converge very slowly to the root r. But they do converge; that is, $\lim_{n \to \infty} m_n = r$. The method works, and we have at step n a good bound for the error $E_n = r − m_n$, namely, $|E_n| \le h_n$.

Newton's Method   We are still considering the problem of solving the equation $f(x) = 0$ for a root r. Suppose that f is differentiable, so the graph of $y = f(x)$ has a tangent line at each point. If we can find a first approximation x_1 to r by graphing or any other means (see Figure 4), then a better approximation x_2 ought to lie at the intersection of the tangent at $(x_1, f(x_1))$ with the x-axis. Using x_2 as an approximation, we can then find a still better approximation x_3, and so on.

The process can be mechanized so that it is easy to do on a calculator. The equation of the tangent line at $(x_1, f(x_1))$ is

$$y − f(x_1) = f'(x_1)(x − x_1)$$

and its x-intercept x_2 is found by setting $y = 0$ and solving for x. The result is

$$x_2 = x_1 − \frac{f(x_1)}{f'(x_1)}$$

provided $f'(x_1) \ne 0$. More generally, we have the following algorithm, also called a *recursion formula* or an *iteration scheme*.

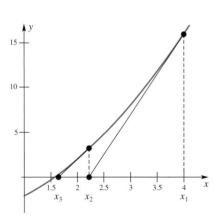

Figure 4

> **Algorithm** **Newton's Method**
>
> Let $f(x)$ be a differentiable function and let x_1 be an initial approximation to the root r of $f(x) = 0$. Let E denote a bound for the error $|r - x_n|$.
> Repeat the following step for $n = 1, 2, \ldots$ until $|x_{n+1} - x_n| < E$:
>
> 1. $\qquad x_{n+1} = x_n - \dfrac{f(x_n)}{f'(x_n)}$

EXAMPLE 2 Use Newton's Method to find the real root r of $f(x) = x^3 - 3x - 5 = 0$ to seven decimal places.

SOLUTION This is the same equation considered in Example 1. Let's use $x_1 = 2.5$ as our first approximation to r, as we did there. Since $f(x) = x^3 - 3x - 5$ and $f'(x) = 3x^2 - 3$, the algorithm is

$$x_{n+1} = x_n - \frac{x_n^3 - 3x_n - 5}{3x_n^2 - 3} = \frac{2x_n^3 + 5}{3x_n^2 - 3}$$

We obtain the following table.

n	x_n
1	2.5
2	2.30
3	2.2793
4	2.2790188
5	2.2790188

After just four steps, we get a repetition of the first eight digits. We feel confident in reporting that $r \approx 2.2790188$, with perhaps some question about the last digit. ∎

EXAMPLE 3 Use Newton's Method to find the positive real root r of $f(x) = 2 - x + \sin x = 0$.

SOLUTION The graph of $y = 2 - x + \sin x$ is shown in Figure 5. We will use the starting value $x_1 = 2$. Since $f'(x) = -1 + \cos x$, the iteration becomes

$$x_{n+1} = x_n - \frac{2 - x_n + \sin x_n}{-1 + \cos x_n}$$

which leads to the following table:

n	x_n
1	2.0
2	2.6420926
3	2.5552335
4	2.5541961
5	2.5541960
6	2.5541960

After just five steps, we get a repetition of the seven digits after the decimal point. We conclude that $r \approx 2.5541960$. ∎

EXAMPLE 4 Use Newton's Method to find the real root r of $f(x) = x - e^{-x} = 0$ to seven decimal places.

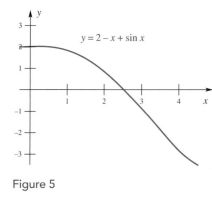

Algorithms

Algorithms have been part of mathematics since people first learned to do long division, but it is computer science that has given algorithmic thinking its present popularity. What is an algorithm? Donald Knuth, dean of computer scientists, responds,

"An algorithm is a precisely defined sequence of rules telling how to produce specified output information from given input information in a finite number of steps."

And what is computer science? According to Knuth,

"It is the study of algorithms."

Figure 5

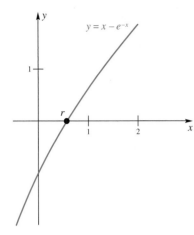

$y = x - e^{-x}$

Figure 6

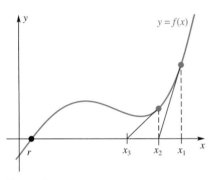

$y = f(x)$

Figure 7

SOLUTION The graph of $y = x - e^{-x}$ is sketched in Figure 6. We use $x_1 = 0.5$ and $x_{n+1} = x_n - (x_n - e^{-x_n})/(1 + e^{-x_n}) = (x_n + 1)/(e^{x_n} + 1)$ to obtain the following table:

n	x_n
1	0.5
2	0.566
3	0.56714
4	0.5671433
5	0.5671433

We conclude that $r \approx 0.5671433$. ∎

Newton's Method creates a *sequence* of successive approximations to the root. (We mentioned sequences briefly in Section 2.4.) It is often the case that Newton's Method produces a sequence $\{x_n\}$ that converges to the root of $f(x) = 0$, that is, $\lim_{n \to \infty} x_n = r$. This is not always the case, however. Figure 7 illustrates what can go wrong (see also Problem 22). For the function in Figure 7, the difficulty is that x_1 is not close enough to r to get a convergent process started. Other difficulties arise if $f'(x)$ is zero or undefined at or near r. When Newton's Method fails to produce approximations that converge to the solution, then you can retry Newton's Method with a different starting point, or use a different method such as the Bisection Method.

The Fixed-Point Algorithm The Fixed-Point Algorithm is simple and straightforward, but it often works.

Suppose that an equation can be written in the form $x = g(x)$. To solve this equation is to find a number r that is unchanged by the function g. We call such a number a **fixed point** of g. To find this number, we propose the following algorithm. Make a first guess x_1. Then let $x_2 = g(x_1)$, $x_3 = g(x_2)$, and so on. If we are lucky, x_n will converge to the root r as $n \to \infty$.

Algorithm **Fixed-Point Algorithm**

Let $g(x)$ be a continuous function, and let x_1 be an initial approximation to the root r of $x = g(x)$. Let E denote a bound for the error $|r - x_n|$.

    Repeat the following step for $n = 1, 2, \ldots$ until $|x_{n+1} - x_n| < E$:

      1. $x_{n+1} = g(x_n)$

EXAMPLE 5 Approximate the solution of $x - e^{-x} = 0$ using the Fixed-Point Algorithm.

SOLUTION We write the equation $x = e^{-x}$ and apply the algorithm $x_{n+1} = e^{-x_n}$ with $x_1 = 0.5$. The results are shown in the accompanying table.

n	x_n	n	x_n	n	x_n
1	0.5	10	0.5675596	19	0.5671408
2	0.6065307	11	0.5669072	20	0.5671447
3	0.5452392	12	0.5672772	21	0.5671425
4	0.5797031	13	0.5670674	22	0.5671438
5	0.5600646	14	0.5671864	23	0.5671430
6	0.5711722	15	0.5671189	24	0.5671435
7	0.5648630	16	0.5671572	25	0.5671432
8	0.5684381	17	0.5671354	26	0.5671433
9	0.5664095	18	0.5671478	27	0.5671433

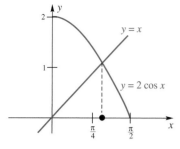

Figure 8

Although it took 27 steps to get a repetition of the first seven digits, the process did produce a sequence that converges and to the right value. Moreover, the process was very easy to carry out. ∎

EXAMPLE 6 Solve $x = 2 \cos x$ using the Fixed-Point Algorithm.

SOLUTION Note first that solving this equation is equivalent to solving the pair of equations $y = x$ and $y = 2 \cos x$. Thus, to get our initial value, we graph these two equations (Figure 8) and observe that the two curves cross at approximately $x = 1$. Taking $x_1 = 1$ and applying the algorithm $x_{n+1} = 2 \cos x_n$, we obtain the results in the following table.

n	x_n	n	x_n
1	1	6	1.4394614
2	1.0806046	7	0.2619155
3	0.9415902	8	1.9317916
4	1.1770062	9	−0.7064109
5	0.7673820	10	1.5213931

Quite clearly the process is unstable, even though our initial guess is very close to the actual root.

Let's take a different tack. Rewrite the equation $x = 2 \cos x$ as $x = (x + 2 \cos x)/2$ and use the algorithm

$$x_{n+1} = \frac{x_n + 2 \cos x_n}{2}$$

This process produces a convergent sequence, shown in the following table. (The oscillation in the last digit is probably due to round-off errors.)

n	x_n	n	x_n	n	x_n
1	1	7	1.0298054	13	1.0298665
2	1.0403023	8	1.0298883	14	1.0298666
3	1.0261107	9	1.0298588	15	1.0298665
4	1.0312046	10	1.0298693	16	1.0298666
5	1.0293881	11	1.0298655		
6	1.0300374	12	1.0298668		∎

Now we raise an obvious question. Why did the second algorithm yield a convergent sequence, whereas the first one failed to do so? Whether or not the Fixed-Point Algorithm works depends on two factors. One is the formulation of the equation $x = g(x)$. Example 6 demonstrates that an equation such as $x = 2 \cos x$ can be rewritten in a form that yields a different sequence of approximations. In Example 6 the reformulation was $x = (x + 2 \cos x)/2$. In general, there may be many ways to write the equation and the trick is to find one that works. Another factor that affects whether the Fixed-Point Algorithm converges is the closeness of the starting point x_1 to the root r. As we suggested for Newton's Method, if the Fixed-Point Algorithm fails with one starting point, you can try a different one.

Concepts Review

1. The virtues of the Bisection Method are its simplicity and reliability; its vice is its _____.

2. If f is continuous on $[a, b]$, and $f(a)$ and $f(b)$ have opposite signs, then there is a _____ of $f(x) = 0$ between a and b. This follows from the _____ Theorem.

3. The Bisection Method, Newton's Method, and the Fixed-Point Algorithm are examples of _____; that is, they provide a finite sequence of steps that, if followed, will produce a root of an equation to desired accuracy.

4. A point x satisfying $g(x) = x$ is called a _____ of g.

Problem Set 4.7

C *In Problems 1–4, use the Bisection Method to approximate the real root of the given equation on the given interval. Each answer should be accurate to two decimal places.*

1. $x^3 + 2x - 6 = 0$; $[1, 2]$ **2.** $x^4 + 5x^3 + 1 = 0$; $[-1, 0]$

3. $2 \cos x - e^{-x} = 0$; $[1, 2]$

4. $x - 2 + 2 \ln x = 0$; $[1, 2]$

C *In Problems 5–14, use Newton's Method to approximate the indicated root of the given equation accurate to five decimal places. Begin by sketching a graph.*

5. The largest root of $x^3 + 6x^2 + 9x + 1 = 0$

6. The real root of $7x^3 + x - 5 = 0$

7. The largest root of $x - 2 + 2 \ln x = 0$ (see Problem 4)

8. The smallest positive root of $2 \cos x - e^{-x} = 0$ (see Problem 3)

9. The root of $\cos x = 2x$

10. The root of $x \ln x = 2$

11. All real roots of $x^4 - 8x^3 + 22x^2 - 24x + 8 = 0$

12. All real roots of $x^4 + 6x^3 + 2x^2 + 24x - 8 = 0$

13. The positive root of $2x^2 - \sin x = 0$

14. The smallest positive root of $2 \cot x = x$

C **15.** Use Newton's Method to calculate $\sqrt[3]{6}$ to five decimal places. *Hint:* Solve $x^3 - 6 = 0$.

C **16.** Use Newton's Method to calculate $\sqrt[4]{47}$ to five decimal places.

GC *In Problems 17–20, approximate the values of x that give maximum and minimum values of the function on the indicated intervals.*

17. $f(x) = x^4 + x^3 + x^2 + x$; $[-1, 1]$

18. $f(x) = \dfrac{x^3 + 1}{x^4 + 1}$; $[-4, 4]$

19. $f(x) = \dfrac{\sin x}{x}$; $[\pi, 3\pi]$

20. $f(x) = x^2 \sin \dfrac{x}{2}$; $[0, 4\pi]$

C **21.** Kepler's equation $x = m + E \sin x$ is important in astronomy. Use the Fixed-Point Algorithm to solve this equation for x when $m = 0.8$ and $E = 0.2$.

22. Sketch the graph of $y = x^{1/3}$. Obviously, its only x-intercept is zero. Convince yourself that Newton's Method fails to converge to the root of $x^{1/3} = 0$. Explain this failure.

23. In installment buying, one would like to figure out the real interest rate (effective rate), but unfortunately this involves solving a complicated equation. If one buys an item worth $\$P$ today and agrees to pay for it with payments of $\$R$ at the end of each month for k months, then

$$P = \frac{R}{i}\left[1 - \frac{1}{(1 + i)^k}\right]$$

where i is the interest rate per month. Tom bought a used car for $\$2000$ and agreed to pay for it with $\$100$ payments at the end of each of the next 24 months.

(a) Show that i satisfies the equation

$$20i(1 + i)^{24} - (1 + i)^{24} + 1 = 0$$

(b) Show that Newton's Method for this equation reduces to

$$i_{n+1} = i_n - \left[\frac{20i_n^2 + 19i_n - 1 + (1 + i_n)^{-23}}{500i_n - 4}\right]$$

C (c) Find i accurate to five decimal places starting with $i = 0.012$, and then give the annual rate r as a percent ($r = 1200i$).

24. In applying Newton's Method to solve $f(x) = 0$, one can usually tell by simply looking at the numbers $x_1, x_2, x_3, \ldots$ whether the sequence is converging. But even if it converges, say to $\bar{x}$, can we be sure that $\bar{x}$ is a solution? Show that the answer is yes provided f and f' are continuous at $\bar{x}$ and $f'(\bar{x}) \neq 0$.

C *In Problems 25–28, use the Fixed-Point Algorithm with x_1 as indicated to solve the equations to five decimal places.*

25. $x = \dfrac{3}{2} \cos x$; $x_1 = 1$

26. $x = 2 - \sin x$; $x_1 = 2$

27. $x = \sqrt{2.7 + x}$; $x_1 = 1$

28. $x = \sqrt{3.2 + x}$; $x_1 = 47$

GC **29.** Consider the equation $x = 2(x - x^2) = g(x)$.

(a) Sketch the graph of $y = x$ and $y = g(x)$ using the same coordinate system, and thereby approximately locate the positive root of $x = g(x)$.

(b) Try solving the equation by the Fixed-Point Algorithm starting with $x_1 = 0.7$.

(c) Solve the equation algebraically.

GC **30.** Follow the directions of Problem 29 for $x = 5(x - x^2) = g(x)$.

C **31.** Consider $x = \sqrt{1 + x}$.

(a) Apply the Fixed-Point Algorithm starting with $x_1 = 0$ to find x_2, x_3, x_4, and x_5.

(b) Algebraically solve for x in $x = \sqrt{1 + x}$.

(c) Evaluate $\sqrt{1 + \sqrt{1 + \sqrt{1 + \cdots}}}$.

C **32.** Consider $x = \sqrt{5 + x}$.

(a) Apply the Fixed-Point Algorithm starting with $x_1 = 0$ to find x_2, x_3, x_4, and x_5.

(b) Algebraically solve for x in $x = \sqrt{5 + x}$.

(c) Evaluate $\sqrt{5 + \sqrt{5 + \sqrt{5 + \cdots}}}$.

C **33.** Consider $x = 1 + \dfrac{1}{x}$.

(a) Apply the Fixed-Point Algorithm starting with $x_1 = 1$ to find x_2, x_3, x_4, and x_5.

(b) Algebraically solve for x in $x = 1 + \dfrac{1}{x}$.

(c) Evaluate the following expression. (An expression like this is called a **continued fraction**.)

$$1 + \cfrac{1}{1 + \cfrac{1}{1 + \cfrac{1}{1 + \cdots}}}$$

EXPL **34.** Consider the equation $x = x - f(x)/f'(x)$ and suppose that $f'(x) \neq 0$ in an interval $[a, b]$.

(a) Show that if r is in $[a, b]$ then r is a root of the equation $x = x - f(x)/f'(x)$ if and only if $f(r) = 0$.

(b) Show that Newton's Method is a special case of the Fixed-Point Algorithm, in which $g'(r) = 0$.

35. Experiment with the algorithm

$$x_{n+1} = 2x_n - ax_n^2$$

using several different values of a.

(a) Make a conjecture about what this algorithm computes.

(b) Prove your conjecture.

C *After differentiating and setting the result equal to zero, many practical max–min problems lead to an equation that cannot be solved exactly. For the following problems, use a numerical method to approximate the solution to the problem.*

36. A rectangle has two corners on the x-axis and the other two on the curve $y = \cos x$, with $-\pi/2 < x < \pi/2$. What are the dimensions of the rectangle of this type with maximum area? (See Figure 25 of Section 4.4.)

37. Two hallways meet in a right angle as shown in Figure 7 of Section 4.4, except the widths of the hallways are 8.6 feet and 6.2 feet. What is the length of the longest thin rod that can be carried around the corner?

38. An 8-foot-wide hallway makes a turn as shown in Figure 9. What is the length of the longest thin rod that can be carried around the corner?

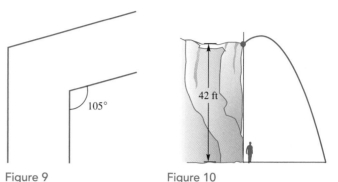

Figure 9   Figure 10

39. An object thrown from the edge of a 42-foot cliff follows the path given by $y = -\dfrac{2x^2}{25} + x + 42$ (Figure 10). An observer stands 3 feet from the bottom of the cliff.

(a) Find the position of the object when it is closest to the observer.

(b) Find the position of the object when it is farthest from the observer.

Answers to Concepts Review: **1.** slowness of convergence **2.** root: Intermediate Value **3.** algorithms **4.** fixed point

---

4.8
Antiderivatives

Most of the mathematical operations that we work with come in inverse pairs: addition and subtraction, multiplication and division, and exponentiation and root taking. In each case, the second operation undoes the first, and vice versa. One reason for our interest in inverse operations is their usefulness in solving equations. For example, solving $x^3 = 8$ involves taking roots. We have been studying differentiation in this chapter and the previous one. If we want to solve equations involving derivatives we will need its inverse, called *antidifferentiation* or *integration*.

> **Definition**
>
> We call F an **antiderivative** of f on the interval I if $D_x F(x) = f(x)$ on I, that is, if $F'(x) = f(x)$ for all x in I.

We said *an* antiderivative rather than *the* antiderivative in our definition. You will soon see why.

EXAMPLE 1 Find an antiderivative of the function $f(x) = 4x^3$ on $(-\infty, \infty)$.

SOLUTION We seek a function F satisfying $F'(x) = 4x^3$ for all real x. From our experience with differentiation, we know that $F(x) = x^4$ is one such function. ∎

A moment's thought will suggest other solutions to Example 1. The function $F(x) = x^4 + 6$ also satisfies $F'(x) = 4x^3$; it too is an antiderivative of $f(x) = 4x^3$. In fact, $F(x) = x^4 + C$, where C is any constant, is an antiderivative of $4x^3$ on $(-\infty, \infty)$ (see Figure 1).

Now we pose an important question. Is *every* antiderivative of $f(x) = 4x^3$ of the form $F(x) = x^4 + C$? The answer is yes. This follows from Theorem 4.6B which says that if two functions have the same derivative, they must differ by a constant.

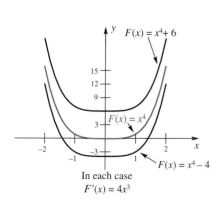

In each case
$F'(x) = 4x^3$

Figure 1

Our conclusion is this. If a function f has an antiderivative, it will have a whole family of them, and each member of this family can be obtained from one of them by the addition of an appropriate constant. We call this family of functions the **general antiderivative** of f. After we get used to this notion, we will often omit the adjective *general*.

EXAMPLE 2 Find the general antiderivative of $f(x) = x^2$ on $(-\infty, \infty)$.

SOLUTION The function $F(x) = x^3$ will not do since its derivative is $3x^2$. But this suggests $F(x) = \frac{1}{3}x^3$, which satisfies $F'(x) = \frac{1}{3} \cdot 3x^2 = x^2$. However, the general antiderivative is $\frac{1}{3}x^3 + C$. ∎

Notation for Antiderivatives Since we used the symbol D_x for the operation of taking a derivative, it would be natural to use A_x for the operation of finding the antiderivative. Thus,

$$A_x(x^2) = \frac{1}{3}x^3 + C$$

This is the notation used by several authors and it was, in fact, used in earlier editions of this book. However, Leibniz's original notation continues to enjoy overwhelming popularity, and we therefore choose to follow him. Rather than A_x, Leibniz used the symbol $\int \ldots dx$. He wrote

$$\int x^2 \, dx = \frac{1}{3}x^3 + C$$

and

$$\int 4x^3 \, dx = x^4 + C$$

Leibniz chose to use the elongated s, $\int$, and the dx for reasons that will not become apparent until the next chapter. For the moment, simply think of $\int \ldots dx$ as indicating the antiderivative with respect to x, just as D_x indicates the derivative with respect to x. Note that

$$D_x \int f(x) \, dx = f(x) \quad \text{and} \quad \int D_x f(x) \, dx = f(x) + C$$

Proving Rules for Antiderivatives

To establish any result of the form

$$\int f(x) \, dx = F(x) + C$$

all we have to do is show that

$$D_x[F(x) + C] = f(x)$$

Theorem A **Power Rule**

If r is any real number except -1, then

$$\int x^r \, dx = \frac{x^{r+1}}{r+1} + C$$

Proof The derivative of the right side is

$$D_x\left[\frac{x^{r+1}}{r+1} + C\right] = \frac{1}{r+1}(r+1)x^r = x^r$$ ∎

We make two comments about Theorem A. First, it is meant to include the case $r = 0$; that is,

$$\int 1 \, dx = x + C$$

Second, since no interval I is specified, the conclusion is understood to be valid only on intervals on which x^r is defined. In particular, we must exclude any interval containing the origin if $r < 0$.

Following Leibniz, we shall often use the term **indefinite integral** in place of antiderivative. To antidifferentiate is also to **integrate.** In the symbol $\int f(x) \, dx$, $\int$ is called the **integral sign** and $f(x)$ is called the **integrand.** Thus, we integrate the integrand and thereby evaluate the indefinite integral. Perhaps Leibniz used the adjective *indefinite* to suggest that the indefinite integral always involves an arbitrary constant.

EXAMPLE 3 Find the general antiderivative of $f(x) = x^{4/3}$.

SOLUTION

$$\int x^{4/3}\, dx = \frac{x^{7/3}}{\frac{7}{3}} + C = \tfrac{3}{7}x^{7/3} + C$$ ∎

Note that *to integrate a power of x, we increase the exponent by 1 and divide by the new exponent.*

Other Antiderivative Formulas At the end of Section 3.10, we presented a table of derivative formulas. For every derivative formula, there is a corresponding antiderivative formula. Theorem B gives a number of the important results. The proofs are easy; simply differentiate the right side to get the integrand.

Theorem B **Antidifferentiation Formulas**

(1) $\displaystyle\int \sin x\, dx = -\cos x + C$

(2) $\displaystyle\int \cos x\, dx = \sin x + C$

(3) $\displaystyle\int \frac{1}{x}\, dx = \ln x + C, x > 0$

(4) $\displaystyle\int e^x\, dx = e^x + C$

(5) $\displaystyle\int a^x\, dx = \left(\frac{1}{\ln a}\right)a^x + C$

(6) $\displaystyle\int \sinh x\, dx = \cosh x + C$

(7) $\displaystyle\int \cosh x\, dx = \sinh x + C$

(8) $\displaystyle\int \frac{1}{\sqrt{1 - x^2}}\, dx = \sin^{-1} x + C, -1 < x < 1$

(9) $\displaystyle\int \frac{1}{1 + x^2}\, dx = \tan^{-1} x + C$

The Indefinite Integral Is Linear Recall from Chapter 3 that D_x is a linear operator. This means two things.

1. $D_x[kf(x)] = kD_xf(x)$

2. $D_x[f(x) + g(x)] = D_xf(x) + D_xg(x)$

From these two properties, a third follows automatically.

3. $D_x[f(x) - g(x)] = D_xf(x) - D_xg(x)$

It turns out that $\int \ldots dx$ also has these properties of a linear operator.

Theorem C **Indefinite Integral Is a Linear Operator**

Let f and g have antiderivatives (indefinite integrals) and let k be a constant. Then

(1) $\displaystyle\int kf(x)\, dx = k\int f(x)\, dx$

(2) $\displaystyle\int [f(x) + g(x)]\, dx = \int f(x)\, dx + \int g(x)\, dx$

(3) $\displaystyle\int [f(x) - g(x)]\, dx = \int f(x)\, dx - \int g(x)\, dx$

Proof To show (1) and (2), we simply differentiate the right side and observe that we get the integrand of the left side.

$$D_x\left[k\int f(x)\,dx\right] = kD_x\int f(x)\,dx = kf(x)$$

$$D_x\left[\int f(x)\,dx + \int g(x)\,dx\right] = D_x\int f(x)\,dx + D_x\int g(x)\,dx$$

$$= f(x) + g(x)$$

Property (3) follows from (1) and (2). ∎

EXAMPLE 4 Using the linearity of $\int$, evaluate

(a) $\displaystyle\int (3x^2 + 4x)\,dx$ (b) $\displaystyle\int (u^{3/2} - 3u + 14)\,du$ (c) $\displaystyle\int \left(1/t^2 + \sqrt{t}\right)dt$

SOLUTION

(a)
$$\int (3x^2 + 4x)\,dx = \int 3x^2\,dx + \int 4x\,dx$$
$$= 3\int x^2\,dx + 4\int x\,dx$$
$$= 3\left(\frac{x^3}{3} + C_1\right) + 4\left(\frac{x^2}{2} + C_2\right)$$
$$= x^3 + 2x^2 + (3C_1 + 4C_2)$$
$$= x^3 + 2x^2 + C$$

Two arbitrary constants C_1 and C_2 appeared, but they were combined into one constant, C, a practice we consistently follow.

(b) Note the use of the variable u rather than x. This is fine as long as the corresponding differential symbol is du, since we then have a complete change of notation.

$$\int (u^{3/2} - 3u + 14)\,du = \int u^{3/2}\,du - 3\int u\,du + 14\int 1\,du$$
$$= \tfrac{2}{5}u^{5/2} - \tfrac{3}{2}u^2 + 14u + C$$

(c)
$$\int \left(\frac{1}{t^2} + \sqrt{t}\right)dt = \int (t^{-2} + t^{1/2})\,dt = \int t^{-2}\,dt + \int t^{1/2}\,dt$$
$$= \frac{t^{-1}}{-1} + \frac{t^{3/2}}{\frac{3}{2}} + C = -\frac{1}{t} + \frac{2}{3}t^{3/2} + C$$ ∎

Generalized Power Rule Recall the Chain Rule as applied to a power of a function. If $u = g(x)$ is a differentiable function and r is a real number $(r \neq -1)$, then

$$D_x\left[\frac{u^{r+1}}{r+1}\right] = u^r \cdot D_x u$$

or, in functional notation,

$$D_x\left(\frac{[g(x)]^{r+1}}{r+1}\right) = [g(x)]^r \cdot g'(x)$$

From this we obtain an important rule for indefinite integrals.

> **Theorem D** **Generalized Power Rule**
>
> Let g be a differentiable function and r a real number different from -1. Then
> $$\int [g(x)]^r g'(x)\, dx = \frac{[g(x)]^{r+1}}{r+1} + C$$

To apply Theorem D, we must be able to recognize the functions g and g' in the integrand.

EXAMPLE 5 Evaluate

(a) $\displaystyle\int (x^4 + 3x)^{30}(4x^3 + 3)\, dx$ (b) $\displaystyle\int \sin^{10} x \cos x\, dx$

SOLUTION

(a) Let $g(x) = x^4 + 3x$; then $g'(x) = 4x^3 + 3$. Thus, by Theorem D,

$$\int (x^4 + 3x)^{30}(4x^3 + 3)\, dx = \int [g(x)]^{30} g'(x)\, dx = \frac{[g(x)]^{31}}{31} + C$$
$$= \frac{(x^4 + 3x)^{31}}{31} + C$$

(b) Let $g(x) = \sin x$; then $g'(x) = \cos x$. Thus,

$$\int \sin^{10} x \cos x\, dx = \int [g(x)]^{10} g'(x)\, dx = \frac{[g(x)]^{11}}{11} + C = \frac{\sin^{11} x}{11} + C \quad\blacksquare$$

Example 5 shows why Leibniz used the differential dx in his notation $\int \ldots dx$. If we let $u = g(x)$, then $du = g'(x)\, dx$ and the conclusion of Theorem D is

$$\int u^r\, du = \frac{u^{r+1}}{r+1} + C, \qquad r \neq -1$$

which is the ordinary power rule with u as the variable. Thus, the generalized power rule is just the ordinary power rule applied to functions. But, in applying it, we must always make sure that we have du to go with u^r. The following examples illustrate what we mean.

EXAMPLE 6 Evaluate

(a) $\displaystyle\int (x^3 + 6x)^5(6x^2 + 12)\, dx$ (b) $\displaystyle\int (x^2 + 4)^{10} x\, dx$

SOLUTION

(a) Let $u = x^3 + 6x$; then $du = (3x^2 + 6)\, dx$. Thus, $(6x^2 + 12)\, dx = 2(3x^2 + 6)\, dx = 2\, du$, and so

$$\int (x^3 + 6x)^5(6x^2 + 12)\, dx = \int u^5 2\, du = 2\left[\frac{u^6}{6} + C\right]$$
$$= \frac{u^6}{3} + 2C = \frac{(x^3 + 6x)^6}{3} + K$$

Constants in Example 6

Two things should be noted about our solution. First, the fact that $(6x^2 + 12)\, dx$ is $2\, du$ instead of du caused no trouble; the constant 2 could be moved in front of the integral sign by linearity. Second, we wound up with an arbitrary constant of $2C$. This is still an arbitrary constant; we called it K.

(b) Let $u = x^2 + 4$; then $du = 2x\,dx$. Thus,

$$\int (x^2 + 4)^{10} x\,dx = \int (x^2 + 4)^{10} \cdot \frac{1}{2} \cdot 2x\,dx$$

$$= \frac{1}{2} \int u^{10}\,du$$

$$= \frac{1}{2}\left(\frac{u^{11}}{11} + C\right) = \frac{(x^2 + 4)^{11}}{22} + K \qquad \blacksquare$$

EXAMPLE 7 Evaluate

(a) $\displaystyle\int (1 + \sinh x)^4 \cosh x\,dx$ 　　(b) $\displaystyle\int \frac{e^x}{(1 + e^x)^4}\,dx$

SOLUTION

(a) Here we let $u = 1 + \sinh x$, so that $du = \cosh x\,dx$. Thus,

$$\int (1 + \sinh x)^4 \cosh x\,dx = \int u^4\,du = \frac{u^5}{5} + C = \frac{\sinh^5 x}{5} + C$$

(b) The substitution is less obvious here. What we must look for is a functon of x raised to a power, times the derivative of that function. Since $D_x(1 + e^x) = e^x$, this suggests letting $u = 1 + e^x$, so that $du = e^x\,dx$. Thus,

$$\int \frac{e^x}{(1 + e^x)^4}\,dx = \int (1 + e^x)^{-4}\,(e^x\,dx)$$

$$= \int u^{-4}\,du = \frac{u^{-3}}{-3} + C = -\frac{1}{3}(1 + e^x)^{-3} + C \qquad \blacksquare$$

The restriction $x > 0$ in the antiderivative formula for $\int 1/x\,dx$ (part 3 of Theorem B) is sometimes a nuisance. The next example addresses this issue.

EXAMPLE 8 Show that

(a) $D_x \ln |x| = \dfrac{1}{x}$, $x \neq 0$ 　　(b) $\displaystyle\int \frac{1}{x}\,dx = \ln |x| + C$, $x \neq 0$

(c) $\displaystyle\int \frac{1}{x - a}\,dx = \ln |x - a| + C$, $x \neq a$

SOLUTION

(a) We must consider two cases. For $x > 0$, $|x| = x$, and

$$D_x \ln |x| = D_x \ln x = \frac{1}{x}$$

For $x < 0$, $|x| = -x$, and we apply the Chain Rule.

$$D_x \ln |x| = D_x \ln (-x) = \frac{1}{(-x)} D_x(-x) = -\frac{1}{x}(-1) = \frac{1}{x}$$

Figure 2 suggests why this is the case. Since $\ln |x|$ is an even function, the slope at the point c $(c > 0)$ is $1/c$, while the slope at $-c$ is the negative of $1/c$, that is, $-1/c$.

(b) The integral formula follows from part (a) since

$$D_x (\ln |x| + C) = \frac{1}{x}$$

(c) Differentiation of the right side, but this time using the Chain Rule, gives

$$D_x (\ln |x - a| + C) = \frac{1}{x - a} D_x (x - a) = \frac{1}{x - a} \qquad \blacksquare$$

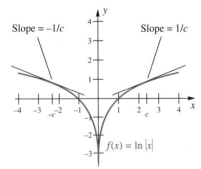

Slope $= -1/c$ 　　Slope $= 1/c$

$f(x) = \ln |x|$

Figure 2

EXAMPLE 9 Evaluate $\displaystyle\int \frac{x}{10 - x^2}\, dx$.

SOLUTION Let $u = 10 - x^2$, so $du = -2x\, dx$. Then

$$\int \frac{x}{10 - x^2}\, dx = -\frac{1}{2} \int \frac{-2x}{10 - x^2}\, dx = -\frac{1}{2} \int \frac{1}{u}\, du$$

$$= -\frac{1}{2} \ln|u| + C = -\frac{1}{2} \ln|10 - x^2| + C \qquad \blacksquare$$

When the integrand is the quotient of two polynomials (that is, a rational function) and the numerator is of equal or greater degree than the denominator, always *divide the denominator into the numerator first.*

EXAMPLE 10 Find $\displaystyle\int \frac{x^2 - x}{x + 1}\, dx$.

SOLUTION By long division (Figure 3),

$$\frac{x^2 - x}{x + 1} = x - 2 + \frac{2}{x + 1}$$

Hence,

$$\int \frac{x^2 - x}{x + 1}\, dx = \int (x - 2)\, dx + 2 \int \frac{1}{x + 1}\, dx$$

$$= \frac{x^2}{2} - 2x + 2 \int \frac{1}{x + 1}\, dx$$

$$= \frac{x^2}{2} - 2x + 2 \ln|x + 1| + C \qquad \blacksquare$$

$$
\begin{array}{r}
x - 2 \\
x + 1 \overline{)\,x^2 - x} \\
\underline{x^2 + x} \\
-2x \\
\underline{-2x - 2} \\
2
\end{array}
$$

Figure 3

Concepts Review

1. The Power Rule for derivatives says that $d(x^r)/dx =$ _____. The Power Rule for integrals says that $\int x^r\, dx =$ _____.

2. The Generalized Power Rule for integrals says that $\int$ _____ $dx = [f(x)]^{r+1}/(r + 1) + C, r \neq -1$.

3. $\int (x^4 + 3x^2 + 1)^8(4x^3 + 6x)\, dx =$ _____.

4. By linearity, $\int [c_1 f(x) + c_2 g(x)]\, dx =$ _____.

Problem Set 4.8

Find the general antiderivative $F(x) + C$ for each of the following.

1. $f(x) = 5$

2. $f(x) = x - 4$

3. $f(x) = x^2 + \pi$

4. $f(x) = 3x^2 + \sqrt{3}$

5. $f(x) = x^{5/4}$

6. $f(x) = 3x^{2/3}$

7. $f(x) = 1/\sqrt[3]{x^2}$

8. $f(x) = 7x^{-3/4}$

9. $f(x) = x^2 - x$

10. $f(x) = 3x^2 - \pi x$

11. $f(x) = 4x^5 - x^3$

12. $f(x) = x^{100} + x^{99}$

13. $f(x) = 27x^7 + 3x^5 - 45x^3 + \sqrt{2}x$

14. $f(x) = x^2(x^3 + 5x^2 - 3x + \sqrt{3})$

15. $f(x) = \dfrac{3}{x^2} - \dfrac{2}{x^3}$

16. $f(x) = \dfrac{\sqrt{2x}}{x} + \dfrac{3}{x^5}$

17. $f(x) = \dfrac{4x^6 + 3x^4}{x^3}$

18. $f(x) = \dfrac{x^6 - x}{x^3}$

19. $f(x) = x - \cosh x$

20. $f(x) = x^2 + e^x$

In Problems 21–28, evaluate the indicated indefinite integrals.

21. $\displaystyle\int (x^2 + x)\, dx$

22. $\displaystyle\int (x^3 + \sqrt{x})\, dx$

23. $\displaystyle\int (x + 1)^2\, dx$

24. $\displaystyle\int (z + \sqrt{2}z)^2\, dz$

25. $\displaystyle\int \frac{(z^2 + 1)^2}{\sqrt{z}}\, dz$

26. $\displaystyle\int \frac{s(s + 1)^2}{\sqrt{s}}\, ds$

27. $\displaystyle\int (\sin \theta - \cos \theta)\, d\theta$

28. $\displaystyle\int (t^2 - 2 \cos t)\, dt$

In Problems 29–40, use the methods of Examples 5 and 6 to evaluate the indefinite integrals.

29. $\displaystyle\int (\sqrt{2}x + 1)^3 \sqrt{2}\, dx$

30. $\displaystyle\int (\pi x^3 + 1)^4 3\pi x^2\, dx$

31. $\displaystyle\int (5x^2 + 1)(5x^3 + 3x - 8)^6\, dx$

32. $\displaystyle\int (5x^2 + 1)\sqrt{5x^3 + 3x - 2}\, dx$

33. $\displaystyle\int 3t\sqrt[3]{2t^2 - 11}\, dt$

34. $\displaystyle\int \frac{3y}{\sqrt{2y^2 + 5}}\, dy$

35. $\displaystyle\int x^2\sqrt{x^3 + 4}\, dx$

36. $\displaystyle\int (x^3 + x)\sqrt{x^4 + 2x^2}\, dx$

37. $\displaystyle\int \sin x\, (1 + \cos x)^4\, dx$

38. $\displaystyle\int \sin x \cos x\, \sqrt{1 + \sin^2 x}\, dx$

39. $\displaystyle\int (1 + e^x)^2\, e^x\, dx$

40. $\displaystyle\int \frac{\sinh x}{1 + \cosh x}\, dx$

In Problems 41–46, $f''(x)$ is given. Find $f(x)$ by antidifferentiating twice. Note that in this case your answer should involve two arbitrary constants, one from each antidifferentiation. For example, if $f''(x) = x$, then $f'(x) = x^2/2 + C_1$ and $f(x) = x^3/6 + C_1 x + C_2$. The constants C_1 and C_2 cannot be combined because $C_1 x$ is not a constant.

41. $f''(x) = 3x + 1$ **42.** $f''(x) = -2x + 3$

43. $f''(x) = \sqrt{x}$ **44.** $f''(x) = x^{4/3}$

45. $f''(x) = \dfrac{x^4 + 1}{x^3}$ **46.** $f''(x) = 2\sqrt[3]{x + 1}$

47. Prove the formula

$$\int [f(x)g'(x) + g(x)f'(x)]\, dx = f(x)g(x) + C$$

Hint: See the box in the margin next to Theorem A.

48. Prove the formula

$$\int \frac{g(x)f'(x) - f(x)g'(x)}{g^2(x)}\, dx = \frac{f(x)}{g(x)} + C$$

49. Use the formula from Problem 47 to find

$$\int \left[\frac{x^2}{2\sqrt{x - 1}} + 2x\sqrt{x - 1}\right] dx$$

50. Use the formula from Problem 47 to find

$$\int \left[\frac{-x^3}{(2x + 5)^{3/2}} + \frac{3x^2}{\sqrt{2x + 5}}\right] dx$$

51. Find $\displaystyle\int f''(x)\, dx$ if $f(x) = x\sqrt{x^3 + 1}$.

52. Prove the formula

$$\int \frac{2g(x)f'(x) - f(x)g'(x)}{2[g(x)]^{3/2}} = \frac{f(x)}{\sqrt{g(x)}} + C$$

53. Prove the formula

$$\int f^{m-1}(x)g^{n-1}(x)[nf(x)g'(x) + mg(x)f'(x)]\, dx$$
$$= f^m(x)g^n(x) + C$$

54. Evaluate the indefinite integral

$$\int \sin^3[(x^2 + 1)^4]\cos[(x^2 + 1)^4](x^2 + 1)^3 x\, dx$$

Hint: Let $u = \sin(x^2 + 1)^4$.

55. Evaluate $\displaystyle\int |x|\, dx$.   **56.** Evaluate $\displaystyle\int \sin^2 x\, dx$.

CAS **57.** Some software packages can evaluate indefinite integrals. Use your software on each of the following.

(a) $\displaystyle\int 6\sin(3(x - 2))\, dx$ (b) $\displaystyle\int \sin^3(x/6)\, dx$

(c) $\displaystyle\int (x^2\cos 2x + x\sin 2x)\, dx$

EXPL CAS **58.** Let $F_0(x) = x\sin x$ and $F_{n+1}(x) = \displaystyle\int F_n(x)\, dx$.

(a) Determine $F_1(x)$, $F_2(x)$, $F_3(x)$, and $F_4(x)$.

(b) On the basis of part (a), conjecture the form of $F_{16}(x)$.

Answers to Concepts Review: **1.** rx^{r-1};
$x^{r+1}/(r + 1) + C, r \neq -1$ **2.** $[f(x)]^r f'(x)$
3. $(x^4 + 3x^2 + 1)^9/9 + C$ **4.** $c_1\int f(x)\, dx + c_2\int g(x)\, dx$

4.9

Introduction to Differential Equations

In the previous section, our task was to antidifferentiate (integrate) a function f to obtain a new function F. We wrote

$$\int f(x)\, dx = F(x) + C$$

and this was correct by definition provided $F'(x) = f(x)$. When we evaluate an antiderivative like this we are, in effect, asking this: what function(s) $F(x)$ satisfy the condition $F'(x) = f(x)$? Looking at the problem this way leads us to study *differential equations.*

What Is a Differential Equation?
To motivate our answer, we begin with a simple example.

EXAMPLE 1 Find the xy-equation of the curve that passes through $(-1, 2)$ and whose slope at any point on the curve is equal to twice the x-coordinate of that point.

SOLUTION The condition that must hold at each point (x, y) on the curve is

$$\frac{dy}{dx} = 2x$$

We are looking for a function $y = f(x)$ that satisfies this equation and the additional condition that $y = 2$ when $x = -1$. We suggest two ways of looking at this problem.

Method 1 When an equation has the form $dy/dx = g(x)$, we observe that y must be an antiderivative of $g(x)$; that is,

$$y = \int g(x)\, dx$$

In our case,

$$y = \int 2x\, dx = x^2 + C$$

Method 2 Think of dy/dx as a quotient of two differentials. When we multiply both sides of $dy/dx = 2x$ by dx, we get

$$dy = 2x\, dx$$

Next we integrate the differentials on both sides, equate the results, and simplify.

$$\int dy = \int 2x\, dx$$
$$y + C_1 = x^2 + C_2$$
$$y = x^2 + C_2 - C_1$$
$$y = x^2 + C$$

The second method works in a wide variety of problems that are not of the simple form $dy/dx = g(x)$, as we shall see.

The solution $y = x^2 + C$ represents the family of curves illustrated in Figure 1. From this family, we must choose the one for which $y = 2$ when $x = -1$; thus, we want

$$2 = (-1)^2 + C$$

We conclude that $C = 1$ and therefore that $y = x^2 + 1$. ■

The equations $dy/dx = 2x$ and $dy = 2x\, dx$ are called *differential equations*. Other examples are

$$\frac{dy}{dx} = 2xy + \sin x$$

$$y\, dy = (x^3 + 1)\, dx$$

$$\frac{d^2y}{dx^2} + 3\frac{dy}{dx} - 2xy = 0$$

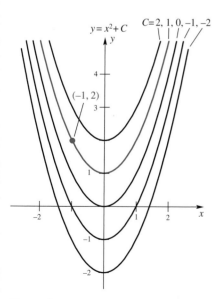

Figure 1

Any equation in which the unknown is a function and that involves derivatives (or differentials) of this unknown function is called a **differential equation.** A function that, when substituted in the differential equation yields an equality, is called a **solution** of the differential equation. Thus, to solve a differential equation is to find an unknown *function*. In general, this is a difficult job and one about which many thick books have been written. Here we consider only the simplest type, **first-order separable** differential equations. These are equations involving just the first derivative of the unknown function and are such that the variables can be separated, one on each side of the equation.

Separation of Variables   Consider the differential equation

$$\frac{dy}{dx} = \frac{x + 3x^2}{y^2}$$

If we multiply both sides by $y^2\, dx$, we obtain

$$y^2\, dy = (x + 3x^2)\, dx$$

In this form, the differential equation has its variables separated; that is, the y terms are on one side of the equation and the x terms are on the other. In separated form, we can solve the differential equation using Method 2 (integrate both sides, equate the results, and simplify), as we now illustrate.

EXAMPLE 2   Solve the differential equation

$$\frac{dy}{dx} = \frac{x + 3x^2}{y^2}$$

Then find that solution for which $y = 6$ when $x = 0$.

SOLUTION   As noted earlier, the given equation leads to

$$y^2\, dy = (x + 3x^2)\, dx$$

Thus,

$$\int y^2\, dy = \int (x + 3x^2)\, dx$$

$$\frac{y^3}{3} + C_1 = \frac{x^2}{2} + x^3 + C_2$$

$$y^3 = \frac{3x^2}{2} + 3x^3 + (3C_2 - 3C_1) = \frac{3x^2}{2} + 3x^3 + C$$

$$y = \sqrt[3]{\frac{3x^2}{2} + 3x^3 + C}$$

To find the constant C, we use the condition $y = 6$ when $x = 0$. This gives

$$6 = \sqrt[3]{C}$$

$$216 = C$$

Thus,

$$y = \sqrt[3]{\frac{3x^2}{2} + 3x^3 + 216}$$

To check our work we can substitute this result in both sides of the original differential equation to see that it gives an equality. We should also check that $y = 6$ when $x = 0$.

Substituting in the left side, we get

$$\frac{dy}{dx} = \frac{1}{3}\left(\frac{3x^2}{2} + 3x^3 + 216\right)^{-2/3}(3x + 9x^2) = \frac{x + 3x^2}{\left(\frac{3}{2}x^2 + 3x^3 + 216\right)^{2/3}}$$

On the right side, we get

$$\frac{x + 3x^2}{y^2} = \frac{x + 3x^2}{\left(\frac{3}{2}x^2 + 3x^3 + 216\right)^{2/3}}$$

As expected, the two expressions are equal. When $x = 0$, we have

$$y = \sqrt[3]{\frac{3 \cdot 0^2}{2} + 3 \cdot 0^3 + 216} = \sqrt[3]{216} = 6$$

Thus, $y = 6$ when $x = 0$, as we expected. ■

Motion Problems   Recall that if $s(t)$, $v(t)$, and $a(t)$ represent the position, velocity, and acceleration, respectively, at time t of an object moving along a coordinate line then

$$v(t) = s'(t) = \frac{ds}{dt}$$

$$a(t) = v'(t) = \frac{dv}{dt} = \frac{d^2s}{dt^2}$$

In some earlier work (Section 3.6), we assumed that $s(t)$ was known, and from this we calculated $v(t)$ and $a(t)$. Now we want to consider the reverse process: given the acceleration $a(t)$, find the velocity $v(t)$ and the position $s(t)$.

▮ EXAMPLE 3 Falling-Body Problem

Near the surface of the earth, the acceleration of a falling body due to gravity is 32 feet per second per second, provided that air resistance is neglected. If an object is thrown upward from an initial height of 1000 feet (Figure 2) with an initial velocity of 50 feet per second, find its velocity and height 4 seconds later.

SOLUTION   Let us assume that the height s is measured positively in the upward direction. Then $v = ds/dt$ is initially positive (s is increasing), but $a = dv/dt$ is negative. (The pull of gravity is downward, thus decreasing v). Hence, we start our analysis with the differential equation $dv/dt = -32$, with the additional conditions that $v = 50$ and $s = 1000$ when $t = 0$. Either Method 1 (direct antidifferentiation) or Method 2 (separation of variables) works well.

$$\frac{dv}{dt} = -32$$

$$v = \int -32 \, dt = -32t + C$$

Since $v = 50$ at $t = 0$, we find that $C = 50$, and so

$$\boxed{v = -32t + 50}$$

Now $v = ds/dt$, and so we have another differential equation,

$$\frac{ds}{dt} = -32t + 50$$

When we integrate, we obtain

$$s = \int (-32t + 50) \, dt$$

$$= -16t^2 + 50t + K$$

Since $s = 1000$ at $t = 0$, $K = 1000$ and

$$\boxed{s = -16t^2 + 50t + 1000}$$

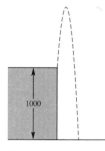

Figure 2

Finally, at $t = 4$,

$$v = -32(4) + 50 = -78 \text{ feet per second}$$
$$s = -16(4)^2 + 50(4) + 1000 = 944 \text{ feet}$$ ∎

We remark that if $v = v_0$ and $s = s_0$ at $t = 0$, the procedure of Example 3 leads to the well-known falling-body formulas:

$$a = -32$$
$$v = -32t + v_0$$
$$s = -16t^2 + v_0 t + s_0$$

EXAMPLE 4 The acceleration of an object moving along a coordinate line is given by $a(t) = (2t + 3)^{-3}$ in meters per second per second. If the velocity at $t = 0$ is 4 meters per second, find the velocity 2 seconds later.

SOLUTION We begin with the differential equation shown in the first line below. To perform the integration in the second line, we multiply and divide by 2, thus preparing the integral for the Generalized Power Rule.

$$\frac{dv}{dt} = (2t + 3)^{-3}$$

$$v = \int (2t + 3)^{-3} \, dt = \frac{1}{2} \int (2t + 3)^{-3} \, 2 \, dt$$

$$= \frac{1}{2} \frac{(2t + 3)^{-2}}{-2} + C = -\frac{1}{4(2t + 3)^2} + C$$

Since $v = 4$ at $t = 0$,

$$4 = -\frac{1}{4(3)^2} + C$$

which gives $C = \frac{145}{36}$. Thus,

$$v = -\frac{1}{4(2t + 3)^2} + \frac{145}{36}$$

At $t = 2$,

$$v = -\frac{1}{4(49)} + \frac{145}{36} \approx 4.023 \text{ meters per second}$$ ∎

EXAMPLE 5 **Escape Velocity (Optional)**

The gravitational attraction F exerted by the earth on an object of mass m at a distance s from the center of the earth is given by $F = -mgR^2/s^2$, where $-g$ ($g \approx 32$ feet per second per second) is the acceleration of gravity at the surface of the earth and R ($R \approx 3960$ miles) is the radius of the earth (Figure 3). Show that an object launched outward from the earth with an initial velocity $v_0 \geq \sqrt{2gR} \approx 6.93$ miles per second will not fall back to the earth. Neglect air resistance in making this calculation.

SOLUTION According to Newton's Second Law, $F = ma$; that is,

$$F = m\frac{dv}{dt} = m\frac{dv}{ds}\frac{ds}{dt} = m\frac{dv}{ds}v$$

Thus,

$$mv\frac{dv}{ds} = -mg\frac{R^2}{s^2}$$

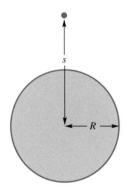

Figure 3

Separating variables gives

$$v \, dv = -gR^2 s^{-2} \, ds$$

$$\int v \, dv = -gR^2 \int s^{-2} \, ds$$

$$\frac{v^2}{2} = \frac{gR^2}{s} + C$$

Now $v = v_0$ when $s = R$, and so $C = \frac{1}{2}v_0^2 - gR$. Consequently,

$$v^2 = \frac{2gR^2}{s} + v_0^2 - 2gR$$

Finally, since $2gR^2/s$ gets small with increasing s, we see that v remains positive if and only if

$$v_0 \geq \sqrt{2gR} \approx \sqrt{(2)\left(\frac{32}{5280}\right)(3960)} \approx 6.93 \text{ miles per second} \qquad \blacksquare$$

Concepts Review

1. $dy/dx = 3x^2 + 1$ and $dy/dx = x/y^2$ are examples of what is called a _____.

2. To solve the differential equation $dy/dx = g(x, y)$ is to find the _____ that, when substituted for y, yields an equality.

3. To solve the differential equation $dy/dx = x^2 y^3$, the first step would be to _____.

4. To solve a falling-body problem near the surface of the earth, we start with the experimental fact that the acceleration a of gravity is -32 feet per second per second; that is, $a = dv/dt = -32$. Solving this differential equation gives $v = ds/dt =$ _____, and solving the resulting differential equation gives $s =$ _____.

Problem Set 4.9

In Problems 1–4, show that the indicated function is a solution of the given differential equation; that is, substitute the indicated function for y to see that it produces an equality.

1. $\dfrac{dy}{dx} + \dfrac{x}{y} = 0; \ y = \sqrt{1 - x^2}$

2. $-x\dfrac{dy}{dx} + y = 0; \ y = Cx$

3. $\dfrac{d^2 y}{dx^2} + y = 0; \ y = C_1 \sin x + C_2 \cos x$

4. $\left(\dfrac{dy}{dx}\right)^2 + y^2 = 1; \ y = \sin(x + C)$ and $y = \pm 1$

In Problems 5–14, first find the general solution (involving a constant C) for the given differential equation. Then find the particular solution that satisfies the indicated condition. (See Example 2.)

5. $\dfrac{dy}{dx} = x^2 + 1; \ y = 1$ at $x = 1$

6. $\dfrac{dy}{dx} = x^{-3} + 2; \ y = 3$ at $x = 1$

7. $\dfrac{dy}{dx} = \dfrac{x}{y}; \ y = 1$ at $x = 1$

8. $\dfrac{dy}{dx} = \sqrt{\dfrac{x}{y}}; \ y = 4$ at $x = 1$

9. $\dfrac{dz}{dt} = t^2 z^2; \ z = 1/3$ at $t = 1$

10. $\dfrac{dy}{dt} = y^4; \ y = 1$ at $t = 0$

11. $\dfrac{ds}{dt} = 16t^2 + 4t - 1; \ s = 100$ at $t = 0$

12. $\dfrac{du}{dt} = u^3(t^3 - t); \ u = 4$ at $t = 0$

13. $\dfrac{dy}{dx} = (2x + 1)^4; \ y = 6$ at $x = 0$

14. $\dfrac{dy}{dx} = -y^2 x(x^2 + 2)^4; \ y = 1$ at $x = 0$

15. Find the xy-equation of the curve through $(1, 2)$ whose slope at any point is three times its x-coordinate (see Example 1).

16. Find the xy-equation of the curve through $(1, 2)$ whose slope at any point is three times the square of its y-coordinate.

In Problems 17–20, an object is moving along a coordinate line subject to the indicated acceleration a (in centimeters per second per second) with the initial velocity v_0 (in centimeters per second) and directed distance s_0 (in centimeters). Find both the velocity v and directed distance s after 2 seconds (see Example 4).

17. $a = t$; $v_0 = 3$, $s_0 = 0$

18. $a = (1 + t)^{-4}$; $v_0 = 0$, $s_0 = 10$

C **19.** $a = \sqrt[3]{2t + 1}$; $v_0 = 0$, $s_0 = 10$

C **20.** $a = (3t + 1)^{-3}$; $v_0 = 4$, $s_0 = 0$

21. A ball is thrown upward from the surface of the earth with an initial velocity of 96 feet per second. What is the maximum height that it reaches? (See Example 3.)

22. A ball is thrown upward from the surface of a planet where the acceleration of gravity is k (a negative constant) feet per second per second. If the initial velocity is v_0, show that the maximum height is $-v_0^2/2k$.

C **23.** On the surface of the moon, the acceleration of gravity is -5.28 feet per second per second. If an object is thrown upward from an initial height of 1000 feet with a velocity of 56 feet per second, find its velocity and height 4.5 seconds later.

C **24.** What is the maximum height that the object of Problem 23 reaches?

25. The rate of change of volume V of a melting snowball is proportional to the surface area S of the ball; that is, $dV/dt = -kS$, where k is a positive constant. If the radius of the ball at $t = 0$ is $r = 2$ and at $t = 10$ is $r = 0.5$, show that $r = -\frac{3}{20}t + 2$.

26. From what height must a ball be dropped in order to strike the ground with a velocity of -136 feet per second?

C **27.** Determine the *escape velocity* for an object launched from each of the following celestial bodies (see Example 5). Here $g \approx 32$ feet per second per second.

	Acceleration of Gravity	Radius (miles)
Moon	$-0.165g$	1,080
Venus	$-0.85g$	3,800
Jupiter	$-2.6g$	43,000
Sun	$-28g$	432,000

28. If the brakes of a car, when fully applied, produce a constant deceleration of 11 feet per second per second, what is the shortest distance in which the car can be braked to a halt from a speed of 60 miles per hour?

29. What constant acceleration will cause a car to increase its velocity from 45 to 60 miles per hour in 10 seconds?

30. A block slides down an inclined plane with a constant acceleration of 8 feet per second per second. If the inclined plane is 75 feet long and the block reaches the bottom in 3.75 seconds, what was the initial velocity of the block?

31. A certain rocket, initially at rest, is shot straight up with an acceleration of $6t$ meters per second per second during the first 10 seconds after blast-off, after which the engine cuts out and the rocket is subject only to gravitational acceleration of -10 meters per second per second. How high will the rocket go?

32. Starting at station A, a commuter train accelerates at 3 meters per second per second for 8 seconds, then travels at constant speed v_m for 100 seconds, and finally brakes (decelerates) to a stop at station B at 4 meters per second per second. Find (a) v_m and (b) the distance between A and B.

33. Starting from rest, a bus increases speed at constant acceleration a_1, then travels at constant speed v_m, and finally brakes to a stop at constant acceleration a_2 $(a_2 < 0)$. It took 4 minutes to travel the 2 miles between stop C and stop D and then 3 minutes to go the 1.4 miles between stop D and stop E.

(a) Sketch the graph of the velocity v as a function of time t, $0 \le t \le 7$.

(b) Find the maximum speed v_m.

(c) If $a_1 = -a_2 = a$, evaluate a.

34. A hot-air balloon left the ground rising at 4 feet per second. Sixteen seconds later, Victoria threw a ball straight up to her friend Colleen in the balloon. At what speed did she throw the ball if it just made it to Colleen?

35. According to Torricelli's Law, the time rate of change of the volume V of water in a draining tank is proportional to the square root of the water's depth. A cylindrical tank of radius $10/\sqrt{\pi}$ centimeters and height 16 centimeters, which was full initially, took 40 seconds to drain.

(a) Write the differential equation for V at time t and the two corresponding conditions.

(b) Solve the differential equation.

(c) Find the volume of water after 10 seconds.

C **36.** The wolf population P in a certain state has been growing at a rate proportional to the cube root of the population size. The population was estimated at 1000 in 1980 and at 1700 in 1990.

(a) Write the differential equation for P at time t with the two corresponding conditions.

(b) Solve the differential equation.

(c) When will the wolf population reach 4000?

37. At $t = 0$, a ball was dropped from a height of 16 feet. It hit the floor and rebounded to a height of 9 feet (Figure 4).

(a) Find a two-part formula for the velocity $v(t)$ that is valid until the ball hits the floor a second time.

(b) At what two times was the ball at height 9 feet?

38. To derive the equation of a hanging cable (catenary), we consider the section AP from the lowest point A to a general point $P(x, y)$ (see Figure 5) and imagine the rest of the cable to have been removed.

The forces acting on the cable are

1. $H = $ horizontal tension pulling at A;
2. $T = $ tangential tension pulling at P;

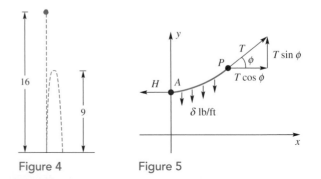

Figure 4   Figure 5

3. $W = \delta s$ = weight of s feet of cable of density δ pounds per foot.

To be in equilibrium, the horizontal and vertical components of T must just balance H and W, respectively. Thus, $T \cos \phi = H$ and $T \sin \phi = W = \delta s$, and so

$$\frac{T \sin \phi}{T \cos \phi} = \tan \phi = \frac{\delta s}{H}$$

But since $\tan \phi = dy/dx$, we get $\dfrac{dy}{dx} = \dfrac{\delta s}{H}$ and therefore

$$\frac{d^2y}{dx^2} = \frac{\delta}{H}\frac{ds}{dx} = \frac{\delta}{H}\sqrt{1 + \left(\frac{dy}{dx}\right)^2}$$

Now show that $y = a \cosh(x/a) + C$ satisfies this differential equation with $a = H/\delta$.

Answers to Concepts Review: 1. differential equation
2. function   **3.** separate variables
4. $-32t + v_0$; $-16t^2 + v_0 t + s_0$

4.10
Exponential Growth and Decay

At the beginning of 2004, the world's population was about 6.4 billion. It is said that by the year 2020 it will reach 7.9 billion. How are such predictions made?

To treat the problem mathematically, let $y = f(t)$ denote the size of the population at time t, where t is the number of years after 2004. Actually, $f(t)$ is an integer, and its graph "jumps" when someone is born or someone dies. However, for a large population, these jumps are so small relative to the total population that we will not go far wrong if we pretend that f is a nice differentiable function.

It seems reasonable to suppose that the increase Δy in population (births minus deaths) during a short time period Δt is proportional to the size of the population at the beginning of the period, and to the length of that period. Thus, $\Delta y = ky\,\Delta t$, or

$$\frac{\Delta y}{\Delta t} = ky$$

In its limiting form, this gives the differential equation

$$\boxed{\frac{dy}{dt} = ky}$$

If $k > 0$, the population is growing; if $k < 0$, it is shrinking. For world population, history indicates that k is about 0.0132 (assuming that t is measured in years), though some agencies report a different figure.

Solving the Differential Equation   We want to solve $dy/dt = ky$ subject to the condition that $y = y_0$ when $t = 0$. Separating variables and integrating, we obtain

$$\frac{dy}{y} = k\,dt$$

$$\int \frac{dy}{y} = \int k\,dt$$

$$\ln y = kt + C$$

Here we know that the population y satisfies $y > 0$ so we can write the antiderivative on the left as $\ln y$ and not worry about the absolute value. The condition $y = y_0$ at $t = 0$ gives $C = \ln y_0$. Thus,

$$\ln y - \ln y_0 = kt$$

or

$$\ln \frac{y}{y_0} = kt$$

Changing to exponential form yields

$$\frac{y}{y_0} = e^{kt}$$

or, finally,

$$\boxed{y = y_0\, e^{kt}}$$

When $k > 0$, this type of growth is called **exponential growth,** and when $k < 0$, it is called **exponential decay.**

Returning to the problem of world population, we choose to measure time t in years after January 1, 2004, and y in billions of people. Thus, $y_0 = 6.4$ and, since $k = 0.0132$,

$$y = 6.4e^{0.0132t}$$

By the year 2020, when $t = 16$, we can predict that y will be about

$$y = 6.4e^{0.0132(16)} \approx 7.9 \text{ billion}$$

EXAMPLE 1 How long will it take world population to double under the assumptions above?

SOLUTION   The question is equivalent to asking "In how many years after 2004 will the population reach 12.8 billion?" We need to solve

$$12.8 = 6.4e^{0.0132t}$$

$$2 = e^{0.0132t}$$

for t. Taking logarithms of both sides gives

$$\ln 2 = 0.0132t$$

$$t = \frac{\ln 2}{0.0132} \approx 53 \text{ years} \qquad \blacksquare$$

If world population will double in the first 53 years after 2004, it will double in any 53-year period; so, for example, it will quadruple in 106 years. More generally, if an exponentially growing quantity doubles from y_0 to $2y_0$ in an initial interval of length T, it will double in *any* interval of length T, since

$$\frac{y(t + T)}{y(t)} = \frac{y_0\, e^{k(t+T)}}{y_0\, e^{kt}} = \frac{y_0\, e^{kT}}{y_0} = \frac{2y_0}{y_0} = 2$$

We call the number T the **doubling time.**

EXAMPLE 2 The number of bacteria in a rapidly growing culture was estimated to be 10,000 at noon and 40,000 after 2 hours. Predict how many bacteria there will be at 5 P.M.

SOLUTION   We assume that the differential equation $dy/dt = ky$ is applicable, so $y = y_0\, e^{kt}$. Now we have two conditions ($y_0 = 10{,}000$ and $y = 40{,}000$ at $t = 2$), from which we conclude that

$$40{,}000 = 10{,}000e^{k(2)}$$

or

$$4 = e^{2k}$$

Taking logarithms yields

$$\ln 4 = 2k$$

or

$$k = \frac{1}{2}\ln 4 = \ln \sqrt{4} = \ln 2$$

Thus,

$$y = 10{,}000e^{(\ln 2)t}$$

and, at $t = 5$, this gives

$$y = 10{,}000e^{0.693(5)} \approx 320{,}000$$ ■

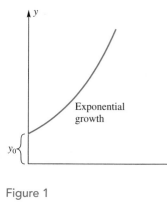

Figure 1

The exponential model $y = y_0 e^{kt}$, $k > 0$, for population growth is flawed since it projects faster and faster growth indefinitely far into the future (Figure 1). In most cases (including that of world population), the limited amount of space and resources will eventually force a slowing of the growth rate. This suggests another model for population growth, called the **logistic model,** in which we assume that the rate of growth is proportional both to the population size y and to the difference $L - y$, where L is the maximum population that can be supported. This leads to the differential equation

$$\frac{dy}{dt} = ky(L - y)$$

Note that for small y, $dy/dt \approx kLy$, which suggests exponential-type growth. But as y nears L, growth is curtailed and dy/dt gets smaller and smaller, producing a growth curve like Figure 2. This model is explored in Problems 34, 35, and 47 of this section and again in Section 7.5.

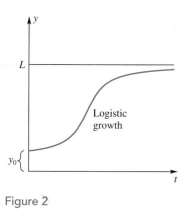

Figure 2

Radioactive Decay Not everything grows; some things decrease over time. For example, radioactive elements *decay*, and they do it at a rate proportional to the amount present. Thus, their change rates also satisfy the differential equation

$$\frac{dy}{dt} = ky$$

but now with k negative. It is still true that $y = y_0 e^{kt}$ is the solution to this equation. A typical graph appears in Figure 3.

▨ **EXAMPLE 3** Carbon 14, an isotope of carbon, is radioactive and decays at a rate proportional to the amount present. Its **half-life** is 5730 years; that is, it takes 5730 years for a given amount of carbon 14 to decay to one-half its original size. If there were 10 grams present originally, how much would be left after 2000 years?

SOLUTION The half-life of 5730 allows us to determine k, since it implies that

$$\frac{1}{2} = 1e^{k(5730)}$$

or, after taking logarithms,

$$-\ln 2 = 5730k$$

$$k = \frac{-\ln 2}{5730} \approx -0.000121$$

Thus,

$$y = 10e^{-0.000121t}$$

At $t = 2000$, this gives

$$y = 10e^{-0.000121(2000)} \approx 7.85 \text{ grams}$$ ■

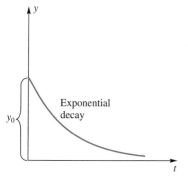

Figure 3

In Problem 17, we show how Example 3 may be used to determine the age of fossils and other once-living things.

Newton's Law of Cooling Newton's Law of Cooling states that the rate at which an object cools (or warms) is proportional to the difference in temperature between the object and the surrounding medium. To be specific, suppose that an object initially at temperature T_0 is placed in a room where the temperature is T_1. If $T(t)$ represents the temperature of the object at time t, then Newton's Law of Cooling says that

$$\frac{dT}{dt} = k(T - T_1)$$

This differential equation is separable and can be solved like the growth and decay problems in this section.

EXAMPLE 4 An object is taken from an oven at 350°F and left to cool in a room at 70°F. If the temperature fell to 250°F in one hour, what would its temperature be three hours after it was removed from the oven?

SOLUTION The differential equation can be written as

$$\frac{dT}{dt} = k(T - 70)$$

$$\frac{dT}{T - 70} = k\, dt$$

$$\int \frac{dT}{T - 70} = \int k\, dt$$

$$\ln|T - 70| = kt + C$$

Since the initial temperature is greater than 70, it seems reasonable that the object's temperature will decrease toward 70; thus $T - 70$ will be positive and the absolute value is unnecessary. This leads to

$$T - 70 = e^{kt+C}$$

$$T = 70 + C_1 e^{kt}$$

where $C_1 = e^C$. Now we apply the initial condition, $T(0) = 350$ to find C_1:

$$350 = T(0) = 70 + C_1 e^{k \cdot 0}$$

$$280 = C_1$$

Thus, the solution of the differential equation is

$$T(t) = 70 + 280 e^{kt}$$

To find k we apply the condition that at time $t = 1$ the temperature was $T(1) = 250$.

$$250 = T(1) = 70 + 280 e^{k \cdot 1}$$

$$280 e^k = 180$$

$$e^k = \frac{180}{280}$$

$$k = \ln\frac{180}{280} \approx -0.44183$$

This gives

$$T(t) = 70 + 280 e^{-0.44183t}$$

See Figure 4. After 3 hours, the temperature is

$$T(3) = 70 + 280 e^{-0.44183 \cdot 3} \approx 144.4°F$$

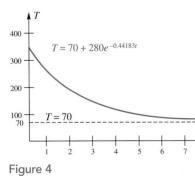

$T = 70 + 280 e^{-0.44183t}$

$T = 70$

Figure 4

Compound Interest We saw in Section 2.6 that if A_0 dollars are put into a bank account that pays an annual rate of interest r, compounded n times per year, it will be worth

$$A(t) = A_0\left(1 + \frac{r}{n}\right)^{nt}$$

dollars after t years. If we let $t \to \infty$, we get continuous compounding of interest, and in this case

$$A(t) = \lim_{n \to \infty} A_0\left(1 + \frac{r}{n}\right)^{nt} = A_0 \lim_{n \to \infty}\left[\left(1 + \frac{r}{n}\right)^{n/r}\right]^{rt} = A_0 e^{rt}$$

Here is another approach to the problem of continuous compounding of interest. Let $A(t)$ be the value at time t of A_0 dollars invested at the interest rate r. To say that interest is compounded continuously is to say that the instantaneous rate of change of A with respect to time is rA; that is,

$$\frac{dA}{dt} = rA$$

This differential equation was solved at the beginning of the section; its solution is $A = A_0 e^{rt}$.

Concepts Review

1. The rate of change dy/dt of a quantity y growing exponentially satisfies the differential equation $dy/dt = $ _____. In contrast, if y is growing logistically toward an upper bound L, $dy/dt = $ _____.

2. If a quantity growing exponentially doubles after T years, it will be _____ times as large after $3T$ years.

3. The time for an exponentially decaying quantity y to go from size y_0 to size $y_0/2$ is called the _____.

4. The number e can be expressed as a limit by $e = \lim_{n \to \infty}$ _____.

Problem Set 4.10

In Problems 1–4, solve the given differential equation subject to the given condition. Note that $y(a)$ denotes the value of y at $t = a$.

1. $\dfrac{dy}{dt} = -6y$, $y(0) = 4$ **2.** $\dfrac{dy}{dt} = 6y$, $y(0) = 1$

3. $\dfrac{dy}{dt} = 0.005y$, $y(10) = 2$

4. $\dfrac{dy}{dt} = -0.003y$, $y(-2) = 3$

5. A bacterial population grows at a rate proportional to its size. Initially, it is 10,000, and after 10 days it is 20,000. What is the population after 25 days? See Example 2.

6. How long will it take the population of Problem 5 to double? See Example 1.

7. How long will it take the population of Problem 5 to triple? See Example 1.

8. The population of the United States was 3.9 million in 1790 and 178 million in 1960. If the rate of growth is assumed proportional to the number present, what estimate would you give for the population in 2000? (Compare your answer with the actual 2000 population, which was 275 million.)

9. The population of a certain country is growing at 3.2% per year; that is, if it is A at the beginning of a year, it is 1.032A at the end of that year. Assuming that it is 4.5 million now, what will it be at the end of 1 year? 2 years? 10 years? 100 years?

10. Determine the proportionality constant k in $dy/dt = ky$ for Problem 9. Then use $y = 4.5e^{kt}$ to find the population after 100 years.

11. A population is growing at a rate proportional to its size. After 5 years, the population size was 164,000. After 12 years, the population size was 235,000. What was the original population size?

12. The mass of a tumor grows at a rate proportional to its size. The first measurement of its mass was 4.0 grams. Four months later its mass was 6.76 grams. How large was the tumor six months before the first measurement? If the instrument can detect tumors of mass 1 gram or greater, would the tumor have been detected at that time?

13. A radioactive substance has a half-life of 700 years. If there were 10 grams initially, how much would be left after 300 years?

14. If a radioactive substance loses 15% of its radioactivity in 2 days, what is its half-life?

15. Cesium-137 and strontium-90 are two radioactive chemicals that were released at the Chernobyl nuclear reactor in April 1986. The half-life of cesium-137 is 30.22 years, and that of strontium-90 is 28.8 years. In what year will the amount of cesium-137 be equal to 1% of what was released? Answer this question for strontium-90.

16. An unknown amount of a radioactive substance is being studied. After two days, the mass is 15.231 grams. After eight days, the mass is 9.086 grams. How much was there initially? What is the half-life of this substance?

17. (Carbon Dating) All living things contain carbon 12, which is stable, and carbon 14, which is radioactive. While a plant or animal is alive, the ratio of these two isotopes of carbon remains unchanged, since the carbon 14 is constantly renewed; after death, no more carbon 14 is absorbed. The half-life of carbon 14 is 5730 years. If charred logs of an old fort show only 70% of the carbon 14 expected in living matter, when did the fort burn down? Assume that the fort burned soon after it was built of freshly cut logs.

18. Human hair from a grave in Africa proved to have only 51% of the carbon 14 of living tissue. When was the body buried?

19. An object is taken from an oven at 300°F and left to cool in a room at 75°F. If the temperature fell to 200°F in $\frac{1}{2}$ hour, what will it be after 3 hours?

20. A thermometer registered -20°C outside and then was brought into a house where the temperature was 24°C. After 5 minutes it registered 0°C. When will it register 20°C?

21. An object initially at 26°C is placed in water having temperature 90°C. If the temperature of the object rises to 70°C in 5 minutes, what will be the temperature after 10 minutes?

22. A batch of brownies is taken from a 350°F oven and placed in a refrigerator at 40°F and left to cool. After 15 minutes, the brownies have cooled to 250°F. When will the temperature of the brownies be 110°F?

23. A dead body is found at 10 P.M. to have temperature 82°F. One hour later the temperature was 76°F. The temperature of the room was a constant 70°F. Assuming that the temperature of the body was 98.6°F when it was alive, estimate the time of death.

24. Solve the differential equation for Newton's Law of Cooling for an arbitrary T_0, T_1, and k, assuming that $T_0 > T_1$. Show that $\lim_{t \to \infty} T(t) = T_1$.

25. If $375 is put in the bank today, what will it be worth at the end of 2 years if interest is 3.5% and is compounded as specified?

(a) Annually   (b) Monthly
(c) Daily   (d) Continuously

26. Do Problem 25 assuming that the interest rate is 4.6%.

27. How long does it take money to double in value for the specified interest rate?

(a) 6% compounded monthly
(b) 6% compounded continuously

28. Inflation between 1999 and 2004 ran at about 2.5% per year. On this basis, what would you expect a car that would have cost $20,000 in 1999 to cost in 2004?

29. Manhattan Island is said to have been bought by Peter Minuit in 1626 for $24. Suppose that Minuit had instead put the

$24 in the bank at 6% interest compounded continuously. What would that $24 have been worth in 2000?

30. If Methuselah's parents had put $100 in the bank for him at birth and he left it there, what would Methuselah have had at his death (969 years later) if interest was 4% compounded annually?

31. Find the value of $1000 at the end of 1 year when the interest is compounded continuously at 5%. This is called the **future value.**

32. Suppose that after 1 year you have $1000 in the bank. If the interest was compounded continuously at 5%, how much money did you put in the bank one year ago? This is called the **present value.**

33. It will be shown later for small x that $\ln(1 + x) \approx x$. Use this fact to show that the doubling time for money invested at p percent compounded annually is about $70/p$ years.

34. The equation for logistic growth is

$$\frac{dy}{dt} = ky(L - y)$$

Show that this differential equation has the solution

$$y = \frac{Ly_0}{y_0 + (L - y_0)e^{-Lkt}}$$

Hint: $\dfrac{1}{y(L - y)} = \dfrac{1}{Ly} + \dfrac{1}{L(L - y)}$.

35. Sketch the graph of the solution in Problem 34 when $y_0 = 6.4$, $L = 16$, and $k = 0.00186$ (a *logistic model* for world population; see the discussion at the beginning of this section). Note that $\lim_{t \to \infty} y = 16$.

36. Show that the differential equation

$$\frac{dy}{dt} = ay + b, \quad y(0) = y_0$$

has solution

$$y = \left(y_0 + \frac{b}{a}\right)e^{at} - \frac{b}{a}$$

Assume that $a \neq 0$.

37. Consider a country with a population of 10 million in 1985, a growth rate of 1.2% per year, and immigration from other countries of 60,000 per year. Use the differential equation of Problem 36 to model this situation and predict the population in 2010. Take $a = 0.012$.

38. Important news is said to diffuse through an adult population of fixed size L at a time rate proportional to the number of people who have not heard the news. Five days after a scandal in City Hall was reported, a poll showed that half the people had heard it. How long will it take for 99% of the people to hear it?

EXPL *Besides providing an easy way to differentiate products, logarithmic differentiation also provides a measure of the **relative** or **fractional rate of change**, defined as y'/y. We explore this concept in Problems 39–42.*

39. Show that the relative rate of change of e^{kt} as a function of t is k.

40. Show that the relative rate of change of any polynomial approaches zero as the independent variable approaches infinity.

41. Prove that if the relative rate of change is a positive constant then the function must represent exponential growth.

42. Prove that if the relative rate of change is a negative constant then the function must represent exponential decay.

43. Assume that (1) world population continues to grow exponentially with growth constant $k = 0.0132$, (2) it takes $\frac{1}{2}$ acre of land to supply food for one person, and (3) there are 13,500,000 square miles of arable land in the world. How long will it be before the world reaches the maximum population? *Note:* There were 6.4 billion people in 2004 and 1 square mile is 640 acres.

GC **44.** The Census Bureau estimates that the growth rate k of the world population will decrease by roughly 0.0002 per year for the next few decades. In 2004, k was 0.0132.

(a) Express k as a function of time t, where t is measured in years since 2004.

(b) Find a differential equation that models the population y for this problem.

(c) Solve the differential equation with the additional condition that the population in 2004 ($t = 0$) was 6.4 billion.

(d) Graph the population y for the next 300 years.

(e) With this model, when will the population reach a maximum? When will the population drop below the 2004 level?

GC **45.** Repeat Exercise 44 under the assumption that k will decrease by 0.0001 per year.

EXPL **46.** Let E be a differentiable function satisfying $E(u + v) = E(u)E(v)$ for all u and v. Find a formula for $E(x)$. *Hint:* First find $E'(x)$.

GC **47.** Using the same axes, draw the graphs for $0 \le t \le 100$ of the following two models for the growth of world population (both described in this section).

(a) Exponential growth: $y = 6.4e^{0.0132t}$

(b) Logistic growth: $y = 102.4/(6 + 10e^{-0.030t})$

Compare what the two models predict for world population in 2010, 2040, and 2090. *Note:* Both models assume that world population was 6.4 billion in 2004 ($t = 0$).

Answers to Concepts Review: **1.** $ky; ky(L - y)$ **2.** 8 **3.** half-life **4.** $\left(1 + \dfrac{1}{n}\right)^n$

4.11 Chapter Review

Concepts Test

Respond with true or false to each of the following assertions. Be prepared to justify your answer.

1. A continuous function defined on a closed interval must attain a maximum value on that interval.

2. If a differentiable function f attains a maximum value at an interior point c of its domain, then $f'(c) = 0$.

3. It is possible for a function to have an infinite number of critical points.

4. A continuous function that is increasing on $(-\infty, \infty)$ must be differentiable everywhere.

5. If $f(x) = 3x^6 + 4x^4 + 2x^2$, then the graph of f is concave up on the whole real line.

6. If f is an increasing differentiable function on an interval I, then $f'(x) > 0$ for all x in I.

7. If $f'(x) > 0$, for all x in I, then f is increasing on I.

8. If $f''(c) = 0$, then f has an inflection point at $(c, f(c))$.

9. A quadratic function has no inflection points.

10. If $f'(x) > 0$ for all x in $[a, b]$, then f attains its maximum value on $[a, b]$ at b.

11. The function $y = \tan^2 x$ has no minimum value.

12. The function $y = 2x^3 + x$ has no maximum or minimum values.

13. The function $y = 2x^3 + x + \tan x$ has no maximum or minimum values.

14. The graph of $y = \dfrac{x^2 - x - 6}{x - 3} = \dfrac{(x + 2)(x - 3)}{x - 3}$ has a vertical asymptote at $x = 3$.

15. The graph of $y = \dfrac{x^2 + 1}{1 - x^2}$ has a horizontal asymptote of $y = -1$.

16. The graph of $y = \dfrac{3x^2 + 2x + \sin x}{x}$ has an oblique asymptote of $y = 3x + 2$.

17. The function $f(x) = \sqrt{x}$ satisfies the hypotheses of the Mean Value Theorem on $[0, 2]$.

18. The function $f(x) = |x|$ satisfies the hypotheses of the Mean Value Theorem on $[-1, 1]$.

19. On the interval $[-1, 1]$, there will be just one point where the tangent line to $y = x^3$ is parallel to the secant line.

20. If $f'(x) = 0$ for all x in (a, b), then f is constant on this interval.

21. If $f'(c) = f''(c) = 0$, then $f(c)$ is neither a maximum nor minimum value.

22. The graph of $y = \sin x$ has infinitely many points of inflection.

23. Among rectangles of fixed area K, the one with maximum perimeter is a square.

24. If the graph of a differentiable function has three x-intercepts, then it must have at least two points where the tangent line is horizontal.

25. The sum of two increasing functions is an increasing function.

26. The product of two increasing functions is an increasing function.

27. If $f'(0) = 0$ and $f''(x) > 0$ for $x \geq 0$, then f is increasing on $[0, \infty)$.

28. If $f'(x) \leq 2$ for all x on the interval $[0, 3]$ and $f(0) = 1$, then $f(3) < 4$.

29. If f is a differentiable function, then f is nondecreasing on (a, b) if and only if $f'(x) \geq 0$ on (a, b).

30. Two differentiable functions have the same derivative on (a, b) if and only if they differ by a constant on (a, b).

31. If $f''(x) > 0$ for all x, then the graph of $y = f(x)$ cannot have a horizontal asymptote.

32. A global maximum value is always a local maximum value.

33. A cubic function $f(x) = ax^3 + bx^2 + cx + d, a \neq 0$, can have at most one local maximum value on any open interval.

34. The linear function $f(x) = ax + b, a \neq 0$, has no minimum value on any open interval.

35. If f is continuous on $[a, b]$ and $f(a)f(b) < 0$, then $f(x) = 0$ has a root between a and b.

36. One of the virtues of the Bisection Method is its rapid convergence.

37. Newton's Method will produce a convergent sequence for the equation $x^{1/3} = 0$.

38. If Newton's Method fails to converge for one starting value, then it will fail to converge for every starting value.

39. If g is continuous on $[a, b]$ and if $a < g(a) < g(b) < b$, then g has a fixed point between a and b.

40. One of the virtues of the Bisection Method is that it always converges.

41. The indefinite integral is a linear operator.

42. $\int [f(x)g'(x) + g(x)f'(x)] \, dx = f(x)g(x) + C.$

43. $y = \cos x$ is a solution to the differential equation $(dy/dx)^2 = 1 - y^2$.

44. All functions that are antiderivatives must have derivatives.

45. If the second derivatives of two functions are equal, then the functions differ at most by a constant.

46. $\int f'(x) \, dx = f(x)$ for every differentiable function f.

47. If $s = -16t^2 + v_0 t$ gives the height at time t of a ball thrown straight up from the surface of the earth, then the ball will hit the ground with velocity $-v_0$.

48. If y is growing exponentially and if y triples between $t = 0$ and $t = t_1$, then y will also triple between $t = 2t_1$ and $t = 3t_1$.

49. The time necessary for $x(t) = Ce^{-kt}$ to drop to half its value is $\dfrac{\ln 2}{\ln k}$.

50. It is to a saver's advantage to have money invested at 5% compounded continuously rather than 6% compounded monthly.

Sample Test Problems

In Problems 1–12, a function f and its domain are given. Determine the critical points, evaluate f at these points, and find the (global) maximum and minimum values.

1. $f(x) = x^2 - 2x; [0, 4]$

2. $f(t) = \dfrac{1}{t}; [1, 4]$

3. $f(z) = \dfrac{1}{z^2}; \left[-2, -\frac{1}{2}\right]$

4. $f(x) = \dfrac{1}{x^2}; [-2, 0)$

5. $f(x) = |x|; \left[-\frac{1}{2}, 1\right]$

6. $f(s) = s + |s|; [-1, 1]$

7. $f(x) = 3x^4 - 4x^3; [-2, 3]$

8. $f(u) = u^2(u - 2)^{1/3}; [-1, 3]$

9. $f(x) = 2x^5 - 5x^4 + 7; [-1, 3]$

10. $f(x) = (x - 1)^3(x + 2)^2; [-2, 2]$

11. $f(\theta) = \sin \theta; [\pi/4, 4\pi/3]$

12. $f(\theta) = \sin^2 \theta - \sin \theta; [0, \pi]$

In Problems 13–19, a function f is given with domain $(-\infty, \infty)$. Indicate where f is increasing and where it is concave down.

13. $f(x) = 3x - x^2$

14. $f(x) = x^9$

15. $f(x) = x^3 - 3x + 3$

16. $f(x) = -2x^3 - 3x^2 + 12x + 1$

17. $f(x) = x^4 - 4x^5$

18. $f(x) = e^{-|x|}$

19. $f(x) = \ln(1 + x^4)$

20. Find where the function g, defined by $g(t) = t^3 + 1/t$, is increasing and where it is decreasing. Find the local extreme values of g. Find the point of inflection. Sketch the graph.

21. Find where the function f, defined by $f(x) = x^2(x - 4)$, is increasing and where it is decreasing. Find the local extreme values of f. Find the point of inflection. Sketch the graph.

22. Find the maximum and minimum values, if they exist, of the function defined by

$$f(x) = \frac{4}{x^2 + 1} + 2$$

In Problems 23–30, sketch the graph of the given function f, labeling all extrema (local and global) and the inflection points and showing any asymptotes. Be sure to make use of f' and f".

23. $f(x) = x^4 - 2x$

24. $f(x) = (x^2 - 1)^2$

25. $f(x) = x\sqrt{x - 3}$

26. $f(x) = \dfrac{x - 2}{x - 3}$

27. $f(x) = 3x^4 - 4x^3$

28. $f(x) = \dfrac{x^2 - 1}{x}$

29. $f(x) = e^{-|x|}$

30. $f(x) = \sin^{-1} x^2$

In Problems 31–36, sketch the graph of the given function f in the region $(-\pi, \pi)$, unless otherwise indicated, labeling all extrema (local and global) and the inflection points and showing any asymptotes. Be sure to make use of f' and f".

31. $f(x) = \cos x - \sin x$

32. $f(x) = \sin x - \tan x$

33. $f(x) = x \tan x; (-\pi/2, \pi/2)$

34. $f(x) = 2x - \cot x; (0, \pi)$

35. $f(x) = \sin x - \sin^2 x$

36. $f(x) = 2 \cos x - 2 \sin x$

37. Sketch the graph of a function F that has all of the following properties:

(a) F is everywhere continuous;

(b) $F(-2) = 3, F(2) = -1$;

(c) $F'(x) = 0$ for $x > 2$;

(d) $F''(x) < 0$ for $x < 2$.

38. Sketch the graph of a function F that has all of the following properties:

(a) F is everywhere continuous;

(b) $F(-1) = 6, F(3) = -2$;

(c) $F'(x) < 0$ for $x < -1, F'(-1) = F'(3) = -2, F'(7) = 0$;

(d) $F''(x) < 0$ for $x < -1, F''(x) = 0$ for $-1 < x < 3$, $F''(x) > 0$ for $x > 3$.

39. Sketch the graph of a function F that has all of the following properties:

(a) F is everywhere continuous;

(b) F has period π;

(c) $0 \le F(x) \le 2, F(0) = 0, F\left(\dfrac{\pi}{2}\right) = 2$;

(d) $F'(x) > 0$ for $0 < x < \dfrac{\pi}{2}, F'(x) < 0$ for $\dfrac{\pi}{2} < x < \pi$;

(e) $F''(x) < 0$ for $0 < x < \pi$.

40. A long sheet of metal, 16 inches wide, is to be turned up at both sides to make a horizontal gutter with vertical sides. How many inches should be turned up at each side for maximum carrying capacity?

41. A fence, 8 feet high, is parallel to the wall of a building and 1 foot from the building. What is the shortest plank that can go over the fence, from the level ground, to prop the wall?

42. A page of a book is to contain 27 square inches of print. If the margins at the top, bottom, and one side are 2 inches and the margin at the other side is 1 inch, what size page would use the least paper?

43. A metal water trough with equal semicircular ends and open top is to have a capacity of 128π cubic feet (Figure 1). Determine its radius r and length h if the trough is to require the least material for its construction.

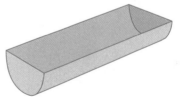

Figure 1

44. Find the maximum and the minimum of the function defined on the closed interval $[-2, 2]$ by

$$f(x) = \begin{cases} \frac{1}{4}(x^2 + 6x + 8), & \text{if } -2 \le x \le 0 \\ -\frac{1}{6}(x^2 + 4x - 12), & \text{if } 0 \le x \le 2 \end{cases}$$

Find where the graph is concave up and where it is concave down. Sketch the graph.

45. For each of the following functions, decide whether the Mean Value Theorem applies on the indicated interval I. If so, find all possible values of c, if not, tell why. Make a sketch.

(a) $f(x) = \dfrac{x^3}{3}; I = [-3, 3]$

(b) $F(x) = x^{3/5} + 1; I = [-1, 1]$

(c) $g(x) = \dfrac{x + 1}{x - 1}; I = [2, 3]$

46. Find the equations of the tangent lines at the inflection points of the graph of

$$y = x^4 - 6x^3 + 12x^2 - 3x + 1$$

47. Let f be a continuous function with $f(1) = -1/4$, $f(2) = 0$, and $f(3) = -1/4$. If the graph of $y = f'(x)$ is as shown in Figure 2, sketch a possible graph for $y = f(x)$.

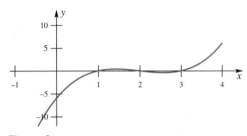

Figure 2

48. Sketch the graph of a function G with all the following properties:

(a) $G(x)$ is continuous and $G''(x) > 0$ for all x in $(-\infty, 0) \cup (0, \infty)$;

(b) $G(-2) = G(2) = 3$;

(c) $\lim_{x \to -\infty} G(x) = 2$, $\lim_{x \to \infty} [G(x) - x] = 0$;

(d) $\lim_{x \to 0^+} G(x) = \lim_{x \to 0^-} G(x) = \infty$.

C **49.** Use the Bisection Method to solve $3x - \cos 2x = 0$ accurate to six decimal places. Use $a_1 = 0$ and $b_1 = 1$.

C **50.** Use Newton's Method to solve $3x - \cos 2x = 0$ accurate to six decimal places. Use $x_1 = 0.5$.

C **51.** Use the Fixed-Point Algorithm to solve $3x - \cos 2x = 0$, starting with $x_1 = 0.5$.

C **52.** Use Newton's Method to find the solution of $x - \tan x = 0$ in the interval $(\pi, 2\pi)$ accurate to four decimal places. *Hint:* Sketch graphs of $y = x$ and $y = \tan x$ using the same axes to get a good initial guess for x_1.

In Problems 53–67, evaluate the indicated antiderivatives.

53. $\int \left(x^3 - 3x^2 + 3\sqrt{x} \right) dx$

54. $\int \frac{2x^4 - 3x^2 + 1}{x^2} dx$

55. $\int \frac{y^3 - 9y \sin y + 26y^{-1}}{y} dy$

56. $\int y\sqrt{y^2 - 4} \, dy$

57. $\int z(2z^2 - 3)^{1/3} dz$

58. $\int \cos^4 x \sin x \, dx$

59. $\int (x + 1) \tan^2(3x^2 + 6x) \sec^2(3x^2 + 6x) \, dx$

60. $\int \frac{t^3}{\sqrt{t^4 + 9}} dt$

61. $\int t^4 (t^5 + 5)^{2/3} dt$

62. $\int \frac{x}{\sqrt{x^2 + 4}} dx$

63. $\int \frac{x^2}{\sqrt{x^3 + 9}} dx$

64. $\int \frac{1}{(y + 1)^2} dy$

65. $\int \frac{2}{(2y - 1)^3} dy$

66. $\int e^t \, dt$

67. $\int \sin 2\theta \, d\theta$

68. $\int \frac{y^2 - 1}{(y^3 - 3y)^2} dy$

69. $\int \frac{(y^2 + y + 1)}{\sqrt[5]{2y^3 + 3y^2 + 6y}} dy$

In Problems 70–78, solve the differential equation subject to the indicated condition.

70. $\frac{dy}{dx} = \sin x$; $y = 2$ at $x = 0$

71. $\frac{dy}{dx} = \frac{1}{\sqrt{x + 1}}$; $y = 18$ at $x = 3$

72. $\frac{dy}{dx} = \csc y$; $y = \pi$ at $x = 0$

73. $\frac{dy}{dt} = \sqrt{2t - 1}$; $y = -1$ at $t = \frac{1}{2}$

74. $\frac{dy}{dt} = t^2 y^4$; $y = 1$ at $t = 1$

75. $\frac{dy}{dt} = 2y$; $y = 7$ at $t = 0$

76. $\frac{dy}{dt} = 6 - y$; $y = 4$ at $t = 0$

77. $\dfrac{dy}{dx} = \dfrac{6x - x^3}{2y}$; $y = 3$ at $x = 0$

78. $\dfrac{dy}{dx} = x \sec y$; $y = \pi$ at $x = 0$

79. A ball is thrown directly upward from a tower 448 feet high with an initial velocity of 48 feet per second. In how many seconds will it strike the ground and with what velocity? Assume that $g = 32$ feet per second per second and neglect air resistance.

80. A town grew exponentially from 10,000 in 1990 to 14,000 in 2000. Assuming that the same type of growth continues, what will the population be in 2010?

81. Suppose that glucose is infused into the bloodstream of a patient at the rate of 3 grams per minute, but that the patient's body converts and removes glucose from its blood at a rate proportional to the amount present (with constant of proportionality 0.02). Let $Q(t)$ be the amount present at time t, with $Q(0) = 120$.

(a) Write the differential equation for Q.

(b) Solve this differential equation. *Hint:* Use the result of Problem 36 in Section 4.11.

(c) Determine what happens to Q in the long run.

In Problems 1–12, find the area of the shaded region.

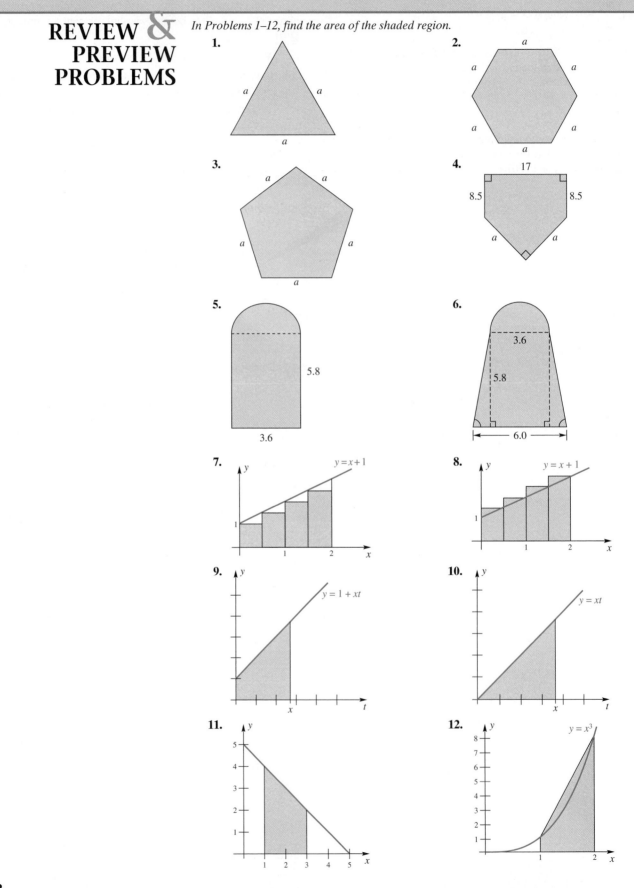

1.

2.

3.

4.

5.

6.

7.

8.

9.

10.

11.

12.

The Definite Integral

5.1
Introduction to Area

Two problems, both from geometry, motivate the two most important ideas in calculus. The problem of finding the tangent line led us to the *derivative*. The problem of finding area will lead us to the *definite integral*.

For polygons (closed plane regions bounded by line segments), the problem of finding area is hardly a problem at all. We start by defining the area of a rectangle to be the familiar length times width, and from this we successively derive the formulas for the area of a parallelogram, a triangle, and any polygon. The sequence of figures in Figure 1 suggests how this is done.

Even in this simple setting, it is clear that area should satisfy five properties.

1. The area of a plane region is a nonnegative (real) number.
2. The area of a rectangle is the product of its length and width (both measured in the same units). The result is in square units, for example, square feet or square centimeters.
3. Congruent regions have equal areas.
4. The area of the union of two regions that overlap only in a line segment is the sum of the areas of the two regions.
5. If one region is contained in a second region, then the area of the first region is less than or equal to that of the second.

When we consider a region with a curved boundary, the problem of assigning area is more difficult. However, over 2000 years ago, Archimedes provided the key to a solution. Consider a sequence of inscribed polygons that approximate the curved region with greater and greater accuracy. For example, for the circle of

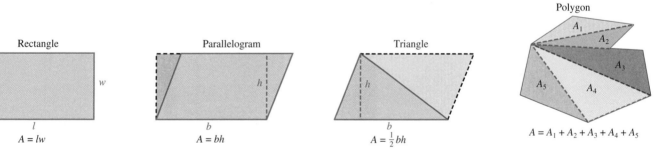

Rectangle
w
l
$A = lw$

Parallelogram
h
b
$A = bh$

Triangle
h
b
$A = \frac{1}{2}bh$

Polygon
A_1
A_2
A_3
A_4
A_5
$A = A_1 + A_2 + A_3 + A_4 + A_5$

Figure 1

radius 1, consider regular *inscribed* polygons $P_1, P_2, P_3, \ldots$ with 4 sides, 8 sides, 16 sides, $\ldots$, as shown in Figure 2. The area of the circle is the limit as $n \to \infty$ of the areas of P_n. Thus, if $A(F)$ denotes the area of a region F, then

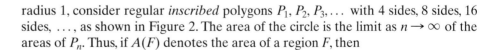

$$A(\text{circle}) = \lim_{n \to \infty} A(P_n)$$

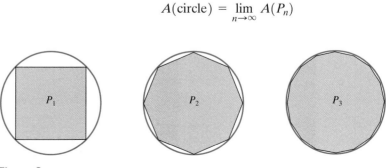

P_1
P_2
P_3

Figure 2

Archimedes went further, considering also *circumscribed* polygons $T_1, T_2, T_3, \ldots$ (Figure 3). He showed that you get the same value for the area of the circle of radius 1 (what we call π) whether you use inscribed or circumscribed polygons. It is just a small step from what he did to our modern treatment of area.

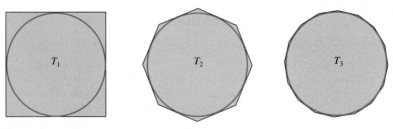

Figure 3

Sigma Notation   Our approach to finding the area of a curved region R will involve the following steps:

1. Approximate the region R by n rectangles where the n rectangles taken together either contain R, producing a **circumscribed polygon,** or are contained in R, producing an **inscribed polygon.**
2. Find the area of each rectangle.
3. Sum the areas of the n rectangles.
4. Take the limit as $n \to \infty$.

If the limit of areas of inscribed and circumscribed polygons is the same, we call this limit the area of the region R.

Step 3, involving summing the areas of rectangles, requires us to have a notation for summation, as well as some of its properties. Consider, for example, the following sums:

$$1^2 + 2^2 + 3^2 + 4^2 + \cdots + 100^2$$

and

$$a_1 + a_2 + a_3 + a_4 + \cdots + a_n$$

To indicate these sums in a compact way, we write these sums as

$$\sum_{i=1}^{100} i^2 \quad \text{and} \quad \sum_{i=1}^{n} a_i$$

respectively. Here Σ (capital Greek sigma), which corresponds to the English S, says that we are to sum (add) all numbers of the form indicated as the *index i* runs through the positive integers, starting with the integer shown below Σ and ending with the integer above Σ. Thus,

$$\sum_{i=2}^{4} a_i b_i = a_2 b_2 + a_3 b_3 + a_4 b_4$$

$$\sum_{j=1}^{n} \frac{1}{j} = \frac{1}{1} + \frac{1}{2} + \frac{1}{3} + \cdots + \frac{1}{n}$$

$$\sum_{k=1}^{4} \frac{k}{k^2 + 1} = \frac{1}{1^2 + 1} + \frac{2}{2^2 + 1} + \frac{3}{3^2 + 1} + \frac{4}{4^2 + 1}$$

If all the c_i in $\sum_{i=1}^{n} c_i$ have the same value, say c, then

$$\sum_{i=1}^{n} c_i = \underbrace{c + c + c + \cdots + c}_{n \text{ terms}}$$

As a result,

$$\sum_{i=1}^{n} c = nc$$

In particular,

$$\sum_{i=1}^{5} 2 = 5(2) = 10 \quad \text{and} \quad \sum_{i=1}^{100}(-4) = 100(-4) = -400$$

Properties of $\sum$ Thought of as an operator, Σ operates on sequences, and it does so in a linear way.

Theorem A   **Linearity of $\sum$**

If c is a constant, then

(1) $\displaystyle\sum_{i=1}^{n} ca_i = c\sum_{i=1}^{n} a_i$;

(2) $\displaystyle\sum_{i=1}^{n}(a_i + b_i) = \sum_{i=1}^{n} a_i + \sum_{i=1}^{n} b_i$;

(3) $\displaystyle\sum_{i=1}^{n}(a_i - b_i) = \sum_{i=1}^{n} a_i - \sum_{i=1}^{n} b_i$.

Proof   The proofs are easy; we consider only (1).

$$\sum_{i=1}^{n} ca_i = ca_1 + ca_2 + \cdots + ca_n = c(a_1 + a_2 + \cdots + a_n) = c\sum_{i=1}^{n} a_i \quad \blacksquare$$

EXAMPLE 1   Suppose that $\displaystyle\sum_{i=1}^{100} a_i = 60$ and $\displaystyle\sum_{i=1}^{100} b_i = 11$. Calculate

$$\sum_{i=1}^{100}(2a_i - 3b_i + 4)$$

SOLUTION

$$\sum_{i=1}^{100}(2a_i - 3b_i + 4) = \sum_{i=1}^{100} 2a_i - \sum_{i=1}^{100} 3b_i + \sum_{i=1}^{100} 4$$
$$= 2\sum_{i=1}^{100} a_i - 3\sum_{i=1}^{100} b_i + \sum_{i=1}^{100} 4$$
$$= 2(60) - 3(11) + 100(4) = 487 \quad \blacksquare$$

EXAMPLE 2   **Collapsing Sums**

Show that:

(a) $\displaystyle\sum_{i=1}^{n}(a_{i+1} - a_i) = a_{n+1} - a_1$

(b) $\displaystyle\sum_{i=1}^{n}\left[(i + 1)^2 - i^2\right] = (n + 1)^2 - 1$

SOLUTION

(a) Here we should resist our inclination to apply linearity and instead write out the sum, hoping for some nice cancellations.

$$\sum_{i=1}^{n} (a_{i+1} - a_i) = (a_2 - a_1) + (a_3 - a_2) + (a_4 - a_3) + \cdots + (a_{n+1} - a_n)$$

$$= -a_1 + a_2 - a_2 + a_3 - a_3 + a_4 - \cdots - a_n + a_{n+1}$$

$$= -a_1 + a_{n+1} = a_{n+1} - a_1$$

(b) This follows immediately from part (a).   ∎

The symbol used for the index does not matter. Thus,

$$\sum_{i=1}^{n} a_i = \sum_{j=1}^{n} a_j = \sum_{k=1}^{n} a_k$$

and all of these are equal to $a_1 + a_2 + \cdots + a_n$. For this reason, the index is sometimes called a **dummy index.**

Some Special Sum Formulas   When finding areas of regions we will often need to consider the sum of the first n positive integers, as well as the sums of their squares, cubes, and so on. There are nice formulas for these; proofs are discussed after Example 4.

1. $\displaystyle\sum_{i=1}^{n} i = 1 + 2 + 3 + \cdots + n = \frac{n(n+1)}{2}$

2. $\displaystyle\sum_{i=1}^{n} i^2 = 1^2 + 2^2 + 3^2 + \cdots + n^2 = \frac{n(n+1)(2n+1)}{6}$

3. $\displaystyle\sum_{i=1}^{n} i^3 = 1^3 + 2^3 + 3^3 + \cdots + n^3 = \left[\frac{n(n+1)}{2}\right]^2$

4. $\displaystyle\sum_{i=1}^{n} i^4 = 1^4 + 2^4 + 3^4 + \cdots + n^4 = \frac{n(n+1)(2n+1)(3n^2+3n-1)}{30}$

EXAMPLE 3   Find a formula for $\displaystyle\sum_{j=1}^{n} (j+2)(j-5)$.

SOLUTION   We make use of linearity and Formulas 1 and 2 from above.

$$\sum_{j=1}^{n} (j+2)(j-5) = \sum_{j=1}^{n} (j^2 - 3j - 10) = \sum_{j=1}^{n} j^2 - 3\sum_{j=1}^{n} j - \sum_{j=1}^{n} 10$$

$$= \frac{n(n+1)(2n+1)}{6} - 3\frac{n(n+1)}{2} - 10n$$

$$= \frac{n}{6}[2n^2 + 3n + 1 - 9n - 9 - 60]$$

$$= \frac{n(n^2 - 3n - 34)}{3} \qquad ∎$$

EXAMPLE 4   How many oranges are in the pyramid shown in Figure 4?

SOLUTION $1^2 + 2^2 + 3^2 + \cdots + 7^2 = \displaystyle\sum_{i=1}^{7} i^2 = \frac{7(8)(15)}{6} = 140$ ∎

Proofs of Special Sum Formulas   To prove Special Sum Formula 1, we start with the identity $(i+1)^2 - i^2 = 2i + 1$, sum both sides, apply Example 2 on the left, and use linearity on the right.

Figure 4

$$(i + 1)^2 - i^2 = 2i + 1$$

$$\sum_{i=1}^{n}[(i + 1)^2 - i^2] = \sum_{i=1}^{n}(2i + 1)$$

$$(n + 1)^2 - 1^2 = 2\sum_{i=1}^{n}i + \sum_{i=1}^{n}1$$

$$n^2 + 2n = 2\sum_{i=1}^{n}i + n$$

$$\frac{n^2 + n}{2} = \sum_{i=1}^{n}i$$

Almost the same technique works to establish Formulas 2, 3, and 4 (Problems 29–31).

Area by Inscribed Polygons Consider the region R bounded by the parabola $y = f(x) = x^2$, the x-axis, and the vertical line $x = 2$ (Figure 5). We refer to R as the region under the curve $y = x^2$ between $x = 0$ and $x = 2$. Our aim is to calculate its area $A(R)$.

Partition (as in Figure 6) the interval $[0, 2]$ into n subintervals, each of length $\Delta x = 2/n$, by means of the $n + 1$ points

$$0 = x_0 < x_1 < x_2 < \cdots < x_{n-1} < x_n = 2$$

Thus,

$$x_0 = 0$$

$$x_1 = \Delta x = \frac{2}{n}$$

$$x_2 = 2 \cdot \Delta x = \frac{4}{n}$$

$$\vdots$$

$$x_i = i \cdot \Delta x = \frac{2i}{n}$$

$$\vdots$$

$$x_{n-1} = (n - 1) \cdot \Delta x = \frac{(n - 1)2}{n}$$

$$x_n = n \cdot \Delta x = n\left(\frac{2}{n}\right) = 2$$

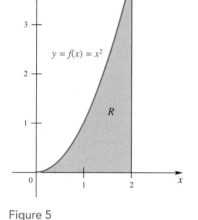

Figure 5

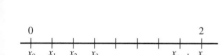

Figure 6

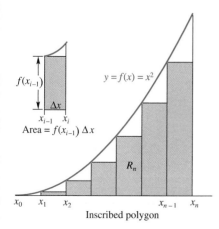

Inscribed polygon

Figure 7

Consider the typical rectangle with base $[x_{i-1}, x_i]$ and height $f(x_{i-1}) = x_{i-1}^2$. Its area is $f(x_{i-1})\,\Delta x$ (see the upper-left part of Figure 7). The union R_n of all such rectangles forms the inscribed polygon shown in the lower-right part of Figure 7. The area $A(R_n)$ can be calculated by summing the areas of these rectangles.

$$A(R_n) = f(x_0)\,\Delta x + f(x_1)\,\Delta x + f(x_2)\,\Delta x + \cdots + f(x_{n-1})\,\Delta x$$

Now

$$f(x_i)\,\Delta x = x_i^2\,\Delta x = \left(\frac{2i}{n}\right)^2 \cdot \frac{2}{n} = \left(\frac{8}{n^3}\right)i^2$$

Thus,

$$A(R_n) = \left[\frac{8}{n^3}(0^2) + \frac{8}{n^3}(1^2) + \frac{8}{n^3}(2^2) + \cdots + \frac{8}{n^3}(n - 1)^2\right]$$

$$= \frac{8}{n^3}[1^2 + 2^2 + \cdots + (n - 1)^2]$$

$$= \frac{8}{n^3}\left[\frac{(n-1)n(2n-1)}{6}\right] \quad \text{(Special Sum Formula 2,}$$
$$\text{with } n-1 \text{ replacing } n)$$

$$= \frac{8}{6}\left(\frac{2n^3 - 3n^2 + n}{n^3}\right)$$

$$= \frac{4}{3}\left(2 - \frac{3}{n} + \frac{1}{n^2}\right)$$

$$= \frac{8}{3} - \frac{4}{n} + \frac{4}{3n^2}$$

We conclude that

$$A(R) = \lim_{n\to\infty} A(R_n) = \lim_{n\to\infty}\left(\frac{8}{3} - \frac{4}{n} + \frac{4}{3n^2}\right) = \frac{8}{3}$$

The diagrams in Figure 8 should help you to visualize what is happening as n gets larger and larger.

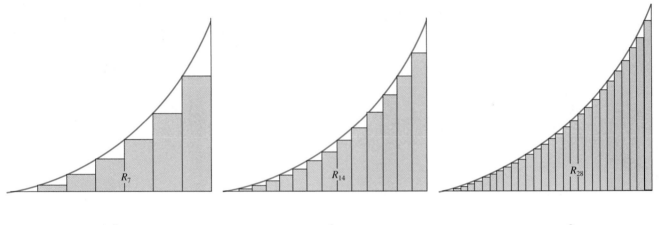

$$A(R_7) \approx \frac{8}{3} - 0.5442 \qquad A(R_{14}) \approx \frac{8}{3} - 0.2789 \qquad A(R_{28}) \approx \frac{8}{3} - 0.1412$$

Figure 8

Area by Circumscribed Polygons Perhaps you are still not convinced that $A(R) = \frac{8}{3}$. We can give more evidence. Consider the rectangle with base $[x_{i-1}, x_i]$ and height $f(x_i) = x_i^2$ (shown at the upper left in Figure 9). Its area is $f(x_i)\,\Delta x$. The union S_n of all such rectangles forms a circumscribed polygon for the region R, as shown at the lower right in Figure 9.

The area $A(S_n)$ is calculated in analogy with the calculation of $A(R_n)$.

$$A(S_n) = f(x_1)\,\Delta x + f(x_2)\,\Delta x + \cdots + f(x_n)\,\Delta x$$

As before, $f(x_i)\,\Delta x = x_i^2\,\Delta x = (8/n^3)i^2$, and so

$$A(S_n) = \left[\frac{8}{n^3}(1^2) + \frac{8}{n^3}(2^2) + \cdots + \frac{8}{n^3}(n^2)\right]$$

$$= \frac{8}{n^3}[1^2 + 2^2 + \cdots + n^2]$$

$$= \frac{8}{n^3}\left[\frac{n(n+1)(2n+1)}{6}\right] \quad \text{(Special Sum Formula 2)}$$

$$= \frac{8}{6}\left[\frac{2n^3 + 3n^2 + n}{n^3}\right]$$

$$= \frac{8}{3} + \frac{4}{n} + \frac{4}{3n^2}$$

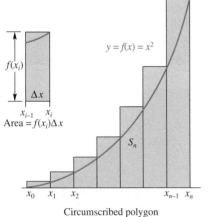

$y = f(x) = x^2$

$f(x_i)$

Δx

x_{i-1} x_i
Area $= f(x_i)\Delta x$

S_n

x_0 x_1 x_2 $\quad x_{n-1}$ x_n

Circumscribed polygon

Figure 9

Again, we conclude that

$$A(R) = \lim_{n \to \infty} A(S_n) = \lim_{n \to \infty} \left(\frac{8}{3} + \frac{4}{n} + \frac{4}{3n^2} \right) = \frac{8}{3}$$

Another Problem—Same Theme Suppose that an object is traveling along the x-axis in such a way that its velocity at time t is given by $v = f(t) = \frac{1}{4}t^3 + 1$ feet per second. How far did it travel between $t = 0$ and $t = 3$? This problem can be solved by the method of differential equations (Section 4.9), but we have something else in mind.

Our starting point is the familiar fact that, if an object travels at constant velocity k over a time interval of length Δt, then the distance traveled is $k \, \Delta t$. But this is just the area of a rectangle, the one shown in Figure 10.

Next consider the given problem, where $v = f(t) = \frac{1}{4}t^3 + 1$. The graph is shown in the top half of Figure 11. Partition the interval $[0, 3]$ into n subintervals of length $\Delta t = 3/n$ by means of points $0 = t_0 < t_1 < t_2 < \cdots < t_n = 3$. Then consider the corresponding circumscribed polygon S_n, displayed in the bottom half of Figure 11 (we could as well have considered the inscribed polygon). Its area, $A(S_n)$, should be a good approximation of the distance traveled, especially if Δt is small, since on each subinterval the actual velocity is almost equal to a constant (the value of v at the end of the subinterval). Moreover, this approximation should get better and better as n gets larger. We are led to the conclusion that the exact distance traveled is $\lim_{n \to \infty} A(S_n)$; that is, it is the area of the region under the velocity curve between $t = 0$ and $t = 3$.

To calculate $A(S_n)$, note that $t_i = 3i/n$, and so the area of the ith rectangle is

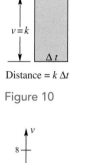

$v = k$

Distance = $k \, \Delta t$

Figure 10

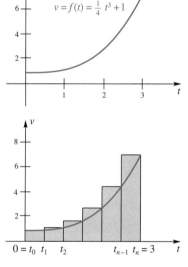

$v = f(t) = \frac{1}{4}t^3 + 1$

Figure 11

$$f(t_i) \, \Delta t = \left[\frac{1}{4} \left(\frac{3i}{n} \right)^3 + 1 \right] \frac{3}{n} = \frac{81}{4n^4} i^3 + \frac{3}{n}$$

Thus,

$$A(S_n) = f(t_1) \, \Delta t + f(t_2) \, \Delta t + \cdots + f(t_n) \, \Delta t$$

$$= \sum_{i=1}^{n} f(t_i) \, \Delta t$$

$$= \sum_{i=1}^{n} \left(\frac{81}{4n^4} i^3 + \frac{3}{n} \right)$$

$$= \frac{81}{4n^4} \sum_{i=1}^{n} i^3 + \sum_{i=1}^{n} \frac{3}{n}$$

$$= \frac{81}{4n^4} \left[\frac{n(n+1)}{2} \right]^2 + \frac{3}{n} \cdot n \qquad \text{(Special Sum Formula 3)}$$

$$= \frac{81}{16} \left[n^2 \frac{(n^2 + 2n + 1)}{n^4} \right] + 3$$

$$= \frac{81}{16} \left(1 + \frac{2}{n} + \frac{1}{n^2} \right) + 3$$

We conclude that

$$\lim_{n \to \infty} A(S_n) = \frac{81}{16} + 3 = \frac{129}{16} \approx 8.06$$

The object traveled about 8.06 feet between $t = 0$ and $t = 3$.

What was true in this example is true for any object moving with positive velocity. *The distance traveled is the area of the region under the velocity curve.*

Concepts Review

1. The value of $\sum_{i=1}^{5} 2i$ is _____, and the value of $\sum_{i=1}^{5} 2$ is _____.

2. If $\sum_{i=1}^{10} a_i = 9$ and $\sum_{i=1}^{10} b_i = 7$, then the value of $\sum_{i=1}^{10}(3a_i - 2b_i) =$ _____ and the value of $\sum_{i=1}^{10}(a_i + 4) =$ _____.

3. The area of a(n) _____ polygon underestimates the area of a region, whereas the area of a(n) _____ polygon overestimates this area.

4. The exact area of the region under the curve $y = [x]$ between 0 and 4 is _____.

Problem Set 5.1

In Problems 1–8, find the value of the indicated sum.

1. $\sum_{k=1}^{6}(k - 1)$

2. $\sum_{i=1}^{6} i^2$

3. $\sum_{k=1}^{7} \frac{1}{k + 1}$

4. $\sum_{l=3}^{8}(l + 1)^2$

5. $\sum_{m=1}^{8}(-1)^m 2^{m-2}$

6. $\sum_{k=3}^{7} \frac{(-1)^k 2^k}{(k + 1)}$

7. $\sum_{n=1}^{6} n \cos(n\pi)$

8. $\sum_{k=-1}^{6} k \sin(k\pi/2)$

In Problems 9–14, write the indicated sum in sigma notation.

9. $1 + 2 + 3 + \cdots + 41$

10. $2 + 4 + 6 + 8 + \cdots + 50$

11. $1 + \frac{1}{2} + \frac{1}{3} + \cdots + \frac{1}{100}$

12. $1 - \frac{1}{2} + \frac{1}{3} - \frac{1}{4} + \cdots - \frac{1}{100}$

13. $a_1 + a_3 + a_5 + a_7 + \cdots + a_{99}$

14. $f(w_1)\,\Delta x + f(w_2)\,\Delta x + \cdots + f(w_n)\,\Delta x$

In Problems 15–18, suppose that $\sum_{i=1}^{10} a_i = 40$ and $\sum_{i=1}^{10} b_i = 50$. Calculate each of the following (see Example 1).

15. $\sum_{i=1}^{10}(a_i + b_i)$

16. $\sum_{n=1}^{10}(3a_n + 2b_n)$

17. $\sum_{p=0}^{9}(a_{p+1} - b_{p+1})$

18. $\sum_{q=1}^{10}(a_q - b_q - q)$

In Problems 19–24, use Special Sum Formulas 1–4 to find each sum.

19. $\sum_{i=1}^{100}(3i - 2)$

20. $\sum_{i=1}^{10}[(i - 1)(4i + 3)]$

21. $\sum_{k=1}^{10}(k^3 - k^2)$

22. $\sum_{k=1}^{10} 5k^2(k + 4)$

23. $\sum_{i=1}^{n}(2i^2 - 3i + 1)$

24. $\sum_{i=1}^{n}(2i - 3)^2$

25. Add both sides of the two equalities below, solve for S, and thereby give another proof of Formula 1.

$$S = 1 + 2 + 3 + \cdots + (n - 2) + (n - 1) + n$$
$$S = n + (n - 1) + (n - 2) + \cdots + 3 + 2 + 1$$

26. Prove the following formula for a **geometric sum:**

$$\sum_{k=0}^{n} ar^k = a + ar + ar^2 + \cdots + ar^n = \frac{a - ar^{n+1}}{1 - r} \quad (r \neq 1)$$

Hint: Let $S = a + ar + \cdots + ar^n$. Simplify $S - rS$ and solve for S.

27. Use Problem 26 to calculate each sum.

(a) $\sum_{k=1}^{10}\left(\frac{1}{2}\right)^k$

(b) $\sum_{k=1}^{10} 2^k$

28. Use a derivation like that in Problem 25 to obtain a formula for the **arithmetic sum:**

$$\sum_{k=0}^{n}(a + kd) = a + (a + d) + (a + 2d) + \cdots + (a + nd)$$

29. Use the identity $(i + 1)^3 - i^3 = 3i^2 + 3i + 1$ to prove Special Sum Formula 2.

30. Use the identity $(i + 1)^4 - i^4 = 4i^3 + 6i^2 + 4i + 1$ to prove Special Sum Formula 3.

31. Use the identity $(i + 1)^5 - i^5 = 5i^4 + 10i^3 + 10i^2 + 5i + 1$ to prove Special Sum Formula 4.

32. Use the diagrams in Figure 12 to establish Formulas 1 and 3.

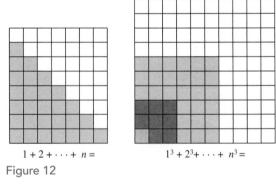

$$1 + 2 + \cdots + n =$$
$$1^3 + 2^3 + \cdots + n^3 =$$

Figure 12

C **33.** In statistics we define the *mean* $\bar{x}$ and the *variance* s^2 of a sequence of numbers $x_1, x_2, \ldots, x_n$ by

$$\bar{x} = \frac{1}{n}\sum_{i=1}^{n} x_i, \qquad s^2 = \frac{1}{n}\sum_{i=1}^{n}(x_i - \bar{x})^2$$

Find $\bar{x}$ and s^2 for the sequence of numbers $2, 5, 7, 8, 9, 10, 14$.

34. Using the definitions in Problem 33, find $\bar{x}$ and s^2 for each sequence of numbers.

(a) $1, 1, 1, 1, 1$

(b) $1001, 1001, 1001, 1001, 1001$

(c) $1, 2, 3$

(d) $1{,}000{,}001; 1{,}000{,}002; 1{,}000{,}003$

35. Use the definitions in Problem 33 to show that each is true.

(a) $\sum_{i=1}^{n}(x_i - \bar{x}) = 0$

(b) $s^2 = \left(\frac{1}{n}\sum_{i=1}^{n} x_i^2\right) - \bar{x}^2$

36. Based on your response to parts (a) and (b) of Problem 34, make a conjecture about the variance of n identical numbers. Prove your conjecture.

37. Let $x_1, x_2, \ldots, x_n$ be any real numbers. Find the value of c that minimizes $\sum_{i=1}^{n} (x_i - c)^2$.

38. In the song *The Twelve Days of Christmas*, my true love gave me 1 gift on the first day, $1 + 2$ gifts on the second day, $1 + 2 + 3$ gifts on the third day, and so on for 12 days.

(a) Find the total number of gifts given in 12 days.

(b) Find a simple formula for T_n, the total number of gifts given during a Christmas of n days.

39. A grocer stacks oranges in a pyramidlike pile. If the bottom layer is rectangular with 10 rows of 16 oranges and the top layer has a single row of oranges, how many oranges are in the stack?

40. Answer the same question in Problem 39 if the bottom layer has 50 rows of 60 oranges.

41. Generalize the result of Problems 39 and 40 to the case of m rows of n oranges.

42. Find a nice formula for the sum

$$\frac{1}{1 \cdot 2} + \frac{1}{2 \cdot 3} + \frac{1}{3 \cdot 4} + \cdots + \frac{1}{n(n+1)}$$

Hint: $\dfrac{1}{i(i+1)} = \dfrac{1}{i} - \dfrac{1}{i+1}$.

In Problems 43–48, find the area of the indicated inscribed or circumscribed polygon.

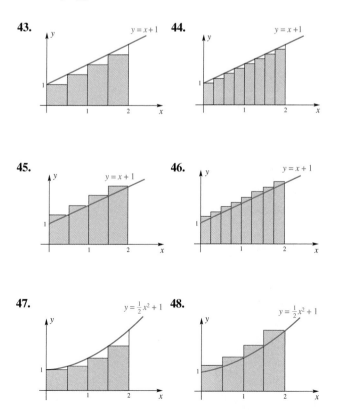

43. $y = x + 1$ **44.** $y = x + 1$

45. $y = x + 1$ **46.** $y = x + 1$

47. $y = \frac{1}{2}x^2 + 1$ **48.** $y = \frac{1}{2}x^2 + 1$

In Problems 49–52, sketch the graph of the given function over the interval $[a, b]$; then divide $[a, b]$ into n equal subintervals. Finally, calculate the area of the corresponding circumscribed polygon.

49. $f(x) = x + 1; a = -1, b = 2, n = 3$

50. $f(x) = 3x - 1; a = 1, b = 3, n = 4$

[C] **51.** $f(x) = x^2 - 1; a = 2, b = 3, n = 6$

[C] **52.** $f(x) = 3x^2 + x + 1; a = -1, b = 1, n = 10$

In Problems 53–58, find the area of the region under the curve $y = f(x)$ over the interval $[a, b]$. To do this, divide the interval $[a, b]$ into n equal subintervals, calculate the area of the corresponding circumscribed polygon, and then let $n \to \infty$. (See the example for $y = x^2$ in the text.)

53. $y = x + 2; a = 0, b = 1$

54. $y = \frac{1}{2}x^2 + 1; a = 0, b = 1$

55. $y = 2x + 2; a = -1, b = 1$. *Hint:* $x_i = -1 + \dfrac{2i}{n}$

56. $y = x^2; a = -2, b = 2$

[≈] **57.** $y = x^3; a = 0, b = 1$

[≈] **58.** $y = x^3 + x; a = 0, b = 1$

59. Suppose that an object is traveling along the x-axis in such a way that its velocity at time t seconds is $v = t + 2$ feet per second. How far did it travel between $t = 0$ and $t = 1$? *Hint:* See the discussion of the velocity problem at the end of this section and use the result of Problem 53.

60. Follow the directions of Problem 59 given that $v = \frac{1}{2}t^2 + 2$. You may use the result of Problem 54.

61. Let A_a^b denote the area under the curve $y = x^2$ over the interval $[a, b]$.

(a) Prove that $A_0^b = b^3/3$. *Hint:* $\Delta x = b/n$, so $x_i = ib/n$; use circumscribed polygons.

(b) Show that $A_a^b = b^3/3 - a^3/3$. Assume that $a \geq 0$.

62. Suppose that an object, moving along the x-axis, has velocity $v = t^2$ meters per second at time t seconds. How far did it travel between $t = 3$ and $t = 5$? See Problem 61.

63. Use the results of Problem 61 to calculate the area under the curve $y = x^2$ over each of the following intervals.

(a) $[0, 5]$ (b) $[1, 4]$ (c) $[2, 5]$

64. From Special Sum Formulas 1–4 you might guess that

$$1^m + 2^m + 3^m + \cdots + n^m = \frac{n^{m+1}}{m+1} + C_n$$

where C_n is a polynomial in n of degree m. Assume that this is true (which it is) and, for $a \geq 0$, let $A_a^b(x^m)$ be the area under the curve $y = x^m$ over the interval $[a, b]$.

(a) Prove that $A_0^b(x^m) = \dfrac{b^{m+1}}{(m+1)}$.

(b) Show that $A_a^b(x^m) = \dfrac{b^{m+1}}{m+1} - \dfrac{a^{m+1}}{m+1}$.

65. Use the results of Problem 64 to calculate each of the following areas.

(a) $A_0^2(x^3)$ (b) $A_1^2(x^3)$ (c) $A_1^2(x^5)$ (d) $A_0^2(x^9)$

66. Derive the formulas $A_n = \frac{1}{2}nr^2 \sin(2\pi/n)$ and $B_n = nr^2 \tan(\pi/n)$ for the areas of the inscribed and circumscribed regular n-sided polygons for a circle of radius r. Then show that $\lim_{n \to \infty} A_n$ and $\lim_{n \to \infty} B_n$ are both πr^2.

Answers to Concepts Review: **1.** 30; 10 **2.** 13; 49
3. inscribed; circumscribed **4.** 6

5.2
The Definite Integral

All the preparations have been made; we are ready to define the definite integral. Both Newton and Leibniz introduced early versions of this concept. However, it was Georg Friedrich Bernhard Riemann (1826–1866) who gave us the modern definition. In formulating this definition, we are guided by the ideas we discussed in the previous section. The first notion is that of a Riemann sum.

Riemann Sums Consider a function f defined on a closed interval $[a, b]$. It may have both positive and negative values on the interval, and it does not even need to be continuous. Its graph might look something like the one in Figure 1.

Consider a partition P of the interval $[a, b]$ into n subintervals (not necessarily of equal length) by means of points $a = x_0 < x_1 < x_2 < \cdots < x_{n-1} < x_n = b$, and let $\Delta x_i = x_i - x_{i-1}$. On each subinterval $[x_{i-1}, x_i]$, pick an arbitrary point $\overline{x}_i$ (which may be an end point); we call it a *sample point* for the ith subinterval. An example of these constructions is shown in Figure 2 for $n = 6$.

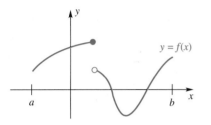

Figure 1

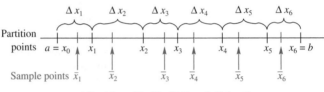

A Partition of $[a, b]$ with Sample Points $\overline{x}_i$

Figure 2

We call the sum

$$R_P = \sum_{i=1}^{n} f(\overline{x}_i)\, \Delta x_i$$

a **Riemann sum** for f corresponding to the partition P. Its geometric interpretation is shown in Figure 3.

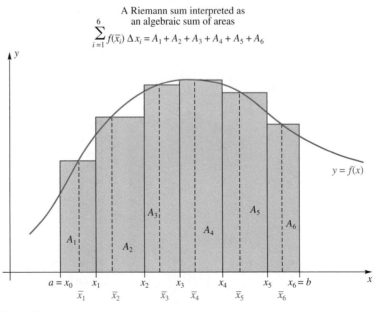

Figure 3

EXAMPLE 1 Evaluate the Riemann sum for $f(x) = x^2 + 1$ on the interval $[-1, 2]$ using the equally spaced partition points $-1 < -0.5 < 0 < 0.5 < 1 < 1.5 < 2$, with the sample point $\bar{x}_i$ being the midpoint of the ith subinterval.

SOLUTION   Note the picture in Figure 4.

$$R_P = \sum_{i=1}^{6} f(\bar{x}_i)\,\Delta x_i$$

$$= \left[f(-0.75) + f(-0.25) + f(0.25) + f(0.75) + f(1.25) + f(1.75) \right](0.5)$$

$$= [1.5625 + 1.0625 + 1.0625 + 1.5625 + 2.5625 + 4.0625](0.5)$$

$$= 5.9375 \qquad \blacksquare$$

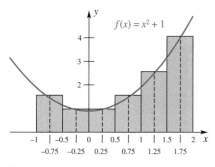

Figure 4

The functions in Figures 3 and 4 were positive. As a consequence of this, the Riemann sum is simply the sum of the areas of the rectangles. But what if f is negative? In this case, a sample point $\bar{x}_i$ with the property that $f(\bar{x}_i) < 0$ will lead to a rectangle that is entirely below the x-axis, and the product $f(\bar{x}_i)\,\Delta x_i$ will be negative. This means that the contribution of such a rectangle to the Riemann sum is negative. Figure 5 illustrates this.

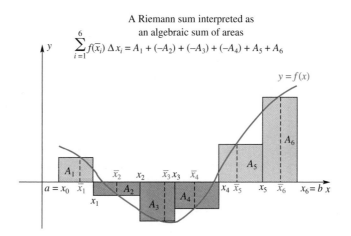

Figure 5

EXAMPLE 2 Evaluate the Riemann sum R_P for

$$f(x) = (x + 1)(x - 2)(x - 4) = x^3 - 5x^2 + 2x + 8$$

on the interval $[0, 5]$ using the partition P with partition points $0 < 1.1 < 2 < 3.2 < 4 < 5$ and the corresponding sample points $\bar{x}_1 = 0.5, \bar{x}_2 = 1.5, \bar{x}_3 = 2.5, \bar{x}_4 = 3.6$, and $\bar{x}_5 = 5$.

SOLUTION

$$R_P = \sum_{i=1}^{5} f(\bar{x}_i)\,\Delta x_i$$

$$= f(\bar{x}_1)\,\Delta x_1 + f(\bar{x}_2)\,\Delta x_2 + f(\bar{x}_3)\,\Delta x_3 + f(\bar{x}_4)\,\Delta x_4 + f(\bar{x}_5)\,\Delta x_5$$

$$= f(0.5)(1.1 - 0) + f(1.5)(2 - 1.1) + f(2.5)(3.2 - 2)$$

$$\quad + f(3.6)(4 - 3.2) + f(5)(5 - 4)$$

$$= (7.875)(1.1) + (3.125)(0.9) + (-2.625)(1.2) + (-2.944)(0.8) + 18(1)$$

$$= 23.9698$$

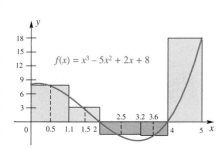

Figure 6

The corresponding geometric picture appears in Figure 6. $\qquad \blacksquare$

Definition of the Definite Integral　Suppose now that P, Δx_i, and $\bar{x}_i$ have the meanings discussed above. Also let $\|P\|$, called the **norm** of P, denote the length of the longest of the subintervals of the partition P. For instance, in Example 1, $\|P\| = 0.5$; in Example 2, $\|P\| = 3.2 - 2 = 1.2$.

Definition　Definite Integral

Let f be a function that is defined on the closed interval $[a, b]$. If

$$\lim_{\|P\|\to 0} \sum_{i=1}^{n} f(\bar{x}_i)\, \Delta x_i$$

exists, we say f that is **integrable** on $[a, b]$. Moreover, $\displaystyle\int_a^b f(x)\, dx$, called the **definite integral** (or Riemann integral) of f from a to b, is then given by

$$\int_a^b f(x)\, dx = \lim_{\|P\|\to 0} \sum_{i=1}^{n} f(\bar{x}_i)\, \Delta x_i$$

The heart of the definition is the final line. The concept captured in that equation grows out of our discussion of area in the previous section. However, we have considerably modified the notion presented there. For example, we now allow f to be negative on part or all of $[a, b]$, we use partitions with subintervals that may be of unequal length, and we allow $\bar{x}_i$ to be *any* point on the ith subinterval. Since we have made these changes, it is important to state precisely how the definite integral relates to area. In general, $\displaystyle\int_a^b f(x)\, dx$ gives the *signed area* of the region trapped between the curve $y = f(x)$ and the x-axis on the interval $[a, b]$, meaning that a positive sign is attached to areas of parts above the x-axis, and a negative sign is attached to areas of parts below the x-axis. In symbols,

$$\int_a^b f(x)\, dx = A_{\text{up}} - A_{\text{down}}$$

where A_{up} and A_{down} are as shown in Figure 7.

The meaning of the word *limit* in the definition of the definite integral is more general than in earlier usage and should be explained. The equality

$$\lim_{\|P\|\to 0} \sum_{i=1}^{n} f(\bar{x}_i)\, \Delta x_i = L$$

means that, corresponding to each $\varepsilon > 0$, there is a $\delta > 0$ such that

$$\left| \sum_{i=1}^{n} f(\bar{x}_i)\, \Delta x_i - L \right| < \varepsilon$$

for all Riemann sums $\displaystyle\sum_{i=1}^{n} f(\bar{x}_i)\, \Delta x_i$ for f on $[a, b]$ for which the norm $\|P\|$ of the associated partition is less than δ. In this case, we say that the indicated limit exists and has the value L.

That was a mouthful, and we are not going to digest it just now. We simply assert that the usual limit theorems also hold for this kind of limit.

Returning to the symbol $\displaystyle\int_a^b f(x)\, dx$, we might call a the lower end point and b the upper end point for the integral. However, most authors use the terminology **lower limit** of integration and **upper limit** of integration, which is fine provided we

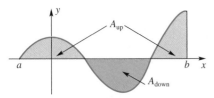

Figure 7

realize that this usage of the word *limit* has nothing to do with its more technical meaning.

In our definition of $\int_a^b f(x)\,dx$, we implicitly assumed that $a < b$. We remove that restriction with the following definitions.

$$\int_a^a f(x)\,dx = 0$$

$$\int_a^b f(x)\,dx = -\int_b^a f(x)\,dx, \quad a > b$$

Thus,

$$\int_2^2 x^3\,dx = 0, \qquad \int_6^2 x^3\,dx = -\int_2^6 x^3\,dx$$

Finally, we point out that x is a **dummy variable** in the symbol $\int_a^b f(x)\,dx$. By this we mean that x can be replaced by any other letter (provided, of course, that it is replaced in each place where it occurs). Thus,

$$\int_a^b f(x)\,dx = \int_a^b f(t)\,dt = \int_a^b f(u)\,du$$

What Functions Are Integrable?   Not every function is integrable on a closed interval $[a, b]$. For example, the unbounded function

$$f(x) = \begin{cases} \dfrac{1}{x^2} & \text{if } x \neq 0 \\[2mm] 1 & \text{if } x = 0 \end{cases}$$

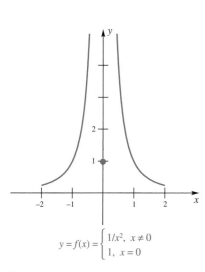

$$y = f(x) = \begin{cases} 1/x^2, & x \neq 0 \\ 1, & x = 0 \end{cases}$$

Figure 8

which is graphed in Figure 8, is not integrable on $[-2, 2]$. It can be shown that for this unbounded function, the Riemann sum can be made arbitrarily large. Therefore, the limit of the Riemann sum over $[-2, 2]$ does not exist.

Even some bounded functions can fail to be integrable, but they have to be pretty complicated (see Problem 39 for one example). Theorem A (below) is the most important theorem about integrability. Unfortunately, it is too difficult to prove here; we leave that for advanced calculus books.

Theorem A   **Integrability Theorem**

If f is bounded on $[a, b]$ and if it is continuous there except at a finite number of points, then f is integrable on $[a, b]$. In particular, if f is continuous on the whole interval $[a, b]$, it is integrable on $[a, b]$.

As a consequence of this theorem, the following functions are integrable on every closed interval $[a, b]$.

1. Polynomial functions
2. Sine and cosine functions
3. Rational functions, provided that the interval $[a, b]$ contains no points where the denominator is 0

Calculating Definite Integrals   Knowing that a function is integrable allows us to calculate its integral by using a **regular partition** (i.e., a partition with equal-length subintervals) and by picking the sample points $\bar{x}_i$ in any way that is convenient for us. Examples 3 and 4 involve polynomials, which we just learned are integrable.

EXAMPLE 3 Evaluate $\int_{-2}^{3} (x + 3) \, dx$.

SOLUTION Partition the interval $[-2, 3]$ into n equal subintervals, each of length $\Delta x = 5/n$. In each subinterval $[x_{i-1}, x_i]$, use $\bar{x}_i = x_i$ as the sample point. Then

$$x_0 = -2$$

$$x_1 = -2 + \Delta x = -2 + \frac{5}{n}$$

$$x_2 = -2 + 2 \Delta x = -2 + 2\left(\frac{5}{n}\right)$$

$$\vdots$$

$$x_i = -2 + i \Delta x = -2 + i\left(\frac{5}{n}\right)$$

$$\vdots$$

$$x_n = -2 + n \Delta x = -2 + n\left(\frac{5}{n}\right) = 3$$

Thus, $f(x_i) = x_i + 3 = 1 + i(5/n)$, and so

$$\sum_{i=1}^{n} f(\bar{x}_i) \, \Delta x_i = \sum_{i=1}^{n} f(x_i) \, \Delta x$$

$$= \sum_{i=1}^{n} \left[1 + i\left(\frac{5}{n}\right)\right] \frac{5}{n}$$

$$= \frac{5}{n} \sum_{i=1}^{n} 1 + \frac{25}{n^2} \sum_{i=1}^{n} i$$

$$= \frac{5}{n}(n) + \frac{25}{n^2}\left[\frac{n(n + 1)}{2}\right] \qquad \text{(Special Sum Formula 1)}$$

$$= 5 + \frac{25}{2}\left(1 + \frac{1}{n}\right)$$

Since P is a regular partition, $\|P\| \to 0$ is equivalent to $n \to \infty$. We conclude that

$$\int_{-2}^{3} (x + 3) \, dx = \lim_{\|P\| \to 0} \sum_{i=1}^{n} f(\bar{x}_i) \, \Delta x_i$$

$$= \lim_{n \to \infty} \left[5 + \frac{25}{2}\left(1 + \frac{1}{n}\right)\right]$$

$$= \frac{35}{2}$$

We can easily check our answer, since the required integral gives the area of the trapezoid in Figure 9. The familiar trapezoidal area formula $A = \frac{1}{2}(a + b)h$ gives $\frac{1}{2}(1 + 6)5 = 35/2$. ∎

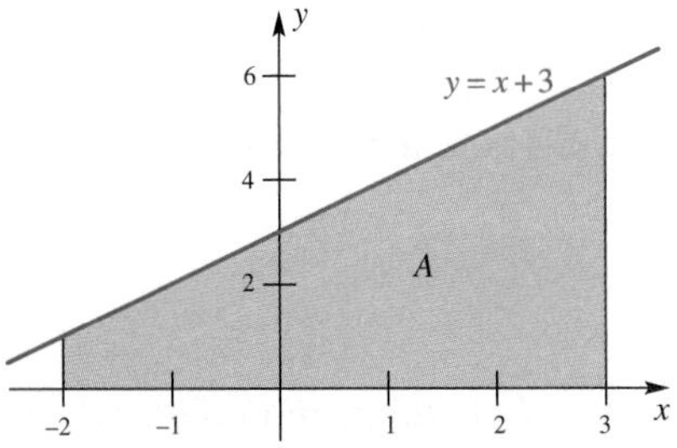

$\int_{-2}^{3}(x + 3) \, dx = A = \frac{35}{2}$

Figure 9

EXAMPLE 4 Evaluate $\int_{-1}^{3} (2x^2 - 8) \, dx$.

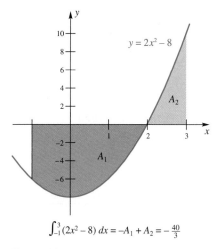

$$\int_{-1}^{3}(2x^2 - 8)\,dx = -A_1 + A_2 = -\tfrac{40}{3}$$

Figure 10

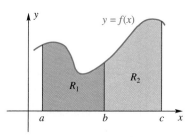

≈ Common Sense

Given the graph of a function, we can always make a rough estimate for the value of a definite integral by using the fact that it is the signed area

$$A_{up} - A_{down}$$

Thus, in Example 4, we might estimate the value of the integral by pretending that the part above the x-axis is a triangle and the part below is a rectangle. Our estimate is

$$\tfrac{1}{2}(1)(10) - (3)(6) = -13$$

SOLUTION   No formulas from elementary geometry will help here. Figure 10 suggests that the integral is equal to $-A_1 + A_2$, where A_1 and A_2 are the areas of the regions below and above the x-axis.

Let P be a regular partition of $[-1, 3]$ into n equal subintervals, each of length $\Delta x = 4/n$. In each subinterval $[x_{i-1}, x_i]$, choose $\bar{x}_i$ to be the right end point, so $\bar{x}_i = x_i$. Then

$$x_i = -1 + i\,\Delta x = -1 + i\left(\frac{4}{n}\right)$$

and

$$f(x_i) = 2x_i^2 - 8 = 2\left[-1 + i\left(\frac{4}{n}\right)\right]^2 - 8$$

$$= -6 - \frac{16i}{n} + \frac{32i^2}{n^2}$$

Consequently,

$$\sum_{i=1}^{n} f(\bar{x}_i)\,\Delta x_i = \sum_{i=1}^{n} f(x_i)\,\Delta x$$

$$= \sum_{i=1}^{n}\left[-6 - \frac{16}{n}i + \frac{32}{n^2}i^2\right]\frac{4}{n}$$

$$= -\frac{24}{n}\sum_{i=1}^{n}1 - \frac{64}{n^2}\sum_{i=1}^{n}i + \frac{128}{n^3}\sum_{i=1}^{n}i^2$$

$$= -\frac{24}{n}(n) - \frac{64}{n^2}\frac{n(n+1)}{2} + \frac{128}{n^3}\frac{n(n+1)(2n+1)}{6}$$

$$= -24 - 32\left(1 + \frac{1}{n}\right) + \frac{128}{6}\left(2 + \frac{3}{n} + \frac{1}{n^2}\right)$$

We conclude that

$$\int_{-1}^{3}(2x^2 - 8)\,dx = \lim_{\|P\|\to 0}\sum_{i=1}^{n} f(\bar{x}_i)\,\Delta x_i$$

$$= \lim_{n\to\infty}\left[-24 - 32\left(1 + \frac{1}{n}\right) + \frac{128}{6}\left(2 + \frac{3}{n} + \frac{1}{n^2}\right)\right]$$

$$= -24 - 32 + \frac{128}{3} = -\frac{40}{3}$$

That the answer is negative is not surprising, since the region below the x-axis appears to be larger than the one above the x-axis (Figure 10). Our answer is close to the estimate given in the margin note COMMON SENSE; this reassures us that our answer is likely to be correct. ∎

The Interval Additive Property   Our definition of the definite integral was motivated by the problem of area for curved regions. Consider the two curved regions R_1 and R_2 in Figure 11 and let $R = R_1 \cup R_2$. It is clear that the areas satisfy

$$A(R) = A(R_1 \cup R_2) = A(R_1) + A(R_2)$$

which suggests that

$$\int_{a}^{c} f(x)\,dx = \int_{a}^{b} f(x)\,dx + \int_{b}^{c} f(x)\,dx$$

We quickly point out that this does not constitute a proof of this fact about integrals, since, first of all, our discussion of area in Section 5.1 was rather informal

Figure 11

and, second, our diagram supposes that f is positive, which it need not be. Nevertheless, definite integrals do satisfy this interval additive property, and they do it no matter how the three points a, b, and c are arranged. We leave the rigorous proof to more advanced works.

Theorem B **Interval Additive Property**

If f is integrable on an interval containing the points a, b, and c, then

$$\int_a^c f(x)\, dx = \int_a^b f(x)\, dx + \int_b^c f(x)\, dx$$

no matter what the order of a, b, and c.

For example,

$$\int_0^2 x^2\, dx = \int_0^1 x^2\, dx + \int_1^2 x^2\, dx$$

which most people readily believe. But it is also true that

$$\int_0^2 x^2\, dx = \int_0^3 x^2\, dx + \int_3^2 x^2\, dx$$

which may seem surprising. If you mistrust the theorem, you might actually evaluate each of the above integrals to see that the equality holds.

Velocity and Position   Near the end of Section 5.1 we explained how the area under the velocity curve is equal to the distance traveled, provided the velocity function $v(t)$ is positive. In general, the position (which could be positive or negative) is equal to the definite integral of the velocity function (which could be positive or negative). More specifically, if $v(t)$ is the velocity of an object at time t, where $t \geq 0$, and if the object is at position 0 at time 0, then the position of the object at time a is $\int_0^a v(t)\, dt$.

EXAMPLE 5   An object at the origin at time $t = 0$ has velocity, measured in meters per second,

$$v(t) = \begin{cases} t/20, & \text{if } 0 \leq t \leq 40 \\ 2, & \text{if } 40 < t \leq 60 \\ 5 - t/20 & \text{if } t > 60 \end{cases}$$

Sketch the velocity curve. Express the object's position at $t = 140$ as a definite integral and evaluate it using formulas from plane geometry.

SOLUTION   Figure 12 shows the velocity curve. The position at time 140 is equal to the definite integral $\int_0^{140} v(t)\, dt$, which we can evaluate using formulas for the area of a triangle and a rectangle and using the Interval Additive Property (Theorem B):

$$\int_0^{140} v(t)\, dt = \int_0^{40} \frac{t}{20}\, dt + \int_{40}^{60} 2\, dt + \int_{60}^{140} \left(5 - \frac{t}{20}\right) dt$$

$$= 40 + 40 + 40 - 40 = 80 \qquad \blacksquare$$

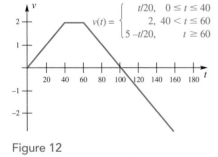

$$v(t) = \begin{cases} t/20, & 0 \leq t \leq 40 \\ 2, & 40 < t \leq 60 \\ 5 - t/20, & t \geq 60 \end{cases}$$

Figure 12

Concepts Review

1. A sum of the form $\sum_{i=1}^{n} f(\overline{x}_i)\, \Delta x_i$ is called a _____.

2. The limit of the sum above for f defined on $[a, b]$ is called a _____ and is symbolized by _____.

3. Geometrically, the definite integral corresponds to a signed area. In terms of A_{up} and A_{down}, $\int_a^b f(x)\, dx = $ _____.

4. Thus, the value of $\int_{-1}^4 x\, dx$ is _____.

Problem Set 5.2

In Problems 1 and 2, calculate the Riemann sum suggested by each figure.

1.

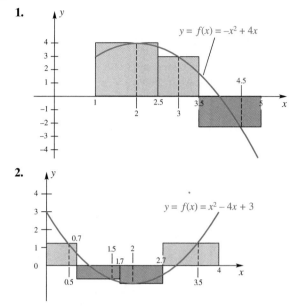

$y = f(x) = -x^2 + 4x$

2.

$y = f(x) = x^2 - 4x + 3$

In Problems 3–6, calculate the Riemann sum $\sum_{i=1}^{n} f(\bar{x}_i)\, \Delta x_i$ for the given data.

3. $f(x) = x - 1; P: 3 < 3.75 < 4.25 < 5.5 < 6 < 7$;
$\bar{x}_1 = 3, \bar{x}_2 = 4, \bar{x}_3 = 4.75, \bar{x}_4 = 6, \bar{x}_5 = 6.5$

4. $f(x) = -x/2 + 3; P: -3 < -1.3 < 0 < 0.9 < 2$;
$\bar{x}_1 = -2, \bar{x}_2 = -0.5, \bar{x}_3 = 0, \bar{x}_4 = 2$

C **5.** $f(x) = x^2/2 + x; [-2, 2]$ is divided into eight equal subintervals, $\bar{x}_i$ is the midpoint.

C **6.** $f(x) = 4x^3 + 1; [0, 3]$ is divided into six equal subintervals, $\bar{x}_i$ is the right end point.

In Problems 7–10, use the given values of a and b and express the given limit as a definite integral.

7. $\lim_{\|P\|\to 0} \sum_{i=1}^{n} (\bar{x}_i)^3\, \Delta x_i; a = 1, b = 3$

8. $\lim_{\|P\|\to 0} \sum_{i=1}^{n} (\bar{x}_i + 1)^3\, \Delta x_i; a = 0, b = 2$

9. $\lim_{\|P\|\to 0} \sum_{i=1}^{n} \dfrac{\bar{x}_i^2}{1 + \bar{x}_i}\, \Delta x_i; a = -1, b = 1$

10. $\lim_{\|P\|\to 0} \sum_{i=1}^{n} (\sin \bar{x}_i)^2\, \Delta x_i; a = 0, b = \pi$

≈ *In Problems 11–16, evaluate the definite integrals using the definition, as in Examples 3 and 4.*

11. $\displaystyle\int_0^2 (x + 1)\, dx$ **12.** $\displaystyle\int_0^2 (x^2 + 1)\, dx$

Hint: Use $\bar{x}_i = 2i/n$.

13. $\displaystyle\int_{-2}^1 (2x + \pi)\, dx$ **14.** $\displaystyle\int_{-2}^1 (3x^2 + 2)\, dx$

Hint: Use $\bar{x}_i = -2 + 3i/n$.

15. $\displaystyle\int_0^5 (x + 1)\, dx$ **16.** $\displaystyle\int_{-10}^{10} (x^2 + x)\, dx$

In Problems 17–22, calculate $\displaystyle\int_a^b f(x)\, dx$, where a and b are the left and right end points for which f is defined, by using the Interval Additive Property and the appropriate area formulas from plane geometry. Begin by graphing the given function.

17. $f(x) = \begin{cases} 2x & \text{if } 0 \le x \le 1 \\ 2 & \text{if } 1 < x \le 2 \\ x & \text{if } 2 < x \le 5 \end{cases}$

18. $f(x) = \begin{cases} 3x & \text{if } 0 \le x \le 1 \\ 2(x - 1) + 2 & \text{if } 1 < x \le 2 \end{cases}$

19. $f(x) = \begin{cases} \sqrt{1 - x^2} & \text{if } 0 \le x \le 1 \\ x - 1 & \text{if } 1 < x \le 2 \end{cases}$

20. $f(x) = \begin{cases} -\sqrt{4 - x^2} & \text{if } -2 \le x \le 0 \\ -2x - 2 & \text{if } 0 < x \le 2 \end{cases}$

21. $f(x) = \sqrt{A^2 - x^2}; -A \le x \le A$

22. $f(x) = 4 - |x|, -4 \le x \le 4$

In Problems 23–26, the velocity function for an object is given. Assuming that the object is at the origin at time $t = 0$, find the position at time $t = 4$.

23. $v(t) = t/60$ **24.** $v(t) = 1 + 2t$

25. $v(t) = \begin{cases} t/2 & \text{if } 0 \le t \le 2 \\ 1 & \text{if } 2 < t \le 4 \end{cases}$

26. $v(t) = \begin{cases} \sqrt{4 - t^2} & \text{if } 0 \le t \le 2 \\ 0 & \text{if } 2 < t \le 4 \end{cases}$

In Problems 27–30, an object's velocity function is graphed. Use this graph to determine the object's position at times $t = 20, 40, 60, 80, 100,$ and 120 assuming the object is at the origin at time $t = 0$.

27.   **28.**

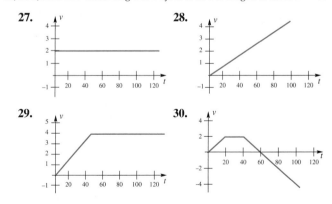

29.   **30.**

31. Recall that $[\![x]\!]$ denotes the greatest integer less than or equal to x. Calculate each of the following integrals. You may use geometric reasoning and the fact that $\displaystyle\int_0^b x^2\, dx = b^3/3$. (The latter is shown in Problem 34.)

(a) $\displaystyle\int_{-3}^3 [\![x]\!]\, dx$ (b) $\displaystyle\int_{-3}^3 [\![x]\!]^2\, dx$

(c) $\displaystyle\int_{-3}^3 (x - [\![x]\!])\, dx$ (d) $\displaystyle\int_{-3}^3 (x - [\![x]\!])^2\, dx$

(e) $\int_{-3}^{3} |x| \, dx$

(f) $\int_{-3}^{3} x|x| \, dx$

(g) $\int_{-1}^{2} |x| [\![x]\!] \, dx$

(h) $\int_{-1}^{2} x^2 [\![x]\!] \, dx$

32. Let f be an odd function and g be an even function, and suppose that $\int_{0}^{1} |f(x)| \, dx = \int_{0}^{1} g(x) \, dx = 3$. Use geometric reasoning to calculate each of the following:

(a) $\int_{-1}^{1} f(x) \, dx$

(b) $\int_{-1}^{1} g(x) \, dx$

(c) $\int_{-1}^{1} |f(x)| \, dx$

(d) $\int_{-1}^{1} [-g(x)] \, dx$

(e) $\int_{-1}^{1} xg(x) \, dx$

(f) $\int_{-1}^{1} f^3(x)g(x) \, dx$

33. Show that $\int_{a}^{b} x \, dx = \frac{1}{2}(b^2 - a^2)$ by completing the following argument. For the partition $a = x_0 < x_1 < \cdots < x_n = b$, choose $\overline{x}_i = \frac{1}{2}(x_{i-1} + x_i)$. Then $R_P = \sum_{i=1}^{n} \overline{x}_i \, \Delta x_i = \frac{1}{2} \sum_{i=1}^{n} (x_i + x_{i-1})(x_i - x_{i-1})$. Now simplify R_P (collapsing sum) and take a limit.

34. Show that $\int_{a}^{b} x^2 \, dx = \frac{1}{3}(b^3 - a^3)$ by an argument like that in Problem 33, but using $\overline{x}_i = \left[\frac{1}{3}(x_{i-1}^2 + x_{i-1}x_i + x_i^2) \right]^{1/2}$. Assume that $0 \le a < b$.

CAS *Many computer algebra systems permit the evaluation of Riemann sums for left end point, right end point, or midpoint evaluations of the function. Using such a system in Problems 35–38, evaluate the 10-subinterval Riemann sums using left end point, right end point, and midpoint evaluations.*

35. $\int_{0}^{2} (x^3 + 1) \, dx$

36. $\int_{0}^{1} \tan x \, dx$

37. $\int_{0}^{1} \cos x \, dx$

38. $\int_{1}^{3} (1/x) \, dx$

39. Prove that the function f defined by

$$f(x) = \begin{cases} 1 & \text{if } x \text{ is rational} \\ 0 & \text{if } x \text{ is irrational} \end{cases}$$

is not integrable on $[0, 1]$. *Hint:* Show that no matter how small the norm of the partition, $\|P\|$, the Riemann sum can be made to have value either 0 or 1.

Answers to Concepts Review: **1.** Riemann sum
2. definite integral; $\int_{a}^{b} f(x) \, dx$ **3.** $A_{up} - A_{down}$ **4.** $\frac{15}{2}$

5.3
The First Fundamental Theorem of Calculus

Calculus is the study of limits, and the two most important limits that you have studied so far are the derivative and the definite integral. The derivative of a function f is

$$f'(x) = \lim_{h \to 0} \frac{f(x + h) - f(x)}{h}$$

and the definite integral is

$$\int_{a}^{b} f(x) \, dx = \lim_{\|P\| \to 0} \sum_{i=1}^{n} f(\overline{x}_i) \, \Delta x_i$$

These two kinds of limits appear to have no connection whatsoever. There is, however, a very close connection, as we shall see in this section.

Newton and Leibniz are usually credited with the simultaneous but independent discovery of calculus. Yet, the concepts of the slope of a tangent line (which led to the derivative) were known earlier, having been studied by Blaise Pascal and Isaac Barrow years before Newton and Leibniz. And Archimedes had studied areas of curved regions 1800 years earlier, in the third century B.C. Why then do Newton and Leibniz get the credit? They understood and exploited the intimate relationship between antiderivatives and definite integrals. This important relationship is called the *First Fundamental Theorem of Calculus*.

The First Fundamental Theorem You have likely met several "fundamental theorems" in your mathematical career. The Fundamental Theorem of Arithmetic says that a whole number factors uniquely into a product of primes. The Fundamental Theorem of Algebra says that an nth-degree polynomial has n roots, counting complex roots and multiplicities. Any "fundamental theorem" should be studied carefully, and then permanently committed to memory.

Near the end of Section 5.1, we studied a problem in which the velocity of an object at time t is given by $v = f(t) = \frac{1}{4}t^3 + 1$. We found that the distance traveled from time $t = 0$ to time $t = 3$ is equal to

$$\lim_{n \to \infty} \sum_{i=1}^{n} f(t_i)\, \Delta t = \frac{129}{16}$$

Using the terminology from Section 5.2, we now see that the distance traveled from time $t = 0$ to time $t = 3$ is equal to the definite integral

$$\lim_{n \to \infty} \sum_{i=1}^{n} f(t_i)\, \Delta t = \int_0^3 f(t)\, dt$$

(Since the velocity is positive for all $t \geq 0$, the distance traveled through time t is equal to the position of the object at time t, assuming that the object started at the origin. If the velocity were negative for some value of t, then the object would be traveling backward at that time t; in such a case, distance traveled would not equal position.) We could use the same reasoning to find that the distance s traveled from time $t = 0$ to time $t = x$ is

$$s(x) = \int_0^x f(t)\, dt$$

The question we now pose is this: What is the derivative of s?

Since the derivative of distance traveled (as long as the velocity is always positive) is the velocity, we have

$$s'(x) = v = f(x)$$

In other words,

$$\frac{d}{dx} s(x) = \frac{d}{dx} \int_0^x f(t)\, dt = f(x)$$

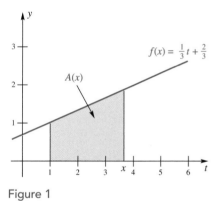

$f(x) = \frac{1}{3}t + \frac{2}{3}$

$A(x)$

Figure 1

Now, define $A(x)$ to be the area under the graph of $y = \frac{1}{3}t + \frac{2}{3}$, above the t-axis, and between the vertical lines $t = 1$ and $t = x$, where $x \geq 1$ (see Figure 1). A function such as this is called an **accumulation function** because it accumulates area under a curve from a fixed value ($t = 1$ in this case) to a variable value ($t = x$ in this case). What is the derivative of A?

The area $A(x)$ is equal to the definite integral

$$A(x) = \int_1^x \left(\frac{2}{3} + \frac{1}{3}t \right) dt$$

In this case we can evaluate this definite integral using a geometrical argument; $A(x)$ is just the area of a trapezoid, so

$$A(x) = (x - 1)\frac{1 + \left(\frac{2}{3} + \frac{1}{3}x \right)}{2} = \frac{1}{6}x^2 + \frac{2}{3}x - \frac{5}{6}$$

With this done, we see that the derivative of A is

$$A'(x) = \frac{d}{dx}\left(\frac{1}{6}x^2 + \frac{2}{3}x - \frac{5}{6} \right) = \frac{1}{3}x + \frac{2}{3}$$

In other words,

$$\frac{d}{dx} \int_1^x \left(\frac{2}{3} + \frac{1}{3}t \right) dt = \frac{2}{3} + \frac{1}{3}x$$

Let's define another accumulation function B as the area under the curve $y = t^2$, above the t-axis, to the right of the origin, and to the left of the line $t = x$,

Terminology

- The indefinite integral $\displaystyle\int f(x)\, dx$ is a *family of functions* of x.

- The definite integral $\displaystyle\int_a^b f(x)\, dx$ is a *number*, provided that a and b are fixed.

- If the upper limit in a definite integral is a variable x, then the definite integral [e.g., $\displaystyle\int_a^x f(t)\, dt$] is a *function of x.*

- A function of the form $$F(x) = \int_a^x f(t)\, dt$$ is called an *accumulation function.*

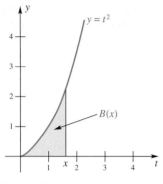

Figure 2

where $x \geq 0$ (see Figure 2). This area is given by the definite integral $\int_0^x t^2 \, dt$. To find this area, we first construct a Riemann sum. We use a regular partition of $[0, x]$ and evaluate the function at the right end point of each subinterval. Then $\Delta t = x/n$ and the right end point of the ith interval is $t_i = 0 + i\Delta t = ix/n$. The Riemann sum is therefore

$$\sum_{i=1}^{n} f(t_i) \, \Delta t = \sum_{i=1}^{n} f\left(\frac{ix}{n}\right) \frac{x}{n}$$

$$= \frac{x}{n} \sum_{i=1}^{n} \left(\frac{ix}{n}\right)^2$$

$$= \frac{x^3}{n^3} \sum_{i=1}^{n} i^2$$

$$= \frac{x^3}{n^3} \frac{n(n + 1)(2n + 1)}{6}$$

The definite integral is the limit of these Riemann sums.

$$\int_0^x t^2 \, dt = \lim_{n \to \infty} \sum_{i=1}^{n} f(t_i) \, \Delta t$$

$$= \lim_{n \to \infty} \frac{x^3}{n^3} \frac{n(n + 1)(2n + 1)}{6}$$

$$= \frac{x^3}{6} \lim_{n \to \infty} \frac{2n^3 + 3n^2 + n}{n^3}$$

$$= \frac{x^3}{6} \cdot 2 = \frac{x^3}{3}$$

Thus, $B(x) = x^3/3$, so the derivative of B is

$$B'(x) = \frac{d}{dx} \frac{x^3}{3} = x^2$$

In other words,

$$\boxed{\frac{d}{dx} \int_0^x t^2 \, dt = x^2}$$

The results of the last three boxed equations suggest that the derivative of an accumulation function is equal to the function being accumulated. But is this *always* the case? And *why* should this be the case?

Suppose that we are using a "retractable" paintbrush to paint the region under a curve. (By retractable, we mean that the brush becomes wider or narrower as it moves left to right so that it just covers the height to be painted. The brush is wide when the integrand values are large and narrow when the integrand values are small. See Figure 3.) With this analogy, the accumulated area is the painted area, and the rate of accumulation is the rate at which the paint is being applied. But the rate at which paint is being applied is equal to the width of the brush, in effect, the height of the function. We can restate this result as follows.

> *The rate of accumulation at $t = x$ is equal to the value of the function being accumulated at $t = x$.*

This, in a nutshell, is the First Fundamental Theorem of Calculus. It is *fundamental* because it links the derivative and the definite integral, the most important kinds of limits you have studied so far.

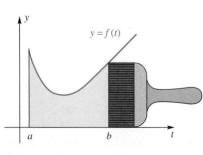

Figure 3

Theorem A **First Fundamental Theorem of Calculus**

Let f be continuous on the closed interval $[a, b]$ and let x be a (variable) point in (a, b). Then

$$\frac{d}{dx} \int_a^x f(t) \, dt = f(x)$$

Sketch of Proof For now, we present a sketch of the proof. This sketch shows the important features of the proof, but a complete proof must wait until after we have established a few other results. For x in $[a, b]$, define $F(x) = \int_a^x f(t) \, dt$. Then for x in (a, b)

$$\frac{d}{dx} \int_a^x f(t) \, dt = F'(x) = \lim_{h \to 0} \frac{F(x + h) - F(x)}{h}$$

$$= \lim_{h \to 0} \frac{1}{h} \left[\int_a^{x+h} f(t) \, dt - \int_a^x f(t) \, dt \right]$$

$$= \lim_{h \to 0} \frac{1}{h} \int_x^{x+h} f(t) \, dt$$

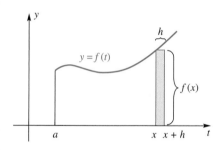

$y = f(t)$

Figure 4

The last line follows from the Interval Additive Property (Theorem 5.2B) and the fact that $\int_x^a f(t) \, dt = -\int_a^x f(t) \, dt$. Now, when h is small, f does not change much over the interval $[x, x + h]$. On this interval, f is roughly equal to $f(x)$, the value of f evaluated at the left end point of the interval (see Figure 4). The area under the curve $y = f(t)$ from x to $x + h$ is approximately equal to the area of the rectangle with width h and height $f(x)$; that is, $\int_x^{x+h} f(t) \, dt \approx hf(x)$. Therefore,

$$\frac{d}{dx} \int_a^x f(t) \, dt \approx \lim_{h \to 0} \frac{1}{h} [hf(x)] = f(x) \qquad \blacksquare$$

Of course, the flaw in this argument is to claim that f does not change over the interval $[x, x + h]$. We will give a complete proof later in this section.

Comparison Properties Consideration of the areas of the regions R_1 and R_2 in Figure 5 suggests another property of definite integrals.

Theorem B **Comparison Property**

If f and g are integrable on $[a, b]$ and if $f(x) \le g(x)$ for all x in $[a, b]$, then

$$\int_a^b f(x) \, dx \le \int_a^b g(x) \, dx$$

In informal but descriptive language, we say that the definite integral preserves inequalities.

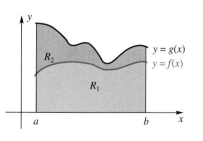

$y = g(x)$
$y = f(x)$
R_2
R_1

Figure 5

Proof Let $P \colon a = x_0 < x_1 < x_2 < \cdots < x_n = b$ be an arbitrary partition of $[a, b]$, and for each i let $\bar{x}_i$ be any sample point on the ith subinterval $[x_{i-1}, x_i]$. We may conclude successively that

$$f(\bar{x}_i) \leq g(\bar{x}_i)$$

$$f(\bar{x}_i) \, \Delta x_i \leq g(\bar{x}_i) \, \Delta x_i$$

$$\sum_{i=1}^{n} f(\bar{x}_i) \, \Delta x_i \leq \sum_{i=1}^{n} g(\bar{x}_i) \, \Delta x_i$$

$$\lim_{\|P\| \to 0} \sum_{i=1}^{n} f(\bar{x}_i) \, \Delta x_i \leq \lim_{\|P\| \to 0} \sum_{i=1}^{n} g(\bar{x}_i) \, \Delta x_i$$

$$\int_a^b f(x) \, dx \leq \int_a^b g(x) \, dx \qquad \blacksquare$$

Theorem C **Boundedness Property**

If f is integrable on $[a, b]$ and $m \leq f(x) \leq M$ for all x in $[a, b]$, then

$$m(b - a) \leq \int_a^b f(x) \, dx \leq M(b - a)$$

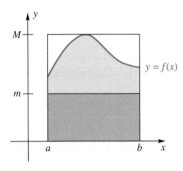

Figure 6

Proof The picture in Figure 6 helps us to understand the theorem. Note that $m(b - a)$ is the area of the lower, small rectangle, $M(b - a)$ is the area of the large rectangle, and $\int_a^b f(x) \, dx$ is the area under the curve.

To prove the right-hand inequality, let $g(x) = M$ for all x in $[a, b]$. Then, by Theorem B,

$$\int_a^b f(x) \, dx \leq \int_a^b g(x) \, dx$$

However, $\int_a^b g(x) \, dx$ is equal to the area of a rectangle with width $b - a$ and height M. Thus,

$$\int_a^b g(x) \, dx = M(b - a)$$

The left-hand inequality is handled similarly. $\qquad \blacksquare$

The Definite Integral Is a Linear Operator   Earlier we learned that D_x, $\int \cdots dx$, and Σ are linear operators. You can add $\int_a^b \cdots dx$ to the list.

Theorem D **Linearity of the Definite Integral**

Suppose that f and g are integrable on $[a, b]$ and that k is a constant. Then kf and $f + g$ are integrable and

(1) $\displaystyle\int_a^b kf(x) \, dx = k \int_a^b f(x) \, dx$

(2) $\displaystyle\int_a^b [f(x) + g(x)] \, dx = \int_a^b f(x) \, dx + \int_a^b g(x) \, dx$

(3) $\displaystyle\int_a^b [f(x) - g(x)] \, dx = \int_a^b f(x) \, dx - \int_a^b g(x) \, dx$

Proof The proofs of (1) and (2) depend on the linearity of Σ and the properties of limits. We show (2).

$$\int_a^b [f(x) + g(x)]\, dx = \lim_{\|P\| \to 0} \sum_{i=1}^n [f(\overline{x}_i) + g(\overline{x}_i)] \Delta x_i$$

$$= \lim_{\|P\| \to 0} \left[\sum_{i=1}^n f(\overline{x}_i)\, \Delta x_i + \sum_{i=1}^n g(\overline{x}_i)\, \Delta x_i \right]$$

$$= \lim_{\|P\| \to 0} \sum_{i=1}^n f(\overline{x}_i)\, \Delta x_i + \lim_{\|P\| \to 0} \sum_{i=1}^n g(\overline{x}_i)\, \Delta x_i$$

$$= \int_a^b f(x)\, dx + \int_a^b g(x)\, dx$$

Part (3) follows from (1) and (2) on writing $f(x) - g(x)$ as $f(x) + (-1)g(x)$. ∎

Proof of the First Fundamental Theorem of Calculus   With these results in hand, we are now ready to prove the First Fundamental Theorem of Calculus.

Proof   In the sketch of the proof presented earlier, we defined $F(x) = \int_a^x f(t)\, dt$, and we established the fact that

$$F(x + h) - F(x) = \int_x^{x+h} f(t)\, dt$$

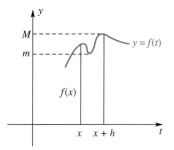

Figure 7

Assume for the moment that $h > 0$ and let m and M be the minimum value and maximum value, respectively, of f on the interval $[x, x + h]$ (Figure 7). By Theorem C,

$$mh \le \int_x^{x+h} f(t)\, dt \le Mh$$

or

$$mh \le F(x + h) - F(x) \le Mh$$

Dividing by h, we obtain

$$m \le \frac{F(x + h) - F(x)}{h} \le M$$

Now m and M really depend on h. Moreover, since f is continuous, both m and M must approach $f(x)$ as $h \to 0$. Thus, by the Squeeze Theorem,

$$\lim_{h \to 0} \frac{F(x + h) - F(x)}{h} = f(x)$$

The case where $h < 0$ is handled similarly. ∎

One theoretical consequence of this theorem is that every continuous function f has an antiderivative F given by the accumulation function

$$F(x) = \int_a^x f(t)\, dt$$

Section 7.6 gives several examples of important functions that are defined as accumulation functions.

EXAMPLE 1 Find $\dfrac{d}{dx}\left[\displaystyle\int_{1}^{x} t^3\, dt\right]$.

SOLUTION   By the First Fundamental Theorem of Calculus,

$$\frac{d}{dx}\left[\int_{1}^{x} t^3\, dt\right] = x^3 \qquad \blacksquare$$

EXAMPLE 2 Find $\dfrac{d}{dx}\left[\displaystyle\int_{2}^{x} \frac{t^{3/2}}{\sqrt{t^2+17}}\, dt\right]$.

SOLUTION   We challenge anyone to do this example by first evaluating the integral. However, by the First Fundamental Theorem of Calculus, it is a trivial problem.

$$\frac{d}{dx}\left[\int_{2}^{x} \frac{t^{3/2}}{\sqrt{t^2+17}}\, dt\right] = \frac{x^{3/2}}{\sqrt{x^2+17}} \qquad \blacksquare$$

EXAMPLE 3 Find $\dfrac{d}{dx}\left[\displaystyle\int_{x}^{4} \tan^2 u \cos u\, du\right], \dfrac{\pi}{2} < x < \dfrac{3\pi}{2}$.

SOLUTION   Use of the dummy variable u rather than t should not bother anyone. However, the fact that x is the lower limit, rather than the upper limit, is troublesome. Here is how we handle this difficulty.

$$\frac{d}{dx}\left[\int_{x}^{4} \tan^2 u \cos u\, du\right] = \frac{d}{dx}\left[-\int_{4}^{x} \tan^2 u \cos u\, du\right]$$

$$= -\frac{d}{dx}\left[\int_{4}^{x} \tan^2 u \cos u\, du\right] = -\tan^2 x \cos x$$

The interchange of the upper and lower limits is allowed if we prefix a negative sign. (Recall that by definition $\displaystyle\int_{b}^{a} f(x)\, dx = -\int_{a}^{b} f(x)\, dx$.) $\qquad \blacksquare$

EXAMPLE 4 Find $D_x\left[\displaystyle\int_{1}^{x^2} (3t-1)\, dt\right]$ in two ways.

SOLUTION   One way to find this derivative is to apply the First Fundamental Theorem of Calculus, although now we have a new complication; the upper limit is x^2 rather than x. This problem is handled by the Chain Rule. We may think of the expression in brackets as

$$\int_{1}^{u} (3t-1)\, dt \qquad \text{where } u = x^2$$

By the Chain Rule, the derivative with respect to x of this composite function is

$$D_u\left[\int_{1}^{u} (3t-1)\, dt\right] \cdot D_x u = (3u-1)(2x) = (3x^2-1)(2x) = 6x^3 - 2x$$

Another way to find this derivative is to evaluate the definite integral first, and then use our rules for derivatives. The definite integral $\displaystyle\int_{1}^{x^2} (3t-1)\, dt$ is the area below the line $y = 3t-1$ between $t=1$ and $t=x^2$ (see Figure 8). Since the area of this trapezoid is $\dfrac{x^2-1}{2}[2+(3x^2-1)] = \dfrac{3}{2}x^4 - x^2 - \dfrac{1}{2}$,

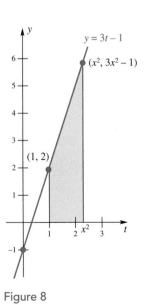

Figure 8

$$\int_{1}^{x^2} (3t - 1)\, dt = \frac{3}{2}x^4 - x^2 - \frac{1}{2}$$

Thus,

$$D_x \int_{1}^{x^2} (3t - 1)\, dt = D_x \left(\frac{3}{2}x^4 - x^2 - \frac{1}{2} \right) = 6x^3 - 2x \qquad \blacksquare$$

Position as Accumulated Velocity In the last section we saw how the position of an object, initially at the origin, is equal to the definite integral of the velocity function. This often leads to accumulation functions, as the next example illustrates.

EXAMPLE 5 An object at the origin at time $t = 0$ has velocity, measured in meters per second,

$$v(t) = \begin{cases} t/20 & \text{if } 0 \le t \le 40 \\ 2 & \text{if } 40 < t \le 60 \\ 5 - t/20 & \text{if } t > 60 \end{cases}$$

When, if ever, does the object return to the origin?

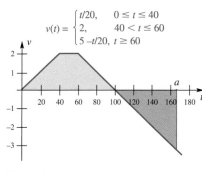

$$v(t) = \begin{cases} t/20, & 0 \le t \le 40 \\ 2, & 40 < t \le 60 \\ 5 - t/20, & t \ge 60 \end{cases}$$

Figure 9

SOLUTION Let $F(a) = \int_0^a v(t)\, dt$ denote the position of the object at time a. The accumulation is illustrated in Figure 9. If the object returns to the origin at some time a, then a must satisfy $F(a) = 0$. The required value of a is certainly greater than 100 because the area below the curve between 0 and 100 must exactly equal the area above the curve and below the x-axis between 100 and a. Therefore,

$$F(a) = \int_0^a v(t)\, dt = \int_0^{100} v(t)\, dt + \int_{100}^a v(t)\, dt$$

$$= \frac{1}{2}40 \cdot 2 + 20 \cdot 2 + \frac{1}{2}40 \cdot 2 + \int_{100}^a (5 - t/20)\, dt$$

$$= 120 + \frac{1}{2}(a - 100)(5 - a/20)$$

$$= -130 + 5a - \frac{1}{40}a^2$$

We must then set $F(a) = 0$. The two solutions to this quadratic equation are $a = 100 \pm 40\sqrt{3}$. Taking the minus sign gives a value less than 100, which cannot be the solution so, we discard it. The other solution is $100 + 40\sqrt{3} \approx 169.3$. Let's check this solution:

$$F(a) = \int_0^{100 + 40\sqrt{3}} v(t)\, dt$$

$$= \int_0^{100} v(t)\, dt + \int_{100}^{100 + 40\sqrt{3}} v(t)\, dt$$

$$= 120 + \frac{1}{2}\left(100 + 40\sqrt{3} - 100\right)\left(5 - \left(100 + 40\sqrt{3}\right)/20\right)$$

$$= 0$$

Thus, the object returns to the origin at time $t = 100 + 40\sqrt{3} \approx 169.3$ seconds. $\blacksquare$

A Way to Evaluate Definite Integrals The next example shows a way (admittedly a rather awkward way) to evaluate a definite integral. If this method seems long and cumbersome, be patient. The next section deals with efficient ways to evaluate definite integrals.

EXAMPLE 6 Let $A(x) = \int_1^x t^3\, dt$.

(a) Let $y = A(x)$, and show that $dy/dx = x^3$.
(b) Find the solution of the differential equation $dy/dx = x^3$ that satisfies $y = 0$ when $x = 1$.
(c) Find $\int_1^4 t^3\, dt$.

SOLUTION

(a) By the First Fundamental Theorem of Calculus,

$$\frac{dy}{dx} = A'(x) = x^3$$

(b) Since the differential equation $dy/dx = x^3$ is separable, we can write

$$dy = x^3\, dx$$

Integrating both sides gives

$$y = \int x^3\, dx = \frac{x^4}{4} + C$$

When $x = 1$, we must have $y = A(1) = \int_1^1 t^3\, dt = 0$. Thus, we choose C so that

$$0 = A(1) = \frac{1^4}{4} + C$$

Therefore, $C = -1/4$. The solution to the differential equation is thus $y = x^4/4 - 1/4$.

(c) Since $y = A(x) = x^4/4 - 1/4$, we have

$$\int_1^4 t^3\, dt = A(4) = \frac{4^4}{4} - \frac{1}{4} = 64 - \frac{1}{4} = \frac{255}{4} \qquad \blacksquare$$

Concepts Review

1. Since $4 \leq x^2 \leq 16$ for all x in $[2, 4]$, the Boundedness Property of the definite integral allows us to say that $\underline{\hspace{1cm}} \leq \int_2^4 x^2\, dx \leq \underline{\hspace{1cm}}$.

2. $\dfrac{d}{dx}\left[\int_1^x \sin^3 t\, dt\right] = \underline{\hspace{1cm}}$.

3. By linearity, $\int_1^4 cf(x)\, dx = c \cdot \underline{\hspace{1cm}}$ and $\int_2^5 \left(x + \sqrt{x}\right) dx = \int_2^5 x\, dx + \underline{\hspace{1cm}}$.

4. If $\int_1^4 f(x)\, dx = 5$ and if $g(x) \leq f(x)$ for all x in $[1, 4]$, then the Comparison Property allows us to say that $\int_1^4 g(x)\, dx \leq \underline{\hspace{1cm}}$.

Problem Set 5.3

In Problems 1–8, find a formula for and graph the accumulation function A(x) that is equal to the indicated area.

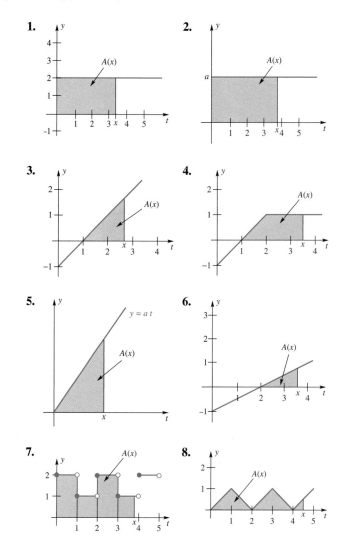

1.

2.

3.

4.

5.

6.

7.

8.

Suppose that $\int_0^1 f(x)\,dx = 2$, $\int_1^2 f(x)\,dx = 3$, $\int_0^1 g(x)\,dx = -1$, *and* $\int_0^2 g(x)\,dx = 4$. *Use properties of definite integrals (linearity, interval additivity, and so on) to calculate each of the integrals in Problems 9–16.*

9. $\int_1^2 2f(x)\,dx$

10. $\int_0^2 2f(x)\,dx$

11. $\int_0^2 [2f(x) + g(x)]\,dx$

12. $\int_0^1 [2f(s) + g(s)]\,ds$

13. $\int_2^1 [2f(s) + 5g(s)]\,ds$

14. $\int_1^1 [3f(x) + 2g(x)]\,dx$

15. $\int_0^2 [3f(t) + 2g(t)]\,dt$

16. $\int_0^2 \left[\sqrt{3}f(t) + \sqrt{2}g(t) + \pi\right]dt$

In Problems 17–26, find G'(x).

17. $G(x) = \int_1^x 2t\,dt$

18. $G(x) = \int_x^1 2t\,dt$

19. $G(x) = \int_0^x \left(2t^2 + \sqrt{t}\right)dt$

20. $G(x) = \int_1^x \cos^3 2t \tan t\,dt;\; -\pi/2 < x < \pi/2$

21. $G(x) = \int_x^{\pi/4} (s - 2) \cot 2s\,ds;\; 0 < x < \pi/2$

22. $G(x) = \int_1^x xt\,dt$ (Be careful.)

23. $G(x) = \int_1^{x^2} e^{-t^2}\,dt$

24. $G(x) = \int_1^{x^2+x} \sqrt{2z + \sin z}\,dz$

25. $G(x) = \int_{-x^2}^x \frac{t^2}{1 + t^2}\,dt$ *Hint:* $\int_{-x^2}^x = \int_{-x^2}^0 + \int_0^x$

26. $G(x) = \int_{\cos x}^{\sin x} t^5\,dt$

In Problems 27–32, find the interval(s) on which the graph of y = f(x), x ≥ 0, is (a) increasing, and (b) concave up.

27. $f(x) = \int_0^x \frac{s}{\sqrt{1 + s^2}}\,ds$

28. $f(x) = \int_0^x \frac{1 + t}{1 + t^2}\,dt$

29. $f(x) = \int_0^x \tan^{-1} u\,du$

30. $f(x) = \int_0^x (t + \sin t)\,dt$

31. $f(x) = \int_1^x \frac{1}{\theta}\,d\theta,\, x > 0$

32. $f(x)$ is the accumulation function $A(x)$ in Problem 8.

In Problems 33–36, use the Interval Additive Property and linearity to evaluate $\int_0^4 f(x)\,dx$. *Begin by drawing a graph of f.*

33. $f(x) = \begin{cases} 2 & \text{if } 0 \le x < 2 \\ x & \text{if } 2 \le x \le 4 \end{cases}$

34. $f(x) = \begin{cases} 1 & \text{if } 0 \le x < 1 \\ x & \text{if } 1 \le x < 2 \\ 4 - x & \text{if } 2 \le x \le 4 \end{cases}$

35. $f(x) = |x - 2|$

36. $f(x) = 3 + |x - 3|$

37. Consider the function $G(x) = \int_0^x f(t)\,dt$, where $f(t)$ oscillates about the line $y = 2$ over the interval $[0, 10]$ and is given by Figure 10.

(a) At what values of x over this region do the local maxima and minima of $G(x)$ occur?

(b) Where does $G(x)$ attain its absolute maximum and absolute minimum?

(c) On what intervals is $G(x)$ concave down?

(d) Sketch a graph of $G(x)$.

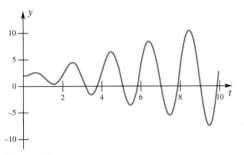

Figure 10

38. Perform the same analysis as you did in Problem 37 for the function $G(x) = \int_0^x f(t)\,dt$ given by Figure 11, where $f(t)$ oscillates about the line $y = 2$ for the interval $[0, 10]$.

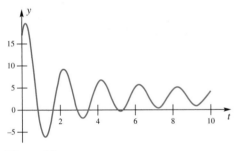

Figure 11

39. Let $F(x) = \int_0^x (t^4 + 1)\,dt$.

(a) Find $F(0)$.

(b) Let $y = F(x)$. Apply the First Fundamental Theorem of Calculus to obtain $dy/dx = F'(x) = x^4 + 1$. Solve the differential equation $dy/dx = x^4 + 1$.

(c) Find the solution to this differential equation that satisfies $y = F(0)$ when $x = 0$.

(d) Show that $\int_0^1 (x^4 + 1)\,dx = \dfrac{6}{5}$.

40. Let $G(x) = \int_0^x \sin t\,dt$.

(a) Find $G(0)$ and $G(2\pi)$.

(b) Let $y = G(x)$. Apply the First Fundamental Theorem of Calculus to obtain $dy/dx = G'(x) = \sin x$. Solve the differential equation $dy/dx = \sin x$.

(c) Find the solution to this differential equation that satisfies $y = G(0)$ when $x = 0$.

(d) Show that $\int_0^\pi \sin x\,dx = 2$.

(e) Find all relative extrema and inflection points of G on the interval $[0, 4\pi]$.

(f) Plot a graph of $y = G(x)$ over the interval $[0, 4\pi]$.

41. Show that $1 \le \int_0^1 \sqrt{1 + x^4}\,dx \le \dfrac{6}{5}$. *Hint:* Explain why $1 \le \sqrt{1 + x^4} \le 1 + x^4$ for x in the closed interval $[0, 1]$; then use the Comparison Property (Theorem B) and the result of Problem 39d.

42. Show that $2 \le \int_0^1 \sqrt{4 + x^4} \le \dfrac{21}{5}$. (See the hint for Problem 41.)

GC *In Problems 43–48, use a graphing calculator to graph each integrand. Then use the Boundedness Property (Theorem C) to find a lower bound and an upper bound for each definite integral.*

43. $\displaystyle\int_0^4 (5 + x^3)\,dx$

44. $\displaystyle\int_2^4 (x + 6)^5\,dx$

45. $\displaystyle\int_1^5 \left(3 + \dfrac{2}{x}\right)dx$

46. $\displaystyle\int_{10}^{20} \left(1 + \dfrac{1}{x}\right)^5 dx$

47. $\displaystyle\int_{4\pi}^{8\pi} \left(5 + \dfrac{1}{20}\sin^2 x\right)dx$

48. $\displaystyle\int_{0.2}^{0.4} (0.002 + 0.0001\cos^2 x)\,dx$

49. Find $\displaystyle\lim_{x \to 0} \dfrac{1}{x}\int_0^x \dfrac{1 + t}{2 + t}\,dt$.

50. Find $\displaystyle\lim_{x \to 1} \dfrac{1}{x - 1}\int_1^x \dfrac{1 + t}{2 + t}\,dt$.

51. Find $f(x)$ if $\displaystyle\int_1^x f(t)\,dt = 2x - 2$.

52. Find $f(x)$ if $\displaystyle\int_0^x f(t)\,dt = x^2$.

53. Find $f(x)$ if $\displaystyle\int_0^{x^2} f(t)\,dt = \tfrac{1}{3}x^3$.

54. Does there exist a function f such that $\displaystyle\int_0^x f(t)\,dt = x + 1$? Explain.

In Problems 55–60, decide whether the given statement is true or false. Then justify your answer.

55. If f is continuous and $f(x) \ge 0$ for all x in $[a, b]$, then $\displaystyle\int_a^b f(x)\,dx \ge 0$.

56. If $\displaystyle\int_a^b f(x)\,dx \ge 0$, then $f(x) \ge 0$ for all x in $[a, b]$.

57. If $\displaystyle\int_a^b f(x)\,dx = 0$, then $f(x) = 0$ for all x in $[a, b]$.

58. If $f(x) \ge 0$ and $\displaystyle\int_a^b f(x)\,dx = 0$, then $f(x) = 0$ for all x in $[a, b]$.

59. If $\displaystyle\int_a^b f(x)\,dx > \int_a^b g(x)\,dx$, then
$$\int_a^b [f(x) - g(x)]\,dx > 0$$

60. If f and g are continuous and $f(x) > g(x)$ for all x in $[a, b]$, then $\left| \int_a^b f(x)\,dx \right| > \left| \int_a^b g(x)\,dx \right|$.

61. The velocity of an object is $v(t) = 2 - |t - 2|$. Assuming that the object is at the origin at time 0, find a formula for its position at time t. (*Hint:* You will have to consider separately the intervals $0 \le t \le 2$, and $t > 2$.) When, if ever, does the object return to the origin?

62. The velocity of an object is

$$v(t) = \begin{cases} 5 & \text{if } 0 \le t \le 100 \\ 6 - t/100 & \text{if } 100 < t \le 700 \\ -1 & \text{if } t > 700 \end{cases}$$

(a) Assuming that the object is at the origin at time 0, find a formula for its position at time t ($t \ge 0$).

(b) What is the farthest to the right of the origin that this object ever gets?

(c) When, if ever, does the object return to the origin?

63. Let f be continuous on $[a, b]$ and thus integrable there. Show that

$$\left| \int_a^b f(x)\,dx \right| \le \int_a^b |f(x)|\,dx$$

Hint: $-|f(x)| \le f(x) \le |f(x)|$; use Theorem B.

64. Suppose that f' is integrable and $|f'(x)| \le M$ for all x. Prove that $|f(x)| \le |f(a)| + M|x - a|$ for every a.

Answers to Concepts Review: **1.** $8; 32$ **2.** $\sin^3 x$

3. $\int_1^4 f(x)\,dx$; $\int_2^5 \sqrt{x}\,dx$ **4.** 5

5.4
The Second Fundamental Theorem of Calculus and the Method of Substitution

The First Fundamental Theorem of Calculus, given in the previous section, gives the inverse relationship between definite integrals and derivatives. Although it is not yet apparent, this relationship gives us a powerful tool for evaluating definite integrals. This tool is called the Second Fundamental Theorem of Calculus, and we will apply it much more often than the First Fundamental Theorem of Calculus.

> **Theorem A** **Second Fundamental Theorem of Calculus**
>
> Let f be continuous (hence integrable) on $[a, b]$, and let F be any antiderivative of f on $[a, b]$. Then
>
> $$\int_a^b f(x)\,dx = F(b) - F(a)$$

Is It Fundamental?

The Second Fundamental Theorem of Calculus is important in providing a powerful tool for evaluating definite integrals. But its deepest significance lies in the link it makes between differentiation and integration, between derivatives and integrals. This link appears in sparkling clarity when we rewrite the conclusion to the theorem with $f(x)$ replaced by $g'(x)$.

$$\int_a^b g'(x)\,dx = g(b) - g(a)$$

Proof For x in the interval $[a, b]$, define $G(x) = \int_a^x f(t)\,dt$. Then, by the First Fundamental Theorem of Calculus, $G'(x) = f(x)$ for all x in (a, b). Thus, G is an antiderivative of f; but F is also an antiderivative of f. From Theorem 4.6B, we conclude that since $F'(x) = G'(x)$, the functions F and G differ by a constant. Thus, for all x in (a, b)

$$F(x) = G(x) + C$$

Since the functions F and G are continuous on the closed interval $[a, b]$ (Problem 81), we have $F(a) = G(a) + C$ and $F(b) = G(b) + C$. Thus, $F(x) = G(x) + C$ on the *closed* interval $[a, b]$.

Since $G(a) = \int_a^a f(t)\,dt = 0$, we have

$$F(a) = G(a) + C = 0 + C = C$$

Therefore,

$$F(b) - F(a) = [G(b) + C] - C = G(b) = \int_a^b f(t)\,dt \qquad \blacksquare$$

In Section 4.8, we defined the *indefinite* integral as an antiderivative. In Section 5.2, we defined the *definite* integral as the limit of a Riemann sum. We used the same word (integral) in both cases, although at the time there seemed to be little in common between the two. Theorem A is fundamental because it shows how indefinite integration (antidifferentiation) and definite integration (signed area) are related. Before going on to examples, ask yourself why we can use the word *any*, in the statement of the theorem.

■ EXAMPLE 1 Show that $\int_a^b k\,dx = k(b-a)$, where k is a constant.

SOLUTION $F(x) = kx$ is an antiderivative of $f(x) = k$. Thus, by the Second Fundamental Theorem of Calculus,

$$\int_a^b k\,dx = F(b) - F(a) = kb - ka = k(b-a) \qquad ■$$

■ EXAMPLE 2 Show that $\int_a^b x\,dx = \dfrac{b^2}{2} - \dfrac{a^2}{2}$.

SOLUTION $F(x) = x^2/2$ is an antiderivative of $f(x) = x$. Therefore,

$$\int_a^b x\,dx = F(b) - F(a) = \frac{b^2}{2} - \frac{a^2}{2} \qquad ■$$

■ EXAMPLE 3 Show that if r is a real number different from -1 and $0 \le a < b$, then

$$\int_a^b x^r\,dx = \frac{b^{r+1}}{r+1} - \frac{a^{r+1}}{r+1}$$

SOLUTION $F(x) = x^{r+1}/(r+1)$ is an antiderivative of $f(x) = x^r$. Thus, by the Second Fundamental Theorem of Calculus,

$$\int_a^b x^r\,dx = F(b) - F(a) = \frac{b^{r+1}}{r+1} - \frac{a^{r+1}}{r+1}$$

If $r < 0$, then we require that $a \ne 0$. Why? ■

It is convenient to introduce a special symbol for $F(b) - F(a)$. We write

$$F(b) - F(a) = \Big[F(x)\Big]_a^b$$

With this notation,

$$\int_2^5 x^2\,dx = \left[\frac{x^3}{3}\right]_2^5 = \frac{125}{3} - \frac{8}{3} = \frac{117}{3} = 39$$

■ EXAMPLE 4 Evaluate $\int_{-1}^2 (4x - 6x^2)\,dx$

(a) using the Second Fundamental Theorem of Calculus directly, and
(b) using linearity (Theorem 5.3D) first.

SOLUTION

(a) $\int_{-1}^2 (4x - 6x^2)\,dx = \Big[2x^2 - 2x^3\Big]_{-1}^2 = (8 - 16) - (2 + 2) = -12$

(b) Using linearity first, we have

$$\int_{-1}^{2} (4x - 6x^2)\, dx = 4 \int_{-1}^{2} x\, dx - 6 \int_{-1}^{2} x^2\, dx$$

$$= 4 \left[\frac{x^2}{2}\right]_{-1}^{2} - 6 \left[\frac{x^3}{3}\right]_{-1}^{2}$$

$$= 4\left(\frac{4}{2} - \frac{1}{2}\right) - 6\left(\frac{8}{3} + \frac{1}{3}\right)$$

$$= -12 \qquad \blacksquare$$

EXAMPLE 5   Evaluate $\int_{1}^{8} (x^{1/3} + x^{4/3})\, dx$.

SOLUTION

$$\int_{1}^{8} (x^{1/3} + x^{4/3})\, dx = \left[\tfrac{3}{4}x^{4/3} + \tfrac{3}{7}x^{7/3}\right]_{1}^{8}$$

$$= \left(\tfrac{3}{4}\cdot 16 + \tfrac{3}{7}\cdot 128\right) - \left(\tfrac{3}{4}\cdot 1 + \tfrac{3}{7}\cdot 1\right)$$

$$= \tfrac{45}{4} + \tfrac{381}{7} \approx 65.68 \qquad \blacksquare$$

EXAMPLE 6   Find $D_x \int_{0}^{x} 3 \sin t\, dt$ in two ways.

SOLUTION   The easy way is to apply the First Fundamental Theorem of Calculus.

$$D_x \int_{0}^{x} 3 \sin t\, dt = 3 \sin x$$

A second way to do this problem is to apply the Second Fundamental Theorem of Calculus to evaluate the integral from 0 to x; then apply the rules of derivatives.

$$\int_{0}^{x} 3 \sin t\, dt = [-3 \cos t]_{0}^{x} = -3 \cos x - (-3 \cos 0) = -3 \cos x + 3$$

Then

$$D_x \int_{0}^{x} 3 \sin t\, dt = D_x(-3 \cos x + 3) = 3 \sin x \qquad \blacksquare$$

In terms of the symbol for the indefinite integral, we may write the conclusion of the Second Fundamental Theorem of Calculus as

$$\int_{a}^{b} f(x)\, dx = \left[\int f(x)\, dx\right]_{a}^{b}$$

The nontrivial part of applying the theorem is always to find the indefinite integral $\int f(x)\, dx$. One of the most powerful techniques for doing this is the method of substitution

The Method of Substitution   In Section 4.8, we introduced the method of substitution for the power rule. This rule can be extended to a more general case as the following theorem shows. An astute reader will see that the substitution rule is nothing more than the Chain Rule in reverse.

Using the Second Fundamental
Theorem of Calculus

The way to use the Second Fundamental Theorem of Calculus to
evaluate a definite integral such as
$\int_a^b f(x)\,dx$, is to

(1) find an antiderivative $F(x)$ of
the integrand $f(x)$, and
(2) substitute the limits and compute $F(b) - F(a)$

This all hinges on being able to find
an antiderivative. It is for this reason
that we return briefly to the evaluation of *indefinite* integrals.

Theorem B **Substitution Rule for Indefinite Integrals**

Let g be a differentiable function and suppose that F is an antiderivative of f.
Then

$$\int f(g(x))g'(x)\,dx = F(g(x)) + C$$

Proof All we need to do to prove this result is to show that the derivative of the
right side is equal to the integrand of the integral on the left. This is a simple application of the Chain Rule.

$$D_x[F(g(x)) + C] = F'(g(x))g'(x) = f(g(x))g'(x) \qquad \blacksquare$$

We normally apply Theorem B as follows. In an integral such as
$\int f(g(x))g'(x)\,dx$ we let $u = g(x)$, so that $du/dx = g'(x)$. Thus, $du = g'(x)\,dx$.
The integral then becomes

$$\int f(\underbrace{g(x)}_{u})\underbrace{g'(x)\,dx}_{du} = \int f(u)\,du = F(u) + C = F(g(x)) + C$$

Thus, if we can find an antiderivative for $f(x)$, we can evaluate $\int f(g(x))g'(x)\,dx$.
The trick to applying the method of substitution is to choose the right substitution to
make. In some cases this substitution is obvious; in other cases it is not so obvious.
Proficiency in applying the method of substitution comes from practice.

Theorem 4.8B gave a number of antidifferentiation formulas. Since those results will be our starting point for most integration problems, that theorem is worth
reviewing now.

EXAMPLE 7 Evaluate $\int \sin 3x\,dx$.

SOLUTION The obvious substitution here is $u = 3x$, so that $du = 3\,dx$. Thus

$$\int \sin 3x\,dx = \int \frac{1}{3}\sin(\underbrace{3x}_{u})\underbrace{3\,dx}_{du}$$

$$= \frac{1}{3}\int \sin u\,du = -\frac{1}{3}\cos u + C = -\frac{1}{3}\cos 3x + C$$

Notice how we had to multiply by $\frac{1}{3}\cdot 3$ in order to have the expression $3\,dx = du$
in the integral. $\blacksquare$

EXAMPLE 8 Evaluate $\int e^{-2x}\,dx$.

SOLUTION The substitution is $u = -2x$, so that $du = -2\,dx$. Thus

$$\int e^{-2x}\,dx = \int \left(-\frac{1}{2}\right)e^{-2x}(-2\,dx) = -\frac{1}{2}\int \exp(\underbrace{-2x}_{u})(\underbrace{-2x\,dx}_{du})$$

$$= -\frac{1}{2}\int e^u\,du = -\frac{1}{2}e^u + C = -\frac{1}{2}e^{-2x} + C \qquad \blacksquare$$

EXAMPLE 9 Evaluate $\int x\sin x^2\,dx$.

SOLUTION   Here the appropriate substitution is $u = x^2$. This gives us $\sin x^2 = \sin u$ in the integrand, but more importantly, the extra x in the integrand can be put with the differential, because $du = 2x\, dx$. Thus

$$\int x \sin x^2 \, dx = \int \frac{1}{2} \sin(\underset{u}{\underbrace{x^2}}) \underset{du}{\underbrace{2x\, dx}}$$

$$= \frac{1}{2} \int \sin u \, du = -\frac{1}{2} \cos u + C = -\frac{1}{2} \cos x^2 + C \qquad \blacksquare$$

No law says that you have to write out the u-substitution. If you can do the substitution mentally, that is fine. Here is an illustration.

EXAMPLE 10   Evaluate $\displaystyle\int x^3 \sqrt{x^4 + 11} \, dx$.

SOLUTION   Mentally, substitute $u = x^4 + 11$.

$$\int x^3 \sqrt{x^4 + 11} \, dx = \frac{1}{4} \int (x^4 + 11)^{1/2} \, (4x^3 \, dx)$$

$$= \frac{1}{6} (x^4 + 11)^{3/2} + C \qquad \blacksquare$$

What Makes This Substitution Work?

Note that in Example 11 the derivative of u is precisely $2x + 1$. This is what makes the substition work. If the expression in parentheses were $3x + 1$ rather than $2x + 1$, the Substitution Rule would not apply and we would have a much more difficult problem.

EXAMPLE 11   Evaluate $\displaystyle\int_0^4 \sqrt{x^2 + x} \, (2x + 1) \, dx$.

SOLUTION   Let $u = x^2 + x$; then $du = (2x + 1) \, dx$. Thus,

$$\int \sqrt{\underset{u}{\underbrace{x^2 + x}}} \underset{du}{\underbrace{(2x + 1) \, dx}} = \int u^{1/2} \, du = \tfrac{2}{3} u^{3/2} + C$$

$$= \tfrac{2}{3}(x^2 + x)^{3/2} + C$$

Therefore, by the Second Fundamental Theorem of Calculus,

$$\int_0^4 \sqrt{x^2 + x} \, (2x + 1) \, dx = \left[\tfrac{2}{3}(x^2 + x)^{3/2} + C \right]_0^4$$

$$= \left[\tfrac{2}{3}(20)^{3/2} + C \right] - [0 + C]$$

$$= \tfrac{2}{3}(20)^{3/2} \approx 59.63 \qquad \blacksquare$$

Note that the C of the indefinite integration cancels out, as it always will, in the definite integration. That is why in the statement of the Second Fundamental Theorem we could use the phrase *any antiderivative*. In particular, we may always choose $C = 0$ in applying the Second Fundamental Theorem.

EXAMPLE 12   Evaluate $\displaystyle\int_0^{\pi/4} \sin^3 2x \cos 2x \, dx$.

SOLUTION   Let $u = \sin 2x$; then $du = 2 \cos 2x \, dx$. Thus,

$$\int \sin^3 2x \cos 2x \, dx = \frac{1}{2} \int \underset{u}{\underbrace{(\sin 2x)^3}} \underset{du}{\underbrace{(2 \cos 2x) \, dx}} = \frac{1}{2} \int u^3 \, du$$

$$= \frac{1}{2} \frac{u^4}{4} + C = \frac{\sin^4 2x}{8} + C$$

Therefore, by the Second Fundamental Theorem of Calculus,

$$\int_0^{\pi/4} \sin^3 2x \cos 2x \, dx = \left[\frac{\sin^4 2x}{8} \right]_0^{\pi/4} = \frac{1}{8} - 0 = \frac{1}{8} \qquad \blacksquare$$

Note that in the two-step procedure illustrated in Examples 11 and 12, we must be sure to express the indefinite integral in terms of x before we apply the Second Fundamental Theorem. This is because the limits, 0 and 4 in Example 11, and 0 and $\pi/4$ in Example 12, apply to x, not to u. But what if, in making the substitution $u = \sin 2x$ in Example 12, we also made the corresponding changes in the limits of integration to u?

If $x = 0$, then $u = \sin(2 \cdot 0) = 0$.

If $x = \pi/4$, then $u = \sin(2(\pi/4)) = \sin(\pi/2) = 1$.

Could we then finish the integration with the definite integral in terms of u? The answer is *yes*.

$$\int_0^{\pi/4} \sin^3 2x \cos 2x \, dx = \left[\frac{1}{2} \frac{u^4}{4} \right]_0^1 = \frac{1}{8} - 0 = \frac{1}{8}$$

Here is the general result, which lets us substitute the limits of integration, thereby producing a procedure with fewer steps.

Substitution in Definite Integrals
To make a substitution in a definite integral, three changes are required:
1. Make the substitution in the integrand.
2. Make the appropriate change in the differential.
3. Change the limits from a and b to $g(a)$ and $g(b)$.

Theorem C **Substitution Rule for Definite Integrals**

Let g have a continuous derivative on $[a, b]$, and let f be continuous on the range of g. Then

$$\int_a^b f(g(x))g'(x) \, dx = \int_{g(a)}^{g(b)} f(u) \, du$$

where $u = g(x)$.

Proof Let F be an antiderivative of f (the existence of F is guaranteed by Theorem 5.3A). Then, by the Second Fundamental Theorem of Calculus,

$$\int_{g(a)}^{g(b)} f(u) \, du = \left[F(u) \right]_{g(a)}^{g(b)} = F(g(b)) - F(g(a))$$

On the other hand, by the Substitution Rule for Indefinite Integrals (Theorem B),

$$\int f(g(x))g'(x) \, dx = F(g(x)) + C$$

and so, again by the Second Fundamental Theorem of Calculus,

$$\int_a^b f(g(x))g'(x) \, dx = \left[F(g(x)) \right]_a^b = F(g(b)) - F(g(a)) \qquad \blacksquare$$

EXAMPLE 13 Evaluate $\displaystyle\int_0^1 \frac{x+1}{(x^2+2x+6)^2} \, dx$.

SOLUTION Let $u = x^2 + 2x + 6$, so $du = (2x+2) \, dx = 2(x+1) \, dx$, and note that $u = 6$ when $x = 0$ and $u = 9$ when $x = 1$. Thus,

$$\int_0^1 \frac{x+1}{(x^2+2x+6)^2} \, dx = \frac{1}{2} \int_0^1 \frac{2(x+1)}{(x^2+2x+6)^2} \, dx$$

$$= \frac{1}{2} \int_6^9 u^{-2} \, du = \left[-\frac{1}{2} \frac{1}{u} \right]_6^9$$

$$= -\frac{1}{18} - \left(-\frac{1}{12} \right) = \frac{1}{36} \qquad \blacksquare$$

EXAMPLE 14 Evaluate $\displaystyle\int_{\pi^2/9}^{\pi^2/4} \frac{\cos\sqrt{x}}{\sqrt{x}} \, dx$.

SOLUTION Let $u = \sqrt{x}$, so $du = dx/(2\sqrt{x})$. Thus,

$$\int_{\pi^2/9}^{\pi^2/4} \frac{\cos\sqrt{x}}{\sqrt{x}}\,dx = 2\int_{\pi^2/9}^{\pi^2/4} \cos\sqrt{x} \cdot \frac{1}{2\sqrt{x}}\,dx$$

$$= 2\int_{\pi/3}^{\pi/2} \cos u\,du$$

$$= \left[2\sin u\right]_{\pi/3}^{\pi/2} = 2 - \sqrt{3}$$

The change in the limits of integration occurred at the second equality. When $x = \pi^2/9$, $u = \sqrt{\pi^2/9} = \pi/3$; when $x = \pi^2/4$, $u = \pi/2$. ∎

EXAMPLE 15 Figure 1 shows the graph of a function f that has a continuous third derivative. The dashed lines are tangent to the graph of $y = f(x)$ at $(1,1)$ and $(5,1)$. Based on what is shown, tell, if possible, whether the following integrals are positive, negative, or zero.

(a) $\displaystyle\int_1^5 f(x)\,dx$ (b) $\displaystyle\int_1^5 f'(x)\,dx$

(c) $\displaystyle\int_1^5 f''(x)\,dx$ (d) $\displaystyle\int_1^5 f'''(x)\,dx$

SOLUTION

(a) The function f is positive for all x in the interval $[1,5]$, and the graph indicates that there is some area above the x-axis. Thus, $\displaystyle\int_1^5 f(x)\,dx > 0$.

(b) By the Second Fundamental Theorem of Calculus,

$$\int_1^5 f'(x)\,dx = f(5) - f(1) = 1 - 1 = 0$$

(c) Again using the Second Fundamental Theorem of Calculus (this time with f' being an antiderivative of f''), we see that

$$\int_1^5 f''(x)\,dx = f'(5) - f'(1) = 0 - (-1) = 1$$

(d) The function f is concave up at $x = 5$, so $f''(5) > 0$, and it is concave down at $x = 1$, so $f''(1) < 0$. Thus,

$$\int_1^5 f'''(x)\,dx = f''(5) - f''(1) > 0$$ ∎

This example illustrates the remarkable property that to evaluate a definite integral all we need to know are the values of an antiderivative at the end points a and b. For example, to evaluate $\displaystyle\int_1^5 f''(x)\,dx$, all we needed to know was $f'(5)$ and $f'(1)$; we did not need to know f' or f'' at any other points.

Accumulated Rate of Change   The Second Fundamental Theorem of Calculus can be restated in this way:

$$\int_a^b F'(t)\,dt = F(b) - F(a)$$

If $F(t)$ measures the amount of some quantity at time t, then the Second Fundamental Theorem of Calculus says that the accumulated rate of change from time $t = a$ to time $t = b$ is equal to the net change in that quantity over the interval $[a, b]$, that is, the amount present at time $t = b$ minus the amount present at time $t = a$.

EXAMPLE 16 Water leaks out of a 55-gallon tank at the rate $V'(t) = 11 - 1.1t$ where t is measured in hours and V in gallons. (See Figure 2.)

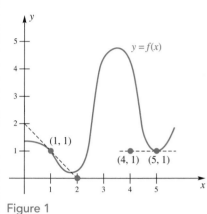

Figure 1

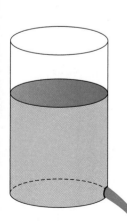

Figure 2

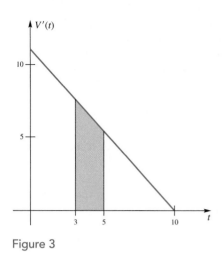

Figure 3

Initially, the tank is full. (a) How much water leaks out of the tank between $t = 3$ and $t = 5$ hours? (b) How long does it take until there are just 5 gallons remaining in the tank?

SOLUTION $V(t)$ represents the amount of water that has leaked out through time t.

(a) The amount that has leaked out between $t = 3$ and $t = 5$ hours is equal to the area under the $V'(t)$ curve from 3 to 5 (Figure 3). Thus

$$V(5) - V(3) = \int_3^5 V'(t)\, dt = \int_3^5 (11 - 1.1t)\, dt = \left[11t - \frac{1.1}{2}t^2\right]_3^5 = 13.2$$

Thus, 13.2 gallons leaked in the two hours between time $t = 3$ and $t = 5$.

(b) Let t_1 denote the time when 5 gallons remain in the tank. Then the amount that has leaked out is equal to 50, so $V(t_1) = 50$. Since the tank was initially full (i.e., nothing has leaked out), we have $V(0) = 0$. Thus,

$$V(t_1) - V(0) = \int_0^{t_1} (11 - 1.1t)\, dt$$

$$50 - 0 = \left[11t - \frac{1.1}{2}t^2\right]_0^{t_1}$$

$$0 = -50 + 11t_1 - 0.55t_1^2$$

The solutions of this last equation are $10\left(11 \pm \sqrt{11}\right)/11$, approximately 6.985 and 13.015. Note that since $\int_0^{10}(11 - 1.1t)\, dt = 55$, the entire tank is drained by time $t = 10$, leading us to discard the latter solution. Thus, 5 gallons remain after 6.985 hours. ∎

Concepts Review

1. If f is continuous on $[a, b]$ and if F is any _____ of f there, then $\int_a^b f(x)\, dx = $ _____.

2. The symbol $\left[F(x)\right]_a^b$ stands for the expression _____.

3. By the Second Fundamental Theorem of Calculus, $\int_c^d F'(x)\, dx = $ _____.

4. Under the substitution $u = x^3 + 1$, the definite integral $\int_0^1 x^2(x^3 + 1)^4\, dx$ transforms to the new definite integral _____.

Problem Set 5.4

In Problems 1–14, use the Second Fundamental Theorem of Calculus to evaluate each definite integral.

1. $\displaystyle\int_0^2 x^3\, dx$

2. $\displaystyle\int_{-1}^2 x^4\, dx$

3. $\displaystyle\int_{-1}^2 (3x^2 - 2x + 3)\, dx$

4. $\displaystyle\int_1^2 (4x^3 + 7)\, dx$

5. $\displaystyle\int_1^4 \frac{1}{w^2}\, dw$

6. $\displaystyle\int_1^3 \frac{2}{t^3}\, dt$

7. $\displaystyle\int_0^4 \sqrt{t}\, dt$

8. $\displaystyle\int_1^8 \sqrt[3]{w}\, dw$

9. $\displaystyle\int_{-4}^{-2} \left(y^2 + \frac{1}{y^3}\right)\, dy$

10. $\displaystyle\int_1^4 \frac{s^4 - 8}{s^2}\, ds$

11. $\displaystyle\int_0^{\pi/2} \cos x\, dx$

12. $\displaystyle\int_{\pi/6}^{\pi/2} 2 \sin t\, dt$

13. $\displaystyle\int_0^1 (2x^4 - 3x^2 + 5)\, dx$

14. $\displaystyle\int_0^1 (x^{4/3} - 2x^{1/3})\, dx$

In Problems 15–34, use the method of substitution to find each of the following indefinite integrals.

15. $\displaystyle\int \sqrt{3x + 2}\, dx$

16. $\displaystyle\int \sqrt[3]{2x - 4}\, dx$

17. $\displaystyle\int \cos(3x + 2)\, dx$

18. $\displaystyle\int \sin(2x - 4)\, dx$

19. $\displaystyle\int \sin(6x - 7)\, dx$

20. $\displaystyle\int \cos\left(\pi v - \sqrt{7}\right)\, dv$

21. $\displaystyle\int x\sqrt{x^2 + 4}\, dx$

22. $\displaystyle\int x^2(x^3 + 5)^9\, dx$

23. $\displaystyle\int x(x^2 + 3)^{-12/7}\, dx$

24. $\displaystyle\int v\left(\sqrt{3v^2 + \pi}\right)^{7/8}\, dv$

25. $\displaystyle\int x \sin(x^2 + 4)\, dx$

26. $\displaystyle\int x^2 \cos(x^3 + 5)\, dx$

27. $\displaystyle\int \frac{x \sin \sqrt{x^2 + 4}}{\sqrt{x^2 + 4}}\, dx$

28. $\displaystyle\int \frac{z \cos\left(\sqrt[3]{z^2 + 3}\right)}{\left(\sqrt[3]{z^2 + 3}\right)^2}\, dz$

29. $\int x^2(x^3 + 5)^8 \exp[(x^3 + 5)^9] \, dx$

30. $\int x^6(7x^7 + \pi)^8 \sinh[(7x^7 + \pi)^9] \, dx$

31. $\int x \cos(x^2 + 4)\sqrt{\sin(x^2 + 4)} \, dx$

32. $\int x^6 \sin(3x^7 + 9)\sqrt[3]{\cos(3x^7 + 9)} \, dx$

33. $\int x^2 \sin(x^3 + 5) \cos^9(x^3 + 5) \, dx$

34. $\int x^{-4} \sec^2(x^{-3} + 1)\sqrt[5]{\tan(x^{-3} + 1)} \, dx$

Hint: $D_x \tan x = \sec^2 x$

In Problems 35–62, use the Substitution Rule for Definite Integrals to evaluate each definite integral.

35. $\int_0^1 (x^2 + 1)^{10}(2x) \, dx$

36. $\int_{-1}^0 \sqrt{x^3 + 1}(3x^2) \, dx$

37. $\int_{-1}^3 \frac{1}{(t + 2)^2} \, dt$

38. $\int_2^{10} \frac{1}{y + 4} \, dy$

39. $\int_5^8 \sqrt{3x + 1} \, dx$

40. $\int_1^7 \frac{1}{\sqrt{2x + 2}} \, dx$

41. $\int_{-3}^3 \sqrt{7 + 2t^2} \, (8t) \, dt$

42. $\int_1^3 \frac{x^2 + 1}{\sqrt{x^3 + 3x}} \, dx$

43. $\int_0^{\pi/2} \cos^2 x \sin x \, dx$

44. $\int_0^{\pi/2} \sin^2 3x \cos 3x \, dx$

45. $\int_0^1 x \, e^{x^2} \, dx$

46. $\int_1^4 \frac{(\sqrt{x} - 1)^3}{\sqrt{x}} \, dx$

47. $\int_0^{\pi/6} \sin^3 \theta \cos \theta \, d\theta$

48. $\int_0^{\pi/6} \frac{\sin \theta}{\cos^3 \theta} \, d\theta$

49. $\int_0^1 \cos(3x - 3) \, dx$

50. $\int_0^{1/2} \sin(2\pi x) \, dx$

51. $\int_0^1 x \sin(\pi x^2) \, dx$

52. $\int_0^\pi x^4 \cos(2x^5) \, dx$

53. $\int_0^{\pi/4} (\cos 2x + \sin 2x) \, dx$

54. $\int_{-\pi/2}^{\pi/2} (\cos 3x + \sin 5x) \, dx$

55. $\int_0^\pi \sin x \, e^{\cos x} \, dx$

56. $\int_{-\pi/2}^{\pi/2} \cos \theta \cos(\pi \sin \theta) \, d\theta$

57. $\int_0^1 x \cos^3(x^2) \sin(x^2) \, dx$

58. $\int_{-\pi/2}^{\pi/2} x^2 \sin^2(x^3) \cos(x^3) \, dx$

59. $\int_0^1 \frac{1}{1 + x^2} \, dx$

60. $\int_{-1}^1 x^2 \cosh x^3 \, dx$

61. $\int_{-5}^5 x \sinh x^2 \, dx$

62. $\int_1^3 \frac{\ln x}{x} \, dx$ *Hint:* Let $u = \ln x$

63. Figure 4 shows the graph of a function f that has a continuous third derivative. The dashed lines are tangent to the graph of $y = f(x)$ at the points $(0, 2)$ and $(3, 0)$. Based on what is shown, tell, if possible, whether the following integrals are positive, negative, or zero.

(a) $\int_0^3 f(x) \, dx$ (b) $\int_0^3 f'(x) \, dx$

(c) $\int_0^3 f''(x) \, dx$ (d) $\int_0^3 f'''(x) \, dx$

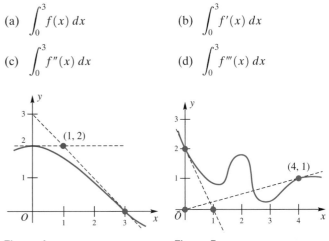

Figure 4   Figure 5

64. Figure 5 shows the graph of a function f that has a continuous third derivative. The dashed lines are tangent to the graph of $y = f(x)$ at the points $(0, 2)$ and $(4, 1)$. Based on what is shown, tell, if possible, whether the following integrals are positive, negative, or zero.

(a) $\int_0^4 f(x) \, dx$ (b) $\int_0^4 f'(x) \, dx$

(c) $\int_0^4 f''(x) \, dx$ (d) $\int_0^4 f'''(x) \, dx$

65. Water leaks out of a 200-gallon storage tank (initially full) at the rate $V'(t) = 20 - t$, where t is measured in hours and V in gallons. How much water leaked out between 10 and 20 hours? How long will it take the tank to drain completely?

66. Oil is leaking at the rate of $V'(t) = 1 - t/110$ from a storage tank that is initially full of 55 gallons. How much leaks out during the first hour? During the tenth hour? How long until the entire tank is drained?

67. The water usage in a small town is measured in gallons per hour. A plot of this rate of usage is shown in Figure 6 for the hours midnight through noon for a particular day. Estimate the total amount of water used during this 12-hour period.

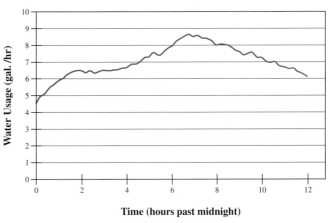

Figure 6

68. Figure 7 shows the rate of oil consumption in million barrels per year for the United States from 1973 to 2003. Approximately how many barrels of oil were consumed between 1990 and 2000?

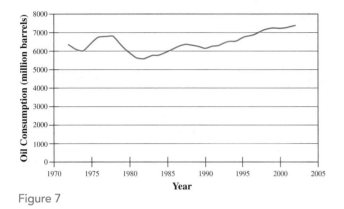

Figure 7

69. Figure 8 shows the power usage, measured in megawatts, for a small town for one day (measured from midnight to midnight). Estimate the energy usage for the day measured in megawatt-hours. *Hint:* Power is the derivative of energy.

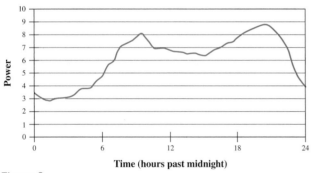

Figure 8

70. The mass, in kilograms, of a rod measured from the left endpoint to the point x meters away is $m(x) = x + x^2/8$. What is the density $\delta(x)$ of the rod, measured in kilograms per meter? Assuming that the rod is 2 meters long, express the total mass of the rod in terms of its density.

71. We claim that

$$\int_a^b x^n\, dx + \int_{a^n}^{b^n} \sqrt[n]{y}\, dy = b^{n+1} - a^{n+1}$$

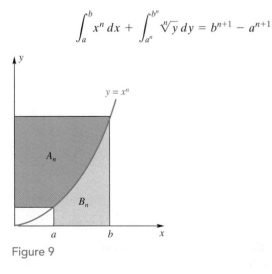

Figure 9

(a) Use Figure 9 to justify this by a geometric argument.

(b) Prove the result using the Second Fundamental Theorem of Calculus.

(c) Show that $A_n = nB_n$.

72. Prove the Second Fundamental Theorem of Calculus following the method suggested in Example 6 of Section 5.3.

In Problems 73–76, first recognize the given limit as a definite integral and then evaluate that integral by the Second Fundamental Theorem of Calculus.

73. $\displaystyle \lim_{n\to\infty} \sum_{i=1}^{n} \left(\frac{3i}{n}\right)^2 \frac{3}{n}$

74. $\displaystyle \lim_{n\to\infty} \sum_{i=1}^{n} \left(\frac{2i}{n}\right)^3 \frac{2}{n}$

75. $\displaystyle \lim_{n\to\infty} \sum_{i=1}^{n} \left[\sin\left(\frac{\pi i}{n}\right)\right] \frac{\pi}{n}$

76. $\displaystyle \lim_{n\to\infty} \sum_{i=1}^{n} \left[1 + \frac{2i}{n} + \left(\frac{2i}{n}\right)^2\right] \frac{2}{n}$

C **77.** Explain why $(1/n^3) \sum_{i=1}^{n} i^2$ should be a good approximation to $\int_0^1 x^2\, dx$ for large n. Now calculate the summation expression for $n = 10$, and evaluate the integral by the Second Fundamental Theorem of Calculus. Compare their values.

78. Evaluate $\displaystyle \int_{-2}^{4} (2[\![x]\!] - 3|x|)\, dx$.

79. Show that $\frac{1}{2}x|x|$ is an antiderivative of $|x|$, and use this fact to get a simple formula for $\displaystyle \int_a^b |x|\, dx$.

80. Find a nice formula for $\displaystyle \int_0^b [\![x]\!]\, dx, b > 0$.

81. Suppose that f is continuous on $[a, b]$.

(a) Let $G(x) = \displaystyle \int_a^x f(t)\, dt$. Show that G is continuous on $[a, b]$.

(b) Let $F(x)$ be any antiderivative of f on $[a, b]$. Show that F is continuous on $[a, b]$.

82. Give an example to show that the accumulation function $G(x) = \displaystyle \int_a^x f(x)\, dx$ can be continuous even if f is not continuous.

Answers to Concepts Review: **1.** antiderivative; $F(b) - F(a)$ **2.** $F(b) - F(a)$ **3.** $F(d) - F(c)$

4. $\displaystyle \int_1^2 \frac{1}{3}u^4\, du$

5.5
The Mean Value Theorem for Integrals and the Use of Symmetry

We know what is meant by the average of a set of n numbers, $y_1, y_2, \ldots, y_n$; we simply add them up and divide by n

$$\bar{y} = \frac{y_1 + y_2 + \cdots + y_n}{n}$$

Can we give meaning to the concept of the average of a function f over an interval $[a, b]$? Well, suppose we take a regular partition of $[a, b]$, say $P: a = x_0 < x_1 < x_2 < \cdots < x_{n-1} < x_n = b$, with $\Delta x = (b - a)/n$. The average of the n values $f(x_1), f(x_2), \ldots, f(x_n)$ is

$$\frac{f(x_1) + f(x_2) + \cdots + f(x_n)}{n} = \frac{1}{n} \sum_{i=1}^{n} f(x_i)$$

$$= \sum_{i=1}^{n} f(x_i) \frac{b - a}{n} \frac{1}{b - a}$$

$$= \frac{1}{b - a} \sum_{i=1}^{n} f(x_i) \, \Delta x$$

This last sum is a Riemann sum for f on $[a, b]$ and therefore

$$\lim_{n \to \infty} \frac{f(x_1) + f(x_2) + \cdots + f(x_n)}{n} = \frac{1}{b - a} \lim_{n \to \infty} \sum_{i=1}^{n} f(x_i) \, \Delta x$$

$$= \frac{1}{b - a} \int_a^b f(x) \, dx$$

This suggests the following definition.

Definition   **Average Value of a Function**

If f is integrable on the interval $[a, b]$, then the **average value** of f on $[a, b]$ is

$$\frac{1}{b - a} \int_a^b f(x) \, dx$$

■ **EXAMPLE 1**   Find the average value of the function defined by $f(x) = x \sin x^2$ on the interval $\left[0, \sqrt{\pi}\right]$. (See Figure 1.)

SOLUTION   The average value is

$$\frac{1}{\sqrt{\pi} - 0} \int_0^{\sqrt{\pi}} x \sin x^2 \, dx$$

To evaluate this integral, we make the substitution $u = x^2$, so that $du = 2x \, dx$. When $x = 0, u = 0$ and when $x = \sqrt{\pi}, u = \pi$. Thus,

$$\frac{1}{\sqrt{\pi}} \int_0^{\sqrt{\pi}} x \sin x^2 \, dx = \frac{1}{\sqrt{\pi}} \int_0^{\pi} \frac{1}{2} \sin u \, du = \frac{1}{2\sqrt{\pi}} \left[-\cos u \right]_0^{\pi} = \frac{1}{2\sqrt{\pi}} (2) = \frac{1}{\sqrt{\pi}} \quad ■$$

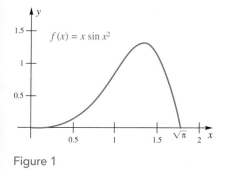

Figure 1

■ **EXAMPLE 2**   Suppose the temperature in degrees Fahrenheit of a metal bar of length 2 feet depends on the position x according to the function $T(x) = 40 + 20x(2 - x)$. Find the average temperature in the bar. Is there a point where the actual temperature equals the average temperature?

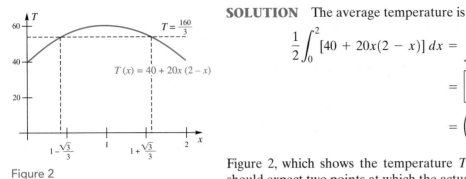

Figure 2

SOLUTION The average temperature is

$$\frac{1}{2}\int_0^2 [40 + 20x(2 - x)]\, dx = \int_0^2 (20 + 20x - 10x^2)\, dx$$

$$= \left[20x + 10x^2 - \frac{10}{3}x^3 \right]_0^2$$

$$= \left(40 + 40 - \frac{80}{3} \right) = \frac{160}{3}\ °F$$

Figure 2, which shows the temperature T as a function of x, indicates that we should expect two points at which the actual temperature equals the average temperature. To find these points, we set $T(x)$ equal to $160/3$ and try to solve for x.

$$40 + 20x(2 - x) = \frac{160}{3}$$

$$3x^2 - 6x + 2 = 0$$

The Quadratic Formula gives

$$x = \frac{1}{3}\left(3 - \sqrt{3}\right) \approx 0.42265 \quad \text{and} \quad x = \frac{1}{3}\left(3 + \sqrt{3}\right) \approx 1.5774$$

Both solutions are between 0 and 2, so there are two points at which the actual temperature equals the average temperature. ■

It seems as if there should always be a value of x with the property that $f(x)$ equals the average value of the function. This is true provided only that the function f is continuous.

The Two Mean Value Theorems

The Mean Value Theorem for Derivatives says that there is some point c in the interval $[a, b]$ at which the average rate of change of f, $(f(b) - f(a))/(b - a)$, equals the instantaneous rate of change, $f'(c)$.

The Mean Value Theorem for Integrals says that there is some point c in the interval $[a, b]$ at which the average value of a function $\frac{1}{b - a}\int_a^b f(t)\, dt$ is equal to the actual value of the function, $f(c)$.

Theorem A **Mean Value Theorem for Integrals**

If f is continuous on $[a, b]$, then there is a number c between a and b such that

$$f(c) = \frac{1}{b - a}\int_a^b f(t)\, dt$$

Proof For $a \le x \le b$ define $G(x) = \int_a^x f(t)\, dt$. By the Mean Value Theorem for Derivatives (applied to G) there is a c in the interval (a, b) such that

$$G'(c) = \frac{G(b) - G(a)}{b - a}$$

Since $G(a) = \int_a^a f(t)\, dt = 0$, $G(b) = \int_a^b f(t)\, dt$, and $G'(c) = f(c)$, this leads to

$$G'(c) = f(c) = \frac{1}{b - a}\int_a^b f(t)\, dt \qquad ■$$

The Mean Value Theorem for Integrals is often expressed as follows: If f is integrable on $[a, b]$, then there exists a c in (a, b) such that

$$\int_a^b f(t)\, dt = (b - a) f(c)$$

When viewed this way, the Mean Value Theorem for Integrals says that there is some c in the interval $[a, b]$ such that the area of the rectangle with height $f(c)$ and width $b - a$ is equal to the area under the curve. In Figure 3, the area under the curve is equal to the area of the rectangle.

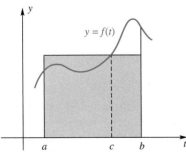

Figure 3

≈ Estimating Integrals

This version of the Mean Value Theorem for Integrals with the accompanying Figure 3 suggests a good way to estimate the value of a definite integral. The area of the region under a curve is equal to the area of a rectangle. One can make a good guess at this rectangle by simply "eyeballing" the region. In Figure 3, the area of the shaded part *above* the curve should match the area of the white part *below* the curve.

EXAMPLE 3 Find all values of c that satisfy the Mean Value Theorem for Integrals for $f(x) = x^2$ on the interval $[-3, 3]$.

SOLUTION The graph of $f(x)$ shown in Figure 4 indicates that there could be two values of c that satisfy the Mean Value Theorem for Integrals. The average value of the function is

$$\frac{1}{3 - (-3)} \int_{-3}^{3} x^2 \, dx = \frac{1}{6}\left[\frac{x^3}{3}\right]_{-3}^{3} = \frac{1}{18}[27 - (-27)] = 3$$

To find the values of c, we solve

$$3 = f(c) = c^2$$
$$c = \pm\sqrt{3}$$

Both $-\sqrt{3}$ and $\sqrt{3}$ are in the interval $[-3, 3]$, so both values satisfy the Mean Value Theorem for Integrals. ∎

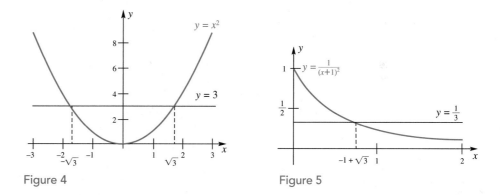

Figure 4   Figure 5

EXAMPLE 4 Find all values of c that satisfy the Mean Value Theorem for Integrals for $f(x) = \dfrac{1}{(x + 1)^2}$ on the interval $[0, 2]$.

SOLUTION The graph of $f(x)$ shown in Figure 5 indicates that there should be one value of c that satisfies the Mean Value Theorem for Integrals. The average value of the function is found by making the substitution $u = x + 1$, $du = dx$, where when $x = 0$, $u = 1$ and when $x = 2$, $u = 3$:

$$\frac{1}{2 - 0} \int_{0}^{2} \frac{1}{(x + 1)^2} \, dx = \frac{1}{2} \int_{1}^{3} \frac{1}{u^2} \, du = \frac{1}{2}\left[-u^{-1}\right]_{1}^{3} = \frac{1}{2}\left(-\frac{1}{3} + 1\right) = \frac{1}{3}$$

To find the value of c we solve

$$\frac{1}{3} = f(c) = \frac{1}{(c + 1)^2}$$
$$c^2 + 2c + 1 = 3$$
$$c = \frac{-2 \pm \sqrt{2^2 - 4(1)(-2)}}{2} = -1 \pm \sqrt{3}$$

Note that $-1 - \sqrt{3} \approx -2.7321$ and $-1 + \sqrt{3} \approx 0.73205$. The only one of these two solutions that is in the interval $[0, 2]$ is $c = -1 + \sqrt{3}$; thus, this is the only value of c that satisfies the Mean Value Theorem for Integrals. ∎

The Use of Symmetry in Evaluating Definite Integrals Recall that an even function is one satisfying $f(-x) = f(x)$, whereas an odd function satisfies

$f(-x) = -f(x)$. The graph of the former is symmetric with respect to the y-axis; the graph of the latter is symmetric with respect to the origin. Here is a useful integration theorem for such functions.

Theorem B **Symmetry Theorem**

If f is an even function, then

$$\int_{-a}^{a} f(x)\, dx = 2 \int_{0}^{a} f(x)\, dx$$

If f is an odd function, then

$$\int_{-a}^{a} f(x)\, dx = 0$$

Proof for Even Functions The geometric interpretation of this theorem is shown in Figures 6 and 7. To justify the results analytically, we first write

$$\int_{-a}^{a} f(x)\, dx = \int_{-a}^{0} f(x)\, dx + \int_{0}^{a} f(x)\, dx$$

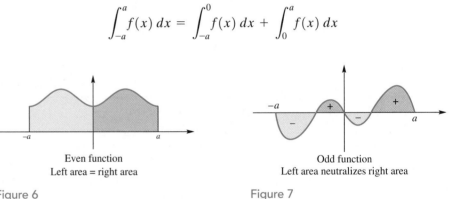

Even function
Left area = right area

Figure 6

Odd function
Left area neutralizes right area

Figure 7

In the first of the integrals on the right, we make the substitution $u = -x, du = -dx$. If f is even, $f(u) = f(-x) = f(x)$ and

$$\int_{-a}^{0} f(x)\, dx = -\int_{-a}^{0} f(-x)(-dx) = -\int_{a}^{0} f(u)\, du = \int_{0}^{a} f(u)\, du = \int_{0}^{a} f(x)\, dx$$

Therefore,

$$\int_{-a}^{a} f(x)\, dx = \int_{0}^{a} f(x)\, dx + \int_{0}^{a} f(x)\, dx = 2\int_{0}^{a} f(x)\, dx$$

The proof for odd functions is left as an exercise (Problem 60). ∎

EXAMPLE 5 Evaluate $\displaystyle\int_{-\pi}^{\pi} \cos\left(\frac{x}{4}\right) dx$.

> Be sure to note the hypotheses of the Symmetry Theorem. The integrand must be even or odd and the interval of integration must be symmetric about the origin. These are restrictive conditions, but it is surprising how often they hold in applications. When they do hold, they can greatly simplify integrations.

SOLUTION Since $\cos(-x/4) = \cos(x/4)$, $f(x) = \cos(x/4)$ is an even function. Thus,

$$\int_{-\pi}^{\pi} \cos\left(\frac{x}{4}\right) dx = 2\int_{0}^{\pi} \cos\left(\frac{x}{4}\right) dx = 8\int_{0}^{\pi} \cos\left(\frac{x}{4}\right) \cdot \frac{1}{4} dx$$

$$= 8\int_{0}^{\pi/4} \cos u\, du = \Big[8 \sin u\Big]_{0}^{\pi/4} = 4\sqrt{2} \quad \blacksquare$$

EXAMPLE 6 Evaluate $\int_{-5}^{5} x^5 e^{-x^2} \, dx$.

SOLUTION $f(x) = x^5 e^{-x^2}$ is an odd function. Thus, the above integral has the value 0. ∎

EXAMPLE 7 Evaluate $\int_{-2}^{2} (x \sin^4 x + x^3 - x^4) \, dx$.

SOLUTION The first two terms in the integrand are odd, and the last is even. Thus, we may write the integral as

$$\int_{-2}^{2} (x \sin^4 x + x^3) \, dx - \int_{-2}^{2} x^4 \, dx = 0 - 2 \int_{0}^{2} x^4 \, dx$$

$$= \left[-2 \frac{x^5}{5} \right]_0^2 = -\frac{64}{5}$$ ∎

EXAMPLE 8 Evaluate $\int_{-\pi}^{\pi} \sin^3 x \cos^5 x \, dx$.

SOLUTION The function $\sin x$ is odd and $\cos x$ is even. An odd function raised to an odd power is odd, so $\sin^3 x$ is odd. An even function raised to any integer power is even, so $\cos^5 x$ is even. An odd function times an even function is odd. Thus the integrand in this integral is an odd function and the interval is symmetric about 0, so the value of this integral is 0. ∎

Use of Periodicity Recall that a function f is *periodic* if there is a number p such that $f(x + p) = f(x)$ for all x in the domain of f. If f is nonconstant, then the smallest such positive number p is called the **period** of f. The trigonometric functions are examples of periodic functions.

Theorem C

If f is periodic with period p, then

$$\int_{a+p}^{b+p} f(x) \, dx = \int_{a}^{b} f(x) \, dx$$

Proof The geometric interpretation can be seen in Figure 8. To prove the result, let $u = x - p$ so that $x = u + p$ and $du = dx$. Then

$$\int_{a+p}^{b+p} f(x) \, dx = \int_{a}^{b} f(u + p) \, du = \int_{a}^{b} f(u) \, du = \int_{a}^{b} f(x) \, dx$$

We could replace $f(u + p)$ by $f(u)$ because f has period p. ∎

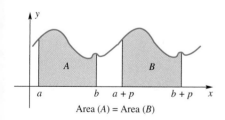

Area (A) = Area (B)

Figure 8

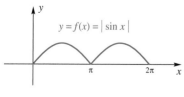

$y = f(x) = |\sin x|$

Figure 9

EXAMPLE 9 Evaluate (a) $\int_{0}^{2\pi} |\sin x| \, dx$ and (b) $\int_{0}^{100\pi} |\sin x| \, dx$.

SOLUTION

(a) Note that $f(x) = |\sin x|$ is periodic with period π (Figure 9). The integral in (a) is thus

$$\int_0^{2\pi} |\sin x| \, dx = \int_0^\pi |\sin x| \, dx + \int_\pi^{2\pi} |\sin x| \, dx$$

$$= \int_0^\pi |\sin x| \, dx + \int_0^\pi |\sin x| \, dx$$

$$= 2 \int_0^\pi \sin x \, dx = 2\big[-\cos x\big]_0^\pi = 2[1 - (-1)] = 4$$

(b) The integral in (b) is

$$\int_0^{100\pi} |\sin x| \, dx = \underbrace{\int_0^\pi |\sin x| \, dx + \int_\pi^{2\pi} |\sin x| \, dx + \cdots + \int_{99\pi}^{100\pi} |\sin x| \, dx}_{\text{100 integrals each equal to } \int_0^\pi \sin x \, dx}$$

$$= 100 \int_0^\pi \sin x \, dx = 100\big[-\cos x\big]_0^\pi = 100(2) = 200 \qquad \blacksquare$$

Note that in Example 9, we had to use symmetry because we can't find an anti-derivative for $|\sin x|$ over the interval $[0, 100\pi]$.

Concepts Review

1. The average value of a function f on the interval $[a, b]$ is _____.

2. The Mean Value Theorem for Integrals says there exists a c in the interval (a, b) such that the average value of the function on $[a, b]$ is equal to _____.

3. If f is an odd function, $\int_{-2}^2 f(x) \, dx =$ _____; if f is an even function, $\int_{-2}^2 f(x) \, dx =$ _____.

4. The function f is periodic if there is a number p such that _____ for all x in the domain of f. The smallest such positive number p is called the _____ of the function.

Problem Set 5.5

In Problems 1–14, find the average value of the function on the given interval.

1. $f(x) = 4x^3$; $[1, 3]$ 2. $f(x) = 5x^2$; $[1, 4]$

3. $f(x) = \dfrac{x}{\sqrt{x^2 + 16}}$; $[0, 3]$

4. $f(x) = \dfrac{x^2}{\sqrt{x^3 + 16}}$; $[0, 2]$

5. $f(x) = 2 + |x|$; $[-2, 1]$ 6. $f(x) = x + |x|$; $[-3, 2]$

7. $f(x) = \cos x$; $[0, \pi]$ 8. $f(x) = \sin x$; $[0, \pi]$

9. $f(x) = e^{-x}$; $[0, 2]$

10. $f(x) = \cosh(2x)$; $[-2, 2]$

11. $F(y) = y(1 + y^2)^3$; $[1, 2]$

12. $g(x) = \tan x \sec^2 x$; $[0, \pi/4]$

13. $h(z) = \dfrac{\sin\sqrt{z}}{\sqrt{z}}$; $[\pi/4, \pi/2]$

14. $G(v) = \dfrac{\sin v \cos v}{\sqrt{1 + \cos^2 v}}$; $[0, \pi/2]$

In Problems 15–28, find all values of c that satisfy the Mean Value Theorem for Integrals on the given interval.

15. $f(x) = \sqrt{x + 1}$; $[0, 3]$ 16. $f(x) = x^2$; $[-1, 1]$

17. $f(x) = 1 - x^2$; $[-4, 3]$ 18. $f(x) = x(1 - x)$; $[0, 1]$

19. $f(x) = |x|$; $[0, 2]$ 20. $f(x) = |x|$; $[-2, 2]$

21. $H(z) = \sin z$; $[-\pi, \pi]$ 22. $g(y) = \cos 2y$; $[0, \pi]$

23. $R(v) = v^2 - v$; $[0, 2]$ 24. $T(x) = x^3$; $[0, 2]$

25. $f(x) = ax + b$; $[1, 4]$ 26. $S(y) = y^2$; $[0, b]$

27. $f(x) = ax + b$; $[A, B]$ 28. $q(y) = ay^2$; $[0, b]$

GC ≈ *Use a graphing calculator to plot the graph of the integrand in Problems 29–32. Then estimate the integral as suggested in the margin note accompanying Theorem B.*

29. $\displaystyle\int_0^{2\pi} (5 + \sin x)^4 \, dx$ 30. $\displaystyle\int_0^2 \big[3 + \sin(x^2)\big] \, dx$

31. $\displaystyle\int_{-1}^1 \frac{2}{1 + x^2} \, dx$ 32. $\displaystyle\int_{10}^{20} \left(1 + \frac{1}{x}\right)^5 \, dx$

33. Figure 10 shows the relative humidity H as a function of time t (measured in days since Sunday) for an office building. Approximate the average relative humidity for the week.

34. Figure 11 shows temperature T as a function of time t (measured in hours past midnight) for one day in St. Louis, Missouri.

(a) Approximate the average temperature for the day.

(b) Must there be a time when the temperature is equal to the average temperature for the day? Explain.

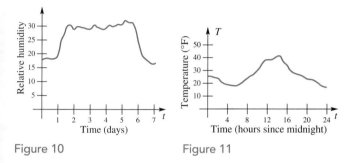

Figure 10   Figure 11

In Problems 35–44, use symmetry to help you evaluate the given integral.

35. $\displaystyle\int_{-\pi}^{\pi} (\sin x + \cos x)\, dx$

36. $\displaystyle\int_{-1}^{1} \frac{x^3}{(1 + x^2)^4}\, dx$

37. $\displaystyle\int_{-\pi/2}^{\pi/2} \frac{\sin x}{1 + \cos x}\, dx$

38. $\displaystyle\int_{-\sqrt[3]{\pi}}^{\sqrt[3]{\pi}} x^2 \cos(x^3)\, dx$

39. $\displaystyle\int_{-\pi}^{\pi} (\sin x + \cos x)^2\, dx$

40. $\displaystyle\int_{-\pi/2}^{\pi/2} z \sin^2(z^3)\cos(z^3)\, dz$

41. $\displaystyle\int_{-1}^{1} (1 + x + x^2 + x^3)\, dx$

42. $\displaystyle\int_{-100}^{100} (v + \sin v + v\cos v + \sin^3 v)^5\, dv$

43. $\displaystyle\int_{-1}^{1} x\, e^{-4x^2}\, dx$

44. $\displaystyle\int_{-\pi/4}^{\pi/4} (|x|\sin^5 x + |x|^2 \tan x)\, dx$

45. How does $\displaystyle\int_{-b}^{-a} f(x)\, dx$ compare with $\displaystyle\int_{a}^{b} f(x)\, dx$ when f is an even function? An odd function?

46. Prove (by a substitution) that
$$\int_{a}^{b} f(-x)\, dx = \int_{-b}^{-a} f(x)\, dx$$

47. Use periodicity to calculate $\displaystyle\int_{0}^{4\pi} |\cos x|\, dx$.

48. Calculate $\displaystyle\int_{0}^{4\pi} |\sin 2x|\, dx$.

49. If f is periodic with period p, then
$$\int_{a}^{a+p} f(x)\, dx = \int_{0}^{p} f(x)\, dx$$

Convince yourself that this is true by drawing a picture and then use the result to calculate $\displaystyle\int_{1}^{1+\pi} |\sin x|\, dx$.

50. Use the result in Problem 49 to calculate
$$\int_{2}^{2+\pi/2} |\sin 2x|\, dx.$$

51. Calculate $\displaystyle\int_{1}^{1+\pi} |\cos x|\, dx$.

52. Prove or disprove that the integral of the average value equals the integral of the function on the interval: $\displaystyle\int_{a}^{b} \bar{f}\, dx = \int_{a}^{b} f(x)\, dx$, where $\bar{f}$ is the average value of the function f over the interval $[a, b]$.

EXPL **53.** Assuming that u and v can be integrated over the interval $[a, b]$ and that the average values over the interval are denoted by $\bar{u}$ and $\bar{v}$, prove or disprove that

(a) $\overline{u + v} = \bar{u} + \bar{v}$;

(b) $\overline{ku} = k\bar{u}$, where k is any constant;

(c) if $u \le v$ then $\bar{u} \le \bar{v}$.

54. Household electric current can be modeled by the voltage $V = \hat{V}\sin(120\pi t + \phi)$, where t is measured in seconds, $\hat{V}$ is the maximum value that V can attain, and ϕ is the phase angle. Such a voltage is usually said to be 60-cycle, since in 1 second the voltage goes through 60 oscillations. The root-mean-square voltage, usually denoted by V_{rms} is defined to be the square root of the average of V^2. Hence
$$V_{rms} = \sqrt{\int_{\phi}^{1+\phi} (\hat{V}\sin(120\pi t + \phi))^2\, dt}$$

A good measure of how much heat a given voltage can produce is given by V_{rms}.

(a) Compute the average voltage over 1 second.

(b) Compute the average voltage over $1/60$ of a second.

(c) Show that $V_{rms} = \dfrac{\hat{V}\sqrt{2}}{2}$ by computing the integral for V_{rms}.

Hint: $\displaystyle\int \sin^2 t\, dt = -\frac{1}{2}\cos t \sin t + \frac{1}{2}t + C.$

(d) If the V_{rms} for household current is usually 120 volts, what is the value $\hat{V}$ in this case?

55. Give a proof of the Mean Value Theorem for Integrals (Theorem A) that does not use the First Fundamental Theorem of Calculus. *Hint:* Apply the Max–Min Existence Theorem and the Intermediate Value Theorem.

56. Integrals that occur frequently in applications are
$$\int_{0}^{2\pi} \cos^2 x\, dx \text{ and } \int_{0}^{2\pi} \sin^2 x\, dx.$$

(a) Using a trigonometric identity, show that
$$\int_{0}^{2\pi} (\sin^2 x + \cos^2 x)\, dx = 2\pi$$

(b) Show from graphical considerations that
$$\int_{0}^{2\pi} \cos^2 x\, dx = \int_{0}^{2\pi} \sin^2 x\, dx$$

(c) Conclude that $\displaystyle\int_{0}^{2\pi} \cos^2 x\, dx = \int_{0}^{2\pi} \sin^2 x\, dx = \pi.$

GC **57.** Let $f(x) = |\sin x| \sin(\cos x)$.

(a) Is f even, odd, or neither?

(b) Note that f is periodic. What is its period?

(c) Evaluate the definite integral of f for each of the following intervals: $[0, \pi/2]$, $[-\pi/2, \pi/2]$, $[0, 3\pi/2]$, $[-3\pi/2, 3\pi/2]$, $[0, 2\pi]$, $[\pi/6, 13\pi/6]$, $[\pi/6, 4\pi/3]$, $[13\pi/6, 10\pi/3]$.

58. Repeat Problem 57 for $f(x) = \sin x \, |\sin(\sin x)|$.

59. Complete the generalization of the Pythagorean Theorem begun in Problem 59 of Section 1.3 by showing that $A + B = C$ in Figure 12, these being the areas of similar regions built on the two legs and the hypotenuse of a right triangle.

(a) Convince yourself that similarity means

$$g(x) = \frac{a}{c}f\left(\frac{c}{a}x\right) \quad \text{and} \quad h(x) = \frac{b}{c}f\left(\frac{c}{b}x\right)$$

(b) Show that $\displaystyle\int_0^a g(x)\,dx + \int_0^b h(x)\,dx = \int_0^c f(x)\,dx.$

60. Prove the Symmetry Theorem for the case of odd functions.

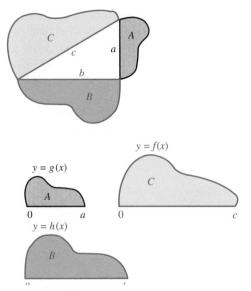

Figure 12

Answers to Concepts Review: **1.** $\dfrac{1}{b-a}\displaystyle\int_a^b f(x)\,dx$

2. $f(c)$ **3.** $0; 2\displaystyle\int_0^2 f(x)\,dx$ **4.** $f(x+p) = f(x)$; period

---

5.6
Numerical Integration

We know that if f is continuous on a closed interval $[a, b]$, then the definite integral

$$\int_a^b f(x)\,dx$$

must exist. Existence is one thing; evaluation is a very different matter. There are many definite integrals that cannot be evaluated by the methods that we have learned, that is, by use of the Second Fundamental Theorem of Calculus. For example, the indefinite integrals

$$\int \sin(x^2)\,dx, \quad \int \sqrt{1 - x^4}\,dx, \quad \int \frac{\sin x}{x}\,dx, \quad \int e^{x^2}\,dx$$

cannot be expressed algebraically in terms of elementary functions, that is, in terms of functions studied in a first calculus course. In Section 5.2 we saw how Riemann sums can be used to approximate a definite integral. In this section we review these Riemann sums and we present two additional methods: the Trapezoidal Rule and the Parabolic Rule.

Riemann Sums In Section 5.2 we introduced the concept of a Riemann sum. Suppose f is defined on $[a, b]$ and we partition the interval $[a, b]$ into n smaller intervals with end points $a = x_0 < x_1 < \cdots < x_{n-1} < x_n = b$. The Riemann sum is then defined to be

$$\sum_{i=1}^{n} f(\bar{x}_i)\,\Delta x_i$$

where $\bar{x}_i$ is some point (possibly even an end point) in the interval $[x_{i-1}, x_i]$, and $\Delta x_i = x_i - x_{i-1}$. For now, we will assume that the partition is *regular*, that is, $\Delta x_i = (b - a)/n$ for all i. Riemann sums were introduced in Section 5.2 with the goal of defining the definite integral as the limit of the Riemann sum. Here we look at the Riemann sum as a way to approximate a definite integral.

We consider the three cases: where the sample point $\bar{x}_i$ is the left end point, the right end point, or the midpoint of $[x_{i-1}, x_i]$. The left end point, right end point, and midpoint of the interval $[x_{i-1}, x_i]$ are

$$\text{left end point} = x_{i-1} = a + (i - 1)\frac{b - a}{n}$$

$$\text{right end point} = x_i = a + i\,\frac{b - a}{n}$$

$$\text{midpoint} = \frac{x_{i-1} + x_i}{2} = \frac{a + (i-1)\frac{b-a}{n} + a + i\frac{b-a}{n}}{2} = a + \left(i - \tfrac{1}{2}\right)\frac{b - a}{n}$$

For a left Riemann sum, we take $\bar{x}_i$ to be x_{i-1}, the left end point:

$$\text{Left Riemann Sum} = \sum_{i=1}^{n} f(\bar{x}_i)\,\Delta x_i = \frac{b - a}{n} \sum_{i=1}^{n} f\left(a + (i - 1)\frac{b - a}{n}\right)$$

For a right Riemann sum, we take $\bar{x}_i$ to be x_i, the right end point:

$$\text{Right Riemann Sum} = \sum_{i=1}^{n} f(\bar{x}_i)\,\Delta x_i = \frac{b - a}{n} \sum_{i=1}^{n} f\left(a + i\,\frac{b - a}{n}\right)$$

For a midpoint Riemann sum, we take $\bar{x}_i$ to be $(x_{i-1} + x_i)/2$, the midpoint of the interval $[x_{i-1}, x_i]$:

$$\text{Midpoint Riemann Sum} = \sum_{i=1}^{n} f(\bar{x}_i)\,\Delta x_i = \frac{b - a}{n} \sum_{i=1}^{n} f\left(a + \left(i - \tfrac{1}{2}\right)\frac{b - a}{n}\right)$$

The figures in the large table on the next page illustrate how these approximations (and two others we will introduce later in this section) work.

EXAMPLE 1 Approximate the definite integral $\displaystyle\int_{1}^{3} \sqrt{4 - x}\, dx$ using left, right, and midpoint Riemann sums with $n = 4$.

SOLUTION Let $f(x) = \sqrt{4 - x}$. We have $a = 1, b = 3$, and $n = 4$, so $(b - a)/n = 0.5$. The values of x_i and $f(x_i)$ are

$$x_0 = 1.0 \qquad f(x_0) = f(1.0) = \sqrt{4 - 1} \approx 1.7321$$

$$x_1 = 1.5 \qquad f(x_1) = f(1.5) = \sqrt{4 - 1.5} \approx 1.5811$$

$$x_2 = 2.0 \qquad f(x_2) = f(2.0) = \sqrt{4 - 2} \approx 1.4142$$

$$x_3 = 2.5 \qquad f(x_3) = f(2.5) = \sqrt{4 - 2.5} \approx 1.2247$$

$$x_4 = 3.0 \qquad f(x_4) = f(3.0) = \sqrt{4 - 3} = 1.0000$$

Using the left Riemann sum, we have the following approximation:

$$\int_{1}^{3} \sqrt{4 - x}\, dx \approx \text{Left Riemann Sum}$$

$$= \frac{b - a}{n}\Big[f(x_0) + f(x_1) + f(x_2) + f(x_3)\Big]$$

$$= 0.5[f(1.0) + f(1.5) + f(2.0) + f(2.5)]$$

$$\approx 0.5(1.7321 + 1.5811 + 1.4142 + 1.2247)$$

$$\approx 2.9761$$

Methods for Approximating $\int_a^b f(x)\,dx$

1. Left Riemann Sum

Area of ith rectangle $= f(x_{i-1})\,\Delta x_i = \dfrac{b-a}{n}f\left(a+(i-1)\dfrac{b-a}{n}\right)$

$$\int_a^b f(x)\,dx \approx \frac{b-a}{n}\sum_{i=1}^{n}f\left(a+(i-1)\frac{b-a}{n}\right)$$

$E_n = \dfrac{(b-a)^2}{2n}\,f'(c)$ for some c in $[a,b]$

2. Right Riemann Sum

Area of ith rectangle $= f(x_i)\,\Delta x_i = \dfrac{b-a}{n}f\left(a+i\dfrac{b-a}{n}\right)$

$$\int_a^b f(x)\,dx \approx \frac{b-a}{n}\sum_{i=1}^{n}f\left(a+i\frac{b-a}{n}\right)$$

$E_n = -\dfrac{(b-a)^2}{2n}\,f'(c)$ for some c in $[a,b]$

3. Midpoint Riemann Sum

Area of ith rectangle $= f\left(\dfrac{x_{i-1}+x_i}{2}\right)\Delta x_i = \dfrac{b-a}{n}f\left(a+\left(i-\dfrac{1}{2}\right)\dfrac{b-a}{n}\right)$

$$\int_a^b f(x)\,dx \approx \frac{b-a}{n}\sum_{i=1}^{n}f\left(a+\left(i-\frac{1}{2}\right)\frac{b-a}{n}\right)$$

$E_n = \dfrac{(b-a)^3}{24n^2}\,f''(c)$ for some c in $[a,b]$

4. Trapezoidal Rule

Area of ith trapezoid $= \dfrac{b-a}{n}\dfrac{f(x_{i-1})+f(x_i)}{2}$

$$\int_a^b f(x)\,dx \approx \frac{b-a}{n}\sum_{i=1}^{n}\frac{f(x_{i-1})+f(x_i)}{2}$$

$$= \frac{b-a}{2n}\left[f(a)+2\sum_{i=1}^{n-1}f\left(a+i\frac{b-a}{n}\right)+f(b)\right]$$

$E_n = -\dfrac{(b-a)^3}{12n^2}\,f''(c)$ for some c in $[a,b]$

5. Parabolic Rule (n must be even)

$$\int_a^b f(x)\,dx \approx \frac{b-a}{3n}[f(x_0)+4f(x_1)+2f(x_2)+4f(x_3)+2f(x_4)+\cdots$$
$$+\,4f(x_{n-3})+2f(x_{n-2})+4f(x_{n-1})+f(x_n)]$$

$$= \frac{b-a}{3n}\left[f(a)+4\sum_{i=1}^{n/2}f\left(a+(2i-1)\frac{b-a}{n}\right)+2\sum_{i=1}^{n/2-1}f\left(a+2i\frac{b-a}{n}\right)+f(b)\right]$$

$E_n = -\dfrac{(b-a)^5}{180n^4}\,f^{(4)}(c)$ for some c in $[a,b]$

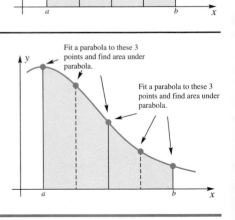

Fit a parabola to these 3 points and find area under parabola.

Fit a parabola to these 3 points and find area under parabola.

The right Riemann sum leads to the following approximation:

$$\int_1^3 \sqrt{4 - x}\, dx \approx \text{Right Riemann Sum}$$

$$= \frac{b - a}{n}\Big[f(x_1) + f(x_2) + f(x_3) + f(x_4)\Big]$$

$$= 0.5\Big[f(1.5) + f(2.0) + f(2.5) + f(3.0)\Big]$$

$$\approx 0.5(1.5811 + 1.4142 + 1.2247 + 1.0000)$$

$$\approx 2.6100$$

Finally, the midpoint Riemann sum approximation to the definite integral is

$$\int_1^3 \sqrt{4 - x}\, dx \approx \text{Midpoint Riemann Sum}$$

$$= \frac{b - a}{n}\left[f\left(\frac{x_0 + x_1}{2}\right) + f\left(\frac{x_1 + x_2}{2}\right) + f\left(\frac{x_2 + x_3}{2}\right) + f\left(\frac{x_3 + x_4}{2}\right)\right]$$

$$= 0.5\left[f(1.25) + f(1.75) + f(2.25) + f(2.75)\right]$$

$$\approx 0.5(1.6583 + 1.5000 + 1.3229 + 1.1180)$$

$$\approx 2.7996$$ ■

In this last example, approximations were not needed because we could have evaluated this integral using the Second Fundamental Theorem of Calculus:

$$\int_1^3 \sqrt{4 - x}\, dx = \left[-\frac{2}{3}(4 - x)^{3/2}\right]_1^3 = -\frac{2}{3}(4 - 3)^{3/2} + \frac{2}{3}(4 - 1)^{3/2}$$

$$= 2\sqrt{3} - \frac{2}{3} \approx 2.7974$$

The midpoint Riemann sum approximation turned out to be the closest. The figures in the large table on the previous page suggest that this will often be the case.

The next example is more realistic, in the sense that it is not possible to apply the Second Fundamental Theorem of Calculus.

EXAMPLE 2 Approximate the definite integral $\int_0^2 \sin x^2\, dx$ using a right Riemann sum with $n = 8$.

SOLUTION Let $f(x) = \sin x^2$. We have $a = 0, b = 2$, and $n = 8$, so $(b - a)/n = 0.25$. Using the right Riemann sum, we have the following approximation:

$$\int_0^2 \sin x^2\, dx \approx \text{Right Riemann Sum}$$

$$= \frac{b - a}{n}\left[\sum_{i=1}^{8} f\left(a + i\frac{b - a}{n}\right)\right]$$

$$= 0.25(\sin 0.25^2 + \sin 0.5^2 + \sin 0.75^2 + \sin 1^2$$

$$+ \sin 1.25^2 + \sin 1.5^2 + \sin 1.75^2 + \sin 2^2)$$

$$\approx 0.69622$$ ■

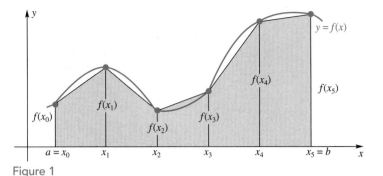

Figure 1

The Trapezoidal Rule Suppose we join the pairs of points $(x_{i-1}, f(x_{i-1}))$ and $(x_i, f(x_i))$ by line segments as shown in Figure 1, thus forming n trapezoids. Then instead of approximating the area under the curve by summing the areas of *rectangles*, we approximate it by summing the areas of the *trapezoids*. This method is called the **Trapezoidal Rule.**

Recalling the area formula shown in Figure 2, we can write the area of the ith trapezoid as

$$A_i = \frac{h}{2}[f(x_{i-1}) + f(x_i)]$$

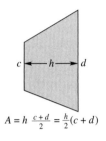

$A = h\,\frac{c+d}{2} = \frac{h}{2}(c + d)$

Figure 2

More accurately, we should say *signed* area, since A_i will be negative for a sub-interval where f is negative. The definite integral $\int_a^b f(x)\,dx$ is approximately equal to $A_1 + A_2 + \cdots + A_n$, that is, to

$$\frac{h}{2}[f(x_0) + f(x_1)] + \frac{h}{2}[f(x_1) + f(x_2)] + \cdots + \frac{h}{2}[f(x_{n-1}) + f(x_n)]$$

This simplifies to the **Trapezoidal Rule:**

Trapezoidal Rule

$$\int_a^b f(x)\,dx \approx \frac{h}{2}\Big[f(x_0) + 2f(x_1) + 2f(x_2) + \cdots + 2f(x_{n-1}) + f(x_n)\Big]$$

$$= \frac{b-a}{2n}\left[f(a) + 2\sum_{i=1}^{n-1} f\left(a + i\frac{b-a}{n}\right) + f(b)\right]$$

■ **EXAMPLE 3** Approximate the definite integral $\int_0^2 \sin x^2\,dx$ using the Trapezoidal Rule with $n = 8$.

SOLUTION This is the same integrand and interval as in Example 2.

$$\int_0^2 \sin x^2\,dx \approx \frac{b-a}{2n}\left[f(a) + 2\sum_{i=1}^{7} f\left(a + i\frac{b-a}{n}\right) + f(b)\right]$$

$$= 0.125\Big[\sin 0^2 + 2(\sin 0.25^2 + \sin 0.5^2 + \sin 0.75^2 + \sin 1^2$$

$$+ \sin 1.25^2 + \sin 1.5^2 + \sin 1.75^2) + \sin 2^2\Big]$$

$$\approx 0.79082$$ ■

Presumably we could get a better approximation by taking n larger; this would be easy to do using a computer. However, while taking n larger reduces the error of the method, it at least potentially increases the error of calculation. It would be unwise, for example, to take $n = 1{,}000{,}000$, since the potential round-off errors would more than compensate for the fact that the error of the method would be minuscule. We will have more to say about errors shortly.

The Parabolic Rule (Simpson's Rule) In the Trapezoidal Rule, we approximated the curve $y = f(x)$ by line segments. It seems likely that we could do better using parabolic segments. Just as before, partition the interval $[a, b]$ into n subintervals of length $h = (b - a)/n$, but this time with n an *even* number. Then fit parabolic segments to neighboring triples of points, as shown in Figure 3.

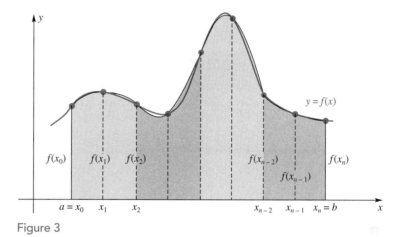

Figure 3

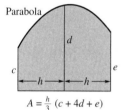

$A = \frac{h}{3}(c + 4d + e)$

Figure 4

Using the area formula in Figure 4 (see Problem 17 for the derivation) leads to an approximation called the **Parabolic Rule.** It is also called **Simpson's Rule,** after the English mathematician Thomas Simpson (1710–1761).

Parabolic Rule (n even)

$$\int_a^b f(x)\, dx \approx \frac{h}{3}\Big[f(x_0) + 4f(x_1) + 2f(x_2) + \cdots + 4f(x_{n-1}) + f(x_n)\Big]$$

$$= \frac{b-a}{3n}\Bigg[f(a) + 4\sum_{i=1}^{n/2} f\Big(a + (2i-1)\frac{b-a}{n}\Big) +$$

$$2\sum_{i=1}^{n/2-1} f\Big(a + 2i\frac{b-a}{n}\Big) + f(b)\Bigg]$$

The pattern of coefficients is $1, 4, 2, 4, 2, 4, 2, \ldots, 2, 4, 1$.

EXAMPLE 4 Approximate the definite integral $\displaystyle\int_0^3 \frac{1}{1 + x^2}\, dx$ using the Parabolic Rule with $n = 6$.

SOLUTION Let $f(x) = 1/(1 + x^2)$, $a = 0$, $b = 3$, and $n = 6$. The x_i's are $x_0 = 0$, $x_1 = 0.5$, $x_2 = 1.0, \ldots, x_6 = 3.0$

$$\int_0^3 \frac{1}{1 + x^2}\, dx \approx \frac{3 - 0}{3 \cdot 6}\Big[f(0) + 4f(0.5) + 2f(1.0) + 4f(1.5) + 2f(2.0) +$$

$$4f(2.5) + f(3.0)\Big]$$

$$\approx \frac{1}{6}(1 + 4 \cdot 0.8 + 2 \cdot 0.5 + 4 \cdot 0.30769 +$$

$$2 \cdot 0.2 + 4 \cdot 0.13793 + 0.1)$$

$$\approx 1.2471 \qquad \blacksquare$$

Error Analysis In any practical use of the approximation methods described in this section, we need to have some idea of the size of the error involved. Fortunately, the methods described in this section have fairly simple error formulas, provided the integrand possesses sufficiently many derivatives. We call E_n the error if it satisfies

$$\int_a^b f(x)\, dx = \text{approximation based on } n \text{ subintervals} + E_n$$

The error formulas are given in the next theorem. The proofs of these results are rather difficult and we omit them here.

Theorem A

Assuming that the required derivatives exist on the interval $[a, b]$, the errors for the left Riemann sum, right Riemann sum, midpoint Riemann sum, Trapezoidal Rule, and Parabolic Rule are

Left Riemann Sum: $E_n = \dfrac{(b - a)^2}{2n} f'(c)$ for some c in $[a, b]$

Right Riemann Sum: $E_n = -\dfrac{(b - a)^2}{2n} f'(c)$ for some c in $[a, b]$

Midpoint Riemann Sum: $E_n = \dfrac{(b - a)^3}{24n^2} f''(c)$ for some c in $[a, b]$

Trapezoidal Rule: $E_n = -\dfrac{(b - a)^3}{12n^2} f''(c)$ for some c in $[a, b]$

Parabolic Rule: $E_n = -\dfrac{(b - a)^5}{180n^4} f^{(4)}(c)$ for some c in $[a, b]$

The most important thing to notice about these error formulas is the position of n, the number of subintervals. In all cases, the n occurs raised to some power in the *denominator*. Thus, as n increases, the error decreases. Also, the larger the exponent on n, the faster the error term will go to zero. For example, the error term for the Parabolic Rule involves an n^4 in the denominator. Since n^4 grows much faster than n^2, the error term for the Parabolic Rule will go to zero faster than the error term for the Trapezoidal Rule or the midpoint Riemann sum rule. Similarly, the error term for the Trapezoidal Rule will go to zero faster than the error term for the left or right Riemann sum rules. One other thing to notice about these error formulas is that they hold "for some c in $[a, b]$." In most practical situations we can never tell what the value of c is. All we can hope to do is obtain an upper bound on how large the error could be. The next example illustrates this.

EXAMPLE 5 Approximate the definite integral $\displaystyle\int_1^4 \frac{1}{1 + x}\, dx$ using the Parabolic Rule with $n = 6$ and give a bound for the absolute value of the error.

SOLUTION Let $f(x) = \dfrac{1}{1 + x}$, $a = 1$, $b = 4$, and $n = 6$. Then

$$\int_1^4 \frac{1}{1 + x}\, dx \approx \frac{b - a}{3n}\Big[f(x_0) + 4f(x_1) + 2f(x_2) + 4f(x_3) + 2f(x_4) + $$
$$4f(x_5) + f(x_6)\Big]$$

$$= \frac{3}{3(6)}\Big[f(1.0) + 4f(1.5) + 2f(2.0) + 4f(2.5) + 2f(3.0) + $$
$$4f(3.5) + f(4.0)\Big]$$

$$\approx \frac{1}{6}(5.4984) \approx 0.9164$$

The error term for the Parabolic Rule involves the fourth derivative of the integrand:

$$f'(x) = -\frac{1}{(1+x)^2}$$

$$f''(x) = \frac{2}{(1+x)^3}$$

$$f'''(x) = -\frac{6}{(1+x)^4}$$

$$f^{(4)}(x) = \frac{24}{(1+x)^5}$$

The question we now face is, how large can $|f^{(4)}(x)|$ be on the interval $[1, 4]$? It is clear that $f^{(4)}(x)$ is a nonnegative decreasing function on this interval, so its absolute value achieves its largest value at the left endpoint, that is, when $x = 1$. The value of the fourth derivative at $x = 1$ is $f^{(4)}(1) = 24/(1 + 1)^5 = 3/4$. Thus

$$|E_6| = \left| -\frac{(b-a)^5}{180n^4}f^{(4)}(c) \right| = \frac{(4-1)^5}{180 \cdot 6^4}|f^{(4)}(c)| \le \frac{(4-1)^5}{180 \cdot 6^4}\frac{3}{4} \approx 0.00078$$

The error is therefore no larger than 0.00078.   ■

In the next example, we turn things around. Rather than specifying n and asking for the error, we give the desired error and ask how large n must be.

EXAMPLE 6 How large must n be in order to guarantee that the absolute value of the error is less than 0.00001 when we use (a) the right Riemann sum, (b) the Trapezoidal Rule, and (c) the Parabolic Rule to estimate $\displaystyle\int_1^4 \frac{1}{1+x}\,dx$?

SOLUTION The derivatives of the integrand $f(x) = 1/(1 + x)$ are given in the previous example.

(a) The absolute value of the error term for the right Riemann sum is

$$|E_n| = \left| -\frac{(4-1)^2}{2n}f'(c) \right| = \frac{3^2}{2n}\left|\frac{1}{(1+c)^2}\right| \le \frac{9}{2n}\frac{1}{(1+1)^2} = \frac{9}{8n}$$

We want $|E_n| \le 0.00001$, so we require

$$\frac{9}{8n} \le 0.00001$$

$$n \ge \frac{9}{8 \cdot 0.00001} = 112{,}500$$

(b) For the Trapezoidal Rule we have

$$|E_n| = \left| -\frac{(4-1)^3}{12n^2}f''(c) \right| = \frac{3^3}{12n^2}\left|\frac{2}{(1+c)^3}\right| \le \frac{54}{12n^2(1+1)^3} = \frac{9}{16n^2}$$

We want $|E_n| \le 0.00001$, so n must satisfy

$$\frac{9}{16n^2} \le 0.00001$$

$$n^2 \ge \frac{9}{16 \cdot 0.00001} = 56{,}250$$

$$n \ge \sqrt{56{,}250} \approx 237.17$$

Thus, $n = 238$ should do it.

(c) For the Parabolic Rule,

$$|E_n| = \left| -\frac{(b-a)^5}{180n^4} f^{(4)}(c) \right| = \frac{3^5}{180n^4} \left| \frac{24}{(1+c)^5} \right| \le \frac{3^5 \cdot 24}{180n^4(1+1)^5} = \frac{81}{80n^4}$$

We want $|E_n| \le 0.00001$, so

$$\frac{81}{80n^4} \le 0.00001$$

$$n^4 \ge \frac{81}{80 \cdot 0.00001} \approx 101{,}250$$

$$n \ge 101{,}250^{1/4} \approx 17.8$$

We must round up to the next even integer (since n must be even for the Parabolic Rule). Thus we require $n = 18$. ∎

Notice how much different the answers were for the three parts in the previous example. Eighteen subintervals for the Parabolic Rule will give about the same accuracy as over 100,000 subintervals for the right Riemann sum! The Parabolic Rule is indeed a powerful method for approximating definite integrals.

Functions Defined by a Table In all the previous examples, the function we integrated was defined over the whole interval of integration. There are many situations where this is not the case. For example, speed is measured every minute, water flow from a tank is measured every 10 seconds, and cross-sectional area is measured every 0.1 millimeter. In all of these cases, the integral has a clearly defined meaning. Although we cannot obtain the integral exactly, we can use the methods of this section to approximate the integral.

■ **EXAMPLE 7** While his father drove from St. Louis to Jefferson City, Chris noted the speed of the car every 10 minutes, that is, every one-sixth of an hour. The table to the left shows these speedometer readings. Use the Trapezoidal Rule to approximate how far they drove.

SOLUTION Let $v(t)$ denote the velocity of the car at time t, where t is measured in hours since the beginning of the trip. If we knew $v(t)$ for all t in the interval $[0, 3.5]$, we could find the distance traveled by taking $\int_0^{3.5} v(t)\, dt$. The problem is, we know $v(t)$ only for 22 values of t: $t_k = k/6$, where $k = 0, 1, 2, \dots, 21$. Figure 5 shows a graph of the information we are given. We partition the interval $[0, 3.5]$ into 21 intervals of width $\frac{1}{6}$ (since 10 minutes is one-sixth of an hour). The Trapezoidal Rule then gives

$$\int_0^{3.5} v(t)\, dt \approx \frac{3.5 - 0}{2 \cdot 21} \left[v(0) + 2\sum_{i=1}^{20} v\left(0 + i\frac{3.5 - 0}{21}\right) + v(21) \right]$$

$$= \frac{3.5}{42} \Big[0 + 2(55 + 57 + 60 + 70 + 70 + 70 + 70 + 19 + 0 + 59$$

$$+ 63 + 65 + 62 + 0 + 0 + 0 + 22 + 38 + 35 + 25) + 0 \Big]$$

$$= 140$$

They drove approximately 140 miles. ∎

Minutes	Speed
0	0
10	55
20	57
30	60
40	70
50	70
60	70
70	70
80	19
90	0
100	59
110	63
120	65
130	62
140	0
150	0
160	0
170	22
180	38
190	35
200	25
210	0

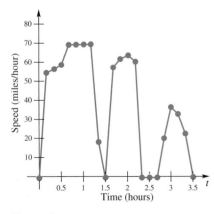

Figure 5

Concepts Review

1. The pattern of coefficients in the Trapezoidal Rule is
_____.

2. The pattern of coefficients in the Parabolic Rule is _____.

3. The error in the Trapezoidal Rule has n^2 in the denominator, whereas the error in the Parabolic Rule has _____ in the

denominator, so we expect the latter to give a better approximation to a definite integral.

4. If f is positive and concave up, then the Trapezoidal Rule will always give a value for $\int_a^b f(x)\, dx$ that is too _____.

Problem Set 5.6

C *In Problems 1–6, use the methods of (1) left Riemann sum, (2) right Riemann sum, (3) Trapezoidal Rule, (4) Parabolic Rule with $n = 8$ to approximate the definite integral. Then use the Second Fundamental Theorem of Calculus to find the exact value of each integral.*

1. $\int_1^3 \frac{1}{x^2}\, dx$

2. $\int_1^3 \frac{1}{x^3}\, dx$

3. $\int_0^2 \sqrt{x}\, dx$

4. $\int_1^3 x\sqrt{x^2 + 1}\, dx$

5. $\int_0^1 x(x^2 + 1)^5\, dx$

6. $\int_1^4 (x + 1)^{3/2}\, dx$

C *In Problems 7–10, use the methods of (1) left Riemann sum, (2) right Riemann sum, (3) midpoint Riemann sum, (4) Trapezoidal Rule, (5) Parabolic Rule with $n = 4, 8, 16$. Present your approximations in a table like this:*

	LRS	RRS	MRS	Trap	Parabolic
$n = 4$					
$n = 8$					
$n = 16$					

7. $\int_1^3 \frac{1}{1 + x^2}\, dx$

8. $\int_1^3 \frac{1}{x}\, dx$

9. $\int_0^2 e^{-x^2/2}\, dx$

10. $\int_1^3 \ln (x^2 + 1)\, dx$

C *In Problems 11–14, determine an n so that the Trapezoidal Rule will approximate the integral with an error E_n satisfying $|E_n| \leq 0.01$. Then, using that n, approximate the integral.*

11. $\int_1^3 \frac{1}{x}\, dx$

12. $\int_1^3 \frac{1}{1 + x}\, dx$

13. $\int_1^4 \sqrt{x}\, dx$

14. $\int_1^3 e^x\, dx$

C *In Problems 15–16, determine an n so that the Parabolic Rule will approximate the integral with an error E_n satisfying $|E_n| \leq 0.01$. Then, using that n, approximate the integral.*

15. $\int_1^3 \frac{1}{x}\, dx$

16. $\int_4^8 \sqrt{x + 1}\, dx$

17. Let $f(x) = ax^2 + bx + c$. Show that

$$\int_{m-h}^{m+h} f(x)\, dx \quad \text{and} \quad \frac{h}{3}[f(m - h) + 4f(m) + f(m + h)]$$

both have the value $(h/3)[a(6m^2 + 2h^2) + b(6m) + 6c]$. This establishes the area formula on which the Parabolic Rule is based.

18. Show that the Parabolic Rule is exact for any cubic polynomial in two different ways.

(a) By direct calculation.

(b) By showing that $E_n = 0$.

Justify your answers to Problems 19–22 two ways: (1) using the properties of the graph of the function, and (2) using the error formulas from Theorem A.

19. If a function f is increasing on $[a, b]$, will the left Riemann sum be larger or smaller than $\int_a^b f(x)\, dx$?

20. If a function f is increasing on $[a, b]$, will the right Riemann sum be larger or smaller than $\int_a^b f(x)\, dx$?

21. If a function f is concave down on $[a, b]$, will the midpoint Riemann sum be larger or smaller than $\int_a^b f(x)\, dx$?

22. If a function f is concave down on $[a, b]$, will the Trapezoidal Rule approximation be larger or smaller than $\int_a^b f(x)\, dx$?

23. Show that the Parabolic Rule gives the exact value of $\int_{-a}^a x^k\, dx$ provided that k is odd.

24. It is interesting that a modified version of the Trapezoidal Rule turns out to be in general more accurate than the Parabolic Rule. This version says that

$$\int_a^b f(x)\, dx \approx T - \frac{[f'(b) - f'(a)]h^2}{12}$$

where T is the standard trapezoidal estimate.

(a) Use this formula with $n = 8$ to estimate $\int_1^3 x^4\, dx$ and note its remarkable accuracy.

(b) Use this formula with $n = 12$ to estimate $\int_0^\pi \sin x\, dx$.

25. Without doing any calculations, rank from smallest to largest the approximations of $\int_0^1 \sqrt{x^2 + 1}\, dx$ for the following methods: left Riemann sum, right Riemann sum, midpoint Riemann sum, Trapezoidal Rule.

26. Without doing any calculations, rank from smallest to largest the approximations of $\int_1^3 (x^3 + x^2 + x + 1)\, dx$ for the following methods: left Riemann sum, right Riemann sum, Trapezoidal Rule, Parabolic Rule.

27. Use the Trapezoidal Rule to approximate the area of the lakeside lot shown in Figure 6. Dimensions are in feet.

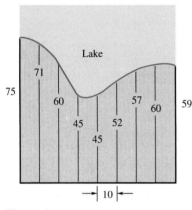

Figure 6

28. Use the Parabolic Rule to approximate the amount of water required to fill a pool shaped like Figure 7 to a depth of 6 feet. All dimensions are in feet.

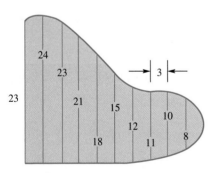

Figure 7

C 29. Figure 8 shows the depth in feet of the water in a river measured at 20-foot intervals across the width of the river. If the river flows at 4 miles per hour, how much water (in cubic feet) flows past the place where these measurements were taken in one day? Use the Parabolic Rule.

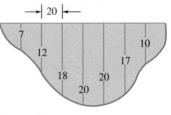

Figure 8

30. On her way to work, Teri noted her speed every 3 minutes. The results are shown in the table below. How far did she drive?

Time (minutes)	0	3	6	9	12	15	18	21	24
Speed (mi/h)	0	31	54	53	52	35	31	28	0

31. Every 12 minutes between 4:00 P.M. and 6:00 P.M., the rate (in gallons per minute) at which water flowed out of a town's water tank was measured. The results are shown in the table below. How much water was used in this 2-hour span?

Time	4:00	4:12	4:24	4:36	4:48	5:00
Flow (gal/min)	65	71	68	78	105	111

Time	5:12	5:24	5:36	5:48	6:00
Flow (gal/min)	108	144	160	152	148

Answers to Concepts Review: **1.** $1, 2, 2, \ldots, 2, 1$ **2.** $1, 4, 2, 4, 2, \ldots, 4, 1$ **3.** n^4 **4.** large

5.7 Chapter Review

Concepts Test

Respond with true or false to each of the following assertions. Be prepared to justify your answer.

1. The indefinite integral is a linear operator.

2. $\int [f(x)g'(x) + g(x)f'(x)]\, dx = f(x)g(x) + C.$

3. All functions that are antiderivatives must have derivatives.

4. If the second derivatives of two functions are equal, then the functions differ at most by a constant.

5. $\int f'(x)\, dx = f(x)$ for every differentiable function f.

6. If $s = -16t^2 + v_0 t$ gives the height at time t of a ball thrown straight up from the surface of the earth with velocity v_0 at time $t = 0$, then the ball will hit the ground with velocity $-v_0$.

7. $\sum_{i=1}^{n} (a_i + a_{i-1}) = a_0 + a_n + 2\sum_{i=1}^{n-1} a_i.$

8. $\sum_{i=1}^{100} (2i - 1) = 10,000.$

9. If $\sum_{i=1}^{10} a_i^2 = 100$ and $\sum_{i=1}^{10} a_i = 20$, then $\sum_{i=1}^{10} (a_i + 1)^2 = 150.$

10. If f is bounded on $[a, b]$, then f is integrable there.

11. $\int_a^a f(x)\, dx = 0.$

12. If $\int_a^b f(x)\, dx = 0$, then $f(x) = 0$ for all x in $[a, b]$.

13. If $\int_a^b [f(x)]^2\, dx = 0$, then $f(x) = 0$ for all x in $[a, b]$.

14. If $a > x$ and $G(x) = \int_a^x f(z)\, dz$, then $G'(x) = -f(x)$.

15. The value of $\int_x^{x+2\pi} (\sin t + \cos t)\, dt$ is independent of x.

16. The operator lim is linear.

17. $\int_{-\pi}^{\pi} \sin^{13} x\, dx = 0.$

18. $\int_1^5 \sin^2 x\, dx = \int_1^7 \sin^2 x\, dx + \int_7^5 \sin^2 x\, dx.$

19. If f is continuous and positive everywhere, then $\int_c^d f(x)\, dx$ is positive.

20. $D_x \left[\int_0^{x^2} \dfrac{1}{1 + t^2}\, dt \right] = \dfrac{1}{1 + x^4}.$

21. $\int_0^{2\pi} |\sin x|\, dx = \int_0^{2\pi} |\cos x|\, dx.$

22. $\int_0^{2\pi} |\sin x|\, dx = 4 \int_0^{\pi/2} \sin x\, dx.$

23. The antiderivatives of odd functions are even functions.

24. If $F(x)$ is an antiderivative of $f(x)$, then $F(5x)$ is an antiderivative of $f(5x)$.

25. If $F(x)$ is an antiderivative of $f(x)$, then $F(2x + 1)$ is an antiderivative of $f(2x + 1)$.

26. If $F(x)$ is an antiderivative of $f(x)$, then $F(x) + 1$ is an antiderivative of $f(x) + 1$.

27. If $F(x)$ is an antiderivative of $f(x)$, then
$$\int f(v(x))\, dx = F(v(x)) + C$$

28. If $F(x)$ is an antiderivative of $f(x)$, then
$$\int f^2(x)\, dx = \tfrac{1}{3} F^3(x) + C$$

29. If $F(x)$ is an antiderivative of $f(x)$, then
$$\int f(x) \dfrac{df}{dx}\, dx = \tfrac{1}{2} F^2(x) + C$$

30. If $f(x) = 4$ on $[0, 3]$, then every Riemann sum for f on the given interval has the value 12.

31. If $F'(x) = G'(x)$ for all x in $[a, b]$, then $F(b) - F(a) = G(b) - G(a)$.

32. If $f(x) = f(-x)$ for all x in $[-a, a]$, then $\int_{-a}^a f(x)\, dx = 0$.

33. If $\bar{z} = \tfrac{1}{2} \int_{-1}^1 z(t)\, dt$, then $z(t) - \bar{z}$ is an odd function for $-1 \le t \le 1$.

34. If $F'(x) = f(x)$ for all x in $[0, b]$, then $\int_0^b f(x)\, dx = F(b)$.

35. $\int_{-99}^{99} (ax^3 + bx^2 + cx)\, dx = 2 \int_0^{99} bx^2\, dx.$

36. If $f(x) \le g(x)$ on $[a, b]$, then $\int_a^b |f(x)|\, dx \le \int_a^b |g(x)|\, dx.$

37. If $f(x) \le g(x)$ on $[a, b]$, then $\left| \int_a^b f(x)\, dx \right| \le \left| \int_a^b g(x)\, dx \right|.$

38. $\left| \sum_{i=1}^n a_i \right| \le \sum_{i=1}^n |a_i|.$

39. If f is continuous on $[a, b]$, then $\left| \int_a^b f(x)\, dx \right| \le \int_a^b |f(x)|\, dx.$

40. $\lim_{n \to \infty} \sum_{i=1}^n \sin \left(\dfrac{2i}{n} \right) \cdot \dfrac{2}{n} = \int_0^2 \sin x\, dx.$

41. If $\|P\| \to 0$, then the number of subintervals in the partition P tends to ∞.

42. We can always express the indefinite integral of an elementary function in terms of elementary functions.

43. For an increasing function, the left Riemann sum will always be less than the right Riemann sum.

44. For a linear function $f(x)$, the midpoint Riemann sum will give the exact value of $\int_a^b f(x)\, dx$ no matter what n is.

45. The Trapezoidal Rule with $n = 10$ will give an estimate for $\int_0^5 x^3\, dx$ that is smaller than the true value.

46. The Parabolic Rule with $n = 10$ will give the exact value of $\int_0^5 x^3\, dx$.

Sample Test Problems

In Problems 1–16, evaluate the indicated integrals.

1. $\int_0^1 \left(x^3 - 3x^2 + 3\sqrt{x} \right) dx$

2. $\int_1^2 \dfrac{2x^4 - 3x^2 + 1}{x^2}\, dx$

3. $\int_1^\pi \dfrac{y^3 - 9y \sin y + 26y^{-1}}{y}\, dy$

4. $\int_4^9 y\sqrt{y^2 - 4}\, dy$

5. $\int_2^8 z(2z^2 - 3)^{1/3}\, dz$

6. $\int_0^{\pi/2} \cos^4 x \sin x\, dx$

7. $\int_0^\pi (x + 1) \tan^2(3x^2 + 6x) \sec^2(3x^2 + 6x)\, dx$

8. $\int_0^2 \dfrac{t^3}{\sqrt{t^4 + 9}}\, dt$

9. $\int_1^2 t^4 (t^5 + 5)^{2/3}\, dt$

10. $\displaystyle\int_2^3 \frac{y^2 - 1}{(y^3 - 3y)^2}\, dy$

11. $\displaystyle\int (x + 1) \sin(x^2 + 2x + 3)\, dx$

12. $\displaystyle\int_1^5 \frac{(y^2 + y + 1)}{\sqrt[3]{2y^3 + 3y^2 + 6y}}\, dy$

13. $\displaystyle\int_{-1}^1 x^2 e^{-x^3}\, dx$

14. $\displaystyle\int_1^2 \frac{\cosh\sqrt{z}}{\sqrt{z}}\, dz$

15. $\displaystyle\int_0^1 e^x \sin e^x\, dx$

16. $\displaystyle\int_0^{\sqrt{\pi/4}} x \cos x^2\, e^{\sin x^2}\, dx$

17. Let P be a regular partition of the interval $[0, 2]$ into four equal subintervals, and let $f(x) = x^2 - 1$. Write out the Riemann sum for f on P, in which $\bar{x}_i$ is the right end point of each subinterval of $P, i = 1, 2, 3, 4$. Find the value of this Riemann sum and make a sketch.

18. If $\displaystyle f(x) = \int_{-2}^x \frac{1}{t + 3}\, dt, -2 \le x$, find $f'(7)$.

19. Evaluate $\displaystyle\int_0^3 \left(2 - \sqrt{x + 1}\right)^2 dx$.

20. If $f(x) = 3x^2\sqrt{x^3 - 4}$, find the average value of f on $[2, 5]$.

21. Evaluate $\displaystyle\int_2^4 \frac{5x^2 - 1}{x^2}\, dx$.

22. Evaluate $\displaystyle\sum_{i=1}^n (3^i - 3^{i-1})$.

23. Evaluate $\displaystyle\sum_{i=1}^{10} (6i^2 - 8i)$.

24. Evaluate each sum.

(a) $\displaystyle\sum_{m=2}^4 \left(\frac{1}{m}\right)$
(b) $\displaystyle\sum_{i=1}^6 (2 - i)$
(c) $\displaystyle\sum_{k=0}^4 \cos\left(\frac{k\pi}{4}\right)$

25. Write in sigma notation.

(a) $\displaystyle\frac{1}{2} + \frac{1}{3} + \frac{1}{4} + \cdots + \frac{1}{78}$

(b) $x^2 + 2x^4 + 3x^6 + 4x^8 + \cdots + 50x^{100}$

26. Sketch the region under the curve $y = 16 - x^2$ between $x = 0$ and $x = 3$, showing the inscribed polygon corresponding to a regular partition of $[0, 3]$ into n subintervals. Find a formula for the area of this polygon and then find the area under the curve by taking a limit.

27. If $\displaystyle\int_0^1 f(x)\, dx = 4, \int_0^2 f(x)\, dx = 2$, and $\displaystyle\int_0^2 g(x)\, dx = -3$, evaluate each integral.

(a) $\displaystyle\int_1^2 f(x)\, dx$
(b) $\displaystyle\int_1^0 f(x)\, dx$

(c) $\displaystyle\int_0^2 3f(u)\, du$
(d) $\displaystyle\int_0^2 [2g(x) - 3f(x)]\, dx$

(e) $\displaystyle\int_0^{-2} f(-x)\, dx$

28. Evaluate each integral.

(a) $\displaystyle\int_0^4 |x - 1|\, dx$
(b) $\displaystyle\int_0^4 [\![x]\!]\, dx$

(c) $\displaystyle\int_0^4 (x - [\![x]\!])\, dx$

Hint: In parts (a) and (b), first sketch a graph.

29. Suppose that $f(x) = f(-x), f(x) \le 0, g(-x) = -g(x)$, $\displaystyle\int_0^2 f(x)\, dx = -4$, and $\displaystyle\int_0^2 g(x)\, dx = 5$. Evaluate each integral.

(a) $\displaystyle\int_{-2}^2 f(x)\, dx$
(b) $\displaystyle\int_{-2}^2 |f(x)|\, dx$

(c) $\displaystyle\int_{-2}^2 g(x)\, dx$
(d) $\displaystyle\int_{-2}^2 [f(x) + f(-x)]\, dx$

(e) $\displaystyle\int_0^2 [2g(x) + 3f(x)]\, dx$
(f) $\displaystyle\int_{-2}^0 g(x)\, dx$

30. Evaluate $\displaystyle\int_{-100}^{100} (x^3 + \sin^5 x)\, dx$.

31. Find c of the Mean Value Theorem for Integrals for $f(x) = 3x^2$ on $[-4, -1]$.

32. Find $G'(x)$ for each function G.

(a) $\displaystyle G(x) = \int_1^x \frac{1}{t^2 + 1}\, dt$

(b) $\displaystyle G(x) = \int_1^{x^2} \frac{1}{t^2 + 1}\, dt$

(c) $\displaystyle G(x) = \int_x^{x^3} \frac{1}{t^2 + 1}\, dt$

33. Find $G'(x)$ for each function G.

(a) $\displaystyle G(x) = \int_1^x \sin^2 z\, dz$

(b) $\displaystyle G(x) = \int_x^{x+1} f(z)\, dz$

(c) $\displaystyle G(x) = \frac{1}{x}\int_0^x f(z)\, dz$

(d) $\displaystyle G(x) = \int_0^x \left(\int_0^u f(t)\, dt\right) du$

(e) $\displaystyle G(x) = \int_0^{g(x)} \left(\frac{d}{du} g(u)\right) du$

(f) $\displaystyle G(x) = \int_0^{-x} f(-t)\, dt$

34. Evaluate each of the following limits by recognizing it as a definite integral.

(a) $\displaystyle\lim_{n\to\infty} \sum_{i=1}^n \sqrt{\frac{4i}{n}} \cdot \frac{4}{n}$
(b) $\displaystyle\lim_{n\to\infty} \sum_{i=1}^n \left(1 + \frac{2i}{n}\right)^2 \frac{2}{n}$

35. Show that if $f(x) = \int_{2x}^{5x} \frac{1}{t}\, dt$, then f is a constant function on $(0, \infty)$.

36. Approximate $\int_{1}^{2} \frac{1}{1 + x^4}\, dx$ using left, right, and midpoint Riemann sums with $n = 8$.

37. Approximate $\int_{1}^{2} \frac{1}{1 + x^4}\, dx$ using the Trapezoidal Rule with $n = 8$, and give an upper bound for the absolute value of the error.

38. Approximate $\int_{0}^{4} \frac{1}{1 + 2x}\, dx$ using the Parabolic Rule with $n = 8$, and give an upper bound for the absolute value of the error.

39. How large must n be for the Trapezoidal Rule in order to approximate $\int_{1}^{2} \frac{1}{1 + x^4}\, dx$ with an error no larger then 0.0001?

40. How large must n be for the Parabolic Rule in order to approximate $\int_{0}^{4} \frac{1}{1 + 2x}\, dx$ with an error no larger then 0.0001?

41. Without doing any calculations, rank from smallest to largest the approximations of $\int_{1}^{6} \frac{1}{x}\, dx$ for the following methods: left Riemann sum, midpoint Riemann sum, Trapezoidal rule.

REVIEW & PREVIEW PROBLEMS

In Problems 1–6, find the length of the solid green line.

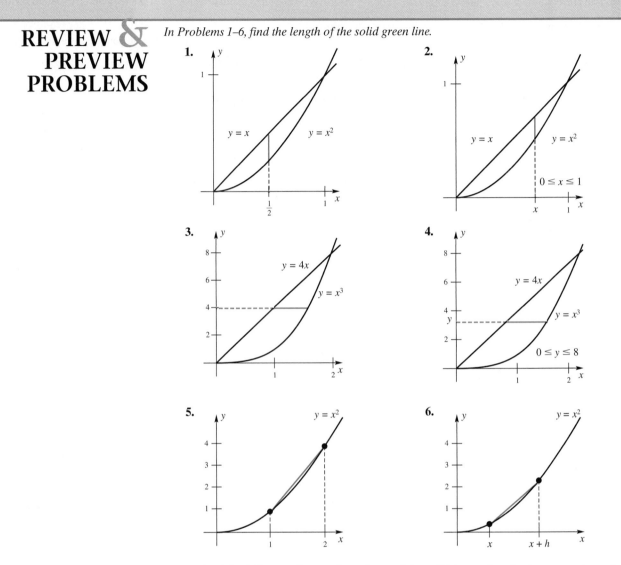

1. *y = x*, *y = x²*

2. *y = x*, *y = x²*, 0 ≤ x ≤ 1

3. *y = 4x*, *y = x³*

4. *y = 4x*, *y = x³*, 0 ≤ y ≤ 8

5. *y = x²*

6. *y = x²*

For each of the following figures, the volume of the solid is equal to the base area times the height. Give the volume of each of these solids.

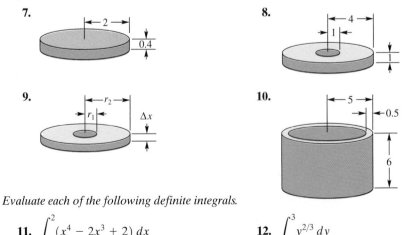

7.

8.

9.

10.

Evaluate each of the following definite integrals.

11. $\displaystyle\int_{-1}^{2} (x^4 - 2x^3 + 2)\, dx$

12. $\displaystyle\int_{0}^{3} y^{2/3}\, dy$

13. $\displaystyle\int_{0}^{2} \left(1 - \frac{x^2}{2} + \frac{x^4}{16}\right) dx$

14. $\displaystyle\int_{1}^{4} \sqrt{1 + \frac{9}{4}x}\, dx$

Applications of the Integral

6.1 The Area of a Plane Region

The brief discussion of area in Section 5.1 served to motivate the definition of the definite integral. With the latter notion now firmly established, we use the definite integral to calculate areas of regions of more and more complicated shapes. As is our practice, we begin with simple cases.

A Region above the x-Axis Let $y = f(x)$ determine a curve in the xy-plane and suppose that f is continuous and nonnegative on the interval $a \le x \le b$ (as in Figure 1). Consider the region R bounded by the graphs of $y = f(x)$, $x = a, x = b$, and $y = 0$. We refer to R as the region under $y = f(x)$ between $x = a$ and $x = b$. Its area $A(R)$ is given by

$$A(R) = \int_a^b f(x)\, dx$$

EXAMPLE 1 Find the area of the region R under $y = x^4 - 2x^3 + 2$ between $x = -1$ and $x = 2$.

SOLUTION The graph of R is shown in Figure 2. A reasonable estimate for the area of R is its base times an average height, say $(3)(2) = 6$. The exact value is

$$A(R) = \int_{-1}^2 (x^4 - 2x^3 + 2)\, dx = \left[\frac{x^5}{5} - \frac{x^4}{2} + 2x \right]_{-1}^2$$

$$= \left(\frac{32}{5} - \frac{16}{2} + 4 \right) - \left(-\frac{1}{5} - \frac{1}{2} - 2 \right) = \frac{51}{10} = 5.1$$

The calculated value 5.1 is close enough to our estimate, 6, to give us confidence in its correctness. ∎

A Region Below the x-Axis Area is a nonnegative number. If the graph of $y = f(x)$ is below the x-axis, then $\int_a^b f(x)\, dx$ is a negative number and therefore cannot be an area. However, it is just the negative of the area of the region bounded by $y = f(x)$, $x = a$, $x = b$, and $y = 0$.

EXAMPLE 2 Find the area of the region R bounded by $y = x^2/3 - 4$, the x-axis, $x = -2$, and $x = 3$.

SOLUTION The region R is shown in Figure 3. Our preliminary estimate for its area is $(5)(3) = 15$. The exact value is

$$A(R) = -\int_{-2}^3 \left(\frac{x^2}{3} - 4 \right) dx = \int_{-2}^3 \left(-\frac{x^2}{3} + 4 \right) dx$$

$$= \left[-\frac{x^3}{9} + 4x \right]_{-2}^3 = \left(-\frac{27}{9} + 12 \right) - \left(\frac{8}{9} - 8 \right) = \frac{145}{9} \approx 16.11$$

We are reassured by the nearness of 16.11 to our estimate. ∎

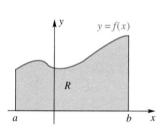

$y = f(x)$

R

a b x

Figure 1

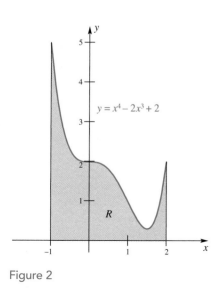

$y = x^4 - 2x^3 + 2$

R

Figure 2

323

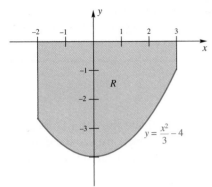

Figure 3

EXAMPLE 3 Find the area of the region R bounded by $y = x^3 - 3x^2 - x + 3$, the segment of the x-axis between $x = -1$ and $x = 2$, and the line $x = 2$.

SOLUTION The region R is shaded in Figure 4. Note that part of it is above the x-axis and part is below. The areas of these two parts, R_1 and R_2, must be calculated separately. You can check that the curve crosses the x-axis at -1, 1, and 3. Thus,

$$A(R) = A(R_1) + A(R_2)$$

$$= \int_{-1}^{1} (x^3 - 3x^2 - x + 3)\, dx - \int_{1}^{2} (x^3 - 3x^2 - x + 3)\, dx$$

$$= \left[\frac{x^4}{4} - x^3 - \frac{x^2}{2} + 3x \right]_{-1}^{1} - \left[\frac{x^4}{4} - x^3 - \frac{x^2}{2} + 3x \right]_{1}^{2}$$

$$= 4 - \left(-\frac{7}{4} \right) = \frac{23}{4}$$

Notice that we could have written this area as one integral using the absolute value symbol,

$$A(R) = \int_{-1}^{2} |x^3 - 3x^2 - x + 3|\, dx$$

but this is no real simplification since, in order to evaluate this integral, we would have to split it into two parts, just as we did above. ∎

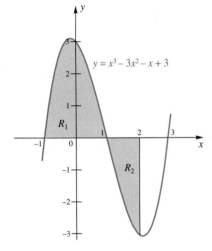

Figure 4

A Helpful Way of Thinking For simple regions of the type considered above, it is quite easy to write down the correct integral. When we consider more complicated regions (e.g., regions between two curves), the task of selecting the right integral is more difficult. However, there is a way of thinking that can be very helpful. It goes back to the definition of area and of the definite integral. Here it is in five steps.

Step 1: Sketch the region.

Step 2: Slice it into thin pieces (strips); label a typical piece.

Step 3: Approximate the area of this typical piece as if it were a rectangle.

Step 4: Add up the approximations to the areas of the pieces.

Step 5: Take the limit as the width of the pieces approaches zero, thus getting a definite integral.

To illustrate, we consider yet another simple example.

EXAMPLE 4 Set up the integral for the area of the region under $y = 1 + \sqrt{x}$ between $x = 0$ and $x = 4$ (Figure 5).

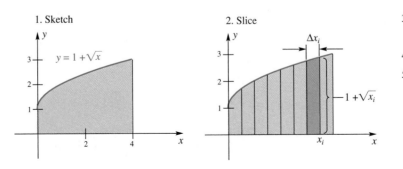

Figure 5

SOLUTION Once we understand this five-step procedure, we can abbreviate it to three: *slice, approximate, integrate*. Think of the word *integrate* as incorporating two steps: (1) add the areas of the pieces and (2) take the limit as the piece width tends to zero. In this process, $\Sigma \ldots \Delta x$ transforms into $\int \ldots dx$ as we take the limit. Figure 6 gives the abbreviated form for the same problem.

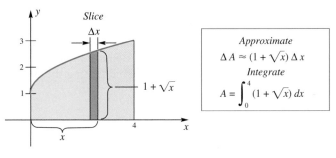

Figure 6 ■

A Region Between Two Curves

Consider curves $y = f(x)$ and $y = g(x)$ with $g(x) \leq f(x)$ on $a \leq x \leq b$. They determine the region shown in Figure 7. We use the *slice, approximate, integrate* method to find its area. Be sure to note that $f(x) - g(x)$ gives the correct height for the thin slice, even when the graph of g goes below the x-axis. In this case $g(x)$ is negative; so subtracting $g(x)$ is the same as adding a positive number. You can check that $f(x) - g(x)$ also gives the correct height, even when both $f(x)$ and $g(x)$ are negative.

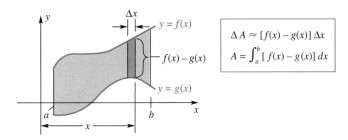

Figure 7

EXAMPLE 5 Find the area of the region between the curves $y = x^4$ and $y = 2x - x^2$.

SOLUTION We start by finding where the two curves intersect. To do this, we need to solve $2x - x^2 = x^4$, a fourth-degree equation, which would usually be difficult to solve. However, in this case $x = 0$ and $x = 1$ are rather obvious solutions. Our sketch of the region, together with the appropriate approximation and the corresponding integral, is shown in Figure 8.

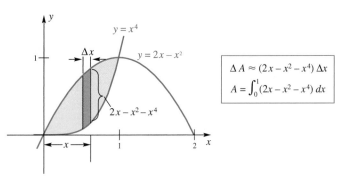

Figure 8

One job remains: to evaluate the integral.

$$\int_0^1 (2x - x^2 - x^4)\, dx = \left[x^2 - \frac{x^3}{3} - \frac{x^5}{5} \right]_0^1 = 1 - \frac{1}{3} - \frac{1}{5} = \frac{7}{15} \qquad \blacksquare$$

EXAMPLE 6 **Horizontal Slicing** Find the area of the region between the parabola $y^2 = 4x$ and the line $4x - 3y = 4$.

SOLUTION We will need the points of intersection of these two curves. The y-coordinates of these points can be found by writing the second equation as $4x = 3y + 4$ and then equating the two expressions for $4x$.

$$y^2 = 3y + 4$$
$$y^2 - 3y - 4 = 0$$
$$(y - 4)(y + 1) = 0$$
$$y = 4, -1$$

When $y = 4$, $x = 4$ and when $y = -1$, $x = \dfrac{1}{4}$, so we conclude that the points of intersection are $(4, 4)$ and $\left(\frac{1}{4}, -1\right)$. The region between the curves is shown in Figure 9.

Now imagine slicing this region vertically. We face a problem, because the lower boundary consists of two different curves. Slices at the extreme left extend from the lower branch of the parabola to its upper branch. For the rest of the region, slices extend from the line to the parabola. To solve the problem with vertical slices requires that we first split our region into two parts, set up an integral for each part, and then evaluate both integrals.

A far better approach is to slice the region horizontally as shown in Figure 10, thus using y rather than x as the integration variable. Note that horizontal slices always go from the parabola (at the left) to the line (at the right). The length of such a slice is the larger x-value $\left(x = \frac{1}{4}(3y + 4) \right)$ minus the smaller x-value $\left(x = \frac{1}{4}y^2 \right)$.

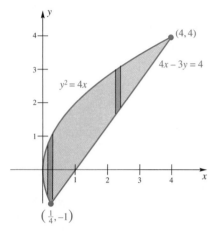

Figure 9

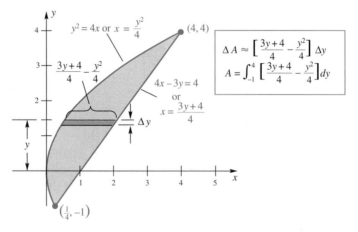

Figure 10

$$A = \int_{-1}^4 \left[\frac{3y + 4 - y^2}{4} \right] dy = \frac{1}{4} \int_{-1}^4 (3y + 4 - y^2)\, dy$$

$$= \frac{1}{4} \left[\frac{3y^2}{2} + 4y - \frac{y^3}{3} \right]_{-1}^4$$

$$= \frac{1}{4} \left[\left(24 + 16 - \frac{64}{3} \right) - \left(\frac{3}{2} - 4 + \frac{1}{3} \right) \right]$$

$$= \frac{125}{24} \approx 5.21$$

There are two items to note: (1) The integrand resulting from a horizontal slicing involves y, not x; and (2) to get the integrand, solve both equations for x and subtract the smaller x-value from the larger. ■

Distance and Displacement   Consider an object moving along a straight line with velocity $v(t)$ at time t. If $v(t) \geq 0$, then $\int_a^b v(t)\, dt$ gives the distance traveled during the time interval $a \leq t \leq b$. However, if $v(t)$ is sometimes negative (which corresponds to the object moving in reverse), then

$$\int_a^b v(t)\, dt = s(b) - s(a)$$

measures the **displacement** of the object, that is, the directed distance from its starting position $s(a)$ to its ending position $s(b)$. To get the **total distance** that the object traveled during $a \leq t \leq b$, we must calculate $\int_a^b |v(t)|\, dt$, the area between the velocity curve and the t-axis.

EXAMPLE 7   An object is at position $s = 3$ at time $t = 0$. Its velocity at time t is $v(t) = 5 \sin 6\pi t$. What is the position of the object at time $t = 2$, and how far did it travel during this time?

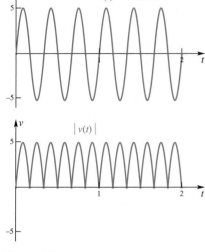

$v(t) = 5 \sin 6\pi t$

$|v(t)|$

Figure 11

SOLUTION   The object's displacement, that is, change in position, is

$$s(2) - s(0) = \int_0^2 v(t)\, dt = \int_0^2 5 \sin 6\pi t\, dt = \left[-\frac{5}{6\pi} \cos 6\pi t \right]_0^2 = 0$$

Thus, $s(2) = s(0) + 0 = 3 + 0 = 3$. The object is at position 3 at time $t = 2$. The total distance traveled is

$$\int_0^2 |v(t)|\, dt = \int_0^2 |5 \sin 6\pi t|\, dt$$

To perform this integration we make use of symmetry (see Figure 11). Thus

$$\int_0^2 |v(t)|\, dt = 12 \int_0^{2/12} 5 \sin 6\pi t\, dt = 60 \left[-\frac{1}{6\pi} \cos 6\pi t \right]_0^{1/6} = \frac{20}{\pi} \approx 6.3662 \quad ■$$

Concepts Review

1. Let R be the region between the curve $y = f(x)$ and the x-axis on the interval $[a, b]$. If $f(x) \geq 0$ for all x in $[a, b]$, then $A(R) =$ _____, but if $f(x) \leq 0$ for all x in $[a, b]$, then $A(R) =$ _____.

2. To find the area of the region between two curves, it is wise to think of the following three-word motto: _____.

3. Suppose that the curves $y = f(x)$ and $y = g(x)$ bound a region R on which $f(x) \leq g(x)$. Then the area of R is given by

$A(R) = \int_a^b$ _____ dx, where a and b are determined by solving the equation _____.

4. If $p(y) \leq q(y)$ for all y in $[c, d]$, then the area $A(R)$ of the region R bounded by the curves $x = p(y)$ and $x = q(y)$ between $y = c$ and $y = d$ is given by $A(R) =$ _____.

Problem Set 6.1

In Problems 1–10, use the three-step procedure (slice, approximate, integrate) to set up and evaluate an integral (or integrals) for the area of the indicated region.

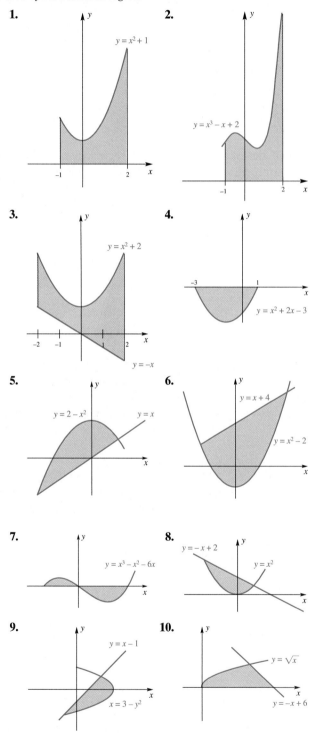

1. $y = x^2 + 1$

2. $y = x^3 - x + 2$

3. $y = x^2 + 2$

4. $y = x^2 + 2x - 3$

5. $y = 2 - x^2$, $y = x$

6. $y = x + 4$, $y = x^2 - 2$

7. $y = x^3 - x^2 - 6x$

8. $y = -x + 2$, $y = x^2$

9. $y = x - 1$, $x = 3 - y^2$

10. $y = \sqrt{x}$, $y = -x + 6$

⊿ *In Problems 11–30, sketch the region bounded by the graphs of the given equations, show a typical slice, approximate its area, set up an integral, and calculate the area of the region. Make an estimate of the area to confirm your answer.*

11. $y = 3 - \frac{1}{3}x^2$, $y = 0$, between $x = 0$ and $x = 3$

12. $y = 5x - x^2$, $y = 0$, between $x = 1$ and $x = 3$

13. $y = (x - 4)(x + 2)$, $y = 0$, between $x = 0$ and $x = 3$

14. $y = x^2 - 4x - 5$, $y = 0$, between $x = -1$ and $x = 4$

15. $y = \frac{1}{4}(x^2 - 7)$, $y = 0$, between $x = 0$ and $x = 2$

16. $y = x^3$, $y = 0$, between $x = -3$ and $x = 3$

17. $y = \sqrt[3]{x}$, $y = 0$, between $x = -2$ and $x = 2$

18. $y = \sqrt{x} - 10$, $y = 0$, between $x = 0$ and $x = 9$

19. $y = (x - 3)(x - 1)$, $y = x$

20. $y = \sqrt{x}$, $y = x - 4$, $x = 0$

21. $y = x^2 - 2x$, $y = -x^2$

22. $y = x^2 - 9$, $y = (2x - 1)(x + 3)$

23. $x = 8y - y^2$, $x = 0$

24. $x = (3 - y)(y + 1)$, $x = 0$

25. $x = -6y^2 + 4y$, $x + 3y - 2 = 0$

26. $x = y^2 - 2y$, $x - y - 4 = 0$

27. $4y^2 - 2x = 0$, $4y^2 + 4x - 12 = 0$

28. $x = 4y^4$, $x = 8 - 4y^4$

29. $y = e^{2x}$, $y = 0$, between $x = 0$ and $x = \ln 2$

30. $y = e^x$, $y = e^{-x}$, between $x = 0$ and $x = 1$

31. Sketch the region R bounded by $y = x + 6$, $y = x^3$, and $2y + x = 0$. Then find its area. *Hint:* Divide R into two pieces.

32. Find the area of the triangle with vertices at $(-1, 4)$, $(2, -2)$, and $(5, 1)$ by integration.

33. An object moves along a line so that its velocity at time t is $v(t) = 3t^2 - 24t + 36$ feet per second. Find the displacement and total distance traveled by the object for $-1 \le t \le 9$.

34. Follow the directions of Problem 33 if $v(t) = \frac{1}{2} + \sin 2t$ and the interval is $0 \le t \le 3\pi/2$.

35. Starting at $s = 0$ when $t = 0$, an object moves along a line so that its velocity at time t is $v(t) = 2t - 4$ centimeters per second. How long will it take to get to $s = 12$? To travel a total distance of 12 centimeters?

36. Consider the curve $y = 1/x^2$ for $1 \le x \le 6$.
(a) Calculate the area under this curve.
(b) Determine c so that the line $x = c$ bisects the area of part (a).
(c) Determine d so that the line $y = d$ bisects the area of part (a).

37. Find the area of the region in the first quadrant below $y = e^{-x}$ above $y = \frac{1}{2}$.

38. Find the area of the region trapped between $y = xe^{-x^2}$ and $y = x/4$. *Hint:* There are two separate regions.

[CAS] **39.** Use the Parabolic Rule with $n = 8$ to approximate the area of the region trapped between $y = 1 - e^{-x^2}$ and $y = e^{-x^2}$.

[CAS] **40.** Use the Parabolic Rule with $n = 8$ to approximate the area of the region trapped between $y = \ln(x + 1)$ and $y = x/4$. *Hint:* One point of intersection is obvious; the other you must approximate.

41. Calculate areas $A, B, C,$ and D in Figure 12. Check by calculating $A + B + C + D$ in one integration.

42. Prove Cavalieri's Principle. (Bonaventura Cavalieri (1598–1647) developed this principle in 1635.) If two regions have the same height at every x in $[a, b]$, then they have the same area (see Figure 13).

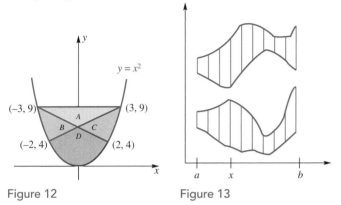

Figure 12

Figure 13

43. Use Cavalieri's Principle (not integration; see Problem 42) to show that the shaded regions in Figure 14 have the same area.

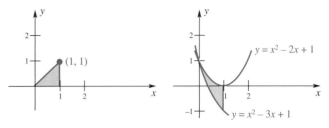

Figure 14

44. Find the area of the region trapped between $y = \sin x$ and $y = \frac{1}{2}, 0 \le x \le 17\pi/6$.

Answers to Concepts Review: 1. $\displaystyle\int_a^b f(x)\,dx; -\int_a^b f(x)\,dx$

2. slice, approximate, integrate **3.** $[g(x) - f(x)]; f(x) = g(x)$

4. $\displaystyle\int_c^d [q(y) - p(y)]\,dy$

6.2
Volumes of Solids: Slabs, Disks, Washers

That the definite integral can be used to calculate *areas* is not surprising; it was invented for that purpose. But uses of the integral go far beyond that application. Many quantities can be thought of as a result of slicing something into small pieces, approximating each piece, adding up, and taking the limit as the pieces shrink in size. This method of slice, approximate, and integrate can be used to find the *volumes* of solids provided that the volume of each slice is easy to approximate.

What is volume? We start with simple solids called *right cylinders*, four of which are shown in Figure 1. In each case, the solid is generated by moving a plane region (the base) through a distance h in a direction perpendicular to that region. And in each case, the volume of the solid is defined to be the area A of the base times the height h; that is,

$$V = A \cdot h$$

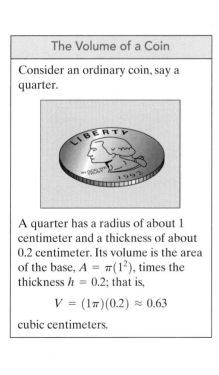

The Volume of a Coin

Consider an ordinary coin, say a quarter.

A quarter has a radius of about 1 centimeter and a thickness of about 0.2 centimeter. Its volume is the area of the base, $A = \pi(1^2)$, times the thickness $h = 0.2$; that is,

$$V = (1\pi)(0.2) \approx 0.63$$

cubic centimeters.

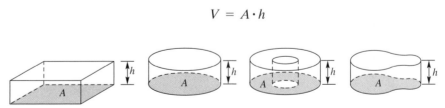

Figure 1

Next consider a solid with the property that cross sections perpendicular to a given line have known area. In particular, suppose that the line is the x-axis and that the area of the cross section at x is $A(x), a \le x \le b$ (Figure 2). We partition the interval $[a, b]$ by inserting points $a = x_0 < x_1 < x_2 < \cdots < x_n = b$. We then pass planes through these points perpendicular to the x-axis, thus slicing the solid into thin **slabs** (Figure 3). The *volume* ΔV_i of a slab should be approximately the volume of a cylinder; that is,

$$\Delta V_i \approx A(\bar{x}_i)\,\Delta x_i$$

(Recall that $\bar{x}_i$, called a *sample point*, is any number in the interval $[x_{i-1}, x_i]$.)

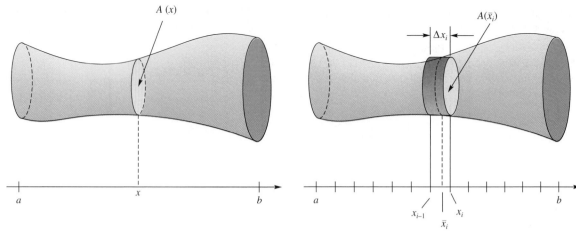

Figure 2

Figure 3

The "volume" V of the solid should be given approximately by the Riemann sum

$$V \approx \sum_{i=1}^{n} A(\overline{x}_i)\, \Delta x_i$$

When we let the norm of the partition approach zero, we obtain a definite integral; this integral is defined to be the **volume** of the solid.

$$V = \int_a^b A(x)\, dx$$

Rather than routinely applying the boxed formula to obtain volumes, we suggest that in each problem you go through the process that led to it. Just as for areas, we call this process *slice, approximate, integrate*. It is illustrated in the examples that follow.

Solids of Revolution: Method of Disks When a plane region, lying entirely on one side of a fixed line in its plane, is revolved about that line, it generates a **solid of revolution.** The fixed line is called the **axis** of the solid of revolution.

As an illustration, if the region bounded by a semicircle and its diameter is revolved about that diameter, it sweeps out a spherical solid (Figure 4). If the region inside a right triangle is revolved about one of its legs, it generates a conical solid (Figure 5). When a circular region is revolved about a line in its plane that does not intersect the circle (Figure 6), it sweeps out a torus (doughnut). In each case, it is possible to represent the volume as a definite integral.

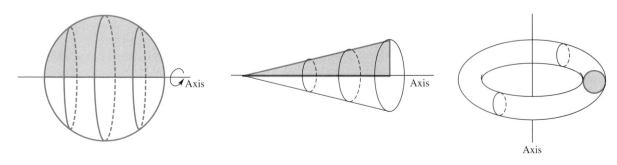

Figure 4

Figure 5

Figure 6

EXAMPLE 1 Find the volume of the solid of revolution obtained by revolving the plane region R bounded by $y = \sqrt{x}$, the x-axis, and the line $x = 4$ about the x-axis.

SOLUTION The region R, with a typical slice, is displayed as the left part of Figure 7. When revolved about the x-axis, this region generates a solid of revolution and the slice generates a disk, a thin coin-shaped object.

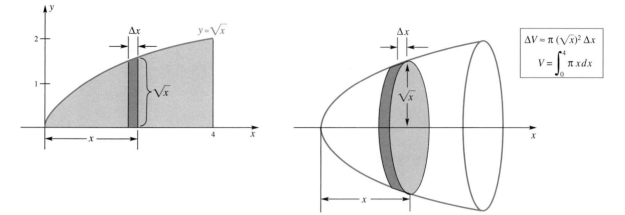

Figure 7

Recalling that the volume of a circular cylinder is $\pi r^2 h$, we approximate the volume ΔV of this disk with $\Delta V \approx \pi(\sqrt{x})^2 \Delta x = \pi x \Delta x$ and then integrate.

$$V = \pi \int_0^4 x\, dx = \pi \left[\frac{x^2}{2} \right]_0^4 = \pi \frac{16}{2} = 8\pi \approx 25.13$$

≈ Is this answer reasonable? The right circular cylinder that contains the solid has volume $V = \pi 2^2 \cdot 4 = 16\pi$. Half this number seems reasonable. ∎

EXAMPLE 2 Find the volume of the solid generated by revolving the region bounded by the curve $y = x^3$, the y-axis, and the line $y = 3$ about the y-axis (Figure 8).

SOLUTION Here we slice horizontally, which makes y the choice for the integration variable. Note that $y = x^3$ is equivalent to $x = \sqrt[3]{y}$ and $\Delta V \approx \pi(\sqrt[3]{y})^2 \Delta y = \pi y^{2/3} \Delta y$.

The volume is therefore

$$V = \pi \int_0^3 y^{2/3}\, dy = \pi \left[\frac{3}{5} y^{5/3} \right]_0^3 = \pi \frac{9\sqrt[3]{9}}{5} \approx 11.76$$

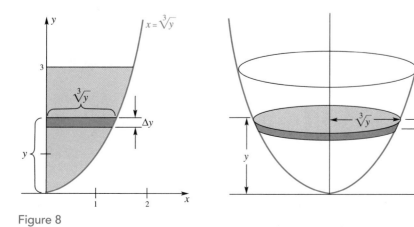

Figure 8

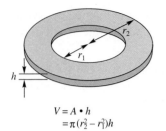

$$V = A \cdot h$$
$$= \pi(r_2^2 - r_1^2)h$$

Figure 9

Method of Washers Sometimes, slicing a solid of revolution results in disks with holes in the middle. We call them **washers.** See the diagram and accompanying volume formula shown in Figure 9.

■ **EXAMPLE 3** Find the volume of the solid generated by revolving the region bounded by the parabolas $y = x^2$ and $y^2 = 8x$ about the x-axis.

SOLUTION The key words are still *slice, approximate, integrate* (see Figure 10).

$$V = \pi \int_0^2 (8x - x^4)\, dx = \pi \left[\frac{8x^2}{2} - \frac{x^5}{5} \right]_0^2 = \frac{48\pi}{5} \approx 30.16$$

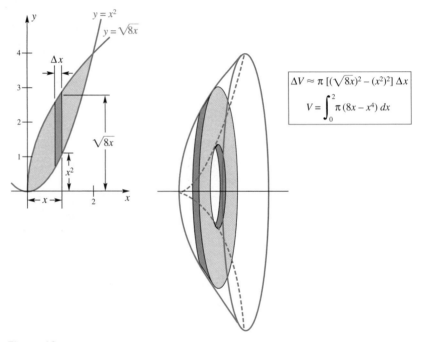

$$\Delta V \approx \pi\left[(\sqrt{8x})^2 - (x^2)^2\right] \Delta x$$
$$V = \int_0^2 \pi(8x - x^4)\, dx$$

Figure 10

■ **EXAMPLE 4** The semicircular region bounded by the curve $x = \sqrt{4 - y^2}$ and the y-axis is revolved about the line $x = -1$. Set up the integral that represents its volume.

SOLUTION Here the outer radius of the washer is $1 + \sqrt{4 - y^2}$ and the inner radius is 1. Figure 11 exhibits the solution. The integral can be simplified. The part above the x-axis has the same volume as the part below it (which manifests itself in an even integrand). Thus, we may integrate from 0 to 2 and double the result.

$$V = \pi \int_{-2}^2 \left[\left(1 + \sqrt{4 - y^2}\right)^2 - 1^2 \right] dy$$

$$= 2\pi \int_0^2 \left[2\sqrt{4 - y^2} + 4 - y^2 \right] dy$$

Now see Problem 37 for a way to evaluate this integral.

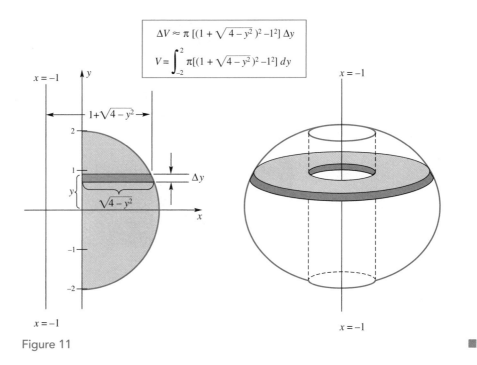

Figure 11

Other Solids with Known Cross Sections So far, our solids have had circular cross sections. However, the method for finding volume works just as well for solids whose cross sections are squares or triangles. In fact, all that is really needed is that the areas of the cross sections can be determined, since, in this case, we can also approximate the volume of the slice—a slab—with this cross section. The volume is then found by integrating.

EXAMPLE 5 Let the base of a solid be the first quadrant plane region bounded by $y = 1 - x^2/4$, the x-axis, and the y-axis. Suppose that cross sections perpendicular to the x-axis are squares. Find the volume of the solid.

SOLUTION When we slice this solid perpendicularly to the x-axis, we get thin square boxes (Figure 12), like slices of cheese.

$$V = \int_0^2 \left(1 - \frac{x^2}{4}\right)^2 dx = \int_0^2 \left(1 - \frac{x^2}{2} + \frac{x^4}{16}\right) dx$$

$$= \left[x - \frac{x^3}{6} + \frac{x^5}{80}\right]_0^2 = 2 - \frac{8}{6} + \frac{32}{80} = \frac{16}{15} \approx 1.07$$

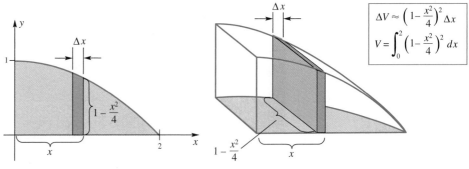

Figure 12

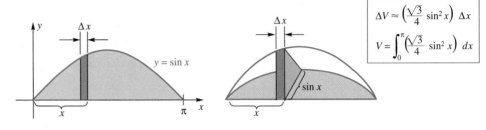

$$A = \frac{1}{2} u \left(\frac{\sqrt{3}}{2} u \right) = \frac{\sqrt{3}}{4} u^2$$

Figure 13

EXAMPLE 6 The base of a solid is the region between one arch of $y = \sin x$ and the x-axis. Each cross section perpendicular to the x-axis is an equilateral triangle sitting on this base. Find the volume of the solid.

SOLUTION We need the fact that the area of an equilateral triangle of side u is $\sqrt{3}\, u^2/4$ (see Figure 13). We proceed as shown in Figure 14.

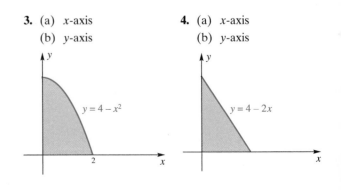

$$\Delta V \approx \left(\frac{\sqrt{3}}{4} \sin^2 x \right) \Delta x$$

$$V = \int_0^\pi \left(\frac{\sqrt{3}}{4} \sin^2 x \right) dx$$

Figure 14

To perform the indicated integration, we use the half-angle formula $\sin^2 x = (1 - \cos 2x)/2$.

$$V = \frac{\sqrt{3}}{4} \int_0^\pi \frac{1 - \cos 2x}{2} dx = \frac{\sqrt{3}}{8} \int_0^\pi (1 - \cos 2x)\, dx$$

$$= \frac{\sqrt{3}}{8} \left[\int_0^\pi 1\, dx - \frac{1}{2} \int_0^\pi \cos 2x \cdot 2\, dx \right]$$

$$= \frac{\sqrt{3}}{8} \left[x - \frac{1}{2} \sin 2x \right]_0^\pi = \frac{\sqrt{3}}{8} \pi \approx 0.68 \qquad ■$$

Concepts Review

1. The volume of a disk of radius r and thickness h is _____.

2. The volume of a washer of inner radius r, outer radius R, and thickness h is _____.

3. If the region R bounded by $y = x^2$, $y = 0$, and $x = 3$ is revolved about the x-axis, the disk at x will have volume $\Delta V \approx$ _____.

4. If the region R of Question 3 is revolved about the line $y = -2$, the washer at x will have volume $\Delta V \approx$ _____.

Problem Set 6.2

In Problems 1–4, find the volume of the solid generated when the indicated region is revolved about the specified axis; slice, approximate, integrate.

1. x-axis

2. x-axis

3. (a) x-axis
  (b) y-axis

4. (a) x-axis
  (b) y-axis

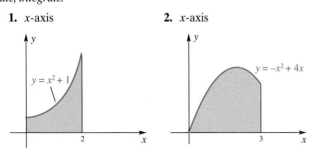

≈ In Problems 5–10, sketch the region R bounded by the graphs of the given equations, and show a typical vertical slice. Then find the volume of the solid generated by revolving R about the x-axis.

5. $y = \dfrac{x^2}{\pi}, x = 4, y = 0$

6. $y = x^3, x = 3, y = 0$

7. $y = \dfrac{1}{x}, x = 2, x = 4, y = 0$

8. $y = e^x, y = \dfrac{e}{x}, y = 0$, between $x = 0$ and $x = 3$

9. $y = \sqrt{9 - x^2}, y = 0$, between $x = -2$ and $x = 3$

10. $y = x^{2/3}, y = 0$, between $x = 1$ and $x = 27$

≈ In Problems 11–16, sketch the region R bounded by the graphs of the given equations and show a typical horizontal slice. Find the volume of the solid generated by revolving R about the y-axis.

11. $x = y^2, x = 0, y = 3$

12. $x = \dfrac{2}{y}, y = 2, y = 6, x = 0$

13. $x = 2\sqrt{y}, y = 4, x = 0$ **14.** $x = y^{2/3}, y = 27, x = 0$

15. $x = y^{3/2}, y = 9, x = 0$ **16.** $x = \sqrt{4 - y^2}, x = 0$

17. Find the volume of the solid generated by revolving about the x-axis the region bounded by the upper half of the ellipse

$$\frac{x^2}{a^2} + \frac{y^2}{b^2} = 1$$

and the x-axis, and thus find the volume of a *prolate spheroid*. Here a and b are positive constants, with $a > b$.

18. Find the volume of the solid generated by revolving about the x-axis the region bounded by the line $y = 6x$ and the parabola $y = 6x^2$.

19. Find the volume of the solid generated by revolving about the x-axis the region bounded by the line $x - 2y = 0$ and the parabola $y^2 = 4x$.

20. Find the volume of the solid generated by revolving about the x-axis the region in the first quadrant bounded by the circle $x^2 + y^2 = r^2$, the x-axis, and the line $x = r - h, 0 < h < r$, and thus find the volume of a *spherical segment* of height h, of a sphere of radius r.

21. Find the volume of the solid generated by revolving about the y-axis the region bounded by the line $y = 4x$ and the parabola $y = 4x^2$.

22. Find the volume of the solid generated by revolving about the line $y = 2$ the region in the first quadrant bounded by the parabolas $3x^2 - 16y + 48 = 0$ and $x^2 - 16y + 80 = 0$ and the y-axis.

23. The base of a solid is the region inside the circle $x^2 + y^2 = 4$. Find the volume of the solid if every cross section by a plane perpendicular to the x-axis is a square. *Hint:* See Examples 5 and 6.

24. Do Problem 23 assuming that every cross section by a plane perpendicular to the x-axis is an isosceles triangle with base on the xy-plane and altitude 4. *Hint:* To complete the evaluation, interpret $\displaystyle\int_{-2}^{2} \sqrt{4 - x^2}\, dx$ as the area of a semicircle.

25. The base of a solid is bounded by one arch of $y = \sqrt{\cos x}, -\pi/2 \le x \le \pi/2$, and the x-axis. Each cross section perpendicular to the x-axis is a square sitting on this base. Find the volume of the solid.

26. The base of a solid is the region bounded by $y = 1 - x^2$ and $y = 1 - x^4$. Cross sections of the solid that are perpendicular to the x-axis are squares. Find the volume of the solid.

27. Find the volume of one octant (one-eighth) of the solid region common to two right circular cylinders of radius 1 whose axes intersect at right angles. *Hint:* Horizontal cross sections are squares. See Figure 15.

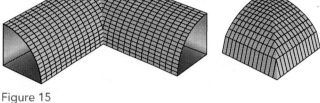

Figure 15

28. Find the volume inside the "+" shown in Figure 16. Assume that both cylinders have radius 2 inches and length 12 inches. *Hint:* The volume is equal to the volume of the first cylinder plus the volume of the second cylinder minus the volume of the region common to both. Use the result of Problem 27.

29. Find the volume inside the "+" in Figure 16, assuming that both cylinders have radius r and length L.

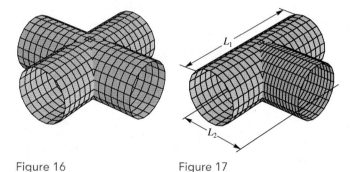

Figure 16   Figure 17

30. Find the volume inside the "T" in Figure 17, assuming that each cylinder has radius $r = 2$ inches and that the lengths are $L_1 = 12$ inches and $L_2 = 8$ inches.

31. Repeat Problem 30 for arbitrary r, L_1, and L_2.

32. The base of a solid is the region R bounded by $y = \sqrt{x}$ and $y = x^2$. Each cross section perpendicular to the x-axis is a semicircle with diameter extending across R. Find the volume of the solid.

33. Find the volume of the solid generated by revolving the region bounded by $y = e^x, y = 0, x = 0$, and $x = \ln 3$ about the x-axis.

34. Find the volume of the solid generated when the region in the first quadrant bounded above by $y = 2$ and on the right by $y = -\ln x$ is revolved about the y-axis.

35. Find the volume of the solid generated by revolving the region in the first quadrant bounded by the curve $y^2 = x^3$, the line $x = 4$, and the x-axis:
(a) about the line $x = 4$;   (b) about the line $y = 8$.

36. Find the volume of the solid generated by revolving the region bounded by the curve $y^2 = x^3$, the line $y = 8$, and the y-axis:

(a) about the line $x = 4$; (b) about the line $y = 8$.

37. Complete the evaluation of the integral in Example 4 by noting that

$$\int_0^2 \left[2\sqrt{4 - y^2} + 4 - y^2\right] dy$$

$$= 2\int_0^2 \sqrt{4 - y^2}\, dy + \int_0^2 (4 - y^2)\, dy$$

Now interpret the first integral as the area of a quarter circle.

38. An open barrel of radius r and height h is initially full of water. It is tilted and water pours out until the water level coincides with a diameter of the base and just touches the rim of the top. Find the volume of water left in the barrel. See Figure 18.

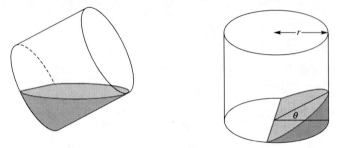

Figure 18   Figure 19

39. A wedge is cut from a right circular cylinder of radius r (Figure 19). The upper surface of the wedge is in a plane through a diameter of the circular base and makes an angle θ with the base. Find the volume of the wedge.

40. (The Water Clock) A water tank is obtained by revolving the curve $y = kx^4$, $k > 0$, about the y-axis.

(a) Find $V(y)$, the volume of water in the tank as a function of its depth y.

(b) Water drains through a small hole according to Torricelli's Law $\left(dV/dt = -m\sqrt{y}\right)$. Show that the water level falls at a constant rate.

41. Show that the volume of a general cone (Figure 20) is $\frac{1}{3}Ah$, where A is the area of the base and h is the height. Use this result to give the formula for the volume of

(a) a right circular cone of radius r and height h;

(b) a regular tetrahedron with edge length r.

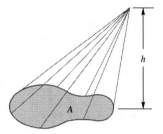

Figure 20

42. State the version of Cavalieri's Principle for volume (see Problem 42 of Section 6.1).

43. Apply Cavalieri's Principle for volumes to the two solids shown in Figure 21. (One is a hemisphere of radius r; the other is a cylinder of radius r and height r with a right circular cone of radius r and height r removed.) Assuming that the volume of a right circular cone is $\frac{1}{3}\pi r^2 h$, find the volume of a hemisphere of radius r.

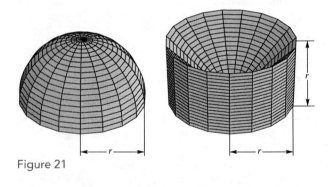

Figure 21

Answers to Concepts Review: **1.** $\pi r^2 h$ **2.** $\pi(R^2 - r^2)h$
3. $\pi x^4\, \Delta x$ **4.** $\pi[(x^2 + 2)^2 - 4]\, \Delta x$

Techniques of Integration and Differential Equations

7.1

Basic Integration Rules

Our repertoire of functions now includes all the elementary functions. These are the constant functions, the power functions, the algebraic functions, the logarithmic and exponential functions, the trigonometric and inverse trigonometric functions, and all functions obtained from them by addition, subtraction, multiplication, division, and composition. Thus,

$$f(x) = \frac{e^x + e^{-x}}{2} = \cosh x$$

$$g(x) = (1 + \cos^4 x)^{1/2}$$

$$h(x) = \frac{3^{x^2 - 2x}}{\ln(x^2 + 1)} - \sin[\cos(\cosh x)]$$

are elementary functions.

Differentiation of an elementary function is straightforward, requiring only a systematic use of the rules that we have learned. And the result is always an elementary function. Integration (antidifferentiation) is a far different matter. It involves a few techniques and a large bag of tricks; what is worse, it does not always yield an elementary function. For example, it is known that the antiderivatives of e^{-x^2} and $(\sin x)/x$ are not elementary functions.

The two principal techniques for integration are *substitution* and *integration by parts*. The method of substitution was introduced in Section 5.4; we have used it occasionally in Chapters 5 and 6.

Standard Forms   Effective use of the method of substitution and integration by parts depends on the ready availability of a list of known integrals. One such list (but too long to memorize) appears inside the back cover of this book. The short list shown below is so useful that we think that every calculus student should memorize it.

Standard Integral Forms

Constants, Powers   1. $\int k \, du = ku + C$

2. $\int u^r \, du = \begin{cases} \dfrac{u^{r+1}}{r+1} + C & r \neq -1 \\ \ln|u| + C & r = -1 \end{cases}$

Exponentials   3. $\int e^u \, du = e^u + C$

4. $\int a^u \, du = \dfrac{a^u}{\ln a} + C, a \neq 1, a > 0$

Trigonometric Functions   5. $\int \sin u \, du = -\cos u + C$

6. $\int \cos u \, du = \sin u + C$

7. $\int \sec^2 u \, du = \tan u + C$

8. $\int \csc^2 u \, du = -\cot u + C$

9. $\int \sec u \tan u \, du = \sec u + C$

10. $\int \csc u \cot u \, du = -\csc u + C$

11. $\int \tan u \, du = -\ln|\cos u| + C$

12. $\int \cot u \, du = \ln|\sin u| + C$

Algebraic Functions   13. $\int \dfrac{du}{\sqrt{a^2 - u^2}} = \sin^{-1}\left(\dfrac{u}{a}\right) + C$

14. $\int \dfrac{du}{a^2 + u^2} = \dfrac{1}{a}\tan^{-1}\left(\dfrac{u}{a}\right) + C$

15. $\displaystyle\int \frac{du}{u\sqrt{u^2 - a^2}} = \frac{1}{a}\sec^{-1}\left(\frac{|u|}{a}\right) + C = \frac{1}{a}\cos^{-1}\left(\frac{a}{|u|}\right) + C$

Hyperbolic Functions　16. $\displaystyle\int \sinh u \, du = \cosh u + C$　　17. $\displaystyle\int \cosh u \, du = \sinh u + C$

Substitution in Indefinite Integrals　Suppose that you face an indefinite integral. If it is a standard form, simply write the answer. If not, look for a substitution that will change it to a standard form. If the first substitution that you try does not work, try another. Skill at this, like most worthwhile activities, depends on practice.

　　The method of substitution was given in Theorem 5.4B and is restated here for easy reference.

Theorem A　**Substitution in Indefinite Integrals**

Let g be a differentiable function and suppose that F is an antiderivative of f. Then, if $u = g(x)$,

$$\int f(g(x))g'(x) \, dx = \int f(u) \, du = F(u) + C = F(g(x)) + C$$

EXAMPLE 1　Find $\displaystyle\int \frac{x}{\cos^2(x^2)} \, dx$.

SOLUTION　Look at this integral for a few moments. Since $1/\cos^2 x = \sec^2 x$, you may be reminded of the standard form $\int \sec^2 u \, du$. Let $u = x^2$, $du = 2x \, dx$. Then

$$\int \frac{x}{\cos^2(x^2)} \, dx = \frac{1}{2}\int \frac{1}{\cos^2(x^2)} \cdot 2x \, dx = \frac{1}{2}\int \sec^2 u \, du$$

$$= \frac{1}{2}\tan u + C = \frac{1}{2}\tan(x^2) + C \qquad \blacksquare$$

EXAMPLE 2　Find $\displaystyle\int \frac{3}{\sqrt{5 - 9x^2}} \, dx$.

SOLUTION　Think of $\displaystyle\int \frac{du}{\sqrt{a^2 - u^2}}$. Let $u = 3x$, so $du = 3 \, dx$. Then

$$\int \frac{3}{\sqrt{5 - 9x^2}} \, dx = \int \frac{1}{\sqrt{5 - u^2}} \, du = \sin^{-1}\left(\frac{u}{\sqrt{5}}\right) + C$$

$$= \sin^{-1}\left(\frac{3x}{\sqrt{5}}\right) + C \qquad \blacksquare$$

EXAMPLE 3　Find $\displaystyle\int \frac{6e^{1/x}}{x^2} \, dx$.

SOLUTION　Think of $\int e^u \, du$. Let $u = 1/x$, so $du = (-1/x^2) \, dx$. Then

$$\int \frac{6e^{1/x}}{x^2} \, dx = -6\int e^{1/x}\left(\frac{-1}{x^2} \, dx\right) = -6\int e^u \, du$$

$$= -6e^u + C = -6e^{1/x} + C \qquad \blacksquare$$

EXAMPLE 4 Find $\int \dfrac{e^x}{4 + 9e^{2x}}\, dx$.

SOLUTION Think of $\int \dfrac{1}{a^2 + u^2}\, du$. Let $u = 3e^x$, so $du = 3e^x\, dx$. Then

$$\int \frac{e^x}{4 + 9e^{2x}}\, dx = \frac{1}{3} \int \frac{1}{4 + 9e^{2x}}(3e^x\, dx) = \frac{1}{3} \int \frac{1}{2^2 + u^2}\, du$$

$$= \frac{1}{3} \cdot \frac{1}{2} \tan^{-1}\!\left(\frac{u}{2}\right) + C = \frac{1}{6} \tan^{-1}\!\left(\frac{3e^x}{2}\right) + C \qquad \blacksquare$$

You don't have to write out the u-substitution. If you can do the substitution mentally, that is fine. Here are two illustrations.

EXAMPLE 5 Find $\int x \cos x^2\, dx$

SOLUTION Mentally substitute $u = x^2$.

$$\int x \cos x^2\, dx = \frac{1}{2} \int (\cos x^2)(2x\, dx) = \frac{1}{2} \sin x^2 + C \qquad \blacksquare$$

EXAMPLE 6 Find $\int \dfrac{a^{\tan t}}{\cos^2 t}\, dt$.

SOLUTION Mentally, substitute $u = \tan t$.

$$\int \frac{a^{\tan t}}{\cos^2 t}\, dt = \int a^{\tan t}(\sec^2 t\, dt) = \frac{a^{\tan t}}{\ln a} + C \qquad \blacksquare$$

Substitution in Definite Integrals This topic was also covered in Section 5.4. It is just like substitution in indefinite integrals, but we must remember to make the appropriate change in the limits of integration.

EXAMPLE 7 Find $\int_2^5 t \sqrt{t^2 - 4}\, dt$.

SOLUTION Let $u = t^2 - 4$, so $du = 2t\, dt$; note that when $t = 2, u = 0$, and when $t = 5, u = 21$. Thus,

$$\int_2^5 t \sqrt{t^2 - 4}\, dt = \frac{1}{2} \int_2^5 (t^2 - 4)^{1/2}(2t\, dt)$$

$$= \frac{1}{2} \int_0^{21} u^{1/2}\, du$$

$$= \left[\frac{1}{3} u^{3/2}\right]_0^{21} = \frac{1}{3}(21)^{3/2} \approx 32.08 \qquad \blacksquare$$

EXAMPLE 8 Find $\int_1^3 x^3 \sqrt{x^4 + 11}\, dx$.

SOLUTION Mentally substitute $u = x^4 + 11$.

$$\int_1^3 x^3 \sqrt{x^4 + 11}\, dx = \frac{1}{4} \int_1^3 (x^4 + 11)^{1/2}(4x^3\, dx)$$

$$= \left[\frac{1}{6}(x^4 + 11)^{3/2}\right]_1^3$$

$$= \frac{1}{6}[92^{3/2} - 12^{3/2}] \approx 140.144 \qquad \blacksquare$$

Trigonometric Integrals Some trigonometric integrals can be evaluated using the natural log function.

EXAMPLE 9 Evaluate $\displaystyle\int \tan x \, dx$.

SOLUTION Since $\tan x = \dfrac{\sin x}{\cos x}$ we can make the substitution $u = \cos x$, $du = -\sin x \, dx$, to obtain

$$\int \tan x \, dx = \int \frac{\sin x}{\cos x} dx = \int \frac{-1}{\cos x}(-\sin x \, dx) = -\ln|\cos x| + C \quad \blacksquare$$

Similarly, $\displaystyle\int \cot x \, dx = \ln|\sin x| + C$.

EXAMPLE 10 Evaluate $\displaystyle\int \sec x \csc x \, dx$.

SOLUTION For this one we use the trig identity $\sec x \csc x = \tan x + \cot x$. Then

$$\int \sec x \csc x \, dx = \int (\tan x + \cot x) \, dx = -\ln|\cos x| + \ln|\sin x| + C \quad \blacksquare$$

Manipulating the Integrand Before you make a substitution, you may find it helpful to rewrite the integrand in a more convenient form. Integrals with quadratic expressions in the denominator can often be reduced to standard forms by *completing the square*. Recall that $x^2 + bx$ becomes a perfect square by the addition of $(b/2)^2$.

EXAMPLE 11 Find $\displaystyle\int \frac{7}{x^2 - 6x + 25} dx$

SOLUTION

$$\int \frac{7}{x^2 - 6x + 25} dx = \int \frac{7}{x^2 - 6x + 9 + 16} dx$$

$$= 7 \int \frac{1}{(x - 3)^2 + 4^2} dx$$

$$= \frac{7}{4} \tan^{-1}\left(\frac{x - 3}{4}\right) + C$$

We made the mental substitution $u = x - 3$ and used Formula 14 at the final stage. $\blacksquare$

Concepts Review

1. Differentiation of an elementary function is straightforward, but there are cases where the antiderivative of an elementary function cannot be expressed as a(an) _____.

2. The substitution $u = 1 + x^3$ transforms $\displaystyle\int 3x^2(1 + x^3)^5 \, dx$ to _____.

3. The substitution $u = $ _____ transforms $\displaystyle\int e^x/(4 + e^{2x}) \, dx$ to $\displaystyle\int 1/(4 + u^2) \, du$.

4. The substitution $u = 1 + \sin x$ transforms $\displaystyle\int_0^{\pi/2} (1 + \sin x)^3 \cos x \, dx$ to _____.

Problem Set 7.1

In Problems 1–54, perform the indicated integrations.

1. $\displaystyle\int (x - 2)^5\, dx$

2. $\displaystyle\int \sqrt{3x}\, dx$

3. $\displaystyle\int_0^2 x(x^2 + 1)^5\, dx$

4. $\displaystyle\int_0^1 x\sqrt{1 - x^2}\, dx$

5. $\displaystyle\int \frac{dx}{x^2 + 4}$

6. $\displaystyle\int \frac{e^x}{2 + e^x}\, dx$

7. $\displaystyle\int \frac{x}{x^2 + 4}\, dx$

8. $\displaystyle\int \frac{2t^2}{2t^2 + 1}\, dt$

9. $\displaystyle\int_0^{\sqrt{5}} 6z\sqrt{4 + z^2}\, dz$

10. $\displaystyle\int_0^4 \frac{5}{\sqrt{2t + 1}}\, dt$

11. $\displaystyle\int_0^{\pi/4} \frac{\tan z}{\cos^2 z}\, dz$

12. $\displaystyle\int_{-\pi/4}^{9\pi/4} e^{\cos z}\sin z\, dz$

13. $\displaystyle\int \frac{\sin\sqrt{t}}{\sqrt{t}}\, dt$

14. $\displaystyle\int \frac{2x\, dx}{\sqrt{1 - x^4}}$

15. $\displaystyle\int_0^{\pi/4} \frac{\cos x}{1 + \sin^2 x}\, dx$

16. $\displaystyle\int_0^{3/4} \frac{\sin\sqrt{1 - x}}{\sqrt{1 - x}}\, dx$

17. $\displaystyle\int \frac{3x^2 + 2x}{x + 1}\, dx$

18. $\displaystyle\int \frac{x^3 + 7x}{x - 1}\, dx$

19. $\displaystyle\int \frac{\sin(\ln 4x^2)}{x}\, dx$

20. $\displaystyle\int \frac{\sec^2(\ln x)}{2x}\, dx$

21. $\displaystyle\int \frac{6e^x}{\sqrt{1 - e^{2x}}}\, dx$

22. $\displaystyle\int \frac{x}{x^4 + 4}\, dx$

23. $\displaystyle\int \frac{3e^{2x}}{\sqrt{1 - e^{2x}}}\, dx$

24. $\displaystyle\int \frac{x^3}{x^4 + 4}\, dx$

25. $\displaystyle\int_0^1 t\, 3^{t^2}\, dt$

26. $\displaystyle\int_0^{\pi/6} 2^{\cos x}\sin x\, dx$

27. $\displaystyle\int \frac{\sin x - \cos x}{\sin x}\, dx$

28. $\displaystyle\int \frac{\sin(4t - 1)}{1 - \sin^2(4t - 1)}\, dt$

29. $\displaystyle\int e^x \sec e^x\, dx$ Hint: See Problem 56.

30. $\displaystyle\int e^x \sec^2(e^x)\, dx$

31. $\displaystyle\int \frac{\sec^3 x + e^{\sin x}}{\sec x}\, dx$

32. $\displaystyle\int \frac{(6t - 1)\sin\sqrt{3t^2 - t - 1}}{\sqrt{3t^2 - t - 1}}\, dt$

33. $\displaystyle\int \frac{t^2 \cos(t^3 - 2)}{\sin^2(t^3 - 2)}\, dt$

34. $\displaystyle\int \frac{1 + \cos 2x}{\sin^2 2x}\, dx$

35. $\displaystyle\int \frac{t^2 \cos^2(t^3 - 2)}{\sin^2(t^3 - 2)}\, dt$

36. $\displaystyle\int \frac{\csc^2 2t}{\sqrt{1 + \cot 2t}}\, dt$

37. $\displaystyle\int \frac{e^{\tan^{-1} 2t}}{1 + 4t^2}\, dt$

38. $\displaystyle\int (t + 1)e^{-t^2 - 2t - 5}\, dt$

39. $\displaystyle\int \frac{y}{\sqrt{16 - 9y^4}}\, dy$

40. $\displaystyle\int \cosh 3x\, dx$

41. $\displaystyle\int x^2 \sinh x^3\, dx$

42. $\displaystyle\int \frac{5}{\sqrt{9 - 4x^2}}\, dx$

43. $\displaystyle\int \frac{e^{3t}}{\sqrt{4 - e^{6t}}}\, dt$

44. $\displaystyle\int \frac{dt}{2t\sqrt{4t^2 - 1}}$

45. $\displaystyle\int_0^{\pi/2} \frac{\sin x}{16 + \cos^2 x}\, dx$

46. $\displaystyle\int_0^1 \frac{e^{2x} - e^{-2x}}{e^{2x} + e^{-2x}}\, dx$

47. $\displaystyle\int \frac{1}{x^2 + 2x + 5}\, dx$

48. $\displaystyle\int \frac{1}{x^2 - 4x + 9}\, dx$

49. $\displaystyle\int \frac{dx}{9x^2 + 18x + 10}$

50. $\displaystyle\int \frac{dx}{\sqrt{16 + 6x - x^2}}$

51. $\displaystyle\int \frac{x + 1}{9x^2 + 18x + 10}\, dx$

52. $\displaystyle\int \frac{3 - x}{\sqrt{16 + 6x - x^2}}\, dx$

53. $\displaystyle\int \frac{dt}{t\sqrt{2t^2 - 9}}$

54. $\displaystyle\int \frac{\tan x}{\sqrt{\sec^2 x - 4}}\, dx$

55. Find the length of the curve $y = \ln(\cos x)$ between $x = 0$ and $x = \pi/4$.

56. Establish the identity

$$\sec x = \frac{\sin x}{\cos x} + \frac{\cos x}{1 + \sin x}$$

and then use it to derive the formula

$$\int \sec x\, dx = \ln|\sec x + \tan x| + C$$

57. Evaluate $\displaystyle\int_0^{2\pi} \frac{x|\sin x|}{1 + \cos^2 x}\, dx$. *Hint:* Make the substitution $u = x - \pi$ in the definite integral and then use symmetry properties.

58. Let R be the region bounded by $y = \sin x$ and $y = \cos x$ between $x = -\pi/4$ and $x = 3\pi/4$. Find the volume of the solid obtained when R is revolved about $x = -\pi/4$. *Hint:* Use cylindrical shells to write a single integral, make the substitution $u = x - \pi/4$, and apply symmetry properties.

Answers to Concepts Review: **1.** elementary function

2. $\displaystyle\int u^5\, du$ **3.** e^x **4.** $\displaystyle\int_1^2 u^3\, du$

7.2
Integration by Parts

If integration by substitution fails, it may be possible to use a double substitution, better known as *integration by parts*. This method is based on the integration of the formula for the derivative of a product of two functions.

Let $u = u(x)$ and $v = v(x)$. Then

$$D_x[u(x)v(x)] = u(x)v'(x) + v(x)u'(x)$$

or

$$u(x)v'(x) = D_x[u(x)v(x)] - v(x)u'(x)$$

By integrating both sides of this equation, we obtain

$$\int u(x)v'(x)\,dx = u(x)v(x) - \int v(x)u'(x)\,dx$$

Since $dv = v'(x)\,dx$ and $du = u'(x)\,dx$, the preceding equation is usually written symbolically as follows:

Integration by Parts: Indefinite Integrals

$$\int u\,dv = uv - \int v\,du$$

The corresponding formula for definite integrals is

$$\int_a^b u(x)v'(x)\,dx = \left[u(x)v(x)\right]_a^b - \int_a^b v(x)u'(x)\,dx$$

Figure 1 illustrates a geometric interpretation of integration by parts for definite integrals. We abbreviate this as follows:

Integration by Parts: Definite Integrals

$$\int_a^b u\,dv = \left[uv\right]_a^b - \int_a^b v\,du$$

These formulas allow us to shift the problem of integrating $u\,dv$ to that of integrating $v\,du$. Success depends on the proper choice of u and dv, which comes with practice.

Integration by Parts

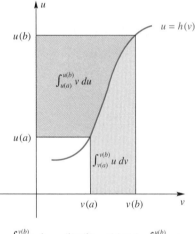

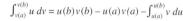

$$\int_{v(a)}^{v(b)} u\,dv = u(b)v(b) - u(a)v(a) - \int_{u(a)}^{u(b)} v\,du$$

Figure 1

EXAMPLE 1 Find $\displaystyle\int x \cos x\,dx$.

SOLUTION We wish to write $x \cos x\,dx$ as $u\,dv$. One possibility is to let $u = x$ and $dv = \cos x\,dx$. Then $du = dx$ and $v = \int \cos x\,dx = \sin x$ (we can omit the arbitrary constant at this stage). Here is a summary of this double substitution in a convenient format.

$$u = x \qquad\qquad dv = \cos x\,dx$$
$$du = dx \qquad\qquad v = \sin x$$

The formula for integration by parts gives

$$\int \underbrace{x}_{u}\ \underbrace{\cos x\,dx}_{dv} = \underbrace{x}_{u}\ \underbrace{\sin x}_{v} - \int \underbrace{\sin x}_{v}\ \underbrace{dx}_{du}$$
$$= x \sin x + \cos x + C$$

We were successful on our first try. Another substitution would be

$$u = \cos x \qquad dv = x \, dx$$

$$du = -\sin x \, dx \qquad v = \frac{x^2}{2}$$

This time the formula for integration by parts gives

$$\int \underbrace{(\cos x)}_{u} \underbrace{x \, dx}_{dv} = \underbrace{(\cos x)}_{u} \underbrace{\frac{x^2}{2}}_{v} - \int \underbrace{\frac{x^2}{2}}_{v} \underbrace{(-\sin x \, dx)}_{du}$$

which is correct but not helpful. The new integral on the right-hand side is more complicated than the original one. Thus, we see the importance of a wise choice for u and dv. ∎

EXAMPLE 2 Find $\displaystyle\int_1^2 \ln x \, dx$.

SOLUTION We make the following substitutions:

$$u = \ln x \qquad dv = dx$$

$$du = \left(\frac{1}{x}\right) dx \qquad v = x$$

Then

$$\int_1^2 \ln x \, dx = [x \ln x]_1^2 - \int_1^2 x \frac{1}{x} dx$$

$$= 2 \ln 2 - \int_1^2 dx$$

$$= 2 \ln 2 - 1 \approx 0.386$$

∎

EXAMPLE 3 Find $\displaystyle\int \arcsin x \, dx$.

SOLUTION We make the substitutions

$$u = \arcsin x \qquad dv = dx$$

$$du = \frac{1}{\sqrt{1 - x^2}} dx \qquad v = x$$

Then

$$\int \arcsin x \, dx = x \arcsin x - \int \frac{x}{\sqrt{1 - x^2}} dx$$

$$= x \arcsin x + \frac{1}{2} \int (1 - x^2)^{-1/2}(-2x \, dx)$$

$$= x \arcsin x + \frac{1}{2} \cdot 2(1 - x^2)^{1/2} + C$$

$$= x \arcsin x + \sqrt{1 - x^2} + C$$

∎

EXAMPLE 4 Find $\displaystyle\int_1^2 t^6 \ln t \, dt$.

SOLUTION   We make the following substitutions

$$u = \ln t \qquad dv = t^6 \, dt$$
$$du = \frac{1}{t} \, dt \qquad v = \frac{1}{7} t^7$$

Then

$$\int_1^2 t^6 \ln t \, dt = \left[\frac{1}{7} t^7 \ln t \right]_1^2 - \int_1^2 \frac{1}{7} t^7 \left(\frac{1}{t} dt \right)$$

$$= \frac{1}{7} (128 \ln 2 - \ln 1) - \frac{1}{7} \int_1^2 t^6 \, dt$$

$$= \frac{128}{7} \ln 2 - \frac{1}{49} [t^7]_1^2$$

$$= \frac{128}{7} \ln 2 - \frac{127}{49} \approx 10.083 \qquad \blacksquare$$

Repeated Integration by Parts   Sometimes it is necessary to apply integration by parts several times.

EXAMPLE 5   Find $\displaystyle\int x^2 \sin x \, dx$.

SOLUTION   Let

$$u = x^2 \qquad dv = \sin x \, dx$$
$$du = 2x \, dx \qquad v = -\cos x$$

Then

$$\int x^2 \sin x \, dx = -x^2 \cos x + 2 \int x \cos x \, dx$$

We have improved our situation (the exponent on x has gone from 2 to 1), which suggests reapplying integration by parts to the integral on the right. Actually, we did this integration in Example 1, so we will make use of the result obtained there.

$$\int x^2 \sin x \, dx = -x^2 \cos x + 2(x \sin x + \cos x + C)$$

$$= -x^2 \cos x + 2x \sin x + 2 \cos x + K \qquad \blacksquare$$

EXAMPLE 6   Find $\displaystyle\int e^x \sin x \, dx$.

SOLUTION   Take $u = e^x$ and $dv = \sin x \, dx$. Then $du = e^x \, dx$ and $v = -\cos x$. Thus,

$$\int e^x \sin x \, dx = -e^x \cos x + \int e^x \cos x \, dx$$

which does not seem to have improved things—but does not leave us any worse off either. So, let's not give up and try integration by parts again. In the integral on the right, let $u = e^x$ and $dv = \cos x \, dx$, so $du = e^x \, dx$ and $v = \sin x$. Then

$$\int e^x \cos x \, dx = e^x \sin x - \int e^x \sin x \, dx$$

When we substitute this in our first result, we get

$$\int e^x \sin x \, dx = -e^x \cos x + e^x \sin x - \int e^x \sin x \, dx$$

By moving the last term to the left side and combining terms, we obtain

$$2 \int e^x \sin x \, dx = e^x (\sin x - \cos x) + C$$

from which

$$\int e^x \sin x \, dx = \frac{1}{2} e^x (\sin x - \cos x) + K$$ ■

The fact that the integral we wanted to find reappeared on the right side is what made Example 6 work.

Reduction Formulas   A formula of the form

$$\int f^n(x) g(x) \, dx = h(x) + \int f^k(x) \, g(x) \, dx$$

where $k < n$, is called a **reduction formula** (the exponent on f is reduced). Such formulas can often be obtained via integration by parts.

■ **EXAMPLE 7**   Derive a reduction formula for $\int \sin^n x \, dx$.

SOLUTION   Let $u = \sin^{n-1} x$ and $dv = \sin x \, dx$. Then

$$du = (n - 1) \sin^{n-2} x \cos x \, dx \quad \text{and} \quad v = -\cos x$$

from which

$$\int \sin^n x \, dx = -\sin^{n-1} x \cos x + (n - 1) \int \sin^{n-2} x \cos^2 x \, dx$$

If we replace $\cos^2 x$ by $1 - \sin^2 x$ in the last integral, we obtain

$$\int \sin^n x \, dx = -\sin^{n-1} x \cos x + (n - 1) \int \sin^{n-2} x \, dx - (n - 1) \int \sin^n x \, dx$$

After combining the first and last integrals above and solving for $\int \sin^n x \, dx$, we get the reduction formula (valid for $n \geq 2$)

$$\int \sin^n x \, dx = \frac{-\sin^{n-1} x \cos x}{n} + \frac{n - 1}{n} \int \sin^{n-2} x \, dx$$ ■

■ **EXAMPLE 8**   Use the reduction formula above to evaluate $\int_0^{\pi/2} \sin^8 x \, dx$.

SOLUTION   Note first that

$$\int_0^{\pi/2} \sin^n x \, dx = \left[\frac{-\sin^{n-1} x \cos x}{n} \right]_0^{\pi/2} + \frac{n - 1}{n} \int_0^{\pi/2} \sin^{n-2} x \, dx$$

$$= 0 + \frac{n - 1}{n} \int_0^{\pi/2} \sin^{n-2} x \, dx$$

Thus,

$$\int_0^{\pi/2} \sin^8 x\, dx = \frac{7}{8} \int_0^{\pi/2} \sin^6 x\, dx$$

$$= \frac{7}{8} \cdot \frac{5}{6} \int_0^{\pi/2} \sin^4 x\, dx$$

$$= \frac{7}{8} \cdot \frac{5}{6} \cdot \frac{3}{4} \int_0^{\pi/2} \sin^2 x\, dx$$

$$= \frac{7}{8} \cdot \frac{5}{6} \cdot \frac{3}{4} \cdot \frac{1}{2} \int_0^{\pi/2} 1\, dx$$

$$= \frac{7}{8} \cdot \frac{5}{6} \cdot \frac{3}{4} \cdot \frac{1}{2} \cdot \frac{\pi}{2} = \frac{35}{256} \pi \quad ■$$

The general formula for $\int_0^{\pi/2} \sin^n x\, dx$ can be found in a similar way (Formula 113 at the back of the book).

Concepts Review

1. The integration-by-parts formula says that $\int u\, dv = $ _____.

2. To apply this formula to $\int x \sin x\, dx$, let $u = $ _____ and $dv = $ _____.

3. Applying the integration-by-parts formula yields the value _____ for $\int_0^{\pi/2} x \sin x\, dx$.

4. A formula that expresses $\int f^n(x)\, g(x)\, dx$ in terms of $\int f^k(x)\, g(x)\, dx$, where $k < n$, is called a _____ formula.

Problem Set 7.2

In Problems 1–36, use integration by parts to evaluate each integral.

1. $\int x e^x\, dx$

2. $\int x e^{3x}\, dx$

3. $\int t e^{5t+\pi}\, dt$

4. $\int (t + 7) e^{2t+3}\, dt$

5. $\int x \cos x\, dx$

6. $\int x \sin 2x\, dx$

7. $\int (t - 3) \cos(t - 3)\, dt$

8. $\int (x - \pi) \sin x\, dx$

9. $\int t \sqrt{t + 1}\, dt$

10. $\int t \sqrt[3]{2t + 7}\, dt$

11. $\int \ln 3x\, dx$

12. $\int \ln(7x^5)\, dx$

13. $\int \arctan x\, dx$

14. $\int \arctan 5x\, dx$

15. $\int \frac{\ln x}{x^2}\, dx$

16. $\int_2^3 \frac{\ln 2x^5}{x^2}\, dx$

17. $\int_1^e \sqrt{t} \ln t\, dt$

18. $\int_1^5 \sqrt{2x} \ln x^3\, dx$

19. $\int z^3 \ln z\, dz$

20. $\int t \arctan t\, dt$

21. $\int \arctan(1/t)\, dt$

22. $\int t^5 \ln(t^7)\, dt$

23. $\int_{\pi/6}^{\pi/2} x \csc^2 x\, dx$

24. $\int_{\pi/6}^{\pi/4} x \sec^2 x\, dx$

25. $\int x^5 \sqrt{x^3 + 4}\, dx$

26. $\int x^{13} \sqrt{x^7 + 1}\, dx$

27. $\int \frac{t^7}{(7 - 3t^4)^{3/2}}\, dt$

28. $\int x^3 \sqrt{4 - x^2}\, dx$

29. $\int \frac{z^7}{(4 - z^4)^2}\, dz$

30. $\int x \cosh x\, dx$

31. $\int x \sinh x\, dx$

32. $\int \frac{\ln x}{\sqrt{x}}\, dx$

33. $\int x(3x + 10)^{49}\, dx$

34. $\int_0^1 t(t - 1)^{12}\, dt$

35. $\int x\, 2^x\, dx$

36. $\int z\, a^z\, dz$

In Problems 37–48, apply integration by parts twice to evaluate each integral (see Examples 5 and 6).

37. $\int x^2 e^x\, dx$

38. $\int x^5 e^{x^2}\, dx$

39. $\int \ln^2 z\, dz$

40. $\int \ln^2 x^{20}\, dx$

41. $\int e^t \cos t\, dt$

42. $\int e^{at} \sin t\, dt$

43. $\int x^2 \cos x\, dx$

44. $\int r^2 \sin r\, dr$

45. $\int \sin(\ln x)\, dx$

46. $\int \cos(\ln x)\, dx$

47. $\int (\ln x)^3\, dx$ *Hint:* Use Problem 39.

48. $\int (\ln x)^4 \, dx$ *Hint:* Use Problems 39 and 47.

In Problems 49–54, use integration by parts to derive the given formula.

49. $\int \sin x \sin 3x \, dx =$
$$-\tfrac{3}{8}\sin x \cos 3x + \tfrac{1}{8}\cos x \sin 3x + C$$

50. $\int \cos 5x \sin 7x \, dx =$
$$-\tfrac{7}{24}\cos 5x \cos 7x - \tfrac{5}{24}\sin 5x \sin 7x + C$$

51. $\int e^{\alpha z} \sin \beta z \, dz = \dfrac{e^{\alpha z}(\alpha \sin \beta z - \beta \cos \beta z)}{\alpha^2 + \beta^2} + C$

52. $\int e^{\alpha z} \cos \beta z \, dz = \dfrac{e^{\alpha z}(\alpha \cos \beta z + \beta \sin \beta z)}{\alpha^2 + \beta^2} + C$

53. $\int x^\alpha \ln x \, dx = \dfrac{x^{\alpha+1}}{\alpha+1}\ln x - \dfrac{x^{\alpha+1}}{(\alpha+1)^2} + C, \alpha \neq -1$

54. $\int x^\alpha (\ln x)^2 \, dx = \dfrac{x^{\alpha+1}}{\alpha+1}(\ln x)^2$
$$- 2\dfrac{x^{\alpha+1}}{(\alpha+1)^2}\ln x + 2\dfrac{x^{\alpha+1}}{(\alpha+1)^3} + C, \alpha \neq -1$$

In Problems 55–61, derive the given reduction formula using integration by parts.

55. $\int x^\alpha e^{\beta x} \, dx = \dfrac{x^\alpha e^{\beta x}}{\beta} - \dfrac{\alpha}{\beta}\int x^{\alpha-1} e^{\beta x} \, dx$

56. $\int x^\alpha \sin \beta x \, dx = -\dfrac{x^\alpha \cos \beta x}{\beta} + \dfrac{\alpha}{\beta}\int x^{\alpha-1} \cos \beta x \, dx$

57. $\int x^\alpha \cos \beta x \, dx = \dfrac{x^\alpha \sin \beta x}{\beta} - \dfrac{\alpha}{\beta}\int x^{\alpha-1} \sin \beta x \, dx$

58. $\int (\ln x)^\alpha \, dx = x(\ln x)^\alpha - \alpha \int (\ln x)^{\alpha-1} \, dx$

59. $\int (a^2 - x^2)^\alpha \, dx =$
$$x(a^2 - x^2)^\alpha + 2\alpha \int x^2(a^2 - x^2)^{\alpha-1} \, dx$$

60. $\int \cos^\alpha x \, dx = \dfrac{\cos^{\alpha-1} x \sin x}{\alpha} + \dfrac{\alpha-1}{\alpha}\int \cos^{\alpha-2} x \, dx$

61. $\int \cos^\alpha \beta x \, dx =$
$$\dfrac{\cos^{\alpha-1} \beta x \sin \beta x}{\alpha \beta} + \dfrac{\alpha-1}{\alpha}\int \cos^{\alpha-2} \beta x \, dx$$

62. Use Problem 55 to derive
$$\int x^4 e^{3x} \, dx = \tfrac{1}{3}x^4 e^{3x} - \tfrac{4}{9}x^3 e^{3x} + \tfrac{4}{9}x^2 e^{3x} - \tfrac{8}{27}xe^{3x} + \tfrac{8}{81}e^{3x} + C$$

63. Use Problems 56 and 57 to derive
$$\int x^4 \cos 3x \, dx = \tfrac{1}{3}x^4 \sin 3x + \tfrac{4}{9}x^3 \cos 3x - \tfrac{4}{9}x^2 \sin 3x$$
$$- \tfrac{8}{27}x \cos 3x + \tfrac{8}{81}\sin 3x + C.$$

64. Use Problem 61 to derive
$$\int \cos^6 3x \, dx = \tfrac{1}{18}\sin 3x \cos^5 3x + \tfrac{5}{72}\sin 3x \cos^3 3x$$
$$+ \tfrac{5}{48}\sin 3x \cos 3x + \tfrac{5}{16}x + C.$$

≈ 65. Find the area of the region bounded by the curve $y = \ln x$, the x-axis, and the line $x = e$.

≈ 66. Find the volume of the solid generated by revolving the region of Problem 65 about the x-axis.

≈ 67. Find the area of the region bounded by the curves $y = 3e^{-x/3}$, $y = 0$, $x = 0$, and $x = 9$. Make a sketch.

≈ 68. Find the volume of the solid generated by revolving the region described in Problem 67 about the x-axis.

≈ 69. Find the area of the region bounded by the graphs of $y = x \sin x$ and $y = x \cos x$ from $x = 0$ to $x = \pi/4$.

≈ 70. Find the volume of the solid obtained by revolving the region under the graph of $y = \sin(x/2)$ from $x = 0$ to $x = 2\pi$ about the y-axis.

≈ 71. Find the centroid (see Section 6.6) of the region bounded by $y = \ln x^2$ and the x-axis from $x = 1$ to $x = e$.

72. Evaluate the integral $\int \cot x \csc^2 x \, dx$ by parts in two different ways:
(a) By differentiating $\cot x$ (b) By differentiating $\csc x$
(c) Show that the two results are equivalent up to a constant.

73. If $p(x)$ is a polynomial of degree n and $G_1, G_2, \ldots, G_{n+1}$, are successive antiderivatives of a function g, then, by repeated integration by parts,
$$\int p(x)g(x) \, dx = p(x)G_1(x) - p'(x)G_2(x) + p''(x)G_3(x) - \cdots$$
$$+ (-1)^n p^{(n)}(x)G_{n+1}(x) + C$$
Use this result to find each of the following:
(a) $\int (x^3 - 2x)e^x \, dx$ (b) $\int (x^2 - 3x + 1) \sin x \, dx$

≈ 74. The graph of $y = x \sin x$ for $x \geq 0$ is sketched in Figure 2.
(a) Find a formula for the area of the nth arch.
(b) The second arch is revolved about the y-axis. Find the volume of the resulting solid.

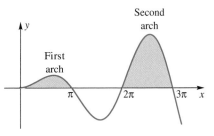

Figure 2

75. The quantity $a_n = \dfrac{1}{\pi}\displaystyle\int_{-\pi}^{\pi} f(x) \sin nx \, dx$ plays an important role in applied mathematics. Show that if $f'(x)$ is continuous on $[-\pi, \pi]$, then $\lim_{n \to \infty} a_n = 0$. *Hint:* Integration by parts.

76. Let $G_n = \sqrt[n]{(n+1)(n+2)\cdots(n+n)}$. Show that $\lim_{n \to \infty}(G_n/n) = 4/e$. *Hint:* Consider $\ln(G_n/n)$, recognize it as a Riemann sum, and use Example 2.

77. Find the error in the following "proof" that $0 = 1$. In $\int (1/t) \, dt$, set $u = 1/t$ and $dv = dt$. Then $du = -t^{-2} \, dt$ and $uv = 1$. Integration by parts gives
$$\int (1/t) \, dt = 1 - \int (-1/t) \, dt$$
or $0 = 1$.

78. Suppose that you want to evaluate the integral

$$\int e^{5x}(4\cos 7x + 6\sin 7x)\,dx$$

and you know from experience that the result will be of the form $e^{5x}(C_1\cos 7x + C_2\sin 7x) + C_3$. Compute C_1 and C_2 by differentiating the result and setting it equal to the integrand.

Many surprising theoretical results can be derived through the use of integration by parts. In all cases, one starts with an integral. We explore two of these results here.

79. Show that

$$\int_a^b f(x)\,dx = [xf(x)]_a^b - \int_a^b xf'(x)\,dx$$

$$= [(x-a)f(x)]_a^b - \int_a^b (x-a)f'(x)\,dx$$

80. Using Problem 79 and replacing f by f', show that

$$f(b) - f(a) = \int_a^b f'(x)\,dx$$

$$= f'(b)(b-a) - \int_a^b (x-a)f''(x)\,dx$$

$$= f'(a)(b-a) - \int_a^b (x-b)f''(x)\,dx$$

81. Show that

$$f(t) = f(a) + \sum_{i=1}^n \frac{f^{(i)}(a)}{i!}(t-a)^i + \int_a^t \frac{(t-x)^n}{n!}f^{(n+1)}(x)\,dx,$$

provided that f can be differentiated $n+1$ times.

82. The *Beta function*, which is important in many branches of mathematics, is defined as

$$B(\alpha, \beta) = \int_0^1 x^{\alpha-1}(1-x)^{\beta-1}\,dx,$$

with the condition that $\alpha \geq 1$ and $\beta \geq 1$.

(a) Show by a change of variables that

$$B(\alpha, \beta) = \int_0^1 x^{\beta-1}(1-x)^{\alpha-1}\,dx = B(\beta, \alpha)$$

(b) Integrate by parts to show that

$$B(\alpha, \beta) = \frac{\alpha-1}{\beta}B(\alpha-1, \beta+1) = \frac{\beta-1}{\alpha}B(\alpha+1, \beta-1)$$

(c) Assume now that $\alpha = n$ and $\beta = m$, and that n and m are positive integers. By using the result in part (b) repeatedly, show that

$$B(n, m) = \frac{(n-1)!\,(m-1)!}{(n+m-1)!}$$

This result is valid even in the case where n and m are not integers, provided that we can give meaning to $(n-1)!$, $(m-1)!$, and $(n+m-1)!$.

83. Suppose that $f(t)$ has the property that $f'(a) = f'(b) = 0$ and that $f(t)$ has two continuous derivatives. Use integration by parts to prove that $\int_a^b f''(t)f(t)\,dt \leq 0$. *Hint:* Use integration by parts by differentiating $f(t)$ and integrating $f''(t)$. This result has many applications in the field of applied mathematics.

84. Derive the formula

$$\int_0^x \left(\int_0^t f(z)\,dz\right)dt = \int_0^x f(t)(x-t)\,dt$$

using integration by parts.

85. Generalize the formula given in Problem 84 to one for an n-fold iterated integral

$$\int_0^x \int_0^{t_1}\cdots\int_0^{t_{n-1}} f(t_n)\,dt_n\ldots dt_1 =$$

$$\frac{1}{(n-1)!}\int_0^x f(t_1)(x-t_1)^{n-1}\,dt_1$$

86. If $P_n(x)$ is a polynomial of degree n, show that

$$\int e^x P_n(x)\,dx = e^x\sum_{j=0}^n (-1)^j \frac{d^j P_n(x)}{dx^j}$$

87. Use the result from Problem 86 to evaluate

$$\int (3x^4 + 2x^2)e^x\,dx$$

Answers to Concepts Review: **1.** $uv - \int v\,du$ **2.** x; $\sin x\,dx$ **3.** 1 **4.** reduction

---

7.3
Some Trigonometric Integrals

When we combine the method of substitution with a clever use of trigonometric identities, we can integrate a wide variety of trigonometric forms. We consider five commonly encountered types.

1. $\displaystyle\int \sin^n x\,dx$ and $\displaystyle\int \cos^n x\,dx$

2. $\displaystyle\int \sin^m x \cos^n x\,dx$

3. $\displaystyle\int \sin mx \cos nx\,dx, \quad \int \sin mx \sin nx\,dx, \quad \int \cos mx \cos nx\,dx$

4. $\displaystyle\int \tan^n x\,dx, \quad \int \cot^n x\,dx$

5. $\displaystyle\int \tan^m x \sec^n x\,dx, \quad \int \cot^m x \csc^n x\,dx$

Useful Identities
Some trigonometric identities need-ed in this section are the following.
Pythagorean Identities
$\sin^2 x + \cos^2 x = 1$
$1 + \tan^2 x = \sec^2 x$
$1 + \cot^2 x = \csc^2 x$
Half-Angle Identities
$\sin^2 x = \dfrac{1 - \cos 2x}{2}$
$\cos^2 x = \dfrac{1 + \cos 2x}{2}$

Type 1 $\left(\int \sin^n x\, dx, \int \cos^n x\, dx \right)$ Consider first the case where n is an odd positive integer. After taking out either the factor $\sin x$ or $\cos x$, use the identity $\sin^2 x + \cos^2 x = 1$.

■ EXAMPLE 1 (*n* **Odd**) Find $\displaystyle\int \sin^5 x\, dx$.

SOLUTION

$$\int \sin^5 x\, dx = \int \sin^4 x \sin x\, dx$$

$$= \int (1 - \cos^2 x)^2 \sin x\, dx$$

$$= \int (1 - 2\cos^2 x + \cos^4 x) \sin x\, dx$$

$$= -\int (1 - 2\cos^2 x + \cos^4 x)(-\sin x\, dx)$$

$$= -\cos x + \tfrac{2}{3}\cos^3 x - \tfrac{1}{5}\cos^5 x + C \qquad\blacksquare$$

■ EXAMPLE 2 (*n* **Even**) Find $\displaystyle\int \sin^2 x\, dx$ and $\displaystyle\int \cos^4 x\, dx$.

SOLUTION Here we make use of half-angle identities.

$$\int \sin^2 x\, dx = \int \frac{1 - \cos 2x}{2}\, dx$$

$$= \frac{1}{2}\int dx - \frac{1}{4}\int (\cos 2x)(2\, dx)$$

$$= \frac{1}{2}x - \frac{1}{4}\sin 2x + C$$

$$\int \cos^4 x\, dx = \int \left(\frac{1 + \cos 2x}{2}\right)^2 dx$$

$$= \frac{1}{4}\int (1 + 2\cos 2x + \cos^2 2x)\, dx$$

$$= \frac{1}{4}\int dx + \frac{1}{4}\int (\cos 2x)(2)\, dx + \frac{1}{8}\int (1 + \cos 4x)\, dx$$

$$= \frac{3}{8}\int dx + \frac{1}{4}\int \cos 2x(2\, dx) + \frac{1}{32}\int \cos 4x(4\, dx)$$

$$= \frac{3}{8}x + \frac{1}{4}\sin 2x + \frac{1}{32}\sin 4x + C \qquad\blacksquare$$

Type 2 $\left(\int \sin^m x \cos^n x\, dx \right)$ If either m or n is an odd positive integer and the other exponent is any number, we factor out $\sin x$ or $\cos x$ and use the identity $\sin^2 x + \cos^2 x = 1$.

■ EXAMPLE 3 (*m* **or** *n* **Odd**) Find $\displaystyle\int \sin^3 x \cos^{-4} x\, dx$.

SOLUTION

$$\int \sin^3 x \cos^{-4} x \, dx = \int (1 - \cos^2 x)(\cos^{-4} x)(\sin x) \, dx$$

$$= -\int (\cos^{-4} x - \cos^{-2} x)(-\sin x \, dx)$$

$$= -\left[\frac{(\cos x)^{-3}}{-3} - \frac{(\cos x)^{-1}}{-1}\right] + C$$

$$= \frac{1}{3}\sec^3 x - \sec x + C$$ ∎

If both m and n are even positive integers, we use half-angle identities to reduce the degree of the integrand. Example 4 gives an illustration.

EXAMPLE 4 **(Both m and n Even)** Find $\int \sin^2 x \cos^4 x \, dx$.

SOLUTION

$$\int \sin^2 x \cos^4 x \, dx$$

$$= \int \left(\frac{1 - \cos 2x}{2}\right)\left(\frac{1 + \cos 2x}{2}\right)^2 dx$$

$$= \frac{1}{8} \int (1 + \cos 2x - \cos^2 2x - \cos^3 2x) \, dx$$

$$= \frac{1}{8} \int \left[1 + \cos 2x - \frac{1}{2}(1 + \cos 4x) - (1 - \sin^2 2x)\cos 2x\right] dx$$

$$= \frac{1}{8} \int \left[\frac{1}{2} - \frac{1}{2}\cos 4x + \sin^2 2x \cos 2x\right] dx$$

$$= \frac{1}{8}\left[\int \frac{1}{2}dx - \frac{1}{8}\int \cos 4x(4 \, dx) + \frac{1}{2}\int \sin^2 2x(2 \cos 2x \, dx)\right]$$

$$= \frac{1}{8}\left[\frac{1}{2}x - \frac{1}{8}\sin 4x + \frac{1}{6}\sin^3 2x\right] + C$$ ∎

Are They Different?

Indefinite integrations may lead to different looking answers. By one method,

$$\int \sin x \cos x \, dx$$

$$= -\int \cos x(-\sin x) \, dx$$

$$= -\tfrac{1}{2}\cos^2 x + C$$

By a second method,

$$\int \sin x \cos x \, dx = \int \sin x(\cos x) \, dx$$

$$= \tfrac{1}{2}\sin^2 x + C$$

But two such answers should differ by at most a constant. Note, however, that

$$\tfrac{1}{2}\sin^2 x + C = \tfrac{1}{2}(1 - \cos^2 x) + C$$

$$= -\tfrac{1}{2}\cos^2 x + \left(\tfrac{1}{2} + C\right)$$

Now reconcile these answers with a third answer.

$$\int \sin x \cos x \, dx = \tfrac{1}{2}\int \sin 2x \, dx$$

$$= -\tfrac{1}{4}\cos 2x + C$$

Type 3 $\left(\int \sin mx \cos nx \, dx, \int \sin mx \sin nx \, dx, \int \cos mx \cos nx \, dx\right)$
Integrals of this type occur in many physics and engineering applications. To handle these integrals, we use the product identities.

1. $\sin mx \cos nx = \dfrac{1}{2}[\sin(m + n)x + \sin(m - n)x]$

2. $\sin mx \sin nx = -\dfrac{1}{2}[\cos(m + n)x - \cos(m - n)x]$

3. $\cos mx \cos nx = \dfrac{1}{2}[\cos(m + n)x + \cos(m - n)x]$

EXAMPLE 5 Find $\int \sin 2x \cos 3x \, dx$.

SOLUTION Apply product identity 1.

$$\int \sin 2x \cos 3x \, dx = \frac{1}{2} \int [\sin 5x + \sin(-x)] \, dx$$

$$= \frac{1}{10} \int \sin 5x (5 \, dx) - \frac{1}{2} \int \sin x \, dx$$

$$= -\frac{1}{10} \cos 5x + \frac{1}{2} \cos x + C \qquad \blacksquare$$

EXAMPLE 6 If m and n are positive integers, show that

$$\int_{-\pi}^{\pi} \sin mx \sin nx \, dx = \begin{cases} 0 & \text{if } m \neq n \\ \pi & \text{if } m = n \end{cases}$$

SOLUTION Apply product identity 2. If $m \neq n$, then

$$\int_{-\pi}^{\pi} \sin mx \sin nx \, dx = -\frac{1}{2} \int_{-\pi}^{\pi} [\cos(m + n)x - \cos(m - n)x] \, dx$$

$$= -\frac{1}{2} \left[\frac{1}{m + n} \sin(m + n)x - \frac{1}{m - n} \sin(m - n)x \right]_{-\pi}^{\pi}$$

$$= 0$$

If $m = n$,

$$\int_{-\pi}^{\pi} \sin mx \sin nx \, dx = -\frac{1}{2} \int_{-\pi}^{\pi} [\cos 2mx - 1] \, dx$$

$$= -\frac{1}{2} \left[\frac{1}{2m} \sin 2mx - x \right]_{-\pi}^{\pi}$$

$$= -\frac{1}{2} [-2\pi] = \pi \qquad \blacksquare$$

EXAMPLE 7 If m and n are positive integers, find

$$\int_{-L}^{L} \sin \frac{m\pi x}{L} \sin \frac{n\pi x}{L} \, dx$$

SOLUTION Let $u = \pi x/L$, $du = \pi dx/L$. If $x = -L$, then $u = -\pi$, and if $x = L$, then $u = \pi$. Thus,

$$\int_{-L}^{L} \sin \frac{m\pi x}{L} \sin \frac{n\pi x}{L} \, dx = \frac{L}{\pi} \int_{-\pi}^{\pi} \sin mu \sin nu \, du$$

$$= \begin{cases} \dfrac{L}{\pi} \cdot 0 & \text{if } m \neq n \\ \dfrac{L}{\pi} \cdot \pi & \text{if } m = n \end{cases}$$

$$= \begin{cases} 0 & \text{if } m \neq n \\ L & \text{if } m = n \end{cases}$$

Here we have used the result of Example 6. $\qquad \blacksquare$

A number of times in this book we have suggested that you should view things from both an algebraic and a geometric point of view. So far, this section has been entirely algebraic, but with definite integrals such as those in Examples 6 and 7, we have an opportunity to view things geometrically.

Figure 1 shows graphs of $y = \sin 3x \sin 2x$ and $y = \sin(3\pi x/10) \sin(2\pi x/10)$. The graphs suggest that the areas above and below the x-axis are the same, leaving $A_{up} - A_{down} = 0$. Examples 6 and 7 confirm this.

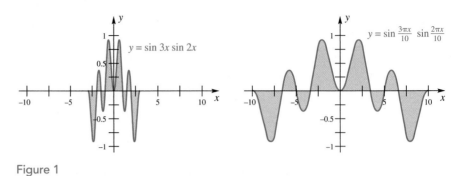

Figure 1

Figure 2 shows graphs of $y = \sin 2x \sin 2x = \sin^2 2x$, $-\pi \le x \le \pi$, and $y = \sin(2\pi x/10) \sin(2\pi x/10) = \sin^2(2\pi x/10)$, $-10 \le x \le 10$. These two graphs look the same, except the one on the right has been stretched horizontally by the factor $10/\pi$. Does it then make sense that the area will increase by this same factor? That would make the shaded area in the figure on the right equal to $10/\pi$ times the shaded area in the figure on the left; that is, the area on the right should be $(10/\pi) \cdot \pi = 10$, which corresponds to the result of Example 7 with $L = 10$.

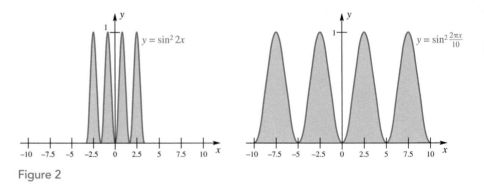

Figure 2

Type 4 $\left(\int \tan^n x \, dx, \int \cot^n x \, dx \right)$ For $n \ge 2$, in the tangent case, factor out $\tan^2 x = \sec^2 x - 1$; in the cotangent case, factor out $\cot^2 x = \csc^2 x - 1$.

EXAMPLE 8 Find $\int \cot^4 x \, dx$.

SOLUTION

$$\int \cot^4 x \, dx = \int \cot^2 x \, (\csc^2 x - 1) \, dx$$

$$= \int \cot^2 x \csc^2 x \, dx - \int \cot^2 x \, dx$$

$$= -\int \cot^2 x \, (-\csc^2 x \, dx) - \int (\csc^2 x - 1) \, dx$$

$$= -\tfrac{1}{3}\cot^3 x + \cot x + x + C$$

■

EXAMPLE 9 Find $\int \tan^5 x \, dx$.

SOLUTION

$$\int \tan^5 x \, dx = \int \tan^3 x \, (\sec^2 x - 1) \, dx$$

$$= \int \tan^3 x \sec^2 x \, dx - \int \tan^3 x \, dx$$

$$= \int \tan^3 x \, (\sec^2 x \, dx) - \int \tan x \, (\sec^2 x - 1) \, dx$$

$$= \int \tan^3 x \, (\sec^2 x \, dx) - \int \tan x \, (\sec^2 x \, dx) + \int \tan x \, dx$$

$$= \tfrac{1}{4} \tan^4 x - \tfrac{1}{2} \tan^2 x - \ln|\cos x| + C$$　　　■

Type 5 $\left(\int \tan^m x \sec^n x \, dx, \int \cot^m x \csc^n x \, dx \right)$

■ **EXAMPLE 10**　(**n Even, m Any Number**)　Find $\displaystyle\int \tan^{-3/2} x \sec^4 x \, dx$.

SOLUTION

$$\int \tan^{-3/2} x \sec^4 x \, dx = \int (\tan^{-3/2} x)(1 + \tan^2 x) \sec^2 x \, dx$$

$$= \int (\tan^{-3/2} x) \sec^2 x \, dx + \int (\tan^{1/2} x) \sec^2 x \, dx$$

$$= -2 \tan^{-1/2} x + \tfrac{2}{3} \tan^{3/2} x + C$$　　　■

■ **EXAMPLE 11**　(**m Odd, n Any Number**)　Find $\displaystyle\int \tan^3 x \sec^{-1/2} x \, dx$.

SOLUTION

$$\int \tan^3 x \sec^{-1/2} x \, dx = \int (\tan^2 x)(\sec^{-3/2} x)(\sec x \tan x) \, dx$$

$$= \int (\sec^2 x - 1) \sec^{-3/2} x \, (\sec x \tan x \, dx)$$

$$= \int \sec^{1/2} x \, (\sec x \tan x \, dx) - \int \sec^{-3/2} x \, (\sec x \tan x \, dx)$$

$$= \tfrac{2}{3} \sec^{3/2} x + 2 \sec^{-1/2} x + C$$　　　■

Concepts Review

1. To handle $\displaystyle\int \cos^2 x \, dx$, we first rewrite it as _____.

2. To handle $\displaystyle\int \cos^3 x \, dx$, we first rewrite it as _____.

3. To handle $\displaystyle\int \sin^2 x \cos^3 x \, dx$, we first rewrite it as _____.

4. To handle $\displaystyle\int_{-\pi}^{\pi} \cos mx \cos nx \, dx$, where $m \neq n$, we use the trigonometric identity _____.

Problem Set 7.3

In Problems 1–28, perform the indicated integrations.

1. $\displaystyle\int \sin^2 x \, dx$

2. $\displaystyle\int \sin^4 6x \, dx$

3. $\displaystyle\int \sin^3 x \, dx$

4. $\displaystyle\int \cos^3 x \, dx$

5. $\displaystyle\int_0^{\pi/2} \cos^5 \theta \, d\theta$

6. $\displaystyle\int_0^{\pi/2} \sin^6 \theta \, d\theta$

7. $\displaystyle\int \sin^5 4x \cos^2 4x \, dx$

8. $\displaystyle\int (\sin^3 2t)\sqrt{\cos 2t} \, dt$

9. $\displaystyle\int \cos^3 3\theta \sin^{-2} 3\theta \, d\theta$

10. $\displaystyle\int \sin^{1/2} 2z \cos^3 2z \, dz$

11. $\displaystyle\int \sin^4 3t \cos^4 3t \, dt$

12. $\displaystyle\int \cos^6 \theta \sin^2 \theta \, d\theta$

13. $\displaystyle\int \sin 4y \cos 5y \, dy$

14. $\displaystyle\int \cos y \cos 4y \, dy$

15. $\displaystyle\int \sin^4\!\left(\frac{w}{2}\right) \cos^2\!\left(\frac{w}{2}\right) dw$

16. $\displaystyle\int \sin 3t \sin t \, dt$

17. $\displaystyle\int x \cos^2 x \sin x \, dx$ *Hint:* Use integration by parts.

18. $\displaystyle\int x \sin^3 x \cos x \, dx$

19. $\displaystyle\int \tan^4 x \, dx$

20. $\displaystyle\int \cot^6 x \, dx$

21. $\displaystyle\int \tan^3 x \, dx$

22. $\displaystyle\int \cot^3 2t \, dt$

23. $\displaystyle\int \tan^5\!\left(\frac{\theta}{2}\right) d\theta$

24. $\displaystyle\int \cot^5 2t \, dt$

25. $\displaystyle\int \tan^{-3} x \sec^4 x \, dx$

26. $\displaystyle\int \tan^{1/2} x \sec^4 x \, dx$

27. $\displaystyle\int \tan^3 x \sec^2 x \, dx$

28. $\displaystyle\int \tan^3 x \sec^{-1/2} x \, dx$

29. Find $\displaystyle\int_{-\pi}^{\pi} \cos mx \cos nx \, dx, m \neq n; m, n$ integers.

30. Find $\displaystyle\int_{-L}^{L} \cos\frac{m\pi x}{L} \cos\frac{n\pi x}{L} dx, m \neq n, m, n$ integers.

≈ **31.** The region bounded by $y = x + \sin x, y = 0, x = \pi$, is revolved about the x-axis. Find the volume of the resulting solid.

≈ **32.** The region bounded by $y = \sin^2(x^2), y = 0$, and $x = \sqrt{\pi/2}$ is revolved about the y-axis. Find the volume of the resulting solid.

33. Let $f(x) = \displaystyle\sum_{n=1}^{N} a_n \sin(nx)$. Use Example 6 to show each of the following for a positive integer m.

(a) $\displaystyle\frac{1}{\pi}\int_{-\pi}^{\pi} f(x) \sin(mx) \, dx = \begin{cases} a_m & \text{if } m \leq N \\ 0 & \text{if } m > N \end{cases}$

(b) $\displaystyle\frac{1}{\pi}\int_{-\pi}^{\pi} f^2(x) \, dx = \sum_{n=1}^{N} a_n^2$

Note: Integrals of this type occur in a subject called *Fourier series*, which has applications to heat, vibrating strings, and other physical phenomena.

34. Show that

$$\lim_{n\to\infty} \cos\frac{x}{2} \cos\frac{x}{4} \cos\frac{x}{8}\cdots\cos\frac{x}{2^n} = \frac{\sin x}{x}$$

by completing the following steps.

(a) $\displaystyle\cos\frac{x}{2} \cos\frac{x}{4}\cdots\cos\frac{x}{2^n} =$

$$\left[\cos\frac{1}{2^n}x + \cos\frac{3}{2^n}x + \cdots + \cos\frac{2^n - 1}{2^n}x\right]\frac{1}{2^{n-1}}$$

(See Problem 46 of Section 1.8.)

(b) Recognize a Riemann sum leading to a definite integral.

(c) Evaluate the definite integral.

35. Use the result of Problem 34 to obtain the famous formula of François Viète (1540–1603):

$$\frac{2}{\pi} = \frac{\sqrt{2}}{2} \cdot \frac{\sqrt{2 + \sqrt{2}}}{2} \cdot \frac{\sqrt{2 + \sqrt{2 + \sqrt{2}}}}{2}\cdots$$

36. The shaded region (Figure 3) between one arch of $y = \sin x, 0 \leq x \leq \pi$, and the line $y = k, 0 \leq k \leq 1$, is revolved about the line $y = k$, generating a solid S. Determine k so that S has

(a) minimum volume and　　(b) maximum volume.

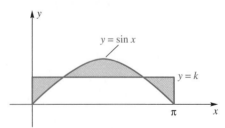

Figure 3

Answers to Concepts Review: **1.** $\int [(1 + \cos 2x)/2] \, dx$
2. $\int(1 - \sin^2 x) \cos x \, dx$　**3.** $\int \sin^2 x(1 - \sin^2 x) \cos x \, dx$
4. $\cos mx \cos nx = \frac{1}{2}[\cos(m + n)x + \cos(m - n)x]$

7.4
Rationalizing Substitutions

Radicals in an integrand are often troublesome and we usually try to get rid of them. Often an appropriate substitution will rationalize the integrand.

Integrands Involving $\sqrt[n]{ax + b}$ If $\sqrt[n]{ax + b}$ appears in an integral, the substitution $u = \sqrt[n]{ax + b}$ will eliminate the radical.

EXAMPLE 1 Find $\displaystyle\int \frac{dx}{x - \sqrt{x}}$.

SOLUTION Let $u = \sqrt{x}$, so $u^2 = x$ and $2u\, du = dx$. Then

$$\int \frac{dx}{x - \sqrt{x}} = \int \frac{2u}{u^2 - u}\, du = 2 \int \frac{1}{u - 1}\, du$$

$$= 2\ln|u - 1| + C = 2\ln|\sqrt{x} - 1| + C \qquad \blacksquare$$

EXAMPLE 2 Find $\displaystyle\int x\sqrt[3]{x - 4}\, dx$.

SOLUTION Let $u = \sqrt[3]{x - 4}$, so $u^3 = x - 4$ and $3u^2\, du = dx$. Then

$$\int x\sqrt[3]{x - 4}\, dx = \int (u^3 + 4)u \cdot (3u^2\, du) = 3\int (u^6 + 4u^3)\, du$$

$$= 3\left[\frac{u^7}{7} + u^4\right] + C = \frac{3}{7}(x - 4)^{7/3} + 3(x - 4)^{4/3} + C \qquad \blacksquare$$

EXAMPLE 3 Find $\displaystyle\int x\sqrt[5]{(x + 1)^2}\, dx$.

SOLUTION Let $u = (x + 1)^{1/5}$, so $u^5 = x + 1$ and $5u^4\, du = dx$. Then

$$\int x(x + 1)^{2/5}\, dx = \int (u^5 - 1)u^2 \cdot 5u^4\, du$$

$$= 5\int (u^{11} - u^6)\, du = \tfrac{5}{12}u^{12} - \tfrac{5}{7}u^7 + C$$

$$= \tfrac{5}{12}(x + 1)^{12/5} - \tfrac{5}{7}(x + 1)^{7/5} + C \qquad \blacksquare$$

Integrands Involving $\sqrt{a^2 - x^2}$, $\sqrt{a^2 + x^2}$ **and** $\sqrt{x^2 - a^2}$ To rationalize these three expressions, we may assume that a is positive and make the following trigonometric substitutions.

Radical	Substitution	Restriction on t
1. $\sqrt{a^2 - x^2}$	$x = a\sin t$	$-\pi/2 \le t \le \pi/2$
2. $\sqrt{a^2 + x^2}$	$x = a\tan t$	$-\pi/2 < t < \pi/2$
3. $\sqrt{x^2 - a^2}$	$x = a\sec t$	$0 \le t \le \pi, t \ne \pi/2$

Now note the simplifications that these substitutions achieve.

1. $\sqrt{a^2 - x^2} = \sqrt{a^2 - a^2\sin^2 t} = \sqrt{a^2\cos^2 t} = |a\cos t| = a\cos t$

2. $\sqrt{a^2 + x^2} = \sqrt{a^2 + a^2\tan^2 t} = \sqrt{a^2\sec^2 t} = |a\sec t| = a\sec t$

3. $\sqrt{x^2 - a^2} = \sqrt{a^2\sec^2 t - a^2} = \sqrt{a^2\tan^2 t} = |a\tan t| = \pm a\tan t$

The restrictions on t allowed us to remove the absolute value signs in the first two cases, but they also achieved something else. These restrictions are exactly the ones we introduced in Section 1.9 in order to make sine, tangent, and secant invertible functions. This means that we can solve the substitution equations for t in each case, and this will allow us to write our final answers in the following examples in terms of x.

EXAMPLE 4 Find $\int \sqrt{a^2 - x^2} \, dx$.

SOLUTION We make the substitution

$$x = a \sin t, \qquad -\frac{\pi}{2} \le t \le \frac{\pi}{2}$$

Then $dx = a \cos t \, dt$ and $\sqrt{a^2 - x^2} = a \cos t$. Thus,

$$\int \sqrt{a^2 - x^2} \, dx = \int a \cos t \cdot a \cos t \, dt = a^2 \int \cos^2 t \, dt$$

$$= \frac{a^2}{2} \int (1 + \cos 2t) \, dt$$

$$= \frac{a^2}{2} \left(t + \frac{1}{2} \sin 2t \right) + C$$

$$= \frac{a^2}{2} (t + \sin t \cos t) + C$$

Now, $x = a \sin t$ is equivalent to $x/a = \sin t$ and, since t was restricted to make the sine function invertible,

$$t = \sin^{-1}\left(\frac{x}{a}\right)$$

Using the right triangle in Figure 1 (as we did in Section 1.9), we see that

$$\cos t = \cos\left[\sin^{-1}\left(\frac{x}{a}\right) \right] = \sqrt{1 - \frac{x^2}{a^2}} = \frac{1}{a}\sqrt{a^2 - x^2}$$

Thus,

$$\int \sqrt{a^2 - x^2} \, dx = \frac{a^2}{2} \sin^{-1}\left(\frac{x}{a}\right) + \frac{x}{2}\sqrt{a^2 - x^2} + C \qquad ■$$

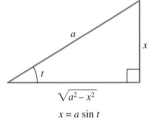

$\sqrt{a^2 - x^2}$

$x = a \sin t$

Figure 1

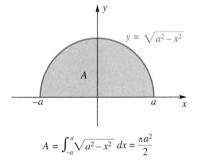

$y = \sqrt{a^2 - x^2}$

A

$-a \qquad a \qquad x$

$A = \int_{-a}^{a} \sqrt{a^2 - x^2} \, dx = \frac{\pi a^2}{2}$

Figure 2

The result in Example 4 allows us to calculate the following definite integral, which represents the area of a semicircle (Figure 2). Thus, calculus confirms a result that we already know.

$$\int_{-a}^{a} \sqrt{a^2 - x^2} \, dx = \left[\frac{a^2}{2} \sin^{-1}\left(\frac{x}{a}\right) + \frac{x}{2}\sqrt{a^2 - x^2} \right]_{-a}^{a} = \frac{a^2}{2}\left[\frac{\pi}{2} + \frac{\pi}{2} \right] = \frac{\pi a^2}{2}$$

EXAMPLE 5 Find $\int \dfrac{dx}{\sqrt{9 + x^2}}$.

SOLUTION Let $x = 3 \tan t$, $-\pi/2 < t < \pi/2$. Then $dx = 3 \sec^2 t \, dt$ and $\sqrt{9 + x^2} = 3 \sec t$.

$$\int \frac{dx}{\sqrt{9 + x^2}} = \int \frac{3 \sec^2 t}{3 \sec t} \, dt = \int \sec t \, dt$$

$$= \ln|\sec t + \tan t| + C$$

The last step, the integration of $\sec t$, was handled in Problem 56 of Section 7.1. Now $\tan t = x/3$, which suggests the triangle in Figure 3, from which we conclude that $\sec t = \sqrt{9 + x^2}/3$. Thus,

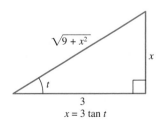

$\sqrt{9 + x^2}$

x

3

$x = 3 \tan t$

Figure 3

$$\int \frac{dx}{\sqrt{9 + x^2}} = \ln\left| \frac{\sqrt{9 + x^2} + x}{3} \right| + C$$

$$= \ln|\sqrt{9 + x^2} + x| - \ln 3 + C$$

$$= \ln|\sqrt{9 + x^2} + x| + K \qquad ■$$

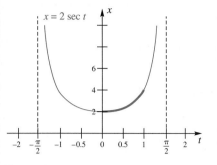

Figure 4

EXAMPLE 6 Calculate $\displaystyle\int_2^4 \frac{\sqrt{x^2 - 4}}{x}\, dx$.

SOLUTION Let $x = 2 \sec t$, where $0 \le t < \pi/2$. Note that the restriction of t to this interval is acceptable, since x is in the interval $2 \le x \le 4$ (see Figure 4). This is important because it allows us to remove the absolute value sign that normally appears when we simplify $\sqrt{x^2 - a^2}$. In our case,

$$\sqrt{x^2 - 4} = \sqrt{4\sec^2 t - 4} = \sqrt{4\tan^2 t} = 2|\tan t| = 2\tan t$$

We now use the theorem on substitution in a definite integral (which requires changing the limits of integration) to write

$$\int_2^4 \frac{\sqrt{x^2 - 4}}{x}\, dx = \int_0^{\pi/3} \frac{2\tan t}{2\sec t}\, 2\sec t \tan t \, dt$$

$$= \int_0^{\pi/3} 2\tan^2 t \, dt = 2\int_0^{\pi/3} (\sec^2 t - 1)\, dt$$

$$= 2\big[\tan t - t\big]_0^{\pi/3} = 2\sqrt{3} - \frac{2\pi}{3} \approx 1.37 \qquad \blacksquare$$

Completing the Square When a quadratic expression of the type $x^2 + Bx + C$ appears under a radical, completing the square will prepare it for a trigonometric substitution.

EXAMPLE 7 Find (a) $\displaystyle\int \frac{dx}{\sqrt{x^2 + 2x + 26}}$ and (b) $\displaystyle\int \frac{2x}{\sqrt{x^2 + 2x + 26}}\, dx$.

SOLUTION

(a) $x^2 + 2x + 26 = x^2 + 2x + 1 + 25 = (x + 1)^2 + 25$. Let $u = x + 1$ and $du = dx$. Then

$$\int \frac{dx}{\sqrt{x^2 + 2x + 26}} = \int \frac{du}{\sqrt{u^2 + 25}}$$

Next let $u = 5\tan t$, $-\pi/2 < t < \pi/2$. Then $du = 5\sec^2 t \, dt$ and $\sqrt{u^2 + 25} = \sqrt{25(\tan^2 t + 1)} = 5\sec t$, so

$$\int \frac{du}{\sqrt{u^2 + 25}} = \int \frac{5\sec^2 t \, dt}{5\sec t} = \int \sec t \, dt$$

$$= \ln|\sec t + \tan t| + C$$

$$= \ln\left|\frac{\sqrt{u^2 + 25}}{5} + \frac{u}{5}\right| + C \qquad \text{(by Figure 5)}$$

$$= \ln|\sqrt{u^2 + 25} + u| - \ln 5 + C$$

$$= \ln|\sqrt{x^2 + 2x + 26} + x + 1| + K$$

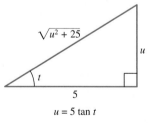

Figure 5

(b) To handle the second integral, we write

$$\int \frac{2x}{\sqrt{x^2 + 2x + 26}}\, dx = \int \frac{2x + 2}{\sqrt{x^2 + 2x + 26}}\, dx - 2\int \frac{1}{\sqrt{x^2 + 2x + 26}}\, dx$$

The first of the integrals on the right is handled by the substitution $u = x^2 + 2x + 26$; the second was just done. We obtain

$$\int \frac{2x}{\sqrt{x^2 + 2x + 26}}\, dx =$$

$$2\sqrt{x^2 + 2x + 26} - 2\ln|\sqrt{x^2 + 2x + 26} + x + 1| + K \qquad \blacksquare$$

Concepts Review

1. To handle $\int x\sqrt{x-3}\,dx$, make the substitution $u = $ _____.

2. To handle an integral involving $\sqrt{4-x^2}$, make the substitution $x = $ _____.

3. To handle an integral involving $\sqrt{4+x^2}$, make the substitution $x = $ _____.

4. To handle an integral involving $\sqrt{x^2-4}$, make the substitution $x = $ _____.

Problem Set 7.4

In Problems 1–16, perform the indicated integrations.

1. $\displaystyle\int x\sqrt{x+1}\,dx$

2. $\displaystyle\int x\sqrt[3]{x+\pi}\,dx$

3. $\displaystyle\int \frac{t\,dt}{\sqrt{3t+4}}$

4. $\displaystyle\int \frac{x^2+3x}{\sqrt{x+4}}\,dx$

5. $\displaystyle\int_1^2 \frac{dt}{\sqrt{t}+e}$

6. $\displaystyle\int_0^1 \frac{\sqrt{t}}{t+1}\,dt$

7. $\displaystyle\int t(3t+2)^{3/2}\,dt$

8. $\displaystyle\int x(1-x)^{2/3}\,dx$

9. $\displaystyle\int \frac{\sqrt{4-x^2}}{x}\,dx$

10. $\displaystyle\int \frac{x^2\,dx}{\sqrt{16-x^2}}$

11. $\displaystyle\int \frac{dx}{(x^2+4)^{3/2}}$

12. $\displaystyle\int_2^3 \frac{dt}{t^2\sqrt{t^2-1}}$

13. $\displaystyle\int_{-2}^{-3} \frac{\sqrt{t^2-1}}{t^3}\,dt$

14. $\displaystyle\int \frac{t}{\sqrt{1-t^2}}\,dt$

15. $\displaystyle\int \frac{2z-3}{\sqrt{1-z^2}}\,dz$

16. $\displaystyle\int_0^\pi \frac{\pi x-1}{\sqrt{x^2+\pi^2}}\,dx$

In Problems 17–26, use the method of completing the square, along with a trigonometric substitution if needed, to evaluate each integral.

17. $\displaystyle\int \frac{dx}{\sqrt{x^2+2x+5}}$

18. $\displaystyle\int \frac{dx}{\sqrt{x^2+4x+5}}$

19. $\displaystyle\int \frac{3x}{\sqrt{x^2+2x+5}}\,dx$

20. $\displaystyle\int \frac{2x-1}{\sqrt{x^2+4x+5}}\,dx$

21. $\displaystyle\int \sqrt{5-4x-x^2}\,dx$

22. $\displaystyle\int \frac{dx}{\sqrt{16+6x-x^2}}$

23. $\displaystyle\int \frac{dx}{\sqrt{4x-x^2}}$

24. $\displaystyle\int \frac{x}{\sqrt{4x-x^2}}\,dx$

25. $\displaystyle\int \frac{2x+1}{x^2+2x+2}\,dx$

26. $\displaystyle\int \frac{2x-1}{x^2-6x+18}\,dx$

27. The region bounded by $y = 1/(x^2+2x+5)$, $y = 0$, $x = 0$, and $x = 1$, is revolved about the x-axis. Find the volume of the resulting solid.

28. The region of Problem 27 is revolved about the y-axis. Find the volume of the resulting solid.

29. Find $\displaystyle\int \frac{x\,dx}{x^2+9}$ by

(a) an algebraic substitution and

(b) a trigonometric substitution. Then reconcile your answers.

30. Find $\displaystyle\int_0^3 \frac{x^3\,dx}{\sqrt{9+x^2}}$ by making the substitutions

$$u = \sqrt{9+x^2}, \quad u^2 = 9+x^2, \quad 2u\,du = 2x\,dx$$

31. Find $\displaystyle\int \frac{\sqrt{4-x^2}}{x}\,dx$ by

(a) the substitution $u = \sqrt{4-x^2}$ and

(b) a trigonometric substitution. Then reconcile your answers.

Hint: $\displaystyle\int \csc x\,dx = \ln|\csc x - \cot x| + C$.

32. Two circles of radius b intersect as shown in Figure 6 with their centers $2a$ apart ($0 \le a \le b$). Find the area of the region of their overlap.

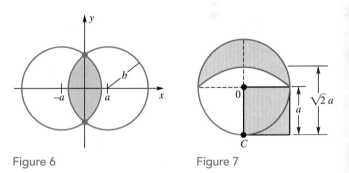

Figure 6   Figure 7

33. Hippocrates of Chios (ca. 430 B.C.) showed that the two shaded regions in Figure 7 have the same area (he squared the lune). Note that C is the center of the lower arc of the lune. Show Hippocrates' result

(a) using calculus and   (b) without calculus.

34. Generalize the idea in Problem 33 by finding a formula for the area of the shaded lune shown in Figure 8.

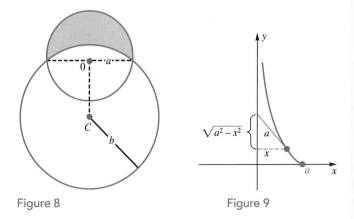

Figure 8   Figure 9

35. Starting at $(a, 0)$, an object is pulled along by a string of length a with the pulling end moving along the positive y-axis (Figure 9). The path of the object is a curve called a **tractrix**

and has the property that the string is always tangent to the curve. Set up a differential equation for the curve and solve it.

7.5
Integration of Rational Functions Using Partial Fractions

A **rational function** is by definition the quotient of two polynomial functions. Examples are

$$f(x) = \frac{2}{(x+1)^3}, \qquad g(x) = \frac{2x+2}{x^2 - 4x + 8}, \qquad h(x) = \frac{x^5 + 2x^3 - x + 1}{x^3 + 5x}$$

Of these, f and g are **proper rational functions,** meaning that the degree of the numerator is less than that of the denominator. An improper (not proper) rational function can always be written as a sum of a polynomial function and a proper rational function. Thus, for example,

$$h(x) = \frac{x^5 + 2x^3 - x + 1}{x^3 + 5x} = x^2 - 3 + \frac{14x + 1}{x^3 + 5x}$$

a result obtained by long division (Figure 1). Since polynomials are easy to integrate, the problem of integrating rational functions is really that of integrating proper rational functions. But can we always integrate proper rational functions? In theory, the answer is yes, though the practical details may be messy. Consider first the integrals of f and g above.

$$\begin{array}{r} x^2 - 3 \\ x^3 + 5x \enclose{longdiv}{x^5 + 2x^3 - x + 1} \\ \underline{x^5 + 5x^3} \\ -3x^3 - x \\ \underline{-3x^3 - 15x} \\ 14x + 1 \end{array}$$

Figure 1

EXAMPLE 1 Find $\displaystyle\int \frac{2}{(x+1)^3}\,dx$.

SOLUTION Think of the substitution $u = x + 1$.

$$\int \frac{2}{(x+1)^3}\,dx = 2\int (x+1)^{-3}\,dx = \frac{2(x+1)^{-2}}{-2} + C$$

$$= -\frac{1}{(x+1)^2} + C \qquad \blacksquare$$

EXAMPLE 2 Find $\displaystyle\int \frac{2x+2}{x^2 - 4x + 8}\,dx$.

SOLUTION Think first of the substitution $u = x^2 - 4x + 8$ for which $du = (2x - 4)\,dx$. Then write the given integral as a sum of two integrals.

$$\int \frac{2x+2}{x^2 - 4x + 8}\,dx = \int \frac{2x - 4}{x^2 - 4x + 8}\,dx + \int \frac{6}{x^2 - 4x + 8}\,dx$$

$$= \ln|x^2 - 4x + 8| + 6\int \frac{1}{x^2 - 4x + 8}\,dx$$

In the second integral, complete the square.

$$\int \frac{1}{x^2 - 4x + 8}\,dx = \int \frac{1}{x^2 - 4x + 4 + 4}\,dx = \int \frac{1}{(x-2)^2 + 4}\,dx$$

$$= \int \frac{1}{(x-2)^2 + 4}\,dx = \frac{1}{2}\tan^{-1}\!\left(\frac{x-2}{2}\right) + C$$

We conclude that

$$\int \frac{2x+2}{x^2 - 4x + 8}\,dx = \ln|x^2 - 4x + 8| + 3\tan^{-1}\!\left(\frac{x-2}{2}\right) + K \qquad \blacksquare$$

It is a remarkable fact that any proper rational function can be written as a sum of *simple* proper rational functions like those illustrated in Examples 1 and 2.

Partial Fraction Decomposition (Linear Factors) To add fractions is a standard algebraic exercise: find a common denominator and add. For example,

$$\frac{2}{x - 1} + \frac{3}{x + 1} = \frac{2(x + 1) + 3(x - 1)}{(x - 1)(x + 1)} = \frac{5x - 1}{(x - 1)(x + 1)} = \frac{5x - 1}{x^2 - 1}$$

It is the reverse process of decomposing a fraction into a sum of simpler fractions that interests us now. We focus on the denominator and consider cases.

EXAMPLE 3 **Distinct Linear Factors** Decompose $(3x - 1)/(x^2 - x - 6)$ and then find its indefinite integral.

SOLUTION Since the denominator factors as $(x + 2)(x - 3)$, it seems reasonable to hope for a decomposition of the following form:

(1) $$\frac{3x - 1}{(x + 2)(x - 3)} = \frac{A}{x + 2} + \frac{B}{x - 3}$$

Our job is, of course, to determine A and B so that (1) is an identity, a task that we find easier after we have multiplied both sides by $(x + 2)(x - 3)$. We obtain

(2) $$3x - 1 = A(x - 3) + B(x + 2)$$

or, equivalently,

(3) $$3x - 1 = (A + B)x + (-3A + 2B)$$

However, (3) is an identity if and only if coefficients of like powers of x on both sides are equal; that is,

$$A + B = 3$$
$$-3A + 2B = -1$$

By solving this pair of equations for A and B, we obtain $A = \frac{7}{5}$, $B = \frac{8}{5}$. Consequently,

$$\frac{3x - 1}{x^2 - x - 6} = \frac{3x - 1}{(x + 2)(x - 3)} = \frac{\frac{7}{5}}{x + 2} + \frac{\frac{8}{5}}{x - 3}$$

and

$$\int \frac{3x - 1}{x^2 - x - 6} \, dx = \frac{7}{5} \int \frac{1}{x + 2} \, dx + \frac{8}{5} \int \frac{1}{x - 3} \, dx$$

$$= \frac{7}{5} \ln|x + 2| + \frac{8}{5} \ln|x - 3| + C \qquad \blacksquare$$

If there was anything difficult about this process, it was the determination of A and B. We found their values by "brute force," but there is an easier way. In (2), which we wish to be an identity (that is, true for *every* value of x), substitute the convenient values $x = 3$ and $x = -2$, obtaining

$$8 = A \cdot 0 + B \cdot 5$$
$$-7 = A \cdot (-5) + B \cdot 0$$

This immediately gives $B = \frac{8}{5}$ and $A = \frac{7}{5}$.

You have just witnessed an odd, but correct, mathematical maneuver. Equation (1) turns out to be an identity (true for all x except -2 and 3) if and only if the essentially equivalent equation (2) is true precisely at -2 and 3. Ask yourself why

---

Solve This D.E.

"Often, there is little resemblance between a differential equation and its solution. Who would suppose that an expression as simple as

$$\frac{dy}{dx} = \frac{1}{a^2 - x^2}$$

could be transformed into

$$y = \frac{1}{2a} \ln\left(\frac{a + x}{a - x}\right) + C$$

This resembles the transformation of a chrysalis into a butterfly."

Silvanus P. Thompson

The method of partial fractions makes this an easy transformation. Do you see how it is done?

this is so. Ultimately it depends on the fact that the two sides of equation (2), both linear polynomials, are identical if they have the same values at any two points.

EXAMPLE 4 **Distinct Linear Factors** Find $\displaystyle\int \frac{5x + 3}{x^3 - 2x^2 - 3x}\, dx$.

SOLUTION Since the denominator factors as $x(x + 1)(x - 3)$, we write

$$\frac{5x + 3}{x(x + 1)(x - 3)} = \frac{A}{x} + \frac{B}{x + 1} + \frac{C}{x - 3}$$

and seek to determine A, B, and C. Clearing the fractions gives

$$5x + 3 = A(x + 1)(x - 3) + Bx(x - 3) + Cx(x + 1)$$

Substitution of the values $x = 0$, $x = -1$, and $x = 3$ results in

$$3 = A(-3)$$
$$-2 = B(4)$$
$$18 = C(12)$$

or $A = -1$, $B = -\frac{1}{2}$, $C = \frac{3}{2}$. Thus,

$$\int \frac{5x + 3}{x^3 - 2x^2 - 3x}\, dx = -\int \frac{1}{x}\, dx - \frac{1}{2}\int \frac{1}{x + 1}\, dx + \frac{3}{2}\int \frac{1}{x - 3}\, dx$$

$$= -\ln|x| - \frac{1}{2}\ln|x + 1| + \frac{3}{2}\ln|x - 3| + C \qquad \blacksquare$$

EXAMPLE 5 **Repeated Linear Factors** Find $\displaystyle\int \frac{x}{(x - 3)^2}\, dx$.

SOLUTION Now the decomposition takes the form

$$\frac{x}{(x - 3)^2} = \frac{A}{x - 3} + \frac{B}{(x - 3)^2}$$

with A and B to be determined. After clearing the fractions, we get

$$x = A(x - 3) + B$$

If we now substitute the convenient value $x = 3$ and any other value, such as $x = 0$, we obtain $B = 3$ and $A = 1$. Thus,

$$\int \frac{x}{(x - 3)^2}\, dx = \int \frac{1}{x - 3}\, dx + 3\int \frac{1}{(x - 3)^2}\, dx$$

$$= \ln|x - 3| - \frac{3}{x - 3} + C \qquad \blacksquare$$

EXAMPLE 6 **Some Distinct, Some Repeated Linear Factors** Find

$$\int \frac{3x^2 - 8x + 13}{(x + 3)(x - 1)^2}\, dx$$

SOLUTION We decompose the integrand in the following way:

$$\frac{3x^2 - 8x + 13}{(x + 3)(x - 1)^2} = \frac{A}{x + 3} + \frac{B}{x - 1} + \frac{C}{(x - 1)^2}$$

Clearing the fractions changes this to

$$3x^2 - 8x + 13 = A(x - 1)^2 + B(x + 3)(x - 1) + C(x + 3)$$

Substitution of $x = 1$, $x = -3$, and $x = 0$ yields $C = 2$, $A = 4$, and $B = -1$. Thus,

$$\int \frac{3x^2 - 8x + 13}{(x + 3)(x - 1)^2} \, dx = 4 \int \frac{dx}{x + 3} - \int \frac{dx}{x - 1} + 2 \int \frac{dx}{(x - 1)^2}$$

$$= 4 \ln|x + 3| - \ln|x - 1| - \frac{2}{x - 1} + C \quad \blacksquare$$

Be sure to note the inclusion of the two fractions $B/(x - 1)$ and $C/(x - 1)^2$ in the decomposition above. The general rule for decomposing fractions with repeated linear factors in the denominator is this: for each factor $(ax + b)^k$ of the denominator, there are k terms in the partial fraction decomposition:

$$\frac{A_1}{ax + b} + \frac{A_2}{(ax + b)^2} + \frac{A_3}{(ax + b)^3} + \cdots + \frac{A_k}{(ax + b)^k}$$

Partial Fraction Decomposition (Quadratic Factors) In factoring the denominator of a fraction, we may well get some quadratic factors, such as $x^2 + 1$, that cannot be factored into linear factors without introducing complex numbers.

EXAMPLE 7 **A Single Quadratic Factor** Decompose $\dfrac{6x^2 - 3x + 1}{(4x + 1)(x^2 + 1)}$ and then find its indefinite integral.

SOLUTION The best we can hope for is a decomposition of the form

$$\frac{6x^2 - 3x + 1}{(4x + 1)(x^2 + 1)} = \frac{A}{4x + 1} + \frac{Bx + C}{x^2 + 1}$$

To determine the constants A, B, and C, we multiply both sides by $(4x + 1)(x^2 + 1)$ and obtain

$$6x^2 - 3x + 1 = A(x^2 + 1) + (Bx + C)(4x + 1)$$

Substitution of $x = -\frac{1}{4}$, $x = 0$, and $x = 1$ yields

$$\frac{6}{16} + \frac{3}{4} + 1 = A\left(\frac{17}{16}\right) \qquad \Rightarrow \qquad A = 2$$

$$1 = 2 + C \qquad \Rightarrow \qquad C = -1$$

$$4 = 4 + (B - 1)5 \qquad \Rightarrow \qquad B = 1$$

Thus,

$$\int \frac{6x^2 - 3x + 1}{(4x + 1)(x^2 + 1)} \, dx = \int \frac{2}{4x + 1} \, dx + \int \frac{x - 1}{x^2 + 1} \, dx$$

$$= \frac{1}{2} \int \frac{4 \, dx}{4x + 1} + \frac{1}{2} \int \frac{2x \, dx}{x^2 + 1} - \int \frac{dx}{x^2 + 1}$$

$$= \frac{1}{2} \ln|4x + 1| + \frac{1}{2} \ln(x^2 + 1) - \tan^{-1} x + C \quad \blacksquare$$

EXAMPLE 8 **A Repeated Quadratic Factor** Find $\displaystyle\int \frac{6x^2 - 15x + 22}{(x + 3)(x^2 + 2)^2} \, dx$.

SOLUTION Here the appropriate decomposition is

$$\frac{6x^2 - 15x + 22}{(x + 3)(x^2 + 2)^2} = \frac{A}{x + 3} + \frac{Bx + C}{x^2 + 2} + \frac{Dx + E}{(x^2 + 2)^2}$$

After considerable work, we discover that $A = 1$, $B = -1$, $C = 3$, $D = -5$, and $E = 0$. Thus,

$$\int \frac{6x^2 - 15x + 22}{(x + 3)(x^2 + 2)^2}\, dx$$

$$= \int \frac{dx}{x + 3} - \int \frac{x - 3}{x^2 + 2}\, dx - 5\int \frac{x}{(x^2 + 2)^2}\, dx$$

$$= \int \frac{dx}{x + 3} - \frac{1}{2}\int \frac{2x}{x^2 + 2}\, dx + 3\int \frac{dx}{x^2 + 2} - \frac{5}{2}\int \frac{2x\, dx}{(x^2 + 2)^2}$$

$$= \ln|x + 3| - \frac{1}{2}\ln(x^2 + 2) + \frac{3}{\sqrt{2}}\tan^{-1}\left(\frac{x}{\sqrt{2}}\right) + \frac{5}{2(x^2 + 2)} + C \quad \blacksquare$$

Summary To decompose a rational function $f(x) = p(x)/q(x)$ into partial fractions, proceed as follows:

Step 1: If $f(x)$ is improper, that is, if $p(x)$ is of degree at least that of $q(x)$, divide $p(x)$ by $q(x)$, obtaining

$$f(x) = \text{a polynomial} + \frac{N(x)}{D(x)}$$

Step 2: Factor $D(x)$ into a product of linear and irreducible quadratic factors with real coefficients. By a theorem of algebra, this is always (theoretically) possible.

Step 3: For each factor of the form $(ax + b)^k$, expect the decomposition to have the terms

$$\frac{A_1}{(ax + b)} + \frac{A_2}{(ax + b)^2} + \cdots + \frac{A_k}{(ax + b)^k}$$

Step 4: For each factor of the form $(ax^2 + bx + c)^m$, expect the decomposition to have the terms

$$\frac{B_1 x + C_1}{ax^2 + bx + c} + \frac{B_2 x + C_2}{(ax^2 + bx + c)^2} + \cdots + \frac{B_m x + C_m}{(ax^2 + bx + c)^m}$$

Step 5: Set $N(x)/D(x)$ equal to the sum of all the terms found in Steps 3 and 4. The number of constants to be determined should equal the degree of the denominator, $D(x)$.

Step 6: Multiply both sides of the equation found in Step 5 by $D(x)$ and solve for the unknown constants. This can be done by either of two methods: (1) Equate co-efficients of like-degree terms or (2) assign convenient values to the variable x.

The Logistic Differential Equation In Section 4.10, we saw that the assumption that the rate of growth of a population is proportional to its size, that is, $y' = ky$, leads to exponential growth. This assumption may be realistic until the available resources in the system are unable to sustain the population. In such a case, more reasonable assumptions are that there is a maximum capacity L that the system can sustain, and that the rate of growth is proportional to the product of the population size y and the "available room" $L - y$. These assumptions lead to the differential equation

$$y' = ky(L - y)$$

This is called the **logistic differential equation.** It is separable and now that we have covered the method of partial fractions, we can perform the necessary integration to solve it.

A Bound for the Answer

The initial population size is 800, and the rate of change in population size, y', is positive, so the population grows. As it nears 2000, the rate of change gets close to zero, so as $t \to \infty$, we have $y \to 2000$. The population at time $t = 2$ should be somewhere between 800 and 2000.

◼ **EXAMPLE 9** A population grows according to the logistic differential equation $y' = 0.0003y(2000 - y)$. The initial population size is 800. Solve this differential equation and use the solution to predict the population size at time $t = 2$.

SOLUTION Writing y' as dy/dt, we see that the differential equation can be written as

$$\frac{dy}{dt} = 0.0003y(2000 - y)$$

$$\frac{dy}{y(2000 - y)} = 0.0003\, dt$$

$$\int \frac{dy}{y(2000 - y)} = \int 0.0003\, dt$$

The integral on the left can be evaluated using the method of partial fractions. We write

$$\frac{1}{y(2000 - y)} = \frac{A}{y} + \frac{B}{2000 - y}$$

which leads to

$$1 = A(2000 - y) + By$$

Substituting $y = 0$ and $y = 2000$ yields

$$1 = 2000A$$

$$1 = 2000B$$

Thus, $A = \dfrac{1}{2000}$ and $B = \dfrac{1}{2000}$, leading to

$$\int \left(\frac{1}{2000y} + \frac{1}{2000(2000 - y)}\right) dy = 0.0003t + C$$

$$\frac{1}{2000}\ln y - \frac{1}{2000}\ln(2000 - y) = 0.0003t + C$$

$$\ln \frac{y}{2000 - y} = 0.6t + 2000C$$

$$\frac{y}{2000 - y} = e^{0.6t + 2000C}$$

$$\frac{y}{2000 - y} = C_1 e^{0.6t}$$

Here, $C_1 = e^{2000C}$. At this point we can use the initial condition $y(0) = 800$ to determine C_1.

$$\frac{800}{2000 - 800} = C_1 e^{0.6 \cdot 0}$$

$$C_1 = \frac{800}{1200} = \frac{2}{3}$$

Thus

$$\frac{y}{2000 - y} = \frac{2}{3}e^{0.6t}$$

$$y = \frac{2}{3}(2000 - y)e^{0.6t}$$

$$y + \frac{2}{3}ye^{0.6t} = \frac{4000}{3}e^{0.6t}$$

$$y = \frac{(4000/3)e^{0.6t}}{1 + (2/3)e^{0.6t}} = \frac{4000/3}{2/3 + e^{-0.6t}}$$

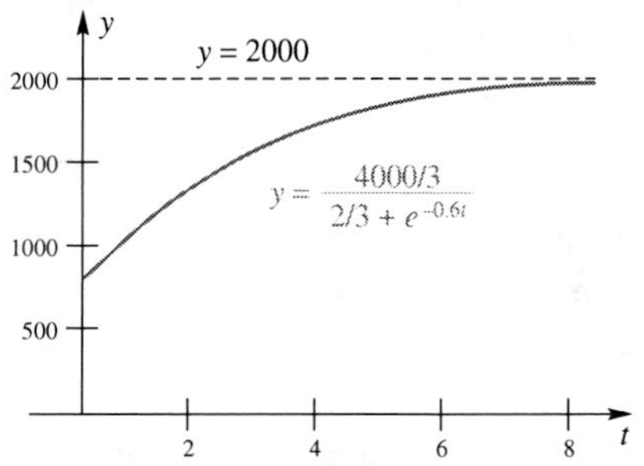

The population at time $t = 2$ is thus

$$y = \frac{4000/3}{2/3 + e^{-0.6 \cdot 2}} \approx 1378$$

A sketch of the population size as a function of t is given in Figure 2. ∎

Figure 2

Concepts Review

1. If the degree of the polynomial $p(x)$ is less than the degree of $q(x)$, then $f(x) = p(x)/q(x)$ is called a _____ rational function.

2. To integrate the improper rational function $f(x) = (x^2 + 4)/(x + 1)$, we first rewrite it as $f(x) = $ _____.

3. If $(x - 1)(x + 1) + 3x + x^2 = ax^2 + bx + c$, then $a = $ _____, $b = $ _____, and $c = $ _____.

4. $(3x + 1)/[(x - 1)^2(x^2 + 1)]$ can be decomposed in the form _____.

Problem Set 7.5

In Problems 1–40, use the method of partial fraction decomposition to perform the required integration.

1. $\int \dfrac{1}{x(x + 1)} \, dx$

2. $\int \dfrac{2}{x^2 + 3x} \, dx$

3. $\int \dfrac{3}{x^2 - 1} \, dx$

4. $\int \dfrac{5x}{2x^3 + 6x^2} \, dx$

5. $\int \dfrac{x - 11}{x^2 + 3x - 4} \, dx$

6. $\int \dfrac{x - 7}{x^2 - x - 12} \, dx$

7. $\int \dfrac{3x - 13}{x^2 + 3x - 10} \, dx$

8. $\int \dfrac{x + \pi}{x^2 - 3\pi x + 2\pi^2} \, dx$

9. $\int \dfrac{2x + 21}{2x^2 + 9x - 5} \, dx$

10. $\int \dfrac{2x^2 - x - 20}{x^2 + x - 6} \, dx$

11. $\int \dfrac{17x - 3}{3x^2 + x - 2} \, dx$

12. $\int \dfrac{5 - x}{x^2 - x(\pi + 4) + 4\pi} \, dx$

13. $\int \dfrac{2x^2 + x - 4}{x^3 - x^2 - 2x} \, dx$

14. $\int \dfrac{7x^2 + 2x - 3}{(2x - 1)(3x + 2)(x - 3)} \, dx$

15. $\int \dfrac{6x^2 + 22x - 23}{(2x - 1)(x^2 + x - 6)} \, dx$

16. $\int \dfrac{x^3 - 6x^2 + 11x - 6}{4x^3 - 28x^2 + 56x - 32} \, dx$

17. $\int \dfrac{x^3}{x^2 + x - 2} \, dx$

18. $\int \dfrac{x^3 + x^2}{x^2 + 5x + 6} \, dx$

19. $\int \dfrac{x^4 + 8x^2 + 8}{x^3 - 4x} \, dx$

20. $\int \dfrac{x^6 + 4x^3 + 4}{x^3 - 4x^2} \, dx$

21. $\int \dfrac{x + 1}{(x - 3)^2} \, dx$

22. $\int \dfrac{5x + 7}{x^2 + 4x + 4} \, dx$

23. $\int \dfrac{3x + 2}{x^3 + 3x^2 + 3x + 1} \, dx$

24. $\int \dfrac{x^6}{(x - 2)^2(1 - x)^5} \, dx$

25. $\int \dfrac{3x^2 - 21x + 32}{x^3 - 8x^2 + 16x} \, dx$

26. $\int \dfrac{x^2 + 19x + 10}{2x^4 + 5x^3} \, dx$

27. $\int \dfrac{2x^2 + x - 8}{x^3 + 4x} \, dx$

28. $\int \dfrac{3x + 2}{x(x + 2)^2 + 16x} \, dx$

29. $\int \dfrac{2x^2 - 3x - 36}{(2x - 1)(x^2 + 9)} \, dx$

30. $\int \dfrac{1}{x^4 - 16} \, dx$

31. $\int \dfrac{1}{(x - 1)^2(x + 4)^2} \, dx$

32. $\int \dfrac{x^3 - 8x^2 - 1}{(x + 3)(x^2 - 4x + 5)} \, dx$

33. $\int \dfrac{(\sin^3 t - 8\sin^2 t - 1)\cos t}{(\sin t + 3)(\sin^2 t - 4\sin t + 5)} \, dt$

34. $\int \dfrac{\cos t}{\sin^4 t - 16} \, dt$

35. $\int \dfrac{x^3 - 4x}{(x^2 + 1)^2} \, dx$

36. $\int \dfrac{(\sin t)(4\cos^2 t - 1)}{(\cos t)(1 + 2\cos^2 t + \cos^4 t)} \, dt$

37. $\int \dfrac{2x^3 + 5x^2 + 16x}{x^5 + 8x^3 + 16x} \, dx$

38. $\int_4^6 \dfrac{x - 17}{x^2 + x - 12} \, dx$

39. $\int_0^{\pi/4} \dfrac{\cos \theta}{(1 - \sin^2 \theta)(\sin^2 \theta + 1)^2} \, d\theta$

40. $\int_1^5 \dfrac{3x + 13}{x^2 + 4x + 3} \, dx$

In Problems 41–44, solve the logistic differential equation representing population growth with the given initial condition. Then use the solution to predict the population size at time $t = 3$.

41. $y' = y(1 - y)$, $y(0) = 0.5$

42. $y' = \dfrac{1}{10}y(12 - y)$, $y(0) = 2$

43. $y' = 0.0003y\,(8000 - y)$, $y(0) = 1000$

44. $y' = 0.001y\,(4000 - y)$, $y(0) = 100$

45. Solve the logistic differential equation for an arbitrary constant of proportionality k, capacity L, and initial condition $y(0) = y_0$.

46. Explain what happens to the solution of the logistic differential equation if the initial population size is *larger* than the maximum capacity.

47. Without solving the logistic equation or referring to its solution, explain how you know that if $y_0 < L$, then the population size is increasing.

48. Consider the logistic equation with initial condition $y(0) = y_0$. Assuming $y_0 < L$, for what values of t is the graph of the population size $y(t)$ concave up?

49. Suppose that the earth will not support a population of more than 16 billion and that there were 2 billion people in 1925 and 4 billion people in 1975. Then, if y is the population t years after 1925, an appropriate model is the logistic differential equation

$$\frac{dy}{dt} = ky(16 - y)$$

(a) Solve this differential equation.

(b) Predict the population in 2015.

(c) When will the population be 9 billion?

50. Do Problem 49 assuming that the upper limit for the population is 10 billion.

51. The Law of Mass Action in chemistry results in the differential equation

$$\frac{dx}{dt} = k(a - x)(b - x), \qquad k > 0, \quad a > 0, \quad b > 0$$

where x is the amount of a substance at time t resulting from the reaction of two others. Assume that $x = 0$ when $t = 0$.

(a) Solve this differential equation in the case $b > a$.

(b) Show that $x \to a$ as $t \to \infty$ (if $b > a$).

(c) Suppose that $a = 2$ and $b = 4$, and that 1 gram of the substance is formed in 20 minutes. How much will be present in 1 hour?

(d) Solve the differential equation if $a = b$.

52. The differential equation

$$\frac{dy}{dt} = k(y - m)(M - y), \quad y(0) = y_0$$

with $k > 0$ and $0 \le m < y_0 < M$ is used to model some growth problems. Solve the equation and find $\lim\limits_{t \to \infty} y$.

53. As a model for the production of trypsin from trypsinogen in digestion, biochemists have proposed the model

$$\frac{dy}{dt} = k(A - y)(B + y)$$

where $k > 0$, A is the initial amount of trypsinogen, and B is the original amount of trypsin. Solve this differential equation.

54. Evaluate

$$\int_{\pi/6}^{\pi/2} \frac{\cos x}{\sin x(\sin^2 x + 1)^2} \, dx$$

Answers to Concepts Review: **1.** proper

2. $x - 1 + \dfrac{5}{x + 1}$ **3.** $2; 3; -1$

4. $\dfrac{A}{x - 1} + \dfrac{B}{(x - 1)^2} + \dfrac{Cx + D}{x^2 + 1}$

CHAPTER 8

Indeterminate Forms and Improper Integrals

8.1
Indeterminate Forms of Type 0/0

Here are three familiar limit problems:

$$\lim_{x\to 0}\frac{\sin x}{x}, \qquad \lim_{x\to 3}\frac{x^2-9}{x^2-x-6}, \qquad \lim_{x\to a}\frac{f(x)-f(a)}{x-a}$$

The first was treated at length in Section 1.4, and the third actually defines the derivative $f'(a)$. The three limits have a common feature. In each case, a quotient is involved and, in each case, both numerator and denominator have 0 as their limits. An attempt to apply part 7 of the Main Limit Theorem (Theorem 2.3A), which says that the limit of a quotient is equal to the quotient of the limits, leads to the nonsensical result 0/0. In fact, the theorem does not apply, since it requires that the limit of the denominator be different from 0. We are not saying that these limits do not exist, only that the Main Limit Theorem will not determine them.

You may recall that an intricate geometric argument led us to the conclusion $\lim_{x\to 0}(\sin x)/x = 1$ (Theorem 2.5B). On the other hand, the algebraic technique of factoring yields

$$\lim_{x\to 3}\frac{x^2-9}{x^2-x-6}=\lim_{x\to 3}\frac{(x-3)(x+3)}{(x-3)(x+2)}=\lim_{x\to 3}\frac{x+3}{x+2}=\frac{6}{5}$$

Would it not be nice to have a standard procedure for handling all problems for which the limits of the numerator and denominator are both 0? That is too much to hope for. However, there is a simple rule that works beautifully on a wide variety of such problems.

L'Hôpital's Rule In 1696, Guillaume François Antoine de l'Hôpital published the first textbook on differential calculus; it included the following rule, which he had learned from his teacher Johann Bernoulli.

Theorem A | **L'Hôpital's Rule for forms of type 0/0**

Suppose that $\lim_{x\to u}f(x)=\lim_{x\to u}g(x)=0$. If $\lim_{x\to u}[f'(x)/g'(x)]$ exists in either the finite or infinite sense (i.e., if this limit is a finite number or $-\infty$ or $+\infty$), then

$$\lim_{x\to u}\frac{f(x)}{g(x)}=\lim_{x\to u}\frac{f'(x)}{g'(x)}$$

Before attempting to prove this theorem, we illustrate it. Note that l'Hôpital's Rule allows us to replace one limit by another, which may be simpler and, in particular, may not have the 0/0 form.

EXAMPLE 1 Use l'Hôpital's Rule to show that

$$\lim_{x\to 0}\frac{\sin x}{x}=1 \quad \text{and} \quad \lim_{x\to 0}\frac{1-\cos x}{x}=0$$

Geometric Interpretation of l'Hôpital's Rule

Study the diagrams below. They should make l'Hôpital's Rule seem quite reasonable. (See Problems 38–42.)

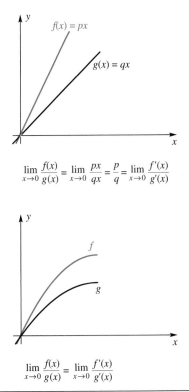

$$\lim_{x\to 0}\frac{f(x)}{g(x)}=\lim_{x\to 0}\frac{px}{qx}=\frac{p}{q}=\lim_{x\to 0}\frac{f'(x)}{g'(x)}$$

$$\lim_{x\to 0}\frac{f(x)}{g(x)}=\lim_{x\to 0}\frac{f'(x)}{g'(x)}$$

SOLUTION We worked pretty hard to demonstrate these two facts in Section 2.5. After noting that trying to evaluate both limits by substitution leads to the form 0/0, we can now establish the desired results in two lines (but see Problem 25). By l'Hôpital's Rule,

$$\lim_{x \to 0} \frac{\sin x}{x} = \lim_{x \to 0} \frac{D_x \sin x}{D_x x} = \lim_{x \to 0} \frac{\cos x}{1} = 1$$

$$\lim_{x \to 0} \frac{1 - \cos x}{x} = \lim_{x \to 0} \frac{D_x(1 - \cos x)}{D_x x} = \lim_{x \to 0} \frac{\sin x}{1} = 0 \qquad \blacksquare$$

EXAMPLE 2 Find $\lim_{x \to 3} \dfrac{x^2 - 9}{x^2 - x - 6}$ and $\lim_{x \to 2^+} \dfrac{x^2 + 3x - 10}{x^2 - 4x + 4}$.

SOLUTION Both limits have the 0/0 form, so, by l'Hôpital's Rule,

$$\lim_{x \to 3} \frac{x^2 - 9}{x^2 - x - 6} = \lim_{x \to 3} \frac{2x}{2x - 1} = \frac{6}{5}$$

$$\lim_{x \to 2^+} \frac{x^2 + 3x - 10}{x^2 - 4x + 4} = \lim_{x \to 2^+} \frac{2x + 3}{2x - 4} = \infty$$

The first of these limits was handled at the beginning of this section by factoring and simplifying. Of course, we get the same answer either way. $\qquad \blacksquare$

EXAMPLE 3 Find $\lim_{x \to 0} \dfrac{\tan 2x}{\ln(1 + x)}$.

SOLUTION Both numerator and denominator have limit 0. Hence,

$$\lim_{x \to 0} \frac{\tan 2x}{\ln(1 + x)} = \lim_{x \to 0} \frac{2 \sec^2 2x}{1/(1 + x)} = \frac{2}{1} = 2 \qquad \blacksquare$$

Sometimes $\lim f'(x)/g'(x)$ also has the indeterminate form 0/0. Then we may apply l'Hôpital's Rule again, as we now illustrate. Each application of l'Hôpital's Rule is flagged with the symbol (L)

EXAMPLE 4 Find $\lim_{x \to 0} \dfrac{\sin x - x}{x^3}$.

SOLUTION By l'Hôpital's Rule applied three times in succession,

$$\lim_{x \to 0} \frac{\sin x - x}{x^3} \overset{(L)}{=} \lim_{x \to 0} \frac{\cos x - 1}{3x^2}$$

$$\overset{(L)}{=} \lim_{x \to 0} \frac{-\sin x}{6x}$$

$$\overset{(L)}{=} \lim_{x \to 0} \frac{-\cos x}{6} = -\frac{1}{6} \qquad \blacksquare$$

Just because we have an elegant rule does not mean that we should use it indiscriminately. In particular, we must always make sure that it applies; that is, we must make sure that the limit has the indeterminate form 0/0. Otherwise, we will be led into all kinds of errors, as we now illustrate.

EXAMPLE 5 Find $\displaystyle\lim_{x\to 0}\frac{1-\cos x}{x^2+3x}$.

SOLUTION We might be tempted to write

$$\lim_{x\to 0}\frac{1-\cos x}{x^2+3x}\overset{L}{\underset{=}{\;}}\lim_{x\to 0}\frac{\sin x}{2x+3}\overset{L}{\underset{=}{\;}}\lim_{x\to 0}\frac{\cos x}{2}=\frac{1}{2}\quad\text{WRONG}$$

The first application of l'Hôpital's Rule was correct; the second was not, since at that stage, the limit did not have the 0/0 form. Here is what we should have done.

$$\lim_{x\to 0}\frac{1-\cos x}{x^2+3x}\overset{L}{\underset{=}{\;}}\lim_{x\to 0}\frac{\sin x}{2x+3}=0\quad\text{RIGHT}$$

We stop differentiating as soon as either the numerator or denominator has a nonzero limit. ∎

Even if the conditions of l'Hôpital's Rule hold, an application of l'Hôpital's Rule may not help us; witness the following example.

EXAMPLE 6 Find $\displaystyle\lim_{x\to\infty}\frac{e^{-x}}{x^{-1}}$.

SOLUTION Since the numerator and denominator both tend to 0, the limit is indeterminate of the form 0/0. Thus, the conditions of Theorem A hold. We may apply l'Hôpital's Rule indefinitely.

$$\lim_{x\to\infty}\frac{e^{-x}}{x^{-1}}\overset{L}{\underset{=}{\;}}\lim_{x\to\infty}\frac{e^{-x}}{x^{-2}}\overset{L}{\underset{=}{\;}}\lim_{x\to\infty}\frac{e^{-x}}{2x^{-3}}=\cdots$$

Clearly, we are only complicating the problem. A better approach is to do a bit of algebra first.

$$\lim_{x\to\infty}\frac{e^{-x}}{x^{-1}}=\lim_{x\to\infty}\frac{x}{e^x}$$

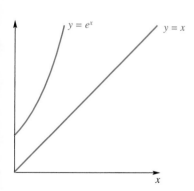

Written this way, the limit is indeterminate of the form ∞/∞, the subject of the next section. However, you should be able to guess that the limit is 0 by considering how much faster e^x grows than x (see Figure 1). A rigorous demonstration will come later (Example 1 of Section 8.2). ∎

Cauchy's Mean Value Theorem The proof of l'Hôpital's Rule depends on an extension of the Mean Value Theorem for Derivatives due to Augustin Louis Cauchy (1789–1857).

Figure 1

Theorem B **Cauchy's Mean Value Theorem**

Let the functions f and g be differentiable on (a, b) and continuous on $[a, b]$. If $g'(x)\neq 0$ for all x in (a, b), then there exists a number c in (a, b) such that

$$\frac{f(b)-f(a)}{g(b)-g(a)}=\frac{f'(c)}{g'(c)}$$

Note that this theorem reduces to the ordinary Mean Value Theorem for Derivatives (Theorem 4.6A) when $g(x)=x$.

Proof It is tempting to apply the ordinary Mean Value Theorem to both numerator and denominator of the left side of the conclusion. If we do this, we obtain

(1) $$f(b) - f(a) = f'(c_1)(b - a)$$

and

(2) $$g(b) - g(a) = g'(c_2)(b - a)$$

for appropriate choices of c_1 and c_2. If only c_1 and c_2 were equal, we could divide the first equality by the second and be done; but there is no reason to hope for such a coincidence. However, this attempt is not a complete failure since (2) yields the valuable information that $g(b) - g(a) \neq 0$, a fact we will need later (this follows from the hypothesis that $g'(x) \neq 0$ for all x in (a, b)).

Recall that the proof of the Mean Value Theorem for Derivatives (Theorem 4.6A) rested on the introduction of an auxiliary function s. If we try to mimic that proof, we are led to the following choice for $s(x)$. Let

$$s(x) = f(x) - f(a) - \frac{f(b) - f(a)}{g(b) - g(a)}[g(x) - g(a)]$$

No division by zero is involved since we earlier established that $g(b) - g(a) \neq 0$. Note further that $s(a) = 0 = s(b)$. Also, s is continuous on $[a, b]$ and differentiable on (a, b), this following from the corresponding facts for f and g. Thus, by the Mean Value Theorem for Derivatives, there is a number c in (a, b) such that

$$s'(c) = \frac{s(b) - s(a)}{b - a} = \frac{0 - 0}{b - a} = 0$$

But

$$s'(c) = f'(c) - \frac{f(b) - f(a)}{g(b) - g(a)}g'(c) = 0$$

so

$$\frac{f'(c)}{g'(c)} = \frac{f(b) - f(a)}{g(b) - g(a)}$$

which is what we wished to prove.   ∎

Proof of L'Hôpital's Rule

Proof Refer back to Theorem A, which actually states several theorems at once. We will prove only the case where L is finite and the limit is the one-sided limit $\lim_{x \to a^+}$.

The hypotheses for Theorem A imply more than they say explicitly. In particular, the existence of $\lim_{x \to a^+}[f'(x)/g'(x)]$ implies that both $f'(x)$ and $g'(x)$ exist in at least a small interval $(a, b]$ and that $g'(x) \neq 0$ there. At a, we do not even know that f and g are defined, but we do know that $\lim_{x \to a^+} f(x) = 0$ and $\lim_{x \to a^+} g(x) = 0$. Thus, we may define (or redefine if necessary) both $f(a)$ and $g(a)$ to be zero, thereby making both f and g (right) continuous at a. All this is to say that f and g satisfy the hypotheses of Cauchy's Mean Value Theorem on $[a, b]$. Consequently, there is a number c in (a, b) such that

$$\frac{f(b) - f(a)}{g(b) - g(a)} = \frac{f'(c)}{g'(c)}$$

or, since $f(a) = 0 = g(a)$,

$$\frac{f(b)}{g(b)} = \frac{f'(c)}{g'(c)}$$

When we let $b \to a^+$, thereby forcing $c \to a^+$, we obtain

$$\lim_{b \to a^+} \frac{f(b)}{g(b)} = \lim_{c \to a^+} \frac{f'(c)}{g'(c)}$$

which is equivalent to what we wanted to prove.

A very similar proof works for the case of left-hand limits and thus for two-sided limits. The proofs for limits at infinity and infinite limits are harder, and we omit them. ∎

Concepts Review

1. L'Hôpital's Rule is useful in finding $\lim_{x \to a}[f(x)/g(x)]$, where both _____ and _____ are zero.

2. L'Hôpital's Rule says that under appropriate conditions $\lim_{x \to a} f(x)/g(x) = \lim_{x \to a}$ _____.

3. From l'Hôpital's Rule, we can conclude that $\lim_{x \to 0}(\tan x)/x = \lim_{x \to 0}$ _____ = _____, but l'Hôpital's Rule gives us no information about $\lim_{x \to 0}(\cos x)/x$ because _____.

4. The proof of l'Hôpital's Rule depends on _____ Theorem.

Problem Set 8.1

In Problems 1–24, find the indicated limit. Make sure that you have an indeterminate form before you apply l'Hôpital's Rule.

1. $\lim_{x \to 0} \dfrac{2x - \sin x}{x}$

2. $\lim_{x \to \pi/2} \dfrac{\cos x}{\frac{1}{2}\pi - x}$

3. $\lim_{x \to 0} \dfrac{x - \sin 2x}{\tan x}$

4. $\lim_{x \to 0} \dfrac{\tan^{-1} 3x}{\sin^{-1} x}$

5. $\lim_{x \to -2} \dfrac{x^2 + 6x + 8}{x^2 - 3x - 10}$

6. $\lim_{x \to 0} \dfrac{x^3 - 3x^2 + x}{x^3 - 2x}$

7. $\lim_{x \to 1^-} \dfrac{x^2 - 2x + 2}{x^2 - 1}$

8. $\lim_{x \to 1} \dfrac{\ln x^2}{x^2 - 1}$

9. $\lim_{x \to \pi/2} \dfrac{\ln(\sin x)^3}{\frac{1}{2}\pi - x}$

10. $\lim_{x \to 0} \dfrac{e^x - e^{-x}}{2 \sin x}$

11. $\lim_{t \to 1} \dfrac{\sqrt{t} - t^2}{\ln t}$

12. $\lim_{x \to 0^+} \dfrac{7^{\sqrt{x}} - 1}{2^{\sqrt{x}} - 1}$

13. $\lim_{x \to 0} \dfrac{\ln \cos 2x}{7x^2}$

14. $\lim_{x \to 0^-} \dfrac{3 \sin x}{\sqrt{-x}}$

15. $\lim_{x \to 0} \dfrac{\tan x - x}{\sin 2x - 2x}$

16. $\lim_{x \to 0} \dfrac{\sin x - \tan x}{x^2 \sin x}$

17. $\lim_{x \to 0^+} \dfrac{x^2}{\sin x - x}$

18. $\lim_{x \to 0} \dfrac{e^x - \ln(1 + x) - 1}{x^2}$

19. $\lim_{x \to 0} \dfrac{\tan^{-1} x - x}{8x^3}$

20. $\lim_{x \to 0} \dfrac{\cosh x - 1}{x^2}$

21. $\lim_{x \to 0^+} \dfrac{1 - \cos x - x \sin x}{2 - 2 \cos x - \sin^2 x}$

22. $\lim_{x \to 0^-} \dfrac{\sin x + \tan x}{e^x + e^{-x} - 2}$

23. $\lim_{x \to 0} \dfrac{\displaystyle\int_0^x \sqrt{1 + \sin t}\, dt}{x}$

24. $\lim_{x \to 0^+} \dfrac{\displaystyle\int_0^x \sqrt{t} \cos t\, dt}{x^2}$

25. In Section 2.5, we worked very hard to prove that $\lim_{x \to 0}(\sin x)/x = 1$; l'Hôpital's Rule allows us to show this in one line. However, even if we had l'Hôpital's Rule, say at the end of Section 2.4, it would not have helped us. Explain why. (We really did need to establish $\lim_{x \to 0} \dfrac{\sin x}{x} = 1$ the way we did in Section 2.5.)

26. Find $\lim_{x \to 0} \dfrac{x^2 \sin(1/x)}{\tan x}$.

Hint: Begin by deciding why l'Hôpital's Rule is not applicable. Then find the limit by other means.

27. For Figure 2, compute the following limits.

(a) $\lim_{t \to 0^+} \dfrac{\text{area of triangle } ABC}{\text{area of curved region } ABC}$

(b) $\lim_{t \to 0^+} \dfrac{\text{area of curved region } BCD}{\text{area of curved region } ABC}$

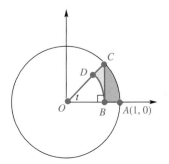

Figure 2

28. In Figure 3, $CD = DE = DF = t$. Find each limit.

(a) $\lim\limits_{t \to 0^+} y$

(b) $\lim\limits_{t \to 0^+} x$

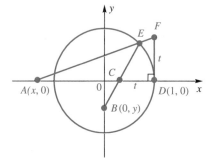

Figure 3

29. Let

$$f(x) = \begin{cases} \dfrac{e^x - 1}{x}, & \text{if } x \neq 0 \\ c, & \text{if } x = 0 \end{cases}$$

What value of c makes $f(x)$ continuous at $x = 0$?

30. Let

$$f(x) = \begin{cases} \dfrac{\ln x}{x - 1}, & \text{if } x \neq 1 \\ c, & \text{if } x = 1 \end{cases}$$

What value of c makes $f(x)$ continuous at $x = 1$?

31. Using the concepts of Section 6.4, you can show that the surface area of the prolate spheroid gotten by rotating the ellipse $x^2/a^2 + y^2/b^2 = 1$ $(a > b)$ about the x-axis is

$$A = 2\pi b^2 + 2\pi ab\left[\frac{a}{\sqrt{a^2 - b^2}} \arcsin \frac{\sqrt{a^2 - b^2}}{a}\right]$$

What should A approach as $a \to b^+$? Use l'Hôpital's Rule to show that this does happen.

32. Determine constants a, b, and c so that

$$\lim_{x \to 1} \frac{ax^4 + bx^3 + 1}{(x - 1)\sin \pi x} = c$$

33. L'Hôpital's Rule in its 1696 form said this: If $\lim\limits_{x \to a} f(x) = \lim\limits_{x \to a} g(x) = 0$, then $\lim\limits_{x \to a} f(x)/g(x) = f'(a)/g'(a)$, provided that $f'(a)$ and $g'(a)$ both exist and $g'(a) \neq 0$. Prove this result without recourse to Cauchy's Mean Value Theorem.

[CAS] *Use a CAS to evaluate the limits in Problems 34–37.*

34. $\lim\limits_{x \to 0} \dfrac{\cos x - 1 + x^2/2}{x^4}$

35. $\lim\limits_{x \to 0} \dfrac{e^x - 1 - x - x^2/2 - x^3/6}{x^4}$

36. $\lim\limits_{x \to 0} \dfrac{1 - \cos(x^2)}{x^3 \sin x}$

37. $\lim\limits_{x \to 0} \dfrac{\tan x - x}{\arcsin x - x}$

[GC] *For Problems 38–41, plot the numerator $f(x)$ and the denominator $g(x)$ in the same graph window for each of these domains: $-1 \leq x \leq 1$, $-0.1 \leq x \leq 0.1$, and $-0.01 \leq x \leq 0.01$. From the plot, estimate the values of $f'(x)$ and $g'(x)$ and use these to approximate the given limit.*

38. $\lim\limits_{x \to 0} \dfrac{3x - \sin x}{x}$

39. $\lim\limits_{x \to 0} \dfrac{\sin x/2}{x}$

40. $\lim\limits_{x \to 0} \dfrac{x}{e^{2x} - 1}$

41. $\lim\limits_{x \to 0} \dfrac{e^x - 1}{e^{-x} - 1}$

[EXPL] **42.** Use the concept of the **linear approximation** to a function (Section 3.11) to explain the geometric interpretation of l'Hôpital's Rule in the marginal box next to Theorem A.

Answers to Concepts Review: **1.** $\lim\limits_{x \to a} f(x); \lim\limits_{x \to a} g(x)$
2. $f'(x)/g'(x)$ **3.** $\sec^2 x$; 1; $\lim\limits_{x \to 0} \cos x \neq 0$ **4.** Cauchy's Mean Value

---

8.2
Other Indeterminate Forms

In the solution to Example 6 of the previous section, we faced the following limit problem.

$$\lim_{x \to \infty} \frac{x}{e^x}$$

This is typical of a class of problems of the form $\lim\limits_{x \to \infty} f(x)/g(x)$, where both numerator and denominator are growing indefinitely large; we call it an indeterminate form of type ∞/∞. It turns out that l'Hôpital's Rule also applies in this situation; that is,

$$\lim_{x \to \infty} \frac{f(x)}{g(x)} = \lim_{x \to \infty} \frac{f'(x)}{g'(x)}$$

A rigorous proof is quite difficult, but there is an intuitive way of seeing that the result has to be true. Imagine that $f(t)$ and $g(t)$ represent the positions of two cars on the t-axis at time t (Figure 1). These two cars, the f-car and the g-car, are on endless journeys with respective velocities $f'(t)$ and $g'(t)$. Now, if

$$\lim_{t \to \infty} \frac{f'(t)}{g'(t)} = L$$

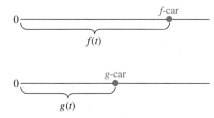

Figure 1

then ultimately the *f*-car travels about *L* times as fast as the *g*-car. It is therefore reasonable to say that, in the long run, it will travel about *L* times as far; that is,

$$\lim_{t \to \infty} \frac{f(t)}{g(t)} = L$$

We do not call this a proof, but it does lend plausibility to a result that we now state formally.

Theorem A **L'Hôpital's Rule for Forms of Type ∞/∞**

Suppose that $\lim_{x \to u} |f(x)| = \lim_{x \to u} |g(x)| = \infty$. If $\lim_{x \to u} [f'(x)/g'(x)]$ exists in either the finite or infinite sense, then

$$\lim_{x \to u} \frac{f(x)}{g(x)} = \lim_{x \to u} \frac{f'(x)}{g'(x)}$$

Here *u* may stand for any of the symbols $a, a^-, a^+, -\infty$, or ∞.

The Indeterminate Form ∞/∞ We use Theorem A to finish Example 6 of the previous section.

EXAMPLE 1 Find $\lim_{x \to \infty} \dfrac{x}{e^x}$.

SOLUTION Both *x* and e^x tend to ∞ as $x \to \infty$. Hence, by l'Hôpital's Rule,

$$\lim_{x \to \infty} \frac{x}{e^x} = \lim_{x \to \infty} \frac{D_x x}{D_x e^x} = \lim_{x \to \infty} \frac{1}{e^x} = 0 \qquad \blacksquare$$

Here is a general result of the same type.

EXAMPLE 2 Show that, if *a* is any positive real number, $\lim_{x \to \infty} \dfrac{x^a}{e^x} = 0$.

SOLUTION Suppose as a special case that $a = 2.5$. Then three applications of l'Hôpital's Rule give

$$\lim_{x \to \infty} \frac{x^{2.5}}{e^x} \overset{\text{L}}{=} \lim_{x \to \infty} \frac{2.5 x^{1.5}}{e^x} \overset{\text{L}}{=} \lim_{x \to \infty} \frac{(2.5)(1.5)x^{0.5}}{e^x} \overset{\text{L}}{=} \lim_{x \to \infty} \frac{(2.5)(1.5)(0.5)}{x^{0.5}e^x} = 0$$

A similar argument works for any $a > 0$. Let *m* denote the greatest integer less than *a*. Then $m + 1$ applications of l'Hôpital's Rule give

$$\lim_{x \to \infty} \frac{x^a}{e^x} \overset{\text{L}}{=} \lim_{x \to \infty} \frac{ax^{a-1}}{e^x} \overset{\text{L}}{=} \lim_{x \to \infty} \frac{a(a-1)x^{a-2}}{e^x} \overset{\text{L}}{=} \cdots \overset{\text{L}}{=} \lim_{x \to \infty} \frac{a(a-1)\cdots(a-m)}{x^{m+1-a}e^x} = 0$$

$\blacksquare$

EXAMPLE 3 Show that, if *a* is any positive real number, $\lim_{x \to \infty} \dfrac{\ln x}{x^a} = 0$.

Figure 2

SOLUTION Both $\ln x$ and x^a tend to ∞ as $x \to \infty$. Hence, by one application of l'Hôpital's Rule,

$$\lim_{x \to \infty} \frac{\ln x}{x^a} \overset{L}{=} \lim_{x \to \infty} \frac{1/x}{ax^{a-1}} = \lim_{x \to \infty} \frac{1}{ax^a} = 0 \quad \blacksquare$$

Examples 2 and 3 say something that is worth remembering: *for sufficiently large x, e^x grows faster as x increases than any constant power of x, whereas $\ln x$ grows more slowly than any constant power of x.* For example, when x is sufficiently large, e^x grows faster than x^{100} and $\ln x$ grows more slowly than $\sqrt[100]{x}$. The chart in the margin and Figure 2 offer additional illustration.

EXAMPLE 4 Find $\displaystyle\lim_{x \to 0^+} \frac{\ln x}{\cot x}$.

SOLUTION As $x \to 0^+$, $\ln x \to -\infty$ and $\cot x \to \infty$, so l'Hôpital's Rule applies.

$$\lim_{x \to 0^+} \frac{\ln x}{\cot x} \overset{L}{=} \lim_{x \to 0^+} \left[\frac{1/x}{-\csc^2 x} \right]$$

This is still indeterminate as it stands, but rather than apply l'Hôpital's Rule again (which only makes things worse), we rewrite the expression in brackets as

$$\frac{1/x}{-\csc^2 x} = -\frac{\sin^2 x}{x} = -\sin x \frac{\sin x}{x}$$

Thus,

$$\lim_{x \to 0^+} \frac{\ln x}{\cot x} = \lim_{x \to 0^+} \left[-\sin x \frac{\sin x}{x} \right] = 0 \cdot 1 = 0 \quad \blacksquare$$

The Indeterminate Forms $0 \cdot \infty$ and $\infty - \infty$ Suppose that $A(x) \to 0$, but $B(x) \to \infty$. What is going to happen to the product $A(x)B(x)$? Two competing forces are at work, tending to pull the product in opposite directions. Which will win this battle, A or B or neither? It depends on whether one is stronger (i.e., doing its job at a faster rate) or whether they are evenly matched. L'Hôpital's Rule will help us to decide, but only after we have transformed the problem to a $0/0$ or ∞/∞ form.

EXAMPLE 5 Find $\displaystyle\lim_{x \to \pi/2} (\tan x \cdot \ln \sin x)$.

SOLUTION Since $\displaystyle\lim_{x \to \pi/2} \ln \sin x = 0$ and $\displaystyle\lim_{x \to \pi/2} |\tan x| = \infty$, this is a $0 \cdot \infty$ indeterminate form. We can rewrite it as a $0/0$ form by the simple device of changing $\tan x$ to $1/\cot x$. Thus,

$$\lim_{x \to \pi/2} (\tan x \cdot \ln \sin x) = \lim_{x \to \pi/2} \frac{\ln \sin x}{\cot x}$$

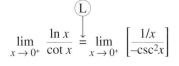

$$\overset{L}{=} \lim_{x \to \pi/2} \frac{\dfrac{1}{\sin x} \cdot \cos x}{-\csc^2 x}$$

$$= \lim_{x \to \pi/2} (-\cos x \cdot \sin x) = 0 \quad \blacksquare$$

EXAMPLE 6 Find $\displaystyle\lim_{x\to1^+}\left(\dfrac{x}{x-1}-\dfrac{1}{\ln x}\right)$.

SOLUTION The first term is growing without bound; so is the second. We say that the limit is an $\infty-\infty$ indeterminate form. L'Hôpital's Rule will determine the result, but only after we rewrite the problem in a form for which the rule applies. In this case, the two fractions must be combined, a procedure that changes the problem to a $0/0$ form. Two applications of l'Hôpital's Rule yield

$$\lim_{x\to1^+}\left(\frac{x}{x-1}-\frac{1}{\ln x}\right)=\lim_{x\to1^+}\frac{x\ln x-x+1}{(x-1)\ln x}\overset{L}{=}\lim_{x\to1^+}\frac{x\cdot1/x+\ln x-1}{(x-1)(1/x)+\ln x}$$

$$=\lim_{x\to1^+}\frac{x\ln x}{x-1+x\ln x}\overset{L}{=}\lim_{x\to1^+}\frac{1+\ln x}{2+\ln x}=\frac{1}{2}$$

∎

The Indeterminate Forms 0^0, ∞^0, 1^∞   We turn now to three indeterminate forms of exponential type. Here the trick is to consider not the original expression, but rather its logarithm. Usually, l'Hôpital's Rule will apply to the logarithm.

EXAMPLE 7 Find $\displaystyle\lim_{x\to0^+}(x+1)^{\cot x}$.

SOLUTION This takes the indeterminate form 1^∞. Let $y=(x+1)^{\cot x}$, so

$$\ln y=\cot x\ln(x+1)=\frac{\ln(x+1)}{\tan x}$$

Using l'Hôpital's Rule for $0/0$ forms, we obtain

$$\lim_{x\to0^+}\ln y=\lim_{x\to0^+}\frac{\ln(x+1)}{\tan x}\overset{L}{=}\lim_{x\to0^+}\frac{\dfrac{1}{x+1}}{\sec^2x}=1$$

Now $y=e^{\ln y}$, and since the exponential function $f(x)=e^x$ is continuous,

$$\lim_{x\to0^+}y=\lim_{x\to0^+}\exp(\ln y)=\exp\left(\lim_{x\to0^+}\ln y\right)=\exp1=e$$

∎

EXAMPLE 8 Find $\displaystyle\lim_{x\to\pi/2^-}(\tan x)^{\cos x}$.

SOLUTION This has the indeterminate form ∞^0. Let $y=(\tan x)^{\cos x}$, so

$$\ln y=\cos x\cdot\ln\tan x=\frac{\ln\tan x}{\sec x}$$

Then

$$\lim_{x\to\pi/2^-}\ln y=\lim_{x\to\pi/2^-}\frac{\ln\tan x}{\sec x}\overset{L}{=}\lim_{x\to\pi/2^-}\frac{\dfrac{1}{\tan x}\cdot\sec^2x}{\sec x\tan x}$$

$$=\lim_{x\to\pi/2^-}\frac{\sec x}{\tan^2x}=\lim_{x\to\pi/2^-}\frac{\cos x}{\sin^2x}=0$$

Therefore,

$$\lim_{x \to \pi/2^-} y = e^0 = 1$$ ∎

Summary We have classified certain limit problems as indeterminate forms, using the seven symbols $0/0$, ∞/∞, $0 \cdot \infty$, $\infty - \infty$, 0^0, ∞^0, and 1^∞. Each involves a competition of opposing forces, which means that the result is not obvious. However, with the help of l'Hôpital's Rule, which applies directly only to the $0/0$ and ∞/∞ forms, we can usually determine the limit.

There are many other possibilities symbolized by, for example, $0/\infty$, $\infty/0$, $\infty + \infty$, $\infty \cdot \infty$, 0^∞, and ∞^∞. Why don't we call these indeterminate forms? Because, in each of these cases, the forces work together, not in competition.

EXAMPLE 9 Find $\lim_{x \to 0^+} (\sin x)^{\cot x}$.

SOLUTION We might call this a 0^∞ form, but it is not indeterminate. Note that $\sin x$ is approaching zero, and raising it to the exponent $\cot x$, an increasingly large number, serves only to make it approach zero faster. Thus,

$$\lim_{x \to 0^+} (\sin x)^{\cot x} = 0$$ ∎

Concepts Review

1. If $\lim_{x \to a} f(x) = \lim_{x \to a} g(x) = \infty$, then l'Hôpital's Rule says that $\lim_{x \to a} f(x)/g(x) = \lim_{x \to a}$ ____.

2. If $\lim_{x \to a} f(x) = 0$ and $\lim_{x \to a} g(x) = \infty$, then $\lim_{x \to a} f(x)g(x)$ is an indeterminate form. To apply l'Hôpital's Rule, we may rewrite this latter limit as ____.

3. Seven indeterminate forms are discussed in this book. They are symbolized by $0/0$, ∞/∞, $0 \cdot \infty$, and ____.

4. e^x grows faster than any power of x, but ____ grows more slowly than any power of x.

Problem Set 8.2

Find each limit in Problems 1–40. Be sure you have an indeterminate form before applying l'Hôpital's Rule.

1. $\displaystyle\lim_{x \to \infty} \frac{\ln x^{10000}}{x}$

2. $\displaystyle\lim_{x \to \infty} \frac{(\ln x)^2}{2^x}$

3. $\displaystyle\lim_{x \to \infty} \frac{x^{10000}}{e^x}$

4. $\displaystyle\lim_{x \to \infty} \frac{3x}{\ln(100x + e^x)}$

5. $\displaystyle\lim_{x \to \pi/2} \frac{3 \sec x + 5}{\tan x}$

6. $\displaystyle\lim_{x \to 0^+} \frac{\ln \sin^2 x}{3 \ln \tan x}$

7. $\displaystyle\lim_{x \to \infty} \frac{\ln(\ln x^{1000})}{\ln x}$

8. $\displaystyle\lim_{x \to (1/2)^-} \frac{\ln(4 - 8x)^2}{\tan \pi x}$

9. $\displaystyle\lim_{x \to 0^+} \frac{\cot x}{\sqrt{-\ln x}}$

10. $\displaystyle\lim_{x \to 0} \frac{2 \csc^2 x}{\cot^2 x}$

11. $\displaystyle\lim_{x \to 0} (x \ln x^{1000})$

12. $\displaystyle\lim_{x \to 0} 3x^2 \csc^2 x$

13. $\displaystyle\lim_{x \to 0} (\csc^2 x - \cot^2 x)$

14. $\displaystyle\lim_{x \to \pi/2} (\tan x - \sec x)$

15. $\displaystyle\lim_{x \to 0^+} (3x)^{x^2}$

16. $\displaystyle\lim_{x \to 0} (\cos x)^{\csc x}$

17. $\displaystyle\lim_{x \to (\pi/2)^-} (5 \cos x)^{\tan x}$

18. $\displaystyle\lim_{x \to 0} \left(\csc^2 x - \frac{1}{x^2} \right)^2$

19. $\displaystyle\lim_{x \to 0} (x + e^{x/3})^{3/x}$

20. $\displaystyle\lim_{x \to (\pi/2)^-} (\cos 2x)^{x - \pi/2}$

21. $\displaystyle\lim_{x \to \pi/2} (\sin x)^{\cos x}$

22. $\displaystyle\lim_{x \to \infty} x^x$

23. $\displaystyle\lim_{x \to \infty} x^{1/x}$

24. $\displaystyle\lim_{x \to 0} (\cos x)^{1/x^2}$

25. $\displaystyle\lim_{x \to 0^+} (\tan x)^{2/x}$

26. $\displaystyle\lim_{x \to -\infty} (e^{-x} - x)$

27. $\displaystyle\lim_{x \to 0^+} (\sin x)^x$

28. $\displaystyle\lim_{x \to 0} (\cos x - \sin x)^{1/x}$

29. $\displaystyle\lim_{x \to 0} \left(\csc x - \frac{1}{x} \right)$

30. $\displaystyle\lim_{x \to \infty} \left(1 + \frac{1}{x} \right)^x$

31. $\displaystyle\lim_{x \to 0^+} (1 + 2e^x)^{1/x}$

32. $\displaystyle\lim_{x \to 1} \left(\frac{1}{x - 1} - \frac{x}{\ln x} \right)$

33. $\displaystyle\lim_{x \to 0} (\cos x)^{1/x}$

34. $\displaystyle\lim_{x \to 0^+} (x^{1/2} \ln x)$

35. $\displaystyle\lim_{x \to \infty} e^{\cos x}$

36. $\displaystyle\lim_{x \to \infty} [\ln(x + 1) - \ln(x - 1)]$

37. $\displaystyle\lim_{x \to 0^+} \frac{x}{\ln x}$

38. $\displaystyle\lim_{x \to 0^+} (\ln x \cot x)$

39. $\displaystyle\lim_{x \to \infty} \frac{\displaystyle\int_1^x \sqrt{1 + e^{-t}}\, dt}{x}$

40. $\displaystyle\lim_{x \to 1^+} \frac{\displaystyle\int_1^x \sin t\, dt}{x - 1}$

41. Find each limit. *Hint:* Transform to problems involving a continuous variable x. Assume that $a > 0$.

(a) $\displaystyle\lim_{n \to \infty} \sqrt[n]{a}$

(b) $\displaystyle\lim_{n \to \infty} \sqrt[n]{n}$

(c) $\displaystyle\lim_{n \to \infty} n(\sqrt[n]{a} - 1)$

(d) $\displaystyle\lim_{n \to \infty} n(\sqrt[n]{n} - 1)$

42. Find each limit.

(a) $\lim\limits_{x \to 0^+} x^x$

(b) $\lim\limits_{x \to 0^+} (x^x)^x$

(c) $\lim\limits_{x \to 0^+} x^{(x^x)}$

(d) $\lim\limits_{x \to 0^+} ((x^x)^x)^x$

(e) $\lim\limits_{x \to 0^+} x^{(x^{(x^x)})}$

43. Graph $y = x^{1/x}$ for $x > 0$. Show what happens for very small x and very large x. Indicate the maximum value.

44. Find each limit.

(a) $\lim\limits_{x \to 0^+} (1^x + 2^x)^{1/x}$

(b) $\lim\limits_{x \to 0^-} (1^x + 2^x)^{1/x}$

(c) $\lim\limits_{x \to \infty} (1^x + 2^x)^{1/x}$

(d) $\lim\limits_{x \to -\infty} (1^x + 2^x)^{1/x}$

45. For $k \geq 0$, find

$$\lim\limits_{n \to \infty} \frac{1^k + 2^k + \cdots + n^k}{n^{k+1}}$$

Hint: Though this has the ∞/∞ form, l'Hôpital's Rule is not helpful. Think of a Riemann sum.

46. Let $c_1, c_2, \ldots, c_n$ be positive constants with $\sum\limits_{i=1}^{n} c_i = 1$, and let $x_1, x_2, \ldots, x_n$ be positive numbers. Take natural logarithms and then use l'Hôpital's Rule to show that

$$\lim\limits_{t \to 0^+} \left(\sum\limits_{i=1}^{n} c_i x_i^t \right)^{1/t} = x_1^{c_1} x_2^{c_2} \cdots x_n^{c_n} = \prod\limits_{i=1}^{n} x_i^{c_i}$$

Here $\prod$ means product; that is, $\prod\limits_{i=1}^{n} a_i$ means $a_1 \cdot a_2 \cdot \cdots \cdot a_n$. In particular, if $a, b, x,$ and y are positive and $a + b = 1$, then

$$\lim\limits_{t \to 0^+} (ax^t + by^t)^{1/t} = x^a y^b$$

47. Verify the last statement in Problem 46 by calculating each of the following.

(a) $\lim\limits_{t \to 0^+} \left(\frac{1}{2} 2^t + \frac{1}{2} 5^t \right)^{1/t}$

(b) $\lim\limits_{t \to 0^+} \left(\frac{1}{5} 2^t + \frac{4}{5} 5^t \right)^{1/t}$

(c) $\lim\limits_{t \to 0^+} \left(\frac{1}{10} 2^t + \frac{9}{10} 5^t \right)^{1/t}$

48. Consider $f(x) = n^2 x e^{-nx}$.

(a) Graph $f(x)$ for $n = 1, 2, 3, 4, 5, 6$ on $[0, 1]$ in the same graph window.

(b) For $x > 0$, find $\lim\limits_{n \to \infty} f(x)$.

(c) Evaluate $\int_0^1 f(x)\, dx$ for $n = 1, 2, 3, 4, 5, 6$.

(d) Guess at $\lim\limits_{n \to \infty} \int_0^1 f(x)\, dx$. Then justify your answer rigorously.

CAS **49.** Find the absolute maximum and minimum points (if they exist) for $f(x) = (x^{25} + x^3 + 2^x)e^{-x}$ on $[0, \infty)$.

Answers to Concepts Review: **1.** $f'(x)/g'(x)$
2. $\lim\limits_{x \to a} f(x)/[1/g(x)]$ or $\lim\limits_{x \to a} g(x)/[1/f(x)]$
3. $\infty - \infty, 0^0, \infty^0, 1^\infty$ **4.** $\ln x$

12.1
Functions of Two or More Variables

Two kinds of functions have been emphasized so far. The first, typified by $f(x) = x^2$, associates with the real number x another real number $f(x)$. We call it a **real-valued function of a real variable.** The second type of function, illustrated by $\mathbf{f}(x) = \langle x^3, e^x \rangle$, associates with the real number x a vector $\mathbf{f}(x)$. We call it a **vector-valued function of a real variable.**

Our interest shifts now to a **real-valued function of two real variables,** that is, a function f (Figure 1) that assigns to each ordered pair (x, y) in some set D of the plane a (unique) real number $f(x, y)$. Examples are

$$(1) \qquad\qquad f(x, y) = x^2 + 3y^2$$

$$(2) \qquad\qquad g(x, y) = 2x\sqrt{y}$$

Note that $f(-1, 4) = (-1)^2 + 3(4)^2 = 49$ and $g(-1, 4) = 2(-1)\sqrt{4} = -4$.

The set D is called the **domain** of the function. If it is not specified, we take D to be the natural domain, that is, the set of all points (x, y) in the plane for which the function rule makes sense and gives a real number value. For $f(x, y) = x^2 + 3y^2$, the natural domain is the whole plane; for $g(x, y) = 2x\sqrt{y}$, it is $\{(x, y): -\infty < x < \infty, y \geq 0\}$. The **range** of a function is its set of values. If $z = f(x, y)$, we call x and y the **independent variables** and z the **dependent variable.**

All that we have said extends in a natural way to real-valued functions of three real variables (or even n real variables). We will feel free to use such functions without further comment.

■ EXAMPLE 1 In the xy-plane, sketch the natural domain for

$$f(x, y) = \frac{\sqrt{y - x^2}}{x^2 + (y - 1)^2}$$

SOLUTION For this rule to make sense, we must exclude $\{(x, y): y < x^2\}$ and the point $(0, 1)$. The resulting domain is shown in Figure 2. ■

Graphs By the **graph** of a function f of two variables, we mean the graph of the equation $z = f(x, y)$. This graph will normally be a surface (Figure 3) and, since to each (x, y) in the domain there corresponds just one value z, each line perpendicular to the xy-plane intersects the surface in at most one point.

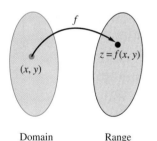

Domain   Range

Figure 1

Figure 2

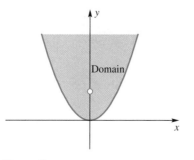

Figure 3

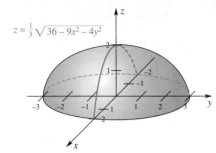

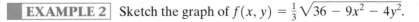

$z = \frac{1}{3}\sqrt{36 - 9x^2 - 4y^2}$

Figure 4

EXAMPLE 2 Sketch the graph of $f(x, y) = \frac{1}{3}\sqrt{36 - 9x^2 - 4y^2}$.

SOLUTION Let $z = \frac{1}{3}\sqrt{36 - 9x^2 - 4y^2}$ and note that $z \geq 0$. If we square both sides and simplify, we obtain the equation

$$9x^2 + 4y^2 + 9z^2 = 36$$

which we recognize as the equation of an ellipsoid (see Section 11.8). The graph of the given function is the upper half of this ellipsoid; it is shown in Figure 4. ■

EXAMPLE 3 Sketch the graph of $z = f(x, y) = y^2 - x^2$.

SOLUTION The graph is a hyperbolic paraboloid (see Section 11.8); it is graphed in Figure 5. ■

Computer Graphs A number of software packages, including *Maple* and *Mathematica*, can produce complicated three-dimensional graphs with ease. In Figures 6 through 9, we show four such graphs. Often, as in these four examples, we choose to show the graph with the y-axis pointing partially toward the viewer, rather than keeping it in the plane of the paper. Also, we often show the axes in a frame around the outside of the graph, rather than in the usual position, which could interfere with our view of the graph. The variable (x or y) indicating the axis is placed near the center of the axis that it represents.

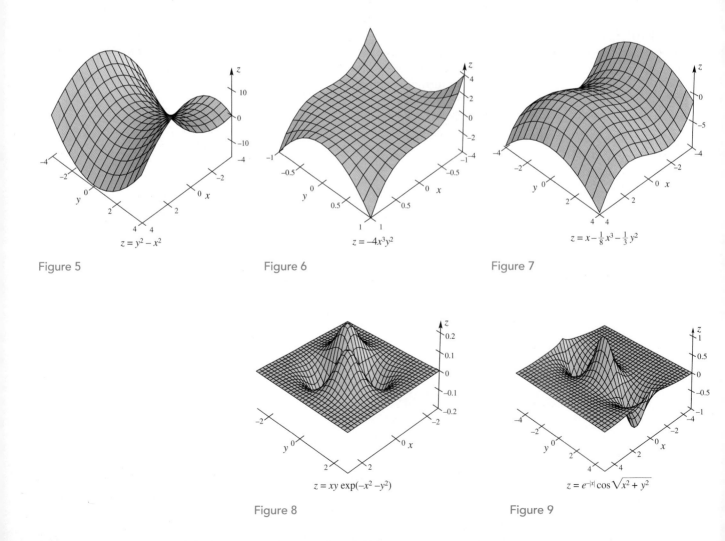

$z = y^2 - x^2$

Figure 5

$z = -4x^3y^2$

Figure 6

$z = x - \frac{1}{8}x^3 - \frac{1}{3}y^2$

Figure 7

$z = xy \exp(-x^2 - y^2)$

Figure 8

$z = e^{-|x|}\cos\sqrt{x^2 + y^2}$

Figure 9

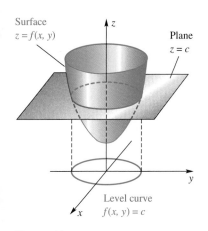

Surface
$z = f(x, y)$

Plane
$z = c$

Level curve
$f(x, y) = c$

Figure 10

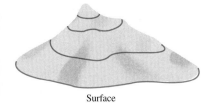

Surface

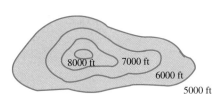

8000 ft   7000 ft

6000 ft

5000 ft

Contour map
with level curves

Figure 11

Contour Map $z = xy$

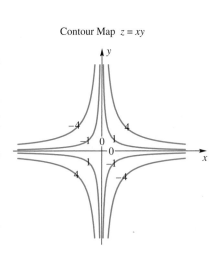

Figure 14

Level Curves

To sketch the surface corresponding to the graph of a function $z = f(x, y)$ of two variables is often very difficult. Map makers have given us another and usually simpler way to picture a surface: the contour map. Each horizontal plane $z = c$ intersects the surface in a curve. The projection of this curve on the xy-plane is called a **level curve** (Figure 10), and a collection of such curves is a **contour plot** or a **contour map.** We show a contour map for a hill-shaped surface in Figure 11.

We will often show contours on the three-dimensional graph itself, as is done in the top diagram in Figure 11. When this is done, we will usually make the y-axis go away from the viewer and the x-axis go to the right. This will help us to see the connection between the three-dimensional plot and the contour plot.

EXAMPLE 4 Draw contour maps for the surfaces corresponding to $z = \frac{1}{3}\sqrt{36 - 9x^2 - 4y^2}$ and $z = y^2 - x^2$ (see Examples 2 and 3, and Figures 4 and 5).

SOLUTION The level curves of $z = \frac{1}{3}\sqrt{36 - 9x^2 - 4y^2}$ corresponding to $z = 0, 1, 1.5, 1.75, 2$ are shown in Figure 12. They are ellipses. Similarly, in Figure 13, we show the level curves of $z = y^2 - x^2$ for $z = -5, -4, -3, \ldots, 2, 3, 4$. These curves are hyperbolas unless $z = 0$. The level curve for $z = 0$ is a pair of intersecting lines. ∎

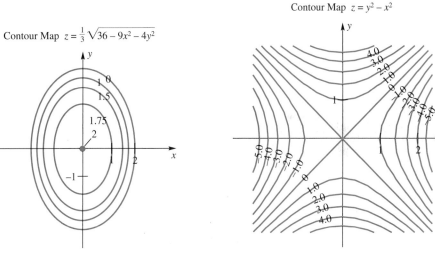

Contour Map $z = \frac{1}{3}\sqrt{36 - 9x^2 - 4y^2}$

Figure 12

Contour Map $z = y^2 - x^2$

Figure 13

EXAMPLE 5 Sketch a contour map for $z = f(x, y) = xy$.

SOLUTION The level curves corresponding to $z = -4, -1, 0, 1, 4$ are shown in Figure 14. It can be shown that they are hyperbolas. Comparing the contour map of Figure 14 with that of Figure 13 suggests that the graph of $z = xy$ might be a hyperbolic paraboloid but with axes rotated through 45°. The suggestion is correct. ∎

Computer Graphs and Level Curves

In Figures 15 through 19, we have drawn five more surfaces, but we now also show the corresponding level curves. A third plot is a three-dimensional plot with level curves on the surface. Note that we have rotated the xy-plane so that the x-axis points to the right, making it easier to relate the surface and the level curves.

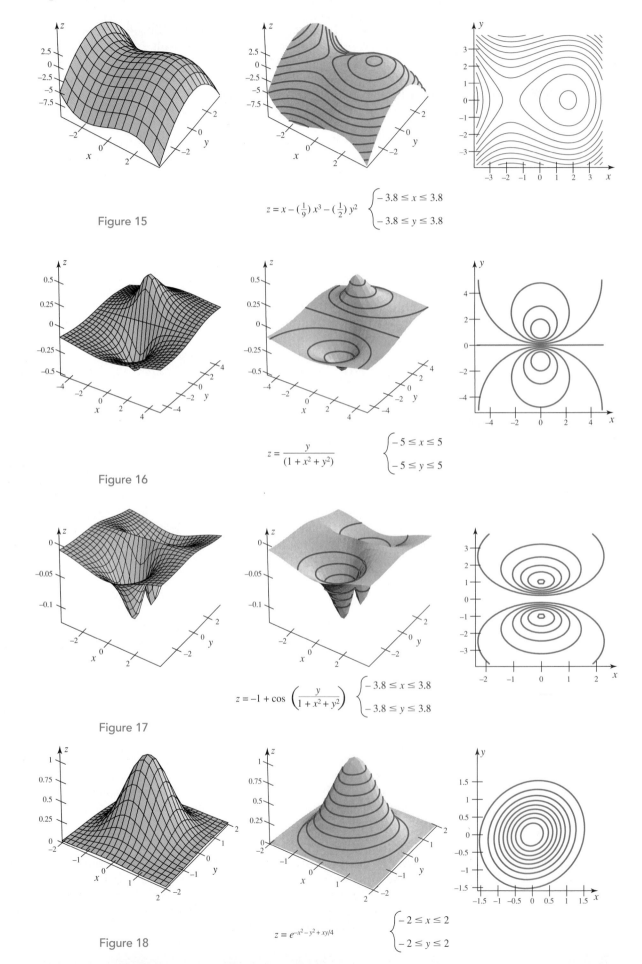

Figure 15

$$z = x - \left(\tfrac{1}{9}\right) x^3 - \left(\tfrac{1}{2}\right) y^2 \quad \begin{cases} -3.8 \le x \le 3.8 \\ -3.8 \le y \le 3.8 \end{cases}$$

Figure 16

$$z = \frac{y}{(1 + x^2 + y^2)} \quad \begin{cases} -5 \le x \le 5 \\ -5 \le y \le 5 \end{cases}$$

Figure 17

$$z = -1 + \cos\left(\frac{y}{1 + x^2 + y^2}\right) \quad \begin{cases} -3.8 \le x \le 3.8 \\ -3.8 \le y \le 3.8 \end{cases}$$

Figure 18

$$z = e^{-x^2 - y^2 + xy/4} \quad \begin{cases} -2 \le x \le 2 \\ -2 \le y \le 2 \end{cases}$$

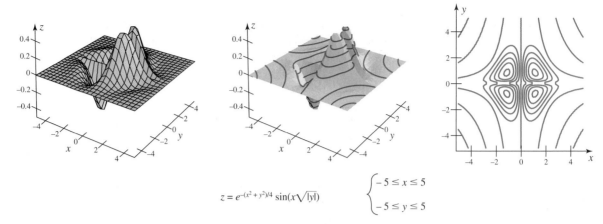

$$z = e^{-(x^2 + y^2)/4} \sin(x\sqrt{|y|})$$

$$\begin{cases} -5 \leq x \leq 5 \\ -5 \leq y \leq 5 \end{cases}$$

Figure 19

Applications of Contour Plots   Contour maps are frequently used to show weather or other conditions at various points on a map. Temperature, for example, varies from place to place. We can envision $T(x, y)$ as being equal to the temperature at the location (x, y). Level curves for equal temperatures are called **isotherms** or **isothermal curves.** Figure 20 shows an isothermal map for the United States.

On April 9, 1917, a strong earthquake centered near the Mississippi river just south of St. Louis was felt as far north as Iowa and as far south as Mississippi. The intensity of an earthquake is measured from I to XII, with higher numbers corresponding to a more severe earthquake. A magnitude VI earthquake will cause physical damage to structures. Figure 21 shows an example of another type of contour map. If we envision the intensity I as a function of the location (x, y), then we can illustrate the earthquake's intensity using a map with level curves corresponding to equal intensity. Curves with constant intensity are called **isoseismic curves.** Figure 21 shows that the regions that experienced an intensity of VI include the St. Louis area and a strip in southeastern Missouri. Much of eastern Missouri and southwestern Illinois experienced an intensity between V and VI. Since Kansas City and Memphis are near the same isoseismic curve, the intensity was about the same in Kansas City and Memphis.

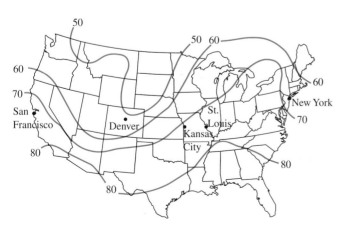

Figure 20

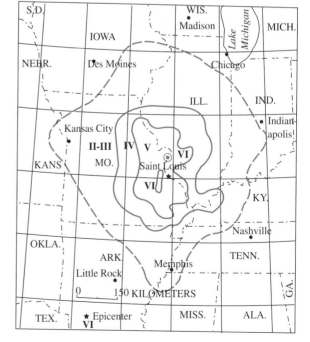

Figure 21

Functions of Three or More Variables A number of quantities depend on three or more variables. For example, the temperature in a large auditorium may depend on the location (x, y, z); this leads to the function $T(x, y, z)$. The velocity of a fluid may depend on the location (x, y, z), as well as on time t; this leads to the function $V(x, y, z, t)$. Finally, the average exam score in a class of 50 students depends on the 50 exam scores $x_1, x_2, \ldots, x_{50}$; this leads to the function $A(x_1, x_2, \ldots, x_{50})$.

We can visualize functions of three variables by plotting **level surfaces**, that is, surfaces in three-dimensional space that lead to a constant value for the function. Functions of four or more variables are much more difficult to visualize. The natural domain of a function of three or more variables is the set of all ordered triples (or quadruples, etc.) for which the function makes sense and gives a real number.

■ **EXAMPLE 6** Find the domain of each function and describe the level surfaces for f.

(a) $f(x, y, z) = \sqrt{x^2 + y^2 + z^2 - 1}$

(b) $g(w, x, y, z) = \dfrac{1}{\sqrt{w^2 + x^2 + y^2 + z^2 - 1}}$

SOLUTION

(a) To avoid roots of negative numbers, the ordered triple (x, y, z) must satisfy $x^2 + y^2 + z^2 - 1 \geq 0$. Thus, the domain for f consists of all points (x, y, z) that are on or outside the unit sphere. Level surfaces for f are surfaces in three-space where $f(x, y, z) = \sqrt{x^2 + y^2 + z^2 - 1} = c$. As long as $c \geq 0$, this relationship leads to $x^2 + y^2 + z^2 = c + 1$, a sphere centered at the origin. Level surfaces are therefore concentric spheres centered at $(0, 0, 0)$.

(b) The ordered quadruple (w, x, y, z) must satisfy $w^2 + x^2 + y^2 + z^2 - 1 > 0$, since we must avoid roots of negative numbers and division by 0. ■

■ **EXAMPLE 7** Let $F(x, y, z) = z - x^2 - y^2$. Describe the level surfaces for F and plot level surfaces for $-1, 0, 1,$ and 2.

SOLUTION The relationship $F(x, y, z) = z - x^2 - y^2 = c$ leads to $z = c + x^2 + y^2$. This is a paraboloid opening upward having vertex at $(0, 0, c)$. The level surfaces are shown in Figure 22. ■

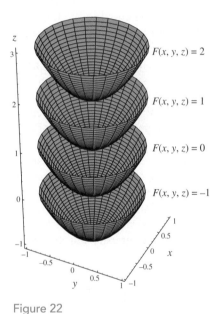

$F(x, y, z) = 2$

$F(x, y, z) = 1$

$F(x, y, z) = 0$

$F(x, y, z) = -1$

Figure 22

Concepts Review

1. A function f determined by $z = f(x, y)$ is called a(n) _____.

2. The projection of the curve $z = f(x, y) = c$ to the xy-plane is called a(n) _____, and a collection of such curves is called a(n) _____.

3. The contour map for $z = x^2 + y^2$ consists of _____.

4. The contour map for $z = x^2$ consists of _____.

Problem Set 12.1

1. Let $f(x, y) = x^2 y + \sqrt{y}$. Find each value.

(a) $f(2, 1)$

(b) $f(3, 0)$

(c) $f(1, 4)$

(d) $f(a, a^4)$

(e) $f(1/x, x^4)$

(f) $f(2, -4)$

What is the natural domain for this function?

2. Let $f(x, y) = y/x + xy$. Find each value.

(a) $f(1, 2)$

(b) $f\left(\tfrac{1}{4}, 4\right)$

(c) $f\left(4, \tfrac{1}{4}\right)$

(d) $f(a, a)$

(e) $f(1/x, x^2)$

(f) $f(0, 0)$

What is the natural domain for this function?

3. Let $g(x, y, z) = x^2 \sin yz$. Find each value.

(a) $g(1, \pi, 2)$

(b) $g(2, 1, \pi/6)$

(c) $g(4, 2, \pi/4)$ C (d) $g(\pi, \pi, \pi)$

4. Let $g(x, y, z) = \sqrt{x} \cos y + z^2$. Find each value.

(a) $g(4, 0, 2)$ (b) $g(-9, \pi, 3)$

(c) $g(2, \pi/3, -1)$ C (d) $g(3, 6, 1.2)$

5. Find $F(f(t), g(t))$ if $F(x, y) = x^2 y$ and $f(t) = t \cos t$, $g(t) = \sec^2 t$.

6. Find $F(f(t), g(t))$ if $F(x, y) = e^x + y^2$ and $f(t) = \ln t^2$, $g(t) = e^{t/2}$.

In Problems 7–16, sketch the graph of f.

7. $f(x, y) = 6$ **8.** $f(x, y) = 6 - x$

9. $f(x, y) = 6 - x - 2y$ **10.** $f(x, y) = 6 - x^2$

11. $f(x, y) = \sqrt{16 - x^2 - y^2}$

12. $f(x, y) = \sqrt{16 - 4x^2 - y^2}$

13. $f(x, y) = 3 - x^2 - y^2$ **14.** $f(x, y) = 2 - x - y^2$

15. $f(x, y) = e^{-(x^2+y^2)}$ **16.** $f(x, y) = x^2/y, y > 0$

In Problems 17–22, sketch the level curve $z = k$ for the indicated values of k.

17. $z = \frac{1}{2}(x^2 + y^2), k = 0, 2, 4, 6, 8$

18. $z = \dfrac{x}{y}, k = -2, -1, 0, 1, 2$

19. $z = \dfrac{x^2}{y}, k = -4, -1, 0, 1, 4$

20. $z = x^2 + y, k = -4, -1, 0, 1, 4$

21. $z = \dfrac{x^2 + 1}{x^2 + y^2}, k = 1, 2, 4$

22. $z = y - \sin x, k = -2, -1, 0, 1, 2$

23. Let $T(x, y)$ be the temperature at a point (x, y) in the plane. Draw the isothermal curves corresponding to $T = \frac{1}{10}, \frac{1}{5}, \frac{1}{2}, 0$ if

$$T(x, y) = \frac{x^2}{x^2 + y^2}$$

24. If $V(x, y)$ is the voltage at a point (x, y) in the plane, the level curves of V are called **equipotential curves.** Draw the equipotential curves corresponding to $V = \frac{1}{2}, 1, 2, 4$ for

$$V(x, y) = \frac{4}{\sqrt{(x - 2)^2 + (y + 3)^2}}$$

25. Figure 20 shows isotherms for the United States.

(a) Which of San Francisco, Denver, and New York had approximately the same temperature as St. Louis?

(b) If you were in Kansas City and wanted to drive toward cooler weather as quickly as possible, in which direction would you travel? What if you wanted to drive toward warmer weather?

(c) If you were leaving Kansas City, in which directions could you go and stay at approximately the same temperature?

26. Figure 23 shows a contour map for barometric pressure in millibars. Level curves for barometric pressure are called **isobars.**

(a) What part of the country had the lowest barometric pressure? The highest?

(b) If you were in St. Louis, in which direction would you have to travel to move as fast as possible toward lower barometric pressure? Higher barometric pressure?

(c) If you were leaving St. Louis, in which directions could you go in order to remain at approximately the same barometric pressure?

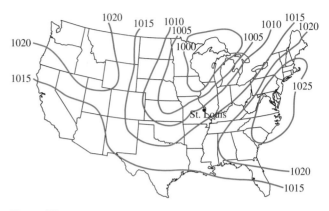

Figure 23

In Problems 27–32, describe geometrically the domain of each of the indicated functions of three variables.

27. $f(x, y, z) = \sqrt{x^2 + y^2 + z^2 - 16}$

28. $f(x, y, z) = \sqrt{x^2 + y^2 - z^2 - 9}$

29. $f(x, y, z) = \sqrt{144 - 16x^2 - 9y^2 - 144z^2}$

30. $f(x, y, z) = \dfrac{(144 - 16x^2 - 16y^2 + 9z^2)^{3/2}}{xyz}$

31. $f(x, y, z) = \ln(x^2 + y^2 + z^2)$

32. $f(x, y, z) = z \ln(xy)$

Describe geometrically the level surfaces for the functions defined in Problems 33–38.

33. $f(x, y, z) = x^2 + y^2 + z^2; k > 0$

34. $f(x, y, z) = 100x^2 + 16y^2 + 25z^2; k > 0$

35. $f(x, y, z) = 16x^2 + 16y^2 - 9z^2$

36. $f(x, y, z) = 9x^2 - 4y^2 - z^2$

37. $f(x, y, z) = 4x^2 - 9y^2$

38. $f(x, y, z) = e^{x^2+y^2+z^2}, k > 0$

39. Find the domain of each function.

(a) $f(w, x, y, z) = \dfrac{1}{\sqrt{w^2 + x^2 + y^2 + z^2}}$

(b) $g(x_1, x_2, \ldots, x_n) = \exp(-x_1^2 - x_2^2 - \cdots - x_n^2)$

(c) $h(x_1, x_2, \ldots, x_n) = \sqrt{1 - (x_1^2 + x_2^2 + \cdots + x_n^2)}$

40. Sketch (as best you can) the graph of the monkey saddle $z = x(x^2 - 3y^2)$. Begin by noting where $z = 0$.

41. The contour map in Figure 24 shows level curves for a mountain 3000 feet high.

(a) What is special about the path to the top labeled AC? What is special about BC?

(b) Make good estimates of the total lengths of path AC and path BC.

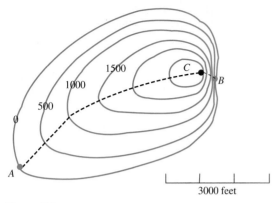

Figure 24

42. Identify the graph of $f(x, y) = x^2 - x + 3y^2 + 12y - 13$, state where it attains its minimum value, and find this minimum value.

CAS *For each of the functions in Problems 43–46, draw the graph and the corresponding contour plot.*

43. $f(x, y) = \sin\sqrt{2x^2 + y^2}$; $-2 \le x \le 2, -2 \le y \le 2$

44. $f(x, y) = \sin(x^2 + y^2)/(x^2 + y^2), f(0, 0) = 1$; $-2 \le x \le 2, -2 \le y \le 2$

45. $f(x, y) = (2x - y^2)\exp(-x^2 - y^2)$; $-2 \le x \le 2$, $-2 \le y \le 2$

46. $f(x, y) = (\sin x \sin y)/(1 + x^2 + y^2)$; $-2 \le x \le 2$, $-2 \le y \le 2$

Answers to Concepts Review: **1.** real-valued function of two real variables **2.** level curve; contour map **3.** concentric circles **4.** parallel lines

---

12.2
Partial Derivatives

Suppose that f is a function of two variables x and y. If y is held constant, say $y = y_0$, then $f(x, y_0)$ is a function of the single variable x. Its derivative at $x = x_0$ is called the **partial derivative of f with respect to x** at (x_0, y_0) and is denoted by $f_x(x_0, y_0)$. Thus,

$$f_x(x_0, y_0) = \lim_{\Delta x \to 0} \frac{f(x_0 + \Delta x, y_0) - f(x_0, y_0)}{\Delta x}$$

Similarly, the partial derivative of f with respect to y at (x_0, y_0) is denoted by $f_y(x_0, y_0)$ and is given by

$$f_y(x_0, y_0) = \lim_{\Delta y \to 0} \frac{f(x_0, y_0 + \Delta y) - f(x_0, y_0)}{\Delta y}$$

Rather than calculate $f_x(x_0, y_0)$ and $f_y(x_0, y_0)$ directly from the boxed definitions, we typically find $f_x(x, y)$ and $f_y(x, y)$ using the standard rules for derivatives; then we substitute $x = x_0$ and $y = y_0$. The key point here is that the rules for differentiating a function of one variable (Chapter 3) work for finding partial derivatives, as long as we hold one variable fixed.

EXAMPLE 1 Find $f_x(1, 2)$ and $f_y(1, 2)$ if $f(x, y) = x^2 y + 3y^3$.

SOLUTION To find $f_x(x, y)$, we treat y as a constant and differentiate with respect to x, obtaining

$$f_x(x, y) = 2xy + 0$$

Thus,

$$f_x(1, 2) = 2 \cdot 1 \cdot 2 = 4$$

Similarly, we treat x as a constant and differentiate with respect to y, obtaining

$$f_y(x, y) = x^2 + 9y^2$$

and so

$$f_y(1, 2) = 1^2 + 9 \cdot 2^2 = 37$$

If $z = f(x, y)$, we use the following alternative notations:

$$f_x(x, y) = \frac{\partial z}{\partial x} = \frac{\partial f(x, y)}{\partial x} \qquad f_y(x, y) = \frac{\partial z}{\partial y} = \frac{\partial f(x, y)}{\partial y}$$

$$f_x(x_0, y_0) = \frac{\partial z}{\partial x}\bigg|_{(x_0, y_0)} \qquad f_y(x_0, y_0) = \frac{\partial z}{\partial y}\bigg|_{(x_0, y_0)}$$

The symbol ∂ is special to mathematics and is called the partial derivative sign. The symbols $\dfrac{\partial}{\partial x}$ and $\dfrac{\partial}{\partial y}$ represent linear operators, much like the linear operators D_x and $\dfrac{d}{dx}$ that we encountered in Chapter 3.

■ EXAMPLE 2 If $z = x^2 \sin(xy^2)$, find $\partial z/\partial x$ and $\partial z/\partial y$.

SOLUTION

$$\frac{\partial z}{\partial x} = x^2 \frac{\partial}{\partial x}[\sin(xy^2)] + \sin(xy^2)\frac{\partial}{\partial x}(x^2)$$

$$= x^2 \cos(xy^2)\frac{\partial}{\partial x}(xy^2) + \sin(xy^2) \cdot 2x$$

$$= x^2 \cos(xy^2) \cdot y^2 + 2x \sin(xy^2)$$

$$= x^2y^2 \cos(xy^2) + 2x \sin(xy^2)$$

$$\frac{\partial z}{\partial y} = x^2 \cos(xy^2) \cdot 2xy = 2x^3y \cos(xy^2)$$ ■

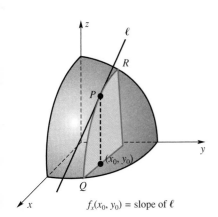

$f_x(x_0, y_0)$ = slope of ℓ

Figure 1

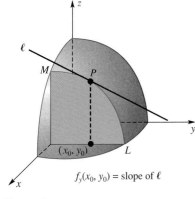

$f_y(x_0, y_0)$ = slope of ℓ

Figure 2

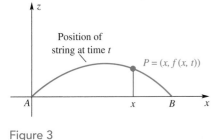

Figure 3

Geometric and Physical Interpretations Consider the surface whose equation is $z = f(x, y)$. The plane $y = y_0$ intersects this surface in the plane curve QPR (Figure 1), and the value of $f_x(x_0, y_0)$ is the slope of the tangent line to this curve at $P(x_0, y_0, f(x_0, y_0))$. Similarly, the plane $x = x_0$ intersects the surface in the plane curve LPM (Figure 2), and $f_y(x_0, y_0)$ is the slope of the tangent line to this curve at P.

Partial derivatives may also be interpreted as (instantaneous) rates of change. Suppose that a violin string is fixed at points A and B and vibrates in the xz-plane. Figure 3 shows the position of the string at a typical time t. If $z = f(x, t)$ denotes the height of the string at the point P with x-coordinate x at time t, then $\partial z/\partial x$ is the slope of the string at P, and $\partial z/\partial t$ is the time rate of change of height of P along the indicated vertical line. In other words, $\partial z/\partial t$ is the vertical velocity of P.

■ EXAMPLE 3 The surface $z = f(x, y) = \sqrt{9 - 2x^2 - y^2}$ and the plane $y = 1$ intersect in a curve as in Figure 1. Find parametric equations for the tangent line at $\left(\sqrt{2}, 1, 2\right)$.

SOLUTION

$$f_x(x, y) = \tfrac{1}{2}(9 - 2x^2 - y^2)^{-1/2}(-4x)$$

and so $f_x\left(\sqrt{2}, 1\right) = -\sqrt{2}$. This number is the slope of the tangent line to the curve at $\left(\sqrt{2}, 1, 2\right)$; that is, $-\sqrt{2}/1$ is the ratio of rise to run along the tangent line. It follows that this line has direction vector $\langle 1, 0, -\sqrt{2}\rangle$ and, since it goes through $\left(\sqrt{2}, 1, 2\right)$,

$$x = \sqrt{2} + t, \qquad y = 1, \qquad z = 2 - \sqrt{2}t$$

provide the required parametric equations. ■

EXAMPLE 4 The volume of a certain gas is related to its temperature T and its pressure P by the gas law $PV = 10T$, where V is measured in cubic inches, P in pounds per square inch, and T in degrees Kelvin. If V is kept constant at 50, what is the rate of change of pressure with respect to temperature when $T = 200$?

SOLUTION Since $P = 10T/V$,

$$\frac{\partial P}{\partial T} = \frac{10}{V}$$

Thus,

$$\left.\frac{\partial P}{\partial T}\right|_{T=200,\,V=50} = \frac{10}{50} = \frac{1}{5}$$

Thus, the pressure is increasing at the rate of $\frac{1}{5}$ pound per square inch per degree Kelvin. ∎

Higher Partial Derivatives Since a partial derivative of a function of x and y is, in general, another function of these same two variables, it may be differentiated partially with respect to either x or y, resulting in four **second partial derivatives** of f.

$$f_{xx} = \frac{\partial}{\partial x}\left(\frac{\partial f}{\partial x}\right) = \frac{\partial^2 f}{\partial x^2} \qquad\qquad f_{yy} = \frac{\partial}{\partial y}\left(\frac{\partial f}{\partial y}\right) = \frac{\partial^2 f}{\partial y^2}$$

$$f_{xy} = (f_x)_y = \frac{\partial}{\partial y}\left(\frac{\partial f}{\partial x}\right) = \frac{\partial^2 f}{\partial y\,\partial x} \qquad\qquad f_{yx} = (f_y)_x = \frac{\partial}{\partial x}\left(\frac{\partial f}{\partial y}\right) = \frac{\partial^2 f}{\partial x\,\partial y}$$

EXAMPLE 5 Find the four second partial derivatives of

$$f(x, y) = xe^y - \sin(x/y) + x^3 y^2$$

SOLUTION

$$f_x(x, y) = e^y - \frac{1}{y}\cos\left(\frac{x}{y}\right) + 3x^2 y^2$$

$$f_y(x, y) = xe^y + \frac{x}{y^2}\cos\left(\frac{x}{y}\right) + 2x^3 y$$

$$f_{xx}(x, y) = \frac{1}{y^2}\sin\left(\frac{x}{y}\right) + 6xy^2$$

$$f_{yy}(x, y) = xe^y + \frac{x^2}{y^4}\sin\left(\frac{x}{y}\right) - \frac{2x}{y^3}\cos\left(\frac{x}{y}\right) + 2x^3$$

$$f_{xy}(x, y) = e^y - \frac{x}{y^3}\sin\left(\frac{x}{y}\right) + \frac{1}{y^2}\cos\left(\frac{x}{y}\right) + 6x^2 y$$

$$f_{yx}(x, y) = e^y - \frac{x}{y^3}\sin\left(\frac{x}{y}\right) + \frac{1}{y^2}\cos\left(\frac{x}{y}\right) + 6x^2 y \qquad ∎$$

Notice that in Example 5, $f_{xy} = f_{yx}$, which is usually the case for the functions of two variables encountered in a first course. A criterion for this equality will be given in Section 12.3 (Theorem C).

Partial derivatives of the third and higher orders are defined analogously, and the notation for them is similar. Thus, if f is a function of the two variables x and y, the third partial derivative of f obtained by differentiating f partially, first with respect to x and then twice with respect to y, will be indicated by

$$\frac{\partial}{\partial y}\left[\frac{\partial}{\partial y}\left(\frac{\partial f}{\partial x}\right)\right] = \frac{\partial}{\partial y}\left(\frac{\partial^2 f}{\partial y\,\partial x}\right) = \frac{\partial^3 f}{\partial y^2\,\partial x} = f_{xyy}$$

Altogether, there are eight third partial derivatives.

More Than Two Variables Let f be a function of three variables, x, y, and z. The **partial derivative of f with respect to x** at (x, y, z) is denoted by $f_x(x, y, z)$ or $\partial f(x, y, z)/\partial x$ and is defined by

$$f_x(x, y, z) = \lim_{\Delta x \to 0} \frac{f(x + \Delta x, y, z) - f(x, y, z)}{\Delta x}$$

Thus, $f_x(x, y, z)$ may be obtained by treating y and z as constants and differentiating with respect to x.

The partial derivatives with respect to y and z are defined in an analogous way. Partial derivatives of functions of four or more variables are defined similarly (see Problem 49). Partial derivatives, such as f_{xy} and f_{xyz}, that involve differentiation with respect to more than one variable are called **mixed partial derivatives.**

EXAMPLE 6 If $f(x, y, z) = xy + 2yz + 3zx$, find f_x, f_y, and f_z.

SOLUTION To get f_x, we think of y and z as constants and differentiate with respect to the variable x. Thus,

$$f_x(x, y, z) = y + 3z$$

To find f_y, we treat x and z as constants and differentiate with respect to y:

$$f_y(x, y, z) = x + 2z$$

Similarly,

$$f_z(x, y, z) = 2y + 3x$$

EXAMPLE 7 If $T(w, x, y, z) = ze^{w^2 + x^2 + y^2}$, find all first partial derivatives and $\dfrac{\partial^2 T}{\partial w \, \partial x}$, $\dfrac{\partial^2 T}{\partial x \, \partial w}$, and $\dfrac{\partial^2 T}{\partial z^2}$.

SOLUTION The four first partials are

$$\frac{\partial T}{\partial w} = \frac{\partial}{\partial w}\left(ze^{w^2 + x^2 + y^2}\right) = 2wze^{w^2 + x^2 + y^2}$$

$$\frac{\partial T}{\partial x} = \frac{\partial}{\partial x}\left(ze^{w^2 + x^2 + y^2}\right) = 2xze^{w^2 + x^2 + y^2}$$

$$\frac{\partial T}{\partial y} = \frac{\partial}{\partial y}\left(ze^{w^2 + x^2 + y^2}\right) = 2yze^{w^2 + x^2 + y^2}$$

$$\frac{\partial T}{\partial z} = \frac{\partial}{\partial z}\left(ze^{w^2 + x^2 + y^2}\right) = e^{w^2 + x^2 + y^2}$$

The other partial derivatives are

$$\frac{\partial^2 T}{\partial w \, \partial x} = \frac{\partial^2}{\partial w \, \partial x}\left(ze^{w^2 + x^2 + y^2}\right) = \frac{\partial}{\partial w}\left(2xze^{w^2 + x^2 + y^2}\right) = 4wxze^{w^2 + x^2 + y^2}$$

$$\frac{\partial^2 T}{\partial x \, \partial w} = \frac{\partial^2}{\partial x \, \partial w}\left(ze^{w^2 + x^2 + y^2}\right) = \frac{\partial}{\partial x}\left(2wze^{w^2 + x^2 + y^2}\right) = 4wxze^{w^2 + x^2 + y^2}$$

$$\frac{\partial^2 T}{\partial z^2} = \frac{\partial^2}{\partial z^2}\left(ze^{w^2 + x^2 + y^2}\right) = \frac{\partial}{\partial z}\left(e^{w^2 + x^2 + y^2}\right) = 0$$

Concepts Review

1. As a limit, $f_x(x_0, y_0)$ is defined by _____ and is called the _____ at (x_0, y_0).

2. If $f(x, y) = x^3 + xy$, then $f_x(1, 2) = $ _____ and $f_y(1, 2) = $ _____.

3. Another notation for $f_{xy}(x, y)$ is _____.

4. If $f(x, y) = g(x) + h(y)$, then $f_{xy}(x, y) = $ _____.

Problem Set 12.2

In Problems 1–16, find all first partial derivatives of each function.

1. $f(x, y) = (2x - y)^4$

2. $f(x, y) = (4x - y^2)^{3/2}$

3. $f(x, y) = \dfrac{x^2 - y^2}{xy}$

4. $f(x, y) = e^x \cos y$

5. $f(x, y) = e^y \sin x$

6. $f(x, y) = (3x^2 + y^2)^{-1/3}$

7. $f(x, y) = \sqrt{x^2 - y^2}$

8. $f(u, v) = e^{uv}$

9. $g(x, y) = e^{-xy}$

10. $f(s, t) = \ln(s^2 - t^2)$

11. $f(x, y) = \tan^{-1}(4x - 7y)$

12. $F(w, z) = w \sin^{-1}\left(\dfrac{w}{z}\right)$

13. $f(x, y) = y \cos(x^2 + y^2)$ **14.** $f(s, t) = e^{t^2 - s^2}$

15. $F(x, y) = 2 \sin x \cos y$ **16.** $f(r, \theta) = 3r^3 \cos 2\theta$

In Problems 17–20, verify that

$$\frac{\partial^2 f}{\partial y \, \partial x} = \frac{\partial^2 f}{\partial x \, \partial y}$$

17. $f(x, y) = 2x^2y^3 - x^3y^5$ **18.** $f(x, y) = (x^3 + y^2)^5$

19. $f(x, y) = 3e^{2x} \cos y$ **20.** $f(x, y) = \tan^{-1} xy$

21. If $F(x, y) = \dfrac{2x - y}{xy}$, find $F_x(3, -2)$ and $F_y(3, -2)$.

22. If $F(x, y) = \ln(x^2 + xy + y^2)$, find $F_x(-1, 4)$ and $F_y(-1, 4)$.

23. If $f(x, y) = \tan^{-1}(y^2/x)$, find $f_x\left(\sqrt{5}, -2\right)$ and $f_y\left(\sqrt{5}, -2\right)$.

24. If $f(x, y) = e^y \cosh x$, find $f_x(-1, 1)$ and $f_y(-1, 1)$.

25. Find the slope of the tangent to the curve of intersection of the surface $36z = 4x^2 + 9y^2$ and the plane $x = 3$ at the point $(3, 2, 2)$.

26. Find the slope of the tangent to the curve of intersection of the surface $3z = \sqrt{36 - 9x^2 - 4y^2}$ and the plane $x = 1$ at the point $\left(1, -2, \sqrt{11}/3\right)$.

27. Find the slope of the tangent to the curve of intersection of the surface $2z = \sqrt{9x^2 + 9y^2 - 36}$ and the plane $y = 1$ at the point $\left(2, 1, \frac{3}{2}\right)$.

28. Find the slope of the tangent to the curve of intersection of the cylinder $4z = 5\sqrt{16 - x^2}$ and the plane $y = 3$ at the point $\left(2, 3, 5\sqrt{3}/2\right)$.

29. The volume V of a right circular cylinder is given by $V = \pi r^2 h$, where r is the radius and h is the height. If h is held fixed at $h = 10$ inches, find the rate of change of V with respect to r when $r = 6$ inches.

30. The temperature in degrees Celsius on a metal plate in the xy-plane is given by $T(x, y) = 4 + 2x^2 + y^3$. What is the rate of change of temperature with respect to distance (measured in feet) if we start moving from $(3, 2)$ in the direction of the positive y-axis?

31. According to the ideal gas law, the pressure, temperature, and volume of a gas are related by $PV = kT$, where k is a constant. Find the rate of change of pressure (pounds per square inch) with respect to temperature when the temperature is $300°$K if the volume is kept fixed at 100 cubic inches.

32. Show that, for the gas law of Problem 31,

$$V \frac{\partial P}{\partial V} + T \frac{\partial P}{\partial T} = 0 \quad \text{and} \quad \frac{\partial P}{\partial V} \frac{\partial V}{\partial T} \frac{\partial T}{\partial P} = -1$$

A function of two variables that satisfies **Laplace's Equation,**

$$\frac{\partial^2 f}{\partial x^2} + \frac{\partial^2 f}{\partial y^2} = 0$$

is said to be **harmonic.** Show that the functions defined in Problems 33 and 34 are harmonic functions.

33. $f(x, y) = x^3y - xy^3$

34. $f(x, y) = \ln(4x^2 + 4y^2)$

35. If $F(x, y) = 3x^4y^5 - 2x^2y^3$, find $\partial^3 F(x, y)/\partial y^3$.

36. If $f(x, y) = \cos(2x^2 - y^2)$, find $\partial^3 f(x, y)/\partial y \, \partial x^2$.

37. Express the following in ∂ notation.

(a) f_{yyy} (b) f_{xxy} (c) f_{xyyy}

38. Express the following in subscript notation.

(a) $\dfrac{\partial^3 f}{\partial x^2 \, \partial y}$ (b) $\dfrac{\partial^4 f}{\partial x^2 \, \partial y^2}$ (c) $\dfrac{\partial^5 f}{\partial x^3 \, \partial y^2}$

39. If $f(x, y, z) = 3x^2y - xyz + y^2z^2$, find each of the following:

(a) $f_x(x, y, z)$ (b) $f_y(0, 1, 2)$ (c) $f_{xy}(x, y, z)$

40. If $f(x, y, z) = (x^3 + y^2 + z)^4$, find each of the following:

(a) $f_x(x, y, z)$ (b) $f_y(0, 1, 1)$ (c) $f_{zz}(x, y, z)$

41. If $f(x, y, z) = e^{-xyz} - \ln(xy - z^2)$, find $f_x(x, y, z)$.

42. If $f(x, y, z) = (xy/z)^{1/2}$, find $f_x(-2, -1, 8)$.

43. A bee was flying upward along the curve that is the intersection of $z = x^4 + xy^3 + 12$ with the plane $x = 1$. At the point $(1, -2, 5)$, it went off on the tangent line. Where did the bee hit the xz-plane? (See Example 3.)

44. Let $A(x, y)$ be the area of a nondegenerate rectangle of dimensions x and y, the rectangle being inside a circle of radius 10. Determine the domain and range for this function.

45. The interval $[0, 1]$ is to be separated into three pieces by making cuts at x and y. Let $A(x, y)$ be the area of any nondegenerate triangle that can be formed from these three pieces. Determine the domain and range for this function.

46. The **wave equation** $c^2 \partial^2 u/\partial x^2 = \partial^2 u/\partial t^2$ and the **heat equation** $c \partial^2 u/\partial x^2 = \partial u/\partial t$ are two of the most important equations in physics (c is a constant). These are called **partial differential equations.** Show each of the following:

(a) $u = \cos x \cos ct$ and $u = e^x \cosh ct$ satisfy the wave equation.

(b) $u = e^{-ct} \sin x$ and $u = t^{-1/2} e^{-x^2/(4ct)}$ satisfy the heat equation.

47. For the contour map for $z = f(x, y)$ shown in Figure 4, estimate each value.

(a) $f_y(1, 1)$ (b) $f_x(-4, 2)$
(c) $f_x(-5, -2)$ (d) $f_y(0, -2)$

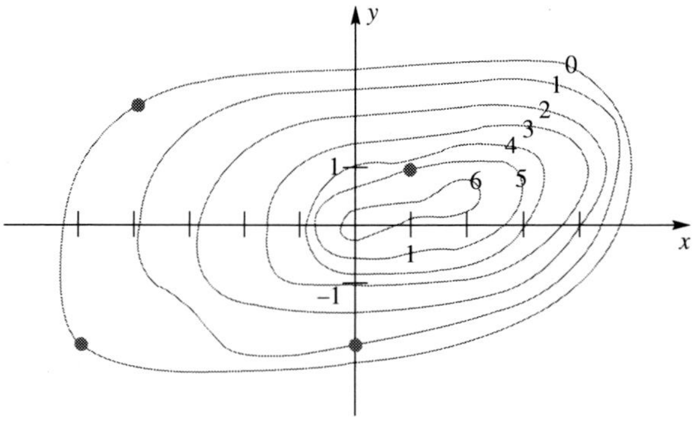

Figure 4

CAS **48.** A CAS can be used to calculate and graph partial derivatives. Draw the graphs of each of the following:

(a) $\sin(x + y^2)$ (b) $D_x \sin(x + y^2)$
(c) $D_y \sin(x + y^2)$ (d) $D_x(D_y \sin(x + y^2))$

49. Give definitions in terms of limits for the following partial derivatives:

(a) $f_y(x, y, z)$ (b) $f_z(x, y, z)$

(c) $G_x(w, x, y, z)$ (d) $\dfrac{\partial}{\partial z}\lambda(x, y, z, t)$

(e) $\dfrac{\partial}{\partial b_2}S(b_0, b_1, b_2, \ldots, b_n)$

50. Find each partial derivative.

(a) $\dfrac{\partial}{\partial w}(\sin w \sin x \cos y \cos z)$ (b) $\dfrac{\partial}{\partial x}[x \ln(wxyz)]$

(c) $\lambda_t(x, y, z, t)$, where $\lambda(x, y, z, t) = \dfrac{t \cos x}{1 + xyzt}$

Answers to Concepts Review:
1. $\lim\limits_{\Delta x \to 0}[f(x_0 + \Delta x, y_0) - f(x_0, y_0)]/\Delta x$; partial derivative of f with respect to x **2.** $5; 1$ **3.** $\partial^2 f/\partial y\, \partial x$ **4.** 0

Appendix

A.1
Mathematical Induction

Often in mathematics we are faced with the task of wanting to establish that a certain proposition P_n is true for every integer $n \geq 1$ (or perhaps every integer $n \geq N$). Here are three examples:

1. P_n: $\quad 1^2 + 2^2 + 3^2 + \cdots + n^2 = \dfrac{n(n+1)(2n+1)}{6}$

2. Q_n: $\quad 2^n > n + 20$

3. R_n: $\quad n^2 - n + 41$ is prime

Proposition P_n is true for every positive integer, and Q_n is true for every integer greater than or equal to 5 (as we will show soon). The third proposition, R_n, is interesting. Note that for $n = 1, 2, 3, \ldots$, the values of $n^2 - n + 41$ are $41, 43, 47, 53, 61, \ldots$ (prime numbers so far). In fact, we will get a prime number for all n's through 40; but at $n = 41$, the formula yields the composite number $1681 = (41)(41)$. Showing the truth of a proposition for 40 (or 40 million) individual cases may make a proposition plausible, but it most certainly does not prove it is true for all n. The chasm between any finite number of cases and *all* cases is infinitely wide.

What is to be done? Is there a procedure for establishing that a proposition P_n is true for *all n*? An affirmative answer is provided by the **Principle of Mathematical Induction.**

Principle of Mathematical Induction

Let $\{P_n\}$ be a sequence of propositions (statements) satisfying these two conditions:

(i) P_N is true (usually N will be 1).

(ii) The truth of P_i implies the truth of $P_{i+1}, i \geq N$.

Then, P_n is true for every integer $n \geq N$.

We do not prove this principle; it is often taken as an axiom, and we hope it seems obvious. After all, if the first domino falls and if each domino knocks over the next one, then the whole row of dominoes will fall. Our efforts will be directed toward illustrating how we use mathematical induction.

EXAMPLE 1 Prove that

$$P_n: \quad 1^2 + 2^2 + 3^2 + \cdots + n^2 = \frac{n(n+1)(2n+1)}{6}$$

is true for all $n \geq 1$.

SOLUTION First, we note that

$$P_1: \quad 1^2 = \frac{1(1+1)(2+1)}{6}$$

is a true statement.

Second, we demonstrate implication (ii). We begin by writing the statements P_i and P_{i+1}.

$$P_i: \quad 1^2 + 2^2 + \cdots + i^2 = \frac{i(i+1)(2i+1)}{6}$$

$$P_{i+1}: \quad 1^2 + 2^2 + \cdots + i^2 + (i+1)^2 = \frac{(i+1)(i+2)(2i+3)}{6}$$

We must show that P_i implies P_{i+1}, so we assume that P_i is true. Then the left side of P_{i+1} can be written as follows (* indicates where P_i is used):

$$[1^2 + 2^2 + \cdots + i^2] + (i + 1)^2 \overset{*}{=} \frac{i(i + 1)(2i + 1)}{6} + (i + 1)^2$$

$$= (i + 1)\frac{2i^2 + i + 6i + 6}{6}$$

$$= \frac{(i + 1)(i + 2)(2i + 3)}{6}$$

This chain of equalities leads to the statement P_{i+1}. Thus, the truth of P_i does imply the truth of P_{i+1}. By the Principle of Mathematical Induction, P_n is true for each positive integer n. ∎

EXAMPLE 2 Prove that P_n: $2^n > n + 20$ is true for each integer $n \geq 5$.

SOLUTION First, we note that P_5: $2^5 > 5 + 20$ is true. Second, we suppose that P_i: $2^i > i + 20$ is true and attempt to deduce from this that P_{i+1}: $2^{i+1} > i + 1 + 20$ is true. But

$$2^{i+1} = 2 \cdot 2^i \overset{*}{>} 2(i + 20) = 2i + 40 > i + 21$$

Read from left to right, this is proposition P_{i+1}. Thus, P_n is true for $n \geq 5$. ∎

EXAMPLE 3 Prove that

$$P_n: x - y \text{ is a factor of } x^n - y^n$$

is true for each integer $n \geq 1$.

SOLUTION Trivially, $x - y$ is a factor of $x - y$, so P_1 is true. Suppose that $x - y$ is a factor of $x^i - y^i$; that is,

$$x^i - y^i = Q(x, y)(x - y)$$

for some polynomial $Q(x, y)$. Then

$$x^{i+1} - y^{i+1} = x^{i+1} - x^i y + x^i y - y^{i+1}$$

$$= x^i(x - y) + y(x^i - y^i)$$

$$\overset{*}{=} x^i(x - y) + y\,Q(x, y)(x - y)$$

$$= [x^i + yQ(x, y)](x - y)$$

Thus, the truth of P_i does imply the truth of P_{i+1}. We conclude by the Principle of Mathematical Induction that P_n is true for all $n \geq 1$. ∎

Problem Set A.1

In Problems 1–8, use the Principle of Mathematical Induction to prove that the given proposition is true for each integer $n \geq 1$.

1. $1 + 2 + 3 + \cdots + n = \dfrac{n(n + 1)}{2}$

2. $1 + 3 + 5 + \cdots + (2n - 1) = n^2$

3. $1 \cdot 2 + 2 \cdot 3 + 3 \cdot 4 + \cdots + n(n + 1) =$

$$\frac{n(n + 1)(n + 2)}{3}$$

4. $1^2 + 3^2 + 5^2 + \cdots + (2n - 1)^2 = \dfrac{n(2n - 1)(2n + 1)}{3}$

5. $1^3 + 2^3 + 3^3 + \cdots + n^3 = \left[\dfrac{n(n + 1)}{2}\right]^2$

6. $1^4 + 2^4 + 3^4 + \cdots + n^4 =$

$$\frac{n(n + 1)(6n^3 + 9n^2 + n - 1)}{30}$$

7. $n^3 - n$ is divisible by 6.

8. $n^3 + (n + 1)^3 + (n + 2)^3$ is divisible by 9.

In Problems 9–12, make a conjecture about the first integer N for which the proposition is true for all $n \geq N$, and then prove the proposition for all $n \geq N$.

9. $3n + 25 < 3^n$

10. $n - 100 > \log_{10} n$

11. $n^2 \leq 2^n$

12. $|\sin nx| \leq n|\sin x|$ for all x

In Problems 13–20, indicate what conclusion about P_n can be drawn from the given information.

13. P_5 is true, and P_i true implies P_{i+2} true.

14. P_1 and P_2 are true, and P_i true implies P_{i+2} true.

15. P_{30} is true, and P_i true implies P_{i-1} true.

16. P_{30} is true, and P_i true implies both P_{i+1} and P_{i-1} true.

17. P_1 is true, and P_i true implies both P_{4i} and P_{i-1} true.

18. P_1 is true, and P_{2i} true implies P_{2i+1} true.

19. P_1 and P_2 are true, and P_i and P_{i+1} true imply P_{i+2} true.

20. P_1 is true, and P_j true for $j \leq i$ implies P_{i+1} true.

In Problems 21–27, decide for what n's the given proposition is true and then use mathematical induction (perhaps in one of the alternative forms that you may have discovered in Problems 13–20) to prove each of the following.

21. $x + y$ is a factor of $x^n + y^n$.

22. The sum of the measures of the interior angles of an n-sided convex (no holes or dents) polygon is $(n - 2)\pi$.

23. The number of diagonals of an n-sided convex polygon is $\dfrac{n(n - 3)}{2}$.

24. $\dfrac{1}{n+1} + \dfrac{1}{n+2} + \dfrac{1}{n+3} + \cdots + \dfrac{1}{2n} > \dfrac{3}{5}$

25. $\left(1 - \dfrac{1}{4}\right)\left(1 - \dfrac{1}{9}\right)\left(1 - \dfrac{1}{16}\right)\cdots\left(1 - \dfrac{1}{n^2}\right) = \dfrac{n+1}{2n}$

26. Let $f_0 = 0, f_1 = 1$, and $f_{n+2} = f_{n+1} + f_n$ for $n \geq 0$ (this is the Fibonacci sequence). Then

$$f_n = \frac{1}{\sqrt{5}}\left[\left(\frac{1 + \sqrt{5}}{2}\right)^n - \left(\frac{1 - \sqrt{5}}{2}\right)^n\right]$$

27. Let $a_0 = 0, a_1 = 1$, and $a_{n+2} = (a_{n+1} + a_n)/2$ for $n \geq 0$. Then

$$a_n = \frac{2}{3}\left[1 - \left(-\frac{1}{2}\right)^n\right]$$

28. What is wrong with the following argument, which purports to show that all people in any set of n people are the same age? The statement is certainly true for a set consisting of one person. Suppose that it is true for any set of i people, and consider a set W of $i + 1$ people. We may think of W as the union of sets X and Y, each consisting of i people (draw a picture, for example, when W has 6 people). By supposition, each of these sets consists of identically aged people. But X and Y overlap (in $X \cap Y$), and so all members of $W = X \cup Y$ also are the same age.

A.2
Proofs of Several Theorems

Theorem A   Main Limit Theorem

Let n be a positive integer, k be a constant, and f and g be functions that have limits at c. Then

1. $\lim\limits_{x \to c} k = k$

2. $\lim\limits_{x \to c} x = c$

3. $\lim\limits_{x \to c} kf(x) = k \lim\limits_{x \to c} f(x)$

4. $\lim\limits_{x \to c}[f(x) + g(x)] = \lim\limits_{x \to c} f(x) + \lim\limits_{x \to c} g(x)$

5. $\lim\limits_{x \to c}[f(x) - g(x)] = \lim\limits_{x \to c} f(x) - \lim\limits_{x \to c} g(x)$

6. $\lim\limits_{x \to c}[f(x) \cdot g(x)] = \lim\limits_{x \to c} f(x) \cdot \lim\limits_{x \to c} g(x)$

7. $\lim\limits_{x \to c} \dfrac{f(x)}{g(x)} = \dfrac{\lim\limits_{x \to c} f(x)}{\lim\limits_{x \to c} g(x)}$, provided $\lim\limits_{x \to c} g(x) \neq 0$

8. $\lim\limits_{x \to c}[f(x)]^n = \left[\lim\limits_{x \to c} f(x)\right]^n$

9. $\lim\limits_{x \to c} \sqrt[n]{f(x)} = \sqrt[n]{\lim\limits_{x \to c} f(x)}$, provided $\lim\limits_{x \to c} f(x) > 0$ when n is even

Proof   We proved parts 1 through 5 near the end of Section 2.3, so we should start with part 6. However, we choose first to prove a special case of part 8:

$$\lim_{x \to c}[g(x)]^2 = \left[\lim_{x \to c} g(x)\right]^2$$

To see this, recall that we have proved that $\lim\limits_{x \to c} x^2 = c^2$ (Example 7 of Section 2.2), and so $f(x) = x^2$ is continuous everywhere. Thus, by the Composite Limit Theorem (Theorem 2.7E),

$$\lim_{x \to c}[g(x)]^2 = \lim_{x \to c} f(g(x)) = f\left[\lim_{x \to c} g(x)\right] = \left[\lim_{x \to c} g(x)\right]^2$$

Next, write

$$f(x)g(x) = \frac{1}{4}\left\{[f(x) + g(x)]^2 - [f(x) - g(x)]^2\right\}$$

and apply parts 3, 4, and 5, plus what we have just proved. Part 6 is proved.

To prove part 7, apply the Composite Limit Theorem with $f(x) = 1/x$ and use Example 8 of Section 2.2. Then

$$\lim_{x \to c} \frac{1}{g(x)} = \lim_{x \to c} f(g(x)) = f\left(\lim_{x \to c} g(x)\right) = \frac{1}{\displaystyle\lim_{x \to c} g(x)}$$

Finally, by part 6,

$$\lim_{x \to c} \frac{f(x)}{g(x)} = \lim_{x \to c}\left[f(x) \cdot \frac{1}{g(x)}\right] = \lim_{x \to c} f(x) \cdot \lim_{x \to c} \frac{1}{g(x)}$$

from which the result follows.

Part 8 follows from repeated use of part 6 (technically, by mathematical induction).

We prove part 9 only for square roots. Let $f(x) = \sqrt{x}$, which is continuous for positive numbers by Example 5 of Section 2.2. By the Composite Limit Theorem,

$$\lim_{x \to c} \sqrt{g(x)} = \lim_{x \to c} f(g(x)) = f\left(\lim_{x \to c} g(x)\right) = \sqrt{\lim_{x \to c} g(x)}$$

which is equivalent to the desired result. ∎

Theorem B **Chain Rule**

If g is differentiable at a and f is differentiable at $g(a)$, then $f \circ g$ is differentiable at a and

$$(f \circ g)'(a) = f'(g(a))g'(a)$$

Proof We offer a proof that generalizes easily to higher dimensions (see Section 12.6). By hypothesis, f is differentiable at $b = g(a)$; that is, there is a number $f'(b)$ such that

(1)
$$\lim_{\Delta u \to 0} \frac{f(b + \Delta u) - f(b)}{\Delta u} = f'(b)$$

Define a function ε depending on Δu by

$$\varepsilon(\Delta u) = \frac{f(b + \Delta u) - f(b)}{\Delta u} - f'(b)$$

and multiply both sides by Δu to obtain

(2)
$$f(b + \Delta u) - f(b) = f'(b)\,\Delta u + \Delta u\,\varepsilon(\Delta u)$$

The existence of the limit in (1) is equivalent to $\varepsilon(\Delta u) \to 0$ as $\Delta u \to 0$ in (2). If, in (2), we replace Δu by $g(a + \Delta x) - g(a)$ and b by $g(a)$, we get

$$f(g(a + \Delta x)) - f(g(a)) = f'(g(a))[g(a + \Delta x) - g(a)]$$
$$+ [g(a + \Delta x) - g(a)]\varepsilon(\Delta u)$$

or, upon dividing both sides by Δx,

(3)
$$\frac{f(g(a + \Delta x)) - f(g(a))}{\Delta x} = f'(g(a))\frac{g(a + \Delta x) - g(a)}{\Delta x}$$
$$+ \frac{g(a + \Delta x) - g(a)}{\Delta x}\varepsilon(\Delta u)$$

In (3), let $\Delta x \to 0$. Since g is differentiable at a, it is continuous there, so $\Delta x \to 0$ forces $\Delta u \to 0$; this, in turn, makes $\varepsilon(\Delta u) \to 0$. We conclude that

$$\lim_{\Delta x \to 0} \frac{f(g(a + \Delta x)) - f(g(a))}{\Delta x} = f'(g(a)) \lim_{\Delta x \to 0} \frac{g(a + \Delta x) - g(a)}{\Delta x} + 0$$

That is, $f \circ g$ is differentiable at a and

$$(f \circ g)'(a) = f'(g(a))g'(a) \qquad \blacksquare$$

Theorem C   **Power Rule**

If r is rational, then x^r is differentiable at any x that is in an open interval on which x^{r-1} is real and

$$D_x(x^r) = rx^{r-1}$$

Proof   Consider first the case where $r = 1/q$, q a positive integer. Recall that $a^q - b^q$ factors as

$$a^q - b^q = (a - b)(a^{q-1} + a^{q-2}b + \cdots + ab^{q-2} + b^{q-1})$$

so

$$\frac{a - b}{a^q - b^q} = \frac{1}{a^{q-1} + a^{q-2}b + \cdots + ab^{q-2} + b^{q-1}}$$

Thus, if $f(t) = t^{1/q}$,

$$f'(x) = \lim_{t \to x} \frac{t^{1/q} - x^{1/q}}{t - x} = \lim_{t \to x} \frac{t^{1/q} - x^{1/q}}{(t^{1/q})^q - (x^{1/q})^q}$$

$$= \lim_{t \to x} \frac{1}{t^{(q-1)/q} + t^{(q-2)/q}x^{1/q} + \cdots + x^{(q-1)/q}}$$

$$= \frac{1}{qx^{(q-1)/q}} = \frac{1}{q}x^{1/q-1}$$

Now, by the Chain Rule, and with p an integer,

$$D_x(x^{p/q}) = D_x[(x^{1/q})^p] = p(x^{1/q})^{p-1} D_x(x^{1/q}) = px^{p/q-1/q}\frac{1}{q}x^{1/q-1} = \frac{p}{q}x^{p/q-1} \quad \blacksquare$$

Theorem D   **Vector Limits**

Let $\mathbf{F}(t) = f(t)\mathbf{i} + g(t)\mathbf{j}$. Then $\mathbf{F}$ has a limit at c if and only if f and g have limits at c. In that case,

$$\lim_{t \to c} \mathbf{F}(t) = \left[\lim_{t \to c} f(t)\right]\mathbf{i} + \left[\lim_{t \to c} g(t)\right]\mathbf{j}$$

Proof   First, note that for any vector $\mathbf{u} = u_1\mathbf{i} + u_2\mathbf{j}$,

$$|u_1| \leq \|\mathbf{u}\| \leq |u_1| + |u_2|$$

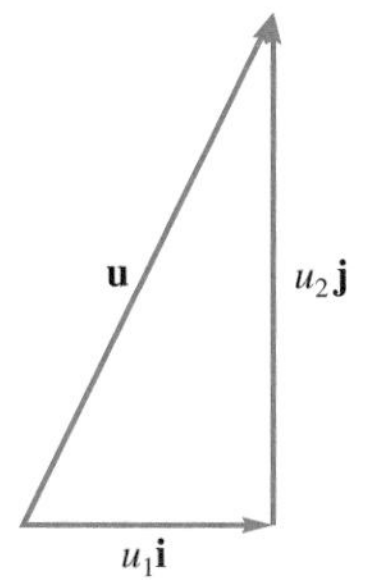

This fact is readily seen from Figure 1.

Now suppose that $\lim_{t \to c} \mathbf{F}(t) = \mathbf{L} = a\mathbf{i} + b\mathbf{j}$. This means that for any $\varepsilon > 0$ there is a corresponding $\delta > 0$ such that

$$0 < |t - c| < \delta \implies \|\mathbf{F}(t) - \mathbf{L}\| < \varepsilon$$

Figure 1

But, by the left part of the boxed inequality,

$$|f(t) - a| \leq \|\mathbf{F}(t) - \mathbf{L}\|$$

and so

$$0 < |t - c| < \delta \implies |f(t) - a| < \varepsilon$$

This shows that $\lim_{t \to c} f(t) = a$. A similar argument establishes that $\lim_{t \to c} g(t) = b$. The first half of our theorem is complete.

Conversely, suppose that

$$\lim_{t \to c} f(t) = a \quad \text{and} \quad \lim_{t \to c} g(t) = b$$

and let $\mathbf{L} = a\,\mathbf{i} + b\,\mathbf{j}$. For any given $\varepsilon > 0$, there is a corresponding $\delta > 0$ such that $0 < |t - c| < \delta$ implies that both

$$|f(t) - a| < \frac{\varepsilon}{2} \quad \text{and} \quad |g(t) - b| < \frac{\varepsilon}{2}$$

Hence, by the right part of the boxed inequality,

$$0 < |t - c| < \delta \implies \|\mathbf{F}(t) - \mathbf{L}\| \leq \frac{\varepsilon}{2} + \frac{\varepsilon}{2} = \varepsilon$$

Thus,

$$\lim_{t \to c} \mathbf{F}(t) = \mathbf{L} = a\,\mathbf{i} + b\,\mathbf{j} = \lim_{t \to c} f(t)\,\mathbf{i} + \lim_{t \to c} g(t)\,\mathbf{j} \qquad \blacksquare$$

Answers to Odd-Numbered Problems

Problem Set 1.1

1. 16 **3.** −148 **5.** $\frac{58}{91}$ **7.** $\frac{1}{24}$ **9.** $\frac{6}{49}$ **11.** $\frac{7}{15}$

13. $\frac{1}{3}$ **15.** 2 **17.** $3x^2 - x - 4$ **19.** $6x^2 - 15x - 9$

21. $9t^4 - 6t^3 + 7t^2 - 2t + 1$ **23.** $x + 2, x \neq 2$

25. $t - 7, t \neq -3$ **27.** $\dfrac{2(3x + 10)}{x(x + 2)}$

29. (a) 0; **(b)** Undefined; **(c)** 0; **(d)** Undefined; **(e)** 0; **(f)** 1

31. 0.08333 . . . **33.** 0.142857 . . . **35.** 3.6666 . . .

37. $\frac{41}{333}$ **39.** $\frac{254}{99}$ **41.** $\frac{1}{5}$

43. Those rational numbers that can be expressed by a terminating decimal followed by zeros

49. Irrational **51.** 20.39230485 **53.** 0.00028307388

55. 0.000691744752 **59.** 132,700,874 ft

61. 651,441 board ft

63. (a) If I stay home from work today then it rains. If I do not stay home from work, then it does not rain. **(b)** If the candidate will be hired then she meets all the qualifications. If the candidate will not be hired then she does not meet all the qualifications.

65. (a) If a triangle is a right triangle, then $a^2 + b^2 = c^2$. If a triangle is not a right triangle, then $a^2 + b^2 \neq c^2$. **(b)** If the measure of angle ABC is greater than 0° and less than 90°, it is acute. If the measure of angle ABC is less than 0° or greater than 90°, then it is not acute.

67. (a) The statement, converse, and contrapositive are all true. **(b)** The statement, converse, and contrapositive are all true.

69. (a) Some isosceles triangles are not equilateral. The negation is true. **(b)** All real numbers are integers. The original statement is true. **(c)** Some natural number is larger than its square. The original statement is true.

71. (a) True; **(b)** False; **(c)** False; **(d)** True; **(e)** True

75. (a) $3 \cdot 3 \cdot 3 \cdot 3 \cdot 3$ or 3^5; **(b)** $2 \cdot 2 \cdot 31$ or $2^2 \cdot 31$ **(c)** $2 \cdot 2 \cdot 3 \cdot 5 \cdot 5 \cdot 17$ or $2^2 \cdot 3 \cdot 5^2 \cdot 17$

81. (a) Rational; **(b)** Rational; **(c)** Rational; **(d)** Irrational

Problem Set 1.2

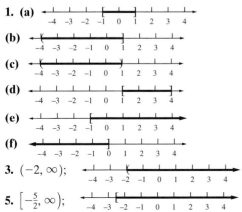

1. (a) **(b)** **(c)** **(d)** **(e)** **(f)**

3. $(-2, \infty)$;

5. $\left[-\frac{5}{2}, \infty\right)$;

7. $(-2, 1)$;

9. $\left[-\frac{1}{2}, \frac{2}{3}\right)$;

11. $\left(-1 - \sqrt{13}, -1 + \sqrt{13}\right)$;

13. $(-\infty, -3) \cup \left(\frac{1}{2}, \infty\right)$;

15. $[-4, 3)$;

17. $(-\infty, 0) \cup \left(\frac{2}{5}, \infty\right)$;

19. $\left(-\infty, \frac{2}{3}\right) \cup \left[\frac{3}{4}, \infty\right)$;

21. $(-2, 1) \cup (3, \infty)$;

23. $\left(-\infty, \frac{3}{2}\right] \cup [3, \infty)$;

25. $(-\infty, -1) \cup (0, 6)$;

27. (a) False; **(b)** True; **(c)** False

31. (a) $(-2, 1)$; **(b)** $(-2, \infty)$; **(c)** No values

33. (a) $[-3, -1] \cup [2, \infty)$; **(b)** $(-\infty, -2] \cup [2, \infty)$; **(c)** $(-2, -1) \cup (1, 2)$

35. $(-\infty, -3] \cup [7, \infty)$ **37.** $\left[-\dfrac{15}{4}, \dfrac{5}{4}\right]$

39. $(-\infty, -7] \cup [42, \infty)$ **41.** $(-\infty, 1) \cup \left(\dfrac{7}{5}, \infty\right)$

43. $\left(-\dfrac{1}{3}, 0\right) \cup \left(0, \dfrac{1}{9}\right)$ **45.** $(-\infty, -1] \cup [4, \infty)$

47. $(-\infty, -6) \cup \left(\frac{1}{3}, \infty\right)$ **53.** $\frac{\varepsilon}{3}$ **55.** $\frac{\varepsilon}{6}$ **57.** 0.0064 in.

59. $\left(-\infty, \frac{7}{3}\right) \cup (5, \infty)$ **61.** $\left(-\frac{4}{5}, \frac{16}{3}\right)$ **77.** $\dfrac{60}{11} \leq R \leq \dfrac{120}{13}$

Problem Set 1.3

1. 2 **3.** $\sqrt{170}$

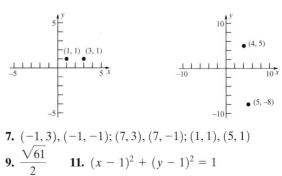

7. $(-1, 3), (-1, -1); (7, 3), (7, -1); (1, 1), (5, 1)$

9. $\dfrac{\sqrt{61}}{2}$ **11.** $(x - 1)^2 + (y - 1)^2 = 1$

13. $(x - 2)^2 + (y + 1)^2 = 25$ **15.** $(x - 2)^2 + (y - 5)^2 = 5$

17. Center $= (-1, 3)$; radius $= \sqrt{10}$

19. Center $= (6, 0)$; radius $= 1$

21. Center $= \left(-2, -\frac{3}{4}\right)$; radius $= \dfrac{\sqrt{13}}{4}$

23. 1   **25.** $\frac{9}{7}$ **27.** $-\frac{5}{3}$ **29.** $y = -x + 4$; $x + y - 4 = 0$

31. $y = 2x + 3$; $2x - y + 3 = 0$

33. $y = \frac{5}{2}x - 2$; $5x - 2y - 4 = 0$

35. Slope $= -\frac{2}{3}$; y-intercept $= \frac{1}{3}$

37. Slope $= -5$; y-intercept $= 4$

39. (a) $y = 2x - 9$; **(b)** $y = -\frac{1}{2}x - \frac{3}{2}$; **(c)** $y = -\frac{2}{3}x - 1$;

(d) $y = \frac{3}{2}x - \frac{15}{2}$; **(e)** $y = -\frac{3}{4}x - \frac{3}{4}$; **(f)** $x = 3$; **(g)** $y = -3$

41. $y = \frac{3}{2}x + 2$ **43.** It lies above the line.

45. $(-1, 2)$; $y = \frac{3}{2}x + \frac{7}{2}$ **47.** $(3, 1)$; $y = -\frac{4}{3}x + 5$

49. Inscribed: $(x - 4)^2 + (y - 1)^2 = 4$;
circumscribed: $(x - 4)^2 + (y - 1)^2 = 8$

55. $d = 2\sqrt{3} + 4$ **61.** $18 + 2\sqrt{17} + 4\pi \approx 38.8$

63. $\dfrac{7}{5}$ **65.** $\dfrac{18}{13}$ **67.** $\dfrac{\sqrt{5}}{5}$ **69.** $y = \frac{3}{5}x + \frac{4}{5}$ **71.** $r = 1$

73. $x + \sqrt{3}y = 12$ and $x - \sqrt{3}y = 12$ **77.** 8

Problem Set 1.4

1.

3.

5.

7.

9.

11.

13.

15.

17.

19.

21.

23.

25.

27.

29.

31.

$(0, 1), (-3, 4)$

33.

$\left(\dfrac{9}{2} - \dfrac{1}{2}\sqrt{11}, -6 + \sqrt{11}\right),$

$\left(\dfrac{9}{2} + \dfrac{1}{2}\sqrt{11}, -6 - \sqrt{11}\right)$

35.

$(\sqrt{2}, \sqrt{2}),$
$(-\sqrt{2}, -\sqrt{2})$

37.

$(-1.65, -3.95),$
$(0.85, 3.55)$

39. (a) (2) **(b)** (1) **(c)** (3) **(d)** (4)

41. Four distinct distances

Problem Set 1.5

1. (a) 0; **(b)** -3; **(c)** 1; **(d)** $1 - k^2$; **(e)** -24; **(f)** $\frac{15}{16}$;
(g) $-2h - h^2$; **(h)** $-2h - h^2$; **(i)** $-4h - h^2$

3. (a) -1; **(b)** -1000; **(c)** 100; **(d)** $\dfrac{1}{y^2 - 1}$; **(e)** $-\dfrac{1}{x + 1}$;

(f) $\dfrac{x^2}{1 - x^2}$

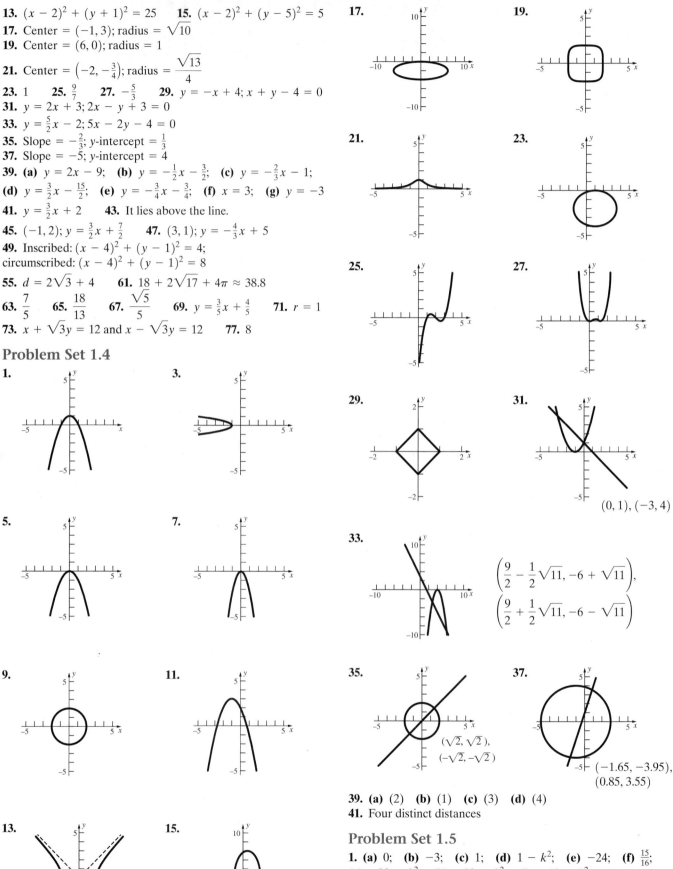

5. (a) Undefined;   **(b)** 2.658;   **(c)** 0.841

7. (a) Not a function;   **(b)** $f(x) = \dfrac{1 - x}{x + 1}$;

(c) $f(x) = \frac{1}{2}(x^2 - 1)$;   **(d)** $f(x) = \dfrac{x}{1 - x}$

9. $4a + 2h$ **11.** $-\dfrac{3}{x^2 - 4x + hx - 2h + 4}$

13. (a) $\{z \in \text{reals}: z \geq -\frac{3}{2}\}$;   **(b)** $\{v \in \text{reals}: v \neq \frac{1}{4}\}$;

(c) $\{x \in \text{reals}: |x| \geq 3\}$;   **(d)** $\{y \in \text{reals}: |y| \leq 5\}$

15. Even

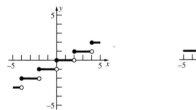

17. Neither

19. Neither

21. Odd

23. Neither

25. Even

27. Neither

29. Neither

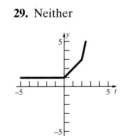

31. $T(x) = 5000 + 805x$, $\{x \in \text{integers}: 0 \leq x \leq 100\}$;
$u(x) = \dfrac{5000}{x} + 805$, $\{x \in \text{integers}: 0 < x \leq 100\}$

33. $E(x) = x - x^2$

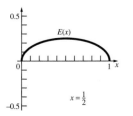

35. $L(x) = \sqrt{h^2 - x^2}$

37. (a) $E(x) = 24 + 0.40x$;   **(b)** 240 miles

39. $A(d) = \dfrac{2d - \pi d^2}{4}$, $\left\{d \in \text{reals}: 0 < d < \dfrac{1}{\pi}\right\}$

41. (a) $B(0) = 0$ **(b)** $B\left(\frac{1}{2}\right) = \frac{1}{2}B(1) = \frac{1}{2} \cdot \frac{1}{6} = \frac{1}{12}$

(c)

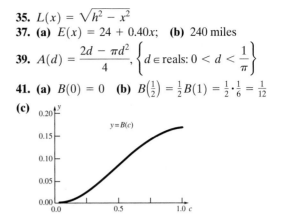

45. (a) $f(1.38) \approx 0.2994$, $f(4.12) \approx 3.6852$

(b)

x	$f(x)$
-4	-4.05
-3	-3.1538
-2	-2.375
-1	-1.8
0	-1.25
1	-0.2
2	1.125
3	2.3846
4	3.55

47.

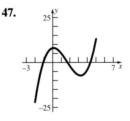

(a) $\{y \in \text{reals}: -22 \leq y \leq 13\}$;
(b) $[-1.1, 1.7] \cup [4.3, 5]$

49.

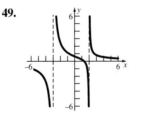

(a) x-intercept $\dfrac{4}{3}$, y-intercept $\dfrac{2}{3}$;
(b) all reals:
(c) $x = -3$, $x = 2$;   **(d)** $y = 0$

Problem Set 1.6

1. (a) 9;   **(b)** 0;   **(c)** $\frac{3}{2}$;   **(d)** 4;   **(e)** 16;   **(f)** 25

3. (a) $t^3 + 1 + \dfrac{1}{t}$;   **(b)** $\dfrac{1}{r^3} + 1$;   **(c)** $\dfrac{1}{r^3 + 1}$;   **(d)** $(z^3 + 1)^3$;

(e) $125t^3 + 1 - \dfrac{1}{5t}$;   **(f)** $\dfrac{1}{t^3} + 1 - t$

5. $(f \circ g)(x) = \sqrt{x^2 + 2x - 3}$; $(g \circ f)(x) = 1 + \sqrt{x^2 - 4}$

7. 1.188   **9.** 4.789

11. (a) $g(x) = \sqrt{x}$, $f(x) = x + 7$;
(b) $g(x) = x^{15}$, $f(x) = x^2 + x$

13. $p = f \circ g \circ h$ if $f(x) = 1/x$, $g(x) = \sqrt{x}$, $h(x) = x^2 + 1$;
$p = f \circ g \circ h$ if $f(x) = 1/\sqrt{x}$, $g(x) = x + 1$, $h(x) = x^2$

15. **17.**

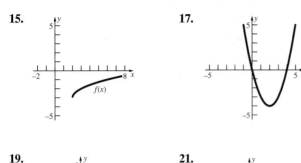

19. **21.**

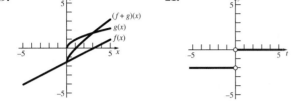

25. $f^{-1}(2) = 4$ **27.** No inverse   **29.** $f^{-1}(2) \approx -1.3$

31. $f^{-1}(x) = x - 1$ **33.** $f^{-1}(x) = x^2 - 1, x \geq 0$

35. $f^{-1}(x) = 3 - \dfrac{1}{x}$ **37.** $f^{-1}(x) = -\dfrac{\sqrt{x}}{2}$

39. $f^{-1}(x) = 1 + \sqrt[3]{x}$ **41.** $f^{-1}(x) = \dfrac{1 + x}{1 - x}$

43. $f^{-1}(x) = \left(\dfrac{2 - x}{x - 1}\right)^{1/3}$ **45.** $V = \dfrac{4\pi h^3}{27}$; $h = 3\sqrt[3]{\dfrac{V}{4\pi}}$

47. $(-\infty, -0.25]$ or $[-0.25, \infty)$; then

$f^{-1}(x) = \frac{1}{4}\left(-1 - \sqrt{8x + 33}\right)$ or $f^{-1}(x) = \frac{1}{4}\left(-1 + \sqrt{8x + 33}\right)$

49. **(a)** neither   **(b)** PF   **(c)** RF   **(d)** PF
(e) RF   **(f)** neither

51. $D(t) = \begin{cases} 400t & \text{if } 0 \leq t \leq 1 \\ \sqrt{250{,}000t^2 - 180{,}000t + 90{,}000} & \text{if } t > 1 \end{cases}$

55. **(a)** $f^{-1}(x) = -\dfrac{dx - b}{cx - a}$ **(b)** $f(x)$ would be a constant
function or undefined.   **(c)** $a = -d$ or f is the identity function.

57. **(a)** $\dfrac{1}{1 - x}$;   **(b)** x;   **(c)** $1 - x$

61. $f_1^{-1} = f_1,\ f_2^{-1} = f_2,\ f_3^{-1} = f_3,\ f_4^{-1} = f_5,\ f_5^{-1} = f_4,\ f_6^{-1} = f_6$

63.

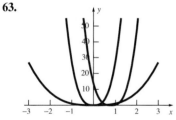

65.

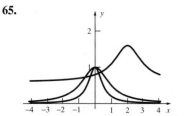

Problem Set 1.7

1.

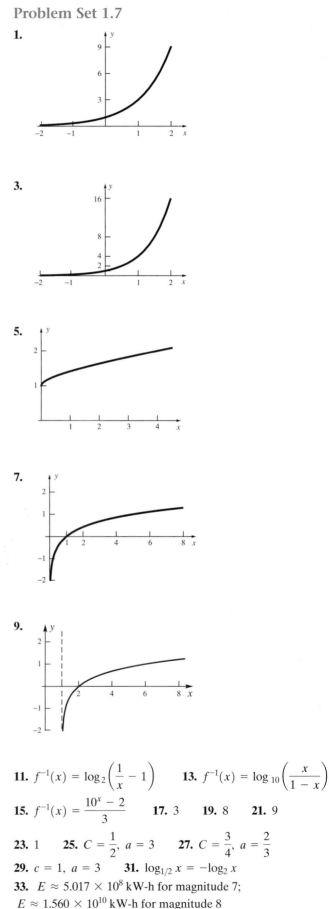

3.

5.

7.

9.

11. $f^{-1}(x) = \log_2\left(\dfrac{1}{x} - 1\right)$ **13.** $f^{-1}(x) = \log_{10}\left(\dfrac{x}{1 - x}\right)$

15. $f^{-1}(x) = \dfrac{10^x - 2}{3}$ **17.** 3   **19.** 8   **21.** 9

23. 1   **25.** $C = \dfrac{1}{2}, a = 3$ **27.** $C = \dfrac{3}{4}, a = \dfrac{2}{3}$

29. $c = 1,\ a = 3$ **31.** $\log_{1/2} x = -\log_2 x$

33. $E \approx 5.017 \times 10^8$ kW-h for magnitude 7;
$E \approx 1.560 \times 10^{10}$ kW-h for magnitude 8

35. $r = 2^{1/12} \approx 1.0595$; frequency of $\overline{C} = 440\sqrt[4]{2} \approx 523.25$

Problem Set 1.8

1. (a) $\frac{\pi}{6}$; **(b)** $\frac{\pi}{4}$; **(c)** $-\frac{\pi}{3}$; **(d)** $\frac{4\pi}{3}$; **(e)** $-\frac{37\pi}{18}$; **(f)** $\frac{\pi}{18}$;

3. (a) 0.5812; **(b)** 0.8029; **(c)** −1.1624; **(d)** 4.1907;
(e) −6.4403; **(f)** 0.1920;

5. (a) 68.37; **(b)** 0.8845; **(c)** 0.4855; **(d)** −0.3532;

7. (a) 46.097; **(b)** 0.0789

9. (a) $\frac{\sqrt{3}}{3}$; **(b)** −1; **(c)** $-\sqrt{2}$; **(d)** 1; **(e)** 1; **(f)** −1

15. (a)   **(b)**

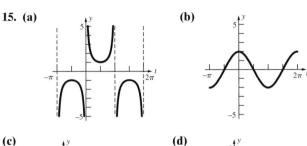

(c)   **(d)**

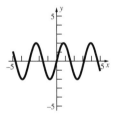

17. Period = π; Amplitude = 2

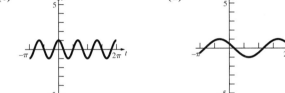

19. Period = $\frac{\pi}{2}$; shift: 2 units up

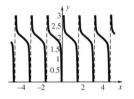

21. Period = π; amplitude = 7; shift: 21 units up, $\frac{3}{2}$ units left

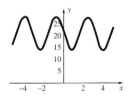

23. Period = $\frac{\pi}{2}$; shift: $\frac{\pi}{6}$ units right

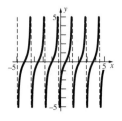

25. (a) Even; **(b)** Even; **(c)** Odd; **(d)** Even; **(e)** Even;
(f) Odd

27. $\frac{1}{4}$ **29.** $\frac{1}{8}$ **31.** $\frac{2-\sqrt{2}}{4}$

35. 336 rev/min   **37.** 28 rev/sec

39. (a) $\frac{\pi}{3}$; **(b)** $\frac{5\pi}{6}$

41. (a) 0.1419; **(b)** 1.8925; **(c)** 1.7127

43. 25 cm^2 **45.** $r^2 \sin\frac{t}{2}\cos\frac{t}{2} + \frac{\pi r^2}{2}\sin^2\frac{t}{2}$ **47.** 67.5°F

49. As t increases, the point on the rim of the wheel will move around the circle of radius 2.
(a) $x(2) \approx 1.902$; $y(2) \approx 0.618$; $x(6) \approx -1.176$;
$y(6) \approx -1.618$; $x(10) = 0$; $y(10) = 2$; $x(0) = 0$; $y(0) = 2$
(b) $x(t) = -2\sin\left(\frac{\pi}{5}t\right)$, $y(t) = 2\cos\left(\frac{\pi}{5}t\right)$
(c) The point is at $(2,0)$ when $\frac{\pi}{5}t = \frac{\pi}{2}$; that is, when $t = \frac{5}{2}$.

51. (c) $A_1\sin(\omega t + \phi_1) + A_2\sin(\omega t + \phi_2) + A_3\sin(\omega t + \phi_3)$
$= (A_1\cos\phi_1 + A_2\cos\phi_2 + A_3\cos\phi_3)\sin\omega t$
$\quad + (A_1\sin\phi_1 + A_2\sin\phi_2 + A_3\sin\phi_3)\cos\omega t$

53. (a)   **(b)**

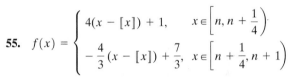

(c)

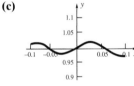

55. $f(x) = \begin{cases} 4(x - [\![x]\!]) + 1, & x \in \left[n, n + \frac{1}{4}\right) \\ -\frac{4}{3}(x - [\![x]\!]) + \frac{7}{3}, & x \in \left[n + \frac{1}{4}, n + 1\right) \end{cases}$

where n is an integer

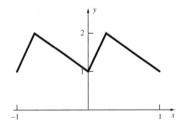

Problem Set 1.9

1. $\frac{\pi}{4}$ **3.** $-\frac{\pi}{3}$ **5.** $\frac{\pi}{3}$ **7.** $-\frac{\pi}{6}$ **9.** 0.4567   **11.** 0.1115

13. 0.3113   **15.** 2.038   **17.** 0.6259   **19.** $\theta = \sin^{-1}\frac{x}{8}$

21. $\theta = \sin^{-1}\frac{5}{x}$ **23.** $\theta = \tan^{-1}\frac{3}{x} - \tan^{-1}\frac{1}{x}$ **25.** $\frac{1}{9}$ **27.** $\frac{56}{65}$

35. (a) $f^{-1}(x) = \frac{1}{2}\arccos\frac{x}{3}$, $0 \le x \le \frac{\pi}{2}$

(b) $f^{-1}(x) = \frac{1}{3}\arcsin\frac{x}{2}$, $-\frac{\pi}{6} \le x \le \frac{\pi}{6}$

(c) $f^{-1}(x) = \arctan 2x$, $-\frac{\pi}{2} < x < \frac{\pi}{2}$

(d) $f^{-1}(x) = \frac{1}{\arcsin x}$, $x < -\frac{2}{\pi}$ or $x > \frac{2}{\pi}$

Chapter Review 1.10

Concepts Test

1. False   **3.** False   **5.** False   **7.** True   **9.** True
11. True   **13.** True   **15.** True   **17.** True   **19.** True
21. True   **23.** True   **25.** True   **27.** True   **29.** True
31. True   **33.** True   **35.** False   **37.** False   **39.** True
41. False   **43.** False   **45.** True   **47.** False   **49.** True
51. True   **53.** False   **55.** True   **57.** False   **59.** True
61. False   **63.** True   **65.** False   **67.** False   **69.** False

Sample Test Problems

1. (a) $2, \frac{25}{4}, \frac{4}{25}$;   (b) $1, 9, 49$;   (c) $64, 8, \frac{1}{8}$;
7. 2.66

9. $\left\{x: x < \frac{1}{3}\right\}; \left(-\infty; \frac{1}{3}\right);$

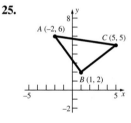

11. $\left\{x: \frac{1}{3} \le x \le 3\right\}; \left[\frac{1}{3}, 3\right];$

13. $\left\{t: \frac{3}{7} \le t \le \frac{5}{3}\right\}; \left[\frac{3}{7}, \frac{5}{3}\right];$

15. $\{x: -4 \le x \le 3\}; [-4, 3];$

17. $\left\{x: x \le -\frac{1}{2} \text{ or } x > 1\right\}; \left(-\infty, -\frac{1}{2}\right] \cup (1, \infty);$

19. Any negative number   **21.** $t \le 5$

25.

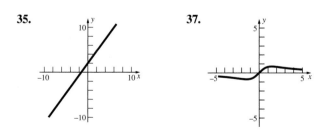

27. $(x - 6)^2 + (y - 2)^2 = 20$ **29.** 5
31. (a) $y = \frac{2}{9}x + \frac{13}{9}$;   (b) $y = \frac{3}{2}x + 4$;   (c) $y = \frac{4}{3}x + \frac{11}{3}$;
(d) $x = -2$;   (e) $y = x + 3$
33. (b)

35.   **37.**

39. $(0, 4)$ and $(3, 7)$
41. (a) $-\frac{1}{2}$;   (b) 4;   (c) Does not exist;   (d) $\frac{1}{t} - \frac{1}{t-1}$;
(e) $\frac{t}{1+t} - t$
43. (a) $\{x \in \text{reals}: x \ne -1, 1\}$;   (b) $\{x \in \text{reals}: |x| \le 2\}$;

45. (a)   (b)

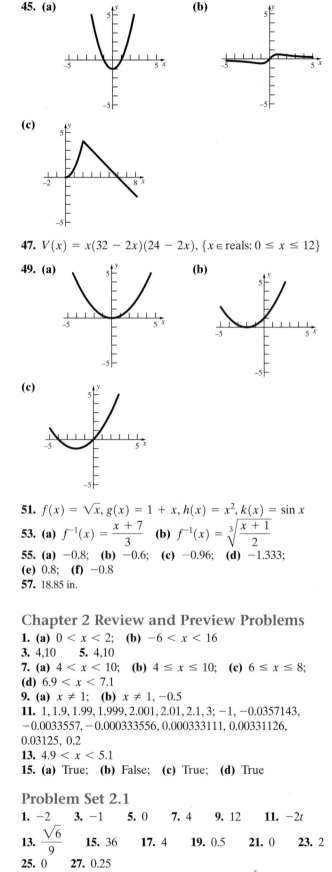

(c)

47. $V(x) = x(32 - 2x)(24 - 2x), \{x \in \text{reals}: 0 \le x \le 12\}$
49. (a)   (b)

(c)

51. $f(x) = \sqrt{x}, g(x) = 1 + x, h(x) = x^2, k(x) = \sin x$
53. (a) $f^{-1}(x) = \dfrac{x + 7}{3}$ (b) $f^{-1}(x) = \sqrt[3]{\dfrac{x + 1}{2}}$
55. (a) -0.8;   (b) -0.6;   (c) -0.96;   (d) -1.333;
(e) 0.8;   (f) -0.8
57. 18.85 in.

Chapter 2 Review and Preview Problems

1. (a) $0 < x < 2$;   (b) $-6 < x < 16$
3. 4,10   **5.** 4,10
7. (a) $4 < x < 10$;   (b) $4 \le x \le 10$;   (c) $6 \le x \le 8$;
(d) $6.9 < x < 7.1$
9. (a) $x \ne 1$;   (b) $x \ne 1, -0.5$
11. $1, 1.9, 1.99, 1.999, 2.001, 2.01, 2.1, 3$; $-1, -0.0357143$,
$-0.0033557, -0.000333556, 0.000333111, 0.00331126$,
$0.03125, 0.2$
13. $4.9 < x < 5.1$
15. (a) True;   (b) False;   (c) True;   (d) True

Problem Set 2.1

1. -2 **3.** -1 **5.** 0   **7.** 4   **9.** 12   **11.** $-2t$
13. $\dfrac{\sqrt{6}}{9}$ **15.** 36   **17.** 4   **19.** 0.5   **21.** 0   **23.** 2
25. 0   **27.** 0.25
29. (a) 2;   (b) 1;   (c) Does not exist;   (d) $\frac{5}{2}$;   (e) 2;
(f) Does not exist;   (g) 2;   (h) 1;   (i) 2.5
31. (a) 2;   (b) undefined;   (c) 2;   (d) 4;   (e) does not exist;
(f) does not exist

33.

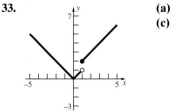

(a) 0;   **(b)** Does not exist;
(c) 2;   **(d)** 2

35.

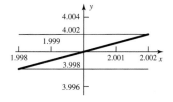

(a) 0;   **(b)** Does not exist;   **(c)** 1;
(d) $\frac{1}{2}$

37. Does not exist
39. (a) Does not exist;   **(b)** 0
41. $a = -1, 0, 1$
43. (a) Does not exist;   **(b)** −1;   **(c)** −3;   **(d)** Does not exist
45. (a) 1;   **(b)** 0;   **(c)** −1;   **(d)** −1
47. Does not exist   **49.** 0   **51.** $\frac{1}{2}$ **53.** Does not exist
55. 6   **57.** −3

Problem Set 2.2
1. $0 < |t - a| < \delta \Rightarrow |f(t) - M| < \varepsilon$
3. $0 < |z - d| < \delta \Rightarrow |h(z) - P| < \varepsilon$
5. $0 < c - x < \delta \Rightarrow |f(x) - L| < \varepsilon$
7. 0.001

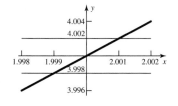

9. 0.0019

31. (b), (c)
33. (a) $\dfrac{x^3 - x^2 - 2x - 4}{x^4 - 4x^3 + x^2 + x + 6}$;   **(b)** No;   **(c)** 3

Problem Set 2.3
1. 3   **3.** −3   **5.** −5   **7.** 2   **9.** −1   **11.** 2   **13.** 0
15. −4   **17.** $-\frac{2}{3}$ **19.** $\frac{3}{2}$ **21.** $\dfrac{x+2}{5}$ **23.** −1
25. $\sqrt{10}$ **27.** −6   **29.** 6   **31.** 12   **33.** $-\frac{1}{4}$ **41.** 0
43. 0   **45.** $\frac{2}{5}$ **47.** −1   **51. (a)** 1;   **(b)** 0

Problem Set 2.4
1. 1   **3.** −1   **5.** −1   **7.** $\frac{1}{2}$ **9.** $\dfrac{3}{\pi}$ **11.** $\dfrac{3}{\sqrt{2}}$
13. 2   **15.** $\frac{1}{2}$ **17.** ∞ **19.** 2   **21.** 0   **23.** $-\infty$

25. 1   **27.** ∞ **29.** ∞ **31.** ∞ **33.** $-\infty$ **35.** 5
37. 0   **39.** −1   **41.** $-\infty$

43. Horizontal asymptote $y = 0$
Vertical asymptote $x = -1$

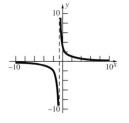

45. Horizontal asymptote $y = 2$
Vertical asymptote $x = 3$

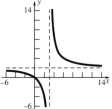

47. Horizontal asymptote $y = 0$
No vertical asymptotes

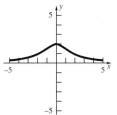

49. The oblique asymptote is $y = 2x + 3$.
51. (a) We say that $\lim\limits_{x \to c^+} f(x) = -\infty$ if for each negative
number M there corresponds a $\delta > 0$ such that
$0 < x - c < \delta \Rightarrow f(x) < M$.
(b) We say that $\lim\limits_{x \to c^-} f(x) = \infty$ if for each positive number M
there corresponds a $\delta > 0$ such that
$0 < c - x < \delta \Rightarrow f(x) > M$.
55. (a) Does not exist.   **(b)** 0   **(c)** 1   **(d)** ∞ **(e)** 0
(f) $\frac{1}{2}$ **(g)** Does not exist.   **(h)** 0
57. $\frac{3}{2}$ **59.** $-\dfrac{3}{2\sqrt{2}}$ **61.** 1   **63.** ∞ **65.** −1
67. $-\infty$ **69.** e **71.** 1

Problem Set 2.5
1. 1   **3.** 1   **5.** $\frac{1}{2}$ **7.** 3   **9.** $\frac{1}{2\pi}$ **11.** 0   **13.** 7
15. 0   **17.** 0

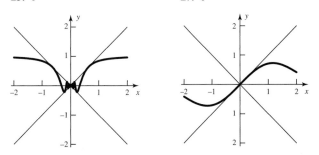

19. 2

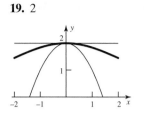

Problem Set 2.6

1. 25   **3.** x^3 **5.** $\cos x$ **7.** $3\ln x - 3x$ **9.** $3x^2$
11. (a) D **(b)** B **(c)** C **(d)** A

13.   **15.**

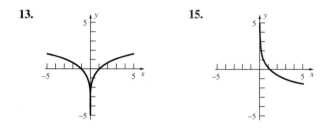

17.

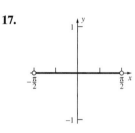

19. (a) $\dfrac{1}{e}$; **(b)** e^3; **(c)** e^2; **(d)** $\dfrac{1}{e^2}$
21. (a) 1.792; **(b)** 0.406; **(c)** 4.396; **(d)** 0.3465;
(e) -3.584; **(f)** 3.871
23. $\ln\dfrac{(x+1)^2}{x}$ **25.** $\ln\dfrac{x^2(x-2)}{x+2}$
27. (a) \$401.71 **(b)** \$402.15 **(c)** \$402.19 **(d)** \$402.19
29. (a) 11.58 yrs. **(b)** 11.55 yrs.
31. \$133.6 billion   **33.** 1.544   **35.** 0.1747
37. 4.08746   **39.** 1.9307

Problem Set 2.7

1. Continuous
3. Not continuous; $\lim\limits_{x\to 3}\dfrac{3}{x-3}$ and $h(3)$ do not exist.
5. Not continuous; $\lim\limits_{t\to 3}\dfrac{|t-3|}{t-3}$ and $h(3)$ do not exist.
7. Continuous   **9.** Not continuous; $h(3)$ does not exist.
11. Continuous   **13.** Continuous   **15.** Continuous
17. $(-\infty, -5), [-5, 4], (4, 6), [6, 8], (8, \infty)$
19. Define $f(3) = -12$.   **21.** Define $H(1) = \tfrac{1}{2}$.
23. Define $F(-1) = -\sin 2$.   **25.** $3, \pi$
27. Every $\theta = n\pi + \tfrac{\pi}{2}$ where n is any integer.   **29.** -1
31. $(-\infty, -2] \cup [2, \infty)$ **33.** 1
35. Every $t = n + \tfrac{1}{2}$ where n is any integer.

37.   **39.**

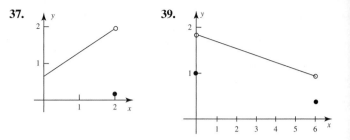

41. Continuous.
43. Discontinuous: removable, define $f(0) = 1$
45. Discontinuous, removable, redefine $g(0) = 1$
47. Discontinuous: nonremovable.
49. $[-5, 5]$ **51.** $[-1, 1]$ **53.** $[1, \infty]$

55. The function is continuous on the intervals
$(0, 1], (1, 2], (2, 3], \ldots$

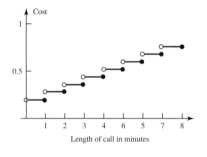

57. The function is continuous on the intervals
$(0, 0.25], (0.25, 0.375], (0.375, 0.5], \ldots$

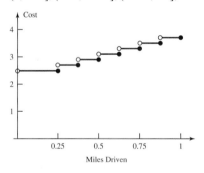

61. The interval $[0.6, 0.7]$ contains the solution.

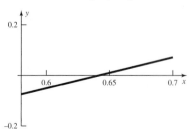

71. Yes, g is continuous.

77. (a) Domain $\left[-\dfrac{3}{4}, \dfrac{3}{4}\right]$, Range $\{-3/4, 0, 3/4\}$

(b) Discontinuous at $x = 0$ **(c)** $-\dfrac{3}{4}, 0, \dfrac{3}{4}$

Chapter Review 2.8

Concepts Test

1. False   **3.** False   **5.** False   **7.** True   **9.** False
11. True   **13.** False   **15.** True   **17.** False   **19.** False
21. False   **23.** True   **25.** True   **27.** True   **29.** True
31. False   **33.** True

Sample Test Problems

1. 0   **3.** 2   **5.** $\dfrac{1}{8}$ **7.** $\dfrac{1}{2}$ **9.** 4   **11.** -1 **13.** -1

15. $\dfrac{5}{3}$ **17.** 1   **19.** ∞ **21.** ∞

25. (a) $x = -1, 1$ **(b)** $f(-1) = -1$
27. (a) 14   **(b)** -12 **(c)** -2 **(d)** -2 **(e)** 5   **(f)** 0
29. $a = 2, b = -1$ **31.** Vertical: none, Horizontal $y = 0$
33. Vertical: $x = -1, 1$, Horizontal: $y = 1$
35. Vertical: $x = \pm\pi/4, \pm3\pi/4, \pm5\pi/4, \dots$, Horizontal: none
37. $[-2, 2]$

Chapter 3 Review and Preview Problems

1. (a) 4   **(b)** 4.41   **(c)** 0.41   **(d)** 4.1   **(e)** $a^2 + 2ah + h^2$
(f) $2ah + h^2$ **(g)** $2a + h$ **(h)** $2a$
3. (a) $\sqrt{2} \approx 1.41$ **(b)** $\sqrt{2.1} \approx 1.45$ **(c)** 0.035   **(d)** 0.35
(e) $\sqrt{a + h}$ **(f)** $\sqrt{a + h} - \sqrt{a}$ **(g)** $\left(\sqrt{a + h} - \sqrt{a}\right)/h$
(h) $\dfrac{1}{2\sqrt{a}}$

5. (a) $a^3 + 3a^2b$ **(b)** $a^4 + 4a^3b$ **(c)** $a^5 + 5a^4b$
7. $\sin(x + h) = \sin x \cos h + \cos x \sin h$
9. (a) $(10, 0), (10, 0), (10, 0)$ **(b)** $t = 1/4$
11. (a) North plane has traveled 600 miles. East plane has
traveled 400 miles.   **(b)** 721 miles   **(c)** 840 miles
13. e^{-2} **15.** $e^{1/3}$

Problem Set 3.1

1. 4

3. -2 **5.** $\dfrac{5}{2}$

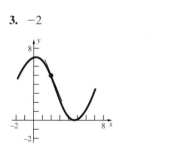

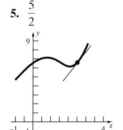

7. (a), (b)   **(c)** 2;   **(d)** 2.01;   **(e)** 2

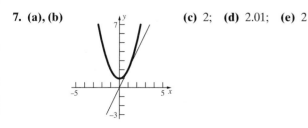

9. $-4, -2, 0, 2, 4$

11.

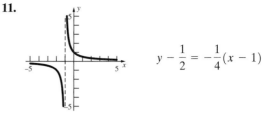

$$y - \frac{1}{2} = -\frac{1}{4}(x - 1)$$

13. (a) 16 ft;   **(b)** 48 ft;   **(c)** 80 ft/s;   **(d)** 96.16 ft/s;
(e) 96 ft/s
15. (a) $\dfrac{1}{\sqrt{2\alpha + 1}}$ ft/s;   **(b)** 1.5 sec
17. (a) 0.02005 g;   **(b)** 2.005 g/h;   **(c)** 2 g/h
19. (a) 49 g/cm;   **(b)** 27 g/cm
21. 4   **23.** 29,167 gal/h; 75,000 gal/h
25. (a) 0.5 °F/day   **(b)** 0.067 °F/day   **(c)** January and July
(d) March and November
27. (a) Increasing   **(b)** Decreasing
29. 24π km²/day
31.

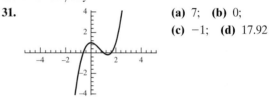

(a) 7;   **(b)** 0;
(c) -1;   **(d)** 17.92

33. 2.818

Problem Set 3.2

1. 2   **3.** 5   **5.** 2   **7.** 6x   **9.** $2ax + b$
11. $3x^2 + 4x$ **13.** $-\dfrac{2}{x^2}$ **15.** $-\dfrac{12x}{(x^2 + 1)^2}$
17. $-\dfrac{7}{(x - 4)^2}$ **19.** $\dfrac{3}{2\sqrt{3x}}$ **21.** $-\dfrac{3}{2(x - 2)^{3/2}}$
23. $2x - 3$ **25.** $-\dfrac{5}{(x - 5)^2}$ **27.** $f(x) = 2x^3$ at $x = 5$
29. $f(x) = x^2$ at $x = 2$ **31.** $f(x) = x^2$ at x
33. $f(t) = \dfrac{2}{t}$ at t **35.** $f(x) = \cos x$ at x

37.

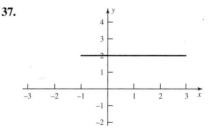

39.

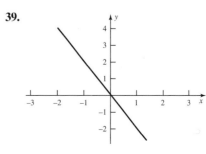

41.

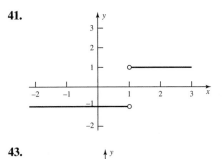

43.

45. 1.5   **47.** −0.1667   **49.** 0.0081   **51.** 2x
53. −1/(x + 1)²   **55.** 2/(x + 1)²   **57.** −½, 1, ⅔, −3

59.

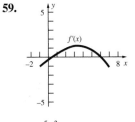

61. (a) $\frac{5}{2}, \frac{3}{2}, 1.8, -0.6$; **(b)** 0.5; **(c)** 5; **(d)** 3, 5; **(e)** 1, 3, 5;
(f) 0; **(g)** −0.7, 1.5, (5, 7)

63.

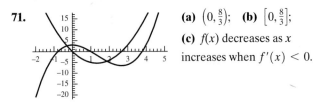

65. f is short-dashed; $g = f'$ is solid; g' is long-dashed
67. $m = 4, b = -4$
69. (a) m; **(b)** $-m$

71.

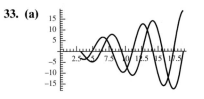

(a) $\left(0, \frac{8}{3}\right)$; **(b)** $\left[0, \frac{8}{3}\right]$;
(c) $f(x)$ decreases as x
increases when $f'(x) < 0$.

Problem Set 3.3

1. $4x$ **3.** π **5.** $-4x^{-3}$ **7.** $-\frac{\pi}{x^2}$ **9.** $-\frac{500}{x^6}$

11. $2x + 2$ **13.** $4x^3 + 3x^2 + 2x + 1$

15. $7\pi x^6 - 10x^4 + 10x^{-3}$ **17.** $-\frac{9}{x^4} - 4x^{-5}$

19. $-\frac{2}{x^2} + \frac{2}{x^3}$ **21.** $-\frac{1}{2x^2} + 2$ **23.** $3x^2 + 1$

25. $8x + 4$ **27.** $5x^4 + 6x^2 + 2x$

29. $5x^4 + 42x^2 + 2x - 51$ **31.** $60x^3 - 30x^2 - 32x + 14$

33. $-\frac{6x}{(3x^2 + 1)^2}$ **35.** $\frac{-8x + 3}{(4x^2 - 3x + 9)^2}$ **37.** $\frac{2}{(x + 1)^2}$

39. $\frac{6x^2 + 20x + 3}{(3x + 5)^2}$ **41.** $\frac{4x^2 + 4x - 5}{(2x + 1)^2}$ **43.** $\frac{x^2 - 1}{(x^2 + 1)^2}$

45. (a) 23; **(b)** 4; **(c)** $-\frac{17}{9}$

49. $y = 1$ **51.** $(0, 0)$ and $\left(\frac{2}{3}, -\frac{4}{27}\right)$

53. $(2.817, 0.563)$ and $(-2.817, -0.563)$

55. (a) -24 ft/s; **(b)** 1.25 s

57. $y = 2x + 1, y = -2x + 9$ **59.** $3\sqrt{5}$

61. 681 cm³ per week

Problem Set 3.4

1. $2 \cos x - 3 \sin x$ **3.** 0   **5.** $\sec x \tan x$ **7.** $\sec^2 x$

9. $\sec^2 x$ **11.** $\cos^2 x - \sin^2 x$ **13.** $\frac{x \cos x - \sin x}{x^2}$

15. $-x^2 \sin x + 2x \cos x$ **17.** $2 \tan x \sec^2 x$

19. $y - 0.5403 = -0.8415(x - 1)$ **21.** $-2 \sin^2 x + 2 \cos^2 x$

23. $30\sqrt{3}$ ft/sec   **25.** $y = x$

27. $x = \frac{\pi}{4} + k\frac{\pi}{2}$ where k is an integer.

33. (a)   **(b)** 6; 5;
(c) $f(x) = x \sin x$ with $a = 0$ and $b = \pi$ is a counterexample;
(d) 24.93

Problem Set 3.5

1. $15(1 + x)^{14}$ **3.** $-10(3 - 2x)^4$

5. $11(3x^2 - 4x + 3)(x^3 - 2x^2 + 3x + 1)^{10}$

7. $-\frac{5}{(x + 3)^6}$ **9.** $(2x + 1) \cos(x^2 + x)$

11. $-3 \sin x \cos^2 x$ **13.** $-\frac{6(x + 1)^2}{(x - 1)^4}$

15. $-\frac{3x^2 + 12x}{(x + 2)^2} \sin\left(\frac{3x^2}{x + 2}\right)$

17. $2(3x - 2)(3 - x^2)(9 + 4x - 9x^2)$

19. $\frac{(x + 1)(3x - 11)}{(3x - 4)^2}$ **21.** $4x(x^2 + 4)$

23. $\frac{51(3t - 2)^2}{(t + 5)^4}$ **25.** $\frac{(6t + 47)(3t - 2)^2}{(t + 5)^2}$

27. $\frac{3 \sin^2 x(\cos x \cos 2x + 2 \sin x \sin 2x)}{\cos^4 2x}$ **29.** 9.6

31. 1.4183   **33.** $4(2x + 3) \sin^3(x^2 + 3x) \cos(x^2 + 3x)$

35. $-3 \sin t \sin^2(\cos t) \cos(\cos t)$

37. $-8\theta \cos^3(\sin \theta^2) \sin(\sin \theta^2)(\cos \theta^2)$

39. $-2 \cos[\cos(\sin 2x)] \sin(\sin 2x)(\cos 2x)$

41. 2   **43.** 1   **45.** −1   **47.** $2F'(2x)$

49. $-2(F(t))^{-3}F'(t)$ **51.** $4(1 + F(2z))F'(2z)$

53. $-\sin xF'(\cos x)$ **55.** $2F'(2x) \sec^2(F(2x))$

57. $2F(x)F'(x) \sin F(x) \cos F(x) + F'(x) \sin^2 F(x)$

59. $-2 \sin 1$ **61.** −1   **63.** $x = \pi/4 + k\pi, k = 0, \pm 1, \pm 2, \ldots$

65. $y = -\frac{1}{2}x + \frac{3}{4}$ **67.** $x = 3/2$

69. (a) $(10 \cos 8\pi t, 10 \sin 8\pi t)$; **(b)** 80π cm/s

71. (a) $(\cos 2\pi t, \sin 2\pi t)$; **(b)** $\sin 2\pi t + \sqrt{25 - \cos^2 2\pi t}$;

(c) $2\pi \cos 2\pi t \left(1 + \dfrac{\sin 2\pi t}{\sqrt{25 - \cos^2 2\pi t}}\right)$

73. 0.38 in/min   **75.** $x_0 = \pi/3$; $\theta = 1.25$ rad.

79. $\cot x |\sin x|$ **81.** 16

Problem Set 3.6

1. 6   **3.** 162   **5.** $-343 \cos(7x)$ **7.** $-\dfrac{6}{(x-1)^4}$

9. 2   **11.** $\frac{1}{2}$ **13.** $2\pi^2$ **15.** -900

19. (a) 0; **(b)** 0; **(c)** 0

21. $f''(-5) = -24$; $f''(3) = 24$

23. (a) $v(t) = 12 - 4t$; $a(t) = -4$ **(b)** $(-\infty, 3)$; **(c)** $(3, \infty)$;

(d) All t; **(e)**

25. (a) $v(t) = 3t^2 - 18t + 24$; $a(t) = 6t - 18$;

(b) $(-\infty, 2) \cup (4, \infty)$; **(c)** $(2, 4)$; **(d)** $(-\infty, 3)$;

(e)

27. (a) $v(t) = 2t - \dfrac{16}{t^2}$; $a(t) = 2 + \dfrac{32}{t^3}$; **(b)** $(2, \infty)$;

(c) $(0, 2)$; **(d)** No t;

(e)

29. $v(1) = 11$; $v(4) = -16$

31. (a) $\frac{3}{4}$ s; **(b)** $\frac{1}{2}$ s, $\frac{3}{4}$ s; **(c)** 0 s, $\frac{3}{2}$ s

33. (a) 48 ft/s; **(b)** $\frac{3}{2}$ s; **(c)** 292 ft; **(d)** 5.77 s; **(e)** 137 ft/s

35. 581 ft/s   **37.** $(-\infty, -2) \cup (1, 4)$

39. $D_x^n(uv) = \displaystyle\sum_{k=0}^{n} \binom{n}{k} D_x^{n-k}(u) D_x^k(v)$ where $\binom{n}{k}$ is the binomial

coefficient $\dfrac{n!}{(n-k)!k!}$.

41. (a)   **(b)** -1.2826

Problem Set 3.7

1. $\dfrac{x}{y}$ **3.** $-\dfrac{y}{x}$ **5.** $\dfrac{1 - y^2}{2xy}$ **7.** $\dfrac{12x^2 + 7y^2}{6y^2 - 14xy}$

9. $\dfrac{y^3 - \dfrac{5y}{2\sqrt{5xy}}}{\dfrac{5x}{2\sqrt{5xy}} + 2 - 2y - 3xy^2}$ **11.** $-\dfrac{y}{x}$

13. $y - 3 = -\frac{9}{7}(x - 1)$ **15.** $y = 1$

17. $y + 1 = \frac{1}{2}(x - 1)$ **19.** $5x^{2/3} + \dfrac{1}{2\sqrt{x}}$

21. $\dfrac{1}{3\sqrt[3]{x^2}} - \dfrac{1}{3\sqrt[3]{x^4}}$ **23.** $\dfrac{3x - 2}{2\sqrt[4]{(3x^2 - 4x)^3}}$

25. $-\dfrac{6x^2 + 4}{3\sqrt[3]{(x^3 + 2x)^5}}$ **27.** $\dfrac{2x + \cos x}{2\sqrt{x^2 + \sin x}}$

29. $-\dfrac{x^2 \cos x + 2x \sin x}{3\sqrt[3]{(x^2 \sin x)^4}}$ **31.** $-\dfrac{(x + 1) \sin(x^2 + 2x)}{2\sqrt[4]{[1 + \cos(x^2 + 2x)]^3}}$

33. $\dfrac{ds}{dt} = -\dfrac{s^2 + 3t^2}{2st}$; $\dfrac{dt}{ds} = -\dfrac{2st}{s^2 + 3t^2}$

35. $\sqrt{3}y + x = 0$, $\sqrt{3}y - x = 0$

37. (a) $y' = -\dfrac{y}{x + 3y^2}$; **(b)** $y'' = \dfrac{2xy}{(x + 3y^2)^3}$

39. -15;   **45.** $\theta \approx 2.0344$ rad

47. $y = 2(x + 4)$; $y = 2(x - 4)$ **49.** $\frac{13}{3}$

Problem Set 3.8

1. 1296 in.^{3}/s   **3.** 392 mi/h   **5.** 471 mi/h   **7.** 0.258 ft/s

9. 0.0796 ft/s   **11.** $\frac{1}{12}$ ft/min   **13.** 1.018 in.^{2}/s

15. 15.71 km/min

17. (a) $\frac{1}{2}$ ft/s; **(b)** $\frac{5}{2}$ ft/s **(c)** $\frac{1}{24}$ rad/s

19. 110 ft/s   **21.** -0.016 ft/h   **23.** 13.33 ft/s

25. 4049 ft^3/hr

27. (a) -1.125 ft/s; **(b)** -0.08 ft/s^2

29. (b) 3 hours

31. $\frac{16}{3}$ ft/s when the girl is at least 30 ft from the light pole and $\frac{80}{17}$ ft/s when she is less than 30 ft from the pole.

Problem Set 3.9

7. $(f^{-1})'(3) \approx \frac{1}{3}$ **9.** $(f^{-1})'(3) \approx -\frac{1}{3}$

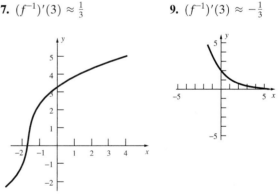

11. $\frac{1}{16}$ **13.** $\frac{1}{4}$ **15.** $\dfrac{2x + 3}{x^2 + 3x + \pi}$ **17.** $\dfrac{3}{x - 4}$ **19.** $\dfrac{3}{x}$

21. $2x + 4x \ln x + \frac{3}{x}(\ln x)^2$ **23.** $\dfrac{1}{\sqrt{x^2 + 1}}$ **25.** $\frac{1}{243}$

27. e^{x+2} **29.** $\dfrac{e^{\sqrt{x+2}}}{2\sqrt{x + 2}}$ **31.** $2x$ **33.** $x^2 e^x(x + 3)$

35. $x\sqrt{e^{x^2}} + \dfrac{x}{|x|} e^{\sqrt{x^2}}$ **37.** $-\dfrac{y}{x}$ **39.** $2 \cdot 6^{2x} \ln 6$

41. $\dfrac{1}{\ln 3}$ **43.** $3^z \left[\dfrac{1}{z + 5} + \ln(z + 5) \ln 3\right]$

45. $10^{x^2} 2x \ln 10 + 20x^{19}$

47. $(\pi + 1)x^{\pi} + (\pi + 1)^x \ln(\pi + 1)$

49. $(x^2 + 1)^{\ln x}\left(\dfrac{\ln(x^2 + 1)}{x} + \dfrac{2x \ln x}{x^2 + 1}\right)$ **51.** $\sin 1$

53. $-\dfrac{x^3 + 33x^2 + 8}{2(x^3 - 4)^{3/2}}$ **55.** $-\dfrac{10x^2 + 219x - 118}{6(x - 4)^2(x + 13)^{1/2}(2x + 1)^{4/3}}$

57. 1

Problem Set 3.10

1. $2 \sinh x \cosh x = \sinh 2x$
3. $10 \sinh x \cosh x = 5 \sinh 2x$ **5.** $3 \sinh(3x + 1)$
7. $\coth x$ **9.** $x^2 \sinh x + 2x \cosh x$
11. $\cosh 3x \cosh x + 3 \sinh 3x \sinh x$
13. $2 \tanh x \cosh 2x + \sinh 2x \operatorname{sech}^2 x$

15. $\dfrac{2x}{\sqrt{x^4 + 1}}$ **17.** $-\dfrac{1}{2(x^2 - 3x + 2)}$

19. $\dfrac{3x}{\sqrt{9x^2 - 1}} + \cosh^{-1} 3x$ **21.** $\dfrac{1}{\sqrt{x^2 - 1}\cosh^{-1} x}$

23. $-\csc^2 x \operatorname{sech}^2(\cot x)$ **25.** $\dfrac{4x}{\sqrt{1 - 4x^4}}$

27. $x^2\left[\dfrac{xe^x}{1 + e^{2x}} + 3 \tan^{-1}(e^x)\right]$ **29.** $\dfrac{3(\tan^{-1} x)^2}{1 + x^2}$

31. $\dfrac{3}{|x|\sqrt{x^6 - 1}}$ **33.** $\dfrac{3(1 + \sin^{-1} x)^2}{\sqrt{1 - x^2}}$ **35.** $\dfrac{2}{x[1 + (\ln x^2)^2]}$

37.

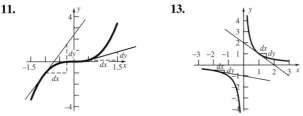

$y = \sinh x$ and
$y = \ln\left(x + \sqrt{x^2 + 1}\right)$
are inverse functions.

39. $y = 758 - 128 \cosh \dfrac{x}{128}$ **41.** $\frac{1}{13}$ rad/s   **43.** 1 rev/min

45. 3.96×10^{-4} rad/s

Problem Set 3.11

1. $dy = (2x + 1)\,dx$ **3.** $dy = -8(2x + 3)^{-5}\,dx$
5. $dy = 3(\sin x + \cos x)^2(\cos x - \sin x)\,dx$

7. $dy = \left[\dfrac{1 - e^x}{x} - e^x \ln x\right]dx$

9. $ds = \frac{3}{2}(2t + \csc^2 t)\sqrt{t^2 - \cot t + 2}\,dt$

11.   **13.**

15. (a) $\Delta y = -\frac{1}{3}$ (b) $\Delta y = -0.3$
17. (a) $\Delta y = 67$ $dy = 34$ (b) $\Delta y \approx 0.1706$ $dy = 0.17$
19. 5.9917   **21.** 39.27 cm^3 **23.** 893 ft^3 **25.** 12.6 ft
27. 4189 ± 62.8 cm^3; relative error ≈ 0.015

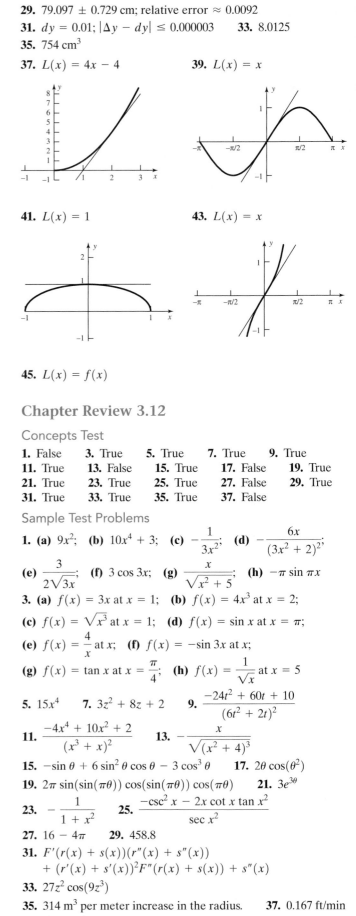

29. 79.097 ± 0.729 cm; relative error ≈ 0.0092
31. $dy = 0.01$; $|\Delta y - dy| \leq 0.000003$ **33.** 8.0125
35. 754 cm^3
37. $L(x) = 4x - 4$ **39.** $L(x) = x$

41. $L(x) = 1$ **43.** $L(x) = x$

45. $L(x) = f(x)$

Chapter Review 3.12

Concepts Test

1. False   **3.** True   **5.** True   **7.** True   **9.** True
11. True   **13.** False   **15.** True   **17.** False   **19.** True
21. True   **23.** True   **25.** True   **27.** False   **29.** True
31. True   **33.** True   **35.** True   **37.** False

Sample Test Problems

1. (a) $9x^2$;   (b) $10x^4 + 3$;   (c) $-\dfrac{1}{3x^2}$;   (d) $-\dfrac{6x}{(3x^2 + 2)^2}$;

(e) $\dfrac{3}{2\sqrt{3x}}$;   (f) $3 \cos 3x$;   (g) $\dfrac{x}{\sqrt{x^2 + 5}}$;   (h) $-\pi \sin \pi x$

3. (a) $f(x) = 3x$ at $x = 1$;   (b) $f(x) = 4x^3$ at $x = 2$;
(c) $f(x) = \sqrt{x^3}$ at $x = 1$;   (d) $f(x) = \sin x$ at $x = \pi$;
(e) $f(x) = \dfrac{4}{x}$ at x;   (f) $f(x) = -\sin 3x$ at x;
(g) $f(x) = \tan x$ at $x = \dfrac{\pi}{4}$;   (h) $f(x) = \dfrac{1}{\sqrt{x}}$ at $x = 5$

5. $15x^4$ **7.** $3z^2 + 8z + 2$ **9.** $\dfrac{-24t^2 + 60t + 10}{(6t^2 + 2t)^2}$

11. $\dfrac{-4x^4 + 10x^2 + 2}{(x^3 + x)^2}$ **13.** $-\dfrac{x}{\sqrt{(x^2 + 4)^3}}$

15. $-\sin \theta + 6 \sin^2 \theta \cos \theta - 3 \cos^3 \theta$ **17.** $2\theta \cos(\theta^2)$

19. $2\pi \sin(\sin(\pi\theta)) \cos(\sin(\pi\theta)) \cos(\pi\theta)$ **21.** $3e^{3\theta}$

23. $-\dfrac{1}{1 + x^2}$ **25.** $\dfrac{-\csc^2 x - 2x \cot x \tan x^2}{\sec x^2}$

27. $16 - 4\pi$ **29.** 458.8
31. $F'(r(x) + s(x))(r''(x) + s''(x))$
$+ (r'(x) + s'(x))^2 F''(r(x) + s(x)) + s''(x)$
33. $27z^2 \cos(9z^3)$
35. 314 m^3 per meter increase in the radius.   **37.** 0.167 ft/min
39. (a) $(1, 3)$ (b) $a(1) = -6, a(3) = 6$;   (c) $(2, \infty)$

41. (a) $\dfrac{1-x}{y}$;   **(b)** $-\dfrac{y^2+2xy}{x^2+2xy}$;   **(c)** $\dfrac{x^2y^3-x^2}{y^2-x^3y^2}$;

(d) $\dfrac{2x-\sin(xy)-xy\cos(xy)}{x^2\cos(xy)}$;   **(e)** $-\dfrac{\tan(xy)+xy\sec^2(xy)}{x^2\sec^2(xy)}$

(f) $-\dfrac{1}{2x}e^{-xy}-\dfrac{y}{x}$

43. 0.0714

45. (a) 84;   **(b)** 23;   **(c)** 20;   **(d)** 26

47. 104 mi/h

49. (a) $\cot\theta\,|\sin\theta|$;   **(b)** $-\tan\theta\,|\cos\theta|$

(c) $\dfrac{|\tan\theta|}{\sin\theta\cos\theta}$ **(d)** $\dfrac{|\sinh x|}{\tanh x}$

Chapter 4 Review and Preview Problems

1. $(2,3)$ **3.** $(-\infty,0]\cup[1,2]$

5. $(-\infty,-2)\cup[0,2)\cup(2,\infty)$

7. $8(2x+1)^3$ **9.** $-2(x^2-1)\sin 2x+2x\cos 2x$

11. $6(\sec^2 3x)(\tan 3x)$ **13.** $(-x^2-x+1)\,e^{-x^2/2}$

15. $x=k\pi$, where k is an integer

17. $x=(2k+1)\pi/2$, where k is an integer

19. $\dfrac{\sqrt{x^2+1}}{4}+\dfrac{4-x}{10}$

21. (a) x^2+3 is one such function

(b) $-\cos x+8$ is one such function

(c) $\dfrac{1}{3}x^3+\dfrac{1}{2}x^2+x+2$ is one such function

Problem Set 4.1

1. Critical points: $-2,0,2,4$; maximum value 10; minimum value 1

3. Critical points: $-2,-1,0,1,2,3,4$; maximum value 3; minimum value 1

5. Critical points: $-4,-2,0$; maximum value 4, minimum value 0

7. Critical points: $-2,-\frac{3}{2},1$; maximum value 4, minimum value $-\frac{9}{4}$

9. Critical points: $-1,1$; no maximum value, minimum value -1

11. Critical points: $-1,0,3$; maximum value 1, minimum value e^{-9}

13. Critical points: $-2,-1,0,1,2$; maximum value 10; minimum value 1

15. Critical point: 0; maximum value 1, no minimum value

17. Critical points: $-\frac{\pi}{4},\frac{\pi}{6}$; maximum value $\frac{1}{2}$, minimum value $-\dfrac{1}{\sqrt{2}}$

19. Critical points: $0,1,3$; maximum value 2, minimum value 0

21. Critical points: $-1,0,27$; maximum value 3, minimum value -1

23. Critical points: $-1,-\dfrac{\sqrt{2}}{2},\dfrac{\sqrt{2}}{2},2$; maximum value $\dfrac{\sqrt{2}}{2}e^{-1/2}$; minimum value $-\dfrac{\sqrt{2}}{2}e^{-1/2}$

25. Critical points: $-\dfrac{\pi}{4},0,\dfrac{\pi}{4}$; maximum value $\dfrac{\pi^2\sqrt{2}}{16}$; minimum value: 0

27. (a) Critical points: $-1,2-\dfrac{\sqrt{33}}{3},2+\dfrac{\sqrt{33}}{3},5$; maximum value ≈ 2.04; minimum value ≈ -26.04

(b) Critical points: $-1,-0.4836,2-\dfrac{\sqrt{33}}{3},0.7172,2+\dfrac{\sqrt{33}}{3},5$; maximum value ≈ 26.04; minimum value $=0$

29. Answers will vary. One possibility:

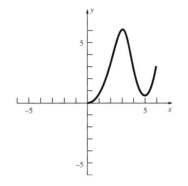

31. Answers will vary. One possibility:

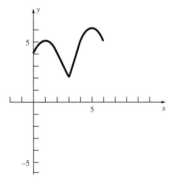

33. Answers will vary. One possibility:

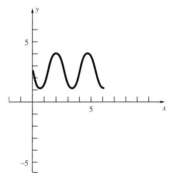

35. Answers will vary. One possibility:

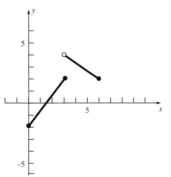

Problem Set 4.2

1. Increasing on $(-\infty, \infty)$

3. Increasing on $[-1, \infty)$, decreasing on $(-\infty, -1]$

5. Increasing on $(-\infty, 1] \cup [2, \infty)$, decreasing on $[1, 2]$

7. Increasing on $[2, \infty)$, decreasing on $(-\infty, 2]$

9. Increasing on $\left[0, \frac{\pi}{2}\right] \cup \left[\frac{3\pi}{2}, 2\pi\right]$, decreasing on $\left[\frac{\pi}{2}, \frac{3\pi}{2}\right]$

11. Concave up for all x; no inflection points

13. Concave up on $(0, \infty)$, concave down on $(-\infty, 0)$; inflection point $(0, 0)$

15. Concave up on $(-\infty, -1) \cup (4, \infty)$, concave down on $(-1, 4)$; inflection points $(-1, -19)$ and $(4, -499)$

17. Concave up for all x; no inflection points

19. Increasing on $(-\infty, -2] \cup [2, \infty)$, decreasing on $[-2, 2]$; concave up on $(0, \infty)$, concave down on $(-\infty, 0)$

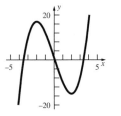

21. Increasing on $[1, \infty)$, decreasing on $(-\infty, 1]$; concave up on $(-\infty, 0) \cup \left(\frac{2}{3}, \infty\right)$, concave down on $\left(0, \frac{2}{3}\right)$

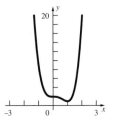

23. Increasing on $(-\infty, -1] \cup [1, \infty)$, decreasing on $[-1, 1]$; concave up on $\left(-\frac{1}{\sqrt{2}}, 0\right) \cup \left(\frac{1}{\sqrt{2}}, \infty\right)$, concave down on $\left(-\infty, -\frac{1}{\sqrt{2}}\right) \cup \left(0, \frac{1}{\sqrt{2}}\right)$.

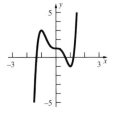

25. Increasing on $\left[0, \frac{\pi}{2}\right]$, decreasing on $\left[\frac{\pi}{2}, \pi\right]$; concave down on $(0, \pi)$.

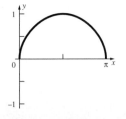

27. Increasing on $(-\infty, 0]$, decreasing on $[0, \infty)$; concave up on $\left(-\infty, -\frac{\sqrt{2}}{2}\right)$ and on $\left(\frac{\sqrt{2}}{2}, \infty\right)$, concave down on $\left(-\frac{\sqrt{2}}{2}, \frac{\sqrt{2}}{2}\right)$

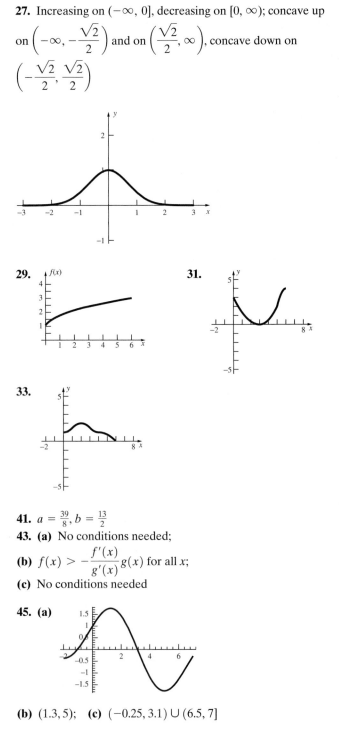

29.

31.

33.

41. $a = \frac{39}{8}, b = \frac{13}{2}$

43. **(a)** No conditions needed;

(b) $f(x) > -\dfrac{f'(x)}{g'(x)} g(x)$ for all x;

(c) No conditions needed

45. **(a)**

(b) $(1.3, 5)$;   **(c)** $(-0.25, 3.1) \cup (6.5, 7]$

(d)

(e)

47. $[-0.598, 0.680]$

49. (a) $\dfrac{ds}{dt} = ks, k$ a constant; **(b)** $\dfrac{d^2s}{dt^2} > 0$

(c) $\dfrac{d^3s}{dt^3} < 0, \dfrac{d^2s}{dt^2} > 0$ **(d)** $\dfrac{d^2s}{dt^2} = 10$ mph/min

(e) $\dfrac{ds}{dt}$ and $\dfrac{d^2s}{dt^2}$ are approaching zero. **(f)** $\dfrac{ds}{dt}$ is constant.

51. (a) $\dfrac{dC}{dt} > 0, \dfrac{d^2C}{dt^2} > 0$, where C is the car's cost. Concave up.

(b) $f(t)$ is oil consumption at time t. $\dfrac{df}{dt} < 0, \dfrac{d^2f}{dt^2} > 0$.
Concave up.

(c) $\dfrac{dP}{dt} > 0, \dfrac{d^2P}{dt^2} < 0$, where P is world population. Concave down.

(d) $\dfrac{d\theta}{dt} > 0, \dfrac{d^2\theta}{dt^2} > 0$, where θ is the angle that the tower makes with the vertical. Concave up.

(e) $P = f(t)$ is profit at time t. $\dfrac{dP}{dt} > 0, \dfrac{d^2P}{dt^2} < 0$. Concave down.

(f) R is revenue at time t. $R < 0, \dfrac{dR}{dt} > 0$. Could be either concave up or down.

53. $h(t) = \sqrt[3]{\dfrac{2400}{\pi}t + 27000} - 30$ **55.**

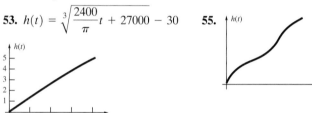

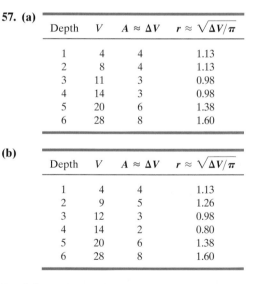

57. (a)

Depth	V	$A \approx \Delta V$	$r \approx \sqrt{\Delta V/\pi}$
1	4	4	1.13
2	8	4	1.13
3	11	3	0.98
4	14	3	0.98
5	20	6	1.38
6	28	8	1.60

(b)

Depth	V	$A \approx \Delta V$	$r \approx \sqrt{\Delta V/\pi}$
1	4	4	1.13
2	9	5	1.26
3	12	3	0.98
4	14	2	0.80
5	20	6	1.38
6	28	8	1.60

Problem Set 4.3

1. Critical points: $0, 4$; local minimum at $x = 4$; local maximum at $x = 0$

3. No critical points; no local minima or maxima on $\left(0, \frac{\pi}{4}\right)$

5. Critical point: 0; local minimum at $\theta = 0$

7. Critical points $-2, 2$; local minimum at $x = -2$, local maximum at $x = 2$

9. Critical point 0; local minimum at 0

11. Critical points: $-1, 1$; local minimum value $f(1) = -2$; local maximum value $f(-1) = 2$

13. Critical points $0, \frac{3}{2}$; local minimum value $H\left(\frac{3}{2}\right) = -\frac{27}{16}$; no local maximum

15. Critical point: 2; no local minimum values; local maximum value $g(2) = \pi$

17. No critical points
No local minimum or maximum values

19. No critical points
No local minimum or maximum values

21. Maximum value $f(\pi/4) = 1$; minimum value $f(0) = f(\pi/2) = 0$

23. Maximum value $g(4) = \dfrac{1}{6}$; minimum value $g(0) = 0$

25. Maximum value $F(9/16) = 9/4$; minimum value $F(4) = -4$

27. Minimum value $f(\tan^{-1}(4/3)) = 125$; no maximum value

29. Maximum value $H(-2) = H(2) = 3$; minimum value $H(-1) = H(1) = 0$

31. Maximum value $f(1) = e^{-1}$; minimum value $f(0) = 0$

33. Local minimum at $x = 0$

35. Local minimum at $x = 4$; local maximum at $x = 3$

37. No local extrema

39. Answers will vary. One possibility:

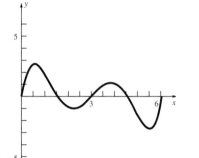

41. Answers will vary. One possibility:

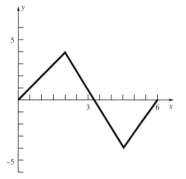

43. Answers will vary. One possibility:

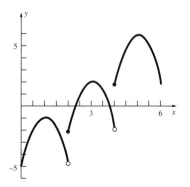

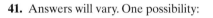

47. f has an inflection point at c.

Problem Set 4.4

1. -4 and 4　**3.** $\frac{1}{16}$　**5.** $\left(-\frac{3}{\sqrt{2}}, \frac{9}{2}\right), \left(\frac{3}{\sqrt{2}}, \frac{9}{2}\right)$　**7.** $\frac{1}{2}$

9. 1024 in^3　**11.** $x = 10 \text{ ft}, y = 40 \text{ ft}$

13. $x = 15\sqrt{3} \text{ ft}, y = 20\sqrt{3} \text{ ft}$

15. $x = \frac{10\sqrt{5}}{\sqrt{3}} \text{ ft}, y = 6\sqrt{15} \text{ ft}$　**17.** $P(2\sqrt{2}, 2), Q(0, 0)$

19. $\frac{6}{\sqrt{7}}$ miles down the shore from P　**21.** At the town

23. about 8:09 A.M.　**25.** $\frac{4\pi\sqrt{3}}{9}r^3$

27. $h = \sqrt{2}r, x = \frac{r}{\sqrt{2}}$ where $h = $ height of the cylinder,
$x = $ radius of the cylinder, $r = $ radius of the sphere

29. **(a)** 43.50 cm from one end; shorter length bent to form square
(b) No cut, wire bent to form square

31. height $= \left(\frac{3V}{\pi}\right)^{1/3}$, radius $= \frac{1}{2}\left(\frac{3V}{\pi}\right)^{1/3}$

33. $r = \sqrt{A}, \theta = 2$　**35.** 4 by 8

37. $r = \sqrt{A/(6\pi)}, \quad h = 2r$
39. Maximum area is for a square.　**41.** $\pi/3$
43. $x = 1, y = 3, z = 3$

45. **(a)** $x = 2a/3$ maximizes area of A.
(b) $x = 2a/3$ minimizes area of B.
(c) $x = 3a/4$ minimizes length z.

47. **(a)** $L' = 3, L = 4, \phi = 90°$;　**(b)** $L' = 5, L = 12, \phi = 90°$;
(c) $\phi = 90°, L = \sqrt{m^2 - h^2}, L' = h$

49. $t \approx 13.8279$, distance ≈ 0.047851 million miles

51. $5\sqrt{5} \text{ ft}$

53. **(a)** $b = \left(\sum_{i=1}^{n} x_i y_i - 5\sum_{i=1}^{n} x_i\right) \Big/ \sum_{i=1}^{n} x_i^2$　**(b)** $b \approx 3.0119$

(c) 50.179 hours

55. $p(n) = 300 - \frac{n}{2}; R(n) = 300n - \frac{n^2}{2}$

57. $n = 200$

59. \$1.92 per unit; \$1.33

61. **(a)** $R(x) = 20x + 4x^2 - \frac{x^3}{3}; \frac{dR}{dx} = 20 + 8x - x^2$

(b) $0 \le x \le 10$　**(c)** 4

63. $x_1 = 25, \frac{dR}{dx} = 0$ at x_1

65. **(a)** No.
(b) $x = 500$.
67. $P(300) = \$2410$

Problem Set 4.5

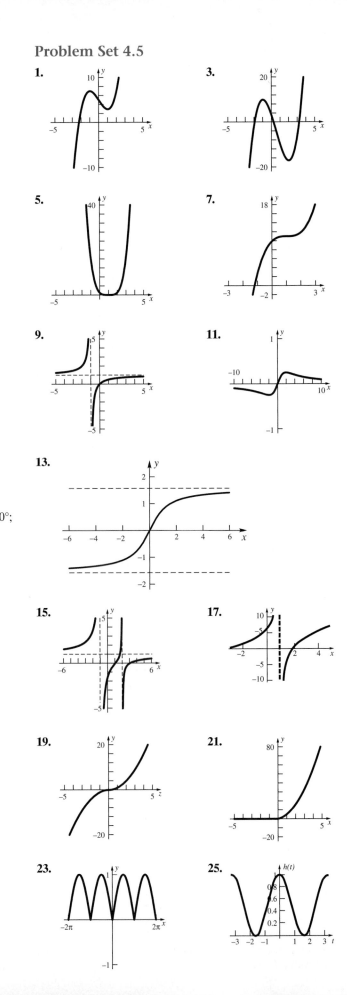

1.

3.

5.

7.

9.

11.

13.

15.

17.

19.

21.

23.

25.

27.

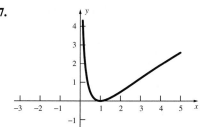

29.

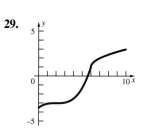

31.

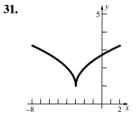

33.

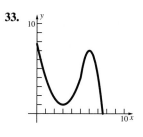

35.

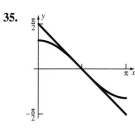

37.

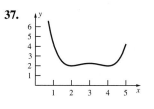

39.

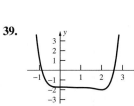

43.

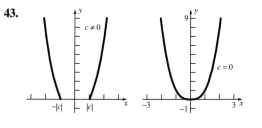

45.

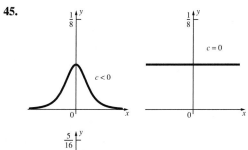

47.

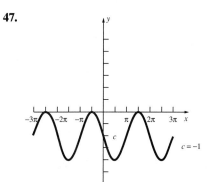

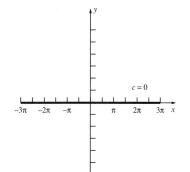

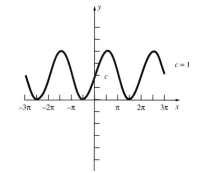

49.

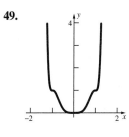

51. (a) Not possible;   **(b)** Not possible;

(c)

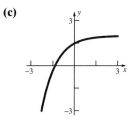

53. (a)

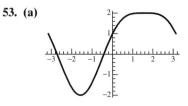

Global minimum: $f\left(-\frac{\pi}{2}\right) = -2$

Global maximum: $f\left(\frac{\pi}{2}\right) = 2$

Inflection points: $\left(-\frac{\pi}{6}, -\frac{1}{4}\right), \left(-\frac{5\pi}{6}, -\frac{1}{4}\right)$

(b)

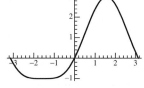

Global minimum: $f\left(-\frac{\pi}{2}\right) = -1$

Global maximum: $f\left(\frac{\pi}{2}\right) = 3$

Inflection points: $\left(\frac{\pi}{6}, \frac{5}{4}\right), \left(\frac{5\pi}{6}, \frac{5}{4}\right)$

(c)

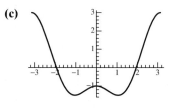

Global minimum: $f\left(-\frac{\pi}{3}\right) = f\left(\frac{\pi}{3}\right) = -1.5$

Global maximum: $f(-\pi) = f(\pi) = 3$

Inflection points: $\approx(-2.206, 0.890), (-0.568, -1.265),$
$(0.568, -1.265), (2.206, 0.890)$

(d)

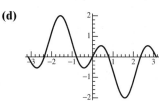

Global minimum: $f\left(\frac{\pi}{2}\right) = -2$

Global maximum: $f\left(-\frac{\pi}{2}\right) = 2$

Inflection points: $(0, 0), \approx(-2.126, 0.755), (-1.016, 0.755),$
$(1.016, -0.755), (2.126, -0.755)$

(e)

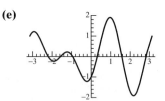

Global minimum: $f(2.17) \approx -1.9$
Global maximum: $f(0.97) \approx 1.9$
Inflection points: $\left(-\frac{\pi}{2}, 0\right), \left(\frac{\pi}{2}, 0\right), \approx(-2.469, 0.542),$
$(-0.673, -0.542), (0.413, 0.408), (2.729, -0.408)$

55. (a) Increasing on $(-\infty, -3] \cup [-1, 0]$: decreasing on
$[-3, -1] \cup [0, \infty)$;
(b) Concave up on $(-2, 0) \cup (0, 2)$; concave down on
$(-\infty, -2) \cup (2, \infty)$;
(c) Local maximum at $x = -3$; local minimum at $x = -1$;
(d) $x = -2, 2$

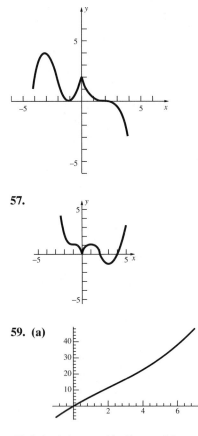

57.

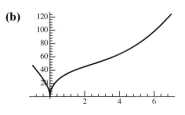

59. (a)

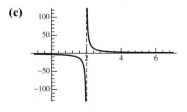

Global minimum: $f(-1) \approx -6.9$
Global maximum: $f(7) \approx 48.0$
Inflection point: $\approx(2.02, 11.4)$

(b)

Global minimum: $f(0) = 0$
Global maximum: $f(7) \approx 124.4$
Inflection point: $\approx(2.34, 48.09)$

(c)

No global minimum or maximum.
No inflections points.

(d)

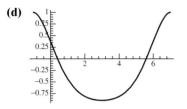

Global minimum: $f(3) \approx -0.9$
Global maximum: $f(-1) = f(7) \approx 1.0$
Inflection points: $\approx(0.05, 0.3), (5.9, 0.3)$

Problem Set 4.6

1. $1 < c < 2$

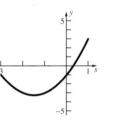

3. $c = 0$

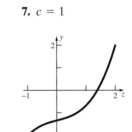

5. $c = -1$

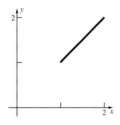

7. $c = 1$

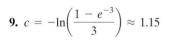

9. $c = -\ln\left(\dfrac{1 - e^{-3}}{3}\right) \approx 1.15$

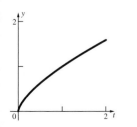

11. $c = \frac{16}{27} \approx 0.59$

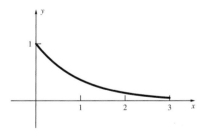

13. $c = \left(\frac{3}{5}\right)^{3/2} \approx 0.46$

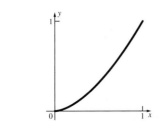

15. $c = \pm\frac{\pi}{2}$

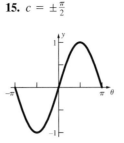

17. Does not apply, $T(\theta)$ not continuous at $\theta = \frac{\pi}{2}$

19. $c = \sqrt{2} \approx 1.41$

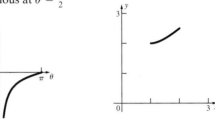

21. Does not apply, $f(x)$ is not differentiable at $x = 0$

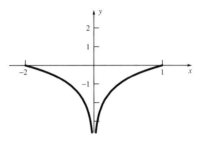

23. $\approx 1.5, 3.75, 7$

Problem Set 4.7

1. 1.46   **3.** 1.45   **5.** -0.12061 **7.** 1.37015
9. 0.45018   **11.** 2, 0.58579, 3.41421   **13.** 0.48095
15. 1.81712
17. Minimum $f(-0.60583) \approx -0.32645$; Maximum $f(1) = 4$
19. Minimum $f(4.493409) \approx -0.21723$
Maximum $f(7.725252) \approx 0.128375$
21. 0.9643   **23. (c)** $i = 0.0151308$; $r = 18.157\%$
25. 0.91486   **27.** 2.21756

29. (a)   **(b)** 0.5;   **(c)** $\frac{1}{2}$;

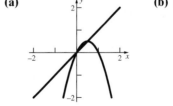

31. (a) $x_1 = 0$, $x_2 = 1$, $x_3 = 1.4142136$, $x_4 = 1.553774$,
$x_5 = 1.5980532$;   **(b)** $x = \frac{1}{2}(1 + \sqrt{5}) \approx 1.618034$
(c) $x = 1.618034$
33. (a) $x_1 = 1$, $x_2 = 2$, $x_3 = 1.5$, $x_4 \approx 1.6666667$, $x_5 = 1.6$
(b) $x = \dfrac{1 + \sqrt{5}}{2} \approx 1.618034$.   **(c)** $\dfrac{1 + \sqrt{5}}{2} \approx 1.618034$.
35. (a) The algorithm computes the root of $\frac{1}{x} - a = 0$ for x_1
close to $\frac{1}{a}$.   **37.** 20.84 ft.
39. (a) $(28.0279, 7.1828)$ **(b)** $(6.7728, 45.1031)$

Problem Set 4.8

1. $5x + C$ **3.** $\frac{1}{3}x^3 + \pi x + C$ **5.** $\frac{4}{9}x^{9/4} + C$

7. $3\sqrt[3]{x} + C$ **9.** $\frac{1}{3}x^3 - \frac{1}{2}x^2 + C$ **11.** $\frac{2}{3}x^6 - \frac{1}{4}x^4 + C$

13. $\frac{27}{8}x^8 + \frac{1}{2}x^6 - \frac{45}{4}x^4 + \frac{\sqrt{2}}{2}x^2 + C$ **15.** $-\frac{3}{x} + \frac{1}{x^2} + C$

17. $x^4 + \frac{3}{2}x^2 + C$ **19.** $\frac{1}{2}x^2 - \sinh x + C$

21. $\frac{1}{3}x^3 + \frac{1}{2}x^2 + C$ **23.** $\frac{1}{3}(x + 1)^3 + C$

25. $\frac{2}{9}z^{9/2} + \frac{4}{5}z^{5/2} + 2z^{1/2} + C$ **27.** $-\cos\theta - \sin\theta + C$

29. $\frac{1}{4}(\sqrt{2}x + 1)^4 + C$ **31.** $\frac{1}{21}(5x^3 + 3x - 8)^7 + C$

33. $\frac{9}{16}\sqrt[3]{(2t^2 - 11)^4} + C$ **35.** $\frac{2}{9}(x^3 + 4)^{3/2} + C$

37. $-\frac{1}{5}(1 + \cos x)^5 + C$ **39.** $\frac{1}{3}(1 + e^x)^2 + C$

41. $\frac{1}{2}x^3 + \frac{1}{2}x^2 + C_1x + C_2$ **43.** $\frac{4}{15}x^{5/2} + C_1x + C_2$

45. $\frac{1}{6}x^3 + \frac{1}{2x} + C_1x + C_2$ **49.** $x^2\sqrt{x - 1} + C$

51. $\dfrac{5x^3 + 2}{2\sqrt{x^3 + 1}} + C$

55. $\frac{1}{2}x^2 + C$ if $x \geq 0$, $-\frac{1}{2}x^2 + C$ if $x < 0$

57. **(a)** $-2\cos(3(x - 2)) + C$ **(b)** $\dfrac{1}{2}\cos\dfrac{x}{2} - \dfrac{9}{2}\cos\dfrac{x}{6} + C$ **(c)** $\dfrac{1}{2}x^2 \sin 2x + C$

Problem Set 4.9

5. $y = \frac{1}{3}x^3 + x + C$; $y = \frac{1}{3}x^3 + x - \frac{1}{3}$

7. $y = \pm\sqrt{x^2 + C}$; $y = \sqrt{x^2}$ **9.** $z = \dfrac{3}{C - t^3}$; $z = \dfrac{3}{10 - t^3}$

11. $s = \frac{16}{3}t^3 + 2t^2 - t + C$; $s = \frac{16}{3}t^3 + 2t^2 - t + 100$

13. $y = \frac{1}{10}(2x + 1)^5 + C$; $y = \frac{1}{10}(2x + 1)^5 + \frac{59}{10}$

15. $y = \frac{3}{2}x^2 + \frac{1}{2}$ **17.** $v = 5$ cm/s; $s = \frac{22}{3}$ cm

19. $v \approx 2.83$ cm/s; $s \approx 12.6$ cm   **21.** 144 ft

23. $v = 32.24$ ft/s; $s = 1198.54$ ft

27. Moon: ≈ 1.470 mi/s; Venus: ≈ 6.257 mi/s
Jupiter: ≈ 36.812 mi/s; Sun: ≈ 382.908 mi/s

29. 2.2 ft/s^2 **31.** 5500 m

33. (a)
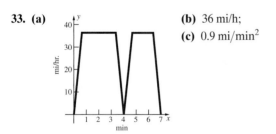
(b) 36 mi/h;
(c) 0.9 mi/min^2

35. (a) $\dfrac{dV}{dt} = C_1\dfrac{\sqrt{V}}{10}$, $V(0) = 1600$, $V(40) = 0$;

(b) $V = \frac{1}{400}(-20t + 800)^2$;   **(c)** 900 cm^3

37. (a) $v(t) = \begin{cases} -32t & \text{for } 0 \leq t < 1 \\ -32(t - 1) + 24 & \text{for } 1 < t \leq 2.5 \end{cases}$

(b) $t \approx 0.66, 1.75$ s

Problem Set 4.10

1. $y = 4e^{-6t}$ **3.** $y = 2e^{0.005(t-10)}$ **5.** 56,569

7. 15.8 days   **9.** 4.64 million; 4.79 million; 6.17 million; 105 million

11. 126,839   **13.** 7.43 g

15. $t_c \approx 201$ yrs(2187) $t_s \approx 191$ yrs(2177)

17. 2950 years ago   **19.** 81.6°F   **21.** 83.7°C   **23.** 8:45 pm

25. (a) $401.71   **(b)** $402.15   **(c)** $402.19   **(d)** $402.19

27. (a) 11.58 yrs.   **(b)** 11.55 yrs.

29. $133.6 billion   **31.** $1051.27   **33.** $t = \dfrac{100 \ln 2}{p}$

35.
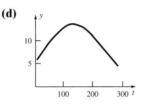

37. 15.25 million   **43.** 75.25 years from 2004

45. (a) $k = 0.0132 - 0.0001t$ **(b)** $y' = (0.0132 - 0.0001t)y$
(c) $y = 6.4^{0.0132t - 0.00005t^2}$

(d)
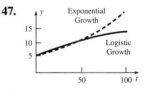

(e) The maximum population will occur when $t = 132$, which is year 2136. The model predicts that the population will return to the 2004 level in year 2268.

47.
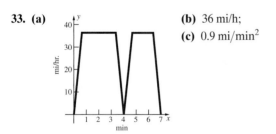

Exponential growth: 6.93 billion in 2010; 10.29 billion in 2040; 19.92 billion in 2090:
Logistic growth: 7.13 billion in 2010; 10.90 billion in 2040; 15.15 billion in 2090

Chapter Review 4.11

Concepts Test

1. True   **3.** True   **5.** True   **7.** True   **9.** True
11. False   **13.** True   **15.** True   **17.** True   **19.** False
21. False   **23.** False   **25.** True   **27.** True   **29.** True
31. False   **33.** True   **35.** True   **37.** False   **39.** True
41. True   **43.** True   **45.** False   **47.** True   **49.** False

Sample Test Problems

1. Critical points: 0, 1, 4; minimum value $f(1) = -1$; maximum value $f(4) = 8$

3. Critical points: $-2, -\frac{1}{2}$; minimum value $f(-2) = \frac{1}{4}$; maximum value $f\left(-\frac{1}{2}\right) = 4$

5. Critical points: $-\frac{1}{2}, 0, 1$; minimum value $f(0) = 0$; maximum value $f(1) = 1$

7. Critical points: $-2, 0, 1, 3$; minimum value $f(1) = -1$; maximum value $f(3) = 135$

9. Critical points: $-1, 0, 2, 3$; minimum value $f(2) = -9$; maximum value $f(3) = 88$

11. Critical points: $\frac{\pi}{4}, \frac{\pi}{2}, \frac{4\pi}{3}$; minimum value $f\left(\frac{4\pi}{3}\right) \approx -0.87$;
maximum value $f\left(\frac{\pi}{2}\right) = 1$

13. Increasing: $\left(-\infty, \frac{3}{2}\right]$; concave down: $(-\infty, \infty)$

15. Increasing: $(-\infty, -1] \cup [1, \infty)$; concave down: $(-\infty, 0)$

17. Increasing: $\left[0, \frac{1}{5}\right]$; concave down: $\left(\frac{3}{20}, \infty\right)$

19. Increasing: $[0, \infty)$; concave down: $(-\infty, -3^{1/4})$ and $(3^{1/4}, \infty)$

21. Increasing: $\left(-\infty, 0\right] \cup \left[\frac{8}{3}, \infty\right)$; decreasing: $\left[0, \frac{8}{3}\right]$;

Local minimum value $f\left(\frac{8}{3}\right) = -\frac{256}{27}$

Local maximum value $f(0) = 0$

Inflection point: $\left(\frac{4}{3}, -\frac{128}{27}\right)$

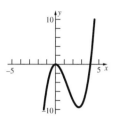

23.

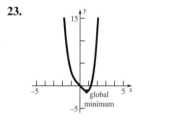

25.

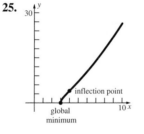

27.

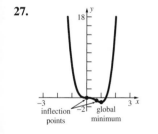

29.

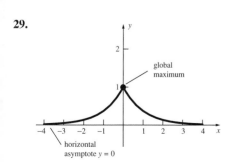

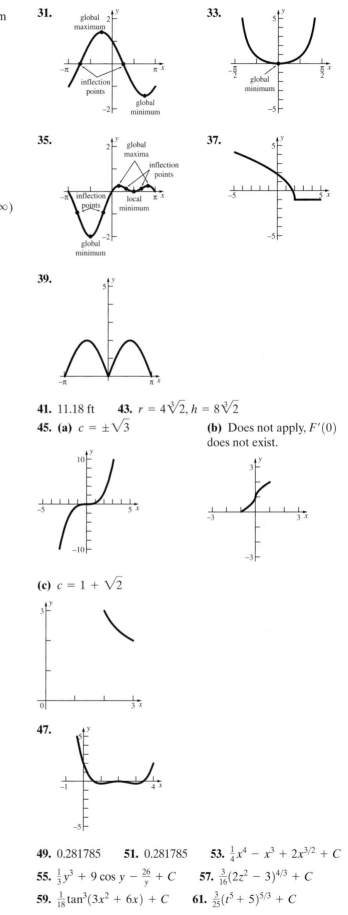

31.

33.

35.

37.

39.

41. 11.18 ft   **43.** $r = 4\sqrt[3]{2}, h = 8\sqrt[3]{2}$

45. (a) $c = \pm\sqrt{3}$ **(b)** Does not apply, $F'(0)$ does not exist.

(c) $c = 1 + \sqrt{2}$

47.

49. 0.281785   **51.** 0.281785   **53.** $\frac{1}{4}x^4 - x^3 + 2x^{3/2} + C$

55. $\frac{1}{3}y^3 + 9\cos y - \frac{26}{y} + C$ **57.** $\frac{3}{16}(2z^2 - 3)^{4/3} + C$

59. $\frac{1}{18}\tan^3(3x^2 + 6x) + C$ **61.** $\frac{3}{25}(t^5 + 5)^{5/3} + C$

63. $\frac{2}{3}\sqrt{x^3+9}+C$ **65.** $-\frac{1}{2(2y-1)^2}+C$

67. $\frac{1}{2}\cos2\theta+C$ **69.** $\frac{5}{24}(2y^3+3y^2+6y)^{4/5}+C$

71. $y=2\sqrt{x+1}+14$ **73.** $y=\frac{1}{3}(2t-1)^{3/2}-1$

75. $y=7e^{2t}$ **77.** $y=\sqrt{3x^2-\frac{1}{4}x^4+9}$ **79.** 7 s; -176 ft/s

81. (a) $Q'(t)=3-0.02Q$ **(b)** $Q(t)=150-30e^{-0.02t}$

(c) $Q(t)\to150$ grams as $t\to\infty$

Chapter 5 Review and Preview Problems

1. $\frac{\sqrt{3}}{4}a^2$ **3.** $\frac{5}{4}a^2\cot36°$ **5.** $3.6\cdot5.8+\frac{1}{2}\pi(1.8)^2\approx25.97$

7. 3.5   **9.** $\frac{1}{2}x^2+x$ **11.** 6

Problem Set 5.1

1. 15   **3.** $\frac{481}{280}$ **5.** $\frac{85}{2}$ **7.** 3   **9.** $\sum_{i=1}^{41}i$ **11.** $\sum_{i=1}^{100}\frac{1}{i}$

13. $\sum_{i=1}^{50}a_{2i-1}$ **15.** 90   **17.** -10 **19.** 14,950

21. 2640   **23.** $\frac{4n^3-3n^2-n}{6}$

27. (a) $1-\left(\frac{1}{2}\right)^{10}$;   **(b)** $2^{11}-2$

33. $\bar{x}=55/7\approx7.86$; $s^2\approx12.41$ **37.** $c=\bar{x}$ **39.** 715

41. $S=\dfrac{m(m+1)(3n-m+1)}{6}$ **43.** $\frac{7}{2}$ **45.** $\frac{9}{2}$ **47.** $\frac{23}{8}$

49. $A=6$ **51.** $A=\frac{1243}{216}$

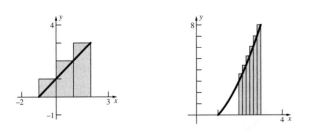

53. $\frac{5}{2}$ **55.** 4   **57.** $\frac{1}{4}$ **59.** $2\frac{1}{2}$ ft

63. (a) $\frac{125}{3}$;   **(b)** 21;   **(c)** 39

65. (a) 4;   **(b)** $\frac{15}{4}$;   **(c)** 10.5;   **(d)** 102.4

Problem Set 5.2

1. 5.625   **3.** 15.6875   **5.** 2.625   **7.** $\int_1^3 x^3\,dx$

9. $\int_{-1}^1\frac{x^2}{1+x}\,dx$ **11.** 4   **13.** $3\pi-3$ **15.** $\frac{35}{2}$

17. $\frac{27}{2}$ **19.** $\frac{1}{2}+\frac{\pi}{4}$ **21.** $\frac{1}{2}\pi A^2$ **23.** $\frac{2}{15}$ **25.** 3

27. 40, 80, 120, 160, 200, 240   **29.** 20, 80, 160, 240, 320, 400

31. (a) -3;   **(b)** 19;   **(c)** 3;   **(d)** 2;   **(e)** 9;   **(f)** 0;

(g) 1;   **(h)** 2

35. Left: 5.24; Right: 6.84; Midpoint: 5.98

37. Left: 0.8638; Right: 0.8178; Midpoint: 0.8418

Problem Set 5.3

1. $A(x)=2x$

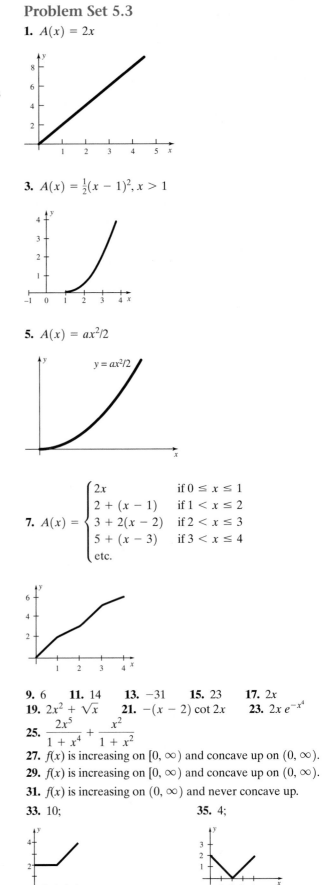

3. $A(x)=\frac{1}{2}(x-1)^2$, $x>1$

5. $A(x)=ax^2/2$

7. $A(x)=\begin{cases}2x & \text{if } 0\le x\le1\\2+(x-1) & \text{if } 1<x\le2\\3+2(x-2) & \text{if } 2<x\le3\\5+(x-3) & \text{if } 3<x\le4\\ \text{etc.}\end{cases}$

9. 6   **11.** 14   **13.** -31 **15.** 23   **17.** $2x$

19. $2x^2+\sqrt{x}$ **21.** $-(x-2)\cot2x$ **23.** $2xe^{-x^4}$

25. $\frac{2x^5}{1+x^4}+\frac{x^2}{1+x^2}$

27. $f(x)$ is increasing on $[0,\infty)$ and concave up on $(0,\infty)$.

29. $f(x)$ is increasing on $[0,\infty)$ and concave up on $(0,\infty)$.

31. $f(x)$ is increasing on $(0,\infty)$ and never concave up.

33. 10;   **35.** 4;

37. (a) Local minima at 0, ≈3.8, ≈5.8, ≈7.9, ≈9.9;
local maxima at ≈3.1, ≈5.0, ≈7.1, ≈9.0, 10
(b) $G(0) = 0$ is global minimum, $G(9)$ is global maximum
(c) G is concave down on ≈(0.7, 1.5), (2.5, 3.5), (4.5, 5.5),
(6.5, 7.5), (8.5, 9.5)

(d)

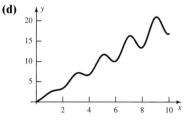

39. (a) 0   **(b)** $\frac{1}{5}x^5 + x + C$ **(c)** $\frac{1}{5}x^5 + x$ **(d)** $\frac{6}{5}$

43. Lower bound 20;
upper bound 276

45. Lower bound $\frac{68}{5}$;
upper bound 20

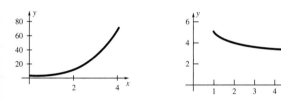

47. Lower bound 20π; upper bound $\frac{101}{5}\pi$

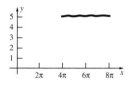

49. $\frac{1}{2}$ **51.** 2   **53.** $\sqrt{x}/2$ **55.** True   **57.** False
59. True
61. $s(t) = \begin{cases} t^2/2, & 0 \le t \le 2 \\ -4 + 4t - t^2/2, & t > 2 \end{cases}$
$t = 4 + 2\sqrt{2} \approx 6.83$

Problem Set 5.4

1. 4   **3.** 15   **5.** $\frac{3}{4}$ **7.** $\frac{16}{3}$ **9.** $\frac{1783}{96}$ **11.** 1   **13.** $\frac{22}{5}$
15. $\frac{2}{9}(3x + 2)^{3/2} + C$ **17.** $\frac{1}{3}\sin(3x + 2) + C$
19. $-\frac{1}{6}\cos(6x - 7) + C$ **21.** $\frac{1}{3}(x^2 + 4)^{3/2} + C$
23. $-\frac{7}{10}(x^2 + 3)^{-5/7} + C$ **25.** $-\frac{1}{2}\cos(x^2 + 4) + C$
27. $-\cos\sqrt{x^2 + 4} + C$ **29.** $\frac{1}{27}\exp[(x^3 + 5)] + C$
31. $\frac{1}{3}[\sin(x^2 + 4)]^{3/2} + C$ **33.** $-\frac{1}{30}\cos^{10}(x^3 + 5) + C$
35. $\frac{2047}{11}$ **37.** $\frac{4}{5}$ **39.** $\frac{122}{9}$ **41.** 0   **43.** $\frac{1}{3}$
45. $\frac{1}{2}(e - 1)$ **47.** $\frac{1}{64}$ **49.** $\frac{\sin 3}{3}$ **51.** $\frac{1}{\pi}$ **53.** 1
55. $e - e^{-1}$ **57.** $\dfrac{1 - \cos^4 1}{8}$ **59.** $\frac{\pi}{4}$ **61.** 0
63. (a) positive,   **(b)** negative,   **(c)** negative,   **(d)** positive
65. 50 gallons; 20 hours   **67.** 84.8 gallons   **69.** 145.2
73. 9   **75.** 2

Problem Set 5.5

1. 40   **3.** $\frac{1}{3}$ **5.** $\frac{17}{6}$ **7.** 0   **9.** $\frac{1}{2}(1 - e^{-2})$ **11.** $\frac{609}{8}$
13. $\frac{8}{\pi}\left(-\cos\sqrt{\frac{\pi}{2}} + \cos\sqrt{\frac{\pi}{4}}\right)$ **15.** $\frac{115}{81}$ **17.** $\frac{\sqrt{39}}{3}$
19. $c = 1$ **21.** $c = 0$ **23.** $c = \frac{\sqrt{21} + 3}{6}$ **25.** $c = \frac{5}{2}$
27. $(A + B)/2$
29. ≈1250π **31.** ≈3.2

33. ≈25   **35.** 0   **37.** 0   **39.** 2π **41.** $\frac{8}{3}$ **43.** 0
45. Even: $\displaystyle\int_{-b}^{-a} f(x)\,dx = \int_{a}^{b} f(x)\,dx$;

Odd: $\displaystyle\int_{-b}^{-a} f(x)\,dx = -\int_{a}^{b} f(x)\,dx$

47. 8   **49.** 2   **51.** 2
57. (a) Even;   **(b)** 2π

(c)

Interval	Value of Integral
$\left[0, \frac{\pi}{2}\right]$	0.46
$\left[-\frac{\pi}{2}, \frac{\pi}{2}\right]$	0.92
$\left[0, \frac{3\pi}{2}\right]$	−0.46
$\left[-\frac{3\pi}{2}, \frac{3\pi}{2}\right]$	−0.92
$[0, 2\pi]$	0
$\left[\frac{\pi}{6}, \frac{13\pi}{6}\right]$	0
$\left[\frac{\pi}{6}, \frac{4\pi}{3}\right]$	−0.44
$\left[\frac{13\pi}{6}, \frac{10\pi}{3}\right]$	−0.44

Problem Set 5.6

1. 0.7877, 0.5654, 0.6766, 0.6671, $\frac{2}{3}$
3. 1.6847, 2.0382, 1.8615, 1.8755, $\frac{4\sqrt{2}}{3}$
5. 3.4966, 7.4966, 5.4966, 5.2580, 5.25

7.

	LRS	RRS	MRS	Trap	Parabolic
$n = 4$	0.5728	0.3728	0.4590	0.4728	0.4637
$n = 8$	0.5159	0.4159	0.4625	0.4659	0.4636
$n = 16$	0.4892	0.4392	0.4634	0.4642	0.4636

9.

	LRS	RRS	MRS	Trap	Parabolic
$n = 4$	1.4068	0.9745	1.1991	1.1907	1.1962
$n = 8$	1.3030	1.0868	1.1970	1.1949	1.1963
$n = 16$	1.2500	1.1419	1.1965	1.1959	1.1963

11. 12, 1.1007   **13.** 8, 4.6637   **15.** 6, 1.0989   **19.** smaller
21. larger   **25.** LRS < Trap < MRS < RRS
27. 4570 ft^2 **29.** 1,074,585,600 ft^3
31. Using a right Riemann sum ≈13,740 gallons

Chapter Review 5.7

Concepts Test

1. True   **3.** True   **5.** False   **7.** True   **9.** True
11. True   **13.** False   **15.** True   **17.** True   **19.** False
21. True   **23.** True   **25.** False   **27.** False   **29.** False
31. True   **33.** False   **35.** True   **37.** False   **39.** True
41. True   **43.** True   **45.** False

Sample Test Problems

1. $\frac{5}{4}$ **3.** $\frac{50}{3} - \frac{26}{\pi} + \frac{\pi^3}{3} - 9\cos 1$

5. $\frac{1}{16}\left[-15\left(-125 + \sqrt[3]{5}\right)\right]$ **7.** $\frac{1}{18}\tan^3(3\pi^2 + 6\pi)$

9. 46.9   **11.** $-\frac{1}{2}\cos(x^2 + 2x + 3) + C$

13. $\frac{1}{3}(e - e^{-1})$ **15.** $\cos 1 - \cos e$

17. $\frac{7}{4}$

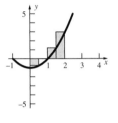

19. $\frac{5}{6}$ **21.** $\frac{39}{4}$ **23.** 1870

25. (a) $\displaystyle\sum_{n=2}^{78}\frac{1}{n}$;   (b) $\displaystyle\sum_{n=1}^{50}nx^{2n}$

27. (a) -2;   (b) -4;   (c) 6;   (d) -12;   (e) -2
29. (a) -8;   (b) 8;   (c) 0;   (d) -16;   (e) -2 (f) -5
31. $c = -\sqrt{7}$
33. (a) $\sin^2 x$;   (b) $f(x + 1) - f(x)$

(c) $-\dfrac{1}{x^2}\displaystyle\int_0^x f(z)\,dz + \dfrac{1}{x}f(x)$;   (d) $\displaystyle\int_0^x f(t)\,dt$;

(e) $g'(g(x))g'(x)$;   (f) $-f(x)$
37. 0.2043   **39.** 372   **41.** MRS $<$ Trap $<$ LRS

Chapter 6 Review and Preview Problems

1. $\dfrac{1}{4}$ **3.** $\sqrt[3]{4} - 1$ **5.** $\sqrt{10}$ **7.** 1.6π

9. $[\pi(r_2^2 - r_1^2)]\,\Delta x$ **11.** $\dfrac{51}{10}$ **13.** $\dfrac{16}{15}$

Problem Set 6.1

1. 6   **3.** $\frac{40}{3}$ **5.** $\frac{9}{2}$ **7.** $\frac{253}{12}$ **9.** $\frac{9}{2}$

11. 6   **13.** 24

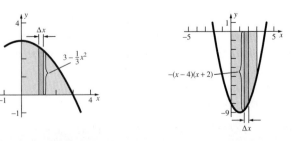

15. $\frac{17}{6}$ **17.** $3\sqrt[3]{2}$

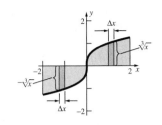

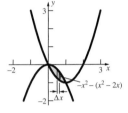

19. $\dfrac{13\sqrt{13}}{6}$ **21.** $\dfrac{1}{3}$

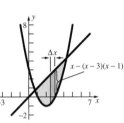

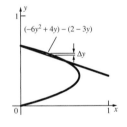

23. $\dfrac{256}{3}$ **25.** $\dfrac{1}{216}$

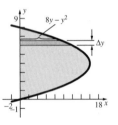

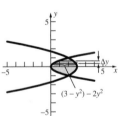

27. 4   **29.** $\dfrac{3}{2}$

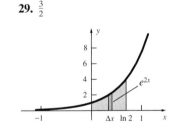

31. 22

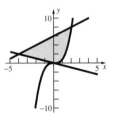

33. 130 ft; 194 ft   **35.** 6 s; $2 + 2\sqrt{2}$ s
37. $\frac{1}{2}(1 - \ln 2)$ **39.** 1.03257
41. Area $(A) = 9$; $A(B) = \frac{37}{6}$; $A(C) = \frac{37}{6}$; $A(D) = \frac{44}{3}$;
Area$(A + B + C + D) = 36$

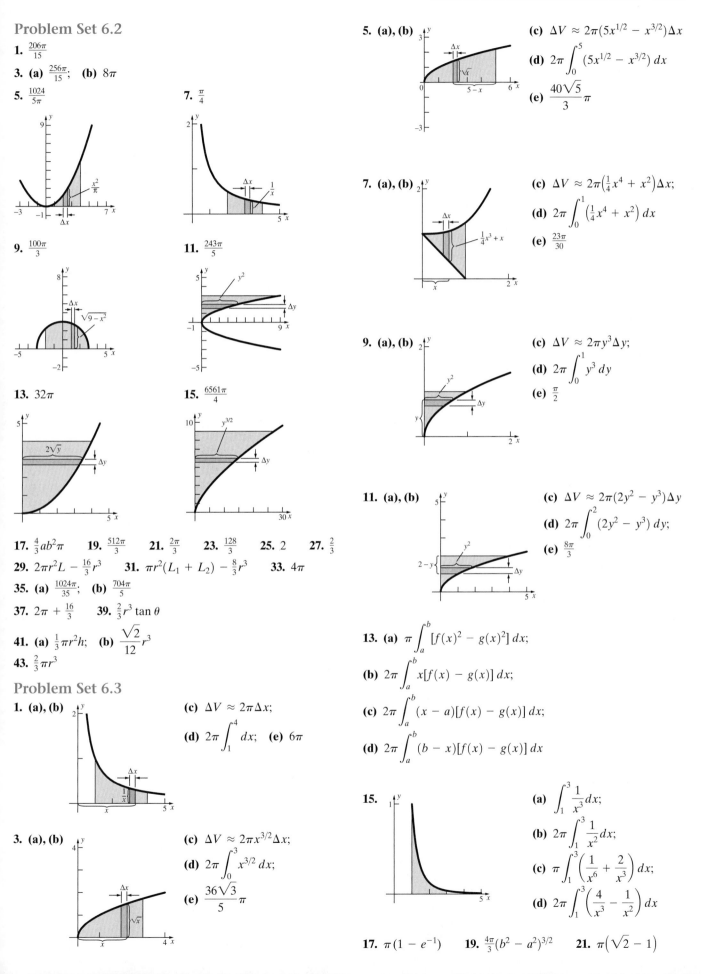

Problem Set 6.2

1. $\frac{206\pi}{15}$

3. (a) $\frac{256\pi}{15}$;   **(b)** 8π

5. $\frac{1024}{5\pi}$

7. $\frac{\pi}{4}$

9. $\frac{100\pi}{3}$

11. $\frac{243\pi}{5}$

13. 32π

15. $\frac{6561\pi}{4}$

17. $\frac{4}{3}ab^2\pi$ **19.** $\frac{512\pi}{3}$ **21.** $\frac{2\pi}{3}$ **23.** $\frac{128}{3}$ **25.** 2   **27.** $\frac{2}{3}$

29. $2\pi r^2 L - \frac{16}{3}r^3$ **31.** $\pi r^2(L_1 + L_2) - \frac{8}{3}r^3$ **33.** 4π

35. (a) $\frac{1024\pi}{35}$;   **(b)** $\frac{704\pi}{5}$

37. $2\pi + \frac{16}{3}$ **39.** $\frac{2}{3}r^3 \tan\theta$

41. (a) $\frac{1}{3}\pi r^2 h$;   **(b)** $\frac{\sqrt{2}}{12}r^3$

43. $\frac{2}{3}\pi r^3$

Problem Set 6.3

1. (a), (b)
(c) $\Delta V \approx 2\pi\Delta x$;
(d) $2\pi\int_1^4 dx$;   **(e)** 6π

3. (a), (b)
(c) $\Delta V \approx 2\pi x^{3/2}\Delta x$;
(d) $2\pi\int_0^3 x^{3/2}\,dx$;
(e) $\frac{36\sqrt{3}}{5}\pi$

5. (a), (b)
(c) $\Delta V \approx 2\pi(5x^{1/2} - x^{3/2})\Delta x$
(d) $2\pi\int_0^5 (5x^{1/2} - x^{3/2})\,dx$
(e) $\frac{40\sqrt{5}}{3}\pi$

7. (a), (b)
(c) $\Delta V \approx 2\pi\left(\frac{1}{4}x^4 + x^2\right)\Delta x$;
(d) $2\pi\int_0^1 \left(\frac{1}{4}x^4 + x^2\right)dx$
(e) $\frac{23\pi}{30}$

9. (a), (b)
(c) $\Delta V \approx 2\pi y^3 \Delta y$;
(d) $2\pi\int_0^1 y^3\,dy$
(e) $\frac{\pi}{2}$

11. (a), (b)
(c) $\Delta V \approx 2\pi(2y^2 - y^3)\Delta y$
(d) $2\pi\int_0^2 (2y^2 - y^3)\,dy$;
(e) $\frac{8\pi}{3}$

13. (a) $\pi\int_a^b [f(x)^2 - g(x)^2]\,dx$;

(b) $2\pi\int_a^b x[f(x) - g(x)]\,dx$;

(c) $2\pi\int_a^b (x - a)[f(x) - g(x)]\,dx$;

(d) $2\pi\int_a^b (b - x)[f(x) - g(x)]\,dx$

15.
(a) $\int_1^3 \frac{1}{x^3}\,dx$;

(b) $2\pi\int_1^3 \frac{1}{x^2}\,dx$;

(c) $\pi\int_1^3 \left(\frac{1}{x^6} + \frac{2}{x^3}\right)dx$;

(d) $2\pi\int_1^3 \left(\frac{4}{x^3} - \frac{1}{x^2}\right)dx$

17. $\pi(1 - e^{-1})$ **19.** $\frac{4\pi}{3}(b^2 - a^2)^{3/2}$ **21.** $\pi\left(\sqrt{2} - 1\right)$

23. (a) $\frac{2\pi}{15}$; **(b)** $\frac{\pi}{6}$; **(c)** $\frac{\pi}{60}$

25. $\frac{1}{3}rS$

Problem Set 6.4

1. $\frac{1}{54}\left(181\sqrt{181} - 13\sqrt{13}\right)$ **3.** 9   **5.** $\frac{595}{144}$ **7.** $\sinh 4$

9. $\frac{1}{3}\left(2\sqrt{2} - 1\right)$ **11.** 4π

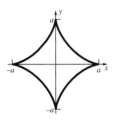

13. $2\sqrt{5}$ **15.** $\int_{0}^{2}\sqrt{1 + e^{-2t}}\, dt \approx 2.22144$

17. $\int_{0}^{\pi/2}\sqrt{\cos^2 t + 4\sin^2 2t}\, dt \approx 2.3241$

19. $6a$

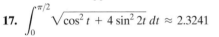

21. $8a$

23. (a) $\frac{2}{5}\left(4\sqrt{2} - 1\right)$; **(b)** 16

25. $6\sqrt{37}\pi$ **27.** $248\sqrt{2}\pi/9$ **29.** $\frac{\pi}{27}\left(10\sqrt{10} - 1\right)$

31. $4\pi r^2$

33. $\pi\left(e^2\sqrt{1 + e^4} + \ln(e^2 + \sqrt{1 + e^4}) - \sqrt{2}\right.$

$\left. - \ln\left(\sqrt{2} + 1\right)\right)$

37. (b) $\frac{64}{3}\pi a^2$

39. $n = 1: L \approx 1.41; n = 2: L \approx 1.48; n = 4: L \approx 1.60$
$n = 10: L \approx 1.75; n = 100: L \approx 1.95; n = 10{,}000: L \approx 2$

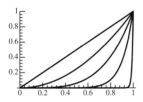

Problem Set 6.5

1. 1.5 ft-lb   **3.** 0.012 Joules   **7.** 18 ft-lb   **9.** 52,000 ft-lb
11. 76,128 ft-lb   **13.** 125,664 ft-lb   **17.** 2075.83 in.-lb
19. 350,000 ft-lb   **21.** 952,381 mi-lb   **23.** 43,200 ft-lb
25. 1684.8 pounds   **27.** 1684.8 pounds   **29.** 16.64 pounds

33. 76,363 pounds   **35.** $\frac{3mh}{4} + 15m$ **37.** $\dfrac{8475}{32}$ ft-lb

Problem Set 6.6

1. $\frac{5}{21}$ **3.** $\frac{21}{5}$ **5.** $M_y = 17, M_x = -3; \bar{x} = 1, \bar{y} = -\frac{3}{17}$

9. $\bar{x} = 0, \bar{y} = \frac{4}{5}$ **11.** $\bar{x} = \frac{4}{5}, \bar{y} = \frac{2}{7}$

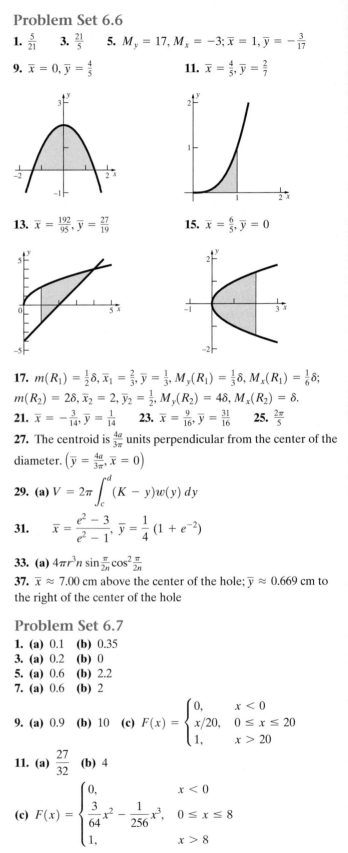

13. $\bar{x} = \frac{192}{95}, \bar{y} = \frac{27}{19}$ **15.** $\bar{x} = \frac{6}{5}, \bar{y} = 0$

17. $m(R_1) = \frac{1}{2}\delta, \bar{x}_1 = \frac{2}{3}, \bar{y} = \frac{1}{3}, M_y(R_1) = \frac{1}{3}\delta, M_x(R_1) = \frac{1}{6}\delta;$
$m(R_2) = 2\delta, \bar{x}_2 = 2, \bar{y}_2 = \frac{1}{2}, M_y(R_2) = 4\delta, M_x(R_2) = \delta.$

21. $\bar{x} = -\frac{3}{14}, \bar{y} = \frac{1}{14}$ **23.** $\bar{x} = \frac{9}{16}, \bar{y} = \frac{31}{16}$ **25.** $\frac{2\pi}{5}$

27. The centroid is $\frac{4a}{3\pi}$ units perpendicular from the center of the diameter. $\left(\bar{y} = \frac{4a}{3\pi}, \bar{x} = 0\right)$

29. (a) $V = 2\pi\displaystyle\int_{c}^{d}(K - y)w(y)\, dy$

31. $\bar{x} = \dfrac{e^2 - 3}{e^2 - 1}, \bar{y} = \dfrac{1}{4}\left(1 + e^{-2}\right)$

33. (a) $4\pi r^3 n \sin\frac{\pi}{2n}\cos^2\frac{\pi}{2n}$

37. $\bar{x} \approx 7.00$ cm above the center of the hole; $\bar{y} \approx 0.669$ cm to the right of the center of the hole

Problem Set 6.7

1. (a) 0.1   **(b)** 0.35
3. (a) 0.2   **(b)** 0
5. (a) 0.6   **(b)** 2.2
7. (a) 0.6   **(b)** 2

9. (a) 0.9   **(b)** 10   **(c)** $F(x) = \begin{cases} 0, & x < 0 \\ x/20, & 0 \le x \le 20 \\ 1, & x > 20 \end{cases}$

11. (a) $\dfrac{27}{32}$ **(b)** 4

(c) $F(x) = \begin{cases} 0, & x < 0 \\ \dfrac{3}{64}x^2 - \dfrac{1}{256}x^3, & 0 \le x \le 8 \\ 1, & x > 8 \end{cases}$

13. (a) 0.6875   **(b)** 2.4

(c) $F(x) = \begin{cases} 0, & x < 0 \\ \dfrac{1}{16}x^3 - \dfrac{3}{256}x^4, & 0 \le x \le 4 \\ 1, & x > 4 \end{cases}$

15. (a) $\dfrac{1}{2}$ **(b)** 2

(c) $F(x) = \begin{cases} 0, & x < 0 \\ \dfrac{1}{2} - \dfrac{1}{2}\cos\dfrac{\pi x}{4}, & 0 \le x \le 4 \\ 1, & x > 4 \end{cases}$

17. (a) $\dfrac{1}{3}$ **(b)** $\dfrac{4}{3}\ln 4$ **(c)** $F(x) = \begin{cases} 0, & x < 1 \\ \dfrac{4x - 4}{3x}, & 1 \le x \le 4 \\ 1, & x > 4 \end{cases}$

21. $\dfrac{a + b}{2}$ **23.** $k = \dfrac{6}{125}$

25. (a) $\dfrac{1}{4}$ **(b)** $\dfrac{1}{8}$ **(c)** 2

(d) $F(x) = \begin{cases} 0, & \text{if } x < 0 \\ x^2/8, & \text{if } 0 \le x \le 2 \\ -x^2/8 + x - 1, & \text{if } 2 < x \le 4 \\ 1, & \text{if } x > 4 \end{cases}$

(e) $F(y) = \begin{cases} 0, & \text{if } y < 0 \\ y^2/28800, & \text{if } 0 \le y \le 120 \\ -y^2/28800 + y/60 - 1, & \text{if } 120 < y \le 240 \\ 1, & \text{if } y > 240 \end{cases}$

27. (a) $\approx 95{,}802{,}719$ **(b)** ≈ 0.884 **(c)** 0.2625

(d) For $0 \le x \le 0.6$, $F(x) \approx 6.3868 \times 10^6 x^{15}$
$- 3.2847 \times 10^7 x^{14} + 7.4284 \times 10^7 x^{13} - 9.6569 \times 10^7 x^{12}$
$+ 7.9011 \times 10^7 x^{11} - 4.1718 \times 10^7 x^{10} + 1.3906 \times 10^7 x^9$
$- 2.6819 \times 10^6 x^8 + 2.2987 \times 10^5 x^7$

(e) $F(25.4y)$ where F is as in (d)

29. $G(y) = \begin{cases} 0, & y < 0 \\ \sqrt{y^2 - 1}, & 0 \le y \le \sqrt{2} \\ 1, & y > \sqrt{2} \end{cases}$

$g(y) = y/\sqrt{y^2 - 1}, 0 \le y \le \sqrt{2}.$

33. $F(x) = \begin{cases} 0, & x < 0 \\ 0.8, & 0 \le x < 1 \\ 0.9, & 1 \le x < 2 \\ 0.95, & 2 \le x < 3 \\ 1, & x \ge 3 \end{cases}$

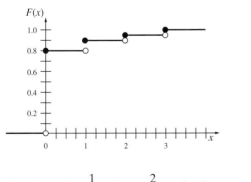

35. (a) 1   **(b)** $\dfrac{1}{12}$ **(c)** $\dfrac{2}{(y + 1)^2}$ for $0 \le y \le 1$ **(d)** 0.38629

37. $2, \dfrac{32}{7}$ **39.** $\dfrac{4}{7}$

Chapter Review 6.8

Concepts Test

1. False   **3.** False   **5.** True   **7.** False   **9.** False
11. False   **13.** True   **15.** True   **17.** True   **19.** True
21. True   **23.** True

Sample Test

1. $\dfrac{1}{6}$ **3.** $\dfrac{\pi}{6}$ **5.** $\dfrac{5\pi}{6}$

7. $V(S_1) = \dfrac{\pi}{30}; V(S_2) = \dfrac{\pi}{6}; V(S_3) = \dfrac{7\pi}{10}; V(S_4) = \dfrac{5\pi}{6}$

9. 205,837 ft-lb   **11. (a), (b)** $\dfrac{32}{3}$ **13.** $\dfrac{2048\pi}{15}$

15. $\dfrac{53}{6}$ **17.** 36   **19.** $\pi \displaystyle\int_a^b [f^2(x) - g^2(x)]\, dx$

21. $M_y = \delta \displaystyle\int_a^b x[f(x) - g(x)]\, dx$

$M_x = \dfrac{\delta}{2} \displaystyle\int_a^b [f^2(x) - g^2(x)]\, dx$

23. $2\pi \displaystyle\int_a^b f(x)\sqrt{1 + [f'(x)]^2}\, dx$

$+ 2\pi \displaystyle\int_a^b g(x)\sqrt{1 + [g'(x)]^2}\, dx$

$+ \pi[f^2(a) - g^2(a)] + \pi[f^2(b) - g^2(b)]$

25. (a) $\dfrac{3}{4}$ **(b)** $\dfrac{6 - x}{18}$ for $0 \le x \le 6$ **(c)** 2

Chapter 7 Review and Preview Problems

1. $-\dfrac{1}{2}\cos 2x + C$ **3.** $-\dfrac{1}{2}\cos x^2 + C$ **5.** $\ln|\sec t| + C$

7. $\dfrac{1}{3}(x^2 + 2)^{3/2} + C$ **9.** $\ln x$ **11.** $x^2 \sin x$

13. $\sin^2 x = \dfrac{1 - \cos 2x}{2}$ **15.** $\cos^4 x = \left(\dfrac{1 + \cos 2x}{2}\right)^2$

17. $\cos 3x \cos 5x = \dfrac{\cos 8x + \cos 2x}{2}$ **19.** $|a|\cos t$

21. $|a| \cdot |\tan t|$ **23.** $\dfrac{2x - 1}{x(1 - x)}$ **25.** $\dfrac{5x + 3}{x(x + 1)(x - 3)}$

Problem Set 7.1

1. $\dfrac{1}{6}(x - 2)^6 + C$ **3.** 1302   **5.** $\dfrac{1}{2}\tan^{-1}\left(\dfrac{x}{2}\right) + C$

7. $\dfrac{1}{2}\ln(x^2 + 4) + C$ **9.** 38   **11.** $\dfrac{1}{2}$ **13.** $-2\cos\sqrt{t} + C$

15. $\tan^{-1}\dfrac{\sqrt{2}}{2}$ **17.** $\dfrac{3}{2}x^2 - x + \ln|x + 1| + C$

19. $-\dfrac{1}{2}\cos(\ln 4x^2) + C$ **21.** $6\sin^{-1}(e^x) + C$

23. $-3\sqrt{1 - e^{2x}} + C$ **25.** $1/\ln 3$ **27.** $x - \ln|\sin x| + C$

29. $\ln|\sec e^x + \tan e^x| + C$ **31.** $\tan x + e^{\sin x} + C$

33. $-\dfrac{1}{3\sin(t^3 - 2)} + C$ **35.** $-\dfrac{1}{3}[\cot(t^3 - 2) + t^3] + C$

37. $\dfrac{1}{2}e^{\tan^{-1}2t} + C$ **39.** $\dfrac{1}{6}\sin^{-1}\left(\dfrac{3y^2}{4}\right) + C$

41. $\dfrac{1}{3}\cosh x^3 + C$ **43.** $\dfrac{1}{3}\sin^{-1}\left(\dfrac{e^{3t}}{2}\right) + C$ **45.** $\dfrac{1}{4}\tan^{-1}\left(\dfrac{1}{4}\right)$

47. $\dfrac{1}{2}\tan^{-1}\left(\dfrac{x + 1}{2}\right) + C$ **49.** $\dfrac{1}{3}\tan^{-1}(3x + 3) + C$

51. $\dfrac{1}{18}\ln|9x^2 + 18x + 10| + C$ **53.** $\dfrac{1}{3}\sec^{-1}\left(\dfrac{|\sqrt{2}t|}{3}\right) + C$

55. $\ln(\sqrt{2} + 1)$ **57.** π^2

Problem Set 7.2

1. $xe^x - e^x + C$ **3.** $\frac{1}{5}te^{5t+\pi} - \frac{1}{25}e^{5t+\pi} + C$

5. $x \sin x + \cos x + C$

7. $(t - 3) \sin(t - 3) + \cos(t - 3) + C$

9. $\frac{2}{3}t(t + 1)^{3/2} - \frac{4}{15}(t + 1)^{5/2} + C$ **11.** $x \ln 3x - x + C$

13. $x \arctan x - \frac{1}{2}\ln(1 + x^2) + C$ **15.** $-\frac{\ln x}{x} - \frac{1}{x} + C$

17. $\frac{2}{9}(e^{3/2} + 2)$ **19.** $\frac{1}{4}z^4 \ln z - \frac{1}{16}z^4 + C$

21. $t \arctan\left(\frac{1}{t}\right) + \frac{1}{2}\ln(1 + t^2) + C$ **23.** $\dfrac{\pi}{2\sqrt{3}} + \ln 2$

25. $\frac{2}{9}x^3(x^3 + 4)^{3/2} - \frac{4}{45}(x^3 + 4)^{5/2} + C$

27. $\dfrac{t^4}{6(7 - 3t^4)^{1/2}} + \frac{1}{9}(7 - 3t^4)^{1/2} + C$

29. $\dfrac{z^4}{4(4 - z^4)} + \frac{1}{4}\ln|4 - z^4| + C$

31. $x \cosh x - \sinh x + C$

33. $\dfrac{x}{150}(3x + 10)^{50} - \dfrac{1}{22950}(3x + 10)^{51} + C$

35. $\dfrac{x}{\ln 2}2^x - \dfrac{1}{(\ln 2)^2}2^x + C$ **37.** $x^2e^x - 2xe^x + 2e^x + C$

39. $z \ln^2 z - 2z \ln z + 2z + C$ **41.** $\frac{1}{2}e^t(\sin t + \cos t) + C$

43. $x^2 \sin x + 2x \cos x - 2 \sin x + C$

45. $\frac{x}{2}[\sin(\ln x) - \cos(\ln x)] + C$

47. $x \ln^3 x - 3x \ln^2 x + 6x \ln x - 6x + C$ **65.** 1

67. $9 - \dfrac{9}{e^3} \approx 8.552$

69. $\dfrac{\sqrt{2}\pi}{4} - 1$ **71.** $\bar{x} = \dfrac{e^2 + 1}{4}, \bar{y} = \dfrac{e - 2}{4}$

73. (a) $(x^3 - 2x)e^x - (3x^2 - 2)e^x + 6xe^x - 6e^x + C$
(b) $(x^2 - 3x + 1)(-\cos x) - (2x - 3)(-\sin x) + 2 \cos x + C$

87. $e^x(3x^4 - 12x^3 + 38x^2 - 76x + 76)$

Problem Set 7.3

1. $\frac{1}{2}x - \frac{1}{4}\sin 2x + C$ **3.** $-\cos x + \frac{1}{3}\cos^3 x + C$ **5.** $\frac{8}{15}$

7. $-\frac{1}{12}\cos^3 4x + \frac{1}{10}\cos^5 4x - \frac{1}{28}\cos^7 4x + C$

9. $-\frac{1}{3}\csc 3\theta - \frac{1}{3}\sin 3\theta + C$

11. $\frac{3}{128}t - \frac{1}{384}\sin 12t + \frac{1}{3072}\sin 24t + C$

13. $\frac{1}{2}\cos y - \frac{1}{18}\cos 9y + C$

15. $\frac{1}{16}w - \frac{1}{32}\sin 2w - \frac{1}{24}\sin^3 w + C$

17. $\frac{1}{3}\left[-x \cos^3 x + \sin x - \frac{1}{3}\sin^3 x\right] + C$

19. $\frac{1}{3}\tan^3 x - \tan x + x + C$ **21.** $\frac{1}{2}\tan^2 x + \ln|\cos x| + C$

23. $\frac{1}{2}\tan^4\left(\frac{\theta}{2}\right) - \tan^2\left(\frac{\theta}{2}\right) - 2 \ln|\cos\frac{\theta}{2}| + C$

25. $-\frac{1}{2}\tan^{-2} x + \ln|\tan x| + C$ **27.** $\frac{1}{4}\tan^4 x + C$

29. 0 for $m \neq n$, since $\sin k\pi = 0$ for all integers k.

31. $\dfrac{\pi^4}{3} + \dfrac{5\pi^2}{2}$

Problem Set 7.4

1. $\frac{2}{5}(x + 1)^{5/2} - \frac{2}{3}(x + 1)^{3/2} + C$

3. $\frac{2}{27}(3t + 4)^{3/2} - \frac{8}{9}(3t + 4)^{1/2} + C$

5. $2\sqrt{2} - 2 - 2e \ln\left(\dfrac{\sqrt{2} + e}{1 + e}\right)$

7. $\frac{2}{63}(3t + 2)^{7/2} - \frac{4}{45}(3t + 2)^{5/2} + C$

9. $2 \ln\left|\dfrac{2 - \sqrt{4 - x^2}}{x}\right| + \sqrt{4 - x^2} + C$

11. $\dfrac{x}{4\sqrt{x^2 + 4}} + C$ **13.** $-\dfrac{\sqrt{2}}{9} - \frac{1}{2}\sec^{-1}(-3) + \dfrac{\sqrt{3}}{8} + \dfrac{\pi}{3}$

15. $-2\sqrt{1 - z^2} - 3 \sin^{-1} z + C$

17. $\ln|\sqrt{x^2 + 2x + 5} + x + 1| + C$

19. $3\sqrt{x^2 + 2x + 5} - 3 \ln|\sqrt{x^2 + 2x + 5} + x + 1| + C$

21. $\frac{9}{2}\sin^{-1}\left(\dfrac{x + 2}{3}\right) + \dfrac{x + 2}{2}\sqrt{5 - 4x - x^2} + C$

23. $\sin^{-1}\left(\dfrac{x - 2}{2}\right) + C$

25. $\ln|x^2 + 2x + 2| - \tan^{-1}(x + 1) + C$

27. $\frac{\pi}{16}\left(\frac{1}{10} + \frac{\pi}{4} - \tan^{-1}\frac{1}{2}\right)$ **29.** $\frac{1}{2}\ln(x^2 + 9) + C$

31. $2 \ln\left|\dfrac{2 - \sqrt{4 - x^2}}{x}\right| + \sqrt{4 - x^2} + C$

35. $\dfrac{dy}{dx} = -\dfrac{\sqrt{a^2 - x^2}}{x}, y = -\sqrt{a^2 - x^2} - a \ln\left|\dfrac{a - \sqrt{a^2 - x^2}}{x}\right|$

Problem Set 7.5

1. $\ln|x| - \ln|x + 1| + C$

3. $-\frac{3}{2}\ln|x + 1| + \frac{3}{2}\ln|x - 1| + C$

5. $3 \ln|x + 4| - 2 \ln|x - 1| + C$

7. $4 \ln|x + 5| - \ln|x - 2| + C$

9. $2 \ln|2x - 1| - \ln|x + 5| + C$

11. $\frac{5}{3}\ln|3x - 2| + 4 \ln|x + 1| + C$

13. $2 \ln|x| - \ln|x + 1| + \ln|x - 2| + C$

15. $\ln|2x - 1| - \ln|x + 3| + 3 \ln|x - 2| + C$

17. $\frac{1}{2}x^2 - x + \frac{8}{3}\ln|x + 2| + \frac{1}{3}\ln|x - 1| + C$

19. $\frac{1}{2}x^2 - 2 \ln|x| + 7 \ln|x + 2| + 7 \ln|x - 2| + C$

21. $\ln|x - 3| - \dfrac{4}{x - 3} + C$

23. $-\dfrac{3}{x + 1} + \dfrac{1}{2(x + 1)^2} + C$

25. $2 \ln|x| + \ln|x - 4| + \dfrac{1}{x - 4} + C$

27. $-2 \ln|x| + \frac{1}{2}\tan^{-1}\left(\frac{x}{2}\right) + 2 \ln|x^2 + 4| + C$

29. $-2 \ln|2x - 1| + \frac{3}{2}\ln|x^2 + 9| + C$

31. $-\dfrac{2}{125}\ln|x - 1| - \dfrac{1}{25(x - 1)}$
$+ \dfrac{2}{125}\ln|x + 4| - \dfrac{1}{25(x + 4)} + C$

33. $\sin t - \frac{50}{13}\ln|\sin t + 3| - \frac{68}{13}\tan^{-1}(\sin t - 2)$
$- \frac{41}{26}\ln|\sin^2 t - 4 \sin t + 5| + C$

35. $\frac{1}{2}\ln|x^2 + 1| + \dfrac{5}{2(x^2 + 1)} + C$

37. $\frac{3}{2}\tan^{-1}\dfrac{x}{2} + \dfrac{2x - 5}{2(x^2 + 4)} + C$

39. $\frac{1}{8}\ln\left(\dfrac{\sqrt{2} + 1}{\sqrt{2} - 1}\right) + \frac{1}{2}\tan^{-1}\dfrac{1}{\sqrt{2}} + \dfrac{1}{6\sqrt{2}}$

41. $y(t) = \dfrac{e^t}{1 + e^t};\ y(3) \approx 0.953$

43. $y(t) = \dfrac{8000e^{2.4t}}{7 + e^{2.4t}};\ y(3) \approx 7958.4$

45. $y(t) = \dfrac{Le^{kLt}}{\left(\dfrac{L - y_0}{y_0}\right) + e^{kLt}}$

47. If $y_0 < L$, then $y'(0) = ky_0(L - y_0) > 0$ and the population is increasing initially.

49. (a) $y = \dfrac{16}{1 + 7e^{-\left(\frac{1}{50}\ln\frac{7}{3}\right)t}}$ **(b)** $y(90) \approx 6.34$ billion

(c) The population will be 9 billion in 2055.

51. (a) $x(t) = \dfrac{ab(1 - e^{(a-b)kt})}{b - ae^{(a-b)kt}}$ **(c)** 1.65 grams

(d) $x(t) = a\left(\dfrac{akt}{akt + 1}\right)$

53. $y(t) = \dfrac{ACe^{(A+B)kt} - B}{1 + Ce^{(A+B)kt}}$

Problem Set 7.6

1. $-\frac{1}{5}e^{-5x}(\frac{1}{5} + x) + C$ **3.** $\frac{1}{2}[\ln 2]^2$

5. $\frac{1}{64}[24x + 8\sin 4x + \sin 8x] + C$

7. $\frac{1}{2}\left(\ln\frac{2}{3} - \ln\frac{3}{5}\right) \approx 0.0527$ **9.** $\frac{2}{15}\left[77\sqrt{7} + 8\sqrt{2}\right] \approx 28.67$

11. 0

13. (a) $\frac{2}{135}(9x - 2)(3x + 1)^{3/2} + C$

(b) $\frac{2}{135}(9e^x - 2)(3e^x + 1)^{3/2} + C$

15. (a) $\dfrac{1}{24}\ln\left|\dfrac{4x + 3}{4x - 3}\right| + C$ **(b)** $\dfrac{1}{24}\ln\left|\dfrac{4e^x + 3}{4e^x - 3}\right| + C$

17. (a) $\dfrac{1}{16}\left[x(4x^2 - 9)\sqrt{9 - 2x^2} + \dfrac{81}{\sqrt{2}}\sin^{-1}\left(\dfrac{\sqrt{2}x}{3}\right)\right] + C$

(b) $\dfrac{1}{16}\left[\sin x(4\sin^2 x - 9)\sqrt{9 - 2\sin^2 x}\right.$

$\left. + \dfrac{81}{\sqrt{2}}\sin^{-1}\left(\dfrac{\sqrt{2}\sin x}{3}\right)\right] + C$

19. (a) $\dfrac{\sqrt{3}}{3}\ln|\sqrt{3}x + \sqrt{5 + 3x^2}| + C$

(b) $\dfrac{\sqrt{3}}{6}\ln|\sqrt{3}x^2 + \sqrt{5 + 3x^4}| + C$

21. (a) $\ln|(t + 1) + \sqrt{t^2 + 2t - 3}| + C$

(b) $\ln\left|\left(t + \dfrac{3}{2}\right) + \sqrt{t^2 + 3t - 5}\right| + C$

23. (a) $\frac{2}{27}(3y - 10)\sqrt{3y + 5} + C$

(b) $\frac{2}{27}(3\sin t - 10)\sqrt{3\sin t + 5} + C$

25. $\frac{1}{12}(\sinh 6t - 6t) + C$

27. $\frac{1}{3}(1 - \cos t)\sqrt{2\cos t + 1} + C$

29. $-\dfrac{2}{5}\sqrt{\cos t + 1}\left[\cos^2 t - \dfrac{4}{3}(\cos t - 2)\right] + C$

31. $\pi - 2 \approx 1.14159$ **33.** $\dfrac{231\pi}{2048} \approx 0.35435$

35. 0.11083   **37.** 1.10577   **39.** $4\ln 2 + 2 \approx 4.77259$

41. $e - 1 \approx 1.71828$ **43.** $e - 1 \approx 1.71828$

45. $c \approx 0.59601$ **47.** $c \approx 0.16668$ **49.** $c \approx 9.2365$

51. $\bar{x} = \dfrac{8}{3(c + 1)}; c = \dfrac{1}{3}$

53. $\bar{x} = \dfrac{cu}{u + 18} + 3$ where $u = -18e^{-c/3}; c \approx 5.7114$

55. (a) $\dfrac{2}{\sqrt{\pi}}e^{-x^2}$ **(b)** $\dfrac{\sin x}{x}$

57. (a) erf(x) is increasing on $(0, \infty)$.

(b) erf(x) is not concave up on $(0, \infty)$.

59. (a) $C(x)$ is increasing on $(0, 1) \cup (\sqrt{3}, 2)$.

(b) $C(x)$ is concave up on $(\sqrt{2}, 2)$.

Problem Set 7.7

1. $y = e^{-x}(x + C)$ **3.** $y = a + C(1 - x^2)^{1/2}$

5. $y = xe^x + Cx$ **7.** $y = 1 + Cx^{-1}$

9. $y = 1 + Ce^{-\int f(x)\, dx}$ **11.** $y = x^4 + 2x$ goes through $(1, 3)$.

13. $y = e^{-x}(1 - x^{-1})$ goes through $(1, 0)$.   **15.** 38.506 lb.

17. $y(t) = 2(60 - t) - \left(\dfrac{1}{1800}\right)(60 - t)^3$

19. $I(t) = 10^{-6}(1 - \exp(-10^6 t))$

21. $I(t) = 0.12\sin 377t$

23. (a) 21.97 min   **(b)** 26.67 min   **(c)** $c > 7.7170$

(d) $400e^{-0.04T} + T = 150$.

25. (a) 200.32 ft   **(b)** $95 - 4T - 95e^{-0.05T} = 0$

Problem Set 7.8

1. $\lim\limits_{t\to\infty} y(t) = 12$ and $y(2) \approx 10.5$

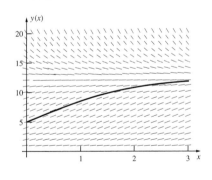

3. $\lim\limits_{t\to\infty} y(t) = 0$ and $y(2) \approx 6$

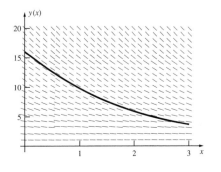

5. The oblique asymptote is $y = x$.

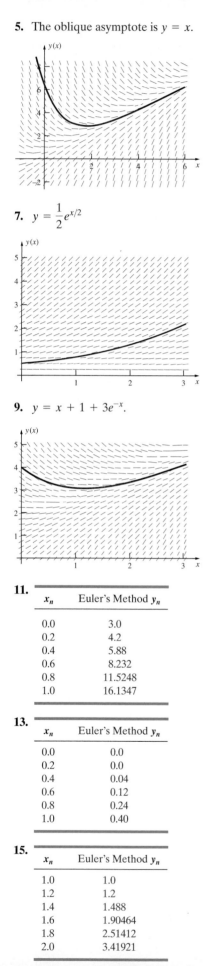

7. $y = \dfrac{1}{2}e^{x/2}$

9. $y = x + 1 + 3e^{-x}$.

11.

x_n	Euler's Method y_n
0.0	3.0
0.2	4.2
0.4	5.88
0.6	8.232
0.8	11.5248
1.0	16.1347

13.

x_n	Euler's Method y_n
0.0	0.0
0.2	0.0
0.4	0.04
0.6	0.12
0.8	0.24
1.0	0.40

15.

x_n	Euler's Method y_n
1.0	1.0
1.2	1.2
1.4	1.488
1.6	1.90464
1.8	2.51412
2.0	3.41921

19. (a) $y(x_1) \approx 0$　**(b)** $y(x_2) \approx 0.00099998$
(c) $y(x_{10}) \approx 0.269097$

21. (a) $\dfrac{\Delta y}{\Delta x} = \dfrac{1}{2}[f(x_0, y_0) + f(x_1, \hat{y}_1)]$
(c) $x_n = x_{n-1} + h$
$\hat{y}_n = y_{n-1} + h \cdot f(x_{n-1}, y_{n-1})$
$y_n = y_{n-1} + \dfrac{h}{2}[f(x_{n-1}, y_{n-1}) + f(x_n, \hat{y}_n)]$

23.

x_n	y_n
0.0	2.0
0.2	1.64
0.4	1.3448
0.6	1.10274
0.8	0.90424
1.0	0.74148

25.

x_n	y_n
0.0	0.0
0.2	0.004
0.4	0.024
0.6	0.076
0.8	0.176
1.0	0.340

27.

x_n	y_n
1.0	2.0
1.2	1.312
1.4	0.80609
1.6	0.46689
1.8	0.25698
2.0	0.13568

Chapter Review 7.9

Concepts Test

1. True　**3.** False　**5.** True　**7.** True　**9.** True
11. False　**13.** True　**15.** True　**17.** False　**19.** True
21. False　**23.** True　**25.** False　**27.** True　**29.** True
31. False

Sample Test Problems

1. 2　**3.** $e - 1$　**5.** $\frac{1}{3}y^3 - \frac{1}{2}y^2 + 2y - 2\ln|1 + y| + C$
7. $\frac{1}{2}\ln|y^2 - 4y + 2| + C$　**9.** $e^t + 2\ln|e^t - 2| + C$
11. $\dfrac{1}{\sqrt{2}}\sin^{-1}\left(\dfrac{x - 1}{3}\right) + C$　**13.** $\dfrac{1}{\sqrt{3}}\ln\left|\sqrt{y^2 + \dfrac{2}{3}} + y\right| + C$
15. $-\ln|\ln|\cos x|| + C$　**17.** $\cosh x + C$
19. $-x\cot x - \frac{1}{2}x^2 + \ln|\sin x| + C$　**21.** $\frac{1}{4}[\ln(t^2)]^2 + C$
23. $-\frac{3}{82}e^{t/3}(9\cos 3t - \sin 3t) + C$
25. $-\frac{1}{2}\cos x - \frac{1}{4}\cos 2x + C$　**27.** $\frac{1}{6}\sec^3(2x) - \frac{1}{2}\sec(2x) + C$
29. $\frac{2}{5}\tan^{5/2} x + \frac{2}{9}\tan^{9/2} x + C$　**31.** $-\sqrt{9 - e^{2y}} + C$
33. $3\sin x + C$　**35.** $\frac{1}{4}\tan^{-1}(e^{4x}) + C$
37. $\frac{2}{3}(w + 5)^{3/2} - 10(w + 5)^{1/2} + C$
39. $-\frac{1}{6}\tan^{-1}\left(\dfrac{\cos^2 y}{3}\right) + C$
41. $\ln|x| - \dfrac{2}{x} - \dfrac{1}{2}\ln|x^2 + 3| + \dfrac{2}{\sqrt{3}}\tan^{-1}\left(\dfrac{x}{\sqrt{3}}\right) + C$

43. (a) $\dfrac{A}{2x + 1} + \dfrac{B}{(2x + 1)^2} + \dfrac{C}{(2x + 1)^3}$

(b) $\dfrac{A}{x - 1} + \dfrac{B}{(x - 1)^2} + \dfrac{C}{2 - x} + \dfrac{D}{(2 - x)^2} + \dfrac{E}{(2 - x)^3}$

(c) $\dfrac{Ax + B}{x^2 + x + 10} + \dfrac{Cx + D}{(x^2 + x + 10)^2}$

(d) $\dfrac{A}{1 - x} + \dfrac{B}{(1 - x)^2} + \dfrac{C}{1 + x} + \dfrac{D}{(1 + x)^2}$

$+ \dfrac{Ex + F}{x^2 - x + 10} + \dfrac{Gx + H}{(x^2 - x + 10)^2}$

(e) $\dfrac{A}{x + 3} + \dfrac{B}{(x + 3)^2} + \dfrac{C}{(x + 3)^3} + \dfrac{D}{(x + 3)^4}$

$+ \dfrac{Ex + F}{x^2 + 2x + 10} + \dfrac{Gx + H}{(x^2 + 2x + 10)^2}$

(f) $\dfrac{Ax + B}{2x^2 + x + 10} + \dfrac{Cx + D}{(2x^2 + x + 10)^2} + \dfrac{Ex + F}{(2x^2 + x + 10)^3}$

45. $\sqrt{5} + 4 \ln\left(\dfrac{1 + \sqrt{5}}{2}\right)$

47. $2\pi \ln \frac{32}{25}$ **49.** $4\pi[2 - \ln 3 - \frac{1}{2}(\ln 3)^2]$ **51.** $\ln 7 - \frac{6}{7}$

53. $\ln\left(\dfrac{2\sqrt{3} + 3}{3}\right)$

55. (a) $\dfrac{\sin x}{2} \sqrt{\sin^2 x + 4} + 2 \ln|\sin x + \sqrt{\sin^2 x + 4}| + C$

(b) $\dfrac{1}{4} \ln\left|\dfrac{1 + 2x}{1 - 2x}\right| + C$

57. $G'(x) = 2x \cos x$, $G''(x) = -2x \sin x + 2\cos x$

59. $y = Cx^{-1}$ **61.** $y = 1 + 2e^{-x^2}$ **63.** $y = -e^x + Ce^{2x}$

Chapter 8 Review and Preview Problems

1. $\dfrac{5}{3}$ **3.** 6   **5.** 2   **7.** 1   **9.** 0   **11.** ∞ **13.** $\dfrac{\pi}{2}$

15.

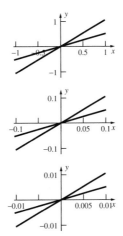

$\lim_{x \to \infty} xe^{-x} = 0.$

17.

$\lim_{x \to \infty} x^3 e^{-x} = 0.$

19.

$\lim_{x \to \infty} x^{10} e^{-x} = 0.$

21.

a	1	2	4	8	16
$1 - e^{-a}$	0.632	0.865	0.982	0.99966	0.999999887

23.

a	1	2	4	8	16
$\ln\left(\sqrt{1 + a^2}\right)$	0.3466	0.8047	1.4166	2.0872	2.7745

25.

a	2	4	8	16
$1 - \dfrac{1}{a}$	0.5	0.75	0.875	0.9375

27.

a	1	1/2	1/4	1/8	1/16
$4 - 2\sqrt{a}$	2	2.58579	3	3.29289	3.5

Problem Set 8.1

1. 1   **3.** -1 **5.** $-\frac{2}{7}$ **7.** $-\infty$ **9.** 0

11. $-\frac{3}{2}$ **13.** $-\frac{2}{7}$ **15.** $-\frac{1}{4}$ **17.** $-\infty$ **19.** $-\frac{1}{24}$

21. $-\infty$ **23.** 1

27. (a) $\frac{3}{4}$; **(b)** $\frac{1}{2}$

29. $c = 1$ **31.** $4\pi b^2$ **35.** $\frac{1}{24}$ **37.** 2

39. The ratio of the slopes is 1/2, indicating that the limit of the ratio should be about 1/2.

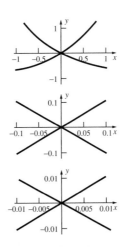

41. The ratio of the slopes is $-1/1 = -1$, indicating that the limit of the ratio should be about -1.

Problem Set 8.2

1. 0 **3.** 0 **5.** 3 **7.** 0 **9.** ∞ **11.** 0 **13.** 1
15. 1 **17.** 0 **19.** e^4 **21.** 1 **23.** 1 **25.** 0
27. 1 **29.** 0 **31.** ∞ **33.** 1
35. Limit does not exist. **37.** 0 **39.** 1
41. (a) 1; **(b)** 1; **(c)** ln a; **(d)** ∞
43. As $x \to 0^+$, $y \to 0$. As $x \to \infty$, $y \to 1$.
Maximum value $e^{1/e}$ at $x = e$.

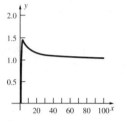

45. $1/(k + 1)$
47. (a) 3.162; **(b)** 4.163; **(c)** 4.562
49. No absolute minimum; absolute maximum at $x \approx 25$

Problem Set 8.3

1. Diverges **3.** $\frac{1}{e}$ **5.** Diverges **7.** 100,000
9. Diverges **11.** Diverges **13.** $\frac{1}{2}(\ln 2 + 1)$ **15.** $-\frac{1}{4}$
17. Diverges **19.** $\frac{\pi}{3}$ **21.** π **23.** $\frac{1}{2}$ **25.** $\frac{1}{2}\ln 3$
29. \$1,250,000

31. (b) $\mu = \dfrac{a + b}{2}$; $\sigma^2 = \dfrac{(b - a)^2}{12}$; **(c)** $\dfrac{1}{5}$

35. (a) $C = 3$ and $M = \dfrac{4 \times 10^4}{3}$; **(b)** $\sigma^2 = \dfrac{4 \times 10^8}{3}$

(c) $^6\!/_{25}$ of one percent earn over \$100,000.

41. $\displaystyle\int_1^{100} \frac{1}{x^2}\,dx = 0.99$; $\displaystyle\int_1^{100} \frac{1}{x^{1.1}}\,dx \approx 3.69$

$\displaystyle\int_1^{100} \frac{1}{x^{1.01}}\,dx \approx 4.50$; $\displaystyle\int_1^{100} \frac{1}{x}\,dx = \ln 100 \approx 4.61$;

$\displaystyle\int_1^{100} \frac{1}{x^{0.99}}\,dx \approx 4.71$

43. $\displaystyle\int_{-1}^1 \frac{1}{\sqrt{2\pi}}\exp\left(-0.5x^2\right)\,dx \approx 0.6827$;

$\displaystyle\int_{-2}^2 \frac{1}{\sqrt{2\pi}}\exp\left(-0.5x^2\right)\,dx \approx 0.9545$;

$\displaystyle\int_{-3}^3 \frac{1}{\sqrt{2\pi}}\exp\left(-0.5x^2\right)\,dx \approx 0.9973$;

$\displaystyle\int_{-4}^4 \frac{1}{\sqrt{2\pi}}\exp\left(-0.5x^2\right)\,dx \approx 0.9999$

Problem Set 8.4

1. $\dfrac{3}{\sqrt[3]{2}}$ **3.** $2\sqrt{7}$ **5.** $\frac{\pi}{2}$ **7.** Diverges **9.** $\frac{21}{2}$
11. $\frac{1}{2}(2^{2/3} - 10^{2/3})$ **13.** Diverges **15.** Diverges
17. Diverges **19.** Diverges **21.** Diverges
23. Diverges **25.** Diverges **27.** $2\sqrt{2}$ **29.** Diverges
31. $\ln(2 + \sqrt{3})$ **35.** 0 **37.** Diverges **41.** 6
43. (a) 3 **45.** No **49.** Converges

55. (a) $C = \beta^{\alpha}/\Gamma(\alpha)$; **(b)** $\mu = \alpha/\beta$; **(c)** $\sigma^2 = \alpha/\beta^2$
57. (a) $\frac{\pi}{2}$; **(b)** π

Chapter Review 8.5

Concepts Test

1. True **3.** False **5.** False **7.** True **9.** True
11. False **13.** True **15.** True **17.** False **19.** True
21. True **23.** True **25.** False

Sample Test Problems

1. 4 **3.** 0 **5.** 2 **7.** 0 **9.** 0 **11.** 1 **13.** 0
15. 0 **17.** 1 **19.** 1 **21.** $\frac{1}{2}e^2$ **23.** Diverges
25. $1 - \frac{\pi}{4}$ **27.** Diverges **29.** $\frac{1}{\ln 2}$ **31.** 6
33. Diverges **35.** $\frac{\pi}{4}$ **37.** 0
39. Converges: $p > 1$; diverges: $p \leq 1$
41. Converges **43.** Diverges

Chapter 9 Review and Preview Problems

1. Original: If $x > 0$, then $x^2 > 0$. (AT)
Converse: If $x^2 > 0$, then $x > 0$.
Contrapositive: If $x^2 \leq 0$, then $x \leq 0$. (AT)
3. Original: f differentiable at $c \Rightarrow f$ continuous at c (AT)
Converse: f continuous at $c \Rightarrow f$ differentiable at c
Contrapositive: f discontinuous at $c \Rightarrow f$ non-differentiable
at c (AT)
5. Original: f right continuous at $c \Rightarrow f$ continuous at c
Converse: f continuous at $c \Rightarrow f$ right continuous at c (AT)
Contrapositive: f discontinuous at $c \Rightarrow f$ not right
continuous at c
7. Original: $f(x) = x^2 \Rightarrow f'(x) = 2x$ (AT)
Converse: $f'(x) = 2x \Rightarrow f(x) = x^2$
Contrapositive: $f'(x) \neq 2x \Rightarrow f(x) \neq x^2$ (AT)
9. $\dfrac{7}{4}$ **11.** $\dfrac{25}{12}$ **13.** $\dfrac{1}{2}$ **15.** 0 **17.** diverges
19. converges **21.** diverges

Problem Set 9.1

1. $\frac{1}{3}$ **3.** 4 **5.** 1 **7.** Diverges **9.** 0 **11.** Diverges
13. 0 **15.** 2 **17.** 0 **19.** e **21.** $a_n = \dfrac{n}{n + 1}$; 1
23. $a_n = (-1)^n\dfrac{n}{2n - 1}$; diverges **25.** $a_n = \dfrac{n}{2n - 1}$; $\dfrac{1}{2}$
27. $a_n = n\sin\dfrac{1}{n}$; 1 **29.** $a_n = \dfrac{2^n}{n^2}$; diverges **31.** $\frac{1}{2}, \frac{5}{4}, \frac{9}{8}, \frac{13}{16}$
33. $\frac{3}{4}, \frac{2}{3}, \frac{5}{8}, \frac{3}{5}$ **35.** $1, \frac{3}{2}, \frac{7}{4}, \frac{15}{8}$ **37.** 2.3028 **39.** $\frac{1}{2}(1 + \sqrt{13})$
41. 1.1118 **43.** $1 - \cos 1$ **51.** No **53.** $\dfrac{\pi}{2\sqrt{3}}$
55. $e^{1/2}$ **57.** e^{-2} **59.** e^{-1}

Problem Set 9.2

1. $\frac{1}{6}$ **3.** $\frac{31}{6}$ **5.** Diverges **7.** -1 **9.** Diverges
11. $\dfrac{e^2}{\pi(\pi - e)}$ **13.** 3 **15.** $\frac{2}{9}$ **17.** $\frac{13}{999}$ **19.** $\frac{1}{2}$
21. 1 **25.** 500 ft **27.** \$4 billion **29.** $\frac{1}{4}$ **31.** $\frac{4}{5}$; No
33. (a) Perimeter is infinite. **(b)** $A = \dfrac{8}{5}\left(\dfrac{81\sqrt{3}}{4}\right)$
35. $111\frac{1}{9}$yd **37.** $\frac{3}{5}$ **39.** $\Pr(X = n) = \left(\dfrac{5}{6}\right)^{n-1}\left(\dfrac{1}{6}\right)$

43. (b) Indefinitely
47. (a) 2;   **(b)** 1
49. (a) $\dfrac{Ce^{kt}}{e^{kt}-1}$;   **(b)** $\frac{8}{3}mg$
51. 1

Problem Set 9.3

1. Diverges   **3.** Diverges   **5.** Diverges   **7.** Diverges
9. Converges   **11.** Converges   **13.** Diverges
15. Diverges   **17.** Diverges   **19.** Converges
21. Converges   **23.** 0.0404   **25.** 0.1974   **27.** $n > 5000$
29. $n > 5000$ **31.** $n > 50$ **33.** $p > 1$
39. 272,404,866

Problem Set 9.4

1. Diverges   **3.** Converges   **5.** Converges
7. Diverges   **9.** Converges   **11.** Diverges; nth-Term Test
13. Converges; Limit Comparison Test
15. Converges; Ratio Test
17. Converges; Limit Comparison Test
19. Converges; Limit Comparison Test
21. Converges; Limit Comparison Test
23. Converges; Ratio Test
25. Converges; Integral Test
27. Diverges; nth Term Test
29. Converges; Comparison Test
31. Converges; Ratio Test
33. Converges; Ratio Test
43. (a) Diverges;   **(b)** Converges;   **(c)** Converges;
(d) Converges;   **(e)** Diverges   **(f)** Converges
45. Converges for $p > 1$, diverges for $p \le 1$.

Problem Set 9.5

1. $|S - S_9| \le 0.065$ **3.** $|S - S_9| \le 0.417$
5. $|S - S_9| \le 0.230$ **13.** Conditionally convergent
15. Divergent   **17.** Conditionally convergent
19. Absolutely convergent   **21.** Conditionally convergent
23. Conditionally convergent   **25.** Absolutely convergent
27. Conditionally convergent   **29.** Divergent
35. (a) $1 + \frac{1}{3} \approx 1.33$;   **(b)** $1 + \frac{1}{3} - \frac{1}{2} \approx 0.833$
45. $\ln 2$

Problem Set 9.6

1. All x **3.** $-1 \le x \le 1$ **5.** $-1 \le x \le 1$
7. $1 < x \le 3$ **9.** $-1 \le x \le 1$ **11.** All x
13. $-1 < x < 1$ **15.** $-1 < x \le 1$ **17.** $-1 \le x \le 1$
19. $-2 < x < 2$ **21.** All x **23.** $0 \le x < 2$
25. $-3 < x < 1$ **27.** $-6 \le x \le -4$
29. If $\lim\limits_{n\to\infty} \dfrac{x_0^n}{n!} \ne 0$, then $\sum \dfrac{x_0^n}{n!}$ will not converge.
31. $\sqrt{2}$ **33.** $\dfrac{1}{4-x}$; $2 < x < 4$
35. (a) $-1 \le x < \frac{1}{3}$;   **(b)** $-\frac{1}{2} < x \le \frac{7}{2}$
37. $S(x) = \dfrac{a_0 + a_1 x + a_2 x^2}{1 - x^3}$, $|x| < 1$

Problem Set 9.7

1. $1 - x + x^2 - x^3 + x^4 - x^5 + \cdots$; 1
3. $1 + 3x + 6x^2 + 10x^3 + \cdots$; 1
5. $\dfrac{1}{2} + \dfrac{3x}{4} + \dfrac{9x^2}{8} + \dfrac{27x^3}{16} + \cdots$; $\dfrac{2}{3}$

7. $x^2 + x^6 + x^{10} + x^{14} + \cdots$; 1
9. $\dfrac{x^2}{2} - \dfrac{x^3}{6} + \dfrac{x^4}{12} - \dfrac{x^5}{20} + \cdots$; 1
11. $2x + \dfrac{2x^3}{3} + \dfrac{2x^5}{5} + \cdots$; 1
13. $1 - x + \dfrac{x^2}{2!} - \dfrac{x^3}{3!} + \dfrac{x^4}{4!} - \dfrac{x^5}{5!} + \cdots$
15. $2 + \dfrac{2x^2}{2!} + \dfrac{2x^4}{4!} + \dfrac{2x^6}{6!} + \cdots$
17. $1 + \dfrac{x^2}{2} + \dfrac{x^3}{3} + \dfrac{3x^4}{8} + \dfrac{11x^5}{30} + \cdots$
19. $x - x^2 + \dfrac{x^3}{6} + \dfrac{x^4}{6} + \dfrac{3x^5}{40} + \cdots$
21. $x + \dfrac{2x^3}{3} + \dfrac{13x^5}{15} - \dfrac{29x^7}{105} + \cdots$
23. $x + \dfrac{x^3}{6} - \dfrac{x^4}{12} + \dfrac{3x^5}{40} - \cdots$
25. (a) $\dfrac{x}{1+x}$;   **(b)** $\dfrac{e^x - (1+x)}{x^2}$;   **(c)** $-\ln(1 - 2x)$
27. $\dfrac{x}{(1-x)^2}$, $-1 < x < 1$
29. (a) $x + \dfrac{x^2}{2} - \dfrac{x^3}{6} - \cdots$;   **(b)** $1 + x + x^2 + \dfrac{5x^3}{6} + \cdots$
31. $\dfrac{x}{2} + \dfrac{3x^2}{4} + \dfrac{7x^3}{8} + \cdots$ **33.** $\dfrac{x}{1 - x - x^2}$ **35.** 3.14159

Problem Set 9.8

1. $x + \dfrac{x^3}{3} + \dfrac{2x^5}{15}$ **3.** $x + x^2 + \dfrac{x^3}{3} - \dfrac{x^5}{30}$
5. $x - \dfrac{x^2}{2} - \dfrac{x^3}{6} + \dfrac{3x^5}{40}$ **7.** $1 + 3x + \dfrac{x^2}{2} + \dfrac{x^4}{24} + \dfrac{x^5}{60}$
9. $1 + x + \dfrac{3x^2}{2} + \dfrac{3x^3}{2} + \dfrac{37x^4}{24} + \dfrac{37x^5}{24}$ **11.** $1 - x + x^3 - x^4$
13. $x^3 - \dfrac{x^5}{2}$ **15.** $2x - \dfrac{x^3}{6} + \dfrac{61x^5}{120}$
17. $1 + \dfrac{3x}{2} + \dfrac{3x^2}{8} - \dfrac{x^3}{16} + \dfrac{3x^4}{128} - \dfrac{3x^5}{256}$
19. $e + e(x - 1) + \dfrac{e}{2}(x - 1)^2 + \dfrac{e}{6}(x - 1)^3$
21. $\dfrac{1}{2} - \dfrac{\sqrt{3}}{2}\left(x - \dfrac{\pi}{3}\right) - \dfrac{1}{4}\left(x - \dfrac{\pi}{3}\right)^2 + \dfrac{\sqrt{3}}{12}\left(x - \dfrac{\pi}{3}\right)^3$
23. $3 + 5(x - 1) + 4(x - 1)^2 + (x - 1)^3$
27. $x + \dfrac{x^3}{6} + \dfrac{3x^5}{40} + \dfrac{5x^7}{112}$ **29.** 0.9045
31. $1 - (x - 1) + (x - 1)^2 - (x - 1)^3 + \cdots$
33. (a) 25;   **(b)** -3;   **(c)** 0;   **(d)** $4e$;   **(e)** -4
35. $x - \dfrac{x^3}{3} + \dfrac{2x^5}{15}$ **41.** $x - \dfrac{x^3}{6} + \dfrac{x^5}{120} - \dfrac{x^7}{5040}$
43. $-2 + x - x^2 - \dfrac{5x^3}{6}$ **45.** $x + \dfrac{x^2}{2} - \dfrac{5x^4}{24} - \dfrac{23x^5}{120}$
47. $x + x^2 + \dfrac{x^3}{3} - \dfrac{x^5}{30}$

Problem Set 9.9

1. $1 + 2x + 2x^2 + \frac{4}{3}x^3 + \frac{2}{3}x^4$; 1.2712   **3.** $2x - \frac{4}{3}x^3$; 0.2377
5. $x - \frac{1}{2}x^2 + \frac{1}{3}x^3 - \frac{1}{4}x^4$; 0.1133   **7.** $x - \frac{1}{3}x^3$; 0.1194

9. $e + e(x - 1) + \frac{e}{2}(x - 1)^2 + \frac{e}{6}(x - 1)^3$

11. $\frac{\sqrt{3}}{3} + \frac{4}{3}\left(x - \frac{\pi}{6}\right) + \frac{4\sqrt{3}}{9}\left(x - \frac{\pi}{6}\right)^2 + \frac{8}{9}\left(x - \frac{\pi}{6}\right)^3$

13. $\frac{\pi}{4} - \frac{1}{2}(x - 1) + \frac{1}{4}(x - 1)^2 - \frac{1}{12}(x - 1)^3$

15. $7 + 2(x - 1) + (x - 1)^2 + (x - 1)^3$

17. $f(x) \approx 1 + x + x^2 + x^3 + x^4$

(a) 1.1111;   **(b)** 1.9375;   **(c)** 4.0951;   **(d)** 31

19.

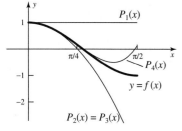

21.

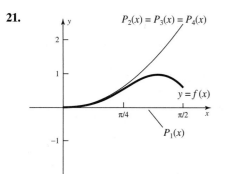

23.

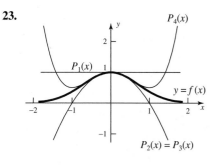

25.

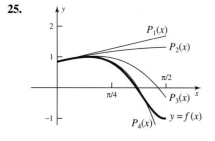

27.

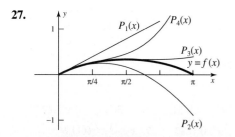

29. $e^6 + 1$ **31.** $2\sqrt{2}\pi$ **33.** $\dfrac{e^4}{3}$ **35.** $\dfrac{17}{10 \ln 2}$

37. $R_6(x) = \dfrac{x^7}{7(2 + c)^7}; 8.719 \times 10^{-6}$

39. $R_6(x) = -\dfrac{\cos c}{5040}\left(x - \dfrac{\pi}{4}\right)^7; 2.685 \times 10^{-8}$

41. $R_6(x) = \dfrac{-(x - 1)^7}{c^8}; 2$ **43.** $n \geq 9$

45. $1 + \dfrac{x}{2} - \dfrac{x^2}{8} + \dfrac{x^3}{16}; |R_3(x)| \leq 0.0276$

47. $1 - \frac{1}{2}x + \frac{3}{8}x^2 - \frac{5}{16}x^3; |R_3(x)| \leq 2.15 \times 10^{-6}$

49. $0.1224; |\text{Error}| \leq 0.00013025$ **51.** $n > 42$

53. $A = \dfrac{1}{2}tr^2 - \dfrac{1}{2}r^2 \sin t; A \approx \dfrac{1}{12}r^2t^3$

55. (c)

	n	n	n
r	(exact)	(approx.)	(rule 72)
0.05	13.892	13.889	14.4
0.10	6.960	6.959	7.2
0.15	4.650	4.649	4.8
0.20	3.495	3.494	3.6

57. $-1 - (x - 1)^2 + (x - 1)^3 + (x - 1)^4$

59. $0.681998; |R_3| \leq 6.19 \times 10^{-8}$

Chapter Review 9.10

Concepts Test

1. False   **3.** True   **5.** False   **7.** False   **9.** True
11. True   **13.** False   **15.** True   **17.** False   **19.** True
21. True   **23.** True   **25.** True   **27.** True   **29.** True
31. True   **33.** False   **35.** True   **37.** True   **39.** True
41. True

Sample Test Problems

1. 3   **3.** e^4 **5.** 1   **7.** 0   **9.** 1   **11.** Diverges

13. $\dfrac{e^2}{e^2 - 1}$ **15.** $\frac{91}{99}$ **17.** $\cos 2$ **19.** Diverges

21. Converges   **23.** Converges   **25.** Diverges
27. Converges   **29.** Diverges   **31.** Converges
33. Conditionally convergent   **35.** Diverges
37. $-1 \leq x \leq 1$ **39.** $3 < x \leq 5$ **41.** $1 < x < 5$
43. $1 - 2x + 3x^2 - 4x^3 + \cdots; -1 < x < 1$

45. $x^2 - \dfrac{x^4}{3} + \dfrac{2x^6}{45} - \dfrac{x^8}{315} + \cdots; \text{all } x$

47. $1 + x - \dfrac{x^2}{2!} - \dfrac{x^3}{3!} + \dfrac{x^4}{4!} + \dfrac{x^5}{5!} - \cdots; \text{all } x$ **49.** $n > 3$

51. (a) $1 + x^3 + x^6$ **(b)** $1 + \dfrac{1}{2}x^2 - \dfrac{1}{8}x^4$ **(c)** $\dfrac{x^2}{2!} - \dfrac{x^3}{3!} + \dfrac{x^4}{4!}$

(d) $x + \dfrac{x^3}{2} + \dfrac{5x^5}{4!}$ **(e)** $x - x^2 + \dfrac{x^3}{3}$ **(f)** $1 - x + x^2$

53. $P(x) = x; 0.2$

55. $P_4(x) = 3 + 9(x - 2) + 4(x - 2)^2 + (x - 2)^3$

57. $f(x) \approx \dfrac{1}{2} - \dfrac{1}{4}(x - 1) + \dfrac{1}{8}(x - 1)^2 - \dfrac{1}{16}(x - 1)^3 + \dfrac{1}{32}(x - 1)^4$

59. $\sin^2 x \approx x^2 - \dfrac{1}{3}x^4; |R_4(x)| < 2.85 \times 10^{-6}$

61. $-0.00269867; \text{Error} < 1.63 \times 10^{-5}$

Chapter 10 Review and Preview Problems

1. (a) $y = x - 1$ **(b)** $y = -x + 3$

3. $(2.4, 2.4), (-2.4, 2.4), (2.4, -2.4), (-2.4, -2.4)$

5. $y = 2\sqrt{3}x + 4$

7. $\left(5, 4\sqrt{3}\right), \left(-5, 4\sqrt{3}\right), \left(5, -4\sqrt{3}\right), \left(-5, -4\sqrt{3}\right)$;
$T_1: 4\sqrt{3}x + 15y = 80\sqrt{3}; T_2: 5\sqrt{3}x - 4y = 9\sqrt{3}; \alpha = 90°$

9. $r = 5; \theta = \sin^{-1}(0.6)$ **11.** $x = y = 4\sqrt{2}$

Problem Set 10.1

1. Focus at $(1, 0)$: directrix $x = -1$

3. Focus at $(0, -3)$; directrix $y = 3$

5. Focus at $\left(\frac{1}{4}, 0\right)$; directrix $x = -\frac{1}{4}$

7. Focus at $\left(0, \frac{3}{4}\right)$; directrix $y = -\frac{3}{4}$

9. $y^2 = 8x$ **11.** $x^2 = -8y$ **13.** $y^2 = -16x$

15. $y^2 = \frac{1}{3}x$ **17.** $x^2 = -\frac{36}{5}y$

19. $y = -2x - 2$; $y = \frac{1}{2}x - \frac{9}{2}$

21. $y = 4x - 8$; $y = -\frac{1}{4}x + 9$

23. $y = \frac{\sqrt{5}}{2}x - \frac{3\sqrt{5}}{2}$; $y = -\frac{2\sqrt{5}}{5}x - \frac{21\sqrt{5}}{5}$

25. $y = -\sqrt{2}x + 3$; $y = \frac{\sqrt{2}}{2}x - 6$

27. $\left(4, 2\sqrt{5}\right)$

29. $y = \frac{3}{2}x - 3$ **35.** 14.8 million mi   **37.** $2p$

39. $L = 4p$ **41.** $y = \frac{\delta x^2}{2H}$

43.

Problem Set 10.2

1. Horizontal ellipse   **3.** Vertical hyperbola

5. Vertical parabola (opens up)   **7.** Vertical ellipse

9.

11.

13.

15.

17. $\frac{x^2}{36} + \frac{y^2}{27} = 1$ **19.** $\frac{x^2}{200} + \frac{y^2}{225} = 1$ **21.** $\frac{x^2}{25} + \frac{y^2}{\frac{225}{21}} = 1$

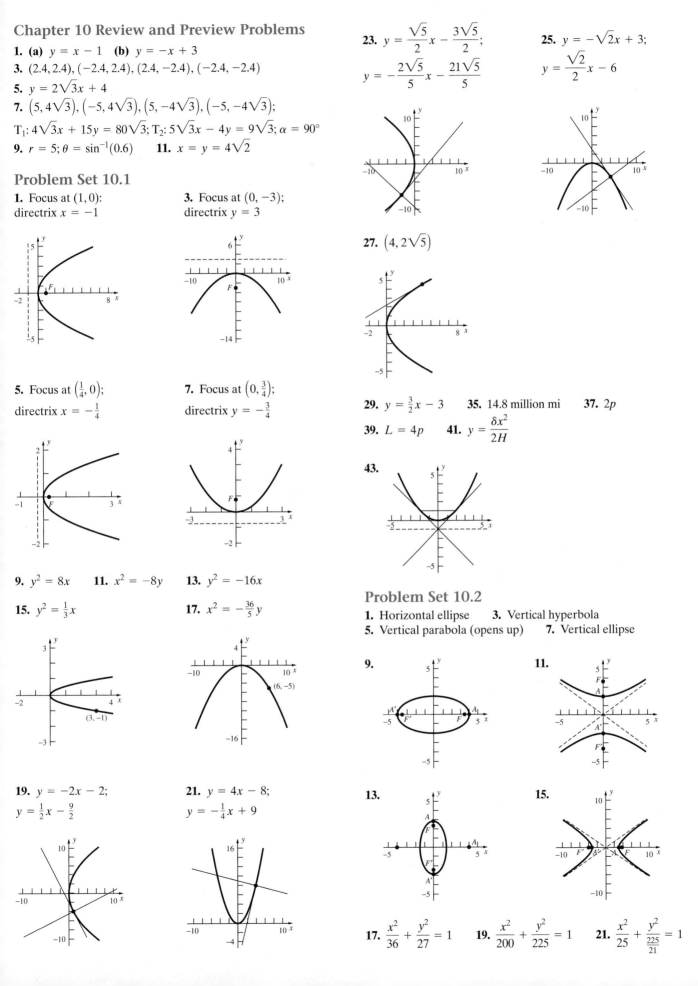

23. $\dfrac{y^2}{16} - \dfrac{x^2}{9} = 1$ **25.** $\dfrac{x^2}{64} - \dfrac{y^2}{16} = 1$ **27.** $\dfrac{x^2}{16} + \dfrac{y^2}{12} = 1$

29. $\dfrac{y^2}{5} - \dfrac{x^2}{20} = 1$ **31.** $\dfrac{x^2}{88} + \dfrac{y^2}{169} = 1$ **33.** $\dfrac{x^2}{36} - \dfrac{y^2}{13} = 1$

35. $x + \sqrt{6}\,y = 9$ **37.** $x - \sqrt{6}\,y = 9$

39. $5x + 12y = 169$ **41.** $y = 13$ **43.** 8.66 ft   **45.** $\dfrac{2b^2}{a}$

47. 0.58 AU   **49.** 0.05175   **51.** $\left(-\sqrt{3}, \frac{3}{2}\right), \left(\sqrt{3}, \frac{3}{2}\right)$

53. $(-7, 3), (7, -3)$ **55.** πab

57. $\dfrac{\pi b^2}{3a^2}\left[(a^2 + b^2)^{3/2} - 3a^2\sqrt{a^2 + b^2} + 2a^3\right]$

59. $a\sqrt{2}$ by $b\sqrt{2}$ **61.** $\left(6, 5\sqrt{3}\right)$

63.

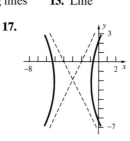

Elliptical mirror

Common focus of parabola and ellipse

F

Parabolic mirror

F'

Other focus of ellipse

69. $\left(\sqrt{\frac{17}{3}}, 5\right)$ **73.** $\dfrac{x^2}{a^2} + \dfrac{y^2}{b^2} = 1$

77.

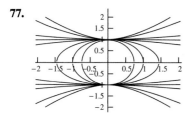

Problem Set 10.3

1. Circle   **3.** Ellipse   **5.** Point   **7.** Parabola
9. Empty set   **11.** Intersecting lines   **13.** Line

15.

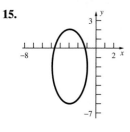

17.

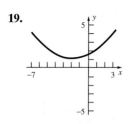

19.

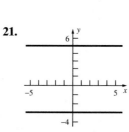

21.

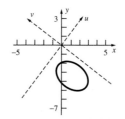

23.

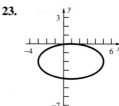

25.

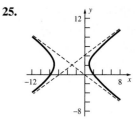

27.

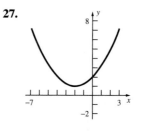

29. Focus at $\left(\frac{21}{20}, 1\right)$; directrix $x = -\frac{29}{20}$ **31.** $(-2, 2), (4, -2)$

33. $\dfrac{(x - 5)^2}{25} + \dfrac{(y - 1)^2}{16} = 1$ **35.** $(x - 2)^2 = 8(y - 3)$

37. $\dfrac{(y - 3)^2}{9} - \dfrac{x^2}{16} = 1$ **39.** $(y - 5)^2 = -16(x - 6)$

41. $\dfrac{x^2}{8} + \dfrac{(y - 2)^2}{4} = 1$

43. $\dfrac{u^2}{4} + \dfrac{v^2}{12} = 1$ **45.** $\dfrac{u^2}{\frac{112}{9}} + \dfrac{v^2}{16} = 1$

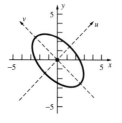

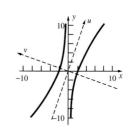

47. $\dfrac{(u - 2)^2}{4} - \dfrac{v^2}{3} = 1$ **49.** $\dfrac{v^2}{4} - \dfrac{u^2}{36} = 1$

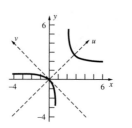

51. $\dfrac{(u + 2)^2}{2} + \dfrac{(v + 3)^2}{4} = 1$

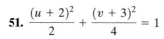

53. (a) $y = x^2 - x$;   **(b)** $x = \frac{1}{4}y^2 - y$;

(c) $\left(x - \frac{5}{2}\right)^2 + \left(y - \frac{5}{2}\right)^2 = \frac{25}{2}$

55. If $K < -1$, the conic is a vertical ellipse. If $K = -1$, the conic is a circle. If $-1 < K < 0$, the conic is a horizontal ellipse. If $K = 0$, the conic is a horizontal parabola. If $K > 0$, the conic is a horizontal hyperbola.

59. $u = x \cos \theta + y \sin \theta$, $v = -x \sin \theta + y \cos \theta$

61. $\left(-\frac{1}{5}, -\frac{7}{5}\right), \left(\frac{1}{5}, \frac{7}{5}\right)$

67. (a) $-2 < B < 2$;   **(b)** $B = 0$;   **(c)** $B < -2$ or $B > 2$;
(d) $B = \pm 2$

Problem Set 10.4

1. (a)   **(b)** Simple; not closed

(c) $y = \frac{2}{3}x$

3. (a)   **(b)** Simple, not closed

(c) $y = \frac{1}{3}(x + 1)$

5. (a)   **(b)** Simple; not closed

(c) $y = \sqrt{4 - x}$

7. (a)   **(b)** Simple; not closed

(c) $y = \frac{1}{x}$

9. (a)   **(b)** Not simple; not closed

(c) $x^2 = y^3 + 4y^2$

11. (a)   **(b)** Simple; not closed

(c) $\dfrac{x^2}{8} + \dfrac{y^2}{18} = 1$

13. (a)   **(b)** Simple; closed

(c) $\dfrac{x^2}{4} + \dfrac{y^2}{9} = 1$

15. (a)   **(b)** Not simple; closed

(c) $\dfrac{x^2}{4} + \dfrac{y^2}{9} = 1$

17. (a)   **(b)** Not simple; closed

(c) $x + y = 9$

19. (a)   **(b)** Not simple; not closed

(c) $y = -8x^2(1 - x^2)$

21. $\dfrac{dy}{dx} = 2\tau; \dfrac{d^2y}{dx^2} = \dfrac{1}{3\tau}$

23. $\dfrac{dy}{dx} = \dfrac{3\sqrt{5}}{4}\theta; \dfrac{d^2y}{dx^2} = \dfrac{3\sqrt{5}}{16\theta}$

25. $\dfrac{dy}{dx} = \cot t; \dfrac{d^2y}{dx^2} = -\csc^3 t$

27. $\dfrac{dy}{dx} = \dfrac{5}{3}\sin t; \dfrac{d^2y}{dx^2} = \dfrac{5}{9}\cos^3 t$

29. $\dfrac{dy}{dx} = \dfrac{(1 - 2t)(1 + t^2)^2}{2t^3(1 - t)^2}$;

$\dfrac{d^2y}{dx^2} = \dfrac{(3t^5 + 7t^4 - 6t^3 + 10t^2 - 9t + 3)(1 + t^2)^2}{4t^5(1 - t)^3}$

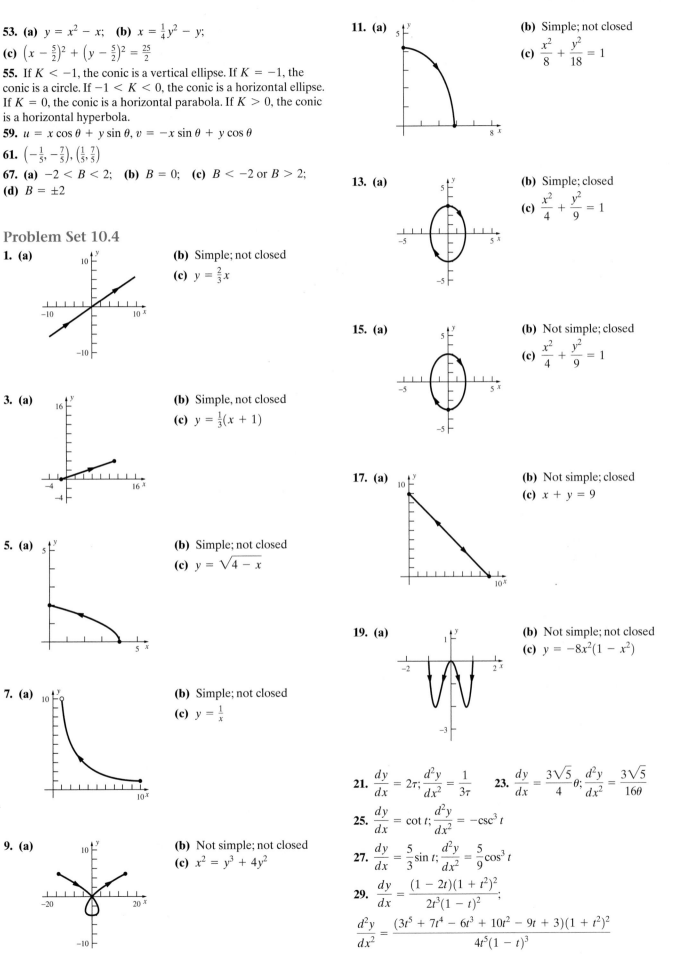

31. $y - 8 = 3(x - 4)$

33. $y + \dfrac{2}{\sqrt{3}} = -2\left(x - \dfrac{4}{\sqrt{3}}\right)$

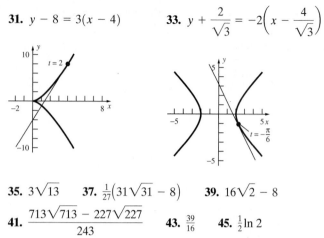

(d)

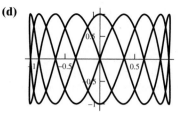

35. $3\sqrt{13}$

37. $\frac{1}{27}(31\sqrt{31} - 8)$

39. $16\sqrt{2} - 8$

41. $\dfrac{713\sqrt{713} - 227\sqrt{227}}{243}$

43. $\frac{39}{16}$

45. $\frac{1}{2}\ln 2$

47. (a) 2π; **(b)** 6π;
(c) The curve in part **(a)** goes around the unit circle once.
The curve in part **(b)** goes around the unit circle three times.

49. $4\pi^2$

51. $4\pi^2$

53. $\frac{2\pi}{3}(29\sqrt{29} - 1)$

55. $-\frac{44}{3}$

57. 8

59.

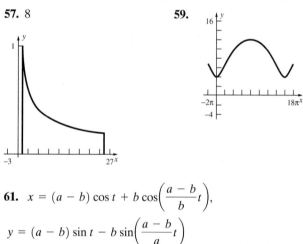

61. $x = (a - b)\cos t + b\cos\left(\dfrac{a - b}{b}t\right),$

$y = (a - b)\sin t - b\sin\left(\dfrac{a - b}{a}t\right)$

65. $L = \dfrac{16a}{3}$

67. (a)

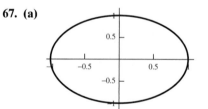

(b)

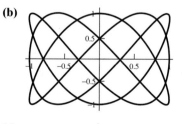

(c)

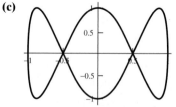

69. a, b, c

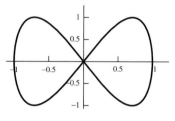

d, e, f

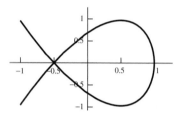

71. (a) $0 \le t \le 2$

(b) $0 \le t \le 1$

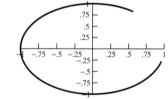

(c) $0.25 \le t \le 2$

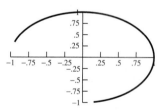

(d) $0 \le t \le 2\pi$

73. (a)

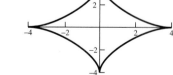

(b)

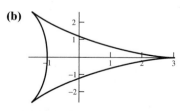

(c)

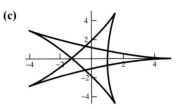

(d)

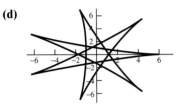

75. Quadrant I for $t > 0$, quadrant II for $-1 < t < 0$, quadrant III for no t, quadrant IV for $t < -1$.

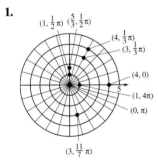

Problem Set 10.5

1.

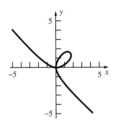

$(1, \frac{1}{2}\pi)$ $(\frac{5}{3}, \frac{1}{2}\pi)$
$(4, \frac{1}{3}\pi)$
$(3, \frac{1}{3}\pi)$
$(4, 0)$
$(1, 4\pi)$
$(0, \pi)$
$(3, \frac{11}{7}\pi)$

3.

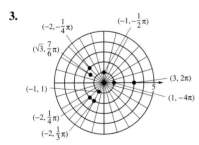

$(-2, -\frac{1}{4}\pi)$ $(-1, -\frac{1}{2}\pi)$
$(\sqrt{3}, \frac{7}{6}\pi)$
$(3, 2\pi)$
$(-1, 1)$
$(1, -4\pi)$
$(-2, \frac{1}{4}\pi)$
$(-2, \frac{1}{3}\pi)$

5.

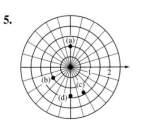

(a) $\left(1, -\frac{3}{2}\pi\right), \left(1, \frac{5}{2}\pi\right), \left(-1, -\frac{1}{2}\pi\right), \left(-1, \frac{3}{2}\pi\right)$

(b) $\left(1, -\frac{3}{4}\pi\right), \left(1, \frac{5}{4}\pi\right), \left(-1, -\frac{7}{4}\pi\right), \left(-1, \frac{9}{4}\pi\right)$

(c) $\left(\sqrt{2}, -\frac{7}{3}\pi\right), \left(\sqrt{2}, \frac{5}{3}\pi\right), \left(-\sqrt{2}, -\frac{4}{3}\pi\right), \left(-\sqrt{2}, \frac{2}{3}\pi\right)$

(d) $\left(\sqrt{2}, -\frac{1}{2}\pi\right), \left(\sqrt{2}, \frac{3}{2}\pi\right), \left(-\sqrt{2}, -\frac{3}{2}\pi\right), \left(-\sqrt{2}, \frac{1}{2}\pi\right)$

7. (a) $(0, 1)$; **(b)** $\left(-\dfrac{\sqrt{2}}{2}, -\dfrac{\sqrt{2}}{2}\right)$; **(c)** $\left(\dfrac{\sqrt{2}}{2}, -\dfrac{\sqrt{6}}{2}\right)$;

(d) $\left(0, -\sqrt{2}\right)$

9. (a) $\left(6, \frac{1}{6}\pi\right)$; **(b)** $\left(4, \frac{5}{6}\pi\right)$; **(c)** $\left(2, \frac{5}{4}\pi\right)$; **(d)** $(0, 0)$

11. $r = \dfrac{2}{3 \sin\theta - \cos\theta}$ **13.** $r = -2\csc\theta$

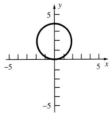

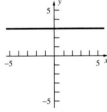

15. $r = 2$

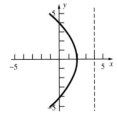

17. $x = 0$ **19.** $x = -3$ **21.** $y = 1$

23. Circle **25.** Line

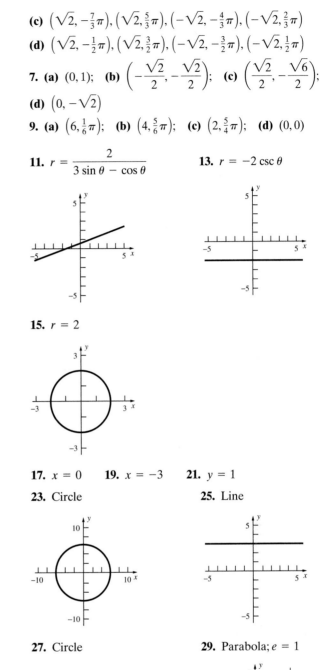

27. Circle **29.** Parabola; $e = 1$

31. Ellipse; $e = \frac{1}{2}$ **33.** Parabola; $e = 1$

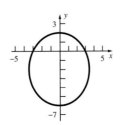

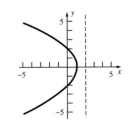

35. Hyperbola; $e = 2$

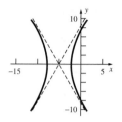

$e = 1.3$

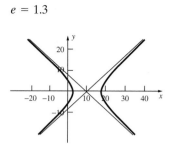

39. $2ed$ **41.** 0.83   **43.** 25 million mi

Problem Set 10.6

45. $e = 0.1$

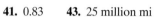

1.

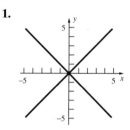

3.

$e = 0.5$

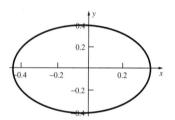

5.

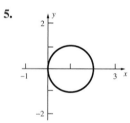

7.

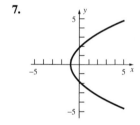

$e = 0.9$

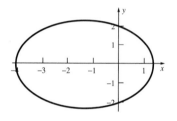

9.

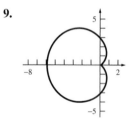

11.

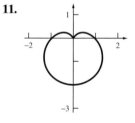

$e = 1$

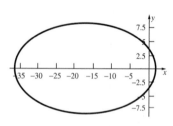

13.

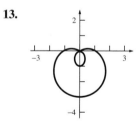

15.

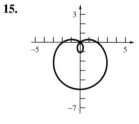

$e = 1.1$

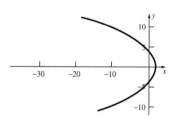

17.

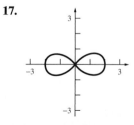

19.

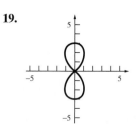

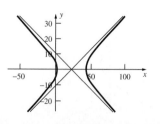

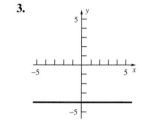

21.

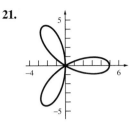

23.

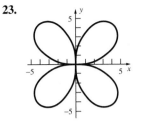

25.

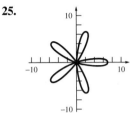

27.

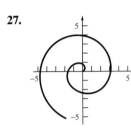

29.

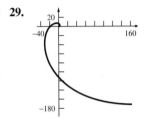

31.

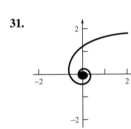

33. $\left(6, \frac{\pi}{3}\right), \left(6, \frac{5\pi}{3}\right)$

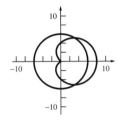

35. $(0,0), \left(\dfrac{3\sqrt{3}}{2}, \dfrac{\pi}{3}\right)$

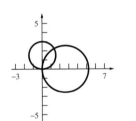

37. $\left(3, \frac{\pi}{6}\right), \left(3, \frac{5\pi}{6}\right), \left(6, \frac{\pi}{2}\right)$

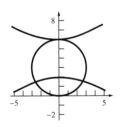

43. (a) $r = \dfrac{45}{\sin \theta}$; **(b)** $r = 6$; **(c)** $r = \pm \dfrac{1}{\sqrt{\cos 2\theta}}$

(d) $r = \pm \dfrac{1}{\sqrt{2 \sin 2\theta}}$; **(e)** $r = \dfrac{2}{\sin \theta - 3 \cos \theta}$;

(f) $r = \dfrac{-2 \sin \theta \pm \sqrt{4 \sin^2 \theta + 6 \cos^2 \theta}}{3 \cos^2 \theta}$;

(g) $r = -\cos \theta + 2 \sin \theta \pm \sqrt{(\cos \theta - 2 \sin \theta)^2 + 25}$;

45. (a) VII **(b)** I **(c)** VIII **(d)** III **(e)** V **(f)** II
(g) VI **(h)** IV

47.

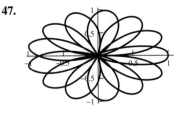

49.

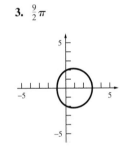

51. (a) The graph for $\phi = 0$ is the graph for $\phi \neq 0$ rotated by ϕ counterclockwise about the pole.
(b) As n increases, the number of "leaves" increases.
53. The spiral will unwind clockwise for $c < 0$. The spiral will unwind counterclockwise for $c > 0$.
55. (a) III; **(b)** IV; **(c)** I; **(d)** II; **(e)** VI; **(f)** V

Problem Set 10.7

1. πa^2

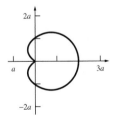

3. $\frac{9}{2}\pi$

5. $\frac{27}{2}\pi$

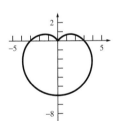

7. $\frac{3}{2}\pi a^2$

9. 9

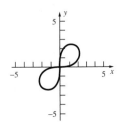

11. $\dfrac{17}{2}\pi - 17 \sin^{-1}\dfrac{3}{4} - \dfrac{9\sqrt{7}}{2}$

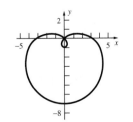

13. $\frac{17}{2}\pi - \frac{17}{2}\cos^{-1}\frac{2}{3} + 3\sqrt{5}$ **15.** 4π

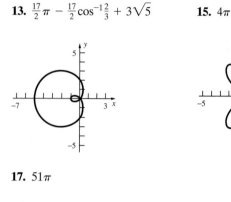

17. 51π

19. $4\sqrt{3} - \frac{4}{3}\pi$ **21.** $9\sqrt{2} - \frac{27}{4}$

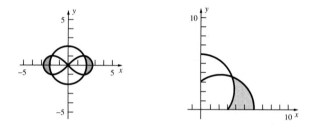

23. (a) $\dfrac{1}{\sqrt{3}}$; (b) -1 (c) $\dfrac{\sqrt{3}}{5}$ (d) $-\dfrac{7}{\sqrt{3}}$

25. $\left(-1, \frac{\pi}{2}\right), \left(3, \frac{3\pi}{2}\right), \left(\frac{1}{2}, \sin^{-1}\frac{1}{4}\right), \left(\frac{1}{2}, \pi - \sin^{-1}\frac{1}{4}\right)$ **27.** $8a$

29. $\frac{1}{2}\pi a^2$ if n is even. $\frac{1}{4}\pi a^2$ if n is odd.

31. (a) $a^2 \tan^{-1}\frac{b}{a} + b^2\left(\frac{\pi}{2} - \tan^{-1}\frac{b}{a}\right) - ab$

33. $a^2\left[(k^2-1)\pi + (2-k^2)\cos^{-1}\left(\frac{k}{2}\right) + \frac{k\sqrt{4-k^2}}{2}\right]$

35. $1.26a$ **37.** 4π; 26.73

39. 63.46

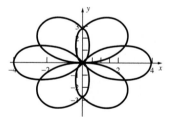

Chapter Review 10.8

Concepts Test

1. False   **3.** False   **5.** True   **7.** True   **9.** False
11. True   **13.** False   **15.** True   **17.** True   **19.** False
21. False   **23.** False   **25.** False   **27.** False   **29.** True
31. False   **33.** True

Sample Test Problems

1. (a) (5); (b) (9); (c) (4); (d) (3); (e) (2); (f) (8);
(g) (8); (h) (1); (i) (7); (j) (6)

3. Ellipse
Foci at $\left(0, \pm\sqrt{5}\right)$
Vertices at $(0, \pm3)$

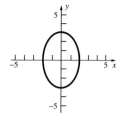

5. Parabola
Focus at $\left(0, -\frac{9}{4}\right)$
Vertex at $(0, 0)$

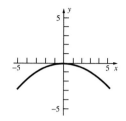

7. Ellipse
Foci at $(\pm4, 0)$
Vertices at $(\pm5, 0)$

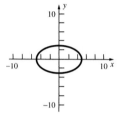

9. Parabola
Focus at $(0, 0)$
Vertex at $\left(0, \frac{5}{4}\right)$

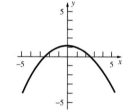

11. $\dfrac{x^2}{16} + \dfrac{y^2}{12} = 1$ **13.** $y^2 = -9x$ **15.** $\dfrac{x^2}{4} - y^2 = 1$

17. $\dfrac{(x-1)^2}{25} + \dfrac{(y-2)^2}{16} = 1$

19. Circle   **21.** Parabola

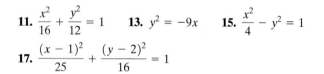

23. $r = \frac{5}{2}$; $s = -\frac{1}{2}$; hyperbola; $4\sqrt{6}$

25. $y = \frac{1}{3}(x-2)$ **27.** $\dfrac{(x+2)^2}{16} + \dfrac{(y-1)^2}{9} = 1$

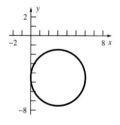

29. $y = -\frac{1}{2}(x-7)$ **31.** $27\sqrt{2}$

33.

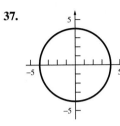

35.

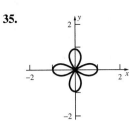

3.

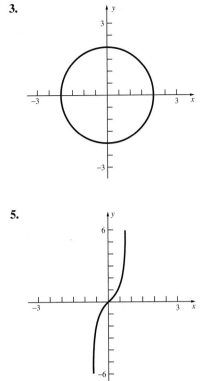

37.

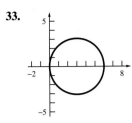

39.

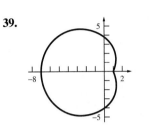

5.

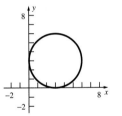

41.

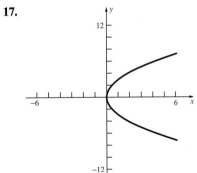

43.

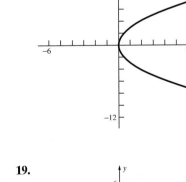

7. $x = h \cdot \cos \theta$
$y = h \cdot \sin \theta$

9. $\dfrac{1}{243}\left[(328)^{3/2} - 8\right] \approx 24.4129$

11. $\pi |a|$ **13.** $(0.8, 2.6)$, distance is $\sqrt{0.8}$

15. (a) $v(t) = 2t - 6; a(t) = 2$ **(b)** $t > 3$

45. $(x - 3)^2 + (y - 3)^2 = 9$

17.

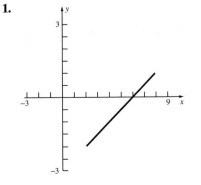

47. -1 **49.** $\dfrac{75}{2}\pi$ **51.** $\dfrac{22}{3}$

53. (a) I;   **(b)** IV;   **(c)** III;   **(d)** II;   **(e)** V

Chapter 11 Review and Preview Problems

1.

19.

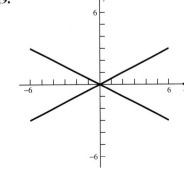

21.

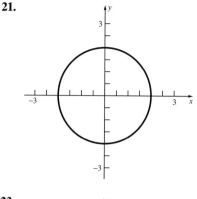

23.

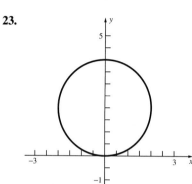

Problem Set 11.1

1. $A(1, 2, 3), B(2, 0, 1), C(-2, 4, 5), D(0, 3, 0), E(-1, -2, -3)$

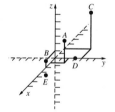

3. $x = 0; x = 0, y = 0$

5. (a) $\sqrt{43}$; **(b)** 5; **(c)** $\sqrt{(e + \pi)^2 + (\pi + 4)^2 + 3}$

9.

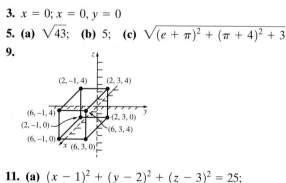

11. (a) $(x - 1)^2 + (y - 2)^2 + (z - 3)^2 = 25$;
(b) $(x + 2)^2 + (y + 3)^2 + (z + 6)^2 = 5$;
(c) $(x - \pi)^2 + (y - e)^2 + (z - \sqrt{2})^2 = \pi$

13. $(6, -7, 4); 10$ **15.** $(\frac{1}{2}, -1, -2); \frac{\sqrt{17}}{2}$

17.   **19.**

21.

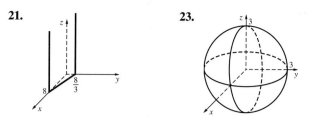

23.

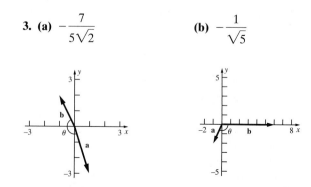

25. $2\sqrt{6}$ **27.** 16.59   **29.** 72   **31.** $2\pi\sqrt{13}$
33. 7.2273   **35.** 34.8394
37. $(x - 1)^2 + (y - 1)^2 + (z - \frac{11}{2})^2 = \frac{53}{4}$
39. $(x - 6)^2 + (y - 6)^2 + (z - 6)^2 = 36$
41. (a) Plane parallel to and 2 units above the xy-plane;
(b) Plane perpendicular to the xy-plane, whose trace in the
xy-plane is the line $x = y$;
(c) Union of the yz-plane $(x = 0)$ and the xz-plane $(y = 0)$;
(d) Union of the three coordinate planes;
(e) Cylinder of radius 2, parallel to the z-axis;
(f) Top half of the sphere with center $(0, 0, 0)$ and radius 3
43. Center $(1, 2, 5)$, radius 4   **45.** $\dfrac{11\pi}{12}$

Problem Set 11.2

1.   **3.**

5. $\frac{1}{2}\mathbf{u} + \frac{1}{2}\mathbf{v}$ **7.** 1
9. $\mathbf{u} + \mathbf{v} = \langle 2, 4 \rangle$; $\mathbf{u} - \mathbf{v} = \langle -4, -4 \rangle$; $\|\mathbf{u}\| = 1$; $\|\mathbf{v}\| = 5$
11. $\mathbf{u} + \mathbf{v} = \langle 10, 14 \rangle$; $\mathbf{u} - \mathbf{v} = \langle 14, 10 \rangle$; $\|\mathbf{u}\| = 12\sqrt{2}$;
$\|\mathbf{v}\| = 2\sqrt{2}$
13. $\mathbf{u} + \mathbf{v} = \langle 2, 4, 0 \rangle$; $\mathbf{u} - \mathbf{v} = \langle -4, -4, 0 \rangle$; $\|\mathbf{u}\| = 1$;
$\|\mathbf{v}\| = 5$
15. $\mathbf{u} + \mathbf{v} = \langle -4, 0, 1 \rangle$; $\mathbf{u} - \mathbf{v} = \langle 6, 0, 1 \rangle$; $\|\mathbf{u}\| = \sqrt{2}$;
$\|\mathbf{v}\| = 5$
17. $\|\mathbf{w}\| \approx 79.34$; S 7.5°W   **19.** 150 N
21. N 2.08° E; 467 mi/h   **23.** 80 mi/h
33. $\alpha + \beta = 143.13°, \beta + \gamma = 126.87°, \alpha + \gamma = 90°$
35. $50/\sqrt{2}$ lbs.

Problem Set 11.3

1. (a) $-12\mathbf{i} + 18\mathbf{j}$; **(b)** -13; **(c)** -28; **(d)** 375;
(e) $-15\sqrt{13}$ **(f)** $13 - \sqrt{13}$

3. (a) $-\dfrac{7}{5\sqrt{2}}$ **(b)** $-\dfrac{1}{\sqrt{5}}$

(c) 0

(d) $-\dfrac{51}{\sqrt{2665}}$

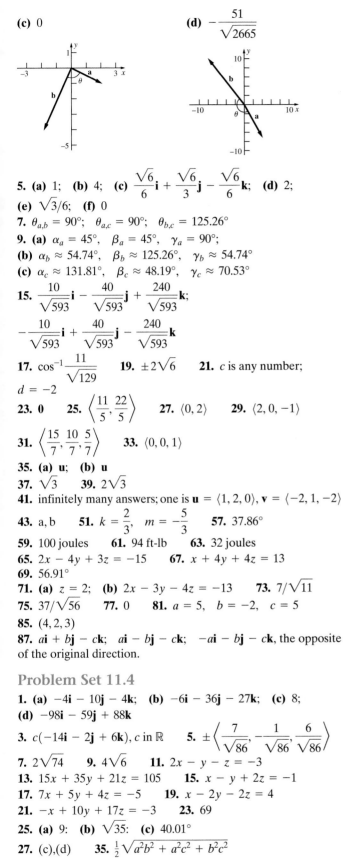

5. (a) 1; **(b)** 4; **(c)** $\dfrac{\sqrt{6}}{6}\mathbf{i} + \dfrac{\sqrt{6}}{3}\mathbf{j} - \dfrac{\sqrt{6}}{6}\mathbf{k}$; **(d)** 2;

(e) $\sqrt{3}/6$; **(f)** 0

7. $\theta_{a,b} = 90°$; $\theta_{a,c} = 90°$; $\theta_{b,c} = 125.26°$

9. (a) $\alpha_a = 45°$, $\beta_a = 45°$, $\gamma_a = 90°$;

(b) $\alpha_b \approx 54.74°$, $\beta_b \approx 125.26°$, $\gamma_b \approx 54.74°$

(c) $\alpha_c \approx 131.81°$, $\beta_c \approx 48.19°$, $\gamma_c \approx 70.53°$

15. $\dfrac{10}{\sqrt{593}}\mathbf{i} - \dfrac{40}{\sqrt{593}}\mathbf{j} + \dfrac{240}{\sqrt{593}}\mathbf{k}$;

$-\dfrac{10}{\sqrt{593}}\mathbf{i} + \dfrac{40}{\sqrt{593}}\mathbf{j} - \dfrac{240}{\sqrt{593}}\mathbf{k}$

17. $\cos^{-1}\dfrac{11}{\sqrt{129}}$ **19.** $\pm2\sqrt{6}$ **21.** c is any number;

$d = -2$

23. 0   **25.** $\left\langle \dfrac{11}{5}, \dfrac{22}{5} \right\rangle$ **27.** $\langle 0, 2 \rangle$ **29.** $\langle 2, 0, -1 \rangle$

31. $\left\langle \dfrac{15}{7}, \dfrac{10}{7}, \dfrac{5}{7} \right\rangle$ **33.** $\langle 0, 0, 1 \rangle$

35. (a) $\mathbf{u}$; **(b)** $\mathbf{u}$

37. $\sqrt{3}$ **39.** $2\sqrt{3}$

41. infinitely many answers; one is $\mathbf{u} = \langle 1, 2, 0 \rangle$, $\mathbf{v} = \langle -2, 1, -2 \rangle$

43. a, b   **51.** $k = \dfrac{2}{3}$, $m = -\dfrac{5}{3}$ **57.** 37.86°

59. 100 joules   **61.** 94 ft-lb   **63.** 32 joules

65. $2x - 4y + 3z = -15$ **67.** $x + 4y + 4z = 13$

69. 56.91°

71. (a) $z = 2$; **(b)** $2x - 3y - 4z = -13$ **73.** $7/\sqrt{11}$

75. $37/\sqrt{56}$ **77.** 0   **81.** $a = 5$, $b = -2$, $c = 5$

85. $(4, 2, 3)$

87. $a\mathbf{i} + b\mathbf{j} - c\mathbf{k}$; $a\mathbf{i} - b\mathbf{j} - c\mathbf{k}$; $-a\mathbf{i} - b\mathbf{j} - c\mathbf{k}$, the opposite of the original direction.

Problem Set 11.4

1. (a) $-4\mathbf{i} - 10\mathbf{j} - 4\mathbf{k}$; **(b)** $-6\mathbf{i} - 36\mathbf{j} - 27\mathbf{k}$; **(c)** 8;

(d) $-98\mathbf{i} - 59\mathbf{j} + 88\mathbf{k}$

3. $c(-14\mathbf{i} - 2\mathbf{j} + 6\mathbf{k})$, c in $\mathbb{R}$ **5.** $\pm\left\langle \dfrac{7}{\sqrt{86}}, -\dfrac{1}{\sqrt{86}}, \dfrac{6}{\sqrt{86}} \right\rangle$

7. $2\sqrt{74}$ **9.** $4\sqrt{6}$ **11.** $2x - y - z = -3$

13. $15x + 35y + 21z = 105$ **15.** $x - y + 2z = -1$

17. $7x + 5y + 4z = -5$ **19.** $x - 2y - 2z = 4$

21. $-x + 10y + 17z = -3$ **23.** 69

25. (a) 9: **(b)** $\sqrt{35}$: **(c)** 40.01°

27. (c),(d)   **35.** $\dfrac{1}{2}\sqrt{a^2b^2 + a^2c^2 + b^2c^2}$

Problem Set 11.5

1. $2\mathbf{i} - \mathbf{j}$ **3.** $\dfrac{1}{2}\mathbf{i} - 4\mathbf{j}$ **5.** $\mathbf{i}$ **7.** Does not exist

9. (a) $\{t \in \mathbb{R} : t \le 3\}$; **(b)** $\{t \in \mathbb{R} : t \le 20\}$

(c) $\{t \in \mathbb{R} : -3 \le t \le 3\}$

11. (a) $\{t \in \mathbb{R} : t \le 3\}$;   **(b)** $\{t \in \mathbb{R} : t < 20, t^2 \text{ not an integer}\}$

(c) $\{t \in \mathbb{R} : -3 \le t \le 3\}$

13. (a) $9(3t + 4)^2\mathbf{i} + 2te^{t^2}\mathbf{j}$; $54(3t + 4)\mathbf{i} + 2(2t^2 + 1)e^{t^2}\mathbf{j}$;

(b) $\sin 2t\mathbf{i} - 3\sin 3t\mathbf{j} + 2t\mathbf{k}$; $2\cos 2t\mathbf{i} - 9\cos 3t\mathbf{j} + 2\mathbf{k}$

15. $-2e^{-2t} - \dfrac{4}{t^3} + \dfrac{4}{t^3}\ln t^2$

17. $-\dfrac{e^{-3t}}{2}\left(\dfrac{6t - 7}{\sqrt{t - 1}} \right)\mathbf{i} + e^{-3t}\left(\dfrac{2}{t} - 3\ln(2t^2) \right)\mathbf{j}$

19. $\mathbf{v}(1) = 4\mathbf{i} + 10\mathbf{j} + 2\mathbf{k}$; $\mathbf{a}(1) = 10\mathbf{j}$; $s(1) = 2\sqrt{30}$

21. $\mathbf{v}(2) = -\dfrac{1}{4}\mathbf{i} - \dfrac{4}{9}\mathbf{j} + 80\mathbf{k}$; $\mathbf{a}(2) = \dfrac{1}{4}\mathbf{i} + \dfrac{26}{27}\mathbf{j} + 160\mathbf{k}$;

$s(2) = \dfrac{\sqrt{8{,}294{,}737}}{36}$

23. $\mathbf{v}(2) = 4\mathbf{j} + \dfrac{2^{2/3}}{3}\mathbf{k}$; $\mathbf{a}(2) = 4\mathbf{j} - \dfrac{1}{9\sqrt[3]{2}}\mathbf{k}$;

$s(2) = \sqrt{16 + \dfrac{2^{4/3}}{9}}$

25. $\mathbf{v}(\pi) = -\mathbf{j} + \mathbf{k}$; $\mathbf{a}(\pi) = \mathbf{i}$, $s(\pi) = \sqrt{2}$

27. $\mathbf{v}\left(\dfrac{\pi}{4}\right) = 2\mathbf{i} + 3e^{\pi/4}\mathbf{j}$; $\mathbf{a}\left(\dfrac{\pi}{4}\right) = 4\mathbf{i} + 3e^{\pi/4}\mathbf{j} + 16\mathbf{k}$;

$s\left(\dfrac{\pi}{4}\right) = \sqrt{4 + 9e^{\pi/2}}$

29. $\mathbf{v}(2) = 2\pi\mathbf{i} + \mathbf{j} - e^{-2}\mathbf{k}$; $\mathbf{a}(2) = 2\pi\mathbf{i} - 2\pi^2\mathbf{j} + e^{-2}\mathbf{k}$;

$s(2) = \sqrt{4\pi^2 + 1 + e^{-4}}$

33. $2\sqrt{2}$ **35.** 144   **37.** $\sqrt{41}$

39. $-6t\sin(3t^2 - 4)\mathbf{i} + 18te^{9t^2 - 12}\mathbf{j}$

41. $(e - 1)\mathbf{i} + (1 - e^{-1})\mathbf{j}$

43. $\mathbf{r}(t) = 5\cos(6t)\mathbf{i} + 5\sin(6t)\mathbf{j}$;

$\mathbf{v}(t) = -30\sin(6t)\mathbf{i} + 30\cos(6t)\mathbf{j}$;

$\|\mathbf{v}(t)\| = 30$; $\mathbf{a}(t) = -180\cos(6t)\mathbf{i} - 180\sin(6t)\mathbf{j}$

45. (b) $R_p = 10R_m$; $t = \dfrac{\pi}{9}$

47. (a) Winding upward around the right circular cylinder $x = \sin t$, $y = \cos t$, as t increases.

(b) Same as part (a), but winding much faster by a factor of $3t^2$.

(c) With standard orientation of the axes, the motion is winding to the right around the right circular cylinder $x = \sin t$, $z = \cos t$.

(d) Spiraling upward, with increasing radius, along the spiral $x = t\sin t$, $y = t\cos t$.

(e) Spiraling upward, with decreasing radius, along the spiral

$x = \dfrac{1}{t^2}\sin t$, $y = \dfrac{1}{t^2}\cos t$.

(f) Spiraling to the right, with increasing radius along the spiral $x = t^2\sin(\ln t)$, $z = t^2\cos(\ln t)$.

Problem Set 11.6

1. $x = 1 + 3t$, $y = -2 + 7t$, $z = 3 + 3t$

3. $x = 4 + t$, $y = 2$, $z = 3 - 2t$

5. $x = 4 + 3t$, $y = 5 + 2t$, $z = 6 + t$; $\dfrac{x - 4}{3} = \dfrac{y - 5}{2} = \dfrac{z - 6}{1}$

7. $x = 1 + t$, $y = 1 + 10t$, $z = 1 + 100t$;

$\dfrac{x - 1}{1} = \dfrac{y - 1}{10} = \dfrac{z - 1}{100}$

9. $\dfrac{x - 4}{27} = \dfrac{y + 5}{-50} = \dfrac{z}{-6}$ **11.** $\dfrac{x + 8}{10} = \dfrac{y}{2} = \dfrac{z + \frac{21}{2}}{9}$

13. $\dfrac{x - 4}{1} = \dfrac{y}{-5} = \dfrac{z - 6}{2}$ **15.** $x = 5t$, $y = -3t$, $z = 4$

17. $x + y + 6z = 11$ **19.** $3x - 2y = 5$

21. (b) $2x + y - z = 7$; **(c)** $(-1, 2, -1)$; **(d)** $\sqrt{6}$

23. $\dfrac{x - 1}{-\sqrt{3}} = \dfrac{y - 3\sqrt{3}}{3} = \dfrac{z - \frac{\pi}{3}}{1}$ **25.** $3x - 4y + 5z = -22$

27. $\left(-\dfrac{1}{2}, 0, \dfrac{37}{4\sqrt{7}}\right)$ **29.** $\left(\dfrac{5}{2}, 1, 0\right)$

31. (a) $\dfrac{8\sqrt{2}}{3}$; **(b)** $\dfrac{3\sqrt{26}}{7}$

Problem Set 11.7

1. $\mathbf{v}(1) = \langle 1, 2 \rangle$; $\mathbf{a}(1) = \langle 0, 2 \rangle$

$\mathbf{T}(1) = \left\langle \dfrac{1}{\sqrt{5}}, \dfrac{2}{\sqrt{5}} \right\rangle$; $\kappa = \dfrac{2}{5^{3/2}}$

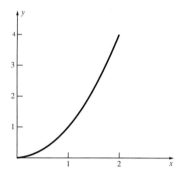

3. $\mathbf{v}(\pi) = \langle 1, 0, -2 \rangle$; $\mathbf{a}(\pi) = \langle 0, 2, 0 \rangle$

$\mathbf{T}(\pi) = \left\langle \dfrac{1}{\sqrt{5}}, 0, -\dfrac{2}{\sqrt{5}} \right\rangle$; $\kappa = \dfrac{2}{5}$

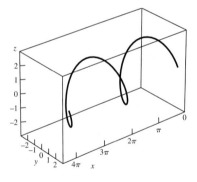

5. $\mathbf{v}(\pi) = \left\langle \dfrac{\pi}{4}, 0, -5 \right\rangle$; $\mathbf{a}(\pi) = \left\langle \dfrac{1}{4}, 5, 0 \right\rangle$

$\mathbf{T}(\pi) = \left\langle \dfrac{\pi}{\sqrt{400 + \pi^2}}, 0, -\dfrac{20}{\sqrt{400 + \pi^2}} \right\rangle$; $\kappa \approx 0.195422$

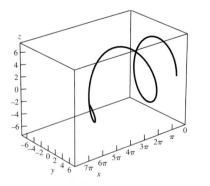

7. $\dfrac{1}{\sqrt{2}}\mathbf{i} + \dfrac{1}{\sqrt{2}}\mathbf{j}; \dfrac{1}{4\sqrt{2}}$ **9.** $-\dfrac{3}{5}\mathbf{i} + \dfrac{4}{5}\mathbf{j}; \dfrac{24\sqrt{2}}{125}$

11. $-\dfrac{2}{\sqrt{13}}\mathbf{i} - \dfrac{3}{\sqrt{13}}\mathbf{j}; \dfrac{6}{13\sqrt{13}}$ **13.** $-\dfrac{1}{\sqrt{2}}\mathbf{i} + \dfrac{1}{\sqrt{2}}\mathbf{j}; \dfrac{1}{\sqrt{2}}$

15. $\kappa = \dfrac{4}{17\sqrt{17}}; R = \dfrac{17\sqrt{17}}{4}$ **17.** $\kappa = \dfrac{2}{3\sqrt{3}}; R = \dfrac{3\sqrt{3}}{2}$

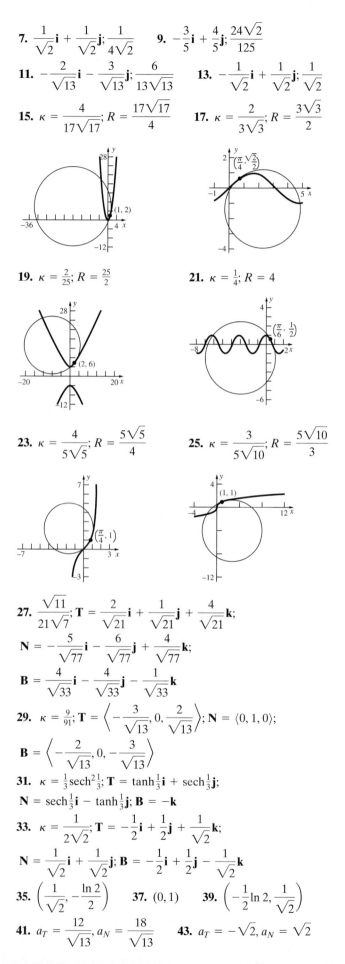

19. $\kappa = \frac{2}{25}; R = \frac{25}{2}$ **21.** $\kappa = \frac{1}{4}; R = 4$

23. $\kappa = \dfrac{4}{5\sqrt{5}}; R = \dfrac{5\sqrt{5}}{4}$ **25.** $\kappa = \dfrac{3}{5\sqrt{10}}; R = \dfrac{5\sqrt{10}}{3}$

27. $\dfrac{\sqrt{11}}{21\sqrt{7}}; \mathbf{T} = \dfrac{2}{\sqrt{21}}\mathbf{i} + \dfrac{1}{\sqrt{21}}\mathbf{j} + \dfrac{4}{\sqrt{21}}\mathbf{k};$

$\mathbf{N} = -\dfrac{5}{\sqrt{77}}\mathbf{i} - \dfrac{6}{\sqrt{77}}\mathbf{j} + \dfrac{4}{\sqrt{77}}\mathbf{k};$

$\mathbf{B} = \dfrac{4}{\sqrt{33}}\mathbf{i} - \dfrac{4}{\sqrt{33}}\mathbf{j} - \dfrac{1}{\sqrt{33}}\mathbf{k}$

29. $\kappa = \dfrac{9}{91}; \mathbf{T} = \left\langle -\dfrac{3}{\sqrt{13}}, 0, \dfrac{2}{\sqrt{13}} \right\rangle; \mathbf{N} = \langle 0, 1, 0 \rangle;$

$\mathbf{B} = \left\langle -\dfrac{2}{\sqrt{13}}, 0, -\dfrac{3}{\sqrt{13}} \right\rangle$

31. $\kappa = \frac{1}{3}\operatorname{sech}^2\frac{1}{3}; \mathbf{T} = \tanh\frac{1}{3}\mathbf{i} + \operatorname{sech}\frac{1}{3}\mathbf{j};$

$\mathbf{N} = \operatorname{sech}\frac{1}{3}\mathbf{i} - \tanh\frac{1}{3}\mathbf{j}; \mathbf{B} = -\mathbf{k}$

33. $\kappa = \dfrac{1}{2\sqrt{2}}; \mathbf{T} = -\dfrac{1}{2}\mathbf{i} + \dfrac{1}{2}\mathbf{j} + \dfrac{1}{\sqrt{2}}\mathbf{k};$

$\mathbf{N} = \dfrac{1}{\sqrt{2}}\mathbf{i} + \dfrac{1}{\sqrt{2}}\mathbf{j}; \mathbf{B} = -\dfrac{1}{2}\mathbf{i} + \dfrac{1}{2}\mathbf{j} - \dfrac{1}{\sqrt{2}}\mathbf{k}$

35. $\left(\dfrac{1}{\sqrt{2}}, -\dfrac{\ln 2}{2}\right)$ **37.** $(0, 1)$ **39.** $\left(-\dfrac{1}{2}\ln 2, \dfrac{1}{\sqrt{2}}\right)$

41. $a_T = \dfrac{12}{\sqrt{13}}, a_N = \dfrac{18}{\sqrt{13}}$ **43.** $a_T = -\sqrt{2}, a_N = \sqrt{2}$

45. $a_T = \dfrac{40a}{3\sqrt{41}}, a_N = \dfrac{3a}{\sqrt{41}}$

47. $a_T(1) = \dfrac{4}{\sqrt{14}}; \quad a_N(1) = 2\sqrt{\dfrac{5}{7}}$

49. $a_T(0) = 0; \quad a_N(0) = \sqrt{2}$

51. $a_T(3) = 36\sqrt{\dfrac{3}{55}}; \quad a_N(3) = 6\sqrt{\dfrac{2}{55}}$

53. $(0,0); (1,0), (-1,0)$

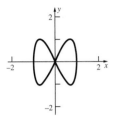

55. The speed is constant; the curvature is zero.
57. $(\cos 5)\mathbf{i} - (\sin 5)\mathbf{j} + 7\mathbf{k}$ **59.** $5\mathbf{T} + 5\mathbf{N}; -\mathbf{i} - 7\mathbf{j}$
61. 72 ft/s   **67.** $P_5(x) = 10x^3 - 15x^4 + 6x^5$ **71.** $\frac{3}{4}$

73. $\dfrac{3}{8\sqrt{2}}$ **75.** $\frac{3}{16}$

79. max ≈ 0.7606; min ≈ 0.1248

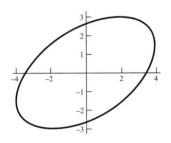

85. $(6,0,8); 8\sqrt{9\pi^2 + 1}$

Problem Set 11.8

1. Elliptic cylinder   **3.** Plane

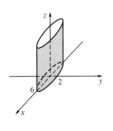

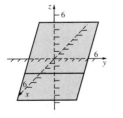

5. Circular cylinder   **7.** Ellipsoid

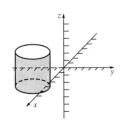

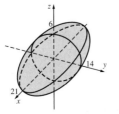

9. Elliptic paraboloid   **11.** Cylinder

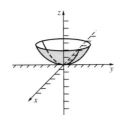

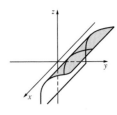

13. Hyperbolic paraboloid   **15.** Elliptic paraboloid

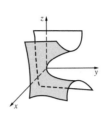

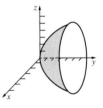

17. Plane   **19.** Hemisphere

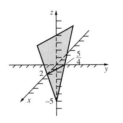

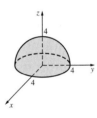

21. (a) Replacing x by $-x$ results in an equivalent equation.
(b) Replacing x by $-x$ and y by $-y$ results in an equivalent equation.
(c) Replacing x by $-x$, y by $-y$, and z by $-z$ results in an equivalent equation.
23. All central ellipsoids are symmetric with respect to
(a) the origin, (b) the x-axis, and the (c) xy-plane.
25. All central hyperboloids of two sheets are symmetric with respect to (a) the origin, (b) the z-axis, and (c) the yz-plane.
27. $y = 2x^2 + 2z^2$ **29.** $4x^2 + 3y^2 + 4z^2 = 12$

31. $\left(0, \pm 2\sqrt{5}, 4\right)$ **33.** $\dfrac{\pi ab(c^2 - h^2)}{c^2}$

35. Major diameter 4; minor diameter $2\sqrt{2}$
37. $x^2 + 9y^2 - 9z^2 = 0$

Problem Set 11.9

1. Cylindrical to Spherical: $\rho = \sqrt{r^2 + z^2}, \cos\phi = \dfrac{z}{\sqrt{r^2 + z^2}}$,
$\theta = \theta$
Spherical to Cylindrical: $r = \rho\sin\phi, z = \rho\cos\phi, \theta = \theta$
3. (a) $\left(3\sqrt{3}, 3, -2\right)$; **(b)** $\left(-2, -2\sqrt{3}, -8\right)$
5. (a) $\left(4\sqrt{2}, \frac{5\pi}{3}, \frac{\pi}{4}\right)$; **(b)** $\left(4, \frac{3\pi}{4}, \frac{\pi}{6}\right)$

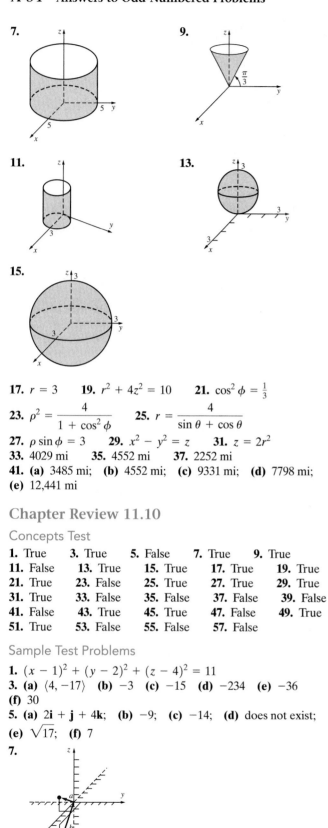

7.

9.

11.

13.

15.

17. $r = 3$ **19.** $r^2 + 4z^2 = 10$ **21.** $\cos^2 \phi = \frac{1}{3}$

23. $\rho^2 = \dfrac{4}{1 + \cos^2 \phi}$ **25.** $r = \dfrac{4}{\sin \theta + \cos \theta}$

27. $\rho \sin \phi = 3$ **29.** $x^2 - y^2 = z$ **31.** $z = 2r^2$

33. 4029 mi   **35.** 4552 mi   **37.** 2252 mi

41. (a) 3485 mi;   **(b)** 4552 mi;   **(c)** 9331 mi;   **(d)** 7798 mi;
(e) 12,441 mi

Chapter Review 11.10

Concepts Test

1. True   **3.** True   **5.** False   **7.** True   **9.** True
11. False   **13.** True   **15.** True   **17.** True   **19.** True
21. True   **23.** False   **25.** True   **27.** True   **29.** True
31. True   **33.** False   **35.** False   **37.** False   **39.** False
41. False   **43.** True   **45.** True   **47.** False   **49.** True
51. True   **53.** False   **55.** False   **57.** False

Sample Test Problems

1. $(x - 1)^2 + (y - 2)^2 + (z - 4)^2 = 11$
3. (a) $\langle 4, -17 \rangle$ **(b)** -3 **(c)** -15 **(d)** -234 **(e)** -36
(f) 30
5. (a) $2\mathbf{i} + \mathbf{j} + 4\mathbf{k}$;   **(b)** -9;   **(c)** -14;   **(d)** does not exist;
(e) $\sqrt{17}$;   **(f)** 7
7.

(a) $3; \sqrt{35}$;   **(b)** $\dfrac{2}{3}, -\dfrac{1}{3}, \dfrac{2}{3}; \dfrac{5}{\sqrt{35}}, \dfrac{1}{\sqrt{35}}, -\dfrac{3}{\sqrt{35}}$;

(c) $\frac{2}{3}\mathbf{i} - \frac{1}{3}\mathbf{j} + \frac{2}{3}\mathbf{k}$;   **(d)** $\cos^{-1}\dfrac{1}{\sqrt{35}}$

9. $c\langle 10, -11, -3 \rangle$, c in $\mathbb{R}$
11. (a) $y = 7$;   **(b)** $x = -5$;   **(c)** $z = -2$;

(d) $3x - 4y + z = -45$
13. 1   **15.** $x = -2 + 8t, y = 1 + t, z = 5 - 8t$
17. $x = 2t, y = 25 + t, z = 16$
19. $\mathbf{r}(t) = \langle 2, -2, 1 \rangle + t\langle 5, -4, -3 \rangle$

21. Tangent line: $\dfrac{x - 2}{1} = \dfrac{y - 2}{2} = \dfrac{z - \frac{8}{3}}{4}$
Normal Plane: $3x + 6y + 12z = 50$
23. $\sqrt{3}(e^5 - e)$ **25.** N 12.22°W; 409.27 mi/h

27. (a) $\left\langle \dfrac{1}{t}, -6t \right\rangle; \left\langle -\dfrac{1}{t^2}, -6 \right\rangle$;
(b) $\langle \cos t, -2 \sin 2t \rangle; \langle -\sin t, -4 \cos 2t \rangle$;
(c) $\langle \sec^2 t, -4t^3 \rangle; \langle 2 \sec^2 t \tan t, -12t^2 \rangle$;

29. $a_T = \dfrac{22}{\sqrt{14}}; a_N = \dfrac{2\sqrt{19}}{\sqrt{14}}$

31. Sphere   **33.** Circular paraboloid

35. Plane   **37.** Ellipsoid

39. (a) $r = 3$;   **(b)** $r^2 = \dfrac{16}{1 + 3 \sin^2 \theta}$;   **(c)** $r^2 = 9z$;
(d) $r^2 + 4z^2 = 10$
41. (a) $\rho = 2$;   **(b)** $\cos^2 \phi = \frac{1}{2}$ (Other forms are possible.);
(c) $\rho^2 = \dfrac{1}{2 \sin^2 \phi \cos^2 \theta - 1}$;   **(d)** $r = \cot \phi \csc \phi$
43. 1.25

Chapter 12 Review and Preview Problems

1. $x^2 + y^2 + z^2 = 64$ **3.** $z = x^2 + 4y^2$

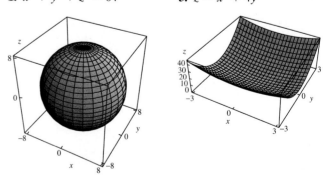

5. (a) $6x^2$;   **(b)** $15x^2$;   **(c)** $3kx^2$;   **(d)** $3ax^2$
7. (a) $2 \cos 2a$;   **(b)** $17 \cos 17a$;   **(c)** $t \cos ta$;   **(d)** $s \cos sa$
9. Continuous and differentiable at $x = 2$
11. Continuous at $x = 4$; not differentiable at $x = 4$

13. maximum value of f on $[0, 4]$ is 5; minimum value is -15

15. $S(r) = 2\pi r^2 + \dfrac{16}{r}$

Problem Set 12.1

1. (a) 5; **(b)** 0; **(c)** 6; **(d)** $a^6 + a^2$; **(e)** $2x^2$;
(f) $(2, -4)$ is not in the domain of f. Domain is set of all (x, y) such that $y > 0$.

3. (a) 0; **(b)** 2; **(c)** 16; **(d)** -4.2469;

5. t^2

7.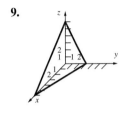

9.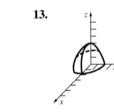

11.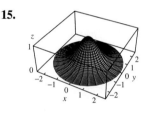

13.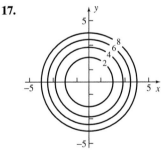

15.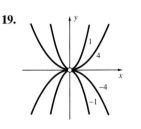

17.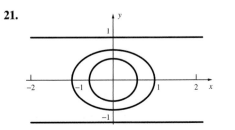

19.

21.

23.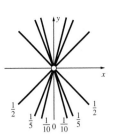

25. (a) San Francisco **(b)** northwest: southeast
(c) southwest or northeast

27. The set of all points on and outside the sphere $x^2 + y^2 + z^2 = 16$.

29. The set of all points on and inside the ellipsoid $x^2/9 + y^2/16 + z^2/1 = 1$.

31. All points in $\mathbb{R}^3$ except the origin $(0, 0, 0)$.

33. The set of all spheres with centers at the origin.

35. A set of hyperboloids of revolution about the z-axis when $k = 0$. When $k \neq 0$, the level surface is an elliptic cone.

37. A set of hyperbolic cylinders parallel to the z-axis when $k \neq 0$. When $k = 0$, the level surface is a pair of planes.

39. (a) All points in $\mathbb{R}^4$ except the origin $(0, 0, 0, 0)$.
(b) All points in $\mathbb{R}^n$.
(c) All points in $\mathbb{R}^n$ that satisfy $x_1^2 + x_2^2 + \cdots + x_n^2 \leq 1$.

41. (a) gentle climb, steep climb; **(b)** 6490 ft, 3060 ft

43.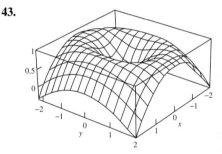

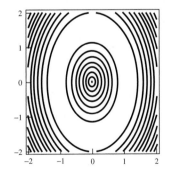

45.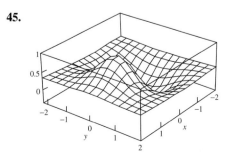

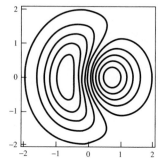

Problem Set 12.2

1. $f_x(x, y) = 8(2x - y)^3; f_y(x, y) = -4(2x - y)^3$

3. $f_x(x, y) = (x^2 + y^2)/(x^2y); f_y(x, y) = -(x^2 + y^2)/(xy^2)$

5. $f_x(x, y) = e^y \cos x; f_y(x, y) = e^y \sin x$

7. $f_x(x, y) = x(x^2 - y^2)^{-1/2}; f_y(x, y) = -y(x^2 - y^2)^{-1/2}$

9. $g_x(x, y) = -ye^{-xy}; g_y(x, y) = -xe^{-xy}$

11. $f_x(x, y) = 4/[1 + (4x - 7y)^2];$
$f_y(x, y) = -7/[1 + (4x - 7y)^2]$

13. $f_x(x, y) = -2xy \sin(x^2 + y^2);$
$f_y(x, y) = -2y^2 \sin(x^2 + y^2) + \cos(x^2 + y^2)$

15. $F_x(x, y) = 2 \cos x \cos y; F_y(x, y) = -2 \sin x \sin y$

17. $f_{xy}(x, y) = 12xy^2 - 15x^2y^4 = f_{yx}(x, y)$

19. $f_{xy}(x, y) = -6e^{2x} \sin y = f_{yx}(x, y)$

21. $F_x(3, -2) = \frac{1}{9}; F_y(3, -2) = -\frac{1}{2}$

23. $f_x(\sqrt{5}, -2) = -\frac{4}{21}; f_y(\sqrt{5}, -2) = -4\sqrt{5}/21$

25. 1   **27.** 3   **29.** 120π **31.** $k/100$

33. $\partial^2 f/\partial x^2 = 6xy; \partial^2 f/\partial y^2 = -6xy$

35. $180x^4y^2 - 12x^2$

37. **(a)** $\partial^3 f/\partial y^3$;   **(b)** $\partial^3 f/\partial y \, \partial x^2$;   **(c)** $\partial^4 f/\partial y^3 \, \partial x$

39. **(a)** $6xy - yz$;   **(b)** 8;   **(c)** $6x - z$

41. $-yze^{-xyz} - y(xy - z^2)^{-1}$ **43.** $(1, 0, 29)$

45. $\{(x, y): x < \frac{1}{2}, y > \frac{1}{2}, y < x + \frac{1}{2}\}$
$\cup \{(x, y): x > \frac{1}{2}, y < \frac{1}{2}, x < y + \frac{1}{2}\}, \{z: 0 < z \leq \sqrt{3}/36\}$

47. **(a)** -4;   **(b)** $\frac{2}{3}$;   **(c)** $\frac{2}{5}$;   **(d)** $\frac{8}{3}$

49. **(a)** $f_y(x, y, z) = \lim\limits_{\Delta y \to 0} \dfrac{f(x, y + \Delta y, z) - f(x, y, z)}{\Delta y}$

(b) $f_z(x, y, z) = \lim\limits_{\Delta z \to 0} \dfrac{f(x, y, z + \Delta z) - f(x, y, z)}{\Delta z}$

(c) $G_x(w, x, y, z) = \lim\limits_{\Delta x \to 0} \dfrac{G(w, x + \Delta x, y, z) - G(w, x, y, z)}{\Delta x}$

(d) $\dfrac{\partial}{\partial z} \lambda(x, y, z, t) = \lim\limits_{\Delta z \to 0} \dfrac{\lambda(x, y, z + \Delta z, t) - \lambda(x, y, z, t)}{\Delta z}$

(e) $\dfrac{\partial}{\partial b_2} S(b_0, b_1, b_2, \ldots, b_n)$

$= \lim\limits_{\Delta b_2 \to 0} \left(\dfrac{S(b_0, b_1, b_2 + \Delta b_2, \ldots, b_n) - S(b_0, b_1, b_2, \ldots, b_n)}{\Delta b_2} \right)$

Problem Set 12.3

1. -18 **3.** $2 - \frac{1}{2}\sqrt{3}$ **5.** $-\frac{5}{2}$;   **7.** 1;

9. Does not exist;   **11.** 0   **13.** 0   **15.** 0

17. Entire plane   **19.** $\{(x, y): x^2 + y^2 < 1\}$

21. $\{(x, y): y \neq x^2\}$ **23.** $\{(x, y): y \leq x + 1\}$

25. All (x, y, z), except $(0, 0, 0)$.

27. The boundary consists of the line segments that form the outer edges of the given rectangle; the set is closed.

29. Boundary: $\{(x, y): x^2 + y^2 = 1\} \cup \{(0, 0)\}$; the set is neither open nor closed.

31. Boundary: $\{(x, y): y = \sin(1/x), x > 0\} \cup \{(x, y): x = 0, y \leq 1\}$; the set is open.

33. $g(x) = 2x$

35. $\lim\limits_{x \to 0} f(x, 0) = \lim\limits_{x \to 0} [0/(x^2 + 0)] = 0$;

$\lim\limits_{x \to 0} f(x, x) = \lim\limits_{x \to 0} [x^2/(x^2 + x^2)] = \frac{1}{2}$

37. **(a)** $\lim\limits_{x \to 0} f(x, mx) = \lim\limits_{x \to 0} mx^3/(x^4 + m^2x^2)$

$= \lim\limits_{x \to 0} mx/(x^2 + m^2) = 0$;

(b) $\lim\limits_{x \to 0} f(x, x^2) = \lim\limits_{x \to 0} x^4/(x^4 + x^4) = \frac{1}{2}$;

(c) $\lim\limits_{(x, y) \to (0, 0)} f(x, y)$ does not exist.

39. **(a)** $\{(x, y, z): x^2 + y^2 = 1, 1 \leq z \leq 2\}$;

(b) $\{(x, y, z): x^2 + y^2 = 1, z = 1\}$;   **(c)** $\{(x, y, z): z = 1\}$;

(d) empty set.

41. **(a)** $\{(x, y): x > 0, y = 0\}$;

(b) $\{(u, v, x, y): \langle x, y \rangle = k\langle u, v \rangle, k > 0, \langle u, v \rangle \neq \langle 0, 0 \rangle\}$

43.

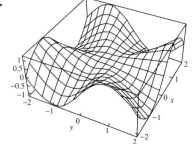

45.

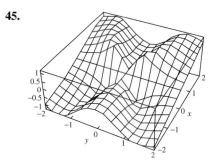

Problem Set 12.4

1. $(2xy + 3y)\mathbf{i} + (x^2 + 3x)\mathbf{j}$ **3.** $e^{xy}(1 + xy)\mathbf{i} + x^2e^{xy}\mathbf{j}$

5. $(x + y)^{-2}[(x^2y + 2xy^2)\mathbf{i} + x^3\mathbf{j}]$

7. $(x^2 + y^2 + z^2)^{-1/2}(x\mathbf{i} + y\mathbf{j} + z\mathbf{k})$

9. $xe^{x-z}[(yx + 2y)\mathbf{i} + x\mathbf{j} - xy\mathbf{k}]$

11. $\langle -21, 16 \rangle, z = -21x + 16y - 60$

13. $\langle 0, -2\pi \rangle, z = -2\pi y + \pi - 1$

15. $w = 7x - 8y - 2z + 3$ **19.** $(1, 2)$

21. **(a)** $x = 2 + t, y = 1, z = 9 + 12t$

(b) $x = 2, y = 1 + 10t, z = 9 + 10t$

(c) $x = 2 - t, y = 1 - t, z = 9 - 22t$

23. $z = -5x + 5y$ **25.** $\mathbf{c} = \langle 1, \frac{1}{2} \rangle$

29.

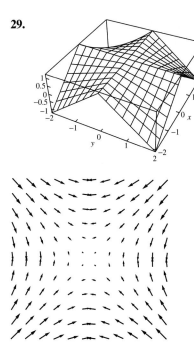

(a) The gradient points in the direction of greatest increase of the function.

(b) No.

Problem Set 12.5

1. $\frac{8}{5}$　　**3.** $3\sqrt{2}/2$　　**5.** $(\sqrt{2} + \sqrt{6})/4$　　**7.** $\frac{52}{3}$

9. $\frac{12}{13}\mathbf{i} - \frac{5}{13}\mathbf{j}$; 13　　**11.** $-\frac{4}{\sqrt{21}}\mathbf{i} + \frac{2}{\sqrt{21}}\mathbf{j} - \frac{1}{\sqrt{21}}\mathbf{k}$; $\sqrt{21}$

13. $(1/\sqrt{5})(-\mathbf{i} + 2\mathbf{j})$

15. $\nabla f(\mathbf{p}) = -4\mathbf{i} + \mathbf{j}$ is perpendicular to the tangent line at $\mathbf{p}$.

17. $\frac{2}{3}$

19. (a) $(0, 0, 0)$;　(b) $-\mathbf{i} + \mathbf{j} - \mathbf{k}$;　(c) yes.

21. $(x^2 + y^2 + z^2)^{-1/2} \cos\sqrt{x^2 + y^2 + z^2} \langle x, y, z \rangle$

23. N 63.43°E　　**25.** Descend: $-300\sqrt{2}e^{-3}$　　**27.** $x = -2y^2$

29. (a) $-10/\sqrt{2 + \pi^2}$ deg/m;　(b) -10 deg/s

31. (a) $(100, 120)$;　(b) $(190, 25)$;　(c) $-\frac{1}{3}, 0, \frac{2}{5}$

33. Leave at about $(-0.1, -5)$.　　**35.** Leave at about $(3, 5)$.

Problem Set 12.6

1. $12t^{11}$　　**3.** $e^{3t}(3\sin 2t + 2\cos 2t) + e^{2t}(3\cos 3t + 2\sin 3t)$

5. $7t^6 \cos(t^7)$　　**7.** $2s^3t - 3s^2t^2$

9. $2(s^2 \sin t \cos t + t \sin^2 s)\exp(s^2 \sin^2 t + t^2 \sin^2 s)$

11. $s^4t(1 + s^4t^2)^{-1/2}$　　**13.** 72　　**15.** $-\frac{1}{2}(\pi + 1)$

17. 244.35 board ft per year　　**19.** $\sqrt{20}$ ft/s

21. $(3x^2 + 4xy)/(3y^2 - 2x^2)$

23. $(y \sin x - \sin y)/(x \cos y + \cos x)$

25. $(yz^3 - 6xz)/(3x^2 - 3xyz^2)$

27. $\partial T/\partial s = (\partial T/\partial x)(\partial x/\partial s) + (\partial T/\partial y)(\partial y/\partial s)$
$+ (\partial T/\partial z)(\partial z/\partial s) + (\partial T/\partial w)(\partial w/\partial s)$

31. $10\sqrt{2} - 3\pi\sqrt{2}$　　**33.** 288 mi/h

Problem Set 12.7

1. $2(x - 2) + 3(y - 3) + \sqrt{3}(z - \sqrt{3}) = 0$

3. $(x - 1) - 3(y - 3) + \sqrt{7}(z - \sqrt{7}) = 0$

5. $x + y - z = 2$　　**7.** $z + 1 = -2\sqrt{3}(x - \frac{1}{3}\pi) - 3y$

9. 0.08; 0.08017992　　**11.** -0.03; -0.03015101

13. $(3, -1, -14)$

15. $\langle 0, 1, 1 \rangle$ is normal to both surfaces at $(0, -1, 2)$

17. $(1, 2, -1)$ and $(-1, -2, 1)$

19. $x = 1 + 32t$; $y = 2 - 19t$; $z = 2 - 17t$　　**21.** 0.004375 lb

23. 7%　　**25.** 20 ± 0.34　　**27.** $V = 9|k|/2$

29. (a) 4.98;　(b) 4.98196;　(c) 4.9819675

Problem Set 12.8

1. $(2, 0)$; local minimum point.

3. $(0, 0)$; saddle point; $\left(\pm\frac{1}{2}, 0\right)$; local minimum points.

5. $(0, 0)$; saddle point.

7. $(1, 2)$; local minimum point.　　**9.** No critical points.

11. Global maximum of 7 at $(1, 1)$; global minimum of -4 at $(0, -1)$.

13. Global maximum of 2 at $(\pm 1, 0)$; global minimum of 0 at $(0, \pm 1)$.

15. Each of the three numbers is $N/3$.　　**17.** A cube.

19. Base 8 ft by 8 ft; depth 4 ft.　　**21.** $3\sqrt{3}(\mathbf{i} + \mathbf{j} + \mathbf{k})$

23. $(0.393, 0.786, 0.772)$; 1.56

25. Width of turned-up sides is 4"; base angle $\frac{2\pi}{3}$

27. (a) maximum value of 8 occurs at $(-1, 2)$

(b) minimum value of -11 occurs at $(4, 0)$

29. Maximum of 3 at $(1, 2)$; minimum of $-\frac{12}{5}$ at $\left(\frac{8}{5}, -\frac{2}{5}\right)$.

31. $y = \frac{7}{10}x + \frac{1}{10}$　　**33.** $x = 50/\sqrt{3}$, $y = 100/\sqrt{1.25}$; \$79,681

35. Maximum of $10 + 3\sqrt{2}$ at $(3/\sqrt{2}, 3/\sqrt{2})$; Minimum of $10 - 3\sqrt{2}$ at $(-3/\sqrt{2}, -3/\sqrt{2})$

37. Length 1.1544 ft, Width 1.1544 ft, Height 1.501 ft

39. $\left(\pm\sqrt{3}/2, -\frac{1}{2}\right)$ where $T = 9/4$; $(0, 1/2)$, where $T = -1/4$

41. Equilateral triangle.

43. Local maximum: $f(1.75, 0) = 1.15$; global maximum: $f(-3.8, 0) = 2.30$

45. Global minimum: $f(0, 1) = f(0, -1) = -0.12$.

47. Global maximum $f(1.13, 0.79) = f(1.13, -0.79) = 0.53$ global minimum $f(-1.13, 0.79) = f(-1.13, -0.79) = -0.53$.

49. Global maximum $f(3, 3) = f(-3, 3) \approx 74.9225$ global minimum $f(1.5708, 0) = f(-1.5708, 0) = -8$.

51. Global maximum: $f(0.67, 0) = 5.06$; global minimum: $f(-0.75, 0) = -3.54$.

53. Global maximum: $f(2.1, 2.1) = 3.5$; global minimum: $f(4.2, 4.2) = -3.5$.

Problem Set 12.9

1. $f(\sqrt{3}, \sqrt{3}) = f(-\sqrt{3}, -\sqrt{3}) = 6$

3. $f(2/\sqrt{5}, -1/\sqrt{5}) = f(-2/\sqrt{5}, 1/\sqrt{5}) = 5$

5. $f\left(\frac{6}{7}, \frac{18}{7}, -\frac{12}{7}\right) = \frac{72}{7}$　　**7.** Base is 4 by 4; depth is 2.

9. $10\sqrt{5}$ ft^3　　**11.** $8abc/(3\sqrt{3})$

13. Maximum is $9\sqrt{3}$ when $\langle x, y, z \rangle = \langle 3\sqrt{3}, 3\sqrt{3}, 3\sqrt{3} \rangle$.

15. Minimum distance is 1.5616 at pt $(0.393, 0.786, 0.772)$

17. Length = Width = 1.1544 ft, Height = 1.501 ft

19. $c_0 = \frac{\pi k}{8 + \pi}$; $p_0 = \frac{4k}{8 + \pi}$; $q_0 = \frac{4k}{8 + \pi}$;

$A(c_0, p_0, q_0) = \frac{k}{4(8 + \pi)} \approx 0.224k^2$ is a minimum value.

21. $f\left(\dfrac{1}{\sqrt{2}}, \dfrac{1}{\sqrt{2}}\right) = 10 + \sqrt{2}$ is the maximum value;

$f\left(-\dfrac{1}{\sqrt{2}}, -\dfrac{1}{\sqrt{2}}\right) = 10 - \sqrt{2}$ is the minimum value

23. $f\left(\dfrac{3\sqrt{3}}{2}, -\dfrac{3}{2}\right) \approx 20.6913$ is the maximum value;

$f(-2, -1) = -3$ is the minimum value

25. $f\left(\dfrac{2}{\sqrt{5}}, \dfrac{8}{\sqrt{5}}\right) \approx 29.9443$ is the maximum value;

$f(x, -1-x) = 0$ for $-\dfrac{1}{5} - \dfrac{2}{5}\sqrt{19} \le x \le -\dfrac{1}{5} + \dfrac{2}{5}\sqrt{19}$
is the minimum value

27. $x = \alpha d/a, y = \beta d/b, z = \gamma d/c$
29. $f(-1, 1, 0) = 3, f(1, -1, 1) = -1$
31. $\sqrt{A}$ is the maximum value of w, where
$A = a_1^2 + a_2^2 + \cdots + a_n^2$
33. $f(4, 0) = -4$ **35.** $f(0, 3) = f(0, -3) = -0.99$

Chapter Review 12.10

Concepts Test
1. True   **3.** True   **5.** True   **7.** False   **9.** True
11. True   **13.** True   **15.** True   **17.** True   **19.** False

Sample Test Problems

1. (a) $\{(x, y): x^2 + 4y^2 \ge 100\}$ **(b)** $\{(x, y): 2x - y \ge 1\}$

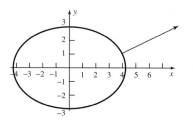

3. $12x^3 y^2 + 14xy^7; 36x^2 y^2 + 14y^7; 24x^3 y + 98xy^6$
5. $e^{-y} \sec^2 x; 2e^{-y} \sec^2 x \tan x; -e^{-y} \sec^2 x$
7. $450x^2 y^4 - 42y^5$ **9.** 1   **11.** Does not exist.
13. (a) $-4\mathbf{i} - \mathbf{j} + 6\mathbf{k};$ **(b)** $-4(\cos 1\mathbf{i} + \sin 1\mathbf{j} - \cos 1\mathbf{k})$
15. $\sqrt{3} + 2$
17. (a) $x^2 + 2y^2 = 18;$ **(b)** $4\mathbf{i} + 2\mathbf{j};$

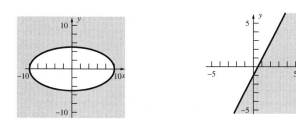

19. $(x^2 + 3y - 4z)/x^2 yz; (-x^2 - 4x)/xy^2 z; (3y - x^2)/xyz^2$
21. $15xy\sqrt{t}/z^3 + 5x^2/tz^3 - 45x^2 ye^{3t}/z^4$
23. $18\mathbf{i} + 16\mathbf{j} - 18\mathbf{k}; 9x + 8y - 9z = 34$ **25.** 0.7728
27. $16\sqrt{3}/3$ **29.** Radius 2; height 4.

Chapter 13 Review and Preview Problems

1.

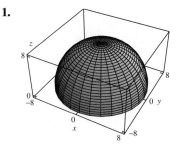

3.

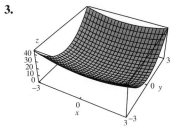

5.

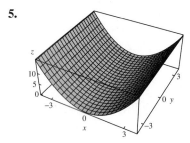

7.

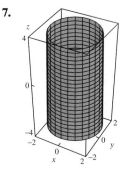

9.

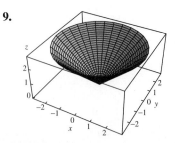

11.

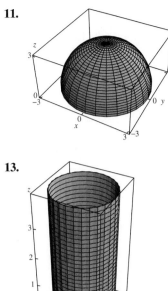

13.

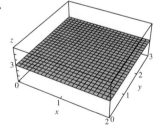

15. $-\dfrac{1}{2}e^{-2x} + C$ **17.** $\dfrac{2a}{\pi}$ **19.** $\dfrac{\pi}{2}$ **21.** $\dfrac{1}{2}\ln 2$

23. $\dfrac{-1 + 37^{3/2}}{12}$ **25.** $\dfrac{\pi}{4}$ **27.** $2\pi\left(\sqrt{a^2 - b^2} - \sqrt{a^2 - c^2}\right)$

29. 36π **31.** $\dfrac{\pi^2}{2}$ **33.** $\dfrac{81\pi}{2}$

Problem Set 13.1

1. 14   **3.** 12   **5.** 4   **7.** 3   **9.** 168   **11.** 520
13. 52.57

15.

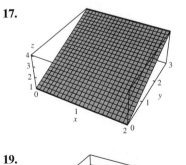

17.

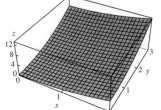

19.

21. 5.5   **25.** $c = 15.30, C = 30.97$
27. (a) -6;   **(b)** 6
29. Number of cubic inches of rain that fell on all Colorado in 1999; average rainfall in Colorado during 1999.
31. Approximately 458.

Problem Set 13.2

1. 48   **3.** $\dfrac{32}{3}$ **5.** $\dfrac{55}{4}$ **7.** 1   **9.** $\pi/2 - 1$

11. $\dfrac{4}{15}\left[31 - 9\sqrt{3}\right] \approx 4.110$ **13.** $1 - \dfrac{1}{2}\ln 3 \approx 0.4507$

15. $\dfrac{9\pi}{4}$ **17.** 0   **19.** 2   **21.** 105   **23.** 112

25.   **27.**

29. 7   **31.** $\dfrac{10}{3}$ **35.** $\dfrac{1}{4}(e - 1)^2$
37. (a) $\dfrac{8}{3}$ **39.** $5 - \sqrt{3} - \sqrt{2}$

Problem Set 13.3

1. $\dfrac{3}{4}$ **3.** 240   **5.** $\dfrac{1}{2}(e^{27} - e)$ **7.** $-\sqrt{2}/(2\pi)$

9. $(3\ln 2 - \pi)/9$ **11.** $e - 2$ **13.** $\dfrac{16}{3}$ **15.** 0   **17.** $\dfrac{27}{70}$

19. $4\tan^{-1} 2 - \ln 5$ **21.** 6   **23.** 20   **25.** 10   **27.** $\dfrac{4}{15}$

29. $-\dfrac{1}{2}\ln(\cos 1)$ **31.** 3π **33.** $\displaystyle\int_0^1 \int_y^1 f(x, y)\, dx\, dy$

35. $\displaystyle\int_0^1 \int_{y^4}^{\sqrt{y}} f(x, y)\, dx\, dy$

37. $\displaystyle\int_{-1}^0 \int_{-x}^1 f(x, y)\, dy\, dx + \int_0^1 \int_x^1 f(x, y)\, dy\, dx$ **39.** $\dfrac{256}{15}$

41. $15\pi/4$ **43.** $\dfrac{1}{3}(1 - \cos 8)$

45. approximately 4,133,000 ft^3

Problem Set 13.4

1. $\dfrac{1}{12}$ **3.** $\dfrac{4}{9}$ **5.** $4\sqrt{2}$ **7.** $2\sqrt{3} + \dfrac{4}{3}\pi \approx 7.653$

9. $\pi a^2/8$ **11.** $8\pi + 6\sqrt{3} \approx 35.525$ **13.** $\dfrac{\pi}{2}$ **15.** $\dfrac{\pi^3}{48}$

17. $\dfrac{\pi}{4}$ **19.** $\pi(e^4 - 1) \approx 168.384$ **21.** $(\pi \ln 2)/8 \approx 0.272$

23. $\pi\left(2 - \sqrt{3}\right)/2 \approx 0.421$ **25.** $\dfrac{1}{12}$ **27.** $81\pi/8 \approx 31.809$

29. $625\left(3\sqrt{3} + 1\right)/12 \approx 322.716$ **31.** $\dfrac{2}{3}\pi d^2(3a - d)$

33. $\dfrac{2}{9}a^3(3\pi - 4)$

Problem Set 13.5

1. $m = 30; \bar{x} = 2; \bar{y} = 1.8$
3. $m = \pi/4; \bar{x} = \pi/2; \bar{y} = 16/(9\pi)$
5. $m \approx 0.1056; \bar{x} \approx 0.281; \bar{y} \approx 0.581$
7. $m = 32/9; \bar{x} = 0; \bar{y} = 6/5$ **9.** $m = \pi; \bar{x} = 0; \bar{y} = \dfrac{3}{\pi}$
11. $I_x \approx 269; I_y \approx 5194; I_z \approx 5463$
13. $I_x = I_y = 5a^5/12; I_z \approx 5a^5/6$

15. $k; 2k; \left(\dfrac{4}{3}, \dfrac{2}{3}\right)$

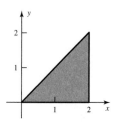

17. The density is proportional to the squared distance from the origin; $\dfrac{25596k}{35}; \left(0, \dfrac{450}{79}\right)$

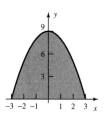

19. The density is proportional to the distance from the origin; $\dfrac{26k\pi}{3}; \left(0, \dfrac{60}{13\pi}\right)$

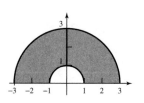

21. $\bar{r} = \sqrt{5/12}\,a \approx 0.6455a$ **23.** $I_x = \pi\delta a^4/4; \bar{r} = a/2$
25. $5\pi\delta a^4/4$ **27.** $\bar{x} = 0, \bar{y} = (15\pi + 32)a/(6\pi + 48)$
29. (a) a^3; **(b)** $7a/12$; **(c)** $11a^5/144$
31. $I_x = \pi k a^4/2, I_y = 17k\pi a^4/2, I_z = 9\pi k a^4$

Problem Set 13.6

1. $\sqrt{61}/3$ **3.** $\pi/3$ **5.** $9 \sin^{-1}\left(\tfrac{2}{3}\right)$ **7.** $8\sqrt{2}$
9. $4\pi a\left(a - \sqrt{a^2 - b^2}\right)$ **11.** $2a^2(\pi - 2)$

13. $\tfrac{1}{6}\pi a^2\left(5\sqrt{5} - 1\right)$ **15.** $\dfrac{(17^{3/2} - 1)\pi}{6}$

17. $\dfrac{D^2\sqrt{A^2 + B^2 + C^2}}{2ABC}$

19. $(h_1 + h_2)/2$
21. $A = \pi b^2, B = 2\pi a^2[1 - \cos(b/a)], C = \pi b^2,$
$D = \pi b^2\left[2a/\left(a + \sqrt{a^2 - b^2}\right)\right], B < A = C < D$
27. (a) 29.3297   **(b)** 15.4233
29. E/F (tie), A/B (tie), C/D (tie)

Problem Set 13.7

1. -40 **3.** $\dfrac{189}{2}$ **5.** 1927.54   **7.** $\dfrac{2}{3}$ **9.** 156

11. $\displaystyle\int_0^1 \int_0^3 \int_0^{(1/6)(12-3x-2y)} f(x, y, z)\, dz\, dy\, dx$

13. $\displaystyle\int_0^2 \int_0^4 \int_0^{y/2} f(x, y, z)\, dx\, dy\, dz$

15. $\displaystyle\int_0^{12/5} \int_{x/3}^{(4-x)/2} \int_0^{4-x-2z} f(x, y, z)\, dy\, dz\, dx$

17. $\displaystyle\int_0^3 \int_{2x/3}^{(9-x)/3} \int_0^{(18-2x-6y)/9} f(x, y, z)\, dz\, dy\, dx$

19. $\displaystyle\int_1^4 \int_0^1 \int_0^{\sqrt{1-z^2}} f(x, y, z)\, dy\, dz\, dx$

21. $\dfrac{128}{15}$ **23.** $4\displaystyle\int_0^1 \int_{x^2}^1 \int_0^{\sqrt{y}} dz\, dy\, dx = 2$

25. $\bar{x} = \bar{y} = \bar{z} = \dfrac{4}{15}$ **27.** $\bar{x} = \bar{y} = \bar{z} = 3a/8$

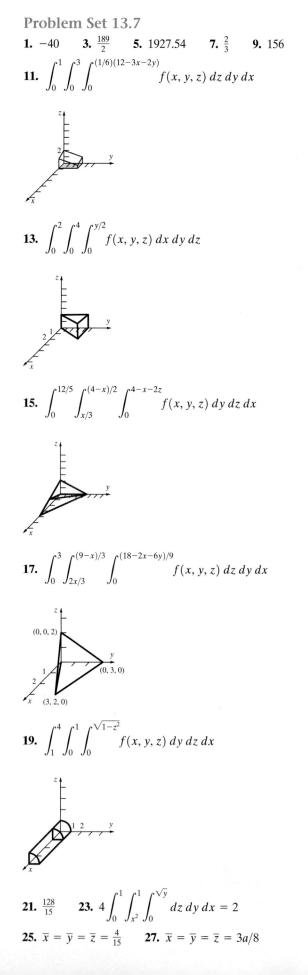

29. $\displaystyle\int_0^1 \int_0^{\sqrt{1-x^2}} \int_0^{\sqrt{1-x^2-y^2}} f(x, y, z)\, dz\, dy\, dx$

31. $\displaystyle\int_0^2 \int_0^{2-z} \int_0^{9-x^2} f(x, y, z)\, dy\, dx\, dz$ **33.** 4

35. Ave $T = 29.54$ **37.** $(\bar{x}, \bar{y}, \bar{z}) = \left(\frac{11}{24}, \frac{25}{12}, \frac{11}{24}\right)$

39. $(\bar{x}, \bar{y}, \bar{z}) = \left(\frac{17}{36}, \frac{17}{36}, \frac{55}{36}\right)$

43. (a) $k = \dfrac{1}{288}$ **(b)** $\dfrac{26}{27}$ **(c)** 9

45. (a) $\dfrac{7}{16}$ **(b)** $\dfrac{1}{4}$ **(c)** 5

47. $x^2/576, 0 \le x \le 12, 9$

Problem Set 13.8

1. Right circular cylinder about the z-axis with radius 3 and height 12; $V = 108\pi$

3. Region under the paraboloid $z = 9 - r^2$ above the xy-plane in that part of the first quadrant satisfying $0 \le \theta \le \dfrac{\pi}{4}$; $V = \dfrac{243\pi}{16}$

5. Sphere centered at the origin with radius a; $V = \dfrac{4}{3}\pi a^3$

7. 8π **9.** $14\pi/3$ **11.** $2\pi(5\sqrt{5} - 4)/3 \approx 15.038$

13. $\bar{x} = \bar{y} = 0$; $\bar{z} = \frac{16}{3}$ **15.** $k\pi(b^4 - a^4)$

17. $\bar{x} = \bar{y} = 0$; $\bar{z} = 2a/5$ **19.** $k\pi^2 a^6/16$ **21.** $\pi/9$

23. $\pi/32$

25. (a) $3a/4$;   **(b)** $3\pi a/16$;   **(c)** $6a/5$

27. (a) $3\pi a \sin \alpha/16\alpha$;   **(b)** $3\pi a/16$

29. $(a + b)(c - 1)/(c + 1)$

Problem Set 13.9

1.

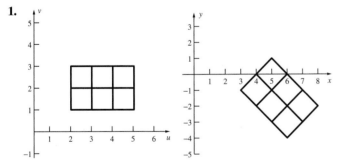

3.

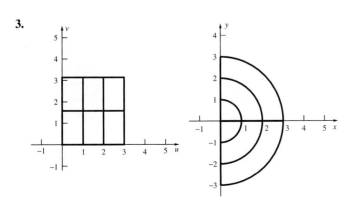

5.

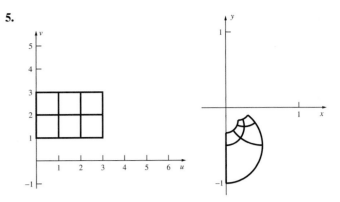

7. Image is the square with corners $(0,0), (2,2), (4,0)$, and $(2, -2)$; $J = -4$.

9. Image is the set of (x, y) that satisfy $y^2 \le x \le y^2 + 1, 0 \le y \le 1$; $J = 2u$.

11. $x = u/2 + v/2$; $y = u/4 - v/4$; $J = -\dfrac{1}{4}$

13. $x = v$; $y = \sqrt{u - v^2}$; $J = -\dfrac{1}{2\sqrt{u - v^2}}$

15. $x = v$; $y = u/v$; $J = -\dfrac{1}{v}$ **17.** 3.15669   **19.** 0

21. $-\rho^2 \sin \phi$

25. (a) $g(u, v) = \begin{cases} e^{-u}, & \text{if } 0 \le v \le u \\ 0, & \text{otherwise} \end{cases}$

(b) $g_U(u) = \begin{cases} ue^{-u}, & \text{if } 0 \le u \\ 0, & \text{otherwise} \end{cases}$

Chapter Review 13.10

Concepts Test

1. True   **3.** True   **5.** True   **7.** False   **9.** True
11. True   **13.** False   **15.** True   **17.** False

Sample Test Problems

1. $\frac{1}{24}$ **3.** $\frac{2}{3}$ **5.** $\displaystyle\int_0^1 \int_0^y f(x, y)\, dx\, dy$

7. $\displaystyle\int_0^{1/2} \int_0^{1-2y} \int_0^{1-2y-z} f(x, y, z)\, dx\, dz\, dy$

9. (a) $8\displaystyle\int_0^a \int_0^{\sqrt{a^2-x^2}} \int_0^{\sqrt{a^2-x^2-y^2}} dz\, dy\, dx$;

(b) $8\displaystyle\int_0^{\pi/2} \int_0^a \int_0^{\sqrt{a^2-r^2}} r\, dz\, dr\, d\theta$;

(c) $8\displaystyle\int_0^{\pi/2} \int_0^{\pi/2} \int_0^a \rho^2 \sin \phi\, d\rho\, d\phi\, d\theta$

11. 0.8857   **13.** $\bar{x} = \frac{13}{6}$; $\bar{y} = \frac{3}{2}$ **15.** 6   **17.** $80\pi k$

19. $ka^2bc/24$ **21.** 0

Chapter 14 Review and Preview Problems

1. $x = 3 \cos t, y = 3 \sin t, 0 \le t < 2\pi$ is one possibility.
3. $x = 2 \cos t, y = 2 \sin t, 0 < t < \pi$ is one possibility.
5. $x = -2 + 5t, y = 2, 0 \le t \le 1$ is one possibility.
7. $x = 9 - t, y = t, 0 < t < 9$ is one possibility.
9. $x = -t, y = 9 - t^2, -3 \le t \le 3$ is one possibility.

11. $\nabla f(x, y) = (x \cos x + \sin x)\mathbf{i} + (\cos y - y \sin y)\mathbf{j}$

13. $\nabla f(x, y, z) = 2x\mathbf{i} + 2y\mathbf{j} + 2z\mathbf{k}$

15. $\nabla f(x, y, z) = (y + z)\mathbf{i} + (x + z)\mathbf{j} + (x + y)\mathbf{k}$

17. $\dfrac{\pi}{2}$ **19.** $\dfrac{3}{4}$ **21.** $\dfrac{14\pi}{3}$

23. The volume in problem 22 is that of a spherical shell centered at $(0, 0, 0)$ with outer radius $= 2$ and inner radius $= 1$.

25. $\left\langle \dfrac{3}{13}, \dfrac{4}{13}, \dfrac{12}{13} \right\rangle$

Problem Set 14.1

1.

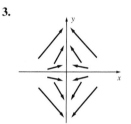

3.

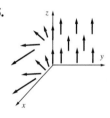

5.

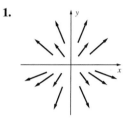

7. $(2x - 3y)\mathbf{i} - 3x\mathbf{j} + 2\mathbf{k}$ **9.** $x^{-1}\mathbf{i} + y^{-1}\mathbf{j} + z^{-1}\mathbf{k}$

11. $e^y \cos z\mathbf{i} + xe^y \cos z\mathbf{j} - xe^y \sin z\mathbf{k}$ **13.** $2yz; z^2\mathbf{i} - 2y\mathbf{k}$

15. $0; 0$ **17.** $2e^x \cos y + 1; 2e^x \sin y\mathbf{k}$

19. (a) Meaningless; **(b)** vector field; **(c)** vector field;
(d) scalar field; **(e)** vector field; **(f)** vector field;
(g) vector field; **(h)** meaningless; **(i)** meaningless;
(j) scalar field; **(k)** meaningless.

25. (a) div $\mathbf{F} = 0$, div $\mathbf{G} < 0$, div $\mathbf{H} = 0$, div $\mathbf{L} > 0$;
(b) clockwise for $\mathbf{H}$, not at all for others.
(c) div $\mathbf{F} = 0$, curl $\mathbf{F} = \mathbf{0}$, div $\mathbf{G} = -2ye^{-y^2}$, curl $\mathbf{G} = \mathbf{0}$,
div $\mathbf{H} = 0$, curl $\mathbf{H} = -2xe^{-x^2}\mathbf{k}$. div $\mathbf{L} = 1/\sqrt{x^2 + y^2}$,
curl $\mathbf{L} = \mathbf{0}$

27.

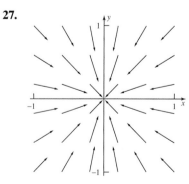

div $\mathbf{F} > 0$. A paddle wheel at the origin will not rotate.

Problem Set 14.2

1. $14(2\sqrt{2} - 1)$ **3.** $2\sqrt{5}$ **5.** $\frac{1}{6}(14\sqrt{14} - 1)$ **7.** $\frac{100}{3}$

9. 144 **11.** 0 **13.** $\frac{17}{6}$ **15.** 19 **17.** $k(17\sqrt{17} - 1)/6$

19. $-\frac{7}{44}$ **21.** $-\frac{1}{2}(a^2 + b^2)$ **23.** $2 - 2/\pi$

25. Work along C_1 is positive; work along C_2 is negative; work along C_3 is zero.

27. 2.25 gal   **29.** $2\pi a^2$ **31.** $4a^2$

33. (a) 27; **(b)** $-297/2$

Problem Set 14.3

1. $f(x, y) = 5x^2 - 7xy + y^2 + C$ **3.** Not conservative.

5. $f(x, y) = \frac{2}{5}x^3 y^{-2} + C$ **7.** $f(x, y) = 2xe^y - ye^x + C$

9. $f(x, y, z) = x^3 + 2y^3 + 3z^3 + C$ **11.** $\ln\left(\dfrac{1}{x^2 + z^2}\right) + C$

13. 14 **15.** $\dfrac{20}{1377}$ **17.** 6 **19.** $-\pi$

23. $f(x, y, z) = \frac{1}{2}k(x^2 + y^2 + z^2)$

25. $\displaystyle\int_C \mathbf{F} \cdot d\mathbf{r} = \int_a^b m\mathbf{r}''(t) \cdot \mathbf{r}'(t)\, dt$

$= \frac{1}{2}m \displaystyle\int_a^b (d/dt)[\mathbf{r}'(t) \cdot \mathbf{r}'(t)]\, dt = \frac{1}{2}m \int_a^b (d/dt)|\mathbf{r}'(t)|^2\, dt$

$= \left[\frac{1}{2}m|\mathbf{r}'(t)|^2\right]_a^b = \frac{1}{2}m[|\mathbf{r}'(b)|^2 - |\mathbf{r}'(a)|^2]$

27. $f(x, y, z) = -gmz$

Problem Set 14.4

1. $-\dfrac{64}{15}$ **3.** $\dfrac{72}{35}$ **5.** 0 **7.** $\dfrac{8}{3}$

9. (a) 0; **(b)** 0
11. (a) 0; **(b)** 0
13. 50 **15.** -2
19. (c) M and N have a discontinuity at $(0, 0)$.
23. $3\pi a^2/8$
27. (a) div $\mathbf{F} = 4$; **(b)** 144
29. (a) div $\mathbf{F} < 0$ in quadrants I and III;
div $\mathbf{F} > 0$ in quadrants II and IV;
(b) $0; -2(1 - \cos 3)^2$

Problem Set 14.5

1. $8\sqrt{3}/3$ **3.** $2 + \pi/3$ **5.** $5\pi/8$ **7.** 6 **9.** 2

11. 20 **13.** $\sqrt{3}ka^4/12$ **15.** $\bar{x} = \bar{y} = \bar{z} = a/3$

17.   **19.**

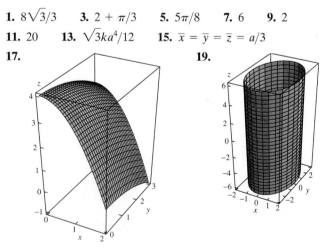

21. $\pi\left[6\sqrt{37} + \ln\sqrt{\dfrac{\sqrt{37}+6}{\sqrt{37}-6}}\right]$

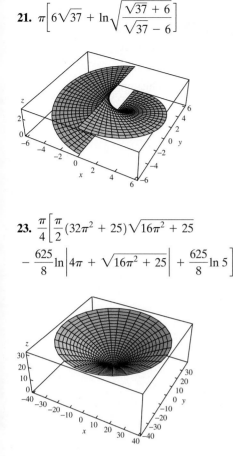

23. $\dfrac{\pi}{4}\left[\dfrac{\pi}{2}(32\pi^2 + 25)\sqrt{16\pi^2 + 25}\right.$

$\left. -\dfrac{625}{8}\ln\left|4\pi + \sqrt{16\pi^2 + 25}\right| + \dfrac{625}{8}\ln 5\right]$

25. $\dfrac{702965k}{32}$

29. (a) 0; **(b)** 0; **(c)** $4\pi a^4$; **(d)** $4\pi a^4/3$; **(e)** $8\pi a^4/3$

31. (a) $4k\pi a^3$; **(b)** $2k\pi a^3$; **(c)** $hk\pi a(a + h)$

Problem Set 14.6

1. 0   **3.** 8   **5.** $3a^2b^2c^2/4$ **7.** $64\pi/3$ **9.** 4π
11. 1176π **13.** 100π

15. $\nabla\cdot\mathbf{F} = 3$ and so $\displaystyle\iint_{\partial S}\mathbf{F}\cdot\mathbf{n}\,dS = \iiint_S 3\,dV = 3V(S)$.

19. (a) $20\pi/3$; **(b)** 4π; **(c)** $16\pi/3$; **(d)** 1; **(e)** 36; **(f)** $12\pi/5$; **(g)** $32\pi\ln 2$

Problem Set 14.7

1. 0   **3.** -2 **5.** -48π **7.** 8π **9.** 2   **11.** $\pi/4$
15. 1/3   **17.** $\frac{4}{3}a^2$ joules

Chapter Review 14.8

Concepts Test

1. True   **3.** False   **5.** True   **7.** False   **9.** True
11. True.

Sample Test Problems

3. $\text{curl}(f\,\nabla f) = f\,\text{curl}(\nabla f) + \nabla f \times \nabla f = \mathbf{0} + \mathbf{0} = \mathbf{0}$
5. (a) $\pi/4$; **(b)** $(3\pi - 5)/6$

7. 47
9. (a) $\frac{1}{2}$; **(b)** $\frac{4}{3}$; **(c)** 0
11. 6π **13.** 0   **15.** $9\pi(3a - 2)/\sqrt{a^2 + b^2 + 1}$

Problem Set 15.1

1. $y = C_1 e^{2x} + C_2 e^{3x}$ **3.** $y = \frac{1}{2}e^x - \frac{1}{2}e^{-7x}$
5. $y = (C_1 + C_2 x)e^{2x}$
7. $y = e^{2x}\left(C_1 e^{\sqrt{3}x} + C_2 e^{-\sqrt{3}x}\right)$
9. $y = 3\sin 2x + 2\cos 2x$
11. $y = e^{-x}(C_1\cos x + C_2\sin x)$
13. $y = C_1 + C_2 x + C_3 e^{-4x} + C_4 e^x$
15. $y = C_1 e^x + C_2 e^{-x} + C_3\cos 2x + C_4\sin 2x$
17. $y = D_1\cosh 2x + D_2\sinh 2x$
19. $y = e^{-x/2}\left[(C_1 + C_2 x)\cos(\sqrt{3}/2)x\right.$
$\left.\qquad +(C_3 + C_4 x)\sin(\sqrt{3}/2)x\right]$
21. $y = (C_1 + C_2\ln x)x^{-2}$
27. $y = 0.5e^{5.16228x} + 0.5e^{-1.162278x}$
29. $y = 1.29099e^{-0.25x}\sin(0.968246x)$

Problem Set 15.2

1. $y = C_1 e^{3x} + C_2 e^{-3x} - \frac{1}{9}x$
3. $y = (C_1 + C_2 x)e^x + x^2 + 5x + 8$
5. $y = C_1 e^{2x} + C_2 e^{3x} + \frac{1}{2}e^x$
7. $y = C_1 e^{-3x} + C_2 e^{-x} - \frac{1}{2}xe^{-3x}$
9. $y = C_1 e^{2x} + C_2 e^{-x} - \frac{3}{5}\sin x + \frac{1}{5}\cos x$
11. $y = C_1\cos 2x + C_2\sin 2x + \frac{1}{2}x\sin 2x$
13. $y = C_1\cos 3x + C_2\sin 3x + \frac{1}{8}\sin x + \frac{1}{13}e^{2x}$
15. $y = e^{2x} - e^{3x} + e^x$ **17.** $y = C_1 e^{2x} + C_2 e^x + \frac{5}{2}x + \frac{19}{4}$
19. $y = C_2\sin x + C_3\cos x - x\sin x - \cos x\ln|\sin x|$
21. $y = D_1 e^x + D_2 e^{2x} + (e^x + e^{2x})\ln(1 + e^{-x})$

Problem Set 15.3

1. $y = 0.1\cos 5t; 2\pi/5$ **3.** 0.5 m/s
5. $y \approx e^{-0.16t}(\cos 8t + 0.02\sin 8t)$ **7.** 14.4 s
9. $Q = 10^{-6}(1 - e^{-t})$
11. (a) $Q = 2.4 \times 10^{-4}\sin 377t$;
  (b) $I = 9.05 \times 10^{-2}\cos 377t$
13. $I \approx 12 \times 10^{-2}\sin 377t$ **17.** $d^2\theta/dt^2 = -(g/L)\sin\theta$

Chapter Review 15.4

Concepts Test

1. False   **3.** True   **5.** True   **7.** True   **9.** False

Sample Test Problems

1. $y = \frac{1}{4}e^x + C_1 e^{-3x} + C_2$ **3.** $y = 3e^{2x} - 3e^x$
5. $y = C_1 e^x + C_2 e^{-x} - 1$ **7.** $y = \left(C_1 + C_2 x + \frac{1}{2}x^2\right)e^{-2x}$
9. $y = e^{-3x}(C_1\cos 4x + C_2\sin 4x)$

11. $y = C_1 + C_2e^{-4x} + C_3e^{2x}$

13. $y = (C_1 + C_2x)e^{\sqrt{2}x} + (C_3 + C_4x)e^{-\sqrt{2}x}$

15. $y = -\cos 4t; 1; \pi/2$ **17.** $I = e^{-t}\sin t$

Problem Set A.1

9. $N = 4$ **11.** $N = 5$ **13.** $P_5, P_7, P_9, \ldots$ are true

15. $P_{30}, P_{29}, P_{28}, \ldots$ are true   **17.** P_i is true for all $i \geq 1$

19. P_i is true for all $i \geq 1$

21. True for $n = 1, 3, 5, \ldots$ Proof is by induction.

23. True for all $n \geq 3$. Proof is by induction.

25. True for all $n \geq 2$. Proof is by induction.

27. True for all $n \geq 0$. Proof is by induction.

Index

Symbols

θ-simple set, 694

A

Abel, Niels Henrik, 487
Absolute convergence, 479
Absolute convergence test, 478
Absolute error, 182
Absolute ratio test, 479
Absolute value function, 32
Absolute values, 11
    continuity of, 108
    as distance, 78
    inequalities involving, 11–12
    properties of, 11
Acceleration, 124, 153
    components of, 600–603
Accumulation function, 281, 367
Addition identities, 57–58
Algorithms, 233
Alternating harmonic series, 476–477
Alternating series, 476–480
    absolute convergence test, 478
    absolute ratio test, 479
    alternating series test, 477–478
    conditionally convergent series, 479–480
    convergence test, 477–478
    Rearrangement Theorem, 480
Amplitude, of trigonometric functions, 54
Angle of inclination, 59
Angles, 56–57
    direction, 571
    of inclination, 59
    rotation of axes of conics, 528
Angular velocity, 143
Anticommutative Law, 577
Antiderivatives, 237–243
    general, 238
    Generalized Power Rule, 241
    notation for, 238
Antidifferentiation, 402
Aphelion, 544
Approximations, 181–183, 404
    derivatives, 181–183
    linear, 183
    tangent planes, 656–657
Arc length, 343–346, 536, 584
    differential of, 346–347
Archimedes, 119, 280, 515
Area, 263–269
    by circumscribed polygons, 264
    by inscribed polygons, 264
    of a plane region, 323–327
        distance and displacement, 326
        region above the x-axis, 323
        region below the x-axis, 323–324
        region between two curves, 325–326
    surface, 702–707
    of a surface of revolution, 347
Asymptote, 31, 92–93
    horizontal, 93

oblique, 94
    vertical, 93
Auxiliary equation, 778
Average value, of a function, 301
Average velocity, 121
    derivatives, 121
Axiom of Completeness, 8
Axis, 330, 512–513
    general equation of a conic section, 527–528
    rotations, 528–530
        determining the angle θ, 529–530
    translations, 525–526

B

Ball, 558
Barrow, Isaac, 280
Basis vectors, 565
Best-fit line, 209–210
Beta function, 384
Binomial Formula, 454
Binomial Series, 495–497
Binormal vector, 601–602
Bisection Method, 113, 230–232
Boundary of a set, 766
Boundary points, 635, 660
Bounded partial sums, 466
Bounded sum test, 466, 475
Boundedness property, 284
Bouyer, Martine, 490
Boyle's Law, 168
Brahe, Tycho, 587

C

Calculators, 404–406
Calculus:
    defined, 71, 82
    differential, 126
    First Fundamental Theorem of, 280–288
    graphing functions using, 216–222
    in polar coordinate system, 549–552
    Second Fundamental Theorem of, 291
Carbon dating, 256
Cardioid, 545
Cartesian coordinates, 16
    in three-space, 557–561
        curves in three-space, 560–561
        Distance Formula, 558
        graphs in three-space, 559–560
        Midpoint Formula, 559
        spheres, 558–559
        triple integrals in, 708–713
Cartesian (rectangular) coordinate system, 539
Catenary, 176, 250
Cauchy, Augustin Louis, 82
Cauchy's Mean Value Theorem, 427–428
Cauchy–Schwarz Inequality for Integrals, 686
Cavalieri's Principle, 336, 697
Center of curvature, for a plane curve, 597–598
Center of mass, 357

and double integrals, 698–700
    and triple integrals in Cartesian coordinates, 711–712
Central conics, 515
Central quadrics, 607
Centroid, 359
Chain Rule, 144–149, 156, 158, 171–172, 177, 286, 293, 402, 534, 649, 653, 744
    applications of, 145–147
    applying more than once, 145–146
    derivatives, 144–149
    first version, for functions of two variables, 649–651
    implicit functions, 652–653
    partial proof of, 148–149
    proof of, 780
    second version, for functions of two variables, 651–652
    three-variable case, 651
    two-variable case, 650
Change of variable formula:
    for double integrals, 723–728
    for triple integrals, 728
Circle of curvature, 597
Circles:
    defined, 17
    equation of, 17–18
    polar equations for, 542–543
Circulation, 755, 774
Closed curve, 532
Closed interval, 8–9
Closed set, 635
Coefficient of friction, 604
Cofunction identities, 57
Coin, volume of, 329
Collapsing series, 460
Common logarithms, 49–50
Comparison properties, 283–284
Comparison test, 471
Completeness property of the real numbers, 456
Completing the square, 526
Complex conjugate, 779
Complex numbers, 2
Components of acceleration, 600–603
    vector forms for, 601
Composite limit theorem, 110
Composition, of functions, 36–37
Compounded continuously, use of term, 102
Computer algebra systems (CAS), 24
    and calculators, 404–406
Computer graphs, 620–621
    and level curves, 621–623
Computers, 3
Concave down, 194–195
Concave side of a curve, 584
Concave up, 194–195
Concavity, 194–198
    inflection points, 197–198
Concavity Theorem, 195
Conchoid, 547

Photo Credits

Fold here

Formula Card
to accompany

CALCULUS, 9/E

Varberg, Purcell, and Rigdon

INTEGRALS

1. $\displaystyle\int u\,dv = uv - \int v\,du$

2. $\displaystyle\int u^n\,du = \frac{1}{n+1}u^{n+1} + C,\ n \neq -1$

3. $\displaystyle\int \frac{1}{u}\,du = \ln|u| + C$

4. $\displaystyle\int e^u\,du = e^u + C$

5. $\displaystyle\int a^u\,du = \frac{a^u}{\ln a} + C$

6. $\displaystyle\int \sin u\,du = -\cos u + C$

7. $\displaystyle\int \cos u\,du = \sin u + C$

8. $\displaystyle\int \sec^2 u\,du = \tan u + C$

9. $\displaystyle\int \csc^2 u\,du = -\cot u + C$

10. $\displaystyle\int \sec u \tan u\,du = \sec u + C$

11. $\displaystyle\int \csc u \cot u\,du = -\csc u + C$

12. $\displaystyle\int \tan u\,du = -\ln|\cos u| + C$

13. $\displaystyle\int \cot u\,du = \ln|\sin u| + C$

14. $\displaystyle\int \sec u\,du = \ln|\sec u + \tan u| + C$

15. $\displaystyle\int \csc u\,du = \ln|\csc u - \cot u| + C$

16. $\displaystyle\int \frac{1}{\sqrt{a^2 - u^2}}\,du = \sin^{-1}\frac{u}{a} + C$

17. $\displaystyle\int \frac{1}{a^2 + u^2}\,du = \frac{1}{a}\tan^{-1}\frac{u}{a} + C$

18. $\displaystyle\int \frac{1}{a^2 - u^2}\,du = \frac{1}{2a}\ln\left|\frac{u + a}{u - a}\right| + C$

19. $\displaystyle\int \frac{1}{u\sqrt{u^2 - a^2}}\,du = \frac{1}{a}\sec^{-1}\left|\frac{u}{a}\right| + C$

DERIVATIVES

$D_x x^r = r x^{r-1}$

$D_x |x| = \dfrac{|x|}{x}$

$D_x \sin x = \cos x$

$D_x \cos x = -\sin x$

$D_x \tan x = \sec^2 x$

$D_x \cot x = -\csc^2 x$

$D_x \sec x = \sec x \tan x$

$D_x \csc x = -\csc x \cot x$

$D_x \sinh x = \cosh x$

$D_x \coth x = -\csch^2 x$

$D_x \cosh x = \sinh x$

$D_x \sech x = -\sech x \tanh x$

$D_x \tanh x = \sech^2 x$

$D_x \csch x = -\csch x \coth x$

$D_x \ln x = \dfrac{1}{x}$

$D_x \log_a x = \dfrac{1}{x \ln a}$

$D_x e^x = e^x$

$D_x a^x = a^x \ln a$

$D_x \sin^{-1} x = \dfrac{1}{\sqrt{1 - x^2}}$

$D_x \cos^{-1} x = \dfrac{-1}{\sqrt{1 - x^2}}$

$D_x \tan^{-1} x = \dfrac{1}{1 + x^2}$

$D_x \sec^{-1} x = \dfrac{1}{|x|\sqrt{x^2 - 1}}$

Fold here

GEOMETRY

Triangles

Pythagorean Theorem
$a^2 + b^2 = c^2$

Right triangle

Angles $\alpha + \beta + \gamma = 180°$

Area $A = \frac{1}{2}bh$

Any triangle

Circles

Circumference $\quad C = 2\pi r$

Area $\qquad\qquad A = \pi r^2$

Cylinders

Surface area $\quad S = 2\pi r^2 + 2\pi r h$

Volume $\qquad\quad V = \pi r^2 h$

Cones

Surface area $\quad S = \pi r^2 + \pi r\sqrt{r^2 + h^2}$

Volume $\qquad\quad V = \frac{1}{3}\pi r^2 h$

Spheres

Surface area $\quad S = 4\pi r^2$

Volume $\qquad\quad V = \frac{4}{3}\pi r^3$

CONVERSIONS

1 inch = 2.54 centimeters

1 liter = 1000 cubic centimeters

1 kilogram ≈ 2.20 pounds

π radians = 180 degrees

1 kilometer ≈ 0.62 miles

1 liter ≈ 1.057 quarts

1 pound ≈ 453.6 grams

1 cubic foot ≈ 7.48 gallons

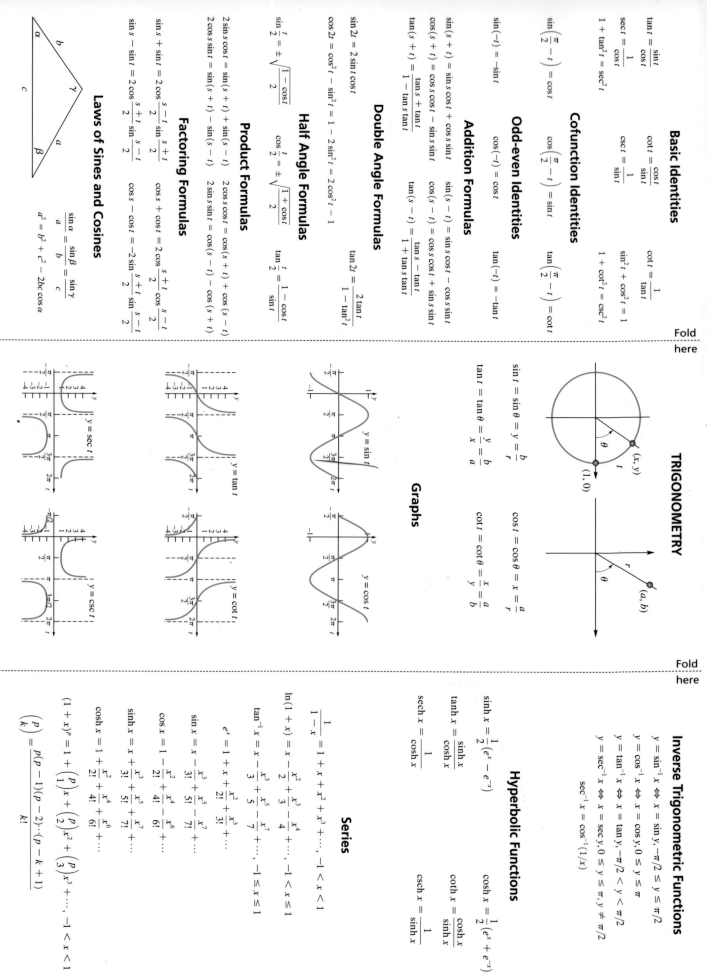

TRIGONOMETRY

Basic Identities

$$\tan t = \frac{\sin t}{\cos t} \qquad \cot t = \frac{\cos t}{\sin t} \qquad \cot t = \frac{1}{\tan t}$$

$$\sec t = \frac{1}{\cos t} \qquad \csc t = \frac{1}{\sin t} \qquad \sin^2 t + \cos^2 t = 1$$

$$1 + \tan^2 t = \sec^2 t \qquad 1 + \cot^2 t = \csc^2 t$$

Cofunction Identities

$$\sin\left(\frac{\pi}{2} - t\right) = \cos t \qquad \cos\left(\frac{\pi}{2} - t\right) = \sin t \qquad \tan\left(\frac{\pi}{2} - t\right) = \cot t$$

Odd-even Identities

$$\sin(-t) = -\sin t \qquad \cos(-t) = \cos t \qquad \tan(-t) = -\tan t$$

Addition Formulas

$$\sin(s + t) = \sin s \cos t + \cos s \sin t \qquad \sin(s - t) = \sin s \cos t - \cos s \sin t$$

$$\cos(s + t) = \cos s \cos t - \sin s \sin t \qquad \cos(s - t) = \cos s \cos t + \sin s \sin t$$

$$\tan(s + t) = \frac{\tan s + \tan t}{1 - \tan s \tan t} \qquad \tan(s - t) = \frac{\tan s - \tan t}{1 + \tan s \tan t}$$

Double Angle Formulas

$$\sin 2t = 2 \sin t \cos t$$

$$\cos 2t = \cos^2 t - \sin^2 t = 1 - 2\sin^2 t = 2\cos^2 t - 1$$

$$\tan 2t = \frac{2 \tan t}{1 - \tan^2 t}$$

Half Angle Formulas

$$\sin \frac{t}{2} = \pm\sqrt{\frac{1 - \cos t}{2}} \qquad \cos \frac{t}{2} = \pm\sqrt{\frac{1 + \cos t}{2}} \qquad \tan \frac{t}{2} = \frac{1 - \cos t}{\sin t}$$

Product Formulas

$$2 \sin s \cos t = \sin(s + t) + \sin(s - t) \qquad 2 \cos s \cos t = \cos(s + t) + \cos(s - t)$$

$$2 \cos s \sin t = \sin(s + t) - \sin(s - t) \qquad 2 \sin s \sin t = \cos(s - t) - \cos(s + t)$$

Factoring Formulas

$$\sin s + \sin t = 2 \cos \frac{s - t}{2} \cos \frac{s + t}{2} \qquad \cos s + \cos t = 2 \cos \frac{s + t}{2} \cos \frac{s - t}{2}$$

$$\sin s - \sin t = 2 \cos \frac{s + t}{2} \sin \frac{s - t}{2} \qquad \cos s - \cos t = -2 \sin \frac{s + t}{2} \sin \frac{s - t}{2}$$

Laws of Sines and Cosines

$$\frac{\sin \alpha}{a} = \frac{\sin \beta}{b} = \frac{\sin \gamma}{c}$$

$$a^2 = b^2 + c^2 - 2bc \cos \alpha$$

Graphs

$$\sin t = \sin \theta = y = \frac{b}{r} \qquad \cos t = \cos \theta = x = \frac{a}{r}$$

$$\tan t = \tan \theta = \frac{y}{x} = \frac{b}{a} \qquad \cot t = \cot \theta = \frac{x}{y} = \frac{a}{b}$$

$$y = \sin t \qquad y = \cos t$$

$$y = \tan t \qquad y = \cot t$$

$$y = \sec t \qquad y = \csc t$$

Inverse Trigonometric Functions

$$y = \sin^{-1} x \Leftrightarrow x = \sin y, \; -\pi/2 \leq y \leq \pi/2$$

$$y = \cos^{-1} x \Leftrightarrow x = \cos y, \; 0 \leq y \leq \pi$$

$$y = \tan^{-1} x \Leftrightarrow x = \tan y, \; -\pi/2 < y < \pi/2$$

$$y = \sec^{-1} x \Leftrightarrow x = \sec y, \; 0 \leq y \leq \pi, y \neq \pi/2$$

$$\sec^{-1} x = \cos^{-1}(1/x)$$

Hyperbolic Functions

$$\sinh x = \frac{1}{2}(e^x - e^{-x}) \qquad \cosh x = \frac{1}{2}(e^x + e^{-x})$$

$$\tanh x = \frac{\sinh x}{\cosh x} \qquad \coth x = \frac{\cosh x}{\sinh x}$$

$$\operatorname{sech} x = \frac{1}{\cosh x} \qquad \operatorname{csch} x = \frac{1}{\sinh x}$$

Series

$$\frac{1}{1 - x} = 1 + x + x^2 + x^3 + \cdots, \; -1 < x < 1$$

$$\ln(1 + x) = x - \frac{x^2}{2} + \frac{x^3}{3} - \frac{x^4}{4} + \cdots, \; -1 < x \leq 1$$

$$\tan^{-1} x = x - \frac{x^3}{3} + \frac{x^5}{5} - \frac{x^7}{7} + \cdots, \; -1 \leq x \leq 1$$

$$e^x = 1 + x + \frac{x^2}{2!} + \frac{x^3}{3!} + \cdots$$

$$\sin x = x - \frac{x^3}{3!} + \frac{x^5}{5!} - \frac{x^7}{7!} + \cdots$$

$$\cos x = 1 - \frac{x^2}{2!} + \frac{x^4}{4!} - \frac{x^6}{6!} + \cdots$$

$$\sinh x = x + \frac{x^3}{3!} + \frac{x^5}{5!} + \frac{x^7}{7!} + \cdots$$

$$\cosh x = 1 + \frac{x^2}{2!} + \frac{x^4}{4!} + \frac{x^6}{6!} + \cdots$$

$$(1 + x)^p = 1 + \binom{p}{1}x + \binom{p}{2}x^2 + \binom{p}{3}x^3 + \cdots, \; -1 < x < 1$$

$$\binom{p}{k} = \frac{p(p - 1)(p - 2)\cdots(p - k + 1)}{k!}$$

Fold here

Fold here